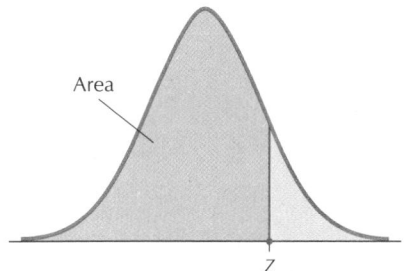

Area

Z

Table C Standard normal distribution (*continued*)

Z	0.00	0.01	0.02	0.03	0.04	0.05	0.06	0.07	0.08	0.09
0.0	0.5000	0.5040	0.5080	0.5120	0.5160	0.5199	0.5239	0.5279	0.5319	0.5359
0.1	0.5398	0.5438	0.5478	0.5517	0.5557	0.5596	0.5636	0.5675	0.5714	0.5753
0.2	0.5793	0.5832	0.5871	0.5910	0.5948	0.5987	0.6026	0.6064	0.6103	0.6141
0.3	0.6179	0.6217	0.6255	0.6293	0.6331	0.6368	0.6406	0.6443	0.6480	0.6517
0.4	0.6554	0.6591	0.6628	0.6664	0.6700	0.6736	0.6772	0.6808	0.6844	0.6879
0.5	0.6915	0.6950	0.6985	0.7019	0.7054	0.7088	0.7123	0.7157	0.7190	0.7224
0.6	0.7257	0.7291	0.7324	0.7357	0.7389	0.7422	0.7454	0.7486	0.7517	0.7549
0.7	0.7580	0.7611	0.7642	0.7673	0.7704	0.7734	0.7764	0.7794	0.7823	0.7852
0.8	0.7881	0.7910	0.7939	0.7967	0.7995	0.8023	0.8051	0.8078	0.8106	0.8133
0.9	0.8159	0.8186	0.8212	0.8238	0.8264	0.8289	0.8315	0.8340	0.8365	0.8389
1.0	0.8413	0.8438	0.8461	0.8485	0.8508	0.8531	0.8554	0.8577	0.8599	0.8621
1.1	0.8643	0.8665	0.8686	0.8708	0.8729	0.8749	0.8770	0.8790	0.8810	0.8830
1.2	0.8849	0.8869	0.8888	0.8907	0.8925	0.8944	0.8962	0.8980	0.8997	0.9015
1.3	0.9032	0.9049	0.9066	0.9082	0.9099	0.9115	0.9131	0.9147	0.9162	0.9177
1.4	0.9192	0.9207	0.9222	0.9236	0.9251	0.9265	0.9279	0.9292	0.9306	0.9319
1.5	0.9332	0.9345	0.9357	0.9370	0.9382	0.9394	0.9406	0.9418	0.9429	0.9441
1.6	0.9452	0.9463	0.9474	0.9484	0.9495	0.9505	0.9515	0.9525	0.9535	0.9545
1.7	0.9554	0.9564	0.9573	0.9582	0.9591	0.9599	0.9608	0.9616	0.9625	0.9633
1.8	0.9641	0.9649	0.9656	0.9664	0.9671	0.9678	0.9686	0.9693	0.9699	0.9706
1.9	0.9713	0.9719	0.9726	0.9732	0.9738	0.9744	0.9750	0.9756	0.9761	0.9767
2.0	0.9772	0.9778	0.9783	0.9788	0.9793	0.9798	0.9803	0.9808	0.9812	0.9817
2.1	0.9821	0.9826	0.9830	0.9834	0.9838	0.9842	0.9846	0.9850	0.9854	0.9857
2.2	0.9861	0.9864	0.9868	0.9871	0.9875	0.9878	0.9881	0.9884	0.9887	0.9890
2.3	0.9893	0.9896	0.9898	0.9901	0.9904	0.9906	0.9909	0.9911	0.9913	0.9916
2.4	0.9918	0.9920	0.9922	0.9925	0.9927	0.9929	0.9931	0.9932	0.9934	0.9936
2.5	0.9938	0.9940	0.9941	0.9943	0.9945	0.9946	0.9948	0.9949	0.9951	0.9952
2.6	0.9953	0.9955	0.9956	0.9957	0.9959	0.9960	0.9961	0.9962	0.9963	0.9964
2.7	0.9965	0.9966	0.9967	0.9968	0.9969	0.9970	0.9971	0.9972	0.9973	0.9974
2.8	0.9974	0.9975	0.9976	0.9977	0.9977	0.9978	0.9979	0.9979	0.9980	0.9981
2.9	0.9981	0.9982	0.9982	0.9983	0.9984	0.9984	0.9985	0.9985	0.9986	0.9986
3.0	0.9987	0.9987	0.9987	0.9988	0.9988	0.9989	0.9989	0.9989	0.9990	0.9990
3.1	0.9990	0.9991	0.9991	0.9991	0.9992	0.9992	0.9992	0.9992	0.9993	0.9993
3.2	0.9993	0.9993	0.9994	0.9994	0.9994	0.9994	0.9994	0.9995	0.9995	0.9995
3.3	0.9995	0.9995	0.9995	0.9996	0.9996	0.9996	0.9996	0.9996	0.9996	0.9997
3.4	0.9997	0.9997	0.9997	0.9997	0.9997	0.9997	0.9997	0.9997	0.9997	0.9998

The cover image for *Discovering Statistics*, 2nd Edition, which shows the Pyramids of Giza, is taken from one of the book's case studies, "The Golden Ratio" (from Chapter 9, "Hypothesis Testing"). Examples of the golden ratio are found in art and architecture throughout the Western world—including the Parthenon, the *Mona Lisa*, and the great pyramids of Egypt. Some mathematicians have argued that the golden ratio is intrinsically pleasing to the human species. Support for this conjecture would be especially strong if evidence were found for the use of the golden ratio in non-Western artistic traditions. In this Case Study, we use hypothesis testing to determine whether the golden ratio is reflected in the non-Western beadwork of the Native American Shoshone tribe.

CASE STUDY — The Golden Ratio

What do Euclid's *Elements*, the Parthenon of ancient Greece, the *Mona Lisa*, and the beadwork of the Shoshone tribe of Native Americans have in common? An appreciation for the *golden ratio*. Suppose we have two quantities A and B, with $A > B > 0$. Then, A/B is called the golden ratio if

$$\frac{A + B}{A} = \frac{A}{B}$$

that is, if the ratio of the sum of the quantities to the larger quantity equals the ratio of the larger to the smaller.

The golden ratio permeates ancient, medieval, Renaissance, and modern art and architecture. For example, the Egyptians constructed their great pyramids using the golden ratio. (Specifically, in Figure 9.1, if $A = \overline{XY}$ is the height from the top vertex to the base, and $B = \overline{YZ}$ is the distance from the center of the base to the edge, then $(A + B)/A = A/B$.) Some mathematicians have said that the golden ratio may be intrinsically pleasing to the human species. Support for this conjecture would be especially strong if evidence was found for the use of the golden ratio in non-Western artistic traditions. In the Case Study on page 462, we use hypothesis testing to determine whether the decorative beaded rectangles sewn by the Shoshone tribe of Native Americans follow the golden ratio.

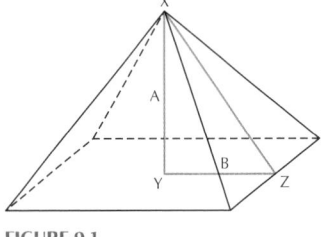

FIGURE 9.1

Learn more as this Case Study unfolds in Chapter 9 (pages 462–463).

CASE STUDY — The Golden Ratio

Euclid's *Elements*, the Parthenon, the *Mona Lisa*, and the beadwork of the Shoshone tribe all have in common an appreciation for the *golden ratio*.

Suppose we have two quantities A and B, with $A > B > 0$. Then A/B is called the *golden ratio* if

that is, if the ratio of the sum of the quantities to the larger quantity equals the ratio of the larger to the smaller (see Figure 9.32).

Euclid wrote about the golden ratio in his *Elements*, calling it the "extreme and mean ratio." The ratio of the width A and height B of the Parthenon, one of the most famous temples in ancient Greece, equals the golden ratio (Figure 9.32). If you enclose the face of Leonardo da Vinci's *Mona Lisa* in a rectangle, the resulting ratio of the long side to the short side follows the golden ratio (Figure 9.33). The golden ratio has a value of approximately 1.618.

Now we will test whether there is evidence for the use of the golden ratio in the artistic traditions of the Shoshone, a Native American tribe from the American West. Figure 9.34 shows a detail of a nineteenth-century Shoshone beaded dress that belonged to Nahtoma, the daughter of Chief Washakie of the Eastern Shoshone.[11] It is intriguing to consider whether Shoshone beaded rectangles such as those on this dress follow the golden ratio.

Instructor's Edition
Discovering Statistics

SECOND EDITION

Daniel T. Larose
Central Connecticut State University

Instructor's Edition Material Written By
Daniel T. Larose
Christina Morian
Lincoln University

W. H. Freeman and Company • New York

Publisher:	Ruth Baruth
Acquisitions Editor:	Karen Carson
Executive Marketing Manager:	Jennifer Somerville
Developmental Editors:	Andrew Sylvester, Shona Burke, Tony Palermino
Senior Media Acquisitions Editor:	Roland Cheyney
Senior Media Editor:	Laura Capuano
Associate Editor:	Katrina Wilhelm
Assistant Media Editor:	Catriona Kaplan
Editorial Assistant:	Tyler Holzer
Photo Editor:	Cecilia Varas
Photo Researcher:	Elyse Rieder
Art Director:	Diana Blume
Senior Project Editor:	Mary Louise Byrd
Illustrations:	Macmillan Publishing Solutions
Production Coordinator:	Paul W. Rohloff
Composition:	Macmillan Publishing Solutions
Printing and Binding:	RR Donnelley

Library of Congress Control Number: 2011934645

Casebound ISBN-13: 978-1-4292-5518-9
ISBN-10: 1-4292-5518-8

Paperback ISBN-13: 978-1-4292-7939-0
ISBN-10: 1-4292-7939-7

Loose-leaf ISBN-13: 978-1-4292-7940-6
ISBN-10: 1-4292-7940-0

Instructor's Edition ISBN-13: 978-1-4292-5687-2
ISBN-10: 1-4292-5687-7

W. H. Freeman and Company
41 Madison Avenue
New York, NY 10010
Houndmills, Basingstoke RG21 6XS, England
www.whfreeman.com

Brief Contents

Available only on CD and Web site: www.whfreeman.com/discostat2e

Contents

1

The Nature of Statistics   3

2

Describing Data Using Graphs and Tables   37

5 Probability   201

6 Probability Distributions   259

10 Two-Sample Inference 499

11 Categorical Data Analysis 555

Available only on CD and Web site: www.whfreeman.com/discostat2e

14 Nonparametric Statistics   14-3

Why I Wrote *Discovering Statistics*

John Naisbitt wrote: "We are drowning in information, but we are starved for knowledge" (*Megatrends: Ten New Directions for Transforming Our Lives,* Warner Books, 1982). As we move deeper into the twenty-first century, the Information Age, the gap between the flood of information and the dearth of knowledge and meaning is ever widening. As statistics instructors, we stand on the front line in the struggle to close this gap, to help our citizen-students sort through the data deluge that daily confronts them, and to help them uncover nuggets of knowledge that have meaning in their lives. This is why I wrote *Discovering Statistics:* to provide a friendly and effective tool that will help instructors connect with their students and teach their students how to discover knowledge and meaning in data.

Discovering Statistics will help your students develop the quantitative and analytical tools needed to understand statistics in today's data-saturated world. The text incorporates unique pedagogical features, such as *Developing Your Statistical Sense, What Do These Numbers Mean?, What Result Would We Expect?,* and the *What If Scenarios.* These features are aimed at anticipating students' questions and helping them understand the value of statistical intuition and interpretation, while at the same time also stressing computational skills. In the Information Age, it is important that students be able not only to find the right answer, but also to explain what the statistical results mean to those who have never taken a statistics course. Thus, the text stresses the importance of interpreting results to others.

In over 20 years of teaching introductory statistics, I have found that this approach works well at motivating students to learn statistics and often to enjoy the study of statistics. My hope is that instructors will find *Discovering Statistics* to be an effective tool for imparting to our twenty-first-century students an appreciation of the power of statistical analysis to extract knowledge from data.

The Introductory Statistics Course

Discovering Statistics is intended for an algebra-based, undergraduate, one- or two-semester course in general introductory statistics for non-majors. The only prerequisite is basic algebra. *Discovering Statistics* will prepare your students to work with data in fields such as psychology, business, nursing, education, and liberal arts, to name a few.

The GAISE guidelines, endorsed by the American Statistical Association, include the following recommendations:

1. Emphasize statistical literacy and develop statistical thinking.
2. Use real data.
3. Stress conceptual understanding rather than mere knowledge of procedures.
4. Foster active learning in the classroom.
5. Use technology for developing conceptual understanding and analyzing data.
6. Use assessments to improve and evaluate student learning.

Discovering Statistics adopts these guidelines verbatim as the course pedagogical objectives, with the following single adjustment: (3) Stress conceptual understanding *in addition to* knowledge of procedures. To these, the text adds two course pedagogical objectives:

7. Use case studies to show how newly acquired analytic tools may be applied to a familiar problem.
8. Encourage student motivation.

Approach of *Discovering Statistics*, Second Edition

Balanced analytical and computational coverage. The text integrates data interpretation and discovery-based methods with complete computational coverage of introductory statistics topics. Through unique and careful use of pedagogy, the text helps students develop their "statistical sense"—understanding the meaning behind the numbers. Equally, the text includes integrated and comprehensive computational coverage, including step-by-step solutions within examples. Select examples include screen shots and computer output from TI-83/84, Excel, Minitab, and CrunchIt!, with keystroke instructions located in the Step-by-Step Technology Guides at the ends of sections.

Communication of results. *Discovering Statistics,* Second Edition, emphasizes how, in the real world and in their future careers, students will need to explain statistical results to others who have never taken a statistics course.

Emphasis on variability. The importance of variability in the introductory statistics curriculum cannot be overstated. Without a solid appreciation of how statistics may vary, there is little chance that students will be able to understand the crucial topic of sampling distributions.

Use of powerful, current examples with real data. The *Deepwater Horizon* oil spill, the use of cell-phone apps, and celebrity-followers on Twitter represent the variety of examples included in *Discovering Statistics,* Second Edition. Example and exercise topics reflect real-world problems and engage the interest of the reader in their solution. Real data (with sources cited) are frequently used to further demonstrate relevance of topics.

New to This Edition

- With streamlined explanations and added examples and exercises, the Second Edition provides in-depth coverage of topics with increased clarity and conciseness. Thus, *Discovering Statistics,* Second Edition, can cover more topics in about the same number of pages as the First Edition.

- Additional topics have been added throughout the text covering Poisson probability distribution, t inference for $\mu_1 - \mu_2$ using pooled variance, Z inference for $\mu_1 - \mu_2$, inference for two independent standard deviations, multiple comparisons in ANOVA, randomized block design in ANOVA, two-way ANOVA, confidence intervals and prediction intervals in regression, and multiple regression. For more information on content coverage, see "Key Chapter Changes" on page xiv.

- An increased number of examples and exercises offers students extra support and provides instructors the flexibility to choose from a variety of relative examples to cover and exercises to assign. Examples and exercises cover a wide range of applications and use updated, real data. The Second Edition contains over 340 examples and 2900 exercises.

- **Now You Can Do Exercises feature,** found in the margin next to most examples, cues students to try related Practicing the Techniques exercises. The intention is not for the instructor to assign each exercise mentioned in this feature. Rather, these callouts are intended to prompt students toward practicing the techniques shown in the example. When working a particular exercise, students can also easily look back through the section to find the callout to a related example.

- **Bringing It All Together** exercises within each section offer a culmination of everything students have learned in a particular section, using a related set of Applying the Concepts exercises to tie together the main concepts and techniques learned.

- **Chapter 9, "Hypothesis Testing,"** has been rewritten to accommodate instructor preference with regard to teaching **(a)** the critical-value method only, **(b)** the p-value method only, or **(c)** both methods.

(a) For those who like to cover the critical-value method but not the *p*-value method, simply cover Section 9.2 but not Section 9.3.

(b) For those who like to cover the *p*-value method but not the critical-value method, cover only Objective 1 from Section 9.2, and then cover Section 9.3.

(c) For those who like to cover both methods, simply cover both Section 9.2 and Section 9.3. For all hypothesis tests, coverage of the critical-value method has been moved ahead of the *p*-value method. This aligns our coverage with that of most other statistics textbooks, making it easier for instructors who have previously taught using a different book, to use *Discovering Statistics*.

- In Chapters 9 and 10, the null hypothesis now always contains an equal sign. For example, the previous usage was

$$H_0 : \mu \leq \mu_0 \quad \text{versus} \quad H_a : \mu > \mu_0$$

The new notation is

$$H_0 : \mu = \mu_0 \quad \text{versus} \quad H_a : \mu > \mu_0$$

- The rejection rules are as follows, to be applied throughout the book:
  - Critical-value method (right-tailed test example): Changed from "Reject H_0 if test statistic $>$ critical value" to "Reject H_0 if test statistic $\geq$ critical-value."
  - *p*-Value method: Changed from "Reject H_0 if *p*-value $< \alpha$" to "Reject H_0 if *p*-value $\leq \alpha$."

- **CrunchIt! Statistical Software** is now included in the Step-by-Step Technology Guides at the end of select sections. This easily accessible and easy-to-use software offers all the basic statistical routines covered in introductory statistics courses.

- **NEW Chapter 14, "Nonparametric Statistics,"** is offered on the book companion CD and Web site: **www.whfreeman.com/discostat2e**.

- **Data sets,** available in a variety of software formats, are each named and marked with an icon in the text. Students can locate the data sets on the CD in the back of the book or at **www.whfreeman.com/discostat2e**.

- The **Try This in Class** feature has been moved to the book CD and is now integrated with the In-Class Activities for each chapter of the Instructor's Edition.

Key Chapter Changes

- **Chapter 2:** Crosstabulations and clustered bar graphs are now covered in Section 2.1, "Graphs and Tables for Categorical Data."

- **Chapter 3:** Quartiles and the interquartile range are now covered in Section 3.4, "Measures of Position and Outliers." Because quartiles are used for the five-number summary and boxplots, this section is now covered before the section on the Empirical Rule and Chebyshev's Rule.

- **Chapter 4** is newly titled "Correlation and Regression." Section 4.1 covers the closely related topics of scatterplots and the correlation coefficient. The regression equation has been changed from $\hat{y} = b_0 + b_1 x$ to $\hat{y} = b_1 x + b_0$, so that instructors who also teach algebra may be comfortable moving from the $y = mx + b$ notation.

- **Chapter 6** is now titled "Probability Distributions." The Case Study is updated using current, real data. Section 6.2 offers new exercises on the geometric, negative binomial, hypergeometric, and multinomial distributions. NEW Section 6.3 covers Poisson probability distribution. Section 6.4 now covers the uniform probability distribution. NEW Section 6.7 covers the normal approximation to the binomial probability distribution.

- **Chapter 7:** The *point estimate* topic has been moved to Section 8.1, where it appears more naturally just before confidence intervals. The awkward term *standard* *deviation of the sampling distribution of the sample mean* has been replaced with the more succinct *standard error of the mean*. Similarly, the *standard deviation of the sampling distribution of the sample proportion* is replaced with *standard error of the proportion*. Normal probability plots are now covered in Section 7.2, just in time for when they are needed. Overall, the coverage has been streamlined so that instructors may get to the Central Limit Theorem more quickly.

- **Chapter 8** opens with a NEW Case Study: Health Effects of the *Deepwater Horizon* Oil Spill. Section 8.1, "Z Interval for the Population Mean," now covers point estimates. The material on the Z confidence interval has been rewritten, making it simpler and increasing the pace.

- **Chapter 9:** The critical-value method is now covered before the *p*-value method. Starting in Section 9.4, in the Applying the Concepts exercises, the method to be used (critical value method or *p*-value method) is not specified. However, the Practicing the Techniques exercises continue to specify which method students should use. The null hypothesis and rejection rule formulas have been changed (see description above). There is a NEW Section 9.7 on probability of a type II error and the power of a hypothesis test.

- **Chapter 10:** The null hypothesis formula has been changed (see description above). Starting with this chapter, coverage of hypothesis testing is moved ahead of confidence intervals for the remainder of the book, in line with common practice. Section 10.2, "Inference for Two Independent Means," covers two new topics: (a) t inference for $\mu_1 - \mu_2$ using pooled variance and (b) Z inference for $\mu_1 - \mu_2$ when σ_1 and σ_2 are known. NEW Section 10.4, "Inference for Two Independent Standard Deviations," introduces the F distribution.

- **Chapter 12:** Three NEW sections—12.2, "Multiple Comparisons," 12.3, "Randomized Block Design," and 12.4, "Two-Way ANOVA"—offer expanded coverage of topics in analysis of variance.

- **Chapter 13:** As in Chapter 4, the regression equation has been changed from $\hat{y} = b_0 + b_1x$ to $\hat{y} = b_1x + b_0$. This includes the population regression equation. The chapter includes two NEW sections: 13.2, "Confidence Intervals and Prediction Intervals," and 13.3, "Multiple Regression."

Features of *Discovering Statistics*, Second Edition

The Second Edition retains many of the successful features from the First Edition.

Case Studies. A Case Study begins each chapter and is developed throughout the section examples, using the new set of tools that the section provides.

The Big Picture. Brief, bulleted lists at the beginning of each chapter look at "where we are coming from, and where we are headed . . . " . (Chapter 2, page 37)

The Big Picture

Where we are coming from, and where we are headed . . .

- In Chapter 1 we learned the basic concepts of statistics, such as population, sample, and types of variables, along with methods of collecting data.

- Here, in Chapter 2, we learn about graphs and tables for summarizing qualitative data and quantitative data, and we examine how to prevent our graphics from being misleading.

- Later, in Chapter 3, we will learn how to describe a data set using numerical measures like statistics rather than graphs and tables.

7.2 Central Limit Theorem for Means

OBJECTIVES By the end of this section, I will be able to . . .

1   Use normal probability plots to assess normality.

2   Describe the sampling distribution of $\bar{x}$ for skewed and symmetric populations as the sample size increases.

3   Apply the Central Limit Theorem for Means to solve probability questions about the sample mean.

1 Assessing Normality Using Normal Probability Plots

Much of the analysis we carry out in this text requires that the sample data come from a population that is normally distributed. But how do we assess whether a data set is normally distributed? Histograms, dotplots, and stem-and-leaf displays may be used.

Matched Objectives. Each section begins with a list of numbered objectives headed "By the end of this section, I will be able to . . .". The objective numbers are matched with the numbered topics within each section as well as the end-of-section summary. (Chapter 7, pages 347, 355)

Section 7.2 Summary

1 Normal probability plots are used to assess the normality of a data set.

2 A simulation study showed that the sampling distribution of $\bar{x}$ for a skewed population achieved approximate normality when n reached 30.

3 The Central Limit Theorem is one of the most important results in statistics and is stated as follows: given a population with mean μ and standard deviation σ, the sampling distribution of the sample mean $\bar{x}$ becomes approximately normal $(\mu, \sigma/\sqrt{n})$ as the sample size gets larger, regardless of the shape of the population.

Developing Your Statistical Sense. This feature empowers students with some useful perspectives that real-world data analysts need to know. Students will learn to think like real-world statistical analysts. This feature implements the GAISE guideline "Develop statistical thinking." (Chapter 9, page 428)

Developing Your Statistical Sense

A Decision Is Not Proof

It is important to understand that the decision to reject or not reject H_0 does not prove anything. The decision represents whether or not there is sufficient evidence against the null hypothesis. This is our best judgment given the data available. You cannot claim to have *proven* anything about the value of a population parameter unless you elicit information from the entire population, which is usually not possible. ◢

What Does This Mean? Feature boxes foster an intuitive approach and interpretation of results. Whenever a new formula or statistic is being introduced, the emphasis is on "What does this really mean?" Developing this understanding is just as important as getting the right answer, especially when the software can do the calculations. In the workplace, students may need to explain to their managers what the statistical results really mean. This feature helps to implement the GAISE guideline "Stress conceptual understanding." (Chapter 8, page 374)

What Does This Confidence Interval Mean?

What does the 90% mean in the phrase *90% confidence interval*? If we take sample after sample for a very long time, then in the long run, the proportion of intervals that will contain the population mean μ will equal 90%.

Interpreting Confidence Intervals

You may use the following generic interpretation for the confidence intervals that you construct: "We are 90% (or 95% or 99% and so on) confident that the population mean _____ (for example, SAT Math score) lies between _____ (lower bound) and _____ (upper bound)." ◢

What If Scenarios. The scenarios help students focus on statistical thinking rather than rote computation. Because of the availability of powerful statistical computer packages, statistical analysis is easy to do badly. The wrong analysis is worse than useless. It can cost companies lots of money, may convince lawmakers to pass bad legislation affecting millions of people, can incorrectly determine effects of pharmaceuticals or environmental pollution, as well as many other serious ramifications. The What If scenarios are extensions of examples or exercises aimed at honing students' critical-thinking skills. In What If exercises, the original problem setup is altered in a specific but nonquantifiable way. Students are then asked to think about how that change would percolate through the results, without recourse to calculations. The exercises as well as the scenarios are marked with the What If? icon. **?** (Chapter 3, page 97)

WHAT IF?

?

Give the Calculator a Rest

What If Scenarios offer you a chance to reflect on how changes in the initial conditions will percolate through the various aspects of a problem. The only requirement is to put your calculator down and think through the problem. You are asked to find the answers by using your knowledge of what the statistics *represent*.

Consider Example 3.6 once again. Now imagine: *what if* there was an incorrect data entry, such as a typo, and the number of Lady Gaga's Twitter followers was greater than 6.6 million people by some unspecified amount.

Describe how and why this change would have affected the following, if at all:

a. The mean number of followers

b. The median number of followers

c. The mode number of followers

Solution

a. Consider Figure 3.3, a dotplot of the number of followers, with the triangle indicating the mean or balance point, at 5.12 followers. Recall that this represents the balance point of the data. As the number of Lady Gaga's Twitter followers increases (arrow), the point at which the data balance (the mean) also moves somewhat to the right. Thus the mean number of followers will increase.

Stepped Example Solutions. In selected examples, students are guided through the key steps needed to work through the calculations and find the solution. (Chapter 9, page 435)

Solution

We may apply the Z test because the sample is large ($n \geq 30$), and the population standard deviation σ is known.

Step 1 **State the hypotheses.** From Example 9.3, our hypotheses are

$$H_0 : \mu = 11 \quad \text{versus} \quad H_a : \mu > 11$$

where μ represents the population mean number of times people use their debit cards per month.

Step 2 **Find Z_{crit} and state the rejection rule.** We have a right-tailed test and level of significance $\alpha = 0.01$, which, from Table 9.4, tell us that $Z_{crit} = 2.33$. Because we have a right-tailed test, the rejection rule will be "Reject H_0 if $Z_{data} \geq Z_{crit}$," that is, "Reject H_0 if $Z_{data} \geq 2.33$" (see Figure 9.4).

Step 3 **Find Z_{data}.** From Example 9.3, we have $Z_{data} = 1$.

Step 4 **State the conclusion and interpretation.** Our rejection rule states that we will reject H_0 if $Z_{data} \geq 2.33$. Since $Z_{data} = 1$, which is *not* ≥ 2.33, the conclusion is to [...] Even though the sample mean of 11.5 exceeds 11, it does not [...] margin to overcome the reasonable doubt that the difference [...] $\bar{x} = 11.5$ and the hypothesized value $\mu_0 = 11$ may have [...] interpret our conclusion as follows: "There is insufficient [...] of significance that the population mean monthly debit card [...] es per month." ∎

What Results Might We Expect?

Note from Figure 9.9 that the sample mean birth weight $\bar{x} = 3276$ grams is close to the hypothesized mean birth weight of $\mu_0 = 3200$ grams. This value of $\bar{x}$ is not extreme and thus does not seem to offer strong evidence that the hypothesized mean birth weight is wrong. Therefore, we might expect to *not reject* the hypothesis that $\mu_0 = 3200$ grams. ◢

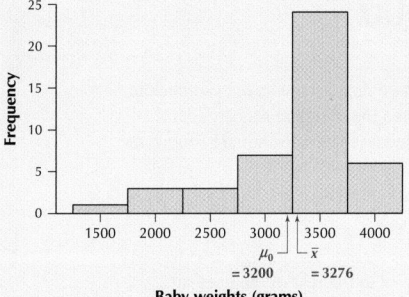

FIGURE 9.9 Sample mean, $\bar{x} = 3276$, is close to hypothesized mean, $\mu_0 = 3200$.

What Results Might We Expect? This feature, located in example solutions, challenges students to predict what the result of a particular problem will be. Students are presented with a graphical view of the situation, and, before performing any calculations, they are asked to bring their intuition and common sense to bear on the problem and to state what results we might expect once we do the number crunching. (Chapter 9, page 443)

Definitions and Formulas. Easily located in highlighted boxes, key definitions and formulas are important for students to understand when working examples and exercises. Important vocabulary and formulas are also listed (with page references) at the end of each chapter. (Chapter 1, page 7)

> The field of **statistics** is the *art* and *science* of
> - collecting,
> - analyzing,
> - presenting, and
> - interpreting data.

Exercises. *Discovering Statistics,* Second Edition, contains a rich and varied collection of section and chapter exercises.

- Clarifying the Concepts (conceptual)
- Practicing the Techniques (skill-based)
- Applying the Concepts (real-world applications)
- **NEW** Bringing It All Together

These exercises bring together everything students have learned in a particular section, using a related set of Applying the Concepts exercises to tie together the main concepts and techniques learned in the section.

- **NEW** Now You Can Do Exercises feature

Connects the Practicing the Techniques exercises to specific examples from the section. For example, in the margin at the end of Example 4.2 on page 160, you will find "Now You Can Do Exercises 13–20." This callout lets the student know that he or she can use the example as a model when completing the exercise set.

Example 4.2 Characterize the relationship between two variables using a scatterplot

Using Figure 4.1, characterize the relationship between lot square footage and lot price.

Solution

Now You Can Do
Exercises 13–20.

The scatterplot in Figure 4.1 most resembles Figure 4.2a, where a positive relationship exists between the variables. Thus, smaller lot sizes tend to be associated with lower prices, and larger lot sizes tend to be associated with higher prices. Put another way, as the lot size increases, the lot price tends to increase as well. ■

At the end of each chapter, **Review Exercises** and a **Chapter Quiz** help to test students' overall understanding of each chapter's concepts and to practice for exams. In the student version of *Discovering Statistics,* the answers to odd-numbered exercises and all chapter quiz exercises are given in the back of the book.

Chapter 3 QUIZ

TRUE OR FALSE
1. True or false: If two data sets have the same mean, median, and mode, then the two data sets are identical.
2. True or false: The variance is the square root of the standard deviation.
3. True or false: The Empirical Rule applies for any data set.

FILL IN THE BLANK
4. An _____ is an extremely large or extremely small data value relative to the rest of the data set.
5. The mean can be viewed as the _____ point of the data.
6. The measure of center that is sensitive to the presence of extreme values is the _____.

Step-by-Step Technology Guide. This feature covers TI-83/84 calculators, Excel, Minitab, and CrunchIt!, providing stepped keystroke instructions for working through selected examples in the text. Screen shots of the results are often provided as well, either within the Step-by-Step Technology Guide or in the corresponding example. (Chapter 4, page 180)

STEP-BY-STEP TECHNOLOGY GUIDE: Regression

We illustrate using Example 4.3, the temperature data (pages 160–161).

TI-83/84
Step 1 Turn diagnostics on as follows. Press **2nd 0**. Scroll down and select **DiagnosticOn** (Figure 4.21). Press **ENTER** twice to turn diagnostics on.
Step 2 Enter the **X (Low Temp)** data in **L1**, and the **Y (High Temp)** data in **L2**.
Step 3 Press **STAT** and highlight **CALC**.
Step 4 Select **LinReg(ax + b)**.
Step 5 On the home screen, **LinReg(ax + b)** appears. Press **ENTER**.

```
CATALOG          ▣
  DependAsk
  DependAuto
  det(
  DiagnosticOff
▸ DiagnosticOn
  dim(
  Disp
```

FIGURE 4.21

EXCEL
Step 1 Enter the x variable in column **A** and the y variable in column **B**.
Step 2 Click on **Data > Data Analysis > Regression** and click **OK**.

Step 3 For **Input Y Range**, select cells **B1–B10**. For **Input X Range**, select cells **A1–A10**. Click **OK**.

MINITAB
Regression
Step 1 Enter the x variable in **C1** and the y variable in **C2**.
Step 2 Click on **Stat > Regression > Regression**.

Step 3 Select the y variable for the **Response Variable** and the x variable for the **Predictor Variable**. Click **OK**.

CRUNCHIT!
Step 1 Click **File . . .** then highlight **Load from Larose2e . . . Chapter 4 . . .** and click on **Example 4.3**.
Step 2 Click **Statistics . . . Regression . . . Simple linear regression**.

Step 3 For **Response variable y** select **High temp**. For **Predictor variable x** select **Low Temp**.
Step 4 For **Display** make sure **Numerical results** is selected. Then click **Calculate**.

 Applets. Interactive statistical applets are located on the CD and the book companion Web site: **www.whfreeman.com/discostat2e**. Applet icons in the text mark the related chapter material and exercises.

 Caution notes. Signaled by the Caution icon, these warnings in the text help students avoid common errors and misconceptions.

Supplements

The following electronic and print supplements are available with *Discovering Statistics,* Second Edition:

 courses.bfwpub.com/discostat2e (Access code required. Available packaged with *Discovering Statistics,* Second Edition, or for purchase online.) StatsPortal is the digital gateway to *Discovering Statistics,* Second Edition, designed to enrich the course and enhance students' study skills through a collection of Web-based tools. StatsPortal integrates a rich suite of diagnostic, assessment, tutorial, and enrichment features, enabling students to master statistics at their own pace. It is organized around the following learning components:

Interactive eBook offers a complete and customizable online version of the text, fully integrated with all the media resources available with *Discovering Statistics,* Second Edition. The eBook allows students to quickly search the text, highlight key areas, and add notes about what they are reading. Instructors can also customize the eBook by adding, removing, and highlighting content.

Resources organizes all the resources for *Discovering Statistics*, Second Edition, into one location for your ease of use. These resources include the following:

- **NEW! Statistical Video Series** consisting of StatClips, StatClips Examples, and Statistically Speaking "Snapshots." View animated lecture videos, whiteboard lessons, and documentary-style footage that illustrate key statistical concepts and help students visualize statistics in real-world scenarios.

- **NEW! *LEARNING*Curve** is a formative assessment tool that tests your students' conceptual knowledge of the material in the text. As your students progress through each Learning Curve activity, the system will customize the questions based on their performance so that they are tested more rigorously in those areas where they need the most work.

- **StatTutor Tutorials** offer over 150 audio-multimedia tutorials, including video, applets, and animations.

- **Stats@Work Simulations** put students in the role of a statistical consultant, helping them to better understand statistics interactively within the context of real-life scenarios. Students are asked to interpret and analyze data presented in report form, as well as to interpret current events.

- **Statistical Applets** help students master key statistical concepts and work exercises from the text.

- **CrunchIt! Statistical Software** allows users to analyze data from any Internet location. Designed with the novice user in mind, the software is not only easily accessible but also easy to use. CrunchIt! offers all the basic statistical routines covered in introductory statistics courses and more.

- **EESEE Case Studies** developed by The Ohio State University Statistics Department, teach students to apply their statistical skills by exploring actual case studies using real data.

- **Student Solutions Manual**

- **WHFStat Macros for Excel**

- **Data sets** are available in ASCII, Excel, TI, Minitab, SPSS, and JMP formats.

- **Statistical Software Manuals** for TI-83/84, Excel, Minitab, SPSS, and JMP are provided.

- **(Instructors Only) NEW! SolutionMaster** is a Web-based version of the instructor's solutions manual. This easy-to-use tool allows instructors to create homework assignments, quizzes, and tests from textbook exercises and generate a separate solution guide. Assignments and solutions can be downloaded in PDF format for convenient printing and posting. For more information or a demonstration, contact your local W. H. Freeman sales representative.

Assignment Center (for instructor use only) organizes assignments and grades through an easy-to-create assignment process providing access to questions from the Test Bank, Web Quizzes, and Exercises from *Discovering Statistics,* Second Edition.

Online Study Center: www.whfreeman.com/osc/discostat2e (access code required; available for purchase online) offers all the resources available in StatsPortal except the eBook and Assignment Center.

Companion Web site: www.whfreeman.com/discostat2e is an open-access Web site that includes statistical applets, data sets, quizzes, and Chapter 14, "Nonparametric Statistics."

Interactive Student CD-ROM is included with every new copy of *Discovering Statistics*. The CD contains access to data sets, applets, and Chapter 14 (also found on the companion Web site).

Printed Student Solutions Manual offers detailed solutions for key exercises from each section of *Discovering Statistics,* Second Edition. ISBN: 1-4292-5706-7

EESEE (Electronic Encyclopedia of Statistical Examples and Exercises) Case Studies. Developed by The Ohio State University Statistics Department, these electronic case studies provide a wide variety of timely, real examples with real data. EESEE case studies are available via an access code–protected Web site. Access codes are included with new copies of the student edition of *Discovering Statistics,* Second Edition (printed behind the CD in the back of the book), or subscriptions can be purchased online. Instructors can access EESEE through the companion Web site.

For Instructors Only

Instructor's Guide with Solutions The printed guide offers teaching tips, chapter commentaries, lists of teaching resources, and solutions to all exercises from *Discovering Statistics*, Second Edition. ISBN: 1-4292-5690-7

Test Bank The Test Bank contains hundreds of multiple-choice questions to generate quizzes and tests. Available in print as well as electronically on CD-ROM (for Windows and Mac), where questions can be downloaded, edited, and resequenced to suit the instructor's needs.

Print Version, ISBN: 1-4292-5700-8
Computerized (CD) Version, ISBN: 1-4292-5699-0

Enhanced Instructor's Resource CD-ROM Allows instructors to search and export (by key term or chapter) all the material from the student CD, plus:

- All text images and tables
- Instructor's Guide with Solutions
- PowerPoint lecture slides
- Test bank files

ISBN: 1-4292-5701-6

Course Management Systems W. H. Freeman and Company provides courses for Blackboard, WebCT (Campus Edition and Vista), and Angel course management systems. They are completely integrated courses that you can easily customize and adapt to meet your teaching goals and course objectives. Visit www.bfwpub.com/lmc for more information.

i-clicker i-clicker is a two-way radio-frequency classroom response solution developed by educators for educators. University of Illinois physicists Tim Stelzer, Gary Gladding, Mats Selen, and Benny Brown created the i-clicker system after using competing classroom response solutions and discovering that they were neither classroom-appropriate nor student-friendly. Each step of i-clicker's development has been informed by teaching and learning. i-clicker is superior to other systems from both pedagogical and technical standpoints. To learn more about packaging i-clicker with this textbook, please contact your local sales rep or visit www .iclicker.com.

Acknowledgments

I would like to join W. H. Freeman and Company in thanking the reviewers who offered comments that assisted in the development and refinement of the Second Edition of *Discovering Statistics*:

Holly Ashton, *Pikes Peak Community College*
John Beyers, *University of Maryland University College*
Dean Burbank, *Gulf Coast State College*
Ferry Butar Butar, *Sam Houston State University*
Ann Cannon, *Cornell College*
Ayona Chatterjee, *University of West Georgia*
Zhao Chen, *Florida Gulf Coast University*
Geoffrey Dietz, *Gannon University*
Wanda Eanes, *Macon State College*
Elaine Fitt, *Bucks County Community College*
Elizabeth Flow-Delwiche, *Community College of Baltimore County*
Joe Gallegos, *Salt Lake Community College*
Dave Gilbert, *Santa Barbara City College*
Donna Gorton, *Butler Community College*
David Gurney, *Southeastern Louisiana University*
Noal Harbertson, *California State University, Fresno and Sacramento*
Steve Hundert, *College of Southern Maryland*
Andreas Lazari, *Valdosta State University*

Ananda Manage, *Sam Houston State University*
Christina Morian, *Lincoln University*
John Nardo, *Oglethorpe University*
Michael Nasab, *Long Beach City College*
Greg Perkins, *Hartnell College*
Rogelio Ruiz, *Riverside Community College*
Fary Sami, *Harford Community College*
Jason Samuels, *Borough of Manhattan Community College*
Mohammed Shayib, *Prairie View A&M University*
Kim Sheppard, *Cecil College*
Marcia Siderow, *California State University, Northridge*
Karen Smith, *University of West Georgia*
Tabrina Smith, *Lake Erie College*
Sherman Sowby, *Brigham Young University*
John Trimboli, *Macon State College*
Cameron Troxell, *Mt. San Antonio College*
Mahbobeh Vezvaei, *Kent State University*
Karin Vorwerk, *Westfield State University*
James Wan, *Long Beach City College*
Tanya Wojtulewicz, *Community College of Baltimore County*

I would also like to thank the many instructors from across the United States and Canada who offered comments on the First Edition:

ARKANSAS George Bratton, *University of Central Arkansas*
ARIZONA Cheryl Ossenfort, *Coconino Community College*
CALIFORNIA Christine Cole, *Moorpark College*; Carol Curtis, *Fresno City College*; Kevin Fox, *Shasta College*; Kristin M. Hartford, *Long Beach City College*; Elizabeth Hamman, *Cypress College*; Sara Jones, *Santa Rosa Junior College*; Wendy Miao, *El Camino College*; Michael A. Nasab, *Long Beach City College*; Keith Oberlander, *Pasadena City College*; Greg Perkins, *Hartnell College*; Zika Perovic, *MiraCosta College*; Ladera Rosenburg, *Long Beach City College*; Sherman Sowby, *California State University, Fresno*; James Wan, *Long Beach City College*; Michael Zeitzew, *El Camino College*
CANADA Susan Chen, *Camosun College*; Shaun Fallat, *University of Regina*; Dorothy Levay, *Brock University*
COLORADO Holly Ashton, *Pikes Peak Community College*; Dean Barchers, *Red Rocks Community College*; Nels Grevstad, *Metropolitan State College of Denver*; Jay Schaffer, *University of Northern Colorado*
DELAWARE Derald E. Wentzien, *Wesley College*
FLORIDA Abraham Biggs, *Broward Community College*; Lisa M. Borzewski, *St. Petersburg College*; Janette H.

Campbell, *Palm Beach Community College*; Zhao Chen, *Florida Gulf Coast University*; Lani Kempner, *Broward Community College*; Nancy Liu, *Miami Dade College*; Panagiotis Nikolopoulos, *Nova Southeastern University*; William Radulovich, *Florida Community College at Jacksonville*; Traci M. Reed, *St. Johns River Community College*; Pali Sen, *University of North Florida*; Jerry Shawver, *Florida Community College at Jacksonville*; Deanna Voehl, *Indian River State College*
GEORGIA Donna Brouillette, *Georgia Perimeter College*; Ayona Chatterjee, *University of West Georgia*; Wanda Eanes, *Macon State College*; Todd Hendricks, *Georgia Perimeter College*; Shahryar Heydari, *Piedmont College*; Barry J. Monk, *Macon State College*; Chandler Pike, *University of Georgia*; Kim Robinson, *Clayton State University*; Howard L. Sanders, *Georgia Perimeter College*; Karen H. Smith, *University of West Georgia*; Martha Tapia, *Berry College*
HAWAII David Ching, *University of Hawai'i at Mānoa*; Eric Matsuoka, *Leeward Community College*
ILLINOIS Virginia Coil, *College of Lake County*; James Cicarelli, *Roosevelt University*; Faye Dang, *Joliet Junior College*; Linda Hoffman, *McKendree University*; Glenn Jablonski, *Triton College*;

Julius Nadas, *Wilbur Wright College*; Stephen G. Zuro, *Joliet Junior College*

INDIANA Ewa Misiolek, *Saint Mary's College*

IOWA Russell Campbell, *University of Northern Iowa*

KANSAS Linda Herndon, *Benedictine College*; James Leininger, *MidAmerica Nazarene University*; Leesa Pohl, *Donnelly College*

KENTUCKY Brooke Buckley, *Northern Kentucky University*; Lloyd Jaisingh, *Morehead State University*; Christopher Schroeder, *Morehead State University*; Marlene Will, *Spalding University*

LOUISIANA Arun K. Agarwal, *Grambling State University*; David Busekist, *Southeastern Louisiana University*; Julien Doucet, *Louisiana State University at Alexandria*; Diane Fisher, *University of Louisiana at Lafayette*; David Gurney, *Southeastern Louisiana University*; Nabendu Pal, *University of Louisiana at Lafayette*; Victor S. Swaim, *Southeastern Louisiana University*

MARYLAND Cathy Hess, *Anne Arundel Community College*; Steven Hundert, *College of Southern Maryland*; Annette Noble, *University of Maryland Eastern Shore*; Steve Prehoda, *Frederick Community College*; Fary Sami, *Harford Community College*; Kim Sheppard, *Cecil College*

MASSACHUSETTS Mary Fowler, *Worcester State College*; LeRoy P. Hammerstrom, *Eastern Nazarene College*; Bonnie Wicklund, *Mount Wachusett Community College*

MICHIGAN Jennifer Borrello, *Grand Rapids Community College*; Lorraine Gregory, *Lake Superior State University*; Linda Reist, *Macomb Community College*; Kathy Zhong, *University of Detroit Mercy*

MINNESOTA Ken Grace, *Anoka-Ramsey Community College*; Mezbahur Rahman, *Minnesota State University, Mankato*

MISSOURI Kathy Carroll, *Drury University*; Christina Morian, *Lincoln University of Missouri*

MONTANA Debra Wiens, *Rocky Mountain College*

NEBRASKA Polly Amstutz, *University of Nebraska at Kearney*; Kathy Woitaszewski, *Central Community College*

NEW JERSEY Robert Thurston, *Rowan University*; Cathleen Zucco-Teveloff, *Rowan University*

NEW YORK David Bernklau, *Long Island University*; Jadwiga Domino, *Medaille College*; Reva Fish, *University at Buffalo*; Maryann Justinger, *Erie Community College*; Michael Kent, *Borough of Manhattan Community College*; William Price, *North Country Community College*; Sharon Testone, *Onondaga Community College*; Nicholas Zaino, *University of Rochester*

NORTH CAROLINA Emma B. Borynski, *Durham Technical Community College*; Ayesha Delpish, *Elon University*; Jackie MacLaughlin, *Central Piedmont Community College*; Jeanette Szwec, *Cape Fear Community College*; John Russell Taylor, *The University of North Carolina at Charlotte*; James Truesdell, *Chowan University*

OHIO G. Andy Chang, *Youngstown State University*; Don Davis, *Lakeland Community College*; Arjun Gupta, *Bowling Green State University*; William *Huepenbecker, BGSU Firelands*; Gaurab Mahapatra, *The University of Akron*; Mahbobeh Vezvaei, *Kent State University*

OKLAHOMA Mickle Duggan, *East Central University*; John Nichols, *Oklahoma Baptist University*; William Warde, *Oklahoma State University*

OREGON Jong Sung Kim, *Portland State University*; Carrie Kyser, *Clackamas Community College*

PENNSYLVANIA Linda M. Myers, *Harrisburg Area Community College*; Sandra Nypaver, *Mount Aloysius College*

SOUTH CAROLINA Diana J. Asmus, *Greenville Technical College*; Thomas Fitzkee, *Francis Marion University*; Erwin Walker, *Clemson University*

TENNESSEE Aniekan Ebiefung, *University of Tennessee at Chattanooga*; Frankie E. Harris, *Southwest Tennessee Community College*; Marc Loizeaux, *University of Tennessee at Chattanooga*; Mary Ella Poteat, *Northeast State Technical Community College*

TEXAS Ananda Bandulasiri, *Sam Houston State University*; Ferry Butar Butar, *Sam Houston State University*; Ola Disu, *Tarrant County College*; Emmett Elam, *Texas Tech University*; Maggie Foster, *Tarrant County College*; Grady Grizzle, *North Lake College*; Jada P. Hill, *Richland College*; Melinda Holt, *Sam Houston State University*; Jianguo Liu, *University of North Texas*; David D. Marshall, *Texas Woman's University*; Melissa Reeves, *East Texas Baptist University*; Ricardo Rodriguez, *Eastfield College*; Daniela Stoevska-Kojouharov, *Tarrant County College*; Jo Tucker, *Tarrant County College*

UTAH Kari Arnoldsen, *Snow College*; Joe Gallegos, *Salt Lake Community College*; Ruth Trygstad, *Salt Lake Community College*

VIRGINIA John Avioli, *Christopher Newport University*; Robert May, *Virginia Highlands Community College*; Mike Shirazi, *Germanna Community College*; Glenn Weber, *Christopher Newport University*; Ken Wissmann, *Shenandoah University*

WASHINGTON Margaret Balachowski, *Everett Community College*; Kelly Brooks, *Pierce College*; Abel Gage, *Skagit Valley College*; John Kellermeier, *Tacoma Community College*

WISCONSIN William K. Applebaugh, *University of Wisconsin – Eau Claire*; David M. Reineke, *University of Wisconsin – La Crosse*; Vicki Whitledge, *University of Wisconsin – Eau Claire*

The Second Edition of *Discovering Statistics* owes much to the untiring efforts of the team of professionals at W. H. Freeman and Company. I would like to thank Elizabeth Widdicombe, Craig Bleyer, Andrew Sylvester, Karen Carson, Mary Louise Byrd, Shona Burke, Jennifer Somerville, Roland Cheyney, and Laura Capuano for contributing their talents to the creation of the book. A big thank you to Tony Palermino, whose development editing greatly improved the text, as well as to Martha Solonche, Ann Cannon, and Christina Morian. Most especially, I would like to thank Ruth Baruth, Mathematics and Statistics Publisher, who recognized the need for a book like *Discovering Statistics* and helped make it a reality.

I also wish to thank Dr. Jeffrey McGowan and Dr. Chun Jin, Chair and Assistant Chair of the Department of Mathematical Sciences at Central Connecticut State University, Dr. Dipak K. Dey, Distinguished Professor and Associate Dean, College of Liberal Arts and Sciences at the University of Connecticut, and Dr. John Judge, Chair of the Department of Mathematics at Westfield State College. Thanks to my daughter and statistician-in-training Chantal Danielle (23) for carrying on the love of statistics to the next generation, and to my twin children Tristan Spring and Ravel Renaissance (12) for demonstrating that there is life beyond the computer screen. Above all, I extend my deepest gratitude to my darling wife of 26 years, Debra J. Larose, for her love, support, and understanding.

About the Author

Since his days of collecting baseball cards as a youngster and scrutinizing the statistics of his favorite players, Dan Larose has loved statistics. He also loved language and writing, so when Dan went to college he majored in French, then philosophy, and finally, in linguistics and computer science. This background in the liberal arts honed his writing ability. However, his love of statistics never left him, so he went on to earn an M.S. (1993) and a Ph.D. in statistics (1996) from the University of Connecticut. Today, Dan is Professor of Statistics in the Department of Mathematical Sciences at Central Connecticut State University (CCSU).

At CCSU, Dan designed, developed, and now directs the world's first online Master of Science degree and Graduate Certificate program in data mining. He has published three books on data mining and one book on SAS programming. *Discovering Knowledge in Data: An Introduction to Data Mining* has been translated into French and Polish, while *Data Mining Methods and Models* and *Data Mining the Web* have been translated into Polish. He is the founder of DataMiningConsultant.com, and his consulting clients include *The Economist* magazine, Microsoft, *Forbes* magazine, the CIT Group, KPMG International, Computer Associates, Deloitte, Inc., Sonalysts, Inc., Booz Allen and Hamilton, and the Hospital for Special Care. His consulting work includes a $750,000 Phase II grant from the Air Force Office of Research, Storage Efficient Data Mining of High Speed Data Streams. He is the Series Editor for the Wiley series on Methods and Applications in Data Mining.

However, his favorite work is imparting a love of statistics to a new generation, and he trusts that *Discovering Statistics* will help to do so.

Dan lives in Tolland, Connecticut, with his wife Debra, twin 12-year olds, Tristan Spring and Ravel Renaissance, and daughter Chantal Danielle, who is a graduate student in the Department of Statistics at UConn.

Examples by Application

Discovering Statistics, Second Edition, presents a wide variety of applications from diverse disciplines. The list below indicates a number of examples and exercises related to different fields. Note that some items appear in more than one category.

Biology and the Environment
Chapter 1: 1.19; **Chapter 2:** 2.17, 2.18; **Chapter 3:** 3.15, 3.16, 3.24, 3.25, 3.27, 3.41; **Chapter 4:** 4.3, 4.7, 4.8, 4.10; **Chapter 6:** 6.38; **Chapter 7:** 7.3, 7.11, 7.12; **Chapter 8:** 8.3, 8.11; **Chapter 9:** 9.1, 9.2, 9.12, 9.25; **Chapter 12:** 12.5, 12.6

Business and Consumer Behavior
Chapter 1: 1.10; **Chapter 3:** 3.3–3.5, 3.10; **Chapter 4:** 4.1, 4.2, 4.5, 4.9; **Chapter 5:** 5.9, 5.17, 5.25, 5.26, 5.30, 5.33; **Chapter 6:** 6.24, 6.25; **Chapter 7:** 7.8–7.10, 7.13–7.16; **Chapter 8:** 8.1, 8.4–8.8, 8.15; **Chapter 9:** 9.15; **Chapter 10:** 10.2, 10.10; **Chapter 11:** 11.1–11.4, 11.7

College Life
Chapter 3: 3.1, 3.18; **Chapter 6:** 6.15, 6.26, 6.39–41; **Chapter 12:** 12.1–12.4

Demographics and Characteristics of People
Chapter 1: 1.1–1.4, 1.11; **Chapter 2:** 2.6–2.8, 2.14; **Chapter 3:** 3.7–3.9, 3.19–3.22, 3.30; **Chapter 5:** 5.6, 5.8, 5.9, 5.14, 5.25; **Chapter 6:** 6.7, 6.16; **Chapter 9:** 9.22–9.24, 9.27; **Chapter 10:** 10.15

Economics and Finance
Chapter 1: 1.5, 1.11; **Chapter 5:** 5.24; **Chapter 7:** 7.2, 7.13–7.16; **Chapter 9:** 9.3, 9.27; **Chapter 10:** 10.10, 10.19

Education and Child Development
Chapter 1: 1.18; **Chapter 2:** 2.10–2.13, 2.21, 2.25; **Chapter 3:** 3.18, 3.23, 3.26, 3.28, 3.29, 3.31, 3.34, 3.39, 3.42–3.46; **Chapter 6:** 6.11–6.13, 6.44, 6.45; **Chapter 7:** 7.4–7.6; **Chapter 8:** 8.2, 8.8, 8.10, 8.16, 8.17; **Chapter 9:** 9.23; **Chapter 10:** 10.4, 10.5; **Chapter 12:** 12.8–12.12

Health and Nutrition
Chapter 1: 1.13, 1.14, 1.15; **Chapter 3:** 3.24, 3.25, 3.27, 3.32, 3.35, 3.41; **Chapter 5:** 5.28, 5.29, 5.41; **Chapter 6:** 6.23, 6.27, 6.28, 6.44, 6.45; **Chapter 7:** 7.7, 7.11, 7.12; **Chapter 8:** 8.12, 8.13; **Chapter 9**: 9.7, 9.10, 9.13, 9.16, 9.19, 9.20, 9.24, 9.26; **Chapter 10:** 10.3, 10.6, 10.8, 10.20; **Chapter 13:** 13.11–13.15

Humanities and Social Sciences
Chapter 1: 1.18; **Chapter 4:** 4.13–4.19; **Chapter 12:** 12.5, 12.6; **Chapter 13:** 13.5, 13.6

International
Chapter 2: 2.19, 2.25; **Chapter 8:** 8.11; **Chapter 9:** 9.10

Law Enforcement and Crime
Chapter 2: 2.19, 2.23; **Chapter 3:** 3.1, 3.30; **Chapter 5:** 5.24; **Chapter 8:** 8.19, 8.20; **Chapter 11:** 11.7

Politics and Voting
Chapter 1: 1.16; **Chapter 2:** 2.20; **Chapter 8:** 8.21

Sports, Leisure, and Entertainment
Chapter 1: 1.9, 1.12, 1.13; **Chapter 2:** 2.15, 2.22, 2.24; **Chapter 3:** 3.2, 3.6, 3.8, 3.9, 3.38; **Chapter 5:** 5.5, 5.13, 5.32, 5.37, 5.44; **Chapter 6:** 6.5, 6.6, 6.15; **Chapter 8:** 8.18; **Chapter 13:** 13.17

Technology and the Internet
Chapter 1: 1.14; **Chapter 2:** 2.1–2.4; **Chapter 3:** 3.6; **Chapter 5:** 5.6, 5.8, 5.14, 5.15, 5.20, 5.42; **Chapter 6:** 6.16–6.19, 6.21, 6.25; **Chapter 7:** 7.10; **Chapter 9:** 9.3, 9.5, 9.9, 9.14, 9.22, 9.23; **Chapter 10:** 10.7, 10.9, 10.12, 10.14, 10.19; **Chapter 11:** 11.1–11.4; **Chapter 12:** 12.13–12.15; **Chapter 13:** 13.1, 13.2, 13.7–13.10

Transportation and Fuel
Chapter 2: 2.5, 2.19, 2.23; **Chapter 3:** 3.1, 3.17; **Chapter 6:** 6.42, 6.43; **Chapter 8:** 8.23; **Chapter 9:** 9.21; **Chapter 11:** 11.8

Exercises by Application

Biology and the Environment
Chapter 1: 2.63, 2.65, 2.70; **Chapter 2:** 1.45–55, 1.79–81, 2.63–68, 3.41–42, R.25; **Chapter 3:** 2.51–54, 3.16, 3.18, 3.21, 5.48–56, 6.9–12, R.1–3; **Chapter 4:** 3.44; **Chapter 5:** 2.91–93; **Chapter 6:** 3.23, 3.25, 4.45, 4.48, 6.29, 6.33, 6.36; **Chapter 7:** 1.47, 1.49–51, 2.30, 2.34; **Chapter 8:** 1.57–58, 1.60, 1.66, 1.69–70, 2.57–58, 2.60, 4.39–40, Q.9–10, Q.15; **Chapter 9:** 3.36, 3.40, 5.41, 6.40; **Chapter 10:** 1.33, 1.37, 2.37, Q.16; **Chapter 13:** 1.33, 2.20, 2.24, 3.37

Business and Consumer Behavior
Chapter 1: 2.64, 2.74–75, R.6, R.8; **Chapter 2:** 1.82–87, 2.43, 3.37–39; **Chapter 3:** 1.52–56, 3.17, 3.20–21; **Chapter 5:** 3.100, 4.50–51, 4.55, 4.57–58, 4.69, 4.70; **Chapter 6:** 2.60, 2.64, 2.67, 3.24, 7.26, 7.31, Q.11; **Chapter 7:** 1.41, 1.45, 3.41, 3.45; **Chapter 8:** 1.59, 1.71, 2.59; **Chapter 9:** 1.21, 2.36, 2.42–43, 3.44–46, 3.57–60, 4.37, 4.40, 4.43–45, 7.20–21, 7.23, R.13, Q.10; **Chapter 10:** 1.31, 1.34–35, 1.38, 1.45–49, 2.29–30, 2.43–44, 3.25, 3.29; **Chapter 11:** 1.28, 2.28, 2.33, R.1; **Chapter 12:** 1.24, 1.36, 3.18, 3.21, 3.25, R.3, R.5, R.16, Q.11; **Chapter 13:** 3.36

Demographics and Characteristics of People
Chapter 1: 1.1–6, 3.37, 3.39, R.4; **Chapter 2:** 1.67–69, 1.88–92, 1.95–97, 2.50–53, R.7–20; **Chapter 3:** 2.59–64, 3.15, 5.31–33; **Chapter 4:** 2.62–64, 3.46–47; **Chapter 5:** 2.80, 3.97, 3.101, 3.103, 3.106–114, R.15–18, Q.13–15; **Chapter 6:** 1.69–70, 2.66, 7.29, 7.32, 7.34, R.6, R.9, R.33–34; **Chapter 7:** 1.40, 1.44, 3.48–51, Q.9–10; **Chapter 8:** 1.62, 1.64, 3.49, 3.53, 3.57, 3.60–62, 4.41, R.28, Q.11; **Chapter 9:** 1.22, 2.40–41, 3.42, 3.47–50, 4.52–56, 5.27–29, 5.31, 6.41, R.4; **Chapter 10:** 2.47; **Chapter 11:** 1.34–35, 1.37, 2.32, R.10, R.12; **Chapter 12:** 1.28–29, 3.20, 3.23; **Chapter 13:** 1.32, 2.18, 2.22, 3.35, Q.10–12

Economics and Finance
Chapter 1: 2.69, 3.39, 3.43–44 **Chapter 2:** 1.70–73, 3.40, 3.44, 4.7; **Chapter 3:** 2.71, 3.17, 5.34–41; **Chapter 4:** 2.65–68, 3.48, 3.68, R.6–8; **Chapter 5:** 1.84, 3.102, 3.104; **Chapter 6:** 4.50, 4.52–53, 6.28, 6.32, 6.41–42, 7.25, 7.30, R.3; **Chapter 7:** 1.41, 1.45, 1.55–59, 2.32, 2.36, 2.40–43; **Chapter 8:** 1.50, 1.54, 1.58, 2.50, 2.58, 2.68, 4.34, 4.36, 4.40, R.4; **Chapter 9:** 1.19, 1.23–24, 2.36, 2.43, 3.39, 5.33, 7.19–22, R.6, R.13–14; **Chapter 10:** 2.31, 2.35–36, 2.42, 3.31, 4.37; **Chapter 11:** 1.39–40, 3.24, 4.24; **Chapter 13:** 1.36, 1.55, 2.27–28, 3.39

Education and Child Development
Chapter 1: 2.76–77, 3.38, R.7, R.9–10; **Chapter 2:** 1.93–94, 2.54–57, R.22; **Chapter 3:** 1.51, 2.55–58, 2.66, 2.68, 2.73, 3.19, 4.64–65, 6.15–19, R.11, Q.16–20; **Chapter 4:** 1.45–48, 1.59–61, 2.51, 2.53, 2.55, 2.57, 3.35, 3.37, 3.39, 3.41, 3.49–53, R.1–5, R9–20; **Chapter 5:** 1.73, 2.74, R.7; **Chapter 6:** 1.63, 1.67, 2.57, 2.61, 4.47, 4.50, 6.35, 6.39, R.6, R.9; **Chapter 7:** 1.42, 1.46, 1.60–64, 2.31, 2.35; **Chapter 8:** 2.50, 2.52, 2.54, 2.56, 2.69, R.17, Q.7, Q.16; **Chapter 9:** 3.35, 3.43, 4.49–51, 6.43, R.14; **Chapter 10:** 1.40–41, 2.32–34, 2.36, 2.38–40, 2.42; **Chapter 11:** 1.27, 1.30–32, 1.36, 1.38, 2.30–31, 2.38–42, R.7; **Chapter 12:** 1.23, 1.25, 1.34–35, 3.19, 3.22, 4.22; **Chapter 13:** 1.35, 1.43, 1.45, 2.19, 2.23, 2.26, R.1–2

The Nature of Statistics

Introduction

The goal of Section 1.1 is to demonstrate to students that the field of statistics provides the tools to understand the experiences of the real people behind the numbers. Section 1.2 covers the building blocks of data analysis, including many basic but crucial concepts that the rest of the book depends on, such as *population, sample, variable, element,* and *observation.* Section 1.3 investigates ways of gathering data, including random sampling, questionnaires, and statistical studies.

From the Author

- **Section 1.1 Data Stories: The People Behind the Numbers**
  - A main thrust of *Discovering Statistics* is student motivation. Section 1.1 tries to ease "stats anxiety" using a few illustrations of how statistics and graphs can be used to tell the story of real people going through real-life experiences. This may help some students relate to the subject more easily. For instance, the new Example 1.3, UFO Sightings, is more fun than the example it replaced. Some instructors like to assign Section 1.1 as reading, and then discuss in the next class.

- **Section 1.2 An Introduction to Statistics**
  - Chapter Case Study, page 8. You may wish to ask your students which best illustrates the difference in people's behavior on Friday the 13th, Table 1.3 or Figure 1.5. Hopefully, the response is Figure 1.5, where every green bar is longer than every yellow bar. Using graphs to help support hypotheses is *discovery-based* statistics, and that is why we titled the book *Discovering Statistics.*
  - There are a lot of definitions in this section. Most are very important and will be used throughout the course. Stress the importance of *statistical inference,* which is usually the goal of the intro stats course.

- **Section 1.3 Gathering Data**
  - You may wish to stress the very important topic of what constitutes a random sample. This phrase is used repeatedly throughout the book.
  - We added three new examples, one each for *Stratified Sampling, Systematic Sampling,* and *Cluster Sampling,* and added a Developing Your Statistical Sense feature for the difference between stratified and cluster sampling.

Teaching Tips

Starting Examples: Use the students in the classroom to illustrate the different types of sampling. To illustrate random sampling, write each person's name on a slip of paper and place all the slips of paper in a box. Then randomly select a certain number of names from the box. To show stratified sampling, divide the students into males and females or freshmen, sophomores, juniors, and seniors.

Instructor's Edition

Discovering Statistics

SECOND EDITION

Then select a random sample from each group. For systematic sampling, have the class count off to some number, such as 1, 2, 3, 1, 2, 3, and so forth. Then all of the 3s can be sampled. Clustered sampling can be demonstrated by randomly selecting a sample of rows or a sample of tables in the classroom, and then sampling everyone in the selected rows or the selected tables.

In-Class Activities

1. Getting to know you. It is often helpful to get to know the students a little better at the beginning of the semester. In this way, *the instructor can tailor his or her pedagogy to the individual life experiences of the students.* For example, students who played basketball or baseball in high school may be interested in sports examples or analogies. Here are some questions that will help the instructor learn more about "where the students are coming from." The instructor should ask the students to write down their responses and pass them in to the instructor.

- What is your name?
- Where are you from (town)?
- What is your major (e.g., communication, business administration)?
- Tell me a little about yourself, your interests, etc.
- What are your long-term goals? (What do you want to be after graduation?)
- What is something that you are really proud of about yourself?
- How do you feel about taking statistics?

2. Sample statistics versus population parameters.

  a. Break up into groups.

  b. What is the proportion of females in your group? Let us define our population to be all the students present in our class today. Is your group a sample or a population? Is the proportion of females in your group a statistic or a parameter?

  c. What is the population proportion of females in your class? In this activity, this proportion can be figured out by counting how many females are in the class and dividing by the number of students in the class, but for interesting real-world problems, population parameters like this are usually unknown. Note how the value of this parameter is a fixed constant, in this case between 0% and 100%.

  d. Make a list of the sample proportions of females for all the different groups. Note how each statistic may be different, so that statistics are not fixed constants but may vary from sample to sample.

Generating Random Data

3. Here is a fun way to generate random samples of students from your class by rolling a pair of dice! (For large lecture classes, it is probably easier to use technology or the *Random Sample* applet to generate a random sample. See the Step-by-Step Technology Guide at the end of Section 1.3 for instructions.) Make a table constructed as follows:

	1	2	3	4	5	6
1						
2						
3						
4						
5						
6						

Print this table on a sheet of paper and pass the paper around the class, having each student choose one cell and write his or her name in the cell. The numbers across the top are for the results of tossing a red die, and the numbers down the left are for the results of tossing a black. When a certain combination of red and black numbers is tossed, the student whose cell that combination refers to becomes part of the sample. In Chapter 5 we will learn that all the cells are equally likely to be picked if the dice are fair. If there are fewer than 36 students in your class, simply write *Roll Again* in the remaining empty cells after all students have chosen their cells. If there are more than 36 students in your class, just make more than one of these tables, and use a third colored die (for example, a green die) to choose which table is to be sampled. If a student is chosen more than once, simply roll again.

Do you think this arrangement will produce random samples? Can you suggest any other arrangements that will produce random samples from the population of students in your class?

4. Now let's take samples of the class.

   a. Let the instructor call the first 10 names on an alphabetical list of those present for class today. Is this a random sample? Why or why not? Find the proportion of females in this sample.

   b. Let the instructor ask those students who watched ESPN this week to raise their hands. Is this a random sample? Why or why not? Find the proportion of females in this group. Is this proportion the same as in (a)? Why doesn't it have to be the same?

   c. Get the dice out and generate a sample using the table(s) you constructed. Is this a random sample? Why or why not? Find the sample proportion of females. Is this the same as in (a) or (b)?

   d. Choose another sample as in (c). Is this a random sample? Find the sample proportion of females. Is it the same as in (a) or (b) or (c)?

Supplements

The following resources are available for instructors and students at the book Web site: www .whfreeman.com/discostat2e. (a) statistical applets, (b) online quizzes, (c) data sets in a variety of formats, (d) EESEE, case studies (access code required), and (e) CrunchIt! (access code required).

Further, the following additional resources are available through StatsPortal and Online Study Center: (a) StatTutor tutorials, (b) Stats@Work simulations, (c) Student and Instructor's Solutions Manuals, (d) Technology Manuals for Excel, Minitab, TI-83/84, and SPSS, (e) WHFStat Add-ins for Excel, (f) Lecture PowerPoint Slides.

StatTutor: Note some of the terminology used in StatTutor differs from that used in *Discovering Statistics*. For example, the elements of a data set are called individuals in StatTutor.

- Individuals and variables
- Explanatory and response variables
- Relationships between qualitative variables
- Experiments
- Randomized comparative experiments

Applets

The *Random Sample* applet is referenced in Chapter 1 to generate random samples. Additionally, it is used for Exercises 51–53 in Section 1.3.

A wealth of activities, tools, and applets can be found at **mathforum.org/mathtools**.

Videos

Against All Odds: Inside Statistics is a telecourse consisting of 26 half-hour programs. It was prepared by COMAP for the Annenberg/Corporation for Public Broadcasting Project. For more information (including free streaming videos), go to **www.learner.org/resources/series65.html**.

- *Against All Odds*
  - Program 1: What Is Statistics?

Web Sites

- This site has several activities that generate random data: **http://mathforum.org/mathtools/sitemap2/ps/**.
- This site has simulations for random data: **http://onlinestatbook.com/index.html**.
- This Texas Instruments Web site has TI-83/84 statistics activities that help to generate random data: **http://education.ti.com/educationportal/sites/US/nonProductSingle/activitybook_83_statistics.html**.

OVERVIEW

1

The Nature of Statistics

CASE STUDY

Does Friday the 13th Change Human Behavior?

Superstitions affect most of us. Some people will never walk under a ladder, while others will alter their path to avoid a black cat. Do you think that people change their behavior on Friday the 13th? Perhaps, suspecting that it may be unlucky, some people might elect to stay home and watch television rather than venture outdoors or drive on the highway.

But how does one go about researching such a question? How would *you* do it? In this chapter, we will learn about a British study that considered this question.

The Big Picture

Where we are coming from, and where we are headed . . .

- The objective of *Discovering Statistics* is to help you understand how to analyze and interpret data, and thereby become a successful citizen in the Information Age.

- Chapter 1 introduces the basic ideas of the field of statistics and the methods for gathering data.

- In Chapter 2 we will learn to summarize the data we have gathered using graphs and tables.

1.1 Data Stories: The People Behind the Numbers

OBJECTIVE By the end of this section, I will be able to . . .

1 Realize that behind each data set lies a story about real people undergoing real-life experiences.

We begin *Discovering Statistics* by sharing some data stories. We hope that these stories will kindle a response in you, be it sympathy or curiosity or concern, for behind every data set lies a story about the lives of real people. Individual people are speaking to us from behind the numbers.

Example 1.1   The reasons Katrina survivors did not evacuate

Hurricane Katrina was the costliest and one of the deadliest hurricanes in American history. Damages exceeded $50 billion and fatalities exceeded 1300, according to the National Oceanic and Atmospheric Administration. In September 2005, a survey was conducted of a group of hurricane survivors who had later been moved to shelters in the Greater Houston area. The respondents who did not evacuate were asked what was their most important reason for not evacuating. Figure 1.1 provides a bar graph of the responses, with Table 1.1 supplying more detailed information. ■

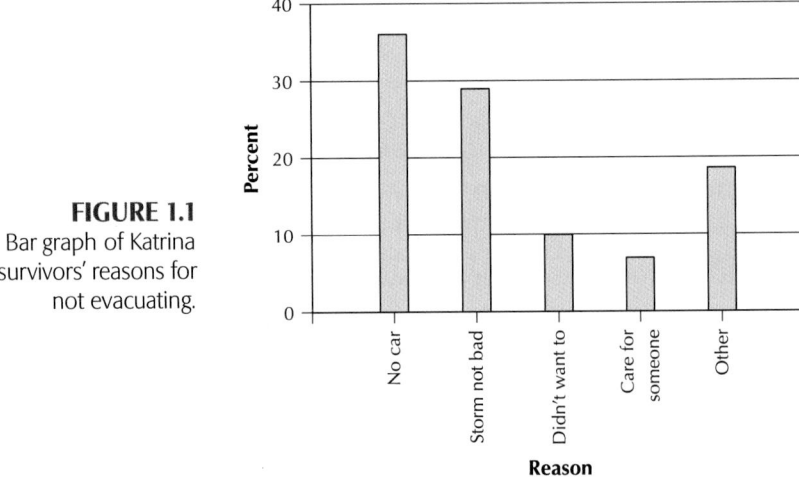

FIGURE 1.1
Bar graph of Katrina survivors' reasons for not evacuating.

Table 1.1 Katrina survivors' most important reasons for not evacuating

Reason	Percent
I did not have a car or a way to leave	36
I thought the storm and its aftermath would not be as bad as they were	29
I just didn't want to leave	10
I had to care for someone who was physically unable to leave	7
All other reasons	18

Example 1.2   Were there gender differences in the emotions experienced immediately after September 11, 2001?

On September 11, 2001, terrorists attacked New York City and Washington, DC. Do you think that men and women felt the same emotions about these attacks? In an NBC News Terrorism Poll conducted the day after the tragic events, the following question was asked: "Which one of the following emotions do you feel the most strongly in response to these terrorist attacks: sadness, fear, anger, disbelief, vulnerability?" Figure 1.2 is called a *clustered bar graph* and shows the results. The dominant emotion felt by the men was anger, while the women tended to feel either sadness, anger, or disbelief. Note how the bar graph makes these findings—that there were indeed systematic differences in the emotions felt by men and women regarding the events of September 11, 2001—crystal clear. We will learn how to construct bar graphs in Chapter 2, "Describing Data Using Graphs and Tables." ■

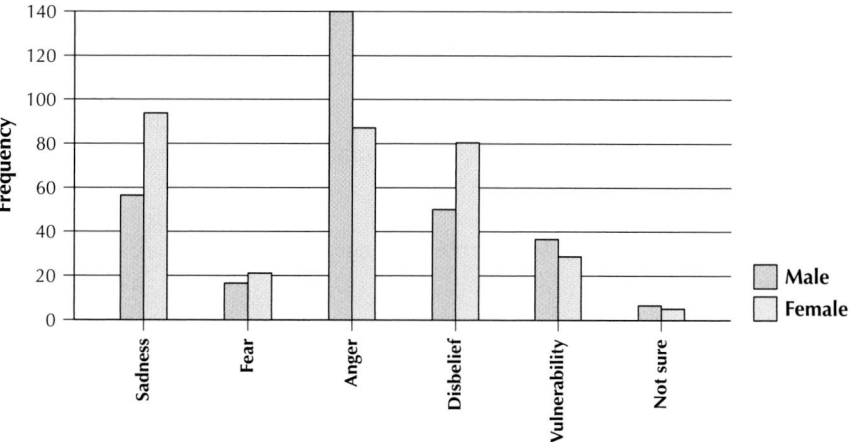

FIGURE 1.2 Clustered bar graph of strongest emotions felt regarding the September 11, 2001, attacks (by gender).

Example 1.3   UFO sightings

Have you or any of your friends sighted any unidentified flying objects (UFOs)? Americans in each of the 50 states have reported seeing UFOs. Figure 1.3 represents a scatterplot of the number of UFO sightings versus state population, for each of the 50 states. Each dot represents a state. The straight line is a regression line which approximates the relationship between UFO sightings and state population. As the state population increases, the number of UFO sightings also tends to increase, which is not surprising.

FIGURE 1.3
A scatterplot of the number of UFO sightings versus state population, showing that UFOs don't mess with Texas.

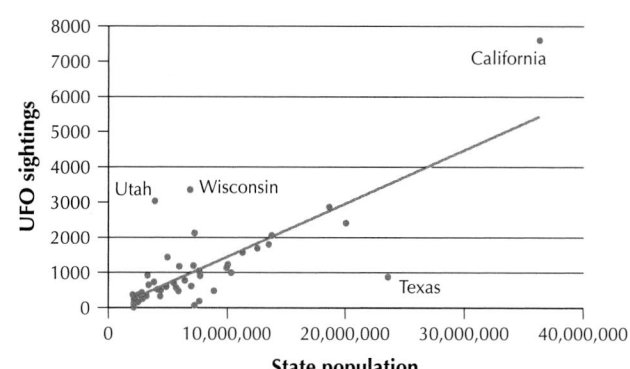

What may be surprising is that the UFOs seem to be attracted to certain states, and to avoid others. States considerably above the regression line have a larger than expected number of UFO sightings for their population size, while states below the line have a smaller than expected number of UFO sightings for their population size. So, there are more sightings than expected in California, Wisconsin, and Utah, given their population size, and fewer than expected in Texas. Why this might occur is open to discussion. Perhaps people in California are more likely to attribute unusual sightings to UFOs than most Americans; perhaps people in Texas are more pragmatic than most Americans. But if the sightings are valid (a big if!), it sure looks like the UFOs don't want to mess with Texas. We will learn how to construct and interpret scatterplots in Chapter 4, "Correlation and Regression," and we will learn how to quantify the relationship between two numerical variables in Chapter 4 and Chapter 13, "Inference in Regression." ∎

Section 1.1 Exercises

Refer to Example 1.1 for Exercises 1–4.

1. Refer to Figure 1.1.
   a. What does the graph say was the most common reason why the Katrina survivors did not evacuate?
   b. What does Table 1.1 say was the most common reason?

2. Refer to Figure 1.1.
   a. Which is more descriptive, the table or the figure?
   b. Why do you think the text in Figure 1.1 has been shortened?

3. If you were writing a news story that sought to display the Katrina survivors in the most sympathetic light, which reasons from Table 1.1 might you emphasize?

4. If you were writing a news story that sought to display the Katrina survivors in a less favorable light, which reasons from Table 1.1 might you emphasize?

Refer to Example 1.2 for Exercises 5 and 6.

5. Do you think the emotions felt were different for men and women? If so, then what evidence from Figure 1.2 would you offer in support of such a view?

6. Suppose you did not believe that the emotions felt were different for men and women. What evidence from Figure 1.2 could be offered in support of that position?

Refer to Example 1.3 for Exercises 7–10.

7. Estimate the following for the state of California.
   a. State population
   b. UFO sightings

8. Estimate the following for the state of Texas.
   c. State population
   d. UFO sightings

9. For a given population size, the expected number of UFO sightings falls on the regression line. For the state of California, what is the expected number of UFO sightings? (*Hint:* It's at the point on the line directly below the dot for California.)

10. For the state of Texas, what is the expected number of UFO sightings?

1.2 An Introduction to Statistics

OBJECTIVES By the end of this section, I will be able to . . .

1 Describe what the field of statistics is.

2 State the meaning of descriptive statistics.

3 Understand that inferential statistics refers to learning about a population by studying a sample from that population.

1 What Is Statistics?

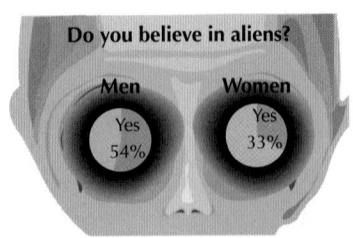

FIGURE 1.4 Graphs comparing percentages of men and women who believe in aliens. (© *USA Today*)

Do you believe in aliens? According to a recent survey, 54% of the men surveyed responded that they believed in aliens, and 33% of the women did (Figure 1.4). These numbers are examples of *statistics,* numbers that describe a group of people or things. Think about these numbers. Here are some questions we could ask about this survey:

- How did the pollsters arrive at these figures?

- Are the figures accurate? Could they be inaccurate?

- Why do pollsters never ask me my opinion about aliens?

- This survey found that more men than women believed in aliens. But is this difference meaningful or just a product of random chance?

These are some of the types of questions we shall be investigating throughout this book.

Examples of Statistics

Many people, including the author, first became interested in statistics as children collecting baseball cards. The back of each card contains the player's statistics season by season. Television networks routinely employ sports statisticians to collect and report statistics about sports figures. Table 1.2, for example, contains batting averages of the league-leading hitters from 2005 to 2009.

Table 1.2 Batting-average leaders, Major League Baseball, 2005–2009

Season	Player	Team	Batting average
2009	Joe Mauer	Minnesota Twins	.365
2008	Chipper Jones	Atlanta Braves	.364
2007	Magglio Ordonez	Detroit Tigers	.363
2006	Joe Mauer	Minnesota Twins	.347
2005	Derrek Lee	Chicago Cubs	.340

The informal meaning of the term *statistic* refers to a number that describes a person, a group, or a set of items. (On page 13, we provide a more precise definition of statistic.) For example, Joe Mauer's batting average of .365 is a statistic, because it is a number that describes his batting performance for the entire 2009 season. Apart from sports, most people become familiar with statistics through exposure to media reports or advertising, such as

- "Polls indicate a majority of Democrats support stem cell research."

- "The median home sales price in Connecticut has climbed in recent months to $250,000."

- "Three out of four dentists surveyed recommend sugarless gum for their patients who chew gum."

You may have noticed that the section title, "What Is Statistics?" refers to statistics in the singular. Why? Because the *field of statistics* involves much more than just collecting and reporting numerical facts. The field of statistics may be defined as follows.

> The field of **statistics** is the *art* and *science* of
> - collecting,
> - analyzing,
> - presenting, and
> - interpreting data.

A statistician, then, is not simply a sports analyst but any person trained in the art and science of statistics. You may be surprised at the inclusion of the word *art* in the definition of statistics. But there is no question that judgment, experience, and even a little intuition are indispensable tools for any statistician's portfolio.

For today's college student, the field of statistics is especially relevant and useful.

- For example, a *business major* may be interested in whether she should consider diversifying her portfolio to tech stocks, based on their price/earnings ratio.

- A *psychology major* may be interested in determining whether there are differences in therapeutic outcomes between traditional counseling methods and a new cognitive approach.

• An *education major* may be interested in whether listening to a Mozart sonata before taking an exam can significantly improve your grade.

The field of statistics can help solve each of these puzzles.

CASE STUDY

Does Friday the 13th Change Human Behavior?

How would researchers go about studying whether superstitions change the way people behave? What kind of evidence would support the hypothesis that Friday the 13th causes a change in human behavior? T. J. Scanlon and his coresearchers thought that if there were fewer vehicles on the road on Friday the 13th than on the previous Friday, this would be evidence that some people were playing it safe on Friday the 13th and staying off the roads.[1] Note that the researchers didn't simply argue about the validity of the Friday the 13th superstition. Such discussions are interesting but largely subjective. What they deemed important is the effect of such a superstition on human behavior and how to measure such an effect as a change in behavior.

Phase 1 **Data collection.** The first phase of a statistical study, as in the definition of statistics, is to *collect* the data. The researchers obtained data kept by the British Department of Transport on the traffic flow through certain junctions of the M25 motorway in England.

Phase 2 **Data analysis.** Next comes the analysis of the data. The authors compared the number of vehicles passing through certain junctions on the M25 motorway on Friday the 13th and the previous Friday during 1990, 1991, and 1992.

Note: There were 10 Friday the 13ths in 1990, 1991, and 1992.

Table 1.3 Traffic through M25 junctions, 1990–1992

Friday the 6th	Friday the 13th	Difference
139,246	138,548	698
134,012	132,908	1104
137,055	136,018	1037
133,732	131,843	1889
123,552	121,641	1911
121,139	118,723	2416
128,293	125,532	2761
124,631	120,249	4382
124,609	122,770	1839
117,584	117,263	321

Table 1.3 shows that, in every instance, the number of vehicles passing through these junctions on Friday the 13th was less than on the preceding Friday. Now, let's examine the data graphically. The clustered bar graph in Figure 1.5 illustrates the difference in the number of vehicles traveling on the M25 motorway on Friday the 6th (in green) and the subsequent Friday the 13th (in yellow) for 10 pairs (clusters) of dates. Note that, *in every instance,* the green bar is longer than its partner yellow

bar. This indicates that the number of vehicles on the motorway *decreased* on Friday the 13th when compared with the previous Friday in every instance.

FIGURE 1.5
Clustered bar graph of motorway traffic.

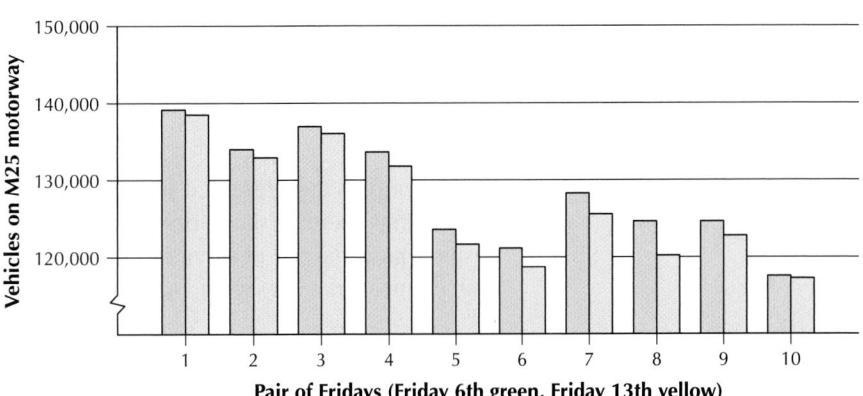

Phase 3 **Data presentation.** The *presentation* of the results is important, and the researchers found a highly respectable journal, the *British Medical Journal,* in which to publish their findings. Other avenues for presentation are delivering a talk at a conference, writing up a report for one's supervisor, or presenting a class project.

Phase 4 **Data interpretation.** Finally, the last facet in our definition of statistics is *interpretation.* It is crucial for those who are performing a statistical study to make their results understandable to nonstatisticians. It is not sufficient for the statistician alone to understand the results. Rather, the statistician must communicate the results clearly, whether in writing or orally. In this case, the researchers chose the decrease in number of vehicles as the criterion on which to base support for their hypothesis that people changed their behavior on Friday the 13th. Their finding of an observable decrease in traffic on Friday the 13th is consistent with their hypothesis. ■

2 Descriptive Statistics: The Building Blocks of Data Analysis

Every data set holds within it a story waiting to be told, as we saw in the Friday the 13th Case Study. To provide us with the tools to uncover these stories we need to learn some simple concepts, *the building blocks of data analysis.*

> **Descriptive statistics** refers to methods for summarizing and organizing the information in a data set.

In **descriptive statistics** we use numbers (such as counts and percents), graphs, and tables to describe the data set, as a first step in data analysis. In Chapters 2 to 4, we will examine descriptive methods much more closely. But first we need to introduce a few terms. Suppose a data analyst for a health maintenance organization (HMO) is collecting data about the patients in a particular hospital, including the diagnosis, length of stay, gender, and total cost. The sources of the information (the patients) are called the **elements.** The patients' characteristics (for example, diagnosis, length of stay) are called the **variables.** Finally, the complete set of characteristics for a particular patient is called an **observation.**

> **Elements, Variables, and Observations**
>
> An **element** is a specific entity about which information is collected.
>
> A **variable** is a characteristic of an element, which can assume different values for different elements.
>
> An **observation** is the set of values of the variables for a given element.

When data are presented in tables and spreadsheets, it is typical practice to have the columns indicate the variables, and the rows to indicate the elements. So, for the hospital patients, the observation (specific values for the set of all the variables) for each element (patient) would appear as a row in the table.

Example 1.4   Elements, variables, and observations

Information was collected on four students from two area colleges and is presented in Table 1.4.
a. What are the elements?
b. What are the variables?
c. List the values that the variable *gender* takes.
d. Provide the observation for Maria.

Table 1.4 Data set of four elements and seven variables

Student	Age	Gender	Ethnicity	No. of children	Marital status	GPA	College
Jamal	19	Male	African American	0	Single	4.00	Western CC
Maria	25	Female	Latina	2	Married	3.95	Northern State Univ.
Chang	20	Female	Asian	0	Single	3.90	Northern State Univ.
Michael	47	Male	European American	3	Divorced	3.75	Western CC

Solution
a. The elements are the students Jamal, Maria, Chang, and Michael.
b. The seven variables are age, gender, ethnicity, number of children, marital status, GPA, and college.
c. The variable *gender* takes values *female* and *male*.
d. Since the observation for Maria consists of the values for the variables in Maria's entire row, her observation is (see the following table) ■

Now You Can Do
Exercises 11–18.

Student	Age	Gender	Ethnicity	No. of children	Marital status	GPA	College
Maria	25	Female	Latina	2	Married	3.95	Northern State Univ.

Notice that we have variables that can take on various types of values, some of which are numbers and some of which are categories. For example, Maria is 25 years old, has two children, and has a GPA of 3.95, each of which is numeric. On the other hand, Maria is Latina, married, and enrolled at Northern State University, characteristics that do not have numeric values but instead are categories. This leads us to define two types of variables: **qualitative** and **quantitative.**

A **qualitative variable** is a variable that may be classified into categories. A **quantitative variable** is a variable that takes numeric values and upon which arithmetical operations such as addition or subtraction may be meaningfully performed.

Qualitative variables are also called *categorical variables*, because they can be grouped into categories. Maria's qualitative variables include her gender, ethnicity, marital status, and college. In contrast, Maria's grade point average is an example of a *quantitative variable*. Other quantitative variables include age and number of children.

Example 1.5 Qualitative or quantitative?

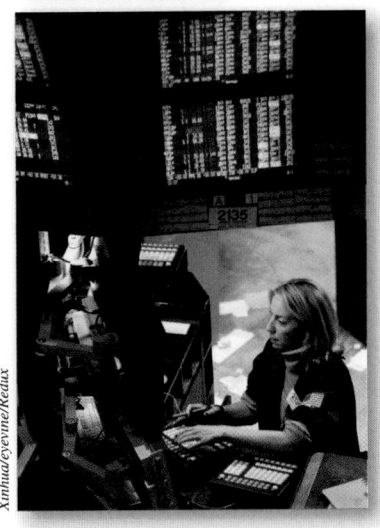

Xinhua/eyevine/Redux

NASDAQ (National Association of Securities Dealers Automated Quotations) is an American stock exchange that includes many technology companies.

Some of the most widespread applications of statistical analysis occur in the business world. Managers examine patterns and trends in data, thereby hoping to increase profitability. Table 1.5 shows the five most active stocks on the New York Stock Exchange (NYSE) and NASDAQ, as reported by *USA Today* for September 10, 2010. (a) What are the elements and the variables of this data set? (b) Which variables are qualitative? Which are quantitative? (c) Provide the observation for Intel Corporation.

Table 1.5 Most active stocks on NYSE and NASDAQ, September 10, 2010

Stock	Exchange	Last	Volume	Change
Citigroup, Inc.	NYSE	$ 3.91	256,441,698	0.00
Bank of America	NYSE	$13.55	85,884,565	+0.05
Intel Corporation	NASDAQ	$17.97	68,824,147	−0.17
Nokia Corporation	NYSE	$ 9.94	64,502,103	+0.18
Microsoft Corporation	NASDAQ	$23.85	58,293,790	−0.46

Solution

a. The *elements* are the five most active stocks traded on the NYSE and NASDAQ on this day in 2010. The *variables* are as follows:
  - Exchange: The exchange where the stock was traded.
  - Last: The most recent trading price for the stock.
  - Volume: How many shares of the stock were traded that day.
  - Change: The change in share price (in dollars) between the opening price and the closing price that day.

b. The exchange, since it can be categorized as either NYSE or NASDAQ, is qualitative. The other variables are quantitative.

c. The observation for Intel includes the exchange and the set of the day's stock data for that company. Intel is traded on the NASDAQ exchange. Its last share price was $17.97 per share, 68,824,147 shares of its stock were traded, and the price decreased by $0.17 per share. ■

Stock	Exchange	Last	Volume	Change
Intel	NASDAQ	$17.97	68,824,147	–0.17

Quantitative variables can be classified as either **discrete** or **continuous.**

Now You Can Do
Exercises 19–22.

Hint: A quantitative variable that must be counted (not measured) is probably a discrete variable, while a quantitative variable that must be measured (not counted) is probably a continuous variable.

A **discrete variable** can take either a finite or a countable number of values. Each value can be graphed as a separate point on a number line, with space between each point. A **continuous variable** can take infinitely many values, forming an interval on the number line, with no space between the points.

Example 1.6 Discrete or continuous?

In Table 1.4, determine whether the following variables are discrete or continuous: (a) number of children and (b) GPA.

Solution

a. Since the number of children per student is finite, the variable *number of children* is discrete.

Now You Can Do
Exercises 23–26.

b. Since GPA can take an infinite number of possible values, for example in the interval 0.0 to 4.0, the variable *GPA* is continuous. ■

Levels of Measurement

Data may be classified according to the following four *levels of measurement*.

- *Nominal data* consist of names, labels, or categories. There is no natural or obvious ordering of nominal data (such as high to low). Arithmetic cannot be carried out on nominal data.

- *Ordinal data* can be arranged in a particular order. However, no arithmetic can be performed on ordinal data.

- *Interval data* are similar to ordinal data, with the extra property that subtraction may be carried out on interval data. There is no *natural zero* for interval data.

- *Ratio data* are similar to interval data, with the extra property that division may be carried out on ratio data. There does exist a natural zero for ratio data.

Example 1.7 Levels of measurement

Identify which level of measurement is represented by the following data.
a. Years covered in European History 101: 1066–1492
b. Annual income of students in Statistics 101 class: $0–$15,000
c. Course grades in English 101: A, B, C, D, F
d. Student gender: male, female

Solution

a. The years 1066 to 1492 represent interval data. There is no natural zero (no "year zero"; the calendar goes from 1 B.C. to A.D. 1). Also, division (1492/1066) does not make sense in terms of years, so that the data are not ratio data. However, subtraction does make sense, in that the course covers 1492 − 1066 = 426 years.

b. Student income represents ratio data. Here division does make sense. That is, someone who made $4000 last year made twice as much as someone who made $2000 last year. Also, some students probably had no income last year, so that $0, the natural zero, also makes sense.

c. Course grades represent ordinal data, since (a) they may be arranged in a particular order, and (b) arithmetic cannot be performed on them. The quantity A − B makes no sense.

d. Student gender represents nominal data, since there is no natural or obvious way that the data may be ordered. Also, no arithmetic can be carried out on student gender. ■

Now You Can Do
Exercises 27–34.

3 Inferential Statistics: How Do We Get There from Here?

© Somos Image/Corbis

A victim of cyberbullying

Descriptive methods of data analysis are widespread and quite informative. However, the modern field of statistics involves much more than simply summarizing a data set. For example, suppose a sociologist claims that one-third of American teenagers have been the targets of cyberbullying, that is, have received a threatening message or have had their emails or text messages forwarded without their consent, an embarrassing picture posted without permission, or rumors spread about them online. How should the sociologist go about collecting evidence to support her claim? One method would be to ask each and every person in the population of all American teenagers. In general, a **population** is the collection of *all* elements (persons, items, or data) of interest in a particular study.

However, to ask every teenager in America about his or her online experiences is a daunting task that is expensive, time-consuming, and, in the end, simply impossible. So, unfortunately, the population proportion of American teenagers who have been the targets of cyberbullying remains *unknown*. This proportion who have been targets of cyberbullying is one characteristic of the population of American teenagers. A characteristic of a population is called a **parameter.** The actual value of a population parameter is often unknown.

A **sample** is a subset of the population from which information is collected. For example, from a sample of 100 teenagers at a local mall, 18 said they had been the targets of cyberbullying. That is, the sample proportion of students who had been targets is 18/100 = 18%. This proportion is a characteristic of the sample and is called a **statistic.** The advantage here is that, since the sample is relatively small, the characteristics of the sample can be determined.

Populations, Parameters, Samples, and Statistics

A **population** is the collection of *all* elements (persons, items, or data) of interest in a particular study. A **parameter** is a characteristic of a population.

A **sample** is a subset of the population from which information is collected. A **statistic** is a characteristic of a sample.

A sample is a subset of a population.

The U.S. Constitution requires that a census be conducted every 10 years. A **census** is the collection of data from every element in the population. As you can imagine, such a task is very difficult and very expensive. In fact, the Census Bureau estimates that the 2000 U.S. census "undercounted the actual U.S. population by over three million individuals."[2]

Because the population you are interested in may be too large to allow you to elicit information from every element, it is often best to gather data from a sample, a subset of that population. Also, time and money often constrain the researcher to choosing a sample rather than studying the entire population. Further, in some experiments, the resource is exhausted when testing is done, for example, in estimating the mean lifetime of light bulbs. Finally, it may be simply impossible to gather information from the entire population, such as when studying the quality of water in Lake Erie.

To estimate the proportion of all American teenagers who have been subjected to cyberbullying, we can use statistical inference. **Statistical inference** refers to learning about the characteristics of a population by studying those characteristics in a subset of the population (that is, in a *sample*). The Pew Internet and American Life Project conducted a survey of 886 teenagers and found that 284 of them (32%) said they had been the targets of cyberbullying.[3] These 886 teenagers represent a sample, and their characteristics can be known. For example, we know that 284 of the 886 teenagers in the sample said they have been subjected to cyberbullying. At this point, the sociologist can make the *inference* that the proportion of *all* American teenagers who have been subjected to cyberbullying is 32%, because this is the proportion in the sample. In doing this, the sociologist is performing *statistical inference.*

> **Statistical inference** consists of methods for estimating and drawing conclusions about population characteristics based on the information contained in a subset (sample) of that population.

"Now wait just a minute," you might object. "How can you say that the proportion of *all* American teenagers who have been subjected to cyberbullying is 32% just because your *sample* proportion is 32%?" Actually, you have a point. We *are* generalizing. We are taking what we know about a portion of the whole (a sample) and using it to draw a conclusion about the whole (the population). But even though the true proportion of American teenagers who have been the targets of cyberbullying is probably not exactly 32%, it is most likely not very far from 32%. The 32% is an *estimate,* an approximation based on sample data. In Chapter 8 we will learn how we can get the estimate as close as we wish to the actual value just by taking a large enough sample.

Finally, we need to point out one further attribute of parameters and statistics. The value of a parameter, even though it is unknown, is a fixed constant. For example, the average age of all persons in your home state (population) at noon today is unknown, but it still exists, and it is a single number. On the other hand, the value of a statistic depends on the sample. For example, a sample of 100 people in your hometown may produce an average age of 31. The average age of a sample of 100 people in a neighboring town may be 32. Later, we will learn that this is because a statistic is a *random variable*.

Of course, to deliver a valid estimate, the sample needs to be *representative* of the population. The sample should not differ systematically in any major characteristic from the population. We will learn more about this in Section 1.3, when we study sampling methods. Table 1.6 summarizes the attributes of a population and a sample.

Parameters are measures from a population, while statistics are measures from a sample. The characteristic associated with the population starts with the same letter, and the same is true for sample.

Table 1.6 Summary of attributes of population and sample

	Population	**Sample**
Thumbnail definition	All elements	Subset of population
Characteristic	Parameter	Statistic
Value	Usually unknown	Usually known
Status	Constant	Depends on sample

| Example 1.8 | Descriptive statistics or statistical inference? |

State whether the following situations illustrate the use of descriptive statistics or statistical inference.

a. In Baltimore County, Maryland, the average amount spent per week on gasoline consumption in a sample of 500 commuters was $75. The county government infers that the average amount spent weekly by all Baltimore County commuters is $75.

b. A sample of 100 residents of Broward County, Florida, yielded 27 residents who work for the government at the local, state, or federal level. Thus, 27% of these 100 residents work for the government.

c. The average age of a sample of 200 residents of Garden City, New York, was 34 years old.

d. In a survey of 1000 citizens in the Seattle, Washington, metropolitan area, 570 said they would pay higher prices in order to reduce greenhouse emissions. City planners conclude that 57% of all Seattle citizens would do so.

Solution

a. **Statistical inference.** A sample was taken, and a sample statistic ($75 per week) was calculated. Then the county government used this statistic to make the *statistical inference* that this was the average amount spent by all Baltimore County commuters.

b. **Descriptive statistics.** Though a sample was taken, there was no attempt to make an inference from this sample of 100 workers to the entire population of Broward County, Florida. So, there is no statistical inference here.

c. **Descriptive statistics.** The average age of 34 years old is a descriptive statistic, since it describes the sample. But no inference is made regarding a larger population.

d. **Statistical inference.** The survey found that 57% of the sample of 1000 citizens would pay higher prices in order to reduce greenhouse emissions. This 57% is a statistic. Then the city planners used this statistic in order to perform statistical inference about the population of all Seattle citizens. ∎

Now You Can Do
Exercises 55–62.

A Statistical Literacy Quiz

Regardless of major, every student in America (indeed, every citizen) needs to become *statistically literate* in order to survive in today's wired society. Why not take this quiz to find out if you are statistically literate? Answer each question true or false.

1. A fair coin is tossed five times and comes up heads each time. That means that tails is "due" and the chances of tails on the next toss is increased.

2. One politician says that the mean income is rising, while another politician says that the median income is falling. One of them has to be lying.

3. Jim is tested for HIV and the test comes back positive. Thus, Jim is HIV-positive.

The correct answer to each question is *false*. Question 1 deals with something called "the Gambler's Fallacy," and we will cover this, along with the explanation for Question 3, in Chapter 5, "Probability." We will deal with Question 2, the quirks of means and medians, in Chapter 3, "Describing Data Numerically."

Section 1.2 Summary

1 The field of statistics is the art and science of collecting, analyzing, presenting, and interpreting data.

2 Descriptive statistics refers to methods for summarizing and organizing the information in a data set. Data sets include information collected on elements. Variables are characteristics of an element, and can take different values for different elements. Variables may be either quantitative or qualitative. A discrete variable is a quantitative variable that can take either a finite or a countable number of possible values. A continuous variable is a quantitative variable that can take an infinite number of possible values. A population is a collection of all elements of interest, while a sample is a subset of the population.

3 Inferential statistics consists of methods for estimating and drawing conclusions about population characteristics based on the information in the sample. The characteristics for a population are called parameters, while the characteristics for a sample are called statistics.

Section 1.2 Exercises

CLARIFYING THE CONCEPTS

1. Write a sentence describing in your own words the field of statistics.

2. True or false: Statistical inference refers to methods for summarizing and organizing the information in a data set.

3. What do we call the entities from which the data are collected?

4. Describe the difference between a qualitative and a quantitative variable.

5. What is another term for a qualitative variable?

6. True or false: The actual value of a population parameter is usually unknown.

7. What is the difference between a sample and a population?

8. Explain what a statistic is.

9. Describe one difference between a statistic and a parameter.

10. What is a census?

PRACTICING THE TECHNIQUES

Refer to Table 1.7 for Exercises 11–14.

TABLE 1.7 Information about four statistics students

Student	Gender	Height	Class rank	Siblings	Math SAT
Michael	Male	67	Sophomore	2	510
Ashley	Female	67	Junior	1	520
Christopher	Male	70	Senior	0	490
Jessica	Female	66	Freshman	3	550

11. What are the elements?

12. List the variables.

13. List the values that the variable *class rank* takes.

14. Provide the observation for Jessica.

Refer to Table 1.8 for Exercises 15–18.

TABLE 1.8 Information about five hospitals

Hospital	Type	Number of floors	HMO ranking	Number of patients per nurse	Year opened
City	General	5	3rd	10.5	1999
Memorial	General	4	4th	12.7	1975
Children's	Specialized	3	1st	5.9	2005
Eldercare	Specialized	2	2nd	7.8	2009
County	General	6	5th	16.2	1967

15. What are the elements?

16. List the variables.

17. List the values that the variable *type* takes.

18. Provide the observation for Children's Hospital.

Refer to Table 1.7 for Exercises 19 and 20.

19. List the quantitative variables.

20. List the qualitative variables.

Refer to Table 1.8 for Exercises 21 and 22.

21. List the quantitative variables.

22. List the qualitative variables.

Refer to Table 1.7 for Exercises 23 and 24.

23. Which variables are discrete?

24. Which variables are continuous?

Refer to Table 1.8 for Exercises 25 and 26.

25. Which variables are discrete?

26. Which variables are continuous?

Refer to Table 1.7 for Exercises 27–30. Identify the variables that represent the following levels of measurement.

27. Nominal data

28. Ordinal data

29. Interval data

30. Ratio data

Refer to Table 1.8 for Exercises 31–34. Identify the variables that represent the following levels of measurement.

31. Nominal data

32. Ordinal data

33. Interval data

34. Ratio data

For Exercises 35–48:
  a. State whether the variable is qualitative or quantitative. If the variable is quantitative, state whether it is discrete or continuous.
  b. Identify the level of measurement represented by the data.

35. The year you were born

36. Whether you own a cell phone or not

37. The price of tea in China

38. The SAT Math score of the person sitting next to you (scores range from 200 to 800)

39. The winning score in next year's Super Bowl
40. The winning team in next year's Super Bowl
41. The rank of the winning Super Bowl team in its division
42. The number of friends on a student's Facebook page
43. Your favorite television show
44. How many contacts you have on your cell phone
45. Your favorite ice cream
46. Your credit card balance
47. How old your car is
48. What model your car is

For Exercises 49–54, identify the population and the sample.
49. A researcher is interested in the median home sales price in Tarrant County, Texas. He collects sales data on 100 home sales.
50. A psychologist is concerned about the health of veterans returning from war. She examines 20 veterans and assesses whether they show signs of post-traumatic stress disorder.
51. A sociologist wants to learn about the number of meetings per year of the 4-H clubs in Maricopa County, Arizona. He collects information from 10 different 4-H clubs in various parts of the county.
52. A physical therapist would like to determine whether a new exercise method can delay the onset of osteoporosis in older women. She chooses 10 of her patients to use the new method.
53. An educator asks a sample of students at Portland Community College whether they would be interested in taking a course online.
54. A financial adviser would like to assess the effect of mergers on price/earnings ratio. She collects data on 50 companies that recently underwent a merger.

For Exercises 55–62, state whether descriptive statistics or statistical inference was used, and explain why.
55. The average price in a sample of 15 homes sold in Jacksonville, Florida, for the week of April 21 was $253,200.
56. According to the Department of Transportation, 60% of all automobile passengers wear seat belts. This is based on a survey of 1000 automobile passengers, of whom 600 wore seat belts.
57. In a sample of 500 subjects, it was found that daily exercise lowered the average cholesterol level by 10%. A medical spokesperson then stated that daily exercise can lower everyone's cholesterol level by 10%.
58. In a sample of 140 traffic fatalities in New York, 75 involved alcohol.
59. The goals-against average for the Charlestown Chiefs hockey team in a sample of 20 games was 3.57 goals per game.
60. The Department of Health and Human Services conducted a survey, where it was found that the percentage of 15- to 18-year-olds using illicit drugs has dropped in the last two years. The department concluded that illicit drug use has fallen among all 15- to 18-year-olds.
61. The average on the first statistics exam for a sample of 10 students in Ms. Reynolds' class was 70.

62. A Department of Homeland Security survey of 750 Americans found that more than half of those surveyed feel safer than they did just after 9/11. The department concluded that more than half of all Americans feel safer than they did just after 9/11.

APPLYING THE CONCEPTS
For Exercises 63–70, do the following:
  a. List the elements and the variables.
  b. Identify the qualitative variables and the quantitative variables.
  c. For each variable, identify the level of measurement.
  d. For each quantitative variable, indicate whether it is discrete or continuous.
  e. Provide the observation for the indicated element.
63. **Endangered Species.** Refer to the following table, which lists four of the endangered animal species in the United States, as listed by **www.earthsendangered.com**. Do (**a**)–(**d**) and then provide the observation for the Florida panther.

Endangered species	Year listed as endangered	Estimated number remaining	Range
Pygmy rabbit	2001	20	Washington State
Florida panther	1973	50	Florida
Red wolf	1967	200	North Carolina
West Indian manatee	1967	2500	Florida

64. **Top Five Employers in Santa Monica, CA.** Refer to the following table. Do (**a**)–(**d**) and then provide the observation for the city of Santa Monica.

Company	Employees	Industry
City of Santa Monica	1892	Government
St. John's Health Center	1755	Health services
The Macerich Company	1605	Real estate
Fremont General Corp.	1600	Insurance
Entravision Corp.	1206	Media company

Source: Santa Monica Chamber of Commerce.

65. **Genetically Engineered Crops.** Genetically engineered (GE) crops are now planted on the majority of acreage in many states around the country. There are three varieties of GE corn: insect-resistant, herbicide-tolerant, and stacked genes. The following table contains the proportion of the corn grown in each of five states that is GE, along with the GE type most prevalent in each state, for 2007.[4] Do (**a**)–(**d**) and then provide the observation for the state of Texas.

State	Proportion of GE corn	Most prevalent type
Texas	79%	Herbicide-tolerant
Missouri	62%	Insect-resistant
Minnesota	86%	Herbicide-tolerant
Ohio	41%	Stacked genes
South Dakota	93%	Stacked genes

66. Crime Statistics for Stillwater, OK. Refer to the following table. Do (**a**)–(**d**) and provide the observation for motor thefts.

Crime type	2005 Total	Per 100,000 people	National per 100,000 people	Compared to national average
Robberies	10	24.4	195.4	Better
Assaults	83	202.4	340.1	Better
Burglaries	317	772.9	814.5	Better
Larceny/thefts	1147	2796.7	2734.7	Worse
Motor thefts	55	134.1	526.5	Better

67. Hospitals near Jackson, MS. Refer to the following table. Do (**a**)–(**d**). What is the observation for Rankin Medical Center?

Hospital	Beds	City	Zip
Hardy Wilson	49	Hazlehurst	39083
Humphreys County	34	Belzoni	39038
Jefferson County	30	Fayette	39069
Lackey Memorial	15	Forest	39074
Leake Memorial	25	Carthage	39051
Madison County	67	Canton	39046
Montfort Jones	72	Kosciusko	39090
Rankin Medical Center	134	Brandon	39042

68. Births and Maternal Age in Westchester County, NY. The following table represents the number of births and the average maternal age for 10 hospitals in northwest Westchester County, New York. Do (**a**)–(**d**). What is the observation for Sleepy Hollow?

Hospital	Births	Average maternal age
Briarcliff Manor	71	34.1
Buchanan	25	31.6
Cortlandt	348	32.2
Croton-on-Hudson	93	33.5
Mount Pleasant	277	32.8
Ossining 1	80	32.1
Ossining 2	371	29.2
Peekskill	365	29.0
Pleasantville	79	32.9
Sleepy Hollow	134	29.2

69. Commodity Prices. The financial company Bloomberg (www.bloomberg.com) reported that, on July 30, 2004, the prices in dollars for the following commodities were oil ($43.80, +1.05%), gold ($393.70, +3.90%), and coffee ($66.45, −1.20%). Do (**a**)–(**d**). What is the observation for gold?

70. Tornado Deaths. The Tornado Project (www .tornadoproject.com) reported the following list of the 10 years with the fewest tornado deaths. Do (**a**)–(**d**). What is the observation for 2004?

Year	Deaths	Year	Deaths
1910	12	1996	26
1986	15	1972	26
2004	16	1980	27
1981	24	1963	27
1962	25	1951	29

71. Radio Ratings. The ratings company Arbitron (www .arbitron.com) reports that 14% of all radio listeners listened to adult contemporary (AC) music. The breakdown within the AC category was Mainstream AC (7.8%), Hot AC (3.7%), Mod AC (0.8%), and Soft AC (1.7%).

   a. What are the elements? Can they be listed? Why or why not?

   b. What are the variables? Are they qualitative or quantitative?

   c. What proportion of AC listeners are Mainstream AC listeners?

72. Refer to Exercise 64 to answer the following questions.

   a. Do these five employers represent a sample or a population?

   b. Could these five companies be considered a representative sample of the number of employees per company for all companies in Santa Monica? Explain.

73. Refer to Exercise 70 to answer the following questions.

   a. Do the data in the table represent a sample or a population?

   b. Could these data be considered a representative sample of the number of annual tornado deaths for all years? Explain.

Light Bulb Lifetime. Use the following information for Exercises 74 and 75. An electrical company has developed a new form of light bulb that it claims lasts longer than current models. The company has 1 million bulbs in its inventory.

74. How do you think the company found evidence for its claim?

75. Suppose you take a representative sample of 100 of the new light bulbs and find the average lifetime to be 2000 hours.

   a. Is this a statistic or a parameter?

   b. Write a sentence that estimates the average lifetime of all the new light bulbs.

BRINGING IT ALL TOGETHER

Largest University Campuses. The National Center for Education Statistics reported that the university campuses with the largest enrollment in 2009 are as shown in the table. Use this information for Exercises 76 and 77.

Campus	Location	Enrollment	Rank
Arizona State	Tempe	55,552	1
Ohio State	Columbus	55,014	2
Central Florida	Orlando	53,537	3
Univ. of Minnesota	Minneapolis/ St. Paul	51,659	4
Univ. of Texas	Austin	51,032	5

76. Do the following:
  a. List the elements.
  b. List the variables.
  c. Identify the qualitative variables.
  d. Identify the quantitative variables.
  e. For each variable, identify the level of measurement.

77. Answer the following:
  a. Do these five campuses represent a sample or a population?
  b. Could these five campuses be considered a representative sample of the enrollment for all university campuses in the United States? Explain.
  c. Provide the observation for Arizona State University.
  d. Write a sentence that describes Ohio State University using the information from its observation.

1.3 Gathering Data

OBJECTIVES By the end of this section, I will be able to . . .

1 Explain what a random sample is, and why we need one.

2 Identify systematic sampling, stratified sampling, cluster sampling, and convenience sampling.

3 Explain selection bias and good questionnaire design.

4 Understand the difference between an observational study and an experiment.

1 Random Sampling

We can use the information gathered from a sample to generalize about the population when it is impractical or impossible to take a census of the entire population. However, if we get a "bad" sample, the information gleaned from the sample will be misleading, with potentially catastrophic consequences. This section introduces a method of sampling that minimizes many potential biases, which could lead to incorrect generalizations about the population. This sampling method is called *random sampling.* Everyday examples of random sampling include (a) randomly selecting lottery numbers from a basket which continuously churns the number-balls, (b) randomly choosing one card from a deck of playing cards that has been well shuffled, and (c) randomly pulling a name out of a hat, after the names have been well stirred. Since random samples are not always practical or desirable, this section also discusses some of the many alternative sampling methods available, including stratified sampling and cluster sampling.

What Is a Random Sample, and Why Do We Need It?

Survey sampling, or polling, has now become so widespread that hardly a day goes by without the results of some new poll or survey making the headlines. Polls are a good example of statistical sampling at work. The pollsters canvass about 1000 or so respondents, analyze the sample results, and then report their statistical inference that, for example, "32% of Americans have used a cell phone to access the Internet."

Today many polls are conducted quite scientifically, and their results are usually very accurate. However, such was not always the case. In 1936, the *Literary Digest* had correctly predicted the past three presidential elections and went to work to predict the winner of the contest between Republican Alf Landon and Democrat Franklin Roosevelt. The magazine sent ballots to 10 million citizens. The results ran strongly in favor of Landon, leading the *Literary Digest* to predict Landon to win the election. About 25% of the ballots were returned, giving the newsweekly a sample size of 2.5 million. George Gallup, on the other hand, was working with a sample size that was about 1000 times *smaller* than the *Literary Digest*'s. However, Gallup predicted a victory for Roosevelt. Clearly, with more data, the *Literary Digest* should have been able to give a more accurate prediction, right? Not necessarily. Roosevelt won in a landslide, and the embarrassed *Literary Digest* later declared bankruptcy.

The problem stemmed from the way that the *Literary Digest* identified its sample. It used lists of people who owned cars and had telephones, which in the 1930s excluded millions of poor and underprivileged people, who overwhelmingly supported Roosevelt. Its sample of 2.5 million therefore was highly biased toward the richer folks, who were less likely to have any great fondness for Roosevelt and his New Deal policies. Gallup, on the other hand, chose his sample more scientifically, and even though his sample size was smaller, it was more representative of the population as a whole.

One inexpensive way of eliminating many types of bias is to make sure your sample is a **random sample.**

Note: When we take a sample, we usually discard any repeated elements because we already have their information.

How the Gallup Organization Obtains a Random Sample

The Gallup Organization (www.gallup.com) has been conducting polls since the 1930s. People often wonder how a random sample of 1000 adults can represent the sentiments of the more than 300 million American adults. How does Gallup obtain a random sample in the first place? Gallup's objective is to make sure that every American has an *equal probability of selection,* that is, an equal chance of being selected, for their poll. Now, where is the place that most Americans are likely to be found? The answer for most Americans is: at home. (Gallup is aware that those who reside on college campuses, on military bases, and in other institutions are thereby not represented, but they usually accept this compromise due to the practical problems of including these institutions.)

In the early days, Gallup conducted interviews in person, going house to house. However, today it is much less expensive to conduct telephone interviews. How does Gallup help to ensure that its telephone sample is truly random? What about the Americans whose phone number is unlisted? The first step is to construct a table of all the telephone exchanges in America, along with an estimate of the proportion of Americans living in that exchange area and the broad characteristics of that population in terms of income, age, ethnicity, education, and so on. Gallup then uses *random digit dialing,* a computer program that generates random four-digit numbers, which are then appended to the telephone exchanges. Thus, each household phone number in America has an equal chance of being included in the sample, regardless of whether it is listed or unlisted. Finally, as of January 1, 2008, Gallup added a data base of cell phone numbers, in order to contact those who can more readily be reached via cell phone.

Example 1.9   Do you prefer watching the Super Bowl or the commercials?

In February 2007, the Gallup Organization used random digit dialing in a poll of Americans who planned to watch the Super Bowl (Indianapolis Colts versus Chicago Bears). One question they asked was whether the subjects preferred to watch the game or the commercials. Does this represent a random sample?

Solution

Since random digit dialing ensures that each household phone number in America has an equal chance of being included in the sample, the sample is random.

A perhaps surprising 33% of respondents reported that they preferred watching the commercials, compared with 66% who preferred watching the game. Gender and age seemed to affect how one responded to this question. Twice the proportion of female viewers (44%) as male viewers (22%) preferred watching the commercials. Among females only, more than twice as many younger (aged 18 to 49) women preferred watching the commercials (56%) as older (aged 50 and over) women (26%). ■

 Random samples may be generated using technology, using the *Random Sample* applet, or using the random number table provided in Table A in the Appendix (page T-2). At the end of this section, we demonstrate how to generate random samples using the TI-83/84 graphing calculator, Excel, and Minitab.

Example 1.10 Generating a random sample using technology

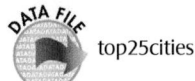 top25cities

Recently, *Inc. Magazine* published a list of the top 25 cities for doing business, shown in Table 1.9. Use the TI-83/84, Excel, or Minitab to generate a random sample of 7 cities from this list.

Table 1.9 Top 25 cities for doing business, according to *Inc. Magazine*

1. Atlanta, GA	10. Suburban Maryland/DC	19. Austin, TX
2. Riverside, CA	11. Orlando, FL	20. Northern Virginia
3. Las Vegas, NV	12. Phoenix, AZ	21. Middlesex, NJ
4. San Antonio, TX	13. Washington, DC, metro area	22. Miami–Hialeah, FL
5. West Palm Beach, FL	14. Tampa–St. Petersburg, FL	23. Orange County, CA
6. Southern New Jersey	15. San Diego, CA	24. Oklahoma City, OK
7. Fort Lauderdale, FL	16. Nassau–Suffolk, NY	25. Albany, NY
8. Jacksonville, FL	17. Richmond–Petersburg, VA	
9. Newark, NJ	18. New Orleans, LA	

Solution

We used the instructions provided in the Step-by-Step Technology Guide at the end of this section (page 30) to create three random samples, listed below. Note that each random sample is different, as yours will be. ■

Random sample 1 using the TI-83/84	Random sample 2 using Excel	Random sample 3 using Minitab
9. Newark, NJ	6. Southern New Jersey	3. Las Vegas, NV
25. Albany, NY	23. Orange County, CA	21. Middlesex, NJ
6. Southern New Jersey	11. Orlando, FL	18. New Orleans, LA
20. Northern Virginia	14. Tampa–St. Petersburg, FL	7. Fort Lauderdale, FL
24. Oklahoma City, OK	25. Albany, NY	2. Riverside, CA
10. Suburban Maryland/DC	7. Fort Lauderdale, FL	25. Albany, NY
1. Atlanta, GA	17. Richmond–Petersburg, VA	10. Suburban Maryland/DC

Now You Can Do
Exercise 23.

2 More Sampling Methods

In certain circumstances, simple random sampling can have shortcomings. A simple random sample may not provide sufficient information about subgroups within the population. For example, suppose you are interested in knowing the proportion of those of Latino descent in Walnut, California, who are registered Democrats. A random sample of size 100 of all the voters in Walnut may yield only 20 of Latino descent, which may be too small a sample to be useful for statistical inference. Therefore, the researcher needs other methods for obtaining samples, depending on the situation and the research question.

Note: Most of the sampling methods mentioned here involve randomness. However, only the simple random sample is used throughout the text. Therefore, whenever you see the phrase *random sample*, it should be understood as *simple random sample.*

Systematic Sampling

Perhaps the easiest method of sampling is systematic sampling, which is used when a random sample is unobtainable. In systematic sampling, each element of the population is numbered, and the sample is obtained by selecting every kth element, where k is some whole number. The first element selected corresponds to a random whole number between 1 and k. The ancient Romans understood well how to use systematic sampling. When a Roman legion mutinied or showed cowardice in battle, every 10th member was selected and summarily executed before his comrades. Literally, the legion was *decimated,* from the Latin *decem,* meaning "ten."

Example 1.11   Systematic sampling

 20richest

Table 1.10 contains the top 20 richest people in the world for the year 2010, according to the annually published *Forbes 400* listing. Obtain a systematic sample from this list, using $k = 4$.

Table 1.10 Twenty richest people in the world

Rank	Name	Net worth ($ billion)	Rank	Name	Net worth ($ billion)
1	Bill Gates	54	11	Larry Page	15
2	Warren Buffett	45	12	Sergey Brin	15
3	Larry Ellison	27	13	Sheldon Adelson	14.7
4	Christy Walton	24	14	George Soros	14.2
5	Charles Koch	21.5	15	Michael Dell	14
6	David Koch	21.5	16	Steve Balmer	13.1
7	Jim Walton	20.1	17	Paul Allen	12.7
8	Alice Walton	20	18	Jeff Bezos	12.6
9	S. Robson Walton	19.7	19	Anne Cox Chambers	12.5
10	Michael Bloomberg	18	20	John Paulson	12.4

Source: Forbes magazine.

Solution

First we randomly select a whole number between 1 and $k = 4$. Suppose we select 2. Thus, our systematic sample will consist of every 4th person in Table 1.10, starting with the 2nd person. That is, our systematic sample will consist of the 2nd, 6th, 10th, 14th, and 18th persons, shown here:

Systematic sample: Warren Buffett, David Koch, Michael Bloomberg, George Soros, Jeff Bezos. ∎

Now You Can Do
Exercise 24.

Stratified Sampling

Often, researchers are interested in investigating characteristics of a certain subgroup of a population, such as those of Latino descent in Walnut, California. In cases like this, the researcher divides the population into subgroups, or *strata,* according to some characteristic, such as race or gender. Then a random sample is taken from each stratum. In this way, the researcher knows that a sample will be obtained from each stratum and that it will be large enough to provide reliable statistical inference for each stratum.

Example 1.12   Stratified sampling

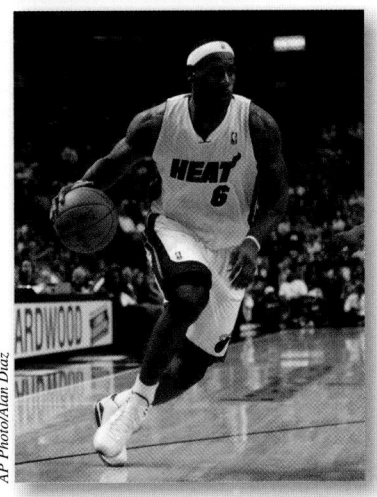

AP Photo/Alan Díaz

LeBron James, of the Miami Heat.

A researcher is interested in analyzing whether there are differences in scoring among the basketball teams in the three divisions of the Eastern Conference of the National Basketball Association (Table 1.11). Obtain a stratified sample of two teams from each division.

Table 1.11 Teams in the three divisions of the Eastern Conference of the National Basketball Association

Atlantic Division	Central Division	Southeast Division
Boston Celtics	Chicago Bulls	Atlanta Hawks
New Jersey Nets	Cleveland Cavaliers	Charlotte Bobcats
New York Knicks	Detroit Pistons	Miami Heat
Philadelphia 76ers	Indiana Pacers	Orlando Magic
Toronto Raptors	Milwaukee Bucks	Washington Wizards

Solution

A random sample of size two was drawn from the teams in each of the three divisions. These six teams are then combined to form our stratified sample of basketball teams. Note that each random sample is different, as yours will be. ■

Atlantic Division	Central Division	Southeast Division
Boston	Chicago	Atlanta
New Jersey	Cleveland	Charlotte
New York	Detroit	Miami
Philadelphia	Indiana	Orlando
Toronto	Milwaukee	Washington

Stratified sample of 6 teams

Boston Celtics
Cleveland Cavaliers
Miami Heat
Milwaukee Bucks
New York Knicks
Orlando Magic

Now You Can Do
Exercise 25.

Cluster Sampling

Cluster sampling is used when the population is widely scattered geographically or poses other logistical difficulties. For example, if we were interested in estimating the mean income of Manhattan residents, it would be time-consuming and expensive to visit 1000 different locations in Manhattan to elicit sample information. In cluster sampling, the population is divided into *clusters,* such as precincts or city blocks. Then several clusters are chosen at random, and all of the elements within the chosen clusters are selected for the sample. One disadvantage of cluster sampling is that the respondents from within a certain cluster will tend to be more similar to each other than the elements of a random sample would be. For example, if one of the clusters in the Manhattan income survey was a Fifth Avenue block, the mean income of residents there would be at the higher end of the income scale.

Example 1.13 | Cluster sampling

Using Table 1.11, consider each division to be a cluster. Construct a cluster sample of the teams in the Eastern Conference by randomly selecting two of the three clusters (divisions).

Solution

Suppose that we randomly select our clusters to be the Atlantic Division and the Southeast Division. Our cluster sample then consists of *all* the teams in both of these divisions, as follows: ■

Atlantic Division	Central Division	Southeast Division
Boston	Chicago	Atlanta
New Jersey	Cleveland	Charlotte
New York	Detroit	Miami
Philadelphia	Indiana	Orlando
Toronto	Milwaukee	Washington

Cluster sample of 10 teams

Atlanta Hawks
Boston Celtics
Charlotte Bobcats
Miami Heat
New Jersey Nets
New York Knicks
Orlando Magic
Philadelphia 76ers
Toronto Raptors
Washington Wizards

Now You Can Do
Exercise 26.

 Developing Your
Statistical Sense

Stratified Sampling versus Cluster Sampling

Stratified sampling and cluster sampling are sometimes confused. To obtain a stratified sample, we (a) divide the population into subgroups (strata, the divisions in Table 1.11), and (b) take a random sample from each subgroup, as shown by the shaded teams in Example 1.12. In cluster sampling, we (a) divide the population into subgroups (the divisions in Table 1.11, this time called clusters), (b) take a random sample of the clusters, as shown by the shaded divisions in Example 1.12, and (c) choose *all* the elements in the selected clusters for our cluster sample. In stratified sampling, we are randomly selecting elements from the subgroups; in cluster sampling, we are randomly selecting the clusters only, not the elements in the clusters. ◢

Convenience Sampling

In convenience sampling, subjects are chosen based on what is convenient for the survey personnel. If you were to estimate the true proportion of females taking an introductory statistics course using only the people in your class, this would considered a convenience sample. As we shall see in Example 1.14, convenience sampling usually does not result in a representative sample.

Example 1.14 | Convenience sampling using online polls

An online newspaper reports that, in an online poll of its readership, 60% say that they get most of their news from online sources. Does this number accurately reflect the proportion of all Americans who get most of their news from online sources?

Solution

No, the sample is not random. Only those Americans who are online already (and already using an online news source) can respond to this online poll. Therefore, the sample is not random, and it is biased. It overestimates the proportion of Americans who get their news from online sources. Further, there is no mechanism to guard against a single person responding repeatedly and getting his or her vote counted multiple times. Online polls are not scientific, and their results should not be considered a true reflection of the sentiments of all Americans. ■

Caution: Surveys, like online polls, that use convenience sampling should be treated with a healthy dose of skepticism. They are not statistically sound.

Example 1.15 Identify the sampling method

For each of the following, identify which type of sampling is represented.
a. Students in your class are divided into females and males. A random sample of size 5 is then drawn from each of the groups.
b. You are interested in estimating the average number of hours dormitory residents spend studying. In each dormitory, one floor is chosen at random and all the students on that floor are interviewed.
c. You are researching the proportion of college students who prefer country music to other forms of music. You obtain a listing of all the students at your college and contact every 20th student on the list.
d. Your campus statistical consulting center uses random digit dialing to locate potential subjects for a political survey.
e. A student is investigating the prevalence of flu on campus this semester, and asks 20 of his friends whether they have had the flu.

Solution

a. This is stratified sampling because (a) the population was divided into subgroups (females and males), and (b) a random sample was drawn from each of the groups.
b. This is cluster sampling because (a) the population was divided into clusters (dormitory floors), (b) a random sample of the clusters (floors) is taken, and (c) all students on that floor (cluster) were selected.
c. This is systematic sampling, where every kth member of the population is taken, with $k = 20$.
d. This is an example of random sampling, as illustrated on page 20.
e. This is convenience sampling, since the student is choosing a sample convenient for him. ■

Now You Can Do
Exercises 7–10.

3 Selection Bias and Questionnaire Design

Here we learn about some common pitfalls in the design and implementation of a survey, including selection bias and the wording of a questionnaire.

The **target population** is the complete collection of all elements that we are interested in studying.

The **potential population** is the collection of elements from the target population that had a chance of being sampled.

Selection bias occurs when the population from which the actual sample is drawn is not representative of the target population, due to an inappropriate sampling method.

Example 1.16 Selection bias

Suppose Ashley would like to estimate the proportion of American voters who would favor abandoning the present system of Social Security in favor of a system where retirement funds would be invested in the stock market. Ashley goes to the mall with her clipboard, and canvasses as many people as she can on Monday between 9 A.M. and 5 P.M. To each person, she asked the question "Do you favor or oppose abandoning the present Social Security system in favor of a system that invests retirement funds in the stock market?"

a. Identify Ashley's target population.
b. Identify Ashley's potential population.
c. Discuss any possible problems.

Solution

a. Ashley's **target population** is the population of all American voters.
b. The collection of all the American voters who visited the mall on Monday between 9 A.M. and 5 P.M. represent her **potential population.**
c. It appears that Ashley's survey may suffer from **selection bias.** The population of people who went to the mall on Monday between 9 A.M. and 5 P.M. is not representative of the target population of all American voters. Since many American voters work on Mondays between 9 A.M. and 5 P.M., they are not elements of the sampled population. Further, the proportion of retirees at the mall during that time was larger than in the target population of all American voters. These retirees tend to oppose strongly any tampering with the Social Security system and would probably tend to respond in the negative to the survey question. ■

Now You Can Do
Exercises 11–14.

Five Factors for Good Questionnaire Design

You may have heard of the aphorism "Be careful what you ask for; you may get it." This warning is certainly relevant to the issue of questionnaire design. The wording of questions can greatly affect the responses. Here are several factors to consider when designing a questionnaire.

1. **Remember: simplicity and clarity.** Do not use four-syllable words when one-syllable words will do. Respondents will be shy about asking you to clarify the question. The result will be confused responses and muddled data.

2. **When reporting results, include the actual question asked.** Be careful about drawing generalizations. The conclusions you draw may not have been what your respondents had in mind when they answered the questions.

3. **Avoid leading questions.** The respondent is often eager to please and will try to tell you what he or she thinks you want to hear. For example, a researcher is interested in determining the proportion of Americans who favor preserving the welfare system. A leading question would be "A child growing up poor in America faces more than his fair share of crime and negligence. Do you support preserving the welfare safety net to help ensure that children are given a fair chance?"

4. **Avoid asking two questions in one.** Avoid questions like "Have you argued with your friends or family in the last month?" This is really two questions in one, and you will not know which question the respondents are answering.

5. **Avoid vague terminology.** Words mean different things to different people. Avoid using terminology like "often" or "sometimes." Instead, try to use specific terms such as "three times a week." If you use ambiguous terms, the data you collect will be ambiguous, and any conclusions you draw will probably not be valid.

Example 1.17 | Questionnaire design

For each of the following questionnaire items, identify which of the five factors for good questionnaire design is violated, if any.

a. Do you oppose the wasteful spending on foreign aid when so many problems confront us here at home?

b. Do you often feel lonely?

c. Do you espouse or disavow the conglomerative confluence of macroeconomic indicators?

d. Have you watched television or downloaded music in the past 24 hours?

e. Do you ever use a cell phone to access the Internet?

Solution

a. This is a leading question, which is clearly trying to influence the respondent's answer.

b. What is meant by "often"? Three times a week? Three times a day? This is vague terminology.

c. This question would only be understood by those who have studied economics, and is neither simple nor clear.

d. This is asking two questions in one. It is possible that respondents have done one or the other, or both.

Now You Can Do
Exercises 15–18.

e. This question is fine. In fact, it is an actual survey question from the Pew Research Center. ∎

4 Experimental Studies and Observational Studies

Two major types of statistical studies are **experimental studies** and **observational studies.** We have seen that researchers can gather data by consulting existing sources, by distributing a questionnaire, or by taking a sample. However, you may not be able to obtain the information you require by using survey or sampling methods. In this case, you may prefer to conduct an experimental study.

Note: What is the difference between an element and a subject? *Subject* is a term usually reserved for statistical studies, while the term *element* can be used for any data set.

> **Experimental Studies**
>
> In an **experimental study**, researchers investigate how varying the predictor variable affects the response variable.
>
> A **predictor variable** (also called an **explanatory variable**) is a characteristic intended to explain differences in the response variable.
>
> A predictor variable that takes the form of a purposeful intervention is called a **treatment.**
>
> A **response variable** is an outcome, a characteristic of the subjects of the experiment presumably brought about by differences in the predictor variable or treatment.
>
> The **subjects** in a statistical study represent the elements from which the data are drawn.

We illustrate experimental studies using the following example.

Example 1.18   Newborn babies and a heartbeat: an experimental study

Thinkstock

A psychologist wanted to test whether the sound of a human heartbeat would help newborn babies grow. A baby nursery at a hospital was set up so that the sound of a human heartbeat could be heard throughout the nursery. The heartbeat sound was played in the nursery for a large batch of newborn children, who were then weighed to determine their weight gain after four days in the nursery. Later, a second batch of children occupied the nursery, but no heartbeat sound was played. These children were also weighed after four days in the nursery. Babies were randomly placed into the two groups. Identify the following:
a. The subjects
b. The predictor variable
c. The treatment
d. The response variable

Solution

a. The babies were the **subjects** of this experimental study.
b. The **predictor variable** is whether or not the heartbeat sound was played in the nursery.
c. The **treatment** is the sound of the human heartbeat.
d. The **response variable** is the baby's weight gain, which is the outcome of the study.

The results were consistent with the psychologist's conjecture; the babies who listened to the heartbeat sound had a greater average weight gain than the babies for whom no heartbeat sound was played. ∎

Now You Can Do
Exercises 27–34.

There are three main factors that should be considered when designing an experimental study: *control, randomization,* and *replication.*

Control.   A control group is necessary to compare against the treatment group, if we wish the results of our experiment to be useful. The control group in the above example is the group of babies for whom the heartbeat sound was not played. Had the psychologist omitted this control group, there would have been nothing to compare his results against. In some experiments, especially in medicine, members of the control group receive a placebo, a nonfunctioning simulated treatment. Sometimes, the symptoms of the members of the control group improve simply by taking the placebo, a phenomenon known as the *placebo effect*.

Randomization.   Many biases can be introduced into an experiment. For example, a well-meaning doctor may want to place underweight high-risk babies in the group with the heartbeat, in the hope that such babies will flourish. To eliminate biases like these, the placement of the subjects into the treatment and control groups should be done randomly.

Replication.   One major theme of statistical investigation is that larger samples are usually better, because they allow more precise inference. In a statistical study, the treatment and the control groups each must contain a large enough number of subjects to allow detection of meaningful differences between the treatment and control. For example, if a researcher examined only three babies with the heartbeat sound and three babies without the heartbeat sound, this would not be a sufficient number of replications. In Chapter 8, "Confidence Intervals," we will learn how large a sample size is sufficient for the needs of a particular study.

Observational Studies

There are circumstances where it is either impossible, impractical, or unethical for the researcher to place subjects into treatment and control groups. For example, suppose we are interested in whether women who work outside the home suffer less depression than women who remain at home with the children. The explanatory variable here is whether or not a woman works outside the home. However, it is not possible for the researcher to take women and randomly separate them into groups that either work outside the home or do not work outside the home.

Sometimes an experimental study is not possible for ethical reasons. Suppose you are interested in whether babies born to chemically dependent mothers display differences in cognitive skills from babies born to mothers who are not chemically dependent. It is clearly not ethical to randomly assign half of the mothers in the study to become chemically dependent during their pregnancy. Therefore, researchers need another type of statistical study: the observational study. In an observational study, the researcher observes whether the subjects' differences in the predictor variable are associated with differences in the response variable. No attempt is made to create differences in the predictor variable.

A sample survey is an example of an observational study. Data about a response variable may be obtained through the survey, along with information about possible predictor variables. No attempt is made to manipulate the variables. The researcher analyzes the information to determine whether differences in the predictor variable are associated with differences in the response variable.

Example 1.19   **Is Ecstasy toxic to your neurons?**

According to the British medical journal *The Lancet*, experimental studies carried out on animals (nonhuman primates, squirrel monkeys, and rodents) have revealed that large doses of the drug Ecstasy (methylene-dioxy-methamphetamine, or MDMA) produce "large and possibly permanent damage" to neural axons in the brain. Explain why the researchers did not carry out their experiment on humans.

Solution

It is not ethical to randomly assign half of the human subjects to receive large doses of the drug Ecstasy, especially in view of its effect on animals. The difficulty of performing experimental studies on humans concerning the effects of controlled substances is addressed by the authors of the *Lancet* study:

> *Only a prospective[experimental] study . . . could definitively show that recreational MDMA use was neurotoxic in human beings. For ethical, political, and legal reasons such a study is unlikely to ever be done. Instead, we have to rely upon evidence from observational studies of recreational MDMA users.*[5] ∎

Now You Can Do
Exercise 47.

A **random sample** (also known as a **simple random sample**) is a sample for which every element has an equal chance of being selected.

The *Random Sample* applet allows you to produce a random sample of up to 100 elements, in the form of a lotto.

STEP-BY-STEP TECHNOLOGY GUIDE: Generating a Random Sample

We illustrate using Example 1.10 (page 21).

TI-83/84

Step 1 Enter a "seed," which can be any nonzero number.
Step 2 Press **STO** ⇒.
Step 3 Press **MATH**, highlight **PRB**, select **1: rand**, and press **ENTER** (see Figure 1.6, which uses 1776 for the seed). Your seed number is now in the calculator's memory.
Step 4 Press **MATH**, highlight **PRB**, and select 5: **randInt(**.
Step 5 Enter **1, N,** *two times* **n**, where N = population size and **n** = sample size. We enter twice the sample size in case there are repeats. For Example 1.10, since **n** = 7, we enter **randInt(1, 25, 14)** and press **ENTER** (Figure 1.7).
Step 6 Store the random sample in list **L1** as follows: press **STO** ⇒, then **2ND**, then **L1** (Figure 1.7). Then press **ENTER**.
Step 7 View the random sample by pressing **STAT**, highlighting **EDIT**, and pressing **ENTER** (Figure 1.8). Note that there is a repeat (**6**). We therefore select the next number, **10**, to round out our sample. The random sample for Example 1.10 is therefore **9, 25, 6, 20, 24, 10, 1** (Figure 1.9).

FIGURE 1.6

FIGURE 1.7

FIGURE 1.8

FIGURE 1.9

EXCEL

Step 1 Select cell **A1**. Click the **Insert Function** icon f_x.
Step 2 For "Search for a function," enter **randbetween**. Click **Go**, then **OK**.
Step 3 For **Bottom**, enter **1**. For **Top**, enter population size **N**. For Example 1.10, **N** = 25. Click **OK**.
Step 4 Cell **A1** now contains a random integer between **1** and **N**. Copy and paste cell **A1** into *twice* as many cells as needed for the sample size **n**, just in case there are repeats. For Example 1.10, copy and paste into cells **A2** to **A14**. The results are shown in Figure 1.10. Note that **8** is repeated, so that our random sample is **8, 2, 20, 16, 23, 7, 22**.

FIGURE 1.10 Excel random sample.

MINITAB

Step 1 Click on **Calc > Random Data > Integer . . .**
Step 2 In the **Generate __ rows of data** section, enter *twice* your desired sample size, just in case there are repeats. For example, if your desired sample size is **7**, enter **14**.
Step 3 In the **Store in column __** section, enter whichever column is convenient for you, such as **C1**.
Step 4 For **Minimum value**, enter **1**. For **Maximum value**, enter your population size, **N**. Click **OK**.
Step 5 The random integers appear in column **C1**. Start from the top and go down the list, omitting any repeats, until you have your sample of size **n**. Our random sample (Figure 1.11) is therefore **3, 18, 2, 11, 21, 7, 25**.

FIGURE 1.11 Minitab random sample.

Excel and Minitab base the seed on the current time, so that you need not set it yourself.

Section 1.3 Summary

1 A random sample is a sample for which every element has an equal chance of being included. A random sample can minimize many potential biases, which could lead to incorrect generalizations about the population.

2 Other sampling methods include stratified sampling, systematic sampling, cluster sampling, and convenience sampling.

3 When constructing a survey, avoid selection bias and follow the five factors for good questionnaire design.

4 There are two types of statistical studies: experimental studies and observational studies. In an experimental study, researchers investigate how varying the predictor variable affects the response variable. It is not always possible to conduct an experimental study, however, and sometimes an observational study is used instead.

Section 1.3 Exercises

CLARIFYING THE CONCEPTS

1. Explain why convenience sampling usually does not result in a representative sample.

2. What type of bias did the *Literary Digest* poll (pages 19–20) exhibit? How did it affect the results?

3. How could the *Literary Digest* have decreased the bias in its poll?

4. Was the *Literary Digest* poll a random sample?

5. Describe what a random sample is.

6. Describe the difference between an observational study and an experimental study.

PRACTICING THE TECHNIQUES

For Exercises 7–10, state which type of sampling is represented.

7. Students in your class are divided into freshmen, sophomores, juniors, and seniors. One of the groups is selected at random and all the students in that group are selected.

8. An instructor in a large lecture course of 300 students would like to get a student sample, and he selects every 10th name from the class roster.

9. You are researching the proportion of college students who prefer country music to other forms of music. You survey all the students in all the classes you are taking this semester.

10. An instructor in a large lecture course of 300 students (two lectures, one lab per week) would like to get a student sample. He takes a random sample of three of the 15 lab sections, and selects all of the students from those three sections.

Use the following information for Exercises 11 and 12. Brandon is trying to estimate the proportion of all college students who are physically fit. He obtains a sample of students working out at the gymnasium on Monday night.

11. Identify the target population and the potential population.

12. Does selection bias exist? Explain why or why not.

Use the following information for Exercises 13 and 14. Michelle would like to determine the proportion of small businesses that who employ at least one college student part-time. She obtains a sample of businesses near the state university.

13. Identify the target population and the potential population.

14. Does selection bias exist? Explain why or why not.

For Exercises 15–18, identify which of the five factors for good questionnaire design is violated, if any.

15. Do you sometimes feel anxiety about your health?

16. Do you support the valiant efforts of our mayor to dispel the lies spread by the corrupt opposition?

17. Do you espouse the diminution of the graduated income tax?

18. Do you support laws restricting invasion of privacy and locking up those responsible for doing so?

For Exercises 19–22, do the following: (**a**) State which type of study is involved, experimental or observational. (**b**) Identify the response variable and the predictor variable.

19. A sociologist would be interested in whether large families (at least four children) attend religious services more often than smaller families do.

20. A financial researcher would be interested in whether companies that give large bonuses to their chief executive officers (at least $1 million per year) have a higher stock price.

21. A manufacturer would be interested in whether a new computer processor will improve the performance of its electronics equipment.

22. A pharmaceutical company would like to see if its new drug will lower high blood pressure.

Refer to Table 1.12 for Exercises 23–26.

TABLE 1.12 College football teams in four major conferences

Big Ten	Southeastern	Atlantic Coast	Pacific Ten
Illinois	Alabama	Boston College	Arizona
Indiana	Arkansas	Clemson	Arizona State
Iowa	Auburn	Duke	California
Michigan	Florida	Florida State	Oregon
Mich. State	Georgia	Georgia Tech	Oregon State
Minnesota	Kentucky	Maryland	Stanford
Northwestern	Louisiana State	Miami	UCLA
Ohio State	Mississippi	North Carolina	USC
Penn State	Miss. State	NC State	Washington
Purdue	South Carolina	Virginia	Wash. State
Wisconsin	Tennessee	Virginia Tech	
	Vanderbilt	Wake Forest	

23. Suppose that we ignore the different conferences, and think of all of these teams as belonging to one big Conference America. Obtain a simple random sample of size 5 teams from Conference America.

24. Suppose the conference chairperson for the Southeastern Conference would like to visit some campuses this year. Obtain a systematic sample of every third team from the Southeastern Conference.

25. Suppose the NCAA wants to form a committee to consider some rule changes for college football, and would like two teams randomly selected from each conference. Obtain a stratified sample of two teams from each conference.

26. Suppose the NCAA is considering a new playoff arrangement for the bowl games, and would like all the teams from two randomly selected conferences to be eligible for this playoff arrangement. Obtain a cluster sample of all the teams from two randomly selected conferences.

Use the following information for Exercises 27–30. Agricultural researchers are investigating whether a new form of pesticide will lead to lower levels of insect damage to crops than the traditional pesticide.

27. Identify the response variable.
28. Identify the predictor variable.
29. What is the treatment?
30. What is the control?

Use the following information for Exercises 31–36. Cholesterol researchers are investigating whether there is any difference between a new medication and a placebo (inactive pill) in lowering LDL cholesterol levels in the bloodstream.

31. Identify the response variable.
32. Identify the predictor variable.
33. What is the treatment?
34. What is the control?
35. Suppose there is a patient with very high LDL cholesterol levels, and so the doctor assigns this patient to the group of patients who receive the new medication rather than the placebo. Which of the experimental factors (control, randomization, replication) did the doctor violate?
36. Use the situation in the previous exercise to discuss why randomization is important.

APPLYING THE CONCEPTS

37. **Contradicting Ann Landers.** "If you had to do it over again, would you have children?" This is the question that advice columnist Ann Landers once asked her readers. It turns out that nearly 70% of the 10,000 responses she received were "No." A professional poll by *Newsday* found that 91% of respondents would have children again. Explain the apparent contradiction between these two surveys using what you have learned in this section.

38. **High School Dropouts.** For the following survey, describe the target population and the potential population, and discuss the potential for selection bias. Researchers are interested in the proportion of high school students in New England who drop out (leave school before graduating). A survey is made of 15 high schools in Greater Boston.

39. **Living Below the Poverty Level.** For the following survey, describe the target population and the potential population, and discuss the potential for selection bias. A sociologist is interested in the proportion of people living below the poverty level in Chicago. He takes a random sample of phone numbers from the Chicago phone directory and asks each respondent his or her annual household income.

40. **Rap or Hip-Hop.** Describe what is wrong, if anything, with the following survey question. "Do you enjoy listening to rap or hip-hop music?"

41. **Financial Ruin.** Describe what is wrong, if anything, with the following survey question: "Do you think that we should tax and spend our way into financial ruin?"

42. **Abortion.** Suppose 67% of female respondents respond affirmatively to the question "Do you support the right of a woman to terminate a pregnancy when her life is in danger?" Would the researcher be justified in reporting, "Two-thirds of women support abortion"?

43. **Most Active Stocks.** Here is a list of the five most active stocks on the NYSE on March 27, 2008.

Stock	Price
Citigroup	$20.98
Merrill Lynch	$40.93
Lehman Brothers	$38.86
Washington Mutual	$10.04
Ford	$ 5.63

a. We are about to select a random sample and determine the lowest price in the sample. Do we know what this price will be before we select the sample? Why or why not?

b. Select a random sample of size 2 from the table.

c. If you take another sample of size 2, is it likely to comprise the same two companies? Why or why not?

d. Which stock in your sample has the lowest price? What is that price?

44. **Most Active Stocks.** Refer to the list of stocks from the previous exercise.

a. We are about to select another random sample and determine the lowest price in the sample. Do we know what this price will be before we select the sample? Do we know whether it will be the same as in the previous exercise? Why or why not?

b. Select another random sample of size 2.

c. Which stock in your new sample has the lowest price? What is that price?

45. **Challenge Exercise.** Compare your answers in Exercise 43(**d**) with those in Exercise 44(**c**). What can we say about a quantity like "the lowest price in a random sample of stocks"?

46. Mediterranean Diet. The American Heart Association reported the following results of an experimental study.[6] Patients who ate a Mediterranean diet had a significantly lower risk of having a second heart attack than did patients who ate a Western diet. Identify the response variable and the predictor variable in this experimental study.

47. Secondhand Smoking and Illness in Children. A 2006 Surgeon General's report found that "the evidence is sufficient to infer a causal relationship" between secondhand tobacco smoke exposure from parental smoking and respiratory illnesses in infants and children.[7]

   a. Given the health risks associated with tobacco use, discuss the ethics of forcing the parents of a treatment group to smoke tobacco.
   b. State whether this report was based on an experimental study or an observational study.

BRINGING IT ALL TOGETHER

Evidence for an Alternative Therapy? Use the following information for Exercises 48–50. A company called QT, Inc. sells "ionized bracelets," called Q-Ray Bracelets, that it claims help to ease pain by balancing the body's flow of "electromagnetic energy." QT, Inc. claims that Q-Ray Bracelets can ease pain caused by cancer, restore well-being, and provide many other health benefits. The Mayo Clinic decided to conduct a statistical study to determine whether the extravagant claims for Q-Ray Bracelets were justified.[8] In the study, 305 subjects wore the Q-Ray "ionized" bracelet and 305 wore a placebo bracelet (identical to the ionized bracelet except for the

ionization) for four weeks, at the end of which certain measures of pain were evaluated and compared between the treatments. The subjects, upon entry to the study, were randomly assigned to receive either the ionized bracelet or the placebo bracelet.

48. Identify the following aspects of this study.
   a. The control
   b. The randomization
   c. The replication
49. Identify the following aspects of this study.
   a. The predictor variable
   b. The treatment
   c. The response variable
50. Does this statistical study represent an experimental study or an observational study? Write a sentence explaining why.

Use the *Random Sample* applet for Exercises 51–53.

51. Generate a random sample of 7 cities from Table 1.9 (page 21).
52. Generate another random sample of 7 cities from Table 1.9. Are all the cities in the two samples the same?
53. Before we generate a third sample of 7 cities, choose a city from Table 1.9.
   a. Will this city appear in the random sample?
   b. Is there any way of telling for certain in advance whether this city will appear in the random sample?
   c. Now go ahead and generate the third random sample of 7 cities. Is your city in the sample?

Chapter 1 Vocabulary

SECTION 1.2
- **Census** (p. 13)
- **Continuous variable** (p. 11)
- **Descriptive statistics** (p. 9)
- **Discrete variable** (p. 11)
- **Element** (p. 10)
- **Observation** (p. 10)
- **Parameter** (p. 13)
- **Population** (p. 13)
- **Qualitative variable** (p. 11)

- **Quantitative variable** (p. 11)
- **Sample** (p. 13)
- **Statistic** (p. 13)
- **Statistical inference** (p. 14)
- **Statistics** (p. 7)
- **Variable** (p. 10)

SECTION 1.3
- **Experimental study** (p. 27)
- **Observational study** (p. 27)

- **Potential population** (p. 25)
- **Predictor variable (explanatory variable)** (p. 27)
- **Random sample** (p. 20)
- **Response variable** (p. 27)
- **Selection bias** (p. 25)
- **Subjects** (p. 27)
- **Target population** (p. 25)
- **Treatment** (p. 27)

Chapter 1 Review Exercises

SECTION 1.2
Refer to Table 1.13 for Exercises 1–3. Table 1.13 contains information on some small sport utility vehicles

(SUVs), as reported by *Consumer Reports* for model year 2010.

TABLE 1.13   2010 Small sport utility vehicles

Car	Cylinders	Passengers	Base price	Customer satisfaction
Subaru Forester	4	5	$20,295	Above average
Honda CR-V	4	5	$21,545	Above average
Nissan Rogue	4	5	$20,340	Average
Mitsubishi Outlander	6	7	$20,840	Average

1. Use Table 1.13 to find each of the following.
   a. List the elements.
   b. Identify the variables.
   c. Identify the qualitative variables.
   d. Identify the quantitative variables.
   e. For each variable, state the level of measurement.
2. Use Table 1.13 to answer the following.
   a. Which small SUV has the lowest base price? The highest?
   b. According to the data, what, if anything, is the difference between the Subaru Forester and the Honda CR-V?
3. Provide the observation for the Subaru Forester.
4. The following table contains population figures for the five most populous states.

State	Pop. (1960, in 1000s)	Pop. (2005, in 1000s)	Increase
California	15,717	36,132	20,415
Texas	9,580	22,860	13,280
New York	16,782	19,255	2,473
Florida	4,952	17,790	12,838
Illinois	10,081	12,763	2,682

   a. Identify the elements and the variables.
   b. Are the variables qualitative or quantitative?
   c. Provide the observation for the state of Florida.
   d. Which three states had the largest population increases? Which two states had the smallest population increases?
5. An electrical company has developed a new form of light bulb that it claims lasts longer than current models. The company has 1 million bulbs in its inventory. Consider the population average lifetime.
   a. What is the only way to find out the population average lifetime of the 1 million bulbs in the inventory?
   b. Suppose someone who worked for you wrote you a memo suggesting that it was crucial to know the exact value of the population average lifetime of all 1 million new light bulbs. How would you respond? What might you suggest instead?

SECTION 1.3
6. Refer to the *Literary Digest* poll discussed in Section 1.3.
   a. What was the target population?
   b. What was the potential population?
   c. What was the sample?
   d. Discuss whether the sample was similar to the target population in all important characteristics.
7. Suppose you are interested in finding out how the statistics grades for your class compare with those of the college as a whole.
   a. Would you use an experimental study or an observational study?
   b. Discuss how this study situation would preclude effective randomization.
8. A long-running television advertisement claimed that "3 out of 4 dentists surveyed recommend sugarless gum for their patients who chew gum."
   a. If in fact only 4 dentists were surveyed, which of the study factors were violated?
   b. Use this situation to discuss why replication is important.
9. Suppose we are interested in determining whether differences exist in the cognitive levels of children from single-parent families and those from two-parent families. Would we use an observational study or an experimental study? Clearly describe why.
10. Referring to the study in the previous exercise, suppose the children from single-parent families showed lower average cognitive skills than children from two-parent families. Does this mean that living in a one-parent family causes lower levels of cognitive skills? Why or why not?

Chapter 1 QUIZ

TRUE OR FALSE
1. True or false: Statistical inference consists of methods for estimating and drawing conclusions about sample characteristics based on the information contained in the population.
2. True or false: A parameter is a characteristic of a sample.

FILL IN THE BLANK
3. Statistics is the art and science of _____, analyzing, presenting, and interpreting data.
4. An _____ is the set of values of all variables for a given element.
5. A statistic is a characteristic of a _____.

SHORT ANSWER

6. Is a sample survey examining the effects of secondhand smoke an example of an experimental study or an observational study?

7. State which type of statistical study is involved in the following. A large pharmaceutical company is interested in whether a new drug will reduce Alzheimer's disease symptoms in elderly patients.

8. For the study in the previous exercise, identify the predictor variable and the response variable.

CALCULATIONS AND INTERPRETATIONS

9. Suppose we are interested in the proportion of left-handed statistics students, and we take a sample to estimate the percent of students in our class who are left-handed.

a. What is the population?
b. What is the sample?
c. What is the variable? Is it quantitative or qualitative?
d. Is the sample proportion likely to be exactly the same as the population proportion? Is it likely to be very far away from the population proportion? Explain.

10. Describe what is wrong, if anything, with the following survey question. "How often would you say that you attend the movie theater: often, occasionally, sometimes, seldom, or never?"

2

Describing Data Using Graphs and Tables

Introduction

In Chapter 2, we apply the adage "A picture is worth a thousand words." Before a researcher can draw conclusions from a data set, he or she must first organize the data, usually into some sort of a table or graph.

Section 2.1 discusses graphs and tables for categorical data, including frequency distributions, relative frequency distributions, bar graphs, Pareto charts, and pie charts.

Sections 2.2 and 2.3 discuss graphs and tables for quantitative data, including frequency distributions, relative frequency distributions, histograms, frequency polygons, stem-and-leaf displays, dotplots, cumulative frequency distributions, cumulative relative frequency distributions, frequency ogives, relative frequency ogives, and time series graphs.

Section 2.4 covers graphical misrepresentations of data.

From the Author

- **Section 2.1 Graphs and Table for Categorical Data**

  - Table 2.1 on page 38 replaced the previous data with the top 20 video games, which represents real data. (Students may mention that a particular game is available for more than one console. If so, then the console listed here is for the better-selling version.)

  - Page 39. Note the question, "Relative to what?" You may wish to mention that this question appears often in this course, as we seek to measure how large is large, or how small is small.

  - Pie charts are challenging to construct manually. Instructors may wish to leave their construction to technology.

  - Crosstabulations (two-way tables) and clustered bar graphs were moved here from Chapter 4, since they represent methods for summarizing data. Example 2.5, Constructing a crosstabulation, is new and uses real data.

- **Section 2.2 Graphs and Table for Quantitative Data**

  - Frequency polygons, page 59. You may wish to mention that these graphs are not technically polygons in a geometric sense, but that this terminology is now widespread.

  - Example 2.14 on page 64 draws Section 2.2 together. Students should realize that the use of a particular graph depends in part on the objective of the data analyst.

- **Section 2.3 Further Graphs and Tables for Quantitative Data**

  - Some instructors find that they do not have time to cover Section 2.3.

- **Section 2.4 Graphical Misrepresentations of Data**

  - Section 2.4 is important for *statistical literacy,* the ability to understand the use of graphs, tables, and statistics in the everyday media. One resource in this area is **www.statlit.org**.

Teaching Tips

Starting Example: It will be helpful for students to see all the graphs and tables for categorical data using one small data set to illustrate construction by hand of the plots. Examples can be collected from students by asking for volunteer information, such as year in school or major—or small data sets may be easily obtained from the Web.

It is also useful for students to see all the graphs and displays for quantitative data using one data set. Once again, the data set should be small and can be collected from students or obtained online. Quiz or exam scores or how long it took them to find a parking space are possible examples.

Using the same data set for both the tables and the graphs gives students an opportunity to comment on the different information that can be obtained from each type of graph.

In-Class Activities

1. Ask students to collect data from the class about the number of children in their families and in the family of 5 other married relatives (uncles, aunts, and so on) or people they know (neighbors, parents of friends, and so on) with children. They can use technology (such as Minitab or TI-83/84) to construct a histogram with 5 to 7 classes. From the information displayed in the histogram, ask students to construct a table showing frequency, cumulative frequency, relative frequency, and cumulative relative frequency distribution. Then have them use the cumulative frequencies and cumulative relative frequencies to construct ogives. They can compare to see if there are differences.

2. A possible activity for constructing crosstabulations and/or clustered bar graphs would be to determine whether gender and major are related by collected information on those variables from the class.

3. Construct a frequency distribution and a relative frequency distribution of the genders of the students in your classroom.

4. Where do you think your favorite sport would fall in the distribution of favorite sports? Construct a frequency distribution and a relative frequency distribution of the favorite sports of the students in your classroom. Where do you fall in this distribution?

5. Where do you think your height would fall in a stem-and-leaf display of the heights of students in your class? Construct such a stem-and-leaf-display, using 1s as leaf units. Did you fall about where you thought you would in this display? How would you describe the shape of the distribution?

APPLET For the following activities, you may randomize using (a) technology, (b) the *Random Sample* applet, or (c) two dice and a 6 by 6 table of students' names.

6. Generate a random sample of 10 students, recording the gender for each student.

   a. Is the distribution of genders the same as for the entire class (viewed as a population)?

   b. If we generated another random sample of 10 students, would the distribution of genders be the same? Why or why not? Would you expect it to be roughly the same or wildly different? How could we make the sample distribution more similar to the population distribution?

7. Generate a random sample of 10 students, recording the height for each student. Construct a dotplot or histogram of the heights.

   a. Is the shape similar to the distribution for the entire class?

   b. If we generated another sample of 10 students, would the shape of the dotplot or histogram be the same as previously? Why or why not? Would you expect it to be roughly the same or wildly different? How could we make the sample distribution more similar to the population distribution?

Supplements

See the descriptions in the Preface for more information about these resources.

- StatTutor:
  - Categorical variables: pie charts
  - Quantitative variables: histograms
  - Interpreting histograms
  - Quantitative variables: stemplots
  - Marginal distributions
  - Time series plots
- Stats@Work Simulation
  - Picture This, Which Graph Is Most Appropriate?; Jan Pepperoni
- EESEE case studies for displaying distributions with graphs
  - Acom size and Oak Tree Page (Question 7 on boxplots; to be revisited in Chapter 3)
  - Billionaires in 1992 (covers variables, histograms, skewness)
  - Brain Size and Intelligence (Question 2 on histograms)
  - Influenza Outbreak of 1918 (Question 1 on time series)
  - The State of SAT (Question 5 on histograms)
  - Historical Farm Data (questions on pie charts and time series)
  - How Many Poets Wrote Cleanness? (questions cover frequency distributions, pie charts, and time series)
  - Surviving the Titanic (Question 3 on the bar graph)
  - Nutrition and Breakfast Cereals (Question 1 on histograms)
  - Habitat of Spotted Owls (Question 1 on the dotplot)

Applets

The *One Variable Statistics and Graphs* and *Random Sample* applets are referenced in Chapter 2 to display histograms, stem-and-leaf displays.

The *One Variable Statistics and Graphs* applet is used for Exercises 63–68 in Section 2.2 and Exercises 14–16 in Section 2.4.

Activities and applets can be found at **http://mathforum.org/mathtools**.

Videos

- *Against All Odds*: **www.learner.org/resources/series65.html**
  - Program 1: What Is Statistics?
  - Program 2: Picturing Distributions

Web Sites

- The following Web site has a collection of class projects, at least one of which deals with the topics of this chapter: **www.amstat.org/publications/jse/v6n3/smith.html**.
- This site has several projects using Excel and Minitab: **www.mathspace.com/NSF_ProbStat/ Teaching_Materials/Primarily_Statistics.htm**.
- This Texas Instruments Web site has a host of TI-83/84 statistics activities: **http://education .ti.com/educationportal/sites/US/nonProductSingle/activitybook_83_statistics.html**.

OVERVIEW

2

Describing Data Using Graphs and Tables

CASE STUDY The Caesar Cipher

Over two thousand years ago, Julius Caesar developed the Caesar Cipher, which was a means of encoding his messages so that enemy generals would not be able to understand them if they were intercepted. He did this by simply shifting each letter in the message a certain number of places. For example, if each letter is shifted one place to the right, then:

The message **MOVE THE ARMY** **NORTH INTO GAUL**	Would be encoded as **NPWF UIF BSNZ** **OPSUI JOUP HBVM**

Where does statistics come in? Well, what if you were an enemy general and you intercepted a message from Caesar to one of his generals? You would not know which shift was being used, so *how could you use statistics to decode the message?* The answer is to make use of your knowledge of modern English letter frequencies (for simplicity, we assume that Caesar was fluent in English, a language that wouldn't develop until hundreds of years later). This, along with the graphs and tables we will find in Section 2.1, will help us decode a secret message in the Case Study on page 45.

The Big Picture

Where we are coming from, and where we are headed . . .

- In Chapter 1 we learned the basic concepts of statistics, such as population, sample, and types of variables, along with methods of collecting data.

- Here, in Chapter 2, we learn about graphs and tables for summarizing qualitative data and quantitative data, and we examine how to prevent our graphics from being misleading.

- Later, in Chapter 3, we will learn how to describe a data set using numerical measures like statistics rather than graphs and tables.

2.1   Graphs and Tables for Categorical Data

OBJECTIVES By the end of this section, I will be able to . . .

1   Construct and interpret a frequency distribution and a relative frequency distribution for qualitative data.

2   Construct and interpret bar graphs and Pareto charts.

3   Construct and interpret pie charts.

4   Construct crosstabulations to describe the relationship between two variables.

5   Construct a clustered bar graph to describe the relationship between two variables.

In Chapter 2, we apply the adage "A picture is worth a thousand words." The human mind can assess information presented in a graph or table better than it can through words and numbers alone. Psychologists sometimes call this innate ability *pattern recognition*. Statistical graphs and tables take advantage of this ability to quickly summarize data.

1   Frequency Distributions and Relative Frequency Distributions

Frequency Distributions

Recall from Chapter 1 that categorical (qualitative) data take values that are non-numeric and are usually classified into categories. In this section we learn graphical and tabular methods for handling categorical data. Let us begin with an example.

Amazon.com tracks the best-selling merchandise on its Web site for many different categories. Table 2.1 shows the 20 best-selling video games of 2010, as reported by Amazon.com, along with the game console. We will analyze the variable *console*, which is a qualitative variable, not quantitative.

Table 2.1 Top 20 video games, September 2010, as reported by Amazon.com

Rank	Game	Console	Rank	Game	Console
1	Halo Reach	Xbox 360	11	New Super Mario Brothers	Wii
2	Final Fantasy XIII	PlayStation 3	12	Madden NFL 11	PlayStation 3
3	Alan Wake	Xbox 360	13	Sports Resort	Wii
4	Lego Rock Band	Xbox 360	14	Just Dance	Wii
5	Sid Meier's Civilization V	Windows	15	Fit	Wii
6	World of Warcraft: Cataclysm	Windows	16	Super Mario Galaxy 2	Wii
7	Call of Duty: Black Ops	Xbox 360	17	Starcraft II: Wings of Liberty	Windows
8	Final Fantasy XIV	Windows	18	Castlevania: Lords of Shadow	PlayStation 3
9	Bioshock 2	Xbox 360	19	Fable III	Xbox 360
10	Resonance of Fate	PlayStation 3	20	Medal of Honor	PlayStation 3

It is not immediately clear from this data set which game console is the most popular choice among the 20 games in the sample. That is why we need ways to summarize the values in a data set. One popular method used to summarize the values in a data set is the **frequency distribution** (or *frequency table*).

> The **frequency**, or **count**, of a category refers to the number of observations in each category. A **frequency distribution** for a qualitative variable is a listing of all the values (for example, categories) that the variable can take, together with the frequencies for each value.

Example 2.1 | Which is the most popular game console?

BLOOMimage/Punchstock Images

Create a frequency distribution for the variable *console* from Table 2.1.

Solution

For each game console, we compute the **frequency;** that is, we **count** how many games used that particular console. Table 2.2 shows the frequency distribution for the variable *console*. For example, five games used the PlayStation 3 game console. The frequency distribution summarizes the data set so that quick observations can be made, such as "The Xbox 360 was the game console used by the greatest number of games in the Amazon.com top 20." ∎

Now You Can Do
Exercises 11 and 15.

Table 2.2 Frequency distribution of console

Console	Frequency
Xbox 360	6
PlayStation 3	5
Wii	5
Windows	4

As the data set gets larger, the need for summarization gets more and more acute. (Imagine if the Amazon.com listing consisted of 1000 games rather than 20.) Take a moment to add up the frequencies in Table 2.2. What do they add up to? This number is the sample size: $n = 20$. Now, is this just a coincidence, or does this happen every time? Actually, this happens every time: the sum of the frequencies equals the sample size, n. One way to check if you made a mistake in forming your frequency distribution table is to add up the frequencies and see if the sum equals the sample size.

Relative Frequency Distributions

Next, suppose you didn't know the size of the sample in the survey. Suppose you were told only that 6 games ran on the Xbox 360. The logical question is "Is that a lot?" If our sample size was only 10 games, then 6 of those games using the Xbox 360 is certainly a lot. However, if our sample size was 1000 games, then only 6 of those games using the Xbox 360 is *not* a lot. So, the number's significance depends on what you compare the 6 games to—that is, "relative to what?" or "compared to what?" In statistics, we compare the frequency of a category with the total sample size to get the **relative frequency.**

> The **relative frequency** of a particular category of a qualitative variable is its frequency divided by the sample size. A **relative frequency distribution** for a qualitative variable is a listing of all values that the variable can take, together with the relative frequencies for each value.

Example 2.2   Relative frequency of game consoles

Create a **relative frequency distribution** for the variable *console* using Table 2.2.

Solution

The relative frequency of the Xbox 360 games is the frequency 6 divided by the sample size 20:

$$\text{relative frequency of Xbox 360} = \frac{\text{frequency}}{\text{sample size}} = \frac{6}{20} = 0.30$$

The relative frequency of the games using the Xbox 360 is 0.30, or 30%. So, if someone told you that 30% of the games used the Xbox 360, without telling you the sample size, you would have a better idea of the relative popularity of that game console. To construct the relative frequency distribution in Table 2.3, divide each frequency in the frequency distribution in Table 2.2 by the sample size 20. ■

Note: The relative frequencies always add up to 1.00, which represents 100%.

Now You Can Do
Exercises 12 and 16.

Table 2.3 Relative frequency distribution of console

Console	Relative frequency
Xbox 360	6/20 = 0.30
PlayStation 3	5/20 = 0.25
Wii	5/20 = 0.25
Windows	4/20 = 0.20

2 Bar Graphs and Pareto Charts

Frequency distributions and relative frequency distributions are tabular, and thus useful for summarizing data sets. The graphical equivalent of a frequency distribution or a relative frequency distribution is called a **bar graph** (or **bar chart**).

> A **bar graph** is used to represent the frequencies or relative frequencies for categorical data. It is constructed as follows:
>
> 1. On the horizontal axis, provide a label for each category.
> 2. Draw rectangles (bars) of equal width for each category. The height of each rectangle represents the frequency or relative frequency for that category. Ensure that the bars are not touching each other.

Example 2.3   Constructing bar graphs

Construct a frequency bar graph and a relative frequency bar graph for the game console distributions in Tables 2.2 and 2.3.

Solution

The bar graphs are provided in Figures 2.1a and 2.1b. Across the horizontal axis are the four console categories. Next, draw rectangles, the heights of which represent either the frequency or the relative frequency for that category, represented on the vertical axis. For example, in Figure 2.1a, the first rectangle (Xbox 360) reaches a height of 6, while the second rectangle reaches only to 5. Note that the rectangles are of equal width, and none of them touch each other. Also notice that the two bar graphs are exactly alike except for the scale indicated on the vertical axis. This is because we divide each frequency by the same number, the sample size, to get the relative frequency. ■

Now You Can Do
Exercises 13 and 17.

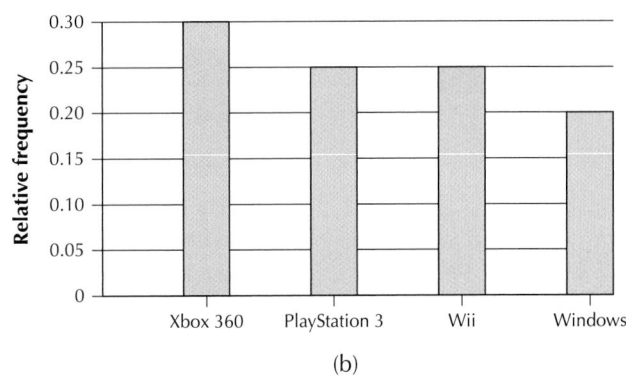

(a)

(b)

FIGURE 2.1 (a) Frequency bar graph; (b) relative frequency bar graph.

The bars in a bar graph may be presented horizontally, especially when the category names are long. Figure 2.2 contains a horizontal bar chart of the top five quarterbacks in the National Football League in 2009, in terms of passing yardage.

FIGURE 2.2
Horizontal bar chart of top five passing quarterbacks, 2009. (*Source:* NFL.com)

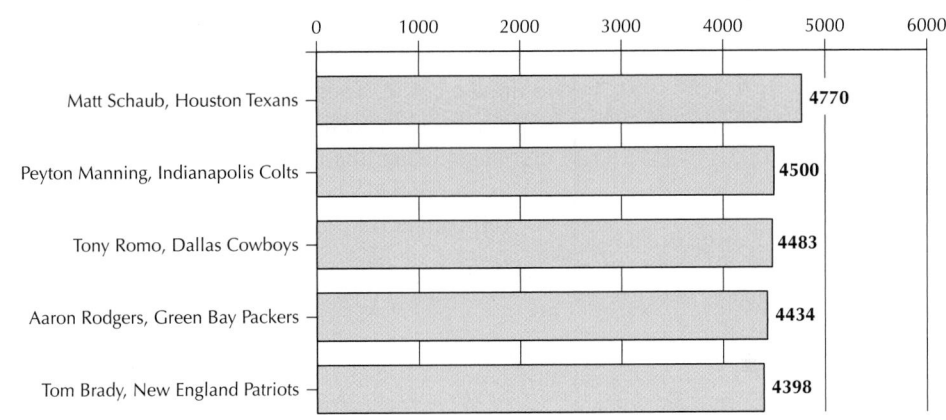

Both Figure 2.1a and Figure 2.1b are examples of **Pareto charts.**

A **Pareto chart** is a bar graph in which the rectangles are presented in decreasing order from left to right.

Figures 2.5a and 2.5b (page 45) are examples of bar graphs that are not Pareto charts.

3 Pie Charts

Pie charts are a common graphical device for displaying the relative frequencies of a categorical variable.

A **pie chart** is a circle divided into sections (that is, slices or wedges), with each section representing a particular category. The size of the section is proportional to the relative frequency of the category.

Pie charts are typically made using technology. However, one can construct a pie chart using a protractor and a compass. Since a circle contains 360 degrees, we need to multiply the relative frequency for each category by 360°. This will tell us how large a slice to make for each category, in terms of degrees.

Example 2.4 | Constructing a pie chart

Construct a pie chart for the game console data from Example 2.2.

Solution

The relative frequencies from Example 2.2 are shown in Table 2.4. We multiply each relative frequency by 360° to get the number of degrees for that section (slice) of the pie chart.

Table 2.4 Finding the number of degrees for each slice of the pie chart

Variable: console	Relative frequency	Multiply by 360°	Degrees for that section
Xbox 360	6/20 = 0.30	0.30 × 360° =	108°
PlayStation 3	5/20 = 0.25	0.25 × 360° =	90°
Wii	5/20 = 0.25	0.25 × 360° =	90°
Windows	4/20 = 0.20	0.20 × 360° =	72°
Total	20/20 = 1.00		360°

Our pie chart will have four slices, one for each console category. Use the compass to draw a circle. Then use the protractor to construct the appropriate angles for each section. From the center of the circle, draw a line to the top of the circle. Measure your first angle using this line. For the Xbox 360, we need an angle of 108°. This angle is shown in Figure 2.3. Then, from there, measure your second angle—in this case, the 90° right angle for PlayStation 3. Continue until your circle is complete. ■

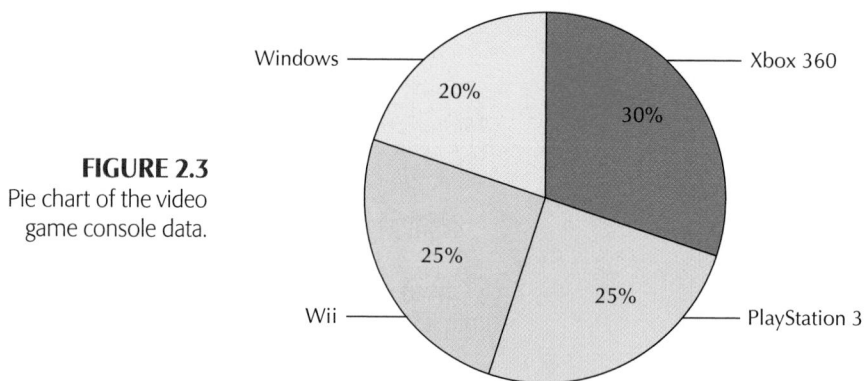

FIGURE 2.3
Pie chart of the video game console data.

Now You Can Do
Exercises 14 and 18.

4 Crosstabulations

So far, we have analyzed only one variable at a time. **Crosstabulation** is a tabular method for simultaneously summarizing the data for two categorical (qualitative) variables.

Steps for Constructing a Crosstabulation

Step 1 Put the categories of one variable at the top of each column, and the categories of the other variable at the beginning of each row.

Step 2 For each row and column combination, enter the number of observations that fall in the two categories.

Step 3 The bottom of the table gives the column totals, and the right-hand column gives the row totals.

Crosstabulations are also known as **two-way tables** or **contingency tables**. We will introduce crosstabulations using an example.

Example 2.5 | Constructing a crosstabulation

Table 2.5 contains information about the size (compact, midsize, or large) and the recommended gasoline (regular or premium) for a sample of ten 2011 automobiles

a. Construct a crosstabulation of the variables *size* and *gasoline*.

b. Identify any patterns.

Table 2.5 Size and recommended gasoline for ten 2011 automobiles

Car	Car size	Recommended gasoline
BMW 328i	Compact	Premium
Chevrolet Camaro	Compact	Regular
Honda Accord	Compact	Regular
Cadillac CTS	Midsize	Premium
Nissan Sentra	Midsize	Regular
Subaru Legacy AWD	Midsize	Premium
Toyota Camry	Midsize	Regular
Ford Taurus	Large	Regular
Hyundai Genesis	Large	Premium
Rolls-Royce	Large	Premium

Source: www.fueleconomy.gov.

Solution

a.

Step 1 We use the values of the two variables to create the crosstabulation given in Table 2.6. Note that the categories for the variable *gasoline* are shown at the top, while the categories for the variable *size* are shown on the left. Each car in the sample is associated with a certain *cell* in the crosstabulation, in the appropriate row and column. For example, the Chevrolet Camaro is one of the two cars that appears in the "Compact" car size row and the "Regular" gasoline column.

Step 2 For each row and column combination in the crosstabulation, enter the number of observations that fall in the two categories.

Step 3 The "Total" column contains the sum of the counts of the cells in each row (category) of the *size* variable, and represents the frequency distribution for this variable. Similarly, the "Total" row along the bottom sums the counts of the cells in each column (category) of the *gasoline* variable, and represents the frequency distribution for this variable. In the lower right-hand corner we have the grand total, which should equal the sample size.

 carsizegas

Table 2.6 Crosstabulation of car size and recommended gasoline

Car size	Recommended Gasoline		Total
	Regular	**Premium**	
Compact	2	1	3
Midsize	2	2	4
Large	1	2	3
Total	5	5	10

b. We can use the crosstabulation to look for patterns in the data set. One possible pattern is the following: Compact cars tend to use regular gasoline while large cars tend to use premium gasoline. Of course, this sample size is too small to form any conclusions about such a relationship. ∎

Now You Can Do
Exercises 27 and 37.

5 Clustered Bar Graphs

Clustered bar graphs are useful for comparing two categorical variables and are often used in conjunction with crosstabulations. Each set of bars in a clustered bar graph represents a single category of one variable across all the categories of the other categorical variable (see Figures 2.4a and 2.4b). This allows the analyst to make comparisons easily. One can construct clustered bar graphs using either frequencies or relative frequencies. To construct a clustered bar graph, identify which of the two categorical variables will define the cluster of bars. Then, for each category of the other variable, draw bars for each category of the clustering variable.

Example 2.6 Constructing clustered bar graphs

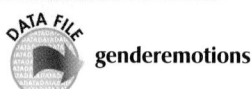
genderemotions

Recall Example 1.2, in Section 1.1 (page 4). (The original survey question read, "Which one of the following emotions do you feel the most strongly in response to these terrorist attacks: sadness, fear, anger, disbelief, vulnerability?")[1] The results are given in the crosstabulation in Table 2.7. Construct a clustered bar graph of the emotions felt, clustered by gender in order to illustrate any differences between males and females.

Table 2.7 Frequency of survey respondents expressing particular emotions, by gender

Gender	Emotion						Total
	Sadness	Fear	Anger	Disbelief	Vulnerability	Not sure	
Female	94	21	87	80	28	4	314
Male	56	16	141	50	36	5	304
Total	150	37	228	130	64	9	618

Solution

Gender is given as the clustering variable. Thus, for each category of the variable *emotion,* we will draw two bars, one representing males and the other representing females. For example, for the first emotion, sadness, we draw one rectangle going up to 56 on the vertical axis, and a separate rectangle going up to 94 on the vertical axis. These two rectangles should touch each other but should not touch any other rectangles. Continue to draw two rectangles for each emotion, one for each of the males' and females' frequencies. The resulting clustered bar graph is shown here as Figure 2.4a. We say that the emotions are *clustered* by gender.

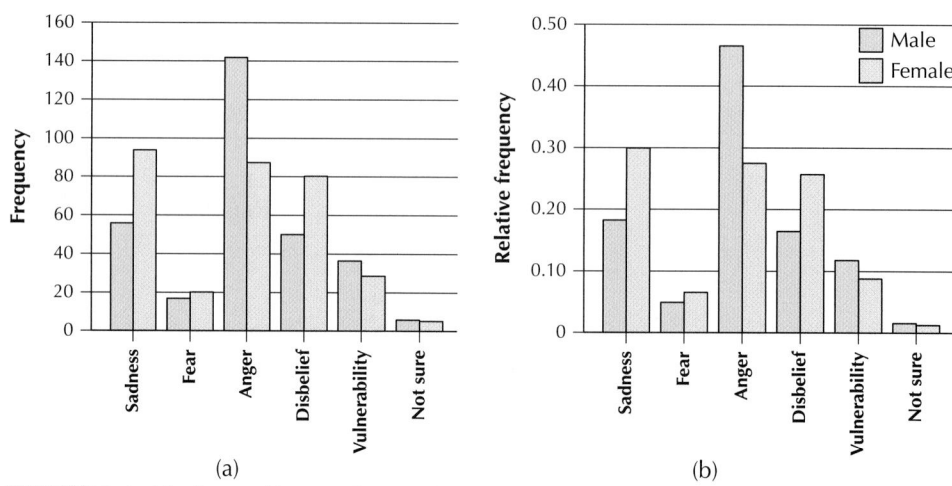

(a)　　　　　　　　　　　　　　　　(b)

FIGURE 2.4 (a) Clustered bar graph using frequencies; (b) clustered bar graph using relative frequencies.

Now, what if females were underrepresented in this survey, so that there were only 100 females and 304 males? Then, direct comparison of the counts would be misleading. When the sample sizes are substantially different, one should use relative frequency clustered bar graphs. The relative frequencies for the frequencies in Table 2.7 are provided in Table 2.8, and the clustered bar graph is given in Figure 2.4b. Note that we divide the counts by the total for that gender, not by the total for the emotion. ■

Note: We can use either *percentage* or *proportion* to describe relative frequency. For example, in Table 2.8, we can say either that the *percentage* of females who expressed sadness was 29.9% or that the *proportion* of females who expressed sadness was 0.299.

Now You Can Do
Exercises 28 and 38.

Table 2.8 Relative frequencies of emotions, by gender

Gender	Emotion						Total
	Sadness	Fear	Anger	Disbelief	Vulnerability	Not sure	
Females	0.299	0.067	0.277	0.255	0.089	0.013	1.000
Males	0.184	0.053	0.464	0.164	0.118	0.016	1.000

© Ancient Art & Architecture Collection Ltd/Alamy

The Caesar Cipher

Recall the Caesar Cipher from the chapter introduction. Suppose we need to decipher the following secret message from Caesar to one of his generals:

LI ZH ZLQ, SLCCD IRU HYHUBRQH (HAWUD SHSSHURQL).

We will make a frequency distribution and bar graph of the letters in the message and then compare them with the bar graph of the letters in the English language given in Figure 2.5a.

We can observe in Figure 2.5a that the letter **E** far outstrips all other letters in the alphabet in frequency. Other high-frequency letters are **A, I, N, O, R, S,** and **T.** Compare this with the frequency distribution of the letters in the coded message, shown in Table 2.9. From this frequency distribution, we can see that **H** is the most frequently occurring letter in the coded message. Other frequently occurring letters are **L, Q, R, S, U,** and **W.** Since **E** is the most frequently occurring letter in English, perhaps this means that **E** is encoded as **H,** the most common letter in our message. The frequency bar graph of letters in the coded message, from Table 2.9, is shown in Figure 2.5b.

(a)

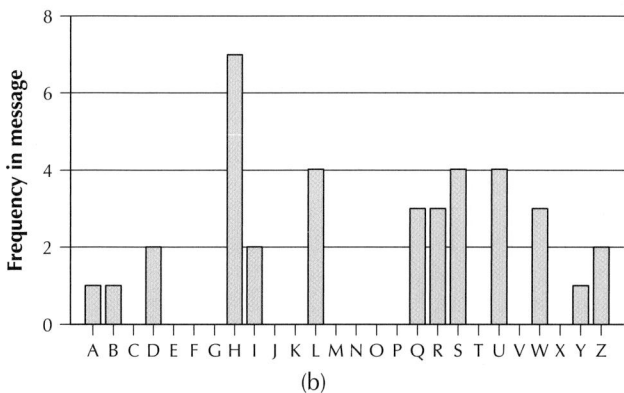

(b)

FIGURE 2.5 (a) Frequency bar graph of English letters; (b) frequency bar graph of letters in coded message.

codeletters

Table 2.9 Frequency distribution of letters in coded message

A	B	C	D	E	F	G	H	I	J	K	L	M
1	1	0	2	0	0	0	7	2	0	0	4	0

N	O	P	Q	R	S	T	U	V	W	X	Y	Z
0	0	0	3	3	4	0	4	0	3	0	1	2

Caesar used a simple shift of the letters for his code. If we substitute **H** for **E,** then the original letters have been shifted three places to the right (**E → F → G → H**). But this may just be an aberration. Is there further evidence for a "right shift of 3"? Let's see if this "right shift of 3" makes sense for the other high-frequency letters in the coded message. To undo a "right shift of 3," we would need to shift the letters in the coded message back three to the left to get the original letters. If the letter **L** is shifted back three places to the left, you get **I,** one of the high-frequency letters in English. Shift the letter **Q** three places, and you get **N,** another letter of high frequency in English. Shift the other letters of high frequency in our coded message, and you get **O, P, R,** and **T,** respectively, all high-frequency letters. There is a strong probability that we have found the correct decoding mechanism.

Let us now proceed to decode the message by shifting every letter in the coded message three places to the left (for example, **L → K → J → I**). It turns out that the decoded message reads

IF WE WIN, PIZZA FOR EVERYONE (EXTRA PEPPERONI).

Small wonder that Caesar went on to win an empire! We have gotten a taste of how the analysis of frequency distributions and bar graphs can be useful for solving problems. ■

STEP-BY-STEP TECHNOLOGY GUIDE: Frequency Distributions, Bar Graphs, and Pie Charts

We use the data set in Table 2.10 to demonstrate how to use technology to construct a frequency distribution, relative frequency distribution, bar graph, and pie chart. Table 2.10 lists the declared majors of 25 randomly selected students at a local business school. (MIS stands for management information systems.)

TABLE 2.10 Declared majors of business school students ⬤ **studentmajor**

Management	MIS	Management	MIS	Marketing
Marketing	Marketing	Management	Finance	Accounting
Accounting	Accounting	MIS	Management	MIS
Management	MIS	Management	Economics	Accounting
Finance	Management	Economics	Marketing	Finance

EXCEL

Frequency Distributions
Step 1 Enter the data in Column A, with the topmost cell indicating the variable name, *Major*.
Step 2 Select cells A1–A26, click **Insert > PivotTable**, and click **OK**.
Step 3 Under **Choose fields to add to report**, select *Major*.
Step 4 Click on *Major* and drag to the **Values** box at the lower right of the screen. The resulting frequency distribution is shown in Figure 2.6. In Excel, this takes the form of a *pivot table*, which is an interactive tabular format.

Clustered Bar Graphs
Step 1 Select the crosstabulation.
Step 2 Click **Insert > Column**.
Step 3 Click **Clustered column**.

Bar Graphs and Pie Charts
Note: Excel can make bar graphs or pie charts using frequency distributions but not from the raw data.

Step 1 Enter the frequency distribution as shown in Figure 2.7.
Step 2 Select cells A1 to B7. For a bar graph, click **Insert > Column**. For a pie chart, click **Insert > Pie**.
Step 3 The resulting frequency bar graph and pie chart are shown in Figures 2.8 and 2.9.

3	Row Labels ▼	Count of Major
4	Accounting	4
5	Economics	2
6	Finance	3
7	Management	7
8	Marketing	4
9	MIS	5
10	**Grand Total**	**25**

FIGURE 2.6

	A	B
1	Major	Count
2	Accounting	4
3	Economics	2
4	Finance	3
5	Management	7
6	Marketing	4
7	MIS	5

FIGURE 2.7

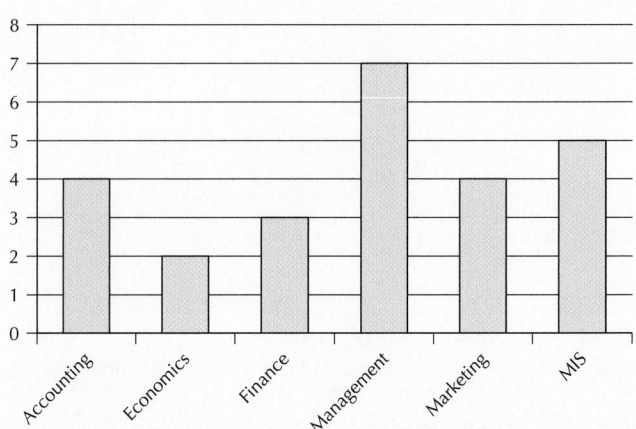

FIGURE 2.8 Excel frequency bar graph.

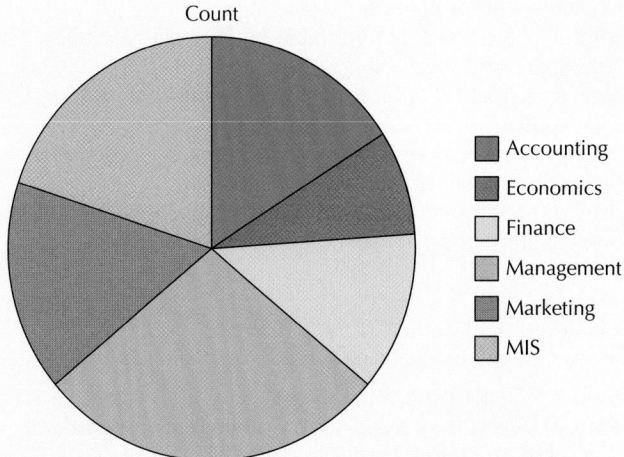

FIGURE 2.9 Excel pie chart.

CRUNCHIT!

Frequency Distributions
Step 1 Click **File . . .** then highlight **Load from Larose2e . . . Chapter 2 . . .** and click on **Table 2.11**.
Step 2 Click **Statistics** and select **Frequency Table**. For **Sample** select **Major**. Then click **Calculate**.

Bar Graphs and Pie Charts
Step 1 Click **File . . .** then highlight **Load from Larose2e . . . Chapter 2 . . .** and click on **Table 2.11**.
Step 2 Click **Graphics** and select **Bar Chart**. For a pie chart select **Pie Chart**.
Step 3 For **Sample** select **Major**. Then click **Calculate**. The resulting bar graph is shown here.

Crosstabulation
We use Table 2.5 from Example 2.5.

Step 1 Click **File** … then highlight **Load from Larose2e . . . Chapter 2 . . .** and click on **Table 2.5**.

MINITAB

Frequency Distributions
Step 1 Name your variable *Major* and enter the data into the **C1** column.
Step 2 Click **Stat > Tables > Tally**.

Bar Graphs
Step 1 Name your variable *Major* and enter the data into the **C1** column.
Step 2 Click **Graph > Bar Chart**. For raw data select **Bars Represent: Counts of Unique Values**, select **Simple,** and

Pie Charts
Step 1 Name your variable *Major* and enter the data into the **C1** column.
Step 2 Click **Graph > Pie Chart**. For raw data select **Chart Counts of unique values**. Then click in the **Variables** box to

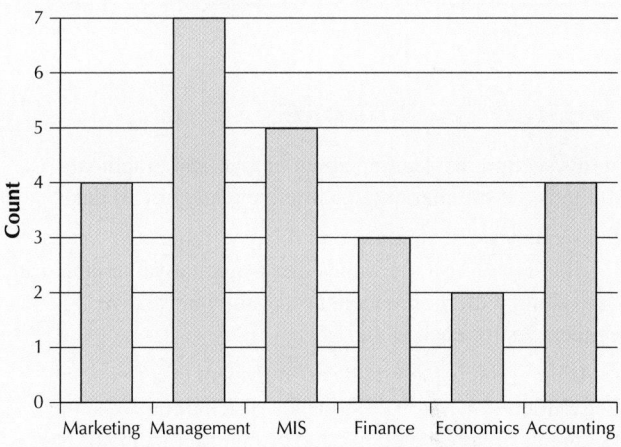

CrunchIt! bar graph.

Step 2 Click **Statistics . . . Contingency Table** and select **Get frequencies**.
Step 3 For **Row variable** select **Size**, and for **Column variable** select **gasoline**. Then click **Calculate**.

Step 3 Under **Display**, select **Counts** and **Percents**.
Step 4 Click inside the **Variables** box until you see your variable *major* listed. Select the variable **C1 *Major,*** and click **Select**. Then click **OK**.

click **OK**. (For summarized data such as a frequency distribution, select **Bars Represent: Values from a Table**, and select **Simple**. Then click **OK**.)
Step 3 In the **listing of variables** box, click on the *Major* variable to select it for analysis. Then click **OK**.

select the variable *Major*, and click **OK**. (For summarized data such as a frequency distribution, select **Chart Data from a Table**. Then select the category variable for **Categorical variable**, and select the variable with the frequencies or relative frequencies for the **Summary variable**. Then click **OK**.)

(Continued)

Crosstabulation of Career Data
Step 1 Enter the data from Table 2.6 (page 43) into two columns, named *size* and *gasoline*.
Step 2 Click **Stat > Tables > Cross-Tabulation and Chi-Square**.
Step 3 For **rows**, select *size;* for **columns**, select *gasoline*. Select **Counts** under **Display**. Then click **OK**.
Step 4 The resulting crosstabulation is shown here. The rows and columns are in alphabetical order.

```
Rows: Size
Columns: Gasoline
    Premium Regular All
Compact   1       2    3
Large     2       1    3
Midsize   2       2    4
All       5       5   10
```

Clustered Bar Graphs
If you have the original data set:

Step 1 Click **Graph > Bar Chart**.
Step 2 Select **Bars Represent: Counts of Unique Values**, and select **Clustered**. Then click **OK**.
Step 3 Select your two categorical variables, and click **OK**.

If you have only the crosstabulation and not the original data:
Step 1 Click **Graph > Bar Chart**.
Step 2 Select **Bars Represent: Values from a Table**, and select **Clustered**. Then click **OK**.
Step 3 For **Graph Variables**, choose the variable that contains the frequencies or relative frequencies. For **Categorical Variables for Grouping**, choose your two categorical variables. Then click **OK**.

Section 2.1 Summary

In this section, we learned about tabular and graphical methods for summarizing qualitative (categorical) data.

1 Frequency distributions and relative frequency distributions list all the values that a qualitative variable can take, along with the frequencies (counts) or relative frequencies for each value.

2 A bar graph is the graphical equivalent of a frequency distribution or a relative frequency distribution. When the rectangles are presented in decreasing order from left to right, the result is a Pareto chart.

3 Pie charts are a common graphical device for displaying the relative frequencies of a categorical variable. A pie chart

is a circle divided into sections (that is, slices or wedges), with each section representing a particular category. The size of the section is proportional to the relative frequency of the category.

4 Crosstabulation summarizes the relationship between two categorical variables. A crosstabulation is a table that gives the counts for each row-column combination, with totals for the rows and columns.

5 Clustered bar graphs are useful for comparing two categorical variables, and are often used in conjunction with crosstabulations.

Section 2.1 Exercises

CLARIFYING THE CONCEPTS
1. Why do we use graphical and tabular methods to summarize data? What's wrong with simply reporting the raw data?
2. What's the difference between a frequency distribution and a relative frequency distribution?
3. True or false: For a given data set, a frequency bar graph and a relative frequency bar graph look alike except for the scale on the vertical axis.
4. True or false: A pie chart is used to represent quantitative data.
5. What should be the sum of the frequencies in a frequency distribution?
6. What should be the sum of the relative frequencies in a relative frequency distribution?
7. In a crosstabulation, the "Total" column represents what? How about the "Total" row?

8. What does the number in the lower right corner of the crosstabulation represent? What should this number be equal to?
9. When is it better to use a relative frequency (rather than a frequency) clustered bar graph?
10. Why can't we use crosstabulations for two numerical variables? Is there some way we could recode the variables in order to use crosstabulations?

PRACTICING THE TECHNIQUES
The political party affiliations of a class of 20 statistics students are shown here. Use this information to construct the table or graph indicated in Exercises 11–14 (Dem = Democrat, Rep = Republican, Ind = Independent).
 politics

Dem Rep Ind Rep Ind Dem Rep Dem Ind Ind
Dem Rep Dem Rep Ind Rep Ind Dem Dem Rep

11. Frequency distribution
12. Relative frequency distribution
13. Bar graph
14. Pie chart

The blood types of a class of 25 nursing students are shown here. The four categories are A, B, AB, and O. Use this information to construct the table or graph indicated in Exercises 15–18. **bloodtypes**

O	A	A	B	A	O	O	A	O
A	A	O	O	O	A	A	B	AB
O	A	A	O	O	B	A		

15. Frequency distribution
16. Relative frequency distribution
17. Bar graph
18. Pie chart

The major and gender of a class of 12 statistics students are recorded here. Use this information to construct the table or graph in Exercises 19–28. **gendermajor**

Major	Gender	Major	Gender
Math	Female	Math	Female
Psychology	Female	Business	Female
Business	Male	Psychology	Male
Math	Male	Psychology	Male
Business	Male	Business	Female
Psychology	Female	Math	Female

19. Frequency distribution of *major*
20. Relative frequency distribution of *major*
21. Bar graph of *major*
22. Pie chart of *major*
23. Frequency distribution of *gender*
24. Relative frequency distribution of *gender*
25. Bar graph of *gender*
26. Pie chart of *gender*
27. Crosstabulation of *major* and *gender*
28. Clustered bar graph of *major*, clustered by *gender*

The class standing and handedness of a group of 14 students are shown here. Use this information to construct the table or graph in Exercises 29–38. **classhands**

Class	Handedness	Class	Handedness
Senior	Right	Junior	Right
Sophomore	Right	Freshman	Right
Senior	Right	Senior	Left
Sophomore	Right	Junior	Left
Sophomore	Right	Senior	Right
Freshman	Right	Junior	Right
Sophomore	Left	Freshman	Left

29. Frequency distribution of *class*
30. Relative frequency distribution of *class*

31. Bar graph of *class*
32. Pie chart of *class*
33. Frequency distribution of *handedness*
34. Relative frequency distribution of *handedness*
35. Bar graph of *handedness*
36. Pie chart of *handedness*
37. Crosstabulation of *class* and *handedness*
38. Clustered bar graph of *class*, clustered by *handedness*

APPLYING THE CONCEPTS

Cell Phone Ownership. Figure 2.10 shows the percentage of cell phone ownership, categorized by level of education. Use Figure 2.10 to answer Exercises 39 and 40.

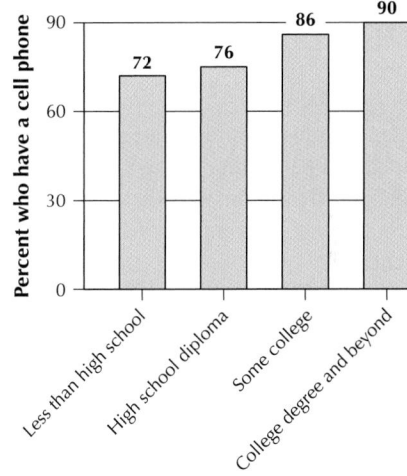

FIGURE 2.10 Cell phone ownership. (*Source:* Amanda Lenhart, *Cell Phones and American Adults,* Pew Internet and American Life Project, September 2, 2010.)

39. Can we use the information in Figure 2.10 to construct a pie chart? Explain why or why not.
40. Is Figure 2.10 a Pareto chart? Explain why or why not.

Cell Phones and the Internet. Figure 2.11 is a pie chart representing the percentage of Americans who access the Internet or email using their cell phones. Use Figure 2.11 to answer Exercises 41 and 42.

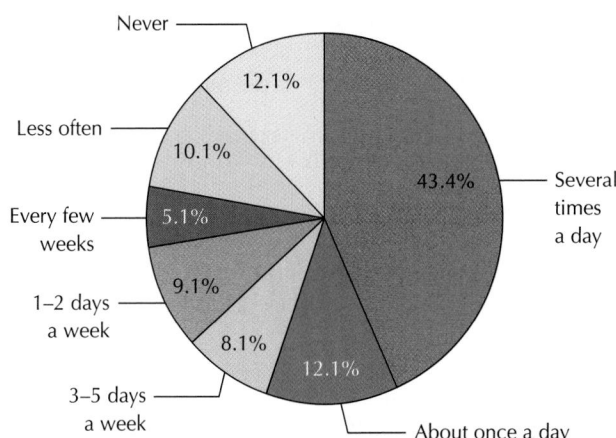

FIGURE 2.11 Percentage using cell phones for Internet or email. (*Source:* Amanda Lenhart, *Cell Phones and American Adults,* Pew Internet and American Life Project, September 2, 2010.)

41. According to this survey:
   a. What is the most common response? What percentage does this represent?
   b. What is the least common response? What percentage does this represent?

42. According to this survey:
   a. What percentage uses the cell phone to access the Internet or email about once a day?
   b. What percentage never uses the cell phone to access the Internet or email?

Sledding Injuries. Every year, about 20,000 children and teenagers visit the emergency room with injuries sustained from snow sledding. Use the horizontal bar graph in Figure 2.12 to answer Exercises 43 and 44.

43. According to this study:
   a. What is the most common category of injury? Estimate the percentage.
   b. Of the specific injuries shown, what is the least common category of injury? What is the percentage?
   c. Is it possible for there to be an injury type that has a lower percentage than traumatic brain injury? Explain.

44. According to this study:
   a. What is the percentage for cuts and bruises?
   b. What is the percentage for strains and sprains?

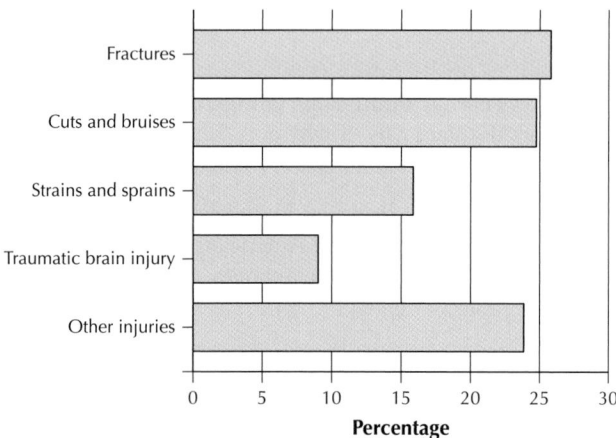

FIGURE 2.12 Most common injuries from sledding. (*Source:* Candace A. Howell, Nicolas G. Nelson, and Lara B. McKenzie, "Pediatric and adolescent sledding-related injuries treated in U.S. emergency departments 1997–2207," *Pediatrics*, 126 (2010): 517–514.)

World Water Usage. See Table 2.11 for Exercises 45–48. For the indicated variable, construct the following:
worldwater
   a. Frequency distribution
   b. Relative frequency distribution
   c. Frequency bar graph
   d. Relative frequency bar graph
   e. Pareto chart, using relative frequencies
   f. Pie chart

TABLE 2.11 **World water usage**

Country	Continent	Climate	Main use
Iraq	Asia	Arid	Irrigation
United States	North America	Temperate	Industry
Pakistan	Asia	Arid	Irrigation
Canada	North America	Temperate	Industry
Madagascar	Africa	Tropical	Irrigation
North Korea	Asia	Temperate	Not reported
Chile	South America	Arid	Irrigation
Bulgaria	Europe	Temperate	Not reported
Afghanistan	Asia	Arid	Irrigation
Iran	Asia	Arid	Irrigation

45. The variable *continent*
46. The variable *climate*
47. The variable *main use*
48. Explain why it is not appropriate to construct a frequency distribution for *country*.

Use Table 2.11 for Exercises 49–54.
49. Construct a crosstabulation of the variables *continent* and *climate*.
50. Construct a crosstabulation of the variables *continent* and *main use*.
51. Construct a crosstabulation of the variables *climate* and *main use*.
52. Construct a clustered bar graph of *continent*, clustered by *climate*.
53. Construct a clustered bar graph of the variable *main use*, clustered by *continent*.
54. Construct a clustered bar graph of the variable *main use*, clustered by *climate*.
55. The table below shows energy-related carbon dioxide emissions (in millions of metric tons), by end-use sector, as reported by the U.S. Energy Information Administration.
co2emissions

Sector	Emissions
Residential	1213.9
Commercial	1034.1
Industrial	1736.0
Transportation	1939.2

Use the table to construct the following:
   a. Relative frequency distribution
   b. Frequency bar graph
   c. Relative frequency bar graph
   d. Pareto chart, using relative frequencies
   e. Pie chart of the relative frequencies
56. Table 2.12 shows the numbers of vehicle models, categorized by vehicle type, examined each year by the U.S. Department of Energy to determine vehicle gas mileage. Use Table 2.12 to construct the following: **cartypemodel**
   a. Relative frequency distribution
   b. Frequency bar graph
   c. Relative frequency bar graph
   d. Pareto chart, using relative frequencies
   e. Pie chart of the relative frequencies

TABLE 2.12

Vehicle type	Number of models
SUVs	370
Compact cars	128
Midsize cars	120
Subcompact cars	110
Standard pickup trucks	106
Large cars	76
Station wagons	62
Small pickup trucks	59
Two-seaters	51
Minicompact cars	43
Vans	38
Minivans	19
Total	1182

Musical Activities. Use the following information for Exercises 57–59. *USA Weekend* conducted a survey of the nation's teenagers, asking them various questions about lifestyle and music. Nearly 60,000 teenagers responded to the poll, conducted in part through *USA Weekend's* Web site. One question was, "Do you listen to music while you are . . . ?" and listed several options. Respondents were asked to select all that apply. The most common responses are shown in the table.

Doing chores	79%
On the computer	73%
Doing homework	72%
Eating meals at home	33%
In the classroom	18%

57. Do you think that the sample is representative of all U.S. teenagers? How might the sample systematically introduce bias?

58. Assuming that the sample size is 60,000, construct a *frequency* bar graph of the five activities listed in the table.

59. Can you construct a pie chart of the five activities listed in the table? Explain precisely why or why not.

Music and Violence. Another poll question asked by *USA Weekend* was "Do you think shock rock and gangsta rap are partly to blame for violence such as school shootings or physical abuse?" The results are shown in the table. Use this information to answer Exercises 60–63.

Yes	31%
No	45%
I've never thought about it	24%

60. Do you think that there may have been other possible responses besides the three above? List at least two other possible responses.

61. Assuming the sample size is 6000, construct a frequency distribution of the responses.

62. Construct a frequency bar graph of the responses.

63. Construct a relative frequency pie chart of the responses.

Astrological Signs. Use the following information for Exercises 64–66. The General Social Survey collects data on social aspects of life in America. Here, 1464 respondents reported their astrological sign. A pie chart of the results is shown here.

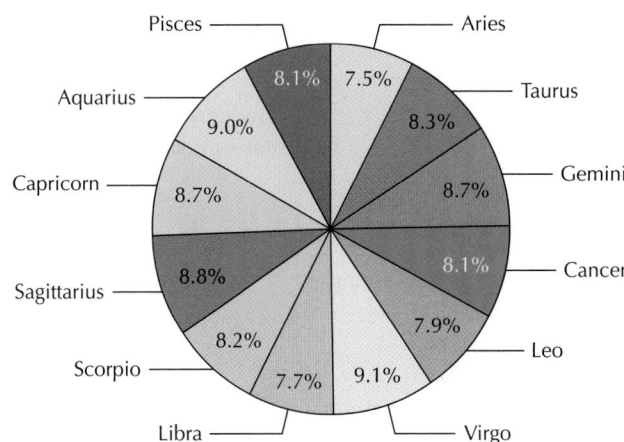

Pie chart of astrological signs.

64. Answer the following:
  a. What is the most common astrological sign?
  b. What is the least common astrological sign?

65. Use the percentages in the pie chart to do the following:
  a. Construct a relative frequency bar graph of the astrological signs.
  b. Construct a relative frequency bar graph, but this time have the *y* axis begin at 7% instead of zero. Describe the difference between the two bar graphs. When would this one be used as opposed to the earlier bar graph?

66. Construct a frequency distribution of the astrological signs. Which sign occurs the least? The most?

Satisfaction with Family Life. Use the following information for Exercises 67–69. The General Social Survey also asked respondents about their amount of satisfaction with family life. Here, 1002 respondents reported their satisfaction levels with family life, as shown in the frequency distribution below. 🔊 **satisfiedfam**

Satisfaction	Frequency
Very great deal	415
Great deal	329
Quite a bit	99
A fair amount	90
Some	27
A little	25
None	17
Total	1002

67. What is your opinion of the categories? Do you think that everyone interprets these phrases in the same way? For example, what is the difference between "quite a bit" and a "great deal"?

68. Construct a Pareto graph of the categories. Do you think that, overall, people are happy with their family lives?

69. Construct a frequency or a relative frequency bar graph of the categories. Do you think that this bar graph reinforces the positive message in the data?

Venture Capital Deals. Use the following information for Exercises 70–73. TheDeal.com reports that the most active venture capital investors, for the 12 months ending July 17, 2007, are as shown in the table. 🐾 **investordeals**

Investor	No. of deals
Intel Capital Corp.	41
New Enterprise Associates	22
Sequoia Capital	19
Venrock Associates	19
Canaan Partners	18
Draper Fisher Jurvetson	18

70. Construct a relative frequency distribution of the number of deals.

71. Construct the following:
 a. Frequency bar graph of the number of deals
 b. Relative frequency bar graph of the number of deals

72. Construct a pie chart of the number of deals.

73. *What if* we doubled each count. How would that affect the following?
 a. Relative frequency distribution of the responses
 b. Relative frequency bar graph of the responses
 c. Pie chart of the responses

Health Insurance Coverage. Use the following information for Exercises 74 and 75. The health insurance coverage of Americans who were younger than 65 years of age in 2005 was reported by the Centers for Disease Control, as shown in the following table.[2] 🐾 **insurancetype**

Type of insurance	Count (in millions)
Private	126.8
Medicaid	13.7
Other	5.7
Uninsured	35.8

74. Construct a relative frequency distribution.
75. Construct a relative frequency bar graph.

Abortion and Rape. Use the following information for Exercises 76–78. Another question asked by the General Social Survey was "Please tell me whether or not you think it should be possible for a pregnant woman to obtain a legal abortion if she became pregnant as a result of rape?"

Here, 934 respondents reported their responses as shown in the bar graph below.

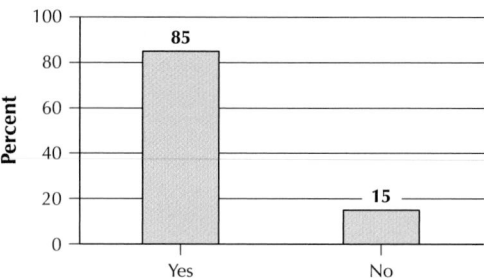

Bar graph of responses: possible for abortion if result of rape?

76. Using the bar graph, construct a frequency distribution of the responses.

77. Using the bar graph, construct a frequency pie chart of the responses.

78. If we wanted to change our frequency pie chart from Exercise 77 to a relative frequency pie chart, would we have to redraw the slices? Explain why or why not.

Don't Mess with Texas (**dontmesswithtexas.org**) is a Texas statewide antilittering organization that identified paper, plastic, metals, and glass as the top four categories of litter by composition. The report also identified tobacco, household, food, and beverages as the top four categories of litter by use. A sample of 12 items of litter had the following characteristics. Use the table to answer Exercises 79–81.
🐾 **litteritems**

Litter item	Composition	Use
1	Paper	Tobacco
2	Plastic	Household
3	Glass	Beverages
4	Paper	Tobacco
5	Metal	Household
6	Plastic	Food
7	Glass	Beverages
8	Paper	Household
9	Metal	Household
10	Plastic	Beverages
11	Paper	Tobacco
12	Plastic	Food

79. Construct a crosstabulation of litter composition by litter use.

80. Construct a clustered bar graph of litter composition and litter use. Cluster by use.

81. Identify any patterns you discover.

Shopping Enjoyment and Gender. Use the information in the crosstabulation for Exercises 82–87. The Pew Internet and American Life Project surveyed 4514 American men and women and asked them, "How much, if at all, do you enjoy shopping?" The results shown in the crosstabulation are missing some entries.

Crosstabulation of shopping enjoyment by gender

| "How much do you enjoy shopping?" | Gender | | Total |
	Male	Female	
A lot		950	1338
Some	582		1255
Only a little	662	497	
Not at all	497		717
Don't know/refused		25	45
Total	2149		4514

82. Fill in the missing entries.
83. Convert the table to a relative frequency crosstabulation. Make it so that the "Male" and "Female" proportions in each row add up to 1.0.
84. Did men or women have the higher proportion of respondents who enjoy shopping
    a. a lot?
    b. some?
    c. only a little?
    d. not at all?
85. What proportion of the respondents are female?
86. What proportion are female, of the respondents who like shopping the following amounts?
    a. a lot
    b. some
    c. only a little
    d. not at all
87. Construct a clustered bar graph of how much the respondents enjoy shopping, clustered by gender.

Religious Preference and Excitement in Life. Use the information in the following table for Exercises 88–92. The General Social Survey asked 967 respondents, "Do you find life exciting, routine, or dull?" along with other questions, including religious preference. Unfortunately, however, not all cell counts are provided.

Crosstabulation of religious preference with excitement in life

| Religious preference | Is Life Exciting or Dull? | | | Total |
	Exciting	Routine	Dull	
Protestant	264		33	623
Catholic	107	128	6	
Jewish	12	8		20
None	38	29	2	69
Other	9	5		14
Total			41	967

88. Fill in the missing entries in the crosstabulation.
89. Convert the table to a relative frequency crosstabulation so that the "Exciting," "Routine," and "Dull" proportions in each row add up to 1.0.
90. Which religious preference (including None and Other) has the largest proportion of those who find life dull?

91. Which religious preference (including None and Other) has the largest proportion of those who find life routine?
92. Which religious preference (including None and Other) has the largest proportion of those who find life exciting?

Educational Goals in Sports. Use your knowledge of Excel or Minitab to solve Exercises 93 and 94. Open the **Goals** data set. The subjects are students in grades four, five, and six from three school districts in Michigan. The students were asked which of the following was most important to them: good grades, sports, or popularity. Information about the students' age, gender, race, and grade was also gathered, as well as whether their school was in an urban, suburban, or rural setting.[3]
93. Generate bar graphs for the following variables.
    a. *Gender.* Estimate the relative frequency of girls in the sample. Of boys.
    b. *Goals.* About what percentage of the students chose "grades" as most important? About what percentage chose "popular"? About what percentage chose "sports"?
94. Generate relative frequency distributions for the following variables.
    a. *Gender.* How close were your estimates in the previous exercise?
    b. *Goals.* How close were your estimates in the previous exercise?

Analysis of Households. For Exercises 95–97, use your knowledge of Excel or Minitab. Open the data set **Household**.
95. How many observations are in this data set? How many variables?
96. Which of the variables are qualitative? Which of the variables are quantitative?
97. What would a relative frequency distribution of the variable *state* look like? A pie chart? A bar graph?

CONSTRUCT YOUR OWN DATA SETS
Environmental Club. Use the following information for Exercises 98–100. You are the president of the College Environmental Club, which has members among all four classes: freshmen, sophomores, juniors, and seniors. The total number of members in the club is 20.
98. Set the frequency of each class so that each class has an equal number of members.
    a. Construct a frequency distribution of the variable *class.*
    b. Construct a relative frequency distribution of the variable *class.*
99. Set the frequency of each class so that there are more sophomores than freshmen, more juniors than sophomores, and more seniors than juniors.
    a. Construct a Pareto chart of the variable *class.*
    b. Construct a pie chart of the variable *class.*
100. Set the frequency of each class so that there are more seniors than any other class while the other three classes have equal numbers.
    a. Construct a frequency bar graph of the variable *class.*
    b. Construct a relative frequency bar graph of the variable *class.*

2.2 Graphs and Tables for Quantitative Data

OBJECTIVES By the end of this section, I will be able to . . .

1   Construct and interpret a frequency distribution and a relative frequency distribution for discrete and continuous data.

2   Use histograms and frequency polygons to summarize quantitative data.

3   Construct and interpret stem-and-leaf displays and dotplots.

4   Recognize distribution shape, symmetry, and skewness.

1 Frequency Distributions and Relative Frequency Distributions

In Section 2.1, we introduced tables and graphs for summarizing qualitative data. However, most of the data sets that we will encounter in this book are quantitative rather than qualitative. Recall from Chapter 1 that quantitative data take on numerical values that arithmetic can be meaningfully performed on. We can apply frequency and relative frequency distributions to quantitative data, just as we did for the qualitative data in Section 2.1

Example 2.7 Frequency distribution and relative frequency distribution for discrete data

The National Center for Missing and Exploited Children (**www.missingkids.com**) keeps an online searchable data base of missing children nationwide. Table 2.13 contains a listing of the 50 children who have gone missing from California and who would have been between 1 and 9 years of age as of March 4, 2007. Suppose we are interested in analyzing the ages of these missing children. Use the data to construct a **frequency distribution** and a **relative frequency distribution** of the variable *age*.

Table 2.13 Missing children and their ages

Child	Age	Child	Age	Child	Age	Child	Age
Amir	5	Carlos	7	Octavio	8	Christian	8
Yamile	5	Ulisses	6	Keoni	6	Mario	8
Kevin	5	Alexander	7	Lance	5	Reya	5
Hilary	8	Adam	4	Mason	5	Elias	1
Zitlalit	7	Sultan	6	Joaquin	6	Maurice	4
Aleida	8	Abril	6	Adriana	6	Samantha	7
Alexia	2	Ramon	6	Christopher	3	Michael	9
Juan	9	Amari	4	Johan	6	Carlos	2
Kevin	2	Joliet	1	Kassandra	4	Lukas	4
Hazel	5	Christopher	4	Hiroki	6	Kayla	4
Melissa	1	Jonathan	8	Kimberly	5	Aiko	3
Kayleen	6	Emil	7	Diondre	4	Lorenzo	9
Mirynda	7	Benjamin	5				

Solution

We can construct the frequency distribution for the variable *age* and can construct the relative frequency distribution by dividing the frequency by the total number of observations, 50. See Table 2.14. ■

Table 2.14 Frequency distribution and relative frequency distribution of *age*

Age	Tally	Frequency	Relative frequency
1	III	3	0.06
2	III	3	0.06
3	II	2	0.04
4	IIII III	8	0.16
5	IIII IIII	9	0.18
6	IIII IIII	10	0.20
7	IIII I	6	0.12
8	IIII I	6	0.12
9	III	3	0.06
Total		50	1.00

Now You Can Do
Exercises 9–12.

We can combine several ages together into "classes," in order to produce a more concise distribution. **Classes** represent a range of data values and are used to group the elements in a data set.

Example 2.8 Frequency and relative frequency distributions using classes

Combine the age data from Example 2.7 into three classes, and construct frequency and relative frequency distributions.

Solution

Let us define the following classes for the age data: 1–3 years old, 4–6 years old, and 7–9 years old. For each class, we group together all the ages in the class. Table 2.15 provides the frequency distribution and relative frequency distribution for these three age classes. ■

Table 2.15 Distributions for the variable *age*, after combining into three classes

Class	Frequency	Relative frequency
1–3	8	0.16
4–6	27	0.54
7–9	15	0.30
Total	50	1.00

Now You Can Do
Exercises 13 and 14.

Developing Your Statistical Sense

Choosing Which Distribution to Use

So which frequency distribution is the "right" one, Table 2.14 or Table 2.15? There is no absolute answer. It depends on the goals of the analysis, as well as other factors. For example, from Table 2.15, we can see that the majority (0.54 = 54%) of missing children are aged 4–6, an observation that was not immediately apparent from Table 2.14. So, combining data values into classes can lead to interesting overall findings. However, whenever data values are combined into classes, some information is lost. For example, it is not possible, using Table 2.15 alone, to determine that age 6 has the highest proportion of missing children. ◢

We use the following to construct frequency distributions and histograms (for a discussion of histograms, see pages 58–59).

> The **lower class limit** of a class equals the smallest value within that class.
>
> The **upper class limit** of a class equals the largest value within that class.
>
> The **class width** equals the difference between the lower class limits of two successive classes.
>
> The **class boundary** of two successive classes is found by taking the sum of the upper class limit of a class and the lower class limit of the class to its right, and dividing this sum by two. The lower class boundary of the leftmost class equals its upper class boundary minus the class width. The upper class boundary of the rightmost class equals its lower class boundary plus the class width.

Example 2.9 Class limits, class widths, and class boundaries

For the classes in Example 2.8, find the following:
a.   The lower class limits and the upper class limits
b.   The class width
c.   The class boundaries

Solution

a.   The following table shows the lower class limits and the upper class limits for the classes in Example 2.8.

Class	Lower class limit (smallest value)	Upper class limit (largest value)
1–3	1	3
4–6	4	6
7–9	7	9

b.   Since our lower class limits are 1, 4, and 7, the class width of each class is 3 because the lower class limits differ by 3. For example, $4 - 1 = 3$.

c.   To find the class boundary of the first and second class, we find the sum of the upper class limit of the first class and the lower class limit of the second class, and divide this sum by 2, giving us $(3 + 4) / 2 = 3.5$. Similarly, the class boundary of the second class with the third class is $(6 + 7) / 2 = 6.5$. The lower class boundary of the leftmost class equals its upper class boundary minus the class width, that is, $3.5 - 3 = 0.5$. The upper class boundary of the rightmost class equals its lower class boundary plus the class width, that is, $6.5 + 3 = 9.5$. ■

Next, we show how to construct frequency distributions for continuous data.

> To construct a frequency distribution for continuous data:
>
> 1.   Choose the number of classes.
>
> 2.   Determine the class width. It is best (though not required) to use the same width for all classes.
>
> 3.   Find the upper and lower class limits. Make sure the classes are nonoverlapping.
>
> 4.   Calculate the class boundaries.
>
> 5.   Find the frequencies of each class.

Example 2.10 Constructing a frequency distribution for continuous data

Twenty management students, in preparation for graduation, took a course to prepare them for a management aptitude test. A simulated test provided the following scores:

77	89	84	83	80	80	83	82	85	92
87	88	87	86	99	93	79	83	81	78

Construct a frequency distribution of these management aptitude test scores.

Solution

Step 1 **Choose the number of classes.**

It is generally recommended that between 5 and 20 classes be used, with the number of classes increasing with the sample size. A small data set such as this will do just fine with 5 classes. In general, choose the number of classes to be large enough to show the variability in the data set, but not so large that many classes are nearly empty.

Step 2 **Determine the class widths.**

First, find the *range* of the data, that is, the difference between the largest and smallest data points. Then, divide this range by the number of classes you chose in Step 1. This gives an estimate of the class width. Here, our largest data value is 99 and our smallest is 77, giving us a *range* of 99 – 77 = 22. In Step 1, we chose 5 classes, so that our estimated class width is 22/5 = 4.4. We will use a convenient class width of 5. It is recommended that each class have the same width.

Step 3 **Find the upper and lower class limits.**

Choose limits so that each data point belongs to only one class. For example, suppose we chose one class to be 75–80 and the next class to be 80–85. Then, to which class would a data value of 80 belong? The classes should not overlap. Therefore, we define the following classes:

75–79   80–84   85–89   90–94   95–99

Note that the lower class limit of the first class, 75, is slightly below that of the smallest value in the data set, 77. Also note that the class width equals 80 – 75 = 5, as desired.

Note: In this example, we have data values that are integers. If the data values, instead, had decimal values, then we would choose the class limits accordingly. For example, if the data values ranged from 75 to 100 but were of the form 75.6, we could choose the class limits of the first class to be 75.0–79.9, the second class to be 80.0–84.9, and so on.

Step 4 **Calculate the class boundaries.**

The class boundary for the first two classes is (79 + 80)/2 = 79.5. Similarly, we may calculate the other class boundaries to be 84.5, 89.5, and 94.5. The lower class boundary of the leftmost class is 79.5 − 5 = 74.5. The upper class boundary of the rightmost class is 94.5 + 5 = 99.5.

Step 5 **Find the frequencies for each class.**

Using these five classes, we now proceed to construct the frequency and relative frequency distributions for the management aptitude test scores (see Table 2.16). We count the number of data values that fall into each class, and we divide each frequency by the sample size (20) to obtain the relative frequency. We see that the majority of the students (0.40 + 0.30 = 0.70) received scores between 80 and 89 and that only one received a score above 94. ■

Now You Can Do
Exercises 15 and 16.

Table 2.16 Distributions for the management aptitude test scores

Class	Tally	Frequency	Relative frequency
75–79	|||	3	0.15
80–84	ℍℍ |||	8	0.40
85–89	ℍℍ		6	0.30
90–94	||	2	0.10
95–99			1	0.05
Total		20	1.00

2 Histograms and Frequency Polygons

Histograms

There are many different methods of summarizing numeric data graphically. One example of a graphical summary for quantitative data is a **histogram.**

> A **histogram** is constructed using rectangles for each class of data. The heights of the rectangles represent the frequencies or relative frequencies of the class. The widths of the rectangles represent the class widths of the corresponding frequency distribution. The class boundaries are placed on the horizontal axis, so that the rectangles are touching each other.

Example 2.11 Constructing a histogram

 mgmttest

Construct a histogram of the frequency of the management aptitude test scores from Example 2.10.

Solution

Step 1 **Find the class limits and draw the horizontal axis.**
Note that the class boundaries for these data were found in Example 2.10: 74.5, 79.5, 84.5, 89.5, 94.5, and 99.5. Draw the horizontal axis, with the numbers 74.5, 79.5, 84.5, 89.5, 94.5, and 99.5, equally spaced along it. The numbers indicate where the rectangles will touch each other.

Step 2 **Determine the frequencies and draw the vertical axis.**
Use the frequencies given in Table 2.16. These will indicate the heights of the five rectangles along the vertical axis. Find the largest frequency, which is 8. It is a good idea to provide a little bit of extra vertical space above the tallest rectangle, so make 9 your highest label along the vertical axis. Then provide equally spaced labels along the vertical axis between 0 and 8.

Step 3 **Draw the rectangles.**
Draw your first rectangle from 74.5 to 79.5, with height 3, the first frequency. Draw the remaining rectangles similarly.

The resulting frequency histogram is shown in Figure 2.13a. The relative frequency histogram is shown in Figure 2.13b. Note that the two histograms have identical shapes and differ only in the labeling along the vertical axis. ∎

Now You Can Do
Exercises 17 and 18.

(a)

(b)

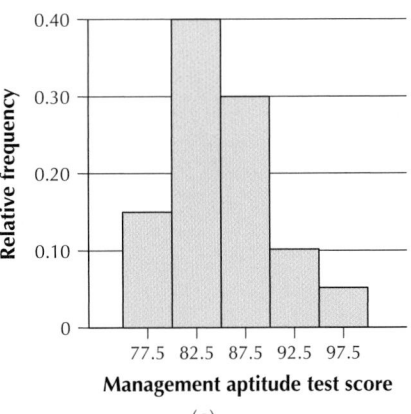
(c)

FIGURE 2.13 (a) Frequency histogram; (b) relative frequency histogram; (c) histogram using midpoints.

Note: Histograms are often presented using class midpoints rather than class boundaries. The class boundaries can be inferred by splitting the difference between the class midpoints. In Figure 2.13c, the upper class boundary for the leftmost class is halfway between 77.5 and 82.5, that is, 80. Otherwise, Figure 2.13c is equivalent to Figure 2.13b.

Note that the histogram, unlike the frequency distribution, provides us with a graphical impression of the data distribution. This characteristic will be crucial later on, when we evaluate the fitness of data sets to undergo certain data analysis methods. Also, notice that the rectangles are contiguous (touching), unlike the rectangles of the bar graphs in Section 2.1. Since the data are quantitative, the horizontal axis in a histogram should be considered as the number line. A **class midpoint** is the average of two consecutive lower class limits. For example, the class midpoint for the leftmost class in Figure 2.13c is $(75 + 80) / 2 = 77.5$.

Shifting the Histogram to the Left

What if we subtracted ten points from each management aptitude test score; how would that affect the frequency histogram in Figure 2.13a? Assume that the number of classes and the class width would stay the same.

Solution

The new class limits and class boundaries would each be ten points lower than the corresponding class limits and class boundaries from Example 2.11. However, the frequencies for each corresponding class would be the same as those from Example 2.11. Thus, the rectangles would look the same, the only difference being that they are "shifted left" ten points along the number line. We discuss more about the shapes of histograms later in this section.

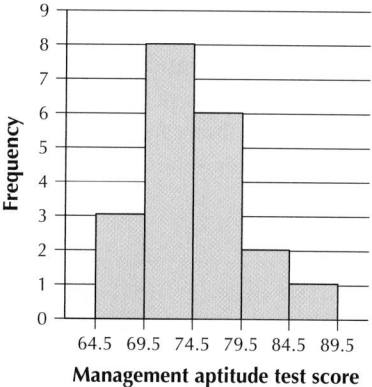

FIGURE 2.13a "Shape" of histogram is unchanged.

The *One Variable Statistics and Graphs* applet can display histograms for a selection of data sets in this textbook, including the management aptitude test scores. The applet allows you to experiment with different class widths.

Frequency Polygons

Frequency polygons provide the same information as histograms, but in a slightly different format.

A **frequency polygon** is constructed as follows. For each class, plot a point at the class midpoint, at a height equal to the frequency for that class. Then join each consecutive pair of points with a line segment.

Example 2.12 Constructing a frequency polygon

mgmttest

Construct a frequency polygon for the management aptitude test data in Example 2.10.

Solution

The midpoints for the classes were calculated for Figure 2.13c. Plot a point for each frequency above each midpoint, and join consecutive points. The result is the frequency polygon in Figure 2.14. ■

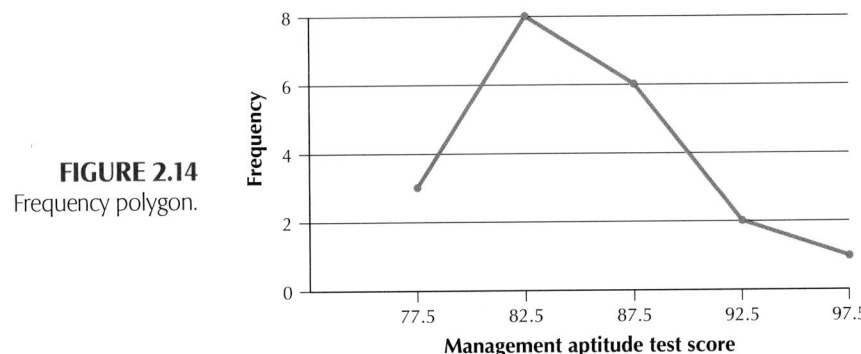

FIGURE 2.14
Frequency polygon.

Now You Can Do
Exercises 19 and 26.

3 Stem-and-Leaf Displays and Dotplots

Stem-and-Leaf Displays

Stem-and-leaf displays were developed by Professor John Tukey of Princeton University in the late 1960s. This type of display generally contains more information than either a frequency distribution or a histogram. We will demonstrate how to construct a stem-and-leaf display in Example 2.13.

Example 2.13 Constructing a stem-and-leaf display

John Tukey, a statistician, who developed the stem-and-leaf display, is said to have coined the term "software."

Construct a stem-and-leaf display for the exam scores of 20 statistics students, given below:

| 57 | 60 | 61 | 65 | 69 | 73 | 74 | 75 | 75 | 75 |
| 76 | 77 | 78 | 81 | 82 | 82 | 85 | 91 | 95 | 98 |

Solution

First, find the leading digits of the numbers. Each number has one of the following as its leading digit: 5, 6, 7, 8, 9. Place these five numbers, called the **stems,** in a column:

5
6
7
8
9

Each number represents the tens place of the exam scores. For example, 5 represents 5 tens. Now consider the ones place of each data value. For example, the first score, 52, has 5 in the tens place (the stem) and 2 in the ones place. Place this number, called the **leaf,** next to its stem:

```
      5 7
stem→ 6   ←leaf
      7
      8
      9
```

The second score, 60, has 6 in the tens place and 0 in the ones place, and the third score, 61, has 6 in the tens place and 1 in the ones place. Write the leaves 0 and 1 next to the stem 6:

```
5 | 7
6 | 01
7 |
8 |
9 |
```

Continue this process with the remaining data, placing each ones value next to its stem. Then, for each stem, order the leaves from left to right in increasing order. This produces the stem-and-leaf display:

```
5 | 7
6 | 0159
7 | 34555678
8 | 1225
9 | 158
```

Notice that the three 75s refer to three different students who happened to get the same grade on the exam. In general, the leaf units represent the smallest decimal place represented in the data values. Then the stem unit consists of the remainder of the number. For example, suppose we have a data value of 127. Then the 7 is the leaf unit, and the 12 is the stem. Or else, suppose our data value is 0.146. Then our leaf unit is the 6 and the stem is the 14. Note that the stem-and-leaf display contains all the information that a histogram turned on its side does. But it also contains more information than a histogram, because the stem-and-leaf display shows the original values.

Split stems may sometimes be used in a stem-and-leaf display to provide a clearer idea of the data distribution when too many data points fall on just a few stems. When using split stems, each stem appears twice, with the leaves 0 to 4 on the upper stem and the leaves 5 to 9 on the lower stem. The above stem-and-leaf display of statistics exam scores would appear as follows when using splits stems:

```
5 | 7
5 |
6 | 01
6 | 59
7 | 34
7 | 555678
8 | 122
8 | 5
9 | 1
9 | 58
```

Now You Can Do
Exercises 20 and 27.

 The *One Variable Statistics and Graphs* applet can display stem-and-leaf displays for a selection of data sets in this textbook, including the statistics exam scores. The applet allows you to experiment with split stems if you like.

Dotplots

A simple but effective graphical display is a **dotplot.** In a dotplot, each data point is represented by a dot above the number line. When the sample size is large, each dot may represent more than one data point. Figure 2.15 is a dotplot of the 20 management aptitude test scores.

Dotplots are useful for comparing two variables. For example, suppose that an instructor taught two different sections of a management course and gave a simulated management aptitude exam in each section (MAT-1 and MAT-2). The instructor could then compare these two groups of scores directly, using a Minitab comparison dotplot, as in Figure 2.16. Although there is much overlap, Section 1 had the highest score, while Section 2 had the three lowest scores. Therefore, it looks as if Section 1 might have done better.

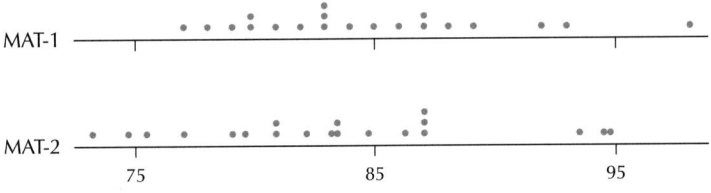

4 Distribution Shape, Symmetry, and Skewness

Frequency distributions are tabular summaries of the set of values that a variable takes. We now generalize the concept of **distribution.**

> The **distribution** of a variable is a table, graph, or formula that identifies the variable values and frequencies for all elements in the data set.

For example, a frequency distribution is a distribution since it is a table that specifies each of the values that a variable can take, along with the frequencies. However, our definition of "distribution" also includes histograms, stem-and-leaf displays, dotplots, and other graphical summaries. (In Chapter 6, we will introduce distributions defined by formulas.) These graphical distributions invite us to consider the shape of a distribution. The *shape* of a distribution is the overall form of a graphical summary, approximated by a smooth curve.

The Bell-Shaped Curve

Figure 2.17 contains the relative frequency histogram of the heights of 1000 college women. Note that there are relatively fewer women in both the left-hand tail (shorter women) and the right-hand tail (taller women). Instead, as height increases from left to right, the relative frequency gradually increases until it reaches a peak near 65 inches tall and then gradually decreases. Thus, the distribution of heights is said to be *bell-shaped.*

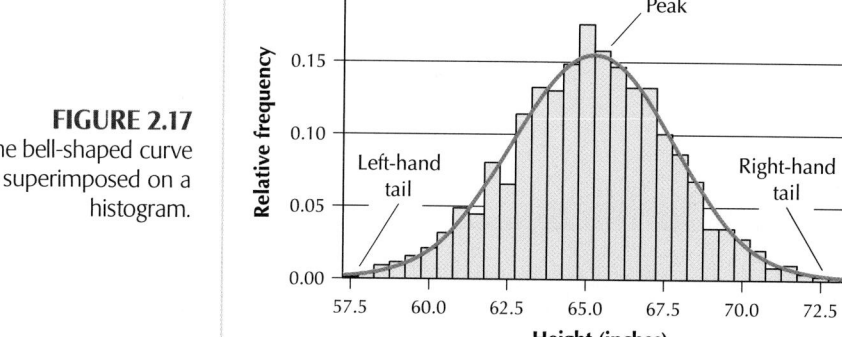

FIGURE 2.17
The bell-shaped curve superimposed on a histogram.

The rectangles represent the actual data. However, the smoothed curve represents an approximation of the overall form of the distribution, and thus the smoothed curve represents the shape of the distribution, which is bell-shaped. The formal name of this bell-shaped distribution is the *normal* distribution. In Chapter 6 we will learn much more about this important distribution, which occurs often in nature and the real world. For example, student heights (within a given gender) follow a bell-shaped distribution. In Chapter 7, we will learn how to assess whether or not a particular distribution is normal (bell-shaped). Starting in Chapter 8, many of the methods for statistical inference we will learn depend on this distribution.

Analyzing the Shape of a Distribution

We next learn some tools for analyzing the shape of a distribution. An image has *symmetry* (or is **symmetric**) if there is a line (axis of symmetry) that splits the image in half so that one side is the mirror image of the other. For example, the butterfly in Figure 2.18 has symmetry, since a line drawn down the middle of the butterfly would create two mirror images of each other. It is important to develop the talent for recognizing which distribution shapes are symmetric.

For example, the smoothed curve in Figure 2.17 is perfectly symmetric. However, the histogram rectangles reflecting the actual data are only nearly symmetric, since a vertical line drawn down the middle of the distribution would not result in two perfect mirror images. *Due to random variation, data from the real world rarely exhibit perfect symmetry.* With this in mind, the data analyst is usually content with the approximate symmetry exhibited by the data (the rectangles) in Figure 2.17.

However, not all distributions are symmetric. In Chapter 8 we will discuss a distribution called the chi-square distribution, which is not symmetric but is **skewed.** It often has a longer "tail" on the right than on the left (see Figure 2.19). Since the right-hand tail is longer, we say that this distribution is *right-skewed.* Examples of right-skewed data are usually found when dealing with money. For example, if we graph the incomes of the families in your home state, the graph will probably be right-skewed. Most of us will lie somewhere in the middle or left with the bulk of the data, while the incomes of folks like Donald Trump and Bill Gates lie far out on the right of the graph, in the right-hand tail. Figure 2.20 shows a *left-skewed* distribution. Good examples of left-skewed data are retirement ages or death ages. Often, exam grade data can be left-skewed, as several students bump up against the 100% boundary on the right, most students are somewhere in the middle, and a few students stagger in with 40s and 50s in the left-hand tail.

FIGURE 2.18
This butterfly is symmetric.
© Burke/ Triolo/Jupiterimages

Note: Only quantitative data, not qualitative data, may be described as symmetric or skewed.

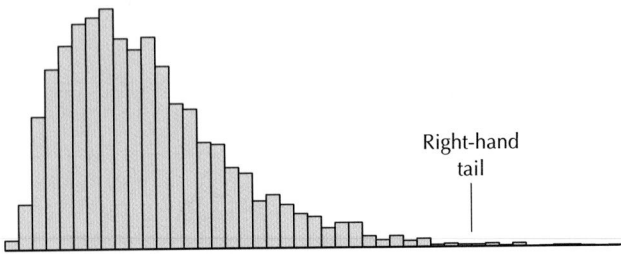

FIGURE 2.19 The chi-square distribution is right-skewed.

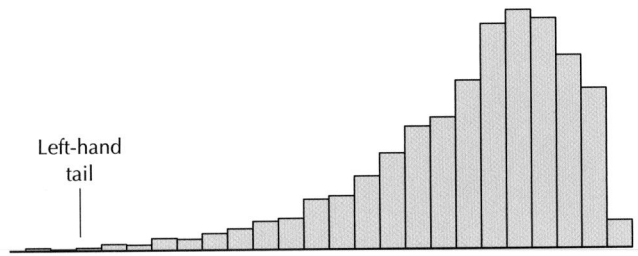

FIGURE 2.20 Some distributions are left-skewed.

Example 2.14   Choosing the appropriate graphical summary

Statistically literate citizens recognize that one may select different graphical summaries, depending on the intention of the presenter. Figures 2.21a, 2.21b, and 2.21c contain a dotplot, a histogram, and a stem-and-leaf display of the average size of households in the 50 states and the District of Columbia. Which graphical summary—the dotplot, the histogram, or the stem-and-leaf display—is most useful if our primary objective is

a. to assess symmetry and skewness?
b. to be able to construct it quickly using paper and pencil?
c. to retain complete knowledge of the original data set?
d. to give a presentation to people who have never had a stats course before?

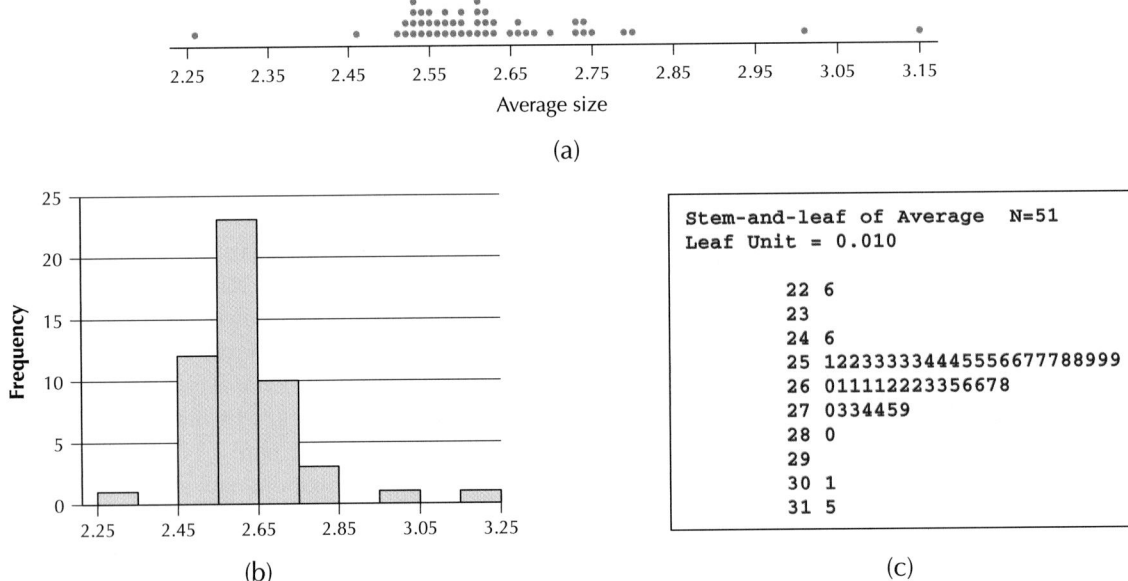

FIGURE 2.21 (a) Dotplot; (b) histogram; (c) stem-and-leaf display. Which is most useful?

Solution

a. All three graphics are good at assessing symmetry and skewness.
b. The dotplot's great asset is its simplicity. It can be quickly drawn, with minimal preparation, in contrast to the other two summaries, which require some organization or calculation.
c. The stem-and-leaf display was invented in order to retain complete knowledge of the data set. Histograms are the least effective in this regard.
d. The histogram is widely used in the real world and is probably the best choice for a presentation in front of those who have not had a stats course before. ∎

Now You Can Do
Exercise 36.

STEP-BY-STEP TECHNOLOGY GUIDE: Quantitative Data

Suppose we would like to produce a histogram of the management aptitude test scores from Example 2.10 (page 57). 🔵 **mgmttest**

TI-83/84

Entering a Data Set
Step 1 Press **STAT**, then press **ENTER**. Highlight the **L1** list.
Step 2 Clear out any old data in **L1**. Press the **up arrow** key, then **CLEAR**, then **ENTER**.
Step 3 Enter the first data value **77** and press **ENTER**.
Step 4 Continue entering data until the entire data set is in **L1** (Figure 2.22).

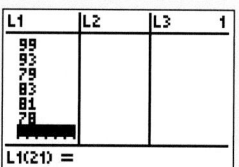

FIGURE 2.22 All data entered.

FIGURE 2.23 Selecting the histogram icon.

Constructing a Histogram
Step 1 Press **2nd**, then **Y=**. In the STAT PLOTS menu, select **1,** and press **ENTER**.
Step 2 Select **ON**, and press **ENTER**. Select the histogram icon (Figure 2.23), and press **ENTER**.
Step 3 Press **ZOOM**, then select **9:ZOOMSTAT**.
Step 4 Press **TRACE**. Selecting each class in turn provides class limits and class frequency. The histogram is given in Figure 2.24.

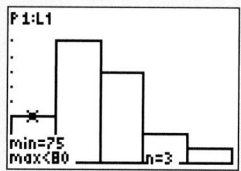

FIGURE 2.24 Histogram with leftmost class selected.

EXCEL

Constructing a Histogram
Make sure the Data Analysis package has been installed on your version of Excel.

Step 1 Click **Data > Data Analysis**.

Step 2 Select **Histogram** and click **OK**.
Step 3 For the *input range*, select the cells in which the data set resides. Then click **OK**.

MINITAB

Constructing a Histogram
Step 1 Enter the management aptitude test scores into column **C1**.
Step 2 Click **Graph > Histogram**.
Step 3 In the **Graph Variables** section, choose **Simple** and click **OK**. Select **C1** *Scores*, and click **Select**. Then click **OK**.
Step 4 The histogram is shown in Figure 2.25. Note that by default Minitab uses midpoints rather than class limits to define the classes. Double-clicking anywhere on the midpoint values (78, 81, . . .) brings up a dialog box providing a wide range of options for changing the number of classes, class limits, etc.

FIGURE 2.25 Minitab histogram.

Constructing a Stem-and-Leaf Display
Step 1 Enter the management aptitude test scores into column **C1**.
Step 2 Click **Graph > Stem-and-Leaf**.
Step 3 Click inside the space indicated **Variables**, select **C1** *Scores*, and click **Select**. Then click **OK**.
Step 4 The output shown in Figure 2.26 tells us that the leaf unit is defined to be ones (1.0). Therefore, the stem unit is tens. (Ignore the leftmost column, which simply provides a cumulative count of the data points from the minimum and maximum.) The first row shows 7 7, indicating a single data point, 77. The second row shows 7 89, indicating two data points, 78 and 79.

```
Stem-and-leaf of MAT
Leaf Unit = 1.0
   1    7  7
   3    7  89
   6    8  001
  10    8  2333
  10    8  45
   8    8  677
   5    8  89
   3    9
   3    9  23
   1    9
   1    9
   1    9  9
```

FIGURE 2.26 Minitab stem-and-leaf display.

(Continued)

Dotplots
Step 1   Enter the management aptitude test scores into column **C1**.

Step 2   Click **Graph . . . Dotplot**. Select **Simple**.
Step 3   In the **Graph Variables** section, select **C1** *Scores* and click **OK**.

CRUNCHIT!

Constructing a Histogram
Step 1   Click **File . . .** then highlight **Load from Larose2e . . . Chapter 2 . . .** and click on **Example 2.10**.
Step 2   Click **Graphics** and select **Histogram**. For **Sample** select **Scores**. (You may optionally select the number of bins, the bin width, and the location for the leftmost lower class limit.) Then click **Calculate**.

Constructing a Dotplot
Step 1   Click **File . . .** then highlight **Load from Larose2e . . . Chapter 2 . . .** and click on **Example 2.10**.
Step 2   Click **Graphics** and select **Dot Plot**. For **Sample** select **Scores**. Then click **Calculate**.

Section 2.2 Summary

In this section, we learned about using graphs and tables for summarizing quantitative (numerical) data.

1 Quantitative variables can be summarized using frequency and relative frequency distributions.

2 Histograms are a graphical display of a frequency or a relative frequency distribution with class intervals on the horizontal axis and the frequencies or relative frequencies on the vertical axis. A frequency polygon is constructed as follows: for each class, plot a point at the class midpoint, at a height equal to the frequency for that class; then join each consecutive pair of points with a line segment.

3 Stem-and-leaf displays contain more information than either a frequency distribution or a histogram, since they retain the original data values in the display. In a dotplot, each data point is represented by a dot above the number line.

4 An image or distribution has symmetry (or is symmetric) if there is a line (axis of symmetry) that splits the image in half so that one side is the mirror image of the other. Nonsymmetric distributions with a long right-hand tail are called right-skewed, while those with a long left-hand tail are called left-skewed.

Section 2.2 Exercises

CLARIFYING THE CONCEPTS

1. Which of the methods for displaying data introduced in this section (frequency and relative frequency distributions, histograms, frequency polygons, stem-and-leaf displays, and dotplots) can be used with both quantitative and qualitative data? Which can be used for quantitative data only?
2. Describe at least one potential benefit of combining classes when constructing a frequency distribution. Describe at least one potential benefit from retaining a larger number of classes.
3. In general, how many classes should be used when constructing a frequency distribution?
4. Describe at least one drawback of choosing class limits that overlap.
5. Describe at least one way that a dotplot may be useful.
6. In your own words, describe what is meant by "symmetry." Provide an example of a shape that is symmetric and an example of a shape that is not symmetric.
7. What are some examples of data sets that are often right-skewed? Left-skewed?

8. For a bar graph (not a Pareto chart), does it matter which order the bars are in? What does this mean for the relevance of symmetry and skewness for summaries of categorical data (such as we studied in Section 2.1)?

PRACTICING THE TECHNIQUES

The following discrete data represent the number of game consoles owned by a random sample of college students. Use the data to construct the table or graph indicated in Exercises 9 and 10.

1	2	0	1	0	2	1	1	0	2	0	1
1	1	0	2	0	0	1	0	2	0	1	1

9. Frequency distribution
10. Relative frequency distribution

The following discrete data represent the ages of a random sample of college students. Use the data to construct the table or graph indicated in Exercises 11–14.

18	21	21	19	20	20	21	22	20
20	19	19	20	18	22	20	21	19

11. Frequency distribution
12. Relative frequency distribution
13. Define the following classes: 18–19, 20–21, and 22–23. Use these classes to construct a frequency distribution.
14. Using the classes in the previous exercise, construct a relative frequency distribution.

The following continuous data represent the pulse rates of a random sample of women. Use the data to construct the table or graph indicated in Exercises 15–21. 🌀 **womenpulse**

75 69 73 84 82 80 74 83 77 78 61 78 87 79 65 72 69 81 62 69

15. Frequency distribution
16. Relative frequency distribution
17. Frequency histogram
18. Relative frequency histogram
19. Frequency polygon
20. Stem-and-leaf display
21. Dotplot

The following continuous data represent the grades on a statistics quiz for a random sample of students. Use the data to construct the table or graph indicated in Exercises 22–28. 🌀 **quizgrades**

95 85 77 82 65 72 76 92 80 74 69 62 79 87 75 75 94 69 70 72

22. Frequency distribution
23. Relative frequency distribution
24. Frequency histogram
25. Relative frequency histogram
26. Frequency polygon
27. Stem-and-leaf display
28. Dotplot
29. A fair die was thrown 100 times, and the values were recorded. The accompanying histogram shows the results.
   a. Which value occurred most frequently?
   b. Which values occurred least frequently?
   c. How often was a 3 observed?
   d. What percentage of times was a 3 observed?

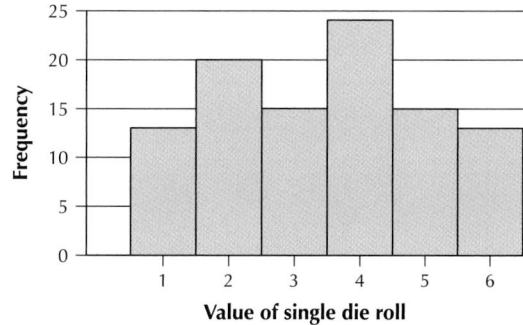

30. A random sample of 1000 police officers was taken, and the number of motor vehicle citations each handed out in a particular week was recorded. The results are shown in the accompanying histogram.

   a. What was the greatest number of citations issued?
   b. What was the fewest number of citations issued?
   c. What was the most frequent number of citations issued? About how many police officers issued this many citations?
   d. Describe the shape of the distribution.
31. A campus-wide statistics midterm worth 50 points resulted in the scores provided in the histogram below.

   a. Which score occurred with the greatest frequency?
   b. Which score occurred with the lowest frequency?
   c. What is the highest score? Lowest score?
   d. Describe the shape of the distribution.
32. A portfolio contains stocks of 19 technology firms. The stock prices are shown in the accompanying histogram.

   a. How many classes are there?
   b. What is the class width? Is it the same for each class?
   c. Is this a frequency histogram or a relative frequency histogram?

33. Refer to the histogram of stock prices.
   a. How could we turn this into a relative frequency histogram? Would the classes or the rectangles be affected?
   b. Suppose we were given a relative frequency histogram instead. How could we turn it into a frequency histogram?
   c. What is the sample size?
34. Refer to the histogram of stock prices.
   a. How many stocks were priced above $27.50?
   b. What is the relative frequency of stocks priced above $27.50?
   c. How many stocks had a price below $15?
   d. What is the relative frequency of stocks with a price below $15?
35. Refer to the histogram of stock prices.
   a. How many stocks are priced between $17.50 and $20?
   b. What is the relative frequency of stocks priced below $5?
   c. Which class has the largest relative frequency? Calculate this relative frequency.
   d. What is the frequency of stocks priced between $10 and $15?
   e. How many stocks had a price of $40?
36. Would you characterize the shape of the stock prices distribution as (a) tending to be symmetric, (b) tending to be right-skewed, (c) tending to be left-skewed?
37. Refer to the accompanying stem-and-leaf display. Reconstruct the data set.

```
Stem-and-leaf of Data   N  = 20
Leaf Unit = 1.0

   2   3
   2   45
   2   67
   2   889
   3   011
   3   2223
   3   5
   3   67
   3   9
   4   0
```

38. Refer to the stem-and-leaf display. Construct a relative frequency distribution, using appropriate values for the class width and the lower class limit of the leftmost class.
39. Refer to the stem-and-leaf display. Construct a frequency histogram.
40. Refer to the stem-and-leaf display. Construct a dotplot.
41. The following frequency polygon represents the quiz scores for a course in introductory statistics.

a. What is the class width?
b. What is the lower class limit of the class that has 45 as its midpoint?
c. What is the upper class limit of the class that has 45 as its midpoint?
d. Which class has the highest frequency?
e. Which class has the lowest frequency?
42. Refer to the frequency polygon of quiz scores.
   a. About how many students scored higher than 82.5?
   b. About how many students scored lower than 52.5?
   c. Can we say how many students scored in the 90s? Why or why not?

APPLYING THE CONCEPTS
43. Small Businesses. The U.S. Census Bureau tracks the number of small businesses per city. The accompanying frequency polygon represents the numbers of small businesses per city (in thousands) for 266 cities nationwide.
   a. What is the class width?
   b. What is the lower class limit of the leftmost class? (*Hint:* Don't forget about the units.)
   c. Which class has the highest frequency?
   d. Which class has the lowest frequency?

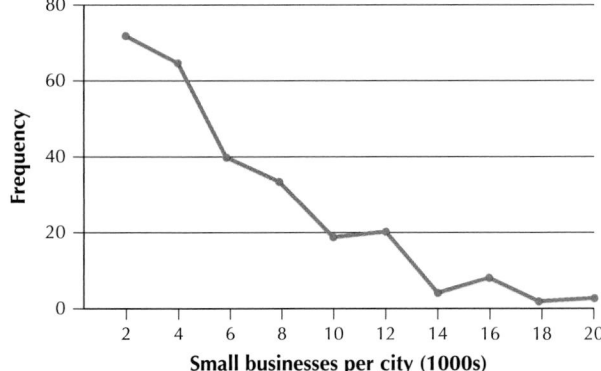

44. Refer to the frequency polygon of small businesses per city.
  a. About how many cities have between 1000 and 3000 small businesses?
  b. About how many cities have more than 19,000 small businesses?
  c. About how many cities have between 9000 and 11,000 small businesses?

45. Countries and Continents. Suppose we are interested in analyzing the variable *continent* for the ten countries in Table 2.17. Construct each of the following tabular or graphical summaries. If not appropriate, explain clearly why we can't use that method. 🐦 **countrycont**
  a. Frequency distribution
  b. Relative frequency distribution
  c. Frequency histogram
  d. Dotplot
  e. Stem-and-leaf display

TABLE 2.17   Countries and continents

Country	Continent
Iraq	Asia
United States	North America
Pakistan	Asia
Canada	North America
Madagascar	Africa
North Korea	Asia
Chile	South America
Bulgaria	Europe
Afghanistan	Asia
Iran	Asia

Miami Arrests. Answer Exercises 46–49 using the information in the following table. The table gives the monthly number of arrests made for the year 2005 by the Miami-Dade Police Department. 🐦 **miamiarrests**

Jan.	751	May	919	Sept.	802
Feb.	650	June	800	Oct.	636
Mar.	909	July	834	Nov.	579
Apr.	881	Aug.	789	Dec.	777

46. Construct a relative frequency distribution of the monthly number of arrests. Use class width of 50 arrests, with the lower class limit of the leftmost class equal to 550.
47. Construct a frequency histogram and relative frequency histogram, using the same classes as in the previous exercise. Which class or classes have the highest frequency? Lowest?
48. Construct a dotplot.
49. Construct a frequency polygon.

New York Townspeople. Use the following information for Exercises 50–53. For towns in New York State, the following histogram provides information on the percentage of the townspeople who are between 18 and 65 years old (data set **New York**). 🐦 **NewYork**

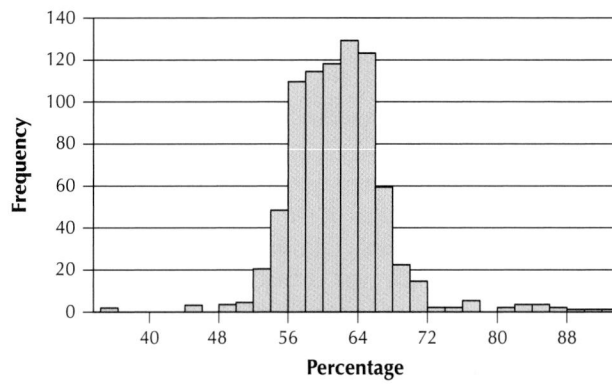

50. Would you characterize the distribution as left-skewed, right-skewed, or fairly symmetrical?
51. Provide an estimate of the "typical" percentage of townspeople who are between 18 and 65 years old. Is this typical value near the middle or near one of the "tails" of the distribution?
52. Provide a rough estimate of the sample size.
53. Would it be possible to construct a stem-and-leaf display, using the information from the histogram? Explain.

Statistics Exam Data. Use the following statistics exam data set from Example 2.13 for Exercises 54–57. 🐦 **statsexam**

57	60	61	65	69	73	74	75	75	75
76	77	78	81	82	82	85	91	95	98

54. Without using a computer, construct the following:
  a. A frequency distribution
  b. A relative frequency distribution
  c. A relative frequency histogram
55. Without using a computer, construct the following:
  a. A dotplot
  b. A frequency polygon
  c. Stem-and-leaf display
56. Compare and contrast the relative usefulness of each of four graphical presentation methods—dotplot, histogram, stem-and-leaf display, and frequency polygon—if our primary objective is
  a. to assess symmetry and skewness.
  b. to be able to construct it quickly using paper and pencil.
  c. to retain complete knowledge of the data set.
  d. to give a presentation to people who have never had a stats course before.

🤔 **57.** *What if* we subtract the same amount (say, 10) from each statistics exam score. Explain how this would affect the following. What would change? What would stay the same?
  a. Relative frequency histogram
  b. Dotplot
  c. Stem-and-leaf display
  d. Frequency polygon

Fats and Cholesterol. For Exercises 58–62, use your knowledge of Excel or Minitab. Open the **Nutrition** data set.

🗱 **Nutrition**

58. How many observations are there in the data set? How many variables?

59. The variable *fat* contains the fat content in grams for each food. Construct a histogram of *fat*. Comment on the symmetry or the skewness of the histogram.

60. Is there a particular type of food whose fat content is particularly large? Which type of food item is this (actually, a set of similar food items)?

61. The variable *cholesterol* contains the cholesterol content in milligrams for each food. Construct a histogram of *cholesterol*. Comment on the symmetry or the skewness of the histogram.

62. Which food item is highest in cholesterol?

🅐 Use the *One Variable Statistics and Graphs* applet for Exercises 63–68. Work with the **Earthquakes** data set, which shows the magnitude on the Richter scale of 57 earthquakes that occurred during the week of October 15–22, 2007. 🗱 **Earthquakes**

63. Click on the **Histogram** tab.
  a. How many classes are there in the histogram?
  b. What is the class width?

64. Click on the leftmost rectangle in the histogram.
  a. What is the frequency for this class?
  b. What are the lower and upper class limits?

65. Click on the number line and drag slowly all the way to the left.
  a. What happens to the number of classes as you drag to the left?

  b. What happens to the class widths as you drag to the left?

66. Click on the number line and drag slowly all the way to the right.
  a. What happens to the number of classes as you drag to the right?
  b. What happens to the class widths as you drag to the right?

67. Click on the **Stem-and-Leaf** tab.
  a. How many stems are there?
  b. Without counting, state how many leaves there are. How do we know this?

68. Select **Split Stems**.
  a. Now how many stems are there?
  b. How many leaves are there?
  c. Which stem-and-leaf display is preferable for the **Earthquakes** data, regular or split stems?

CONSTRUCT YOUR OWN DATA SETS

69. Construct your own right-skewed data set of about 20 values. Just make up the data points, but be sure you know what the data represent (income, housing costs, etc.).
  a. Construct a stem-and-leaf display of your data set.
  b. Construct a dotplot of your data set.

70. Construct your own symmetric data set of about 20 values. Just make up the data points, but be sure you know what the data represent (for example, runs in a baseball game, number of right answers on a quiz).
  a. Construct a stem-and-leaf display of your data set.
  b. Construct a dotplot of your data set.

2.3   Further Graphs and Tables for Quantitative Data

OBJECTIVES By the end of this section, I will be able to . . .

1   Build cumulative frequency distributions and cumulative relative frequency distributions.

2   Create frequency ogives and relative frequency ogives.

3   Construct and interpret time series graphs.

1 Cumulative Frequency Distributions and Cumulative Relative Frequency Distributions

Since quantitative data can be put in ascending order, we can keep track of the accumulated counts at or below a certain value using a **cumulative frequency distribution** or **cumulative relative frequency distribution.** For example, if we list the prices of homes for sale in a neighborhood, a cumulative frequency distribution tells us how many homes are priced at $300,000 or less.

For a discrete variable, a **cumulative frequency distribution** shows the total number of observations *less than or equal to* the category value. For a continuous variable, a **cumulative frequency distribution** shows the total number of observations *less than or equal to* the upper class limit.

A **cumulative relative frequency distribution** shows the proportion of observations less than or equal to the category value (for a discrete variable) or the proportion of observations less than or equal to the upper class limit (for a continuous variable).

| Example 2.15 | Constructing cumulative frequency and cumulative relative frequency distributions |

The first three columns in Table 2.18 contain the frequency distribution and relative frequency distribution for the total 2007 attendance for 25 Major League Baseball teams. Construct a cumulative frequency distribution and a cumulative relative frequency distribution for the attendance figures.

Solution

To find the cumulative frequency for a class, add the frequencies of the classes equal to or below the upper class limit of that class. For example, the cumulative frequency for the class 2.70–3.09 is the sum of the frequency for this class and the frequencies for the classes 1.90–2.29 and 2.30–2.69. The procedure for the cumulative relative frequencies is similar. The results are shown in the last two columns of Table 2.18, where we can see that more than two-thirds (0.68) of these teams had attendance of 3.09 million or less. ∎

Now You Can Do
Exercises 7 and 8.

Table 2.18 Cumulative frequency distribution and cumulative relative frequency distribution

Attendance (millions)	Frequency	Relative frequency	Cumulative frequency	Cumulative relative frequency
1.90–2.29	5	0.20	5	0.20
2.30–2.69	6	0.24	5 + 6 = 11	0.20 + 0.24 = 0.44
2.70–3.09	6	0.24	5 + 6 + 6 = 17	0.44 + 0.24 = 0.68
3.10–3.49	4	0.16	5 + 6 + 6 + 4 = 21	0.68 + 0.16 = 0.84
3.50–3.89	3	0.12	5 + 6 + 6 + 4 + 3 = 24	0.84 + 0.12 = 0.96
3.90–4.29	1	0.04	5 + 6 + 6 + 4 + 3 + 1 = 25	0.96 + 0.04 = 1.00
Total	25	1.00		

2 Ogives

Just as histograms and frequency polygons are the graphical equivalent of frequency distributions, we have the following graphical equivalent of a cumulative frequency distribution.

An **ogive** (pronounced "oh jive") is the graphical equivalent of a cumulative frequency distribution or a cumulative relative frequency distribution. Like a frequency polygon, an ogive consists of a set of plotted points connected by line segments. The *x* coordinates of these points are the upper class limits; the *y* coordinates are the cumulative frequencies or cumulative relative frequencies.

Example 2.16 Constructing an ogive

 bballattend

Construct a relative frequency **ogive** for the attendance data in Table 2.18.

Solution

For the x coordinates, we use the upper class limits for attendance, and for the y coordinates, we use the cumulative relative frequencies. The result is shown in Figure 2.27. ∎

FIGURE 2.27
Ogive for baseball
attendance.

Now You Can Do
Exercises 9 and 10.

> **What Does This Graph Mean?**
>
> The ogive is a graphical representation of a cumulative relative frequency distribution. Thus, the first point (2.29, 0.2) indicates that 20% of the teams had total attendance at or below 2.29 million. The cumulative nature of the graph means that it can never decrease from left to right. The cumulative attendance increases until the rightmost point (4.29, 1.0) indicates that 100% (all) of the teams had total attendance at or below 4.29 million. ◢

3 Time Series Graphs

Data analysts are often interested in how the value of a variable changes over time. Data that are analyzed with respect to time are called *time series data*.

> A graph of time series data is called a **time series plot.** The horizontal axis of a time series plot represents time (for example, hours, days, months, years). The values of the time series data are plotted on the vertical axis, and line segments are drawn to connect the points.

Example 2.17 Constructing a time series plot

Table 2.19 contains the amount of carbon dioxide in parts per million (ppm) found in the atmosphere above Mauna Loa in Hawaii, measured monthly from October 2006 to September 2007. Construct a **time series plot** of these data.

MaunaLoa

Table 2.19 Atmospheric carbon dioxide at Mauna Loa, October 2006 to September 2007

Month	Carbon dioxide (ppm)	Month	Carbon dioxide (ppm)
Oct.	379.03	Apr.	386.37
Nov.	380.17	May	386.54
Dec.	381.85	June	385.98
Jan.	382.94	July	384.35
Feb.	383.86	Aug.	381.85
Mar.	384.49	Sept.	380.58

Source: Dr. Pieter Tans, Earth System Research Laboratory, National Oceanic and Atmospheric Administration, **www.esrl.noaa.gov/gmd/ccgg/trends**.

Solution

We indicate the twelve months October through September on the horizontal axis of the time series plot (Figure 2.28). Then, for each month, we plot the amount of carbon dioxide. Finally, we join the points using line segments. Note that the carbon dioxide level increases from the fall through the winter and peaks in the spring. It then decreases through the summer. In the Step-by-Step Technology Guide, we illustrate how to construct this time series graph using technology. ■

FIGURE 2.28
Time series plot. Carbon dioxide levels at Mauna Loa, Hawaii.

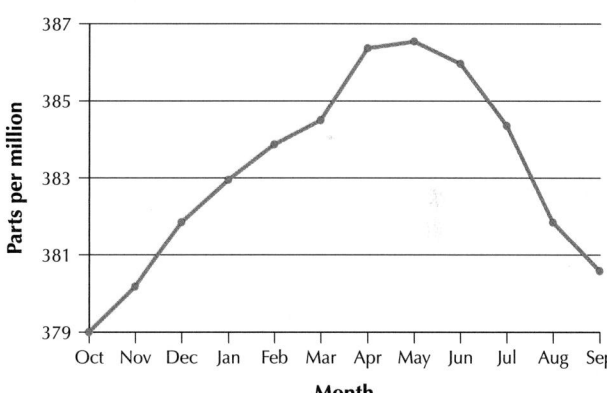

Now You Can Do
Exercises 31 and 32.

Example 2.18   Constructing a time series plot using technology

The data set **Mauna Loa** contains the carbon dioxide levels at Mauna Loa from September 1999 to September 2007. Use technology to construct a time series plot of the data.

Solution

We use the instructions provided in the Step-by-Step Technology Guide at the end of this section. The resulting time series plot is shown in Figure 2.29. (The year on the horizontal axis indicates September of each year. For example "1999" refers to September 1999.)

In Figure 2.29 we observe both a seasonal pattern and a long-term trend. Every autumn and winter, the carbon dioxide level increases, and every summer it decreases. In autumn and winter, leaves and other deciduous vegetation decays, releasing its store of carbon back into the atmosphere. In the spring and summer, the new year's leaves require carbon to grow and extract it from the atmosphere, thereby reducing the atmosphere's carbon dioxide level. Thus, the Earth "inhales" carbon each summer and "exhales" it each winter. However, the carbon dioxide level of each successive September does not quite reach the low level of the previous September. This leads to an overall increasing trend in the amount of carbon dioxide in the atmosphere as we move from 1999 to 2007. ■

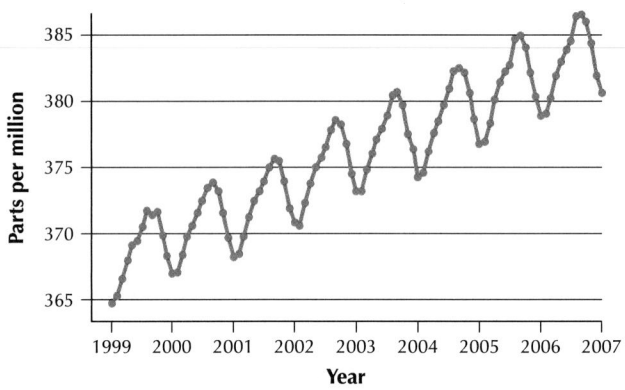

FIGURE 2.29 Watching the Earth breathe. Carbon dioxide levels at Mauna Loa, Hawaii.

STEP-BY-STEP TECHNOLOGY GUIDE: Time Series Plots

We illustrate how to construct a time series plot using Example 2.18 (page 73).

TI-83/84

Step 1 Enter your time index (integers 1, 2, . . .) into list **L1**.
Step 2 Enter the values of your time series variable into list **L2**.
Step 3 Press **2nd**, then **Y=**. In the STAT PLOTS menu, select **1**, and press **ENTER**.
Step 4 Select **ON**, and press **ENTER**. Select the time series icon (Figure 2.30), and press **ENTER**.
Step 5 Press **ZOOM > 9:ZOOMSTAT** and press **ENTER**. The time series plot is shown in Figure 2.31.

FIGURE 2.30 Selecting the time series icon.

FIGURE 2.31 TI-83/84 time series plot.

EXCEL

Step 1 Enter the month data into column **A** (see Figure 2.32).
Step 2 Enter the values of your time series variable into column **B** (see Figure 2.32).
Step 3 Select cells A1–B12 and click **Insert > Line** (in the **Chart** section).
Step 4 Choose the type labeled "Line with markers."

	A	B
1	Oct	379.03
2	Nov	380.17
3	Dec	381.85
4	Jan	382.94
5	Feb	383.86
6	Mar	384.49
7	Apr	386.37
8	May	386.54
9	Jun	385.98
10	Jul	384.35
11	Aug	381.85
12	Sep	380.58

FIGURE 2.32

MINITAB

Step 1 Enter the values of your time series variable into column **C1**.
Step 2 Click **Graph > Time Series Plot . . .**
Step 3 Select **Simple** and click **OK**.
Step 4 For **Series**, double-click on **C1**.

Step 5 Click **Time/Scale**. Select **Calendar > Month**.
Step 6 For **Start value**, enter **10** (for October). For **Increment**, enter **1**.
Step 7 Click **OK** and **OK**.

Section 2.3 Summary

1 A cumulative frequency distribution shows the total number of observations less than or equal to the category value (for a discrete variable) or the upper class limit (for a continuous variable). A cumulative relative frequency distribution shows the proportion of observations less than or equal to the category value (for a discrete variable) or the upper class limit (for a continuous variable).

2 An ogive is the graphical equivalent of a cumulative frequency distribution or a cumulative relative frequency

distribution. The *x* coordinates of the points are the upper class limits; the *y* coordinates are the cumulative frequencies or cumulative relative frequencies.

3 Data that are analyzed with respect to time are called time series data. A graph of time series data is called a time series plot. The horizontal axis of a time series plot represents time (for example, hours, days, months, years). The values of the time series data are plotted on the vertical axis, and line segments are drawn to connect the points.

Section 2.3 Exercises

CLARIFYING THE CONCEPTS

1. Explain the difference between a frequency distribution and a cumulative frequency distribution.

2. Explain the difference between a cumulative frequency distribution and a cumulative relative frequency distribution.

3. What is the graphical equivalent of a cumulative frequency distribution?

4. Explain how to construct an ogive.

5. What do we call data that are analyzed with respect to time?

6. Explain how to construct a time series plot.

PRACTICING THE TECHNIQUES

For Exercises 7–10, use the following relative frequency distribution of the age of students in a particular section of introductory statistics to construct the following graphical summaries of the variable *age*.

Age	Frequency	Relative frequency
17.0–18.9	4	0.2
19.0–20.9	10	0.5
21.0–22.9	6	0.3

7. Cumulative frequency distribution
8. Cumulative relative frequency distribution
9. Frequency ogive
10. Relative frequency ogive

For Exercises 11–14, use the following relative frequency distribution of the height of students in a particular section of introductory statistics to construct the following graphical summaries of the variable *height*.

Height (inches)	Frequency	Relative frequency
60.0–63.9	3	0.12
64.0–67.9	10	0.40
68.0–71.9	10	0.40
72.0–75.9	2	0.08

11. Cumulative frequency distribution
12. Cumulative relative frequency distribution
13. Frequency ogive
14. Relative frequency ogive

For Exercises 15–18, use the histogram from Exercise 29 in Section 2.2 to construct the indicated graph or table.
15. Cumulative frequency distribution
16. Cumulative relative frequency distribution
17. Frequency ogive
18. Relative frequency ogive

For Exercises 19–22, use the histogram from Exercise 32 in Section 2.2 to construct the indicated graph or table.
19. Cumulative frequency distribution
20. Cumulative relative frequency distribution
21. Frequency ogive
22. Relative frequency ogive

For Exercises 23–26, use the frequency distribution from Exercise 15 in Section 2.2 to construct the indicated graph or table.
23. Cumulative frequency distribution
24. Cumulative relative frequency distribution
25. Frequency ogive
26. Relative frequency ogive

For Exercises 27–30, use the frequency distributions from Exercise 22 in Section 2.2 to construct the indicated graph or table.
27. Cumulative frequency distribution
28. Cumulative relative frequency distribution
29. Frequency ogive
30. Relative frequency ogive

31. The following time series data represent the number of songs that Brandon downloaded per month last year, starting in January and ending in December. Construct the time series graph of the data. 🎵 **songdownloads**

2   5   7   10   8   10   18   20   15   12   10   8

32. The following time series data represent the number of friends that Kaitlyn had on her social networking page last year, starting in January and ending in December. Construct the time series graph of the data.

5   7   8   8   10   12   10   12   15   18   20   25

33. Unemployment Rate. The frequency ogive below represents the unemployment rate (in percentages) for 367 cities nationwide.[4]

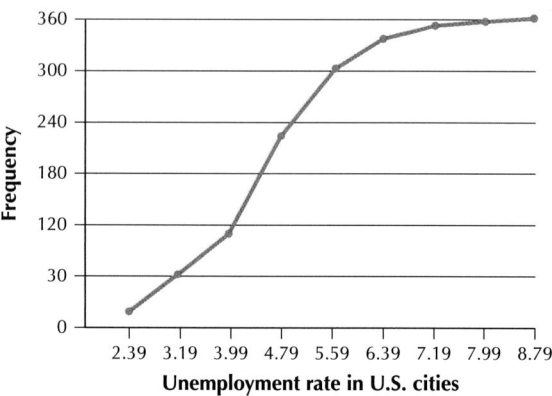

Unemployment rate in U.S. cities

a. What is the class width?
b. What is the upper class limit of the leftmost class?
c. What is the class midpoint of the leftmost class?

34. Refer to the frequency ogive of unemployment rates.
  a. About how many cities have unemployment rates 3.99 and below?
  b. About how many cities have unemployment rates 5.59 and below?
  c. About how many cities have unemployment rates 5.6 and above?

35. HIV/AIDS in Children. The following graph is a time series plot of the number of HIV/AIDS cases in children under 13 in the United States from 1992 to 2004.[5]

HIV/AIDS cases in children, 1992–2004

  a. About how many children had HIV/AIDS in 1992?
  b. About how many children had HIV/AIDS in 2004?

36. Refer to the preceding exercise.
  a. Between which two years do we see the steepest decline in the number of cases?
  b. Overall, does this graph represent encouraging or discouraging news?

APPLYING THE CONCEPTS
Agricultural Exports. For Exercises 37–39, refer to Table 2.20. The table gives the value of agricultural exports (in billions of dollars) from the top 20 U.S. states in 2009. **agriexports**

TABLE 2.20   Agricultural exports (in billions of dollars)

State	Exports	State	Exports
California	12.5	Arkansas	2.6
Iowa	6.5	North Dakota	5.2
Texas	4.7	Ohio	2.7
Illinois	5.5	Florida	2.1
Nebraska	4.8	Wisconsin	2.2
Kansas	4.7	Missouri	2.7
Minnesota	4.3	Georgia	1.8
Washington	3.0	Pennsylvania	1.7
North Carolina	2.9	Michigan	1.6
Indiana	3.1	South Dakota	2.3

Source: U.S. Department of Agriculture.

37. Construct a cumulative frequency distribution of agricultural exports. Start at $0 and use class widths of $2 billion.
  a. How many states have exports of $4 billion or less?
  b. How many states have exports of $6 billion or less?
  c. How many states have exports of more than $6 billion?

38. Construct a cumulative relative frequency distribution of agricultural exports. Start at $0 and use class widths of $2 billion.
  a. What proportion of states have exports of $4 billion or less?
  b. What proportion of states have exports of $6 billion or less?
  c. What proportion of states have exports of more than $6 billion?

39. Use your cumulative relative frequency distribution to construct a relative frequency ogive of agricultural exports.

40. Interest Rates. The following data represent the prime lending rate of interest, as reported by the Federal Reserve, every six months from January 2003 to July 2010.
interestrates

Jan. 2003	4.25	Jan. 2007	8.25
July 2003	4.00	July 2007	8.25
Jan. 2004	4.00	Jan. 2008	6.98
July 2004	4.25	July 2008	5.00
Jan. 2005	5.25	Jan. 2009	3.25
July 2005	6.25	July 2009	3.25
Jan. 2006	7.25	Jan. 2010	3.25
July 2006	8.25	July 2010	3.25

a. Construct a time series plot of the prime lending rate of interest.
b. What trend do you see?

41. Rainfall in Fort Lauderdale. The following data represent the total monthly rainfall (in inches) in 2009 in Fort Lauderdale, Florida, as reported by the U.S. Historical Climatology Network. 🐟 **flrainfall**

Jan.	0.35	July	10.12
Feb.	0.35	Aug.	8.18
Mar.	7.09	Sept.	8.22
Apr.	0.73	Oct.	2.95
May	11.24	Nov.	4.63
June	7.58	Dec.	3.49

a. Construct a time series plot of the data.
b. Is it wetter in summer or winter in Fort Lauderdale?

? 42. In Exercise 41, *what if* we add 3 inches to each month's rainfall amount. Describe how this would affect the time series plot. What would change? What would stay the same?

43. Cigarette Use Among 12th-Graders. Table 2.21 presents the percentages of 12th-graders who smoke cigarettes, for the years 1980–2009. 🐟 **12thsmokers**
a. Construct a time series plot of the data.
b. Describe any trends that you see.

44. Trade Deficit. Table 2.22 presents the annual trade deficits (imports minus exports) for the United States from 1991 to 2009, in billions of dollars. 🐟 **tradedeficits**
a. Construct a time series plot of the data.
b. Describe any trends that you see.

TABLE 2.21   12th-graders who smoke

Year	Percent	Year	Percent
1980	30.5	1995	33.5
1981	29.4	1996	34.0
1982	30.0	1997	36.5
1983	30.3	1998	35.1
1984	29.3	1999	34.6
1985	30.1	2000	31.4
1986	29.6	2001	29.5
1987	29.4	2002	26.7
1988	28.7	2003	24.4
1989	28.6	2004	25.0
1990	29.4	2005	23.2
1991	28.3	2006	21.6
1992	27.8	2007	21.6
1993	29.9	2008	20.4
1994	31.2	2009	20.1

Source: Monitoring the Future study, University of Michigan.

TABLE 2.22   U.S. trade deficits

Year	Trade deficit in $ billions	Year	Trade deficit in $ billions
1991	31	2001	364
1992	39	2002	421
1993	70	2003	494
1994	98	2004	609
1995	96	2005	714
1996	104	2006	759
1997	108	2007	702
1998	166	2008	698
1999	264	2009	374
2000	379		

Source: U.S. Census Bureau.

2.4   Graphical Misrepresentations of Data

OBJECTIVE By the end of this section, I will be able to . . .

1 Understand what can make a graph misleading, confusing, or deceptive.

In the Information Age, when our world is awash in data, it is important for citizens to understand how graphics may be made misleading, confusing, or deceptive. Such an understanding enhances our statistical literacy and makes us less prone to being deceived by misleading graphics.

Eight Common Methods for Making a Graph Misleading
1. Graphing/selecting an inappropriate statistic.
2. Omitting the zero on the relevant scale.
3. Manipulating the scale.
4. Using two dimensions (area) to emphasize a one-dimensional difference.
5. Careless combination of categories in a bar graph.
6. Inaccuracy in relative lengths of bars in a bar graph.
7. Biased distortion or embellishment.
8. Unclear labeling.

Example 2.19 | Inappropriate choice of statistic

Table 2.23 Top five nations for total number of cars stolen in 2000

Country	Cars stolen
1. United States	1,147,300
2. United Kingdom	338,796
3. Japan	309,638
4. France	301,539
5. Italy	243,890

Table 2.24 Top five nations for total number of cars stolen per capita in 2000

Country	Cars stolen per capita
1. Australia	0.00712
2. Denmark	0.00600
3. United Kingdom	0.00567
4. New Zealand	0.00563
5. Norway	0.00516

Now You Can Do
Exercises 3–5.

The United Nations Office on Drugs and Crime reports the statistics, given in Table 2.23, on the top five nations in the world ranked by numbers of cars stolen in 2000. The car thieves seem to be preying on cars in the United States, which has endured nearly as many cars stolen as the next four highest countries put together. (See also the bar graph in Figure 2.33.) However, the United States has a much greater population than these other countries. Is it possible that, *per capita* (per person), the car theft rate in the United States is not so bad?

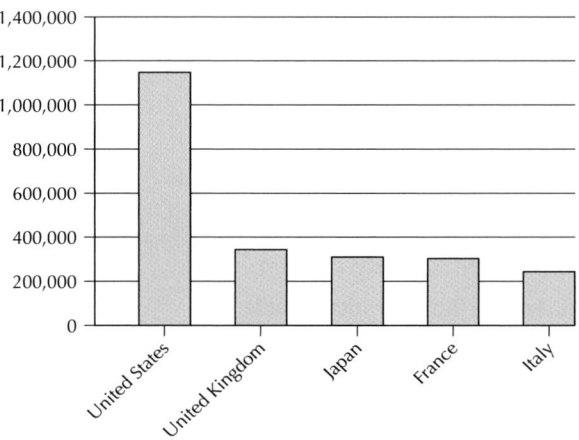

FIGURE 2.33 Bar graph of the top five nations for number of cars stolen in 2000.

Solution

In this case, the total number of cars stolen is an *inappropriate statistic* since the population of the United States is greater than the populations of the other countries. To find the per capita car theft rate, divide the number of cars stolen in a country by that country's population. The resulting list in Table 2.24 of the top five countries for per capita car theft contains a few surprises. Note that the United States has disappeared from the list. It is found in ninth place, with 0.00409 car thefts per capita. ■

> **Developing Your Statistical Sense**
>
> **Choose the Appropriate Statistic**
>
> The bottom line is that *we need to be careful how we use statistics.* Put in an extreme form, "Figures don't lie, but liars figure." One table of statistics tells us the car theft epidemic is striking the United States with special vehemence. The other table asserts the contrary. An American insurance company looking to increase car insurance rates could point to the first table to support its rate request. A citizens group opposing the request could cite the second table. Which table of statistics is true? They both are! We need to be careful how we phrase our research questions and how we choose the type of statistical evidence we use to investigate the research question. ◢

Example 2.20   Omitting the zero

MediaMatters.com reported that **CNN.com** used a misleading graph, reproduced here as Figure 2.34, to exaggerate the difference between the percentages of Democrats and Republicans who agreed with the Florida court's decision to remove the feeding tube from Terri Schiavo in 2005. Explain how Figure 2.34 is misleading.

Solution

Figure 2.34 is misleading because the vertical scale does not begin at zero. **MediaMatters .com** published an amended graphic, reproduced here as Figure 2.35, which includes the zero on the vertical axis and much reduces the apparent difference among the political parties. ▦

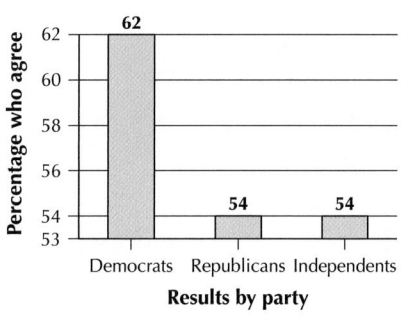

FIGURE 2.34 Omitting the zero is inappropriate.

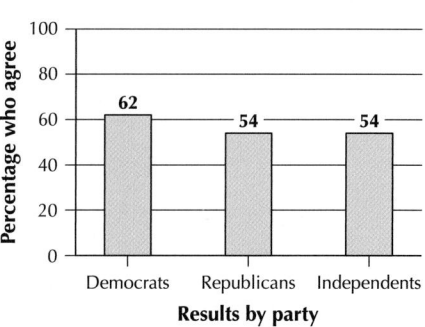

FIGURE 2.35 Appropriate graph.

Example 2.21   Manipulating the scale

Figure 2.36 shows a Minitab relative frequency bar graph of the majors chosen by 25 business school students. Explain how we could manipulate the scale to de-emphasize the differences.

Solution

If we wanted to de-emphasize the differences, we could extend the vertical scale up to its maximum, 1.0 = 100%, to produce the graph in Figure 2.37. ▦

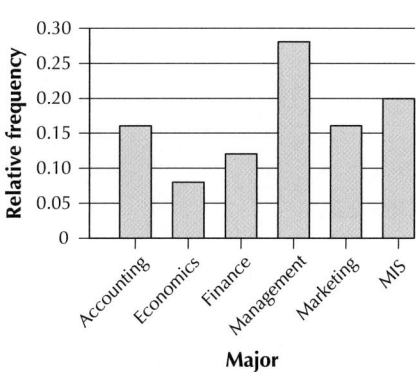

FIGURE 2.36 Well-constructed bar graph.

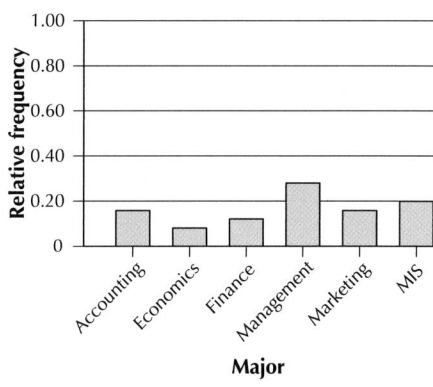

FIGURE 2.37 Inappropriate overextension of vertical scale.

Example 2.22   Using two dimensions for a one-dimensional difference and unclear labeling

Figure 2.38 compares the leaders in career points scored in the NBA All-Star Game among players active in 2007. Explain how this graphic may be misleading.

Solution

The height of the players is supposed to represent the total points, but this is not clearly labeled. Points should be indicated using a vertical axis, but there is no vertical axis at all. Further, note that Shaquille O'Neal dominates the graphic, because his body *area* is larger than the body areas of the other players. This is misleading. All four players should have the same body width, just as all bars in a bar graph have the same width. ■

FIGURE 2.38   This graph uses two dimensions (height and width) to emphasize a one-dimensional (points) difference. *(O'Neal: AP Photo/Alan Diaz; Bryant: AP Photo/Mark J. Terrill; Garnett: AP Photo/ David Zalubowski; Iverson: AP Photo/David Zalubowski.)*

Example 2.23   Careless combination of categories in a bar graph and biased embellishment

Figure 2.39 shows a graphic of how often people have observed drivers running red lights. Explain how this graphic may be considered both confusing and biased.

Solution

One problem with this graphic is that the categories of *seldom* and *never* have been combined, which may not be appropriate. Also, as we learned in Chapter 1, what is "seldom" to one person may not be "seldom" to someone else. A third problem is that the red light of the *Seldom/never* category is lit up, which may be evidence of bias on the part of the designer of the graphic. ■

FIGURE 2.39
Careless combination
of categories.

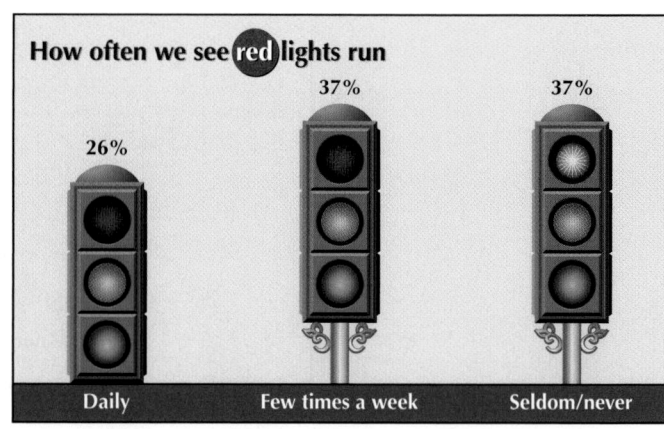

Example 2.24 Inaccuracy in relative lengths of bars in a bar graph and unclear labeling

Figure 2.40 is a horizontal bar graph of the three teams with the most World Series victories in baseball history. Explain what is unclear or misleading about this graph.

Solution

Note that 127 is more than twice as many as 52, and so the Yankees' bar should be more than twice as long as the Cardinals' bar, which it is not. Finally, note the absence of a vertical axis. ■

FIGURE 2.40
Inaccuracy in bar length.

Most World Series Victories

New York Yankees   127

St. Louis Cardinals   52

New York/San Francisco   45

When constructing a histogram, changing the number of classes or the width of the interval can sometimes lead to a completely different-looking distribution. Thus, we need to exercise care when someone shows us a histogram, since it presents, not the data themselves, but one of many ways of classifying the data.

Example 2.25 Presenting the same data set as both symmetric and left-skewed

The National Center for Education Statistics sponsors the Trends in International Mathematics and Science Study (TIMSS). Science tests were administered to eighth-grade students in countries around the world (see Table 2.25). Construct two different histograms, one that shows the data as almost symmetric and one that shows the data as left-skewed.

Table 2.25 Science test scores

Country	Score	Country	Score	Country	Score
Singapore	578	New Zealand	520	Bulgaria	479
Taiwan	571	Lithuania	519	Jordan	475
South Korea	558	Slovak Republic	517	Moldova	472
Hong Kong	556	Belgium	516	Romania	470
Japan	552	Russian Federation	514	Iran	453
Hungary	543	Latvia	513	Macedonia	449
Netherlands	536	Scotland	512	Cyprus	441
United States	527	Malaysia	510	Indonesia	420
Australia	527	Norway	494	Chile	413
Sweden	524	Italy	491	Tunisia	404
Slovenia	520	Israel	488	Philippines	377

Solution

Figure 2.41 is nearly symmetric. But Figure 2.42 is clearly left-skewed. It is important to realize that *both figures are histograms of the very same data set.* Clever choices for the number of classes and the class limits can affect how a histogram presents the data. The reader must therefore beware! The histogram represents a summarization of the data set, and not the data set itself. Analysts may wish to supplement the histogram with other graphical methods, such as dotplots and stem-and-leaf displays, in order to gain a better understanding of the distribution of the data. ■

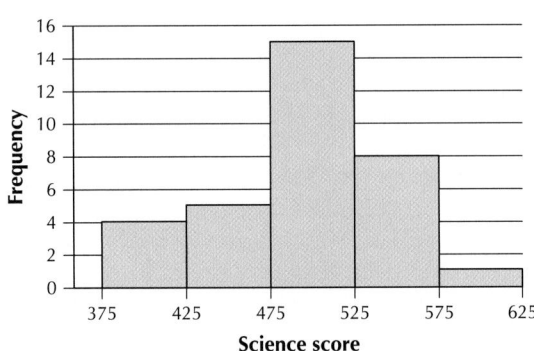

FIGURE 2.41 Nearly symmetric histogram of science test scores.

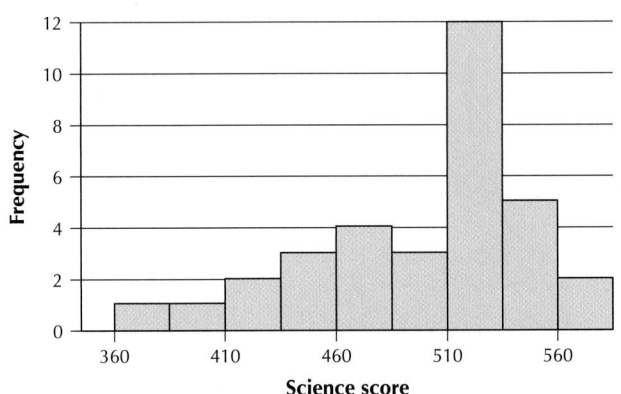

FIGURE 2.42 Left-skewed histogram of the same science test scores.

  The One Variable Statistics and Graphs applet allows you to experiment with the class width and number of classes when constructing a histogram.

Section 2.4 Summary

1 Understanding how graphics are constructed will help you avoid being deceived by misleading graphics. Some common methods for making a graph misleading include manipulating the scale, omitting the zero on the relevant scale, and biased distortion or embellishment.

Section 2.4 Exercises

CLARIFYING THE CONCEPTS

1. Explain in your own words why it is important to be aware of the methods that can be used to make graphics misleading.

2. True or false: What we have learned in this chapter proves that all statistics are misleading.

PRACTICING THE TECHNIQUES

Refer to Example 2.19 for the following exercises.

3. Which do you think is more effective at convincing the American public that a problem exists, Table 2.23 or Figure 2.33?

4. How would factoring in the *number of cars per country* affect the rankings, in your view?

5. If you were an insurance claims adjuster arguing for higher car insurance rates, would you prefer Table 2.23 or Table 2.24? Why?

APPLYING THE CONCEPTS

6. **Eating Bread.** Consider the accompanying graphic (similar to one found in *USA Today*) of the types of bread people eat.
    a. What type of graph is it supposed to represent, among the graphs that we have learned in this chapter?
    b. Consider how the *wheat* category dominates the graph. Which of the eight common methods for misrepresenting data is present here?
    c. Construct a graphic that is not misleading in this way.

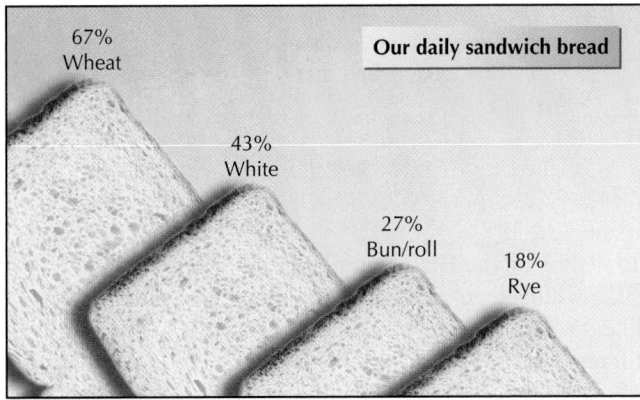

7. Child-Rearing Costs. Consider the accompanying graphic (similar to one found in *USA Today*) of child-rearing costs by type of cost.

    a. Identify one problem with the graphic that makes it misleading.

    b. Construct a graphic that is not misleading in this way.

8. Going to the Game. Consider the accompanying graphic (similar to one found in *USA Today*) of the proportions of people who go to see professional sports events.

    a. Identify two problems with the graphic that make it misleading.

    b. Construct a graphic that is not misleading in these ways.

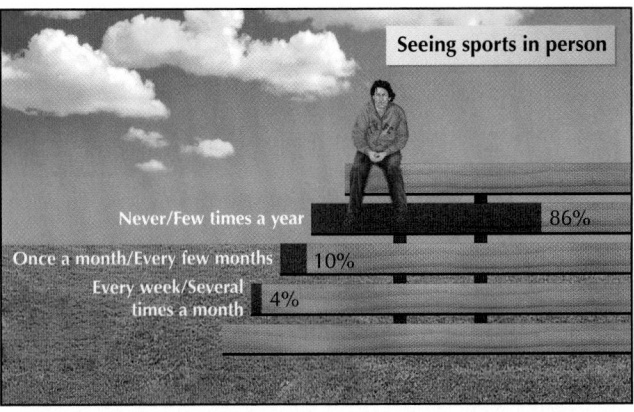

9. Living with AIDS. Consider the accompanying graphic.

    a. What point is the graphic trying to make?

    b. Which of the eight common problems is most obviously present here?

    c. Construct a graphic that is not misleading in this way.

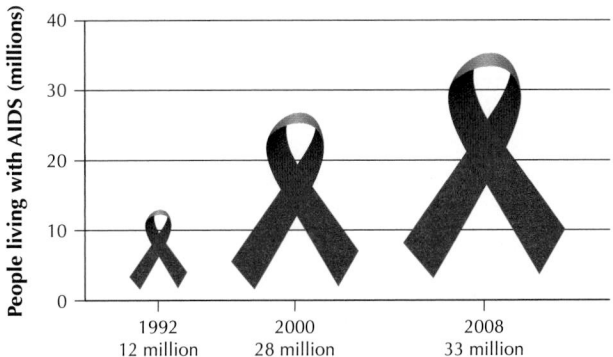

10. What's Your Sign? The General Social Survey collects data on social aspects of life in America. Consider the accompanying bar graph of the results of asking 1464 people what their astrological sign is.

    a. Which of the eight common problems is most obviously present here?

    b. Construct a graphic that is not misleading in this way.

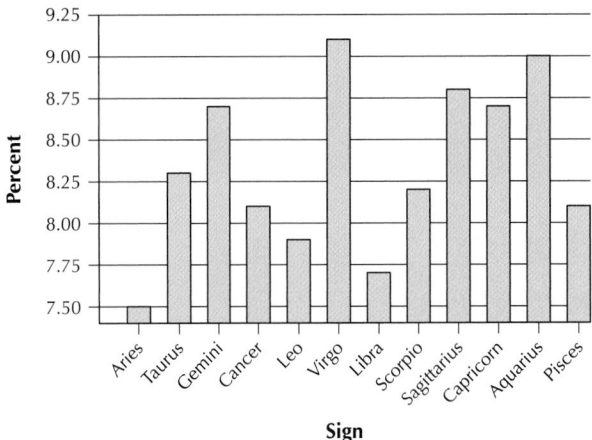

11. American League Shutouts. The bar graph below shows the number of team shutouts in the American League in the 2002 season.

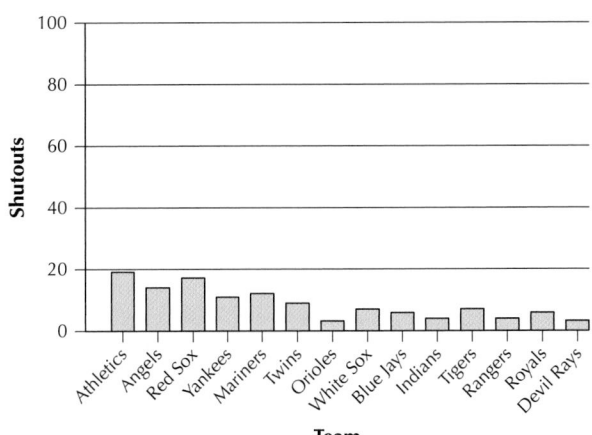

a. Which of the eight common problems is most obviously present here?

b. Construct a graphic that is not misleading in this way.

12. Video Game Consoles. Refer to the video game console data in Table 2.2 on page 39.

a. Construct a bar graph that overemphasizes the difference among the game consoles.

b. Which of the common methods for making graphics misleading are you using in **(a)**?

c. Construct a bar graph that underemphasizes the difference among the game consoles.

d. Which of the common methods for making graphics misleading are you using in **(c)**?

13. Music and Violence. *USA Weekend* conducted a poll that asked, "Do you think shock rock and gangsta rap are partly to blame for violence such as school shootings or physical abuse?" The results are shown in the following table.

Yes	31%
No	45%
I've never thought about it	24%

a. Construct a bar graph that overemphasizes the difference among the responses.

b. Construct a bar graph that underemphasizes the difference among the responses.

c. Construct a bar graph that fairly represents the data.

Use the *One Variable Statistics and Graphs* applet for Exercises 14–16. Work with the TIMSS scores from Example 2.25.

14. Click on the **Histogram** tab. Experiment with the class widths by clicking and dragging on the number line. Produce a histogram that is nearly symmetric, like Figure 2.41.

15. Produce a histogram that is somewhat left-skewed, like Figure 2.42.

16. Click on the **Stem-and-Leaf** tab. The previous two exercises left us with two different ideas as to the shape of the distribution.

a. Now produce a stem-and-leaf display of the TIMSS scores.

b. Compare the regular stem-and-leaf display with the split-stem stem-and-leaf display. Which is preferable for this data set?

c. Use your preferred stem-and-leaf display from **(b)** to describe the shape of the distribution.

d. Which of the two histograms does your description in **(c)** support?

Chapter 2 Vocabulary

SECTION 2.1
- **Bar graph (bar chart)** (p. 40)
- **Clustered bar graph** (p. 44)
- **Crosstabulation (two-way table, contingency table)** (p. 42)
- **Frequency (count)** (p. 39)
- **Frequency distribution** (for qualitative data) (p. 39)
- **Pareto chart** (p. 41)
- **Pie chart** (p. 41)
- **Relative frequency** (for a qualitative variable) (p. 39)
- **Relative frequency distribution** (for qualitative data) (p. 40)

SECTION 2.2
- **Bell-shaped curve** (p. 62)
- **Class** (p. 55)
- **Class boundary** (p. 56)
- **Class limit (lower)** (p. 56)
- **Class limit (upper)** (p. 56)
- **Class midpoint** (p. 59)
- **Class width** (p. 56)

- **Distribution of a variable** (p. 62)
- **Dotplot** (p. 62)
- **Frequency distribution** (for quantitative data) (p. 54)
- **Frequency polygon** (p. 59)
- **Histogram** (p. 58)
- **Relative frequency distribution** (for quantitative data) (p. 54)
- **Skewed distribution** (p. 63)
- **Stem-and-leaf display** (p. 60)
- **Symmetric** (p. 63)

SECTION 2.3
- **Cumulative frequency distribution** (p. 70)
- **Cumulative relative frequency distribution** (p. 70)
- **Ogive** (p. 71)
- **Time series plot (time series graph)** (p. 72)

SECTION 2.4
- **Eight Common Methods for Making a Graph Misleading** (p. 77)

Chapter 2 Review Exercises

SECTION 2.1

1. Parts of Speech. The accompanying bar graph summarizes the frequencies for the various parts of speech in a sample of English words. Should we be interested in determining whether this graph is symmetric or skewed? Clearly explain why or why not.

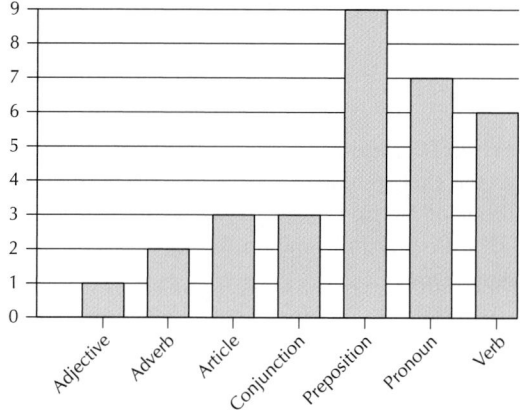

For Exercises 2–6, refer to the bar graph from Exercise 1 to construct the following for the variable *parts of speech.*

2. Relative frequency bar graph
3. Frequency distribution
4. Relative frequency distribution
5. Frequency pie chart
6. Relative frequency pie chart

Happiness in Marriage. The General Social Survey tracks trends in American society through annual surveys. Use the following contingency table for Exercises 7–11.

| Respondents' gender | Happiness of Marriage | | | |
	Very happy	Pretty happy	Not too happy	Total
Male	242	115	9	366
Female	257	149	17	423
Total	499	264	26	789

7. What proportion of the males responded that they were very happy in their marriage?
8. What proportion of the females responded that they were very happy in their marriage?
9. What proportion of the males responded that they were not too happy in their marriage?

10. What proportion of the females responded that they were not too happy in their marriage?
11. Construct a clustered bar graph of the data.

New York Townspeople. For towns in New York State, the accompanying histogram provides information on the percentage of the townspeople who are between 18 and 65 years old (data set **New York**). Refer to the histogram for Exercises 12–14. **NewYork**

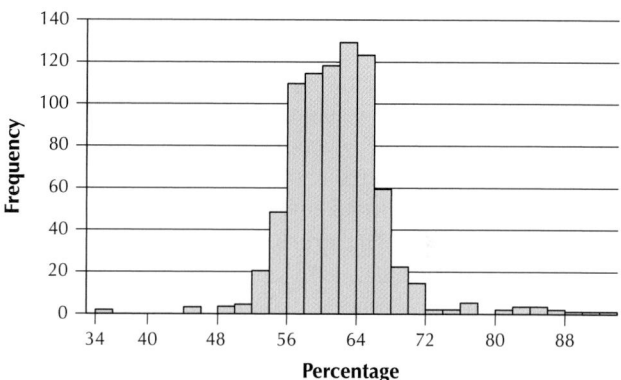

12. Using only the histogram, construct a frequency distribution and a relative frequency distribution of the proportion of townspeople between the ages of 18 and 65. Estimate the frequencies from the histogram.
13. If you had to place a fulcrum under the histogram so that it would balance perfectly like a seesaw, where would you place it?
14. Provide a rough estimate of the relative frequency of towns having 80% or more between 18 and 65 years old.

Households. Use the following information for Exercises 15–20. The data set **Household** contains eight variables' worth of information about the households in all 50 states plus the District of Columbia. The average size of the households is plotted in the accompanying dotplot, reproduced from Figure 2.21a. **Household**

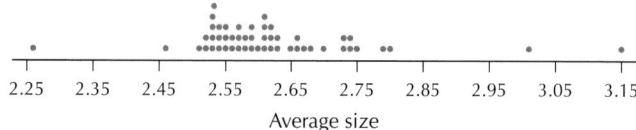

Dotplot of average household size.

15. Construct a frequency distribution of the data.
16. Construct a relative frequency distribution of the data.

17. Construct a frequency histogram of the data.
18. Construct a relative frequency histogram of the data.
19. Construct a frequency polygon of the data.

? **20.** *What if* the data were faulty, and each data point should have had 0.5 added to it. How would that affect the shape of the distribution?

SECTION 2.3
21. Use the data from the stem-and-leaf display in Exercise 37 in Section 2.2 (page 68) to
    a. construct a cumulative frequency distribution.
    b. construct a cumulative relative frequency distribution.
22. **Statistics Exam Data.** Use the data from Exercises 54–57 in Section 2.2 (page 69) to
    a. construct a frequency ogive.
    b. construct a relative frequency ogive.
23. **Miami Arrests.** The Miami-Dade Police Department published the monthly number of arrests made for the year 2005, given in the following table. Construct a time series graph of the data. **miamiarrests**

Jan.	751	May	919	Sept.	802
Feb.	650	June	800	Oct.	636
Mar.	909	July	834	Nov.	579
Apr.	881	Aug.	789	Dec.	777

SECTION 2.4
24. **Sports Clothing.** Consider the accompanying graphic of the types of sports clothing that children own.
    a. What type of graph does it represent, among the graphs that we have learned about in this chapter?
    b. Describe the difference between the representation of the NFL category versus the other categories.
    c. Which of the eight common methods for misrepresenting data is present here?
    d. Construct a graphic that is not misleading in this way.

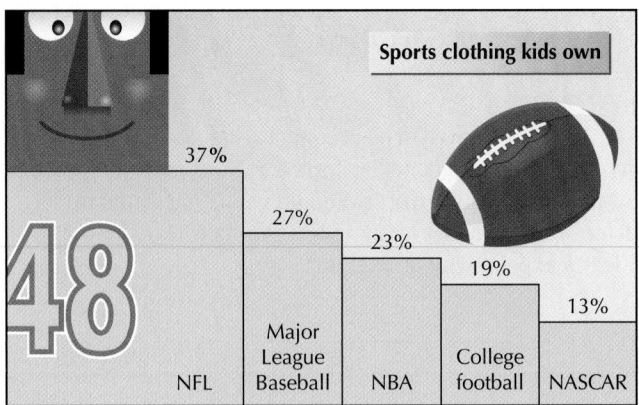

Sports clothing kids own

37% NFL
27% Major League Baseball
23% NBA
19% College football
13% NASCAR

25. **Carbon Dioxide Emissions.** The following table contains the energy-related carbon dioxide emissions (in millions of metric tons), by end-use sector, as reported by the U.S. Energy Information Administration.
co2emissions

Sector	Emissions
Residential	1213.9
Commercial	1034.1
Industrial	1736.0
Transportation	1939.2

a. Construct a bar graph that overemphasizes the differences among the sectors.
b. Which of the common methods for making misleading graphics are you using in (**a**)?
c. Construct a bar graph that underemphasizes the differences among the sectors.
d. Which of the common methods for making graphics misleading are you using in (**c**)?
e. Construct a bar graph that fairly represents the data.

Chapter 2 QUIZ

TRUE OR FALSE

1. True or false: Histograms are superior to stem-and-leaf displays because histograms retain the information contained in the data set.

2. True or false: A histogram always provides a realistic summary of the symmetry or skewness of a data set.

FILL IN THE BLANK

3. The frequencies in a frequency distribution must add up to the _____ _____ [two words].

4. A _____ _____ [two words] for a qualitative variable is a listing of all values that the variable can take, together with the frequencies for each value.

SHORT ANSWER

5. If there is a line that splits an image in half so that one side is the mirror image of the other, we say that the image is what?

6. If the right tail of a distribution is longer than the left tail, we say that the distribution is what?

CALCULATIONS AND INTERPRETATIONS

For Exercises 7–15, refer to the following table, which shows the life expectancy at birth in 2010, as reported by the World Health Organization.[6] **lifeexpect**

Country	Life expectancy
Afghanistan	42
Canada	81
China	74
Ghana	62
India	64
Israel	81
Mexico	76
Russia	68
United Kingdom	80
United States	78

Construct the following:

7. Frequency distribution
8. Relative frequency distribution
9. Cumulative frequency distribution
10. Cumulative relative frequency distribution
11. Frequency bar graph
12. Relative frequency bar graph
13. Pie chart of the relative frequencies
14. Ogive of the frequencies
15. Relative frequency ogive of the frequencies

3

Describing Data Numerically

Introduction

In Chapter 3, students develop numerical summaries to help them discover important characteristics about a data set. They also become acquainted with some powerful and widespread methodologies for applying the tools of descriptive statistics.

Section 3.1 introduces measures of center—the mean, the median, and the mode. Section 3.2 introduces measures of variability—the range, the variance, and the standard deviation. Section 3.3 discusses how to work with grouped data. Section 3.4 introduces us to measures of position, including z-scores, percentiles, percentile ranks, and quartiles, and how to use z-scores to detect outliers. Section 3.5 discusses the five-number summary, boxplots, and how to use the IQR method to detect outliers. Section 3.6 covers Chebyshev's Rule and the Empirical Rule for estimating the proportion of data contained in an interval.

From the Author

- **Section 3.1 Measures of Center**
  - Stress the notion of the mean representing the "balance point" of the data, so that students may check their calculations throughout the remainder of the course.
  - Early in Section 3.1 you may wish to review the definitions of *population* and *sample.*
  - The What-if Scenario, page 97. Usually, this feature is structured in such a way that a calculator will not help. Instead, students need to think about how a change in one aspect of the problem will affect other aspects of the situation.
  - Note that new topics in the Section 3.1 exercises are (a) *trimmed mean,* (b) *midrange,* (c) *harmonic mean,* and (d) *geometric mean.*
  - Constructing Your Own Data Sets, page 103. This is a good way for students to apply their understanding of the concepts, by making up their own list of numbers that satisfies a particular set of conditions.

- **Section 3.2 Measures of Spread**
  - While many (most?) students now learn mean, median, and mode (Section 3.1) in grammar school, not so many learn about the standard deviation or the variance (Section 3.2). So, for most students, most of the material in this section (and subsequent sections) will be new.
  - *Discovering Statistics* stresses what the statistics *mean.* This can be helpful when checking calculations, as, for example, for the standard deviation. If the student understands what a deviation means, and understands that the standard deviation represents a typical deviation, then the student may catch a calculation error. Exercises 49–50 on pages 115–116 are particularly useful for building an intuitive understanding of what the standard deviation means.
  - Note that new topics in the Section 3.2 exercises are (a) *coefficient of variation,* (b) *mean absolute deviation,* and (c) *coefficient of skewness.*

- **Section 3.3 Working with Grouped Data**
  - Some instructors find that they do not have time to cover Section 3.3. If you choose to omit this section, you may wish to cover Objective 1, The Weighted Mean, using the grading policy in your syllabus as an example.
- **Section 3.4 Measures of Position and Outliers**
  - Note that we have moved percentiles to follow z-scores and the z-score method to detect outliers. This follows a more natural progression: applying the mean and standard deviation soon after learning them. We have also moved quartiles and the interquartile range to follow percentiles, as these are related measures.
  - We have added the topic of finding a data value given its z-score. We have also added *percentile ranks*.
- **Section 3.5 Five-Number Summary and Boxplots**
  - We have moved the section on five-number summary and boxplots ahead of the section on the Empirical Rule and Chebyshev's Rule. This is because the boxplot uses the quartiles and the IQR, which were learned in the previous section.
- **Section 3.6 Chebyshev's Rule and the Empirical Rule**
  - Students sometimes have difficulty with the terminology "within 3 standard deviations of the mean." This is why we have devoted an example to illustrating this (Example 3.42, page 146). This is also an early example of an *interval* on the number line, a structure that will return again and again in this course.
  - Example 3.46 on page 150 brings together many of the concepts learned in this chapter.

Teaching Tips

Students may experience a steeper learning curve beginning at Section 3.2. The material in Section 3.1—mean, median, and mode—is often covered in high school or earlier. The material in Section 3.2 on variability is not usually covered in high school and is very important to an understanding of statistics. Stress the concept of *spread*—how spread out a data set is. The more spread out the data, the larger the measure of spread will be, whether it is the range, variance, standard deviation, or interquartile range.

In-Class Activities

1. Access the data set for Old Faithful at the following Web site: **http://research.microsoft .com/en-us/um/people/cmbishop/prml/webdatasets/faithful.txt**.

    The data set consists of 225 values for the variables duration and interruption time in an Excel file. The Yellowstone National Park Web site states that "Old Faithful erupts every 35–120 minutes for 1.5–5 minutes" (**www.yellowstone-natl-park.com/geyser.htm**). Use the data to construct appropriate graphs for the duration times and interruption times for Old Faithful. Ask students,

"What can you say about the distribution of these variables?" Ask them to compute numerical summaries for these two variables. Ask which data set has more variability.

Measures of Center

2. What is your guess of the typical height of all students in your class?

3. Make a dotplot of the heights of the students in your class.

4. Discuss where to place the center of this distribution of student heights. Without crunching any numbers, form a consensus on the location of the center.

5. Calculate the mean, median, and mode of the student heights.

6. Which measure (mean, median, or mode) comes closest to the consensus of where the center is located in (4)?

7. What is the relation between these measures and your guess of the typical height in (2)?

8. Which measure (mean, median, mode, class consensus, your guess) do you think is the best measure of the center of student heights?

Measures of Spread

9. Do you think that the distribution of the heights of all students in your class is more spread out or less spread out than the distribution of the heights of only the females in your class?

10. Would the values of our measures of spread (range, standard deviation) be larger for the entire class or for only the females?

11. Make a dotplot of the heights of only the females in the class. Make sure it uses the same scale as the dotplot for the heights of all the students in the class.

12. Use the two dotplots to assess which group has greater variability.

13. Back up your intuition by calculating and comparing our measures of spread (range, standard deviation) for the two groups.

Supplements

- StatTutor 2.1–2.10
- EESEE case studies for describing data numerically
  - Weighing Trucks in Motion (Question 2 on mean, median, and standard deviation)
  - Acorn Size and Oak Tree Range (Question 7 on boxplots, Question 2 on mean and standard deviation, Question 3 on range and standard deviation)
  - Faculty Salary Comparison (Question 1 on boxplots, Question 3 on weighted averages, Question 4 on ranking and means)

Applets

The *Mean and Median* applet is referenced in Chapter 3 to compute values for the mean and median and for Exercises 79 and 80 in Section 3.1.

Activities and applets that relate to measures of center, spread, and boxplots can be found at **http://mathforum.org/mathtools/tool/12489/**.

The site Online Statistics: An Interactive Multimedia Course of Study has numerous applets and activities: **http://onlinestatbook.com/index.html**.

Videos

- *Against All Odds*: **www.learner.org/resources/series65.html**
  - Program 3: Describing Distributions

Web Sites

- The following Web site has a collection of 20 class projects: **www.amstat.org/publications/jse/v6n3/smith.html**.
- This site has several projects using Excel and Minitab: **www.mathspace.com/NSF_ProbStat/Teaching_Materials/Primarily_Statistics.htm**.
- This site has activities using different technologies: **http://mtsu32.mtsu.edu:11281/classes/math2050_new/coursepack/coursepackindex.htm**.
- This Texas Instruments Web site has a host of TI-83/84 statistics activities: **http://education.ti.com/educationportal/sites/US/nonProductSingle/activitybook_83_statistics.html**.
- This Web site has a host of activities, simulations, and so on relating to elementary statistics: **http://davidmlane.com/hyperstat/ch2_contents.html**.
- This Web site lists other sites that do statistical calculations: **http://statpages.org/**.

63.28...RQP 25.11 ↑ 0.34...WCD

SL 16.42 ↑ 1.93...BJG 18.73 ↓ 1

5 ↓ 0.47...DRZ 29.33 ↑ 2.06...HF

Mark Hooper/Getty Images

OVERVIEW

3

Describing Data Numerically

CASE STUDY

Can the Financial Experts Beat the Darts?

Have you ever wondered whether a bunch of monkeys throwing darts to choose stocks could select a portfolio that performed as well as the stocks carefully chosen by Wall Street experts? The *Wall Street Journal* (**www.wsj.com**) apparently believes that the comparison is worth a look. The *Journal* ran a contest between stocks chosen randomly by *Journal* staff members (rather than monkeys) throwing darts at the *Journal* stock pages (mounted on a board) and stocks chosen by a team of four professional financial experts.

At the end of six months, the *Journal* compared the percentage change in the price of the experts' stocks and the dartboard's stocks. So, who do you think did better? Did the six-figure-salary financial experts put the random dart selections to shame? We examine the results in the Case Study on pages 98 and 113.

The Big Picture

Where we are coming from, and where we are headed . . .

- Chapter 2 showed us graphical and tabular summaries of data.

- Here, in Chapter 3, we "crunch the numbers," that is, develop numerical summaries of data. We examine measures of center, measures of variability, measures of position, and many other numerical summaries of data.

- In Chapter 4, we will learn how to summarize the relationship between two quantitative variables.

3.1 Measures of Center

OBJECTIVES By the end of this section, I will be able to . . .

1   Calculate the mean for a given data set.

2   Find the median, and describe why the median is sometimes preferable to the mean.

3   Find the mode of a data set.

4   Describe how skewness and symmetry affect these measures of center.

In Chapter 3 we learn how to summarize an entire data set with just a few numbers. For example, one numerical summary in baseball is a player's batting average (ratio of hits to at-bats). We know that Derek Jeter of the New York Yankees is a good hitter because his lifetime batting average is .314, which means that he gets hits 31.4% of the time. Most batters in Major League Baseball have a lower average. This simple number summarizes thousands of Jeter's at-bats over his long career. In Section 3.1, we will learn about three numerical measures that tell us where the center of the data lies: the mean, the median, and the mode.

1 The Mean

The mean is often called the arithmetic mean.

The most well known and widely used **measure of center** is the **mean.** In everyday usage, the word *average* is often used to denote the mean.

> To find the **mean** of the values in a data set, simply add up all the numbers and divide by how many numbers you have.

Example 3.1 Motor vehicle thefts at community colleges

Recall from Chapter 1 that a random sample is a sample for which every element has an equal chance of being selected.

Table 3.1 contains a random sample of five community colleges from the thousands of U.S. community colleges, along with the number of motor vehicle thefts that took place in 2009 at each college. Find the mean number of motor vehicle thefts for these five colleges.

Table 3.1 Motor vehicle thefts at community colleges

Amarillo College	1
Columbus State Community College	2
Lone Star College System	1
Mesa Community College	4
Portland Community College	2

Source: U.S. Department of Education, The Campus Safety and Security Data Analysis Cutting Tool (ope.ed.gov/security/), 2010.

Solution

To find the mean, we add up the number of motor vehicle thefts for the five colleges, and divide by the number of colleges, 5:

$$\text{mean number of motor vehicle thefts} = \frac{1 + 2 + 1 + 4 + 2}{5} = 2$$

Now You Can Do Exercises 13–16.

These five community colleges have a mean of 2 motor vehicle thefts. ∎

Notation

Statisticians like to use specialized notation. It is worth learning because it saves a lot of writing and because certain concepts can best be understood using this special notation.

- The **sample size,** which refers to how many observations you have in your sample data set, is always denoted by n. Here, the five colleges from Table 3.1 represent a sample taken from the population (which in this case is all the community colleges in the United States). Thus, here, $n = 5$.

- We denote the *i*th data value by x_i, where *i* is simply an index or counter indicating which data point we are specifying. For example, in Table 3.1, $x_1 = 1$, $x_2 = 2$, $x_3 = 1$, and $x_4 = 4$. The last data value is $x_n = x_5 = 2$.

- The notation for "add them together" is Σ (capital sigma), the Greek letter for "S," because it stands for "Summation." To add up the number of cases for all five colleges, we could write out $1 + 2 + 1 + 4 + 2$, or we could simply represent this sum as Σx_i or, even more simply, as Σx.

- The **sample mean** is called $\bar{x}$ (pronounced "x-bar"). You should try to commit this to long-term memory, since $\bar{x}$ may be the most important symbol used in this book and will return again and again in nearly every chapter.

> The **sample mean** can be written as $\bar{x} = \Sigma x / n$. In plain English, this just means that, in order to find the mean $\bar{x}$, we
>
> 1. Add up all the data values, giving us Σx.
> 2. Divide by how many observations are in the data set, giving us $\Sigma x / n$.

So, for example, the sample mean number of motor vehicle thefts can be written as

$$\bar{x} = \frac{\Sigma x}{n} = \frac{1 + 2 + 1 + 4 + 2}{5} = \frac{10}{5} = 2$$

| **What Does This Number Mean?** | **The Mean as the Balance Point of the Data** |

Let's explore the vehicle theft data a bit further. Consider the dotplot of the number of motor vehicle thefts for each college, given in Figure 3.1. To find out where the mean of the number of motor vehicle thefts lies on this number line, imagine that the dots are little blocks on a ruler or a seesaw and that you must decide where to place the fulcrum so that the ruler balances perfectly. *The place where the data set balances perfectly is the location of the mean.* Placing the fulcrum too far to the right or left would create an imbalance. This data set balances precisely at the sample mean, $\bar{x} = 2$. ◢

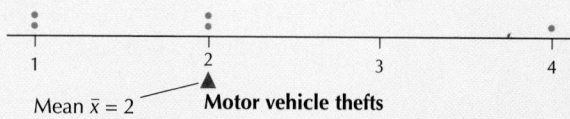

FIGURE 3.1

| **Developing Your Statistical Sense** | **Checking Your Results Against Experience and Common Sense** |

When you have found the balance point, you have found the mean. When you calculate the mean, or have a computer or calculator do it for you, don't just accept whatever value pops out. Make sure the result makes sense. Since the mean always indicates the place where the data values are in balance, the mean is often near the center of the data. If the value you have calculated lies nowhere near the center of the data, then you may want to check your calculations.

For example, suppose we were finding the mean of the vehicle theft data, and we accidentally entered 40 instead of 4 for the number of vehicle thefts for Mesa Community College. Then our value for the mean resulting from this *incorrect* calculation would be

$$\bar{x} = \frac{\Sigma x}{n} = \frac{1 + 2 + 1 + 40 + 2}{5} = \frac{46}{5} = 9.2$$

The mean number of thefts cannot equal 9.2 because all the values in the data set are less than 9.2. The mean can never be larger or smaller than all the values in the data set.

Don't automatically accept the result you get from a computer or calculator. Remember GIGO: Garbage In Garbage Out. If you enter the wrong data, the calculator or computer will not bail you out. Human error is one reason for the explosion of faulty statistical analyses in the newspapers and on the Internet. Now more than ever data analysts must use good judgment. When you calculate a mean, always have an idea of what you *expect* the sample mean to be, that is, at least a ballpark figure. ◢

The Population Mean μ

Greek letters are sometimes used to represent the (usually unknown) population parameters (such as the population mean).

The mean value of a population is usually unknown. For example, we cannot know the mean systolic blood pressure of *all* the residents in your hometown at noon today. Instead, data analysts use *estimation*. We could select a random sample of, say, 30 residents, find the mean systolic blood pressure $\bar{x}$ of this sample, and use this $\bar{x}$ as an estimate of the unknown population mean systolic blood pressure. We denote the **population mean** with μ (mu), which is the Greek letter for "m." The **population size** is denoted by N. When all the values of the population are known, the population mean is calculated as

$$\mu = \frac{\sum x}{N}$$

Example 3.2 Calculating the population mean

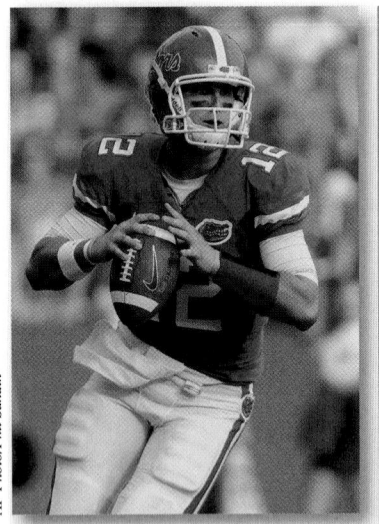

AP Photo/Phil Sandin

Table 3.2 contains the number of victories per team in the Southeast Conference of NCAA football for the 2009 season. Since these teams represent *all* the teams in the conference, then they represent a population.
a. Calculate the population mean number of victories.
b. Suppose a random sample consists of the following four teams: Florida, Arkansas, Georgia, and Tennessee. Calculate the sample mean number of victories for that sample.

Table 3.2 Victories for football teams in the Southeast Conference, 2009 season

Team	Victories	Team	Victories
Alabama	14	Georgia	8
Florida	13	Kentucky	7
Louisiana State	9	South Carolina	7
Mississippi	9	Tennessee	7
Arkansas	8	Mississippi State	5
Auburn	8	Vanderbilt	2

Solution

For calculating the mean, we will adopt the convention of rounding our final calculation to one more decimal place than that in the original data.

a. The population size is the number of teams in the conference, $N = 12$. The population mean number of victories is

$$\mu = \frac{\sum x}{N} = \frac{14 + 13 + 9 + 9 + 8 + 8 + 8 + 7 + 7 + 7 + 5 + 2}{12} = \frac{97}{12} \approx 8.0833 \approx 8.1$$

b. Our sample consists of the following teams: Florida (13 wins), Arkansas (8 wins), Georgia (8 wins), and Tennessee (7 wins), giving us the sample mean number of victories:

$$\bar{x} = \frac{\sum x}{n} = \frac{13 + 8 + 8 + 7}{4} = \frac{36}{4} = 9$$

Now You Can Do
Exercises 17–20.

Of course, a different sample would have yielded a different value for $\bar{x}$. ■

The Mean Is Sensitive to Extreme Values

One drawback of using the mean to measure the center of the data is that the mean is sensitive to the presence of extreme values in the data set. We illustrate this phenomenon with the following example.

Example 3.3 Sensitivity of the mean to extreme values

Table 3.3 Home sales prices in Broward County, Florida

Location	Price
Pembroke Pines	$290,000
Weston	$350,000
Hallandale	$375,000
Miramar	$415,000
Davie	$500,000
Fort Lauderdale	$575,000

Source: www.homes.com.

Table 3.3 contains a sample of 6 home sales prices for Broward County, Florida, for October 4, 2010. We would like to get an idea of the typical home sales price in Broward County. Find the mean sales price of the homes in this sample.

Solution

$$\bar{x} = \frac{\sum x}{n} = \frac{290,000 + 350,000 + 375,000 + 415,000 + 500,000 + 575,000}{6}$$

$$= \frac{2,505,000}{6} = \$417,500$$

Now, suppose that we append a seventh home to our sample, a home in Hillsboro Beach listed for $5,999,998, which is much more expensive than any of the other homes in the sample. Recalculating the mean, we get

$$\bar{x} = \frac{\sum x}{n}$$

$$= \frac{290,000 + 350,000 + 375,000 + 415,000 + 500,000 + 575,000 + 5,999,998}{7}$$

$$= \frac{8,504,998}{7} = \$1,215,000$$

Note that the mean sales price nearly tripled from $417,500 to $1,215,000 when we added this extreme value. Also, this new mean is much higher than every price in the original sample. Thus, it is highly unlikely that this new mean of about $1.2 million is representative of the *typical* sales price of homes in Broward County. This example shows how the mean is sensitive to the presence of extreme values. For situations like this, we prefer a measure of center that is not so sensitive to extreme values. Fortunately, the *median* is just such a measure. ■

2 The Median

Recall that the median strip on a highway is the slice of land in the *middle* of the two lanes of the highway. In statistics, the **median** of a data set is the *middle data value* when the data are put into ascending order. There are two cases, depending on whether the sample size is odd or even.

> **The Median**
>
> The **median** of a data set is the *middle data value* when the data are put into ascending order. Half of the data values lie below the median, and half lie above.
>
> - If the sample size n is odd, then the median is the middle value and lies at the $\left(\frac{n+1}{2}\right)^{\text{th}}$ position when the data are put in ascending order.
> - If the sample size n is even, then the median is the mean of the two middle data values that lie on either side of the $\left(\frac{n+1}{2}\right)^{\text{th}}$ position.

The case when the sample size is even is clear if you hold up four fingers on one hand. Notice that there is no unique finger in the middle. Since there is no middle value when the sample size is even, we take the two data values in the middle and split the difference.

The Median Is Not Sensitive to Extreme Values

Unlike the mean, the median is not sensitive to extreme values. If someone purchases a very expensive house, the mean home sales price will jump, but the median home sales price will be less affected. Let's look at an example of how this would occur.

Example 3.4   Median is not sensitive to extreme values

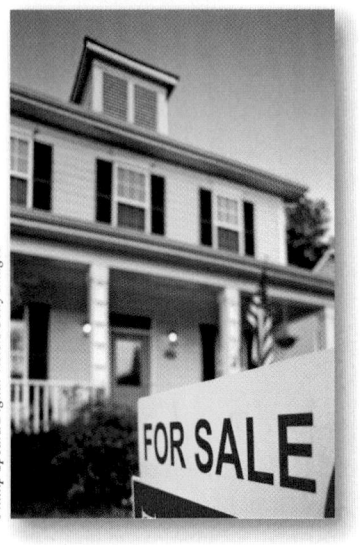

Philip Spears/Digital Vision/Getty Images

Find the median home sales price for the following data:
a. Broward County data from Table 3.3
b. Broward County data from Table 3.3 with the Hillsboro Beach home costing $5,999,998

Solution

a. Fortunately, the data are already presented in ascending order in the table. Since $n = 6$ is even, the median is the mean of the two data values that lie on either side of the $\left(\frac{n+1}{2}\right)^{\text{th}} = \left(\frac{6+1}{2}\right)^{\text{th}} = 3.5$th position. That is, the median is the mean of the 3rd and 4th data values, $375,000 and $415,000. Splitting the difference between these two, we get

$$\text{median price} = \frac{\$375,000 + \$415,000}{2} = \$395,000$$

We note that in Table 3.3 there are exactly as many homes with prices lower than $395,000 as there are homes with prices higher than $395,000.

b. Now, what happens to the median when we add in the $5,999,998 home from Hillsboro Beach? Since $n = 7$ is odd, the median is the unique $\left(\frac{n+1}{2}\right)^{\text{th}} = \left(\frac{7+1}{2}\right)^{\text{th}} = 4$th observation, given by the home in Miramar for $415,000. The extreme value increased the median only from $395,000 to $415,000. Recall that the mean nearly tripled to over $1.2 million. Thus, the median home sales price is a better measure of center because it more accurately reflects the typical sales prices of homes in Broward County. Figure 3.2 shows how the mean (red triangles) changes significantly with the addition of the extreme value, while the median (green triangles) changes relatively little. ■

Because the median is not sensitive to extreme values, we say that it is a *robust*, or *resistant*, measure of center. The mean is neither robust nor resistant.

FIGURE 3.2 The mean (red triangles) is sensitive to extreme values, but the median (green triangles) is not.

Now You Can Do
Exercises 21–24.

 The *Mean and Median* applet allows you to insert your own data values and see how changes in these values affect both the mean and the median.

 Note that the formula $\dfrac{n+1}{2}$ gives the *position*, not the *value*, of the median. For example, the median home sales price for Table 3.3 is *not* $\dfrac{n+1}{2} = \dfrac{6+1}{2} = 3.5$.

Example 3.5 Using technology to find the mean and median

homesales

Find the mean and median of the home sales prices in Table 3.3, using (a) the TI-83/84, (b) Excel, and (c) Minitab.

Solution

Using the instructions in the Step-by-Step Technology Guide on page 99, we get the following output.

a. The first TI-83/84 screen shows $\bar{x} = 417{,}500$ and $n = 6$. The second screen shows the median Med = 395,000.

```
1-Var Stats
x̄=417500
Σx=2505000
Σx²=1.10008E12
Sx=104151.3322
σx=95076.7234
↓n=6
```

```
1-Var Stats
↑n=6
 minX=290000
 Q₁=350000
 Med=395000
 Q₃=500000
 maxX=575000
```

b. The mean and median are shown in the Excel output.

Home Sales Price	
Mean	417500
Standard Error	42519.6
Median	395000
Mode	#N/A

c. The mean and median are shown in the Minitab output. ■

```
Descriptive Statistics:
Home Price

Variable        Mean    Median
Home Price    417500    395000
```

3 The Mode

A third measure of center is called the **mode.** French speakers will recognize that the term *mode* in French refers to *fashion.* The popularity of clothing, cosmetics, music, and even basketball shoes often depends on just which style is in fashion. In a data set, the value that is most "in fashion" is the value that occurs the most.

> The **mode** of a data set is the data value that occurs with the greatest frequency.

Example 3.6   Finding the mean, median, and mode: Twitter followers

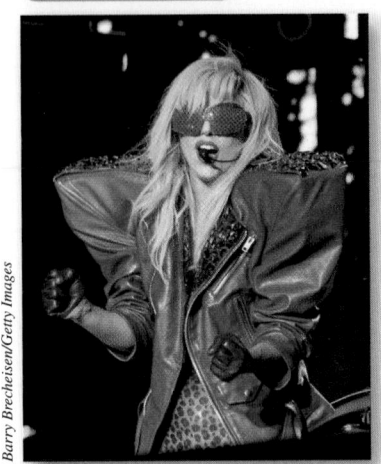

Barry Brecheisen/Getty Images

Lady Gaga

The Web site **twitaholic.com** provides statistics on the number of followers that celebrities have for their Twitter feeds. Table 3.4 provides the top 10 people with the most Twitter followers, as of October 8, 2010.

Table 3.4 Celebrities with the most Twitter followers

Rank	Person	Followers (millions)	Rank	Person	Followers (millions)
1	Lady Gaga	6.6	6	Kim Kardashian	5.0
2	Britney Spears	6.1	7	Taylor Swift	4.4
3	Ashton Kutcher	5.9	8	Oprah Winfrey	4.4
4	Justin Bieber	5.6	9	Katy Perry	4.2
5	Ellen DeGeneres	5.3	10	John Mayer	3.7

Find the (a) mean, (b) median, and (c) mode number of followers.

Solution

a. The sample mean number of followers is

$$\bar{x} = \frac{\sum x}{n} = \frac{6.6 + 6.1 + 5.9 + 5.6 + 5.3 + 5.0 + 4.4 + 4.4 + 4.2 + 3.7}{10}$$

$= 5.11$. The mean number of followers is 5.11 million

b. Since there are 10 people, the median is the mean of the two data values that lie on either side of the $\left(\frac{n+1}{2}\right)^{\text{th}} = \left(\frac{10+1}{2}\right)^{\text{th}} = 5.5$th position. That is, the median is the mean of the 5th and 6th data values, 5.0 million and 5.3 million:

$$\text{median number of followers} = \frac{5.0 + 5.3}{2} = 5.15 \text{ million}$$

c. The mode is the data value that occurs with the greatest frequency. There are two people with 4.4 million followers, Taylor Swift and Oprah Winfrey. No other data value occurs more than once. Therefore the mode is 4.4 million followers. ■

Now You Can Do
Exercises 25–28.

The Excel output on page 95 does not show a mode because no data value occurs more than once in Table 3.3.

One of the strengths of the mode is that it can be used with categorical, or qualitative, data. Suppose you asked your friends to name their favorite flower. Six of them answered "rose," three answered "lily," and one answered "daffodil." Note that these data are categorical, not numerical. Since the most frequently occurring flower is "rose," the rose represents the mode of the variable *favorite flower*. Unfortunately, we cannot use arithmetic with categorical variables, and thus the mean or median for this variable cannot be found.

It may happen that no value occurs more than once, in which case we say there is *no mode*. Or else more than one data value could occur with the greatest frequency, in which case we would say there is more than one mode. Data sets with one mode are *unimodal*; data sets with more than one mode are *multimodal*.

Give the Calculator a Rest

What If Scenarios offer you a chance to reflect on how changes in the initial conditions will percolate through the various aspects of a problem. The only requirement is to put your calculator down and think through the problem. You are asked to find the answers by using your knowledge of what the statistics *represent*.

Consider Example 3.6 once again. Now imagine: *what if* there was an incorrect data entry, such as a typo, and the number of Lady Gaga's Twitter followers was greater than 6.6 million people by some unspecified amount.

Describe how and why this change would have affected the following, if at all:

a. The mean number of followers

b. The median number of followers

c. The mode number of followers

Solution

a. Consider Figure 3.3, a dotplot of the number of followers, with the triangle indicating the mean or balance point, at 5.12 followers. Recall that this represents the balance point of the data. As the number of Lady Gaga's Twitter followers increases (arrow), the point at which the data balance (the mean) also moves somewhat to the right. Thus the mean number of followers will increase.

b. Recall from Example 3.6 that the median is the mean of the 5th and 6th data values, 5.0 million and 5.3 million. In other words, the mean *ignores* most of the data values, including the largest value, which is the only one that has increased. Therefore, the median will remain unchanged.

c. The mode also remains unchanged, since the only data value that occurs more than once is the original mode, 4.4 million followers.

Twitter followers (millions)

FIGURE 3.3 As the number of Lady Gaga's Twitter followers increases, so does the mean.

4 Skewness and Measures of Center

The skewness of a distribution can often tell us something about the relative values of the mean, median, and mode (see Figure 3.4).

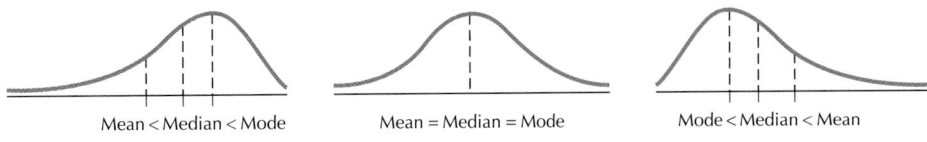

Mean < Median < Mode   Mean = Median = Mode   Mode < Median < Mean

FIGURE 3.4 How skewness affects the mean and median.

How Skewness Affects the Mean and Median

- For a right-skewed distribution, the mean is larger than the median.
- For a left-skewed distribution, the median is larger than the mean.
- For a symmetric unimodal distribution, the mean, median, and mode are fairly close to one another.

Example 3.7 | Mean, median, and skewness

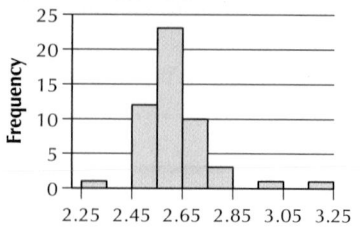

FIGURE 3.5 Household size is somewhat right-skewed.

The histogram of the average size of households in the 50 states and the District of Columbia from Example 2.14 (page 64) is reproduced here as Figure 3.5.

a. Based on the skewness of the distribution, state the relative values of the mean, median, and mode.

b. Use Minitab to verify your claim in (a).

Solution

a. The distribution of average household size is somewhat right-skewed. Thus, from Figure 3.4, we would expect the mean to be greater than the median, which is greater than the mode.

b. The Minitab descriptive statistics are shown here. Note that the mean is greater than the median, which is greater than the mode. ■

Now You Can Do
Exercise 60.

Descriptive Statistics: Size			
Variable	Mean	Median	Mode
Size	2.619	2.590	2.530

Mark Hooper/Getty Images

Note: In exploratory data analysis, we use graphical methods to compare numerical statistics.

CASE STUDY | Can the Financial Experts Beat the Darts?

Recall the contest held by the *Wall Street Journal* to compare the performance of stock portfolios chosen by financial experts and stocks chosen at random by throwing darts at the *Journal* stock pages. We will examine the results of 100 such contests in various ways, using the methods we have learned thus far, and will return to examine them further as we acquire more analysis tools. Let's start by reporting the raw result data. The percentage increase or decrease in stock prices was calculated for the portfolios chosen by the professional financial advisers and by the randomly thrown darts and was compared with the percentage net change in the Dow Jones Industrial Average (DJIA).

Exploratory Data Analysis

Figure 3.6 shows comparative dotplots of the percentage net change in price for the professionally selected portfolio, the randomly selected darts portfolio, and the DJIA, over the course of the 100 contests. First, estimate the mean of each distribution by choosing the balance point of the data. This balance spot is the *mean*. For fun, write down your guess for the mean for the professionals so you can see how close you were when we provide the descriptive statistics later. Now compare this with where you would find the balance spot (mean) for the darts dotplot. Which numerical value is larger, the balance spot for the pros or the darts? Just think: you are comparing the mean portfolio performances for the professionals and the darts without using a formula or a calculator. This is *exploratory data analysis*. You are using *graphical* methods to compare *numerical* statistics.

FIGURE 3.6
Dotplot of the percentage net price change for the professionally selected portfolio, the randomly selected darts portfolio, and the Dow Jones Industrial Average.

Remember: It is often helpful to have a "ballpark" estimate of the mean or other statistics, as a reality check of your calculations.

Hopefully, you discovered that the estimated mean for the pros is greater than the estimated mean for the darts. This is not particularly surprising, is it? Next, find the balance point for the DJIA dotplot. Compare the numerical value for the DJIA balance spot to the mean you found for the dotplot for the pros. Write down your estimate of the means for the DJIA and darts dotplots, so you can see how close you were later. Again, hopefully, you found that the estimated professionals' mean was higher than that of the DJIA. Now, a tougher comparison is to compare the estimated DJIA mean with that of the darts. Which of these two do you think is higher?

Finally, Minitab provides us with the mean percentage net price changes, as shown in Figure 3.7. Over the course of 100 contests, the mean price for the portfolios chosen by the professional financial advisers increased by 10.95%, by 6.793% for the DJIA, and by 4.52% for the random darts portfolio.

FIGURE 3.7
Mean percentage net price change for the professionals, darts, and DJIA.

Variable	N	Mean
Pros	100	10.95
Darts	100	4.52
DJIA	100	6.79

This is evidence in support of the view that financial experts can consistently outperform the market. We return to this Case Study in Section 3.2 (page 113). ■

STEP-BY-STEP TECHNOLOGY GUIDE: Descriptive Statistics

TI-83/84

Step 1 Enter the data in **L1** using the instructions (**STAT > 1: Edit**) found in the Step-by-Step Technology Guide in Section 2.2.
Step 2 Press **STAT**. Use the **right arrow** button to move the cursor so that **CALC** is highlighted.

Step 3 Select **1-Var Stats**, and press **ENTER**.
Step 4 On the home screen, the command **1-Var Stats** is shown. Press **2nd**, then **L1** (above the **1** key) and press **ENTER**.

EXCEL

Step 1 Enter the data in column **A**.
Step 2 Select **Data > Data Analysis**.
Step 3 Select **Descriptive Statistics** and click **OK**.

Step 4 For the **Input Range**, click and drag to select the data in column A.
Step 5 Check **Summary Statistics** and click **OK**.

MINITAB

Step 1 Enter the data in column C1.
Step 2 Select **Stat > Basic Statistics > Display Descriptive Statistics . . .**
Step 3 The variable selection dialog box appears. Select the variable you want to summarize by double-clicking on it until it appears in the **Variables** box.

Step 4 Click **STATISTICS**.
Step 5 Select the desired statistics and click **OK**.

CRUNCHIT!

We will use the data from Example 3.3 (page 93).

Step 1 Click **File . . .** then highlight **Load from Larose2e . . . Chapter 3 . . .** and click on **Example 3.3**.

Step 2 Click **Statistics** and select **Descriptive statistics**. For **Data** select **Prices**. Then click **Calculate**.

Section 3.1 Summary

1 Measures of center are introduced in Section 3.1. The sample mean ($\bar{x}$) represents the sum of the data values in the sample divided by the sample size (n). The population mean (μ) represents the sum of the data values in the population divided by the population size (N). The mean is sensitive to the presence of extreme values.

2 The median occupies the middle position when the data are put in ascending order and is not sensitive to extreme values.

3 The mode is the data value that occurs with the greatest frequency. Modes can be applied to categorical data as well as numerical data but are not always reliable as measures of center.

4 The skewness of a distribution can often tell us something about the relative values of the mean and the median.

Section 3.1 Exercises

CLARIFYING THE CONCEPTS
1. Explain what a measure of center is.
2. Which measure may be used as the balance point of the data set? Explain how this works.
3. Explain what we mean when we say that the mean is sensitive to the presence of extreme values. Explain whether the median is sensitive to extreme values.
4. What are the three measures of center that we learned about in this section?

For Exercises 5–12, either state what is being described or provide the notation.
5. The number of observations in your sample data set
6. The number of observations in your population data set
7. Notation for the ith data value in your data set
8. Notation denoting "add them together"
9. Notation for what we get when we add up all the data values in the sample, and divide by how many observations there are in the sample
10. Notation for what we get when we add up all the data values in the population, and divide by how many observations there are in the sample
11. The middle data value when the data are put in ascending order
12. The data value that occurs with the greatest frequency

PRACTICING THE TECHNIQUES
For the data in Exercises 13–16:
    a. Find the sample size n.
    b. Calculate the sample mean $\bar{x}$.
13. 18, 15, 20, 20, 17
14. 3, 0, 5, −3, 0, −5
15. 75, 65, 90, 80, 85, 75, 100
16. 120, 155, 95, 155, 133

For the data in Exercises 17–20:
    a. Find the population size N.
    b. Calculate the population mean μ.
17. 79, 92, 65, 75, 67, 59, 88
18. −50, −51, −45, 50, 45, 51
19. 1503, 1642, 1298, 1441, 2000
20. 9, 10, 9, 8, 6, 5, 8, 9, 6, 10, 8

For the data in Exercises 21–24, find the median.
21. 18, 15, 20, 20, 17
22. 3, 0, 5, −3, 0, −5
23. 75, 65, 90, 80, 85, 75, 100
24. 120, 155, 95, 155, 133

For the data in Exercises 25–28, find the mode.
25. 18, 15, 20, 20, 17
26. 3, 0, 5, −3, 0, −5
27. 75, 65, 90, 80, 85, 75, 100
28. 120, 155, 95, 155, 133
29. Five friends have just had dinner at the local pizza joint. The total bill came to $30.60. What is the mean cost of each person's meal?
30. Lindsay just bought 4 shirts at the boutique in the mall, costing a total of $84.28. What was the mean cost of each shirt?
31. The mean cost of a sample of 5 items is $20. The cost of four of the items is as follows: $25, $15, $15, $20. What is the cost of the fifth item?
32. The mean size of 4 downloaded music files is 3 Mb (megabytes). The size of three of the files is as follows: 5 Mb, 2 Mb, 3 Mb. What is the length of the fourth music file?
33. The median number of students in a sample of 7 statistics classes is 25. The ordered values are: 20, 22, 24, __, 27, 27, 28. What is the missing value?
34. The median number of academic credits taken in a sample of 6 students is 15. The ordered values are: 12, 12, 14, __, 17, 17. What is the missing value?

Use the following information for Exercises 35–38. Clickstream analysis is the study of how humans behave on the Internet.[1] One measure is the number of new page requests (clicks) that the visitor makes. A sample of the visitors to a particular Web site had the following total numbers of clicks.

1	5	3	4	3	2	3	7

35. Find the sample size n.
36. Calculate the sample mean number of clicks $\bar{x}$.

37. Find the median.

38. Find the mode.

Table 3.5 contains the number of cylinders, the engine size (in liters), the fuel economy (miles per gallon, city driving), and the country of manufacture for six 2011 automobiles. Use this information for Exercises 39–42. 🖥 **cylinderengine**

TABLE 3.5   Cylinders, engine size, and fuel economy for six cars

Vehicle	Cylinders	Engine size	City mpg	Country of manufacture
Cadillac CTS	6	3.0	18	USA
Ford Fusion Hybrid	4	2.5	41	USA
Ford Taurus	6	3.5	18	USA
Honda Civic	4	1.8	25	Japan
Rolls Royce	12	6.7	11	UK
Toyota Camry Hybrid	4	2.4	31	Japan

Source: **www.fueleconomy.gov.**

39. Find the following for the number of cylinders:
 a. Mean **b.** Median **c.** Mode

40. Find the following for the engine size:
 a. Mean **b.** Median **c.** Mode

41. Find the following for the fuel economy:
 a. Mean **b.** Median **c.** Mode

42. Find the mode for country of manufacture.

Use the information in Table 3.6 to answer Exercises 43–46, which gives the number of wins for the top 10 NASCAR racing drivers in various categories. 🖥 **nascar**

TABLE 3.6   Top 10 NASCAR winners in the modern era

Rank	Driver	Total	Super speedways	Short tracks	Road courses
1	Darrell Waltrip	84	18	47	9
2	Dale Earnhardt	76	29	27	3
3	Jeff Gordon	75	15	15	10
4	Cale Yarborough	69	15	29	9
5	Richard Petty	60	19	23	8
6	Bobby Allison	55	24	12	7
7	Rusty Wallace	55	5	25	11
8	David Pearson	45	20	1	4
9	Bill Elliott	44	16	2	4
10	Mark Martin	35	5	7	5

Source: Nascar.com.

43. Refer to the super speedways data. Find the following:
 a. Mean **b.** Median **c.** Mode

44. Refer to the short tracks data. Find the following:
 a. Mean **b.** Median **c.** Mode

45. Refer to the road courses data. Find the following:
 a. Mean **b.** Median **c.** Mode

46. Refer to the totals data. Find the following:
 a. Mean **b.** Median **c.** Mode

Table 3.7 contains the 2009 SAT scores of those students who took the SAT subject tests, as reported by the College Board. Use this information for Exercises 47–50. 🖥 **satsubject**

TABLE 3.7   SAT scores for students who took the SAT subject tests

SAT subject test	SAT Mathematics	SAT Reading	SAT Writing
English Literature	585	599	596
Biology-E	614	594	595
U.S. History	615	617	609
Chemistry	674	615	620
Math Level 1	605	604	600
Math Level 2	655	598	605

47. Calculate the following for the SAT Mathematics test:
 a. Mean **b.** Median

48. Find the following for the SAT Reading test:
 a. Mean **b.** Median

49. Compute the following for the SAT Writing test:
 a. Mean **b.** Median

50. Is there a mode score for any of the three tests? Explain.

APPLYING THE CONCEPTS

51. Liberal Arts Majors. Here are the declared liberal arts majors for a sample of students at a local college:

English	History	Spanish	Art	Theater
Theater	Philosophy	English	Music	Math
Math	Math	History	English	Art
English	History	Spanish	Economics	Math
Music	English	Economics	Theater	Music

 a. What is the mode of this data set? Does this mean that most students at the college are majoring in this subject?

 b. Does the idea of the mean or median of this data set make any sense? Explain clearly why not.

 c. How would you respond to someone who claimed that economics was the most popular major?

For Exercises 52–56, refer to Table 3.8, which lists the top five paperback trade fiction books, for the week of October 9, 2010, as reported by the *New York Times*.

TABLE 3.8   Top five best sellers in paperback trade fiction

Rank	Title	Author	Price
1	The Girl with the Dragon Tattoo	Stieg Larsson	$14.95
2	The Girl Who Played with Fire	Stieg Larsson	$15.95
3	Little Bee	Chris Cleave	$14.00
4	Half Broke Horses	Jeanette Walls	$15.00
5	Cutting for Stone	Abraham Verghese	$15.95

52. Find the mean, median, and mode for the price of these five books on the best-seller list. Suppose a salesperson claimed that the price of a typical book on the best-seller list is less than $14. How would you use these statistics to respond to this claim?

53. Linear Transformations. Add $10 to the price of each book.
  a. Now find the mean of these new prices.
  b. How does this new mean relate to the original mean?
  c. Construct a rule to describe this situation in general.

54. Linear Transformations. Multiply the price of each book by 5.
  a. Now find the mean of these new prices.
  b. How does this new mean relate to the original mean?
  c. Construct a rule to describe this situation in general.

55. Find the mode for the following variables:
  a. Price
  b. Author

56. Explain whether it makes sense to find the mean or median of the variable *author*.

Car Model Years. Refer to Figure 3.8 for Exercises 57–59. The data represent the model year for a sample of cars in a used car lot.

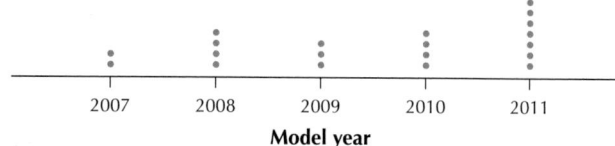

FIGURE 3.8 Dotplot of model year.

57. What are the mean, median, and mode of the model year?

58. Calculate a new statistic "age of the car in 2012" as follows: take the model year and subtract it from 2012.
  a. Find the mode of the car ages.
  b. Find the mean and median of the car ages.

59. What will be the mean, median, and mode of the car ages in 2015?

60. Skewness and Symmetry. Consider the accompanying distributions. What can we say about the values of the mean, median, and mode in relation to one another?

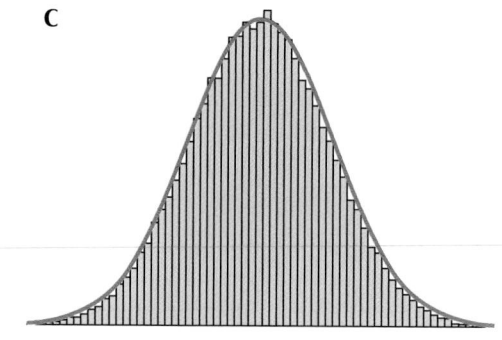

  a. The distribution in A
  b. The distribution in B
  c. The distribution in C

Nutrition Ratings of Breakfast Cereals. Refer to the following information for Exercises 61–64. (Note that Minitab denotes both the sample size and the population size as *N*.)

Descriptive Statistics: Rating						
Variable	N	Mean	Median	TrMean	StDev	SE Mean
Rating	59	45.46	42.00	44.76	14.39	1.87
Variable	Minimum	Maximum	Q1	Q3		
Rating	22.40	93.70	35.25	53.37		

61. Find the following sample statistics.
  a. The sample size
  b. The sample mean
  c. The sample median
  d. The highest and lowest ratings in the sample

62. What do these statistics tell us about the skewness of the distribution?

63. Linear Transformations. If we take each cereal rating and subtract 5 from it, how would that affect the mean, median, and mode? Would it affect each of the measures equally?

64. Linear Transformations. If we cut each of the cereals' ratings in half, how would that affect the mean, median, and mode? Would it affect each of the measures equally?

BRINGING IT ALL TOGETHER
Pulse Rates for Men and Women. To answer Exercises 65–68, refer to Figure 3.9, comparative dotplots of the pulse rates for males and females.[2]

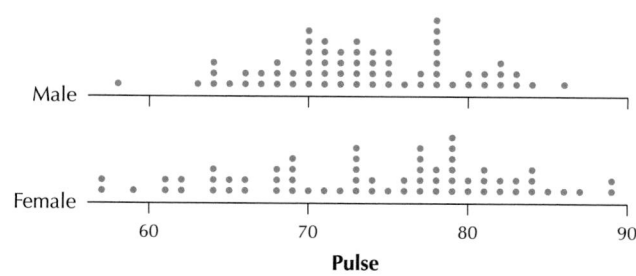

FIGURE 3.9 Comparative dotplots of pulse rates, by gender.

65. Examine Figure 3.9.
  a. Without doing any calculations, what is your impression of which gender, if any, has the higher overall pulse rate?
  b. Find the mean pulse rate for the males by estimating the location of the balance point.
  c. Find the mean pulse rate for the females by estimating the location of the balance point.
  d. Based on (**b**) and (**c**), which gender has the higher mean pulse rate? Does this agree with your earlier impression?

66. Find the following medians.
  a. The median pulse rate for the males
  b. The median pulse rate for the females
  c. Which gender has the higher median pulse rate? Does this agree with your findings for the mean earlier?

67. Find the following modes.
  a. The mode pulse rate for the males
  b. The mode pulse rate for the females
  c. Which gender has the higher mode pulse rate? Does this agree with your findings for the mean earlier?

68. *What if* the fastest pulse rate for the men was a typo and should have been an unspecified lower pulse rate. Describe how and why this change would have affected the following, if at all. Would they increase, decrease, or remain unchanged? Or is there insufficient information to tell what would happen? Explain your answers.
  a. The mean men's pulse rate
  b. The median men's pulse rate
  c. The mode men's pulse rate

69. Trimmed Mean. Because the mean is sensitive to extreme values, the *trimmed mean* was developed as another measure of center. To find the 10% trimmed mean for a data set, omit the largest 10% of the data values and the smallest 10% of the data values, and calculate the mean of the remaining values. Because the most extreme values are omitted, the trimmed mean is *less sensitive,* or *more robust* (*resistant*), than the mean as a measure of center. For the following random sample of women's pulse rates, calculate the following:
  a. The mean
  b. The 10% trimmed mean
  c. The 20% trimmed mean

75 69 73 84 82 80 74 83 77 78 61 78 87 79 65 72 69 81 62 69

70. Challenge Exercise. In general, would you expect the trimmed mean to be larger, smaller, or about the same as the mean, for data sets with the following shapes?
  a. Right-skewed data
  b. Left-skewed data
  c. Symmetric data

71. Midrange. Another measure of center is the *midrange.*

$$\text{midrange} = \frac{\text{largest data value} + \text{smallest data value}}{2}$$

Because the midrange is based on the maximum and minimum values in the data set, it is not a robust statistic, but is sensitive to extreme values. Calculate the midrange for the following data:
  a. The data from Table 3.8
  b. The data from Figure 3.8

72. Harmonic Mean. The *harmonic mean* is a measure of center most appropriately used when dealing with rates, such as miles per hour (mph). The harmonic mean is calculated as

$$\frac{n}{\sum \frac{1}{x}}$$

where n is the sample size, and the x's represent rates, such as the speeds in mph. Emily walked five miles today, but her walking speed slowed as she walked farther. Her walking speed was 5 mph for the first mile, 4 mph for the second mile, 3 mph for the third mile, 2 mph for the fourth mile, and 1 mph for the fifth mile. Calculate her harmonic mean walking speed over the entire five miles.

73. Challenge Exercise. The (arithmetic) mean for Emily's five-mile walk in Exercise 72 is 3 mph. Explain clearly why the value you calculated for the harmonic mean in Exercise 72 makes more sense than this arithmetic mean of 3 mph. (*Hint:* Consider time.)

74. Geometric Mean. The *geometric mean* is a measure of center used to calculate growth rates. Suppose that we have n positive values; then the geometric mean is the nth root of the product of the n values. Jamal has been saving money in an account that has had 4% growth, 6% growth, and 10% growth over the last three years. Calculate the *average growth rate* over these three years. (*Hint:* This is the geometric mean of 1.04, 1.06, and 1.10.)

CONSTRUCT YOUR OWN DATA SETS

75. Construct your own data set with $n = 10$, where the mean, the median, and the mode are all the same. Yes, just make up your own list of numbers, as long as the mean, median, and mode are all the same. Draw a dotplot. Comment on the skewness of the distribution.

76. Construct your own data set with $n = 10$, where the mean is greater than the median, which is greater than the mode. Draw a dotplot. Comment on the skewness of the distribution.

77. Construct your own data set with $n = 10$, where the mode is greater than the median, which is greater than the mean. Draw a dotplot. Comment on the skewness of the distribution.

78. Construct your own data set with $n = 3$. Let the mean and median be equal. Now, alter the three data values so that the mean of the altered data set has increased while the median of the altered data set has decreased.

Use the *Mean and Median* applet for Exercises 79 and 80.

79. Insert three points on the line by clicking just below it, two near the left side and one near the middle.
  a. Click and drag the rightmost point to the right.
  b. Describe what happens to the mean when you do this.
  c. Describe what happens to the median when you do this.

80. Explain why each of the measures behaves the way it does in the previous exercise.

3.2 Measures of Variability

OBJECTIVES By the end of this section, I will be able to . . .

1   Understand and calculate the range of a data set.

2   Explain in my own words what a deviation is.

3   Calculate the variance and the standard deviation for a population or a sample.

1 The Range

In Section 3.1 we learned how to find the center of a data set. Is that all there is to know about a data set? Definitely not! Two data sets can have exactly the same mean, median, and mode and yet be quite different. We need measures that summarize the data set in a different way, namely, the variation or variability of the data. In Section 3.2 we will learn *measures of variability* that will help us answer the question: "How spread out is the data set?"

Example 3.8 Different data sets with the same measures of center

AP Photo/Martin Meissner

DATA FILE volleyball

Table 3.9 contains the heights (in inches) of the players on two volleyball teams.

Table 3.9 Women's volleyball team heights (in inches)

Western Massachusetts University	Northern Connecticut University
60	66
70	67
70	70
70	70
75	72

a. Describe in words and graphs the variability of the heights of the two teams.
b. Verify that the means, medians, and modes for the two teams are equal.

Solution

a. There are some distinct differences between the teams. The Western Massachusetts (WMU) team has a player who is relatively short (60 inches; 5 feet tall) and a player who is very tall (75 inches; 6 feet, 3 inches tall). The Northern Connecticut (NCU) team has players whose heights are all within 6 inches of each other.

b. But despite the differences in (**a**), the mean, median, and mode of the heights for the two teams are precisely the same. As illustrated in Figure 3.10, the mean height (red triangle) for each team is 69 inches, the median height (green triangle) for each team is 70 inches, and the mode height (yellow triangle) for each team is 70 inches.

$$\bar{x}_{\text{WMU}} = \frac{60 + 70 + 70 + 70 + 75}{5} = \frac{345}{5} = 69$$

$$\bar{x}_{\text{NCU}} = \frac{66 + 67 + 70 + 70 + 72}{5} = \frac{345}{5} = 69$$

Clearly, these measures of location do not give us the whole picture. We need **measures of variability** (or **measures of spread** or **measures of dispersion**) that will describe how spread out the data values are. Figure 3.10 illustrates that the heights of the WMU team are *more spread out* than the heights of the NCU team. ■

FIGURE 3.10
Comparative dotplots
of the heights of two
volleyball teams.

Just as there were several measures of the center of a data set, there are also a variety of ways to measure how spread out a data set is. The simplest measure of variability is the **range.**

> The **range** of a data set is the difference between the largest value and the smallest value in the data set:
>
> range = largest value − smallest value

A larger range is an indication of greater variability, or greater spread, in the data set.

Example 3.9 Range of the volleyball teams' heights

Calculate the range of player heights for each of the WMU and NCU teams.

Solution

From Figure 3.10, it is intuitively clear that the heights of the WMU team are more spread out than the heights of the NCU team. Therefore, the range of the WMU team should be larger than the range of the NCU team, reflecting its greater variability.

$$\text{range}_{\text{WMU}} = \text{largest value} - \text{smallest value} = 75 - 60 = 15 \text{ inches}$$

$$\text{range}_{\text{NCU}} = \text{largest value} - \text{smallest value} = 72 - 66 = 6 \text{ inches}$$

Now You Can Do
Exercises 13–24.

The range for WMU is indeed larger than the range for NCU, reflecting WMU's greater variability in height. ■

The range is quite simple to calculate. However, it does have its drawbacks. For example, the range is quite sensitive to extreme values, since it is calculated from the difference of the two most extreme values in the data set. *It completely ignores all of the other data values in the data set.* We would prefer our measure of variability to quantify spread with respect to the center, as well as to actually use all of the available data values. Such a measure is the **standard deviation.**

2 What Is a Deviation?

Before we learn about the standard deviation, we need to get a firm understanding of what a **deviation** means, in the statistical sense. We shall use an example to do this.

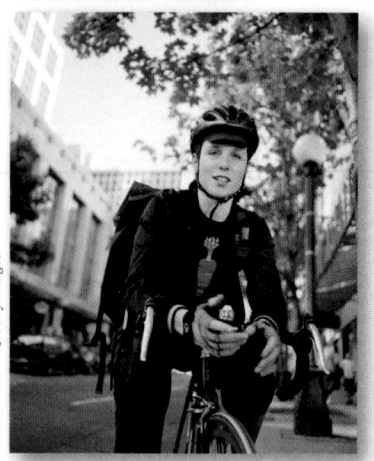

Example 3.10 Amanda and Bethany's delivery service

Amanda and Bethany both deliver documents in midtown Manhattan. Their clients would like to be able to count on a consistent delivery time schedule. Not only do the documents have to arrive in a timely fashion, but the delivery times should not vary a lot. One particularly important client kept careful track of the delivery times (in minutes) for documents delivered by Amanda and Bethany. See Table 3.10 and Figure 3.11. Describe the variability in Amanda's and Bethany's delivery times.

Table 3.10 Delivery times (in minutes) for Amanda and Bethany

Amanda	15	17	12	15	10	16	14	20	16	15
Bethany	5	22	15	25	4	18	10	29	17	5

deliverytime

FIGURE 3.11 Comparative dotplots of Amanda's and Bethany's delivery times.

Solution

Note that Bethany's delivery times vary more than Amanda's. Bethany has some long delivery times, some short, and some of moderate length. On the other hand, Amanda's delivery times are mostly of moderate length. We can say that Bethany's delivery times

- are *more spread out,*
- show *greater variability,*
- have *more variation,*
- are *more dispersed.* ■

You might think that, because the variation in Bethany's delivery times is larger, the mean length of her delivery times is longer as well. Not at all. The two sample means are equal, as shown by the red triangles in Figure 3.11.

$$\bar{x}_{\text{Amanda}} = \frac{\sum x}{n} = \frac{15 + 17 + 12 + 15 + 10 + 16 + 14 + 20 + 16 + 15}{10} = \frac{150}{10} = 15$$

$$\bar{x}_{\text{Bethany}} = \frac{\sum x}{n} = \frac{5 + 22 + 15 + 25 + 4 + 18 + 10 + 29 + 17 + 5}{10} = \frac{150}{10} = 15$$

Some measures of spread, such as the variance or standard deviation, rely on the concept of *deviation.*

Deviation

A **deviation** for a given data value x is the difference between the data value and the mean of the data set. For a sample, the deviation equals $x - \bar{x}$. For a population, the deviation equals $x - \mu$.

- If the data value x is larger than the mean, the deviation will be positive.
- If the data value x is smaller than the mean, the deviation will be negative.
- If the data value x equals the mean, the deviation will be zero.

The deviation can roughly be thought of as the distance between a data value and the mean, except that the deviation can be negative while distance is always positive.

Example 3.11 Calculating the deviations

Calculate the deviations for Amanda's and Bethany's delivery times.

Solution

- Amanda's mean delivery time was $\bar{x} = 15$ minutes. Her first delivery (first data value) also happened to be $x = 15$ minutes long. So the deviation for this first delivery is $x - \bar{x} = 15 - 15 = 0$. A deviation of zero occurs when a data value has the same value as the mean.
- Amanda's second delivery was $x = 17$ minutes long. So the deviation for this data value is $x - \bar{x} = 17 - 15 = 2$. A deviation of 2 implies that this data value lies two units (in this case, minutes) above the mean.
- Amanda's third delivery was 12 minutes long, resulting in a deviation of $x - \bar{x} = 12 - 15 = -3$.

Continuing in this way, we find the deviations for all of Amanda's and Bethany's delivery times, as recorded in Table 3.11. ■

Table 3.11 Delivery times and their deviations

	Delivery									
	1	**2**	**3**	**4**	**5**	**6**	**7**	**8**	**9**	**10**
Amanda's times	15	17	12	15	10	16	14	20	16	15
Amanda's deviations	0	2	−3	0	−5	1	−1	5	1	0
Bethany's times	5	22	15	25	4	18	10	29	17	5
Bethany's deviations	−10	7	0	10	−11	3	−5	14	2	−10

Figure 3.12 illustrates these deviations in comparative dotplots. The green arrows indicate positive deviations, and the red arrows indicate negative deviations from the mean $\bar{x} = 15$. For example, the longest green arrow for Amanda is for her eighth delivery, which took 20 minutes. The deviation for this delivery is $x - \bar{x} = 20 - 15 = 5$. The lower dotplot shows Bethany's delivery times, with positive and negative deviations from the mean $\bar{x} = 15$. Bethany's arrows do seem longer, on average. For a moment, let us consider using the "mean deviation" as a way of measuring the spread. The mean of Amanda's deviations is

$$\text{Amanda's mean deviation} = \frac{0 + 2 + (-3) + 0 + (-5) + 1 + (-1) + 5 + 1 + 0}{10}$$
$$= \frac{0}{10} = 0$$

Deviations equal to zero have no arrows in Figure 3.12.

FIGURE 3.12 Comparative dotplots of delivery time deviations.

You can confirm that Bethany's mean deviation is zero as well. It is not a coincidence that the mean deviation for both Amanda and Bethany equals zero. In fact, *for any conceivable data set, the mean deviation is zero,* since the mean is the unique point on the number line where the negative deviations (the red arrows in Figure 3.12) precisely balance the positive deviations (the green arrows). Hence, the mean deviation is not a useful measure of spread. To avoid this problem, statisticians work with the squared deviations.

3 The Variance and the Standard Deviation

To compute the standard deviation and variance, we consider the squared deviations. Table 3.12 shows the squared deviations for Amanda and Bethany. Note that Bethany's squared deviations are on average larger than Amanda's, reflecting the greater spread in Bethany's delivery times. It is therefore logical to build our measure of spread using the *mean squared deviation*.

Table 3.12 Squared deviations of delivery times for Amanda and Bethany

	Delivery									
	1	2	3	4	5	6	7	8	9	10
Amanda's times	15	17	12	15	10	16	14	20	16	15
Amanda's deviations	0	2	−3	0	−5	1	−1	5	1	0
Amanda's squared deviations	$0^2 = 0$	$2^2 = 4$	$(-3)^2 = 9$	$0^2 = 0$	$(-5)^2 = 25$	$1^2 = 1$	$(-1)^2 = 1$	$5^2 = 25$	$1^2 = 1$	$0^2 = 0$
Bethany's times	5	22	15	25	4	18	10	29	17	5
Bethany's deviations	−10	7	0	10	−11	3	−5	14	2	−10
Bethany's squared deviations	$(-10)^2 = 100$	$7^2 = 49$	$0^2 = 0$	$10^2 = 100$	$(-11)^2 = 121$	$3^2 = 9$	$(-5)^2 = 25$	$14^2 = 196$	$2^2 = 4$	$(-10)^2 = 100$

The Population Variance σ^2

Suppose that we consider Amanda's and Bethany's delivery times to be populations rather than samples. Then the mean of each population is a population mean ($\mu = 15$) rather than a sample mean. Each deviation is $(x - \mu)$, and the mean squared deviation is called the **population variance** and is symbolized by σ^2. This is the lowercase Greek letter *sigma*, not to be confused with the uppercase *sigma* (Σ) used for summation.

Note: Notice that the numerator in σ^2 is a *sum of squares*. Squared numbers can never be negative, so a sum of squares also can never be negative. The denominator, N, the population size, also can never be negative. Thus, σ^2 can never be negative. The only time $\sigma^2 = 0$ is when all the population data values are equal.

The **population variance** σ^2 is the mean of the squared deviations in the population given by the formula

$$\sigma^2 = \frac{\sum(x - \mu)^2}{N}$$

Example 3.12   Calculating the population variances for Amanda and Bethany

Calculate the population variances of the delivery times for Amanda and Bethany.

Solution

Using the squared deviations from Table 3.12, we have

$$\sigma^2 = \frac{\sum(x - \mu)^2}{N} = \frac{0 + 4 + 9 + 0 + 25 + 1 + 1 + 25 + 1 + 0}{10} = \frac{66}{10} = 6.6$$

for Amanda, and

$$\sigma^2 = \frac{\sum(x - \mu)^2}{N} = \frac{100 + 49 + 0 + 100 + 121 + 9 + 25 + 196 + 4 + 100}{10} = \frac{704}{10} = 70.4$$

for Bethany. Clearly, the population variance of the delivery times for Bethany is greater than that for Amanda, thus indicating that Bethany's delivery times have greater variability than Amanda's. ∎

Now You Can Do
Exercises 25a–30a.

However, what is the *meaning* of the values we got for σ^2, 6.6 and 70.4, apart from their comparative value? The problem is that the units of these values are *minutes squared*, which is not a useful measure. Unfortunately, the intuitive meaning of the population variance is not clear.

The Population Standard Deviation σ

In practice, the *standard deviation* is easier to interpret than the variance. The standard deviation is simply the square root of the variance, and by taking the square root, we return the units of measure back to the original data unit (for example, "minutes" rather than "minutes squared"). The symbol for the **population standard deviation** is σ. Conveniently, $\sqrt{\sigma^2} = \sigma$.

Note: σ can never be negative.

> The **population standard deviation** σ is the positive square root of the population variance and is found by
>
> $$\sigma = \sqrt{\frac{\sum(x - \mu)^2}{N}}$$

Example 3.13   Calculating the population standard deviations for Amanda and Bethany

Calculate the population standard deviations of the delivery times for Amanda and Bethany.

Solution

Since Bethany's population variance of 70.4 is larger than Amanda's population variance of 6.6, Bethany's population standard deviation will also be larger, since we are simply taking the square root. We have

$$\sigma = \sqrt{\frac{\sum(x - \mu)^2}{N}} = \sqrt{\frac{66}{10}} = \sqrt{6.6} \approx 2.6$$

for Amanda, and

$$\sigma = \sqrt{\frac{\sum(x - \mu)^2}{N}} = \sqrt{\frac{704}{10}} = \sqrt{70.4} \approx 8.4$$

for Bethany.

The population standard deviation of Bethany's delivery times is 8.4 minutes, which is larger than Amanda's 2.6 minutes. As expected, the greater variability in Bethany's delivery times leads to a larger value for her population standard deviation σ. ■

Now You Can Do
Exercises 25b–30b.

What Do These
Numbers Mean?

Remember that the standard deviation is not the mean deviation, which always equals zero.

The Standard Deviation

So how do we interpret these values for σ? One quick thumbnail interpretation of the standard deviation is that it represents a "typical" deviation. That is, the value of σ represents a *distance from the mean that is representative for that data set.* For example, the typical distance from the mean for Amanda's and Bethany's delivery times is 2.6 minutes and 8.4 minutes, respectively. ◢

Developing Your
Statistical Sense

Communicating the Results

As you study statistics, keep in mind that during your career you will likely need to explain your results to others who have never taken a statistics course. Therefore, you should always keep in mind *how to interpret your results to nonspecialists.* Communication and interpretation of your results can be as important as the results themselves. ◢

Note: In this text, we will work with sample statistics unless the data set is identified as a population.

The Sample Variance s^2 and the Sample Standard Deviation s

In the real world, we usually cannot determine the exact value of the population mean or the population standard deviation. Instead, we use the sample mean and **sample standard deviation** to estimate the population parameters. The **sample variance** also depends on the concept of the mean squared deviation. If the sample mean is $\bar{x}$, and the sample size is n, then we would expect the formula for the sample variance to resemble the formula for the population variance, namely

$$\frac{\sum(x - \bar{x})^2}{n}$$

However, this formula has been found to underestimate the population variance, so that we need to replace the n in the denominator with $n - 1$. We therefore have the following.

> The **sample variance** s^2 is approximately the mean of the squared deviations in the sample and is found by
>
> $$s^2 = \frac{\sum(x - \bar{x})^2}{n - 1}$$

The sample standard deviation s is simply the square root of the sample variance and takes as its symbol the letter s, which is the Roman letter for the Greek σ. The sample standard deviation is perhaps the second most important statistic you will encounter in this book (after the sample mean $\bar{x}$). It is the most commonly used measure of spread. Again, $s = \sqrt{s^2}$.

> The **sample standard deviation** s is the positive square root of the sample variance s^2:
>
> $$s = \sqrt{s^2} = \sqrt{\frac{\sum(x - \bar{x})^2}{n - 1}}$$
>
> The value of s may be interpreted as the typical difference between a data value and the sample mean, for a given data set.

Neither s^2 nor s can ever be negative.

Example 3.14 Calculating the sample variance and the sample standard deviation

Calculate the sample variances and sample standard deviations of Amanda's and Bethany's delivery times.

Solution

Using the squared deviations from Table 3.12, we have the sample variance

$$s^2 = \frac{\sum(x - \bar{x})^2}{n - 1} = \frac{0 + 4 + 9 + 0 + 25 + 1 + 1 + 25 + 1 + 0}{9} = \frac{66}{9} \approx 7.3$$

for Amanda, and the sample variance

$$s^2 = \frac{\sum(x - \bar{x})^2}{n - 1} = \frac{100 + 49 + 0 + 100 + 121 + 9 + 25 + 196 + 4 + 100}{9} = \frac{704}{9} \approx 78.2$$

for Bethany.

We find the sample standard deviations for Amanda's and Bethany's delivery times, as follows. For Amanda, we have

We can say that Amanda's delivery times are *more consistent* than Bethany's, because her value for s is smaller.

$$s = \sqrt{\frac{\sum(x - \bar{x})^2}{n - 1}} = \sqrt{\frac{0 + 4 + 9 + 0 + 25 + 1 + 1 + 25 + 1 + 0}{9}} = \sqrt{\frac{66}{9}} \approx 2.7$$

and for Bethany, we have

$$s = \sqrt{\frac{\sum(x - \bar{x})^2}{n-1}} = \sqrt{\frac{100 + 49 + 0 + 100 + 121 + 9 + 25 + 196 + 4 + 100}{9}} = \sqrt{\frac{704}{9}} \approx 8.8$$

Amanda's delivery times typically differ from the mean $\bar{x} = 15$ by only 2.7 minutes, while Bethany's delivery times typically differ from the mean by 8.8 minutes. ∎

Now You Can Do
Exercises 31–36.

Developing Your Statistical Sense

Less Variation Is Usually Better

Amanda's sample standard deviation of $s = 2.7$ shows a remarkable consistency in her delivery times. Amanda's clients would certainly appreciate this consistency. In most real-world applications, consistency is a great advantage. In statistical data analysis, less variation is often better even though variability is natural and cannot be eliminated. Throughout the text, you will find that smaller variability will lead to
- more precise estimates and
- higher confidence in conclusions. ◢

The above formulas for the variance and standard deviation can sometimes be time-consuming, since each individual deviation needs to be calculated. You may use the following *computational formulas* to simplify your calculations. The computational formulas are equivalent to the above definition formulas.

Computational Formulas for the Variance and Standard Deviation

Population variance:

$$\sigma^2 = \frac{\sum x^2 - \left(\sum x\right)^2 / N}{N}$$

Sample variance:

$$s^2 = \frac{\sum x^2 - \left(\sum x\right)^2 / n}{n-1}$$

Population standard deviation:

$$\sigma = \sqrt{\frac{\sum x^2 - \left(\sum x\right)^2 / N}{N}}$$

Sample standard deviation:

$$s = \sqrt{\frac{\sum x^2 - \left(\sum x\right)^2 / n}{n-1}}$$

where $\sum x^2$ means that you square each data value and then add up the squared data values, and $\left(\sum x\right)^2$ means that you add up all the data values and then square the sum.

A Note on Rounding: In this chapter, *we* typically round to one or two decimal places when *presenting* results. However, when results are to be used for later calculations, students should not round until the last calculation.

Example 3.15 — Calculating the population variance and population standard deviation using the computational formulas

Table 3.13 Farmland in Connecticut

County	Farmland (1000s of acres)
Fairfield	12.8
Hartford	50.2
Litchfield	93.6
Middlesex	17.9
New Haven	26.0
New London	58.9
Tolland	36.8
Windham	61.1

Source: U.S. Bureau of Economic Analysis.

Table 3.13 lists the amount of farmland (in 1000s of acres) in each county in the state of Connecticut. Since the data set contains *all* $N = 8$ counties in Connecticut, it can be considered a population. Calculate the population variance and population standard deviation using the computational formulas.

Solution

Construct a table similar to Table 3.14. The data values (farmland = x) go in the first column, and the squared values go in the second column. Notice that we don't have to find the deviations. Add up the columns to get $\sum x = 357.3$ and $\sum x^2 = 20{,}997.91$, respectively. Then substitute these values into the computational formula for the population variance:

$$\sigma^2 = \frac{\sum x^2 - \left(\sum x\right)^2 / N}{N} = \frac{20{,}997.91 - (357.3)^2 / 8}{8} = 629.9998438 \approx 630.0$$

The population standard deviation is therefore

$$\sigma = \sqrt{\sigma^2} = \sqrt{629.9998438} \approx 25.1$$

The standard deviation of farmland for all counties in Connecticut is about 25,100 acres. ■

Table 3.14 Calculating $\sum x$ and $\sum x^2$

x	x^2
12.8	163.84
50.2	2520.04
93.6	8760.96
17.9	320.41
26.0	676.00
58.9	3469.21
36.8	1354.24
61.1	3733.21
$\sum x = 357.3$	$\sum x^2 = 20{,}997.91$

Example 3.16 Calculating the sample variance and sample standard deviation using the computational formulas

Do you see how this sample is not a random sample?

Suppose we take a sample of the three counties from Table 3.13 that have the most farmland. Calculate the sample variance and sample standard deviation using the computational formulas.

Solution

Table 3.15 shows the calculations required to get $\sum x = 213.6$ and $\sum x^2 = 15{,}963.38$. Then, substituting these values into the computational formula for the sample variance gives us

Table 3.15 Calculating $\sum x$ and $\sum x^2$

x	x^2
93.6	8760.96
61.1	3733.21
58.9	3469.21
$\sum x = 213.6$	$\sum x^2 = 15{,}963.38$

$$s^2 = \frac{\sum x^2 - \left(\sum x\right)^2 / n}{n - 1} = \frac{15{,}963.38 - (213.6)^2 / 3}{3 - 1} \approx 377.53$$

The sample standard deviation is therefore

$$s = \sqrt{s^2} = \sqrt{377.53} \approx 19.4$$

The standard deviation of farmland for this sample of three counties in Connecticut is about 19,400 acres. ■

Example 3.17 Using technology to find the sample variance and sample standard deviation

 gasmileage

Find the sample standard deviation and the sample variance of the city gas mileage for the 2011 cars shown in the following table. Use (a) the TI-83/84, (b) Excel, and (c) Minitab.

Vehicle	City mpg
Cadillac CTS	18
Ford Fusion Hybrid	41
Ford Taurus	18
Honda Civic	25
Rolls Royce Phantom	11
Toyota Camry Hybrid	31

Source: www.fueleconomy.gov.

Solution

Using the instructions in the Step-by-Step Technology Guide on page 99, we obtain the following output:

a. The TI-83/84 output is shown in Figure 3.13a. The sample standard deviation s is given as $Sx = 10.77032961$. The sample variance is $s^2 = (10.77032961)^2 = 116$

b. The Excel output is provided in Figure 3.13b. The sample standard deviation and sample variance are highlighted.

c. The Minitab output is provided in Figure 3.13c. Note that Minitab rounds s to two decimal places. ■

For the TI-83/84, do not confuse Sx, the TI's notation for the sample standard deviation, with σx, which the TI-83/84 uses to label the population standard deviation.

```
1-Var Stats
 x̄=24
 Σx=144
 Σx²=4036
 Sx=10.77032961
 σx=9.831920803
↓n=6
```

FIGURE 3.13a TI-83/84 output.

```
            City mpg
Mean                      24
Standard Error    4.396968653
Median                  21.5
Mode                      18
Standard Deviation 10.77032961
Sample Variance          116
```

FIGURE 3.13b Excel output.

```
Descriptive Statistics: City mpg

Variable    Mean   StDev  Variance  Range
City mpg   24.00   10.77   116.00    30.00
```

FIGURE 3.13c Minitab output.

Mark Hooper/Getty Images

CASE STUDY

Can the Financial Experts Beat the Darts?

Recall from Section 3.1 the *Wall Street Journal* competition between stocks chosen randomly by *Journal* staff members throwing darts and stocks chosen by a team of four financial experts. Note from Figure 3.14 that the DJIA exhibits less variability than the other two portfolios. This smaller variability is due to the fact that the DJIA is made up of 29 component stocks, whereas each portfolio is made up of only 4 stocks. Smaller sample sizes can be associated with increased variability, since an unusual result in one value has a relatively strong effect on the mean when it is not offset by a large sample.

FIGURE 3.14
Comparative dotplots of the net change in prices.

Does the pro portfolio or the darts portfolio show greater variability? It is difficult to determine just by examining Figure 3.14 which has the greater range or standard deviation. We therefore turn to the Minitab descriptive statistics in Figure 3.15. The range for the darts, $72.9 - (-43.0) = 115.9$, is greater than the range for the pros, $75.00 - (-37.80) = 112.80$. But the standard deviation for the darts (19.39) is less than that of the pros (22.25).

FIGURE 3.15
Descriptive statistics for
the portfolios.

```
Descriptive Statistics: Pros, Darts, DJIA

Variable     Mean    StDev    Variance     Range
Pros        10.95    22.25      494.91    112.80
Darts        4.52    19.39      375.91    115.90
DJIA        6.793    8.031      64.505    35.600
```

Measures of spread may disagree about which data set is more variable. However, since the range takes into account only the two most extreme data values, the standard deviation is the preferred measure of spread, since it uses all the data values. Our conclusion, therefore, is that the returns for the professionals exhibit the greater variability.

Why did the pros have more variability than the darts? After all, in finance, high variability is not necessarily advantageous because it is associated with greater *risk*. The professionals evidently chose higher-risk stocks with greater potential for high returns—but also greater potential for losing money. ■

Section 3.2 Summary

1 The simplest measure of variability, or measure of spread, is the range. The range is simply the difference between the maximum and minimum values in a data set, but the range has drawbacks because it relies on the two most extreme data values.

2 A deviation is the difference between a data value and the mean of the data values.

3 The variance and standard deviation are measures of spread that utilize all available data values. The population variance can be thought of as the mean squared deviation. The standard deviation is the square root of the variance. We interpret the value of the standard deviation as the typical deviation, that is, the typical difference between a data value and the mean.

Section 3.2 Exercises

Unless a data set is identified as a population, you can assume that it is a sample.

CLARIFYING THE CONCEPTS
1. Explain what a deviation is.
2. What is the interpretation of the value of the standard deviation?
3. A small business keeps track of the delivery times for a particular supplier. In this instance, which is better, less variability or more variability? Why?
4. State one benefit and one drawback of using the range as a measure of spread.
5. Is the range sensitive or robust? Explain what you mean.
6. The mean of the deviations of any data set always equals what number?
7. True or false: If two data sets have the same mean, median, and mode, then they are identical.
8. What is one benefit of using the standard deviation instead of the range as a measure of spread? What is one drawback?
9. Which measure of spread represents the mean squared deviation for the population?
10. True or false: When using the computational formulas for the variance and standard deviation, you do not need to calculate the individual deviations.

11. When can the sample standard deviation s be negative?
12. When does the sample standard deviation s equal zero?

PRACTICING THE TECHNIQUES
Find the range of the data in Exercises 13–24.
13. 79, 92, 65, 75, 67, 59, 88
14. −50, −51, −45, 50, 45, 51
15. 1503, 1642, 1298, 1441, 2000
16. 9, 10, 9, 8, 6, 5, 8, 9, 6, 10, 8
17. 10, 25, 0, 15, 10
18. 10, 10, 10, 10, 10
19. 18, 15, 20, 20, 17
20. 3, 0, 5, −3, 0, −5
21. 75, 65, 90, 80, 85, 75, 100
22. 120, 155, 95, 155, 133
23. −5, −10, −15, −20
24. 3.14159, 3.14159, 3.14159, 3.14159

For the data in Exercises 25–30, do the following:
    a. Calculate the population variance.
    b. Compute the population standard deviation.

25. 79, 92, 65, 75, 67, 59, 88
26. −50, −51, −45, 50, 45, 51
27. 1503, 1642, 1298, 1441, 2000

28. 9, 10, 9, 8, 6, 5, 8, 9, 6, 10, 8
29. 10, 25, 0, 15, 10
30. 10, 10, 10, 10, 10

For the data in Exercises 31–36, do the following:
    a. Calculate the sample variance.
    b. Compute the sample standard deviation.

31. 18, 15, 20, 20, 17
32. 3, 0, 5, −3, 0, −5
33. 75, 65, 90, 80, 85, 75, 100
34. 120, 155, 95, 155, 133
35. −5, −10, −15, −20
36. 3.14159, 3.14159, 3.14159, 3.14159

For the following exercises, make sure to state your answers in the proper units, such as "years" or "years squared."

Refer to Table 3.5 from the Section 3.1 exercises on page 101 to answer Exercises 37–40. The data represent a sample.
37. Find the following measures of spread for the number of cylinders:
    a. Range
    b. Variance
    c. Standard deviation
38. Find the following measures of spread for the engine size:
    a. Range
    b. Variance
    c. Standard deviation
39. Find the following measures of spread for the fuel economy:
    a. Range
    b. Variance
    c. Standard deviation
40. Is "cylinders squared" easy for nonstatisticians to understand? Which measure do you find to be more easily understood and interpreted for these data, the variance or the standard deviation?

Refer to Table 3.6 on page 101 of the Section 3.1 exercises to answer Exercises 41–44. The data represent a sample.
41. Find the following measures of spread for the super speedway victories:
    a. Range
    b. Variance
    c. Standard deviation
42. Find the following measures of spread for the short track victories:
    a. Range
    b. Variance
    c. Standard deviation
43. Find the following measures of spread for the road course victories:
    a. Range
    b. Variance
    c. Standard deviation

44. Is "victories squared" easy for nonstatisticians to understand? Which measure do you find to be more easily understood and interpreted for these data, the variance or the standard deviation?

APPLYING THE CONCEPTS
NASCAR Winners. Refer to Table 3.6 (page 101) for Exercises 45–48.
45. Construct separate dotplots of the short tracks winners and the road courses winners, using the same scale. Which data set would you say has the greater variability?
46. Construct separate dotplots of the super speedways winners and the road courses winners, using the same scale. Which data set would you say has the greater variability?
47. Refer to Exercise 46. Find the range of each of the two data sets. Which data set has the greater variability? Do these results agree with your judgment above?
48. Refer to Exercise 46. Find the variance and standard deviation of each of the two data sets. Which data set has the greater variability? Do these results agree with your judgment above?
49. Match the histograms in (**a**)–(**d**) to the statistics in (**i**)–(**iv**).
    i. Mean = 75, standard deviation = 20
    ii. Mean = 75, standard deviation = 10
    iii. Mean = 50, standard deviation = 20
    iv. Mean = 50, standard deviation = 10

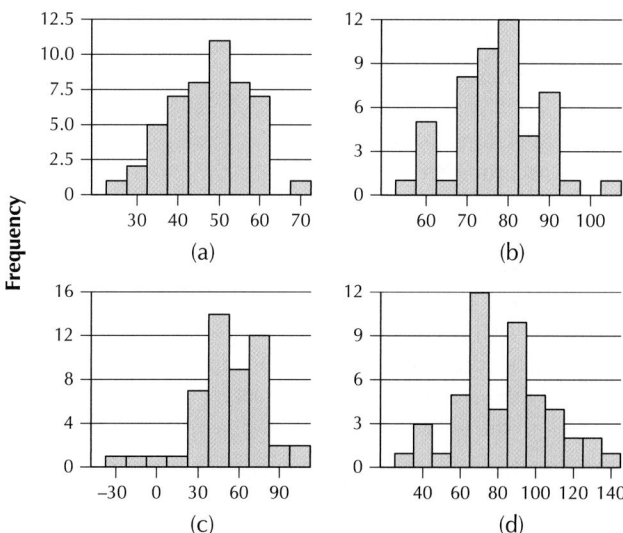

50. Match the histograms in (**a**)–(**d**) (see the next page) to the statistics in (**i**)–(**iv**).
    i. Mean = 1, standard deviation = 1
    ii. Mean = 1, standard deviation = 0.1
    iii. Mean = 0, standard deviation = 1
    iv. Mean = 0, standard deviation = 0.1

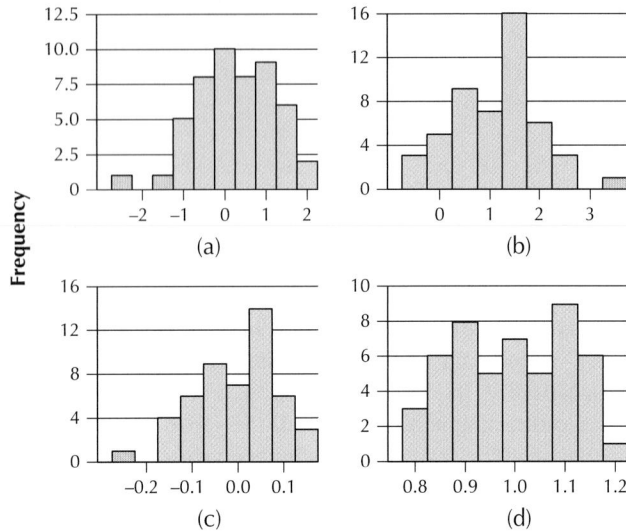

(a)

(b)

(c)

(d)

Zooplankton and Phytoplankton. Refer to the table below for Exercises 51 and 52. *Meta-analysis* refers to the statistical analysis of a set of similar research studies. In a meta-analysis, each data value represents an effect size calculated from the results of a particular study. The table contains effect sizes calculated in a meta-analysis for zooplankton and phytoplankton.[3] 📓 **plankton**

Zooplankton		Phytoplankton	
−2.37	−3.00	10.61	3.04
−0.64	−0.68	2.97	0.65
−2.05	−1.39	1.58	2.55
−1.54	−0.64	2.55	1.05
−6.60	−3.88	5.67	2.11
0.26		1.57	

51. Calculate the ranges for the zooplankton and the phytoplankton.
  a. Which has the greater range?
  b. Which plankton group has the greater variability according to the range?
52. Calculate the standard deviations for the zooplankton and the phytoplankton.
  a. Which has the greater standard deviation?
  b. Which plankton group has the greater variability according to the standard deviation? Does this concur with your answer from the previous exercise?
  c. Without calculating the variances, say which group has the greater variance. How do you know this?

Ant Size. Use the following information for Exercises 53 and 54. A study compared the size of ants from different colonies. The masses (in milligrams) of samples of ants from two different colonies are shown in the accompanying table.[4] 📓 **antcolony**

Colony A		Colony B	
109	134	148	115
120	94	110	101
94	113	110	158
61	111	97	67
72	106	136	114

53. Calculate the range for each ant colony.
  a. Which has the greater range?
  b. Which colony has the greater variability according to the range?
54. Calculate the variance for each colony.
  a. Which has the greater variance?
  b. Which colony has the greater variability according to the variance? Does this concur with your answer from the previous exercise?
  c. Without calculating the standard deviations, say which colony has the greater standard deviation. How do you know this?

SAT Scores. Refer to Table 3.7 (page 101) for Exercises 55–58.
55. Construct dotplots of the SAT Mathematics, the SAT Reading, and the SAT Writing tests. Which test data would you say has the greatest spread (variability)? Why?
56. Find the range and variance for the SAT Mathematics, the SAT Reading, and the SAT Writing tests. Do your findings agree with your judgment from the previous exercise?
57. *Without performing any calculations,* use your results from the previous exercise to state which test has (a) the largest standard deviation, and (b) the smallest standard deviation.
58. Now suppose we omit the Reading test from the data.
  a. *Without recalculating them,* describe how this would affect the values of the measures of spread you found for the SAT Mathematics test and the SAT Writing test.
  b. Now recalculate the three measures of spread for the SAT Mathematics and the SAT Writing test. Was your judgment in (a) supported?

Volleyball Team Heights. Refer to Table 3.9 (page 104) for Exercises 59–61.
59. Consider the deviations for each team.
  a. Would you say that a typical distance from the mean for the WMU team is about 70 inches, about 6 inches, or about 3 inches?
  b. What would you say a typical distance from the mean is for the NCU team?
60. Consider the standard deviations.
  a. Find the standard deviation for each team.
  b. Interpret the meaning of the values you obtained for the standard deviations so that someone who has never studied statistics would understand it.
  c. Which team has the greater variability according to the standard deviation?
61. Suppose that the shortest player on the NCU team was not 66 inches but only 62 inches tall.
  a. *Without recalculating them,* what effect would this change have on the three measures of spread for the NCU data?
  b. Now recalculate the three measures of spread for the NCU data, with the shortest player now 62 inches instead of 66 inches tall. Was your judgment in (a) supported?

Linear Transformations. Women's Volleyball Team Heights. Refer to Table 3.9 (page 104) for Exercises 62–64.

62. Suppose a new player joins the NCU team. She is 7 feet tall (84 inches) and replaces the 72-inch-tall player.

   a. Would you expect the standard deviation to go up or down, and why?

   b. Now find the standard deviation for the team including the new player. Was your intuition correct?

63. Add 4 inches to the height of each player on the WMU team.

   a. Recalculate the range and standard deviation.

   b. Formulate a rule for the behavior of these measures of variability when a constant (like 4) is added to each member of the data set.

64. Starting with the original data, double the height of each player on the NCU team.

   a. Recalculate the range and standard deviation.

   b. Formulate a rule for the range and standard deviation when the data values are doubled.

Coefficient of Variation. The *coefficient of variation* enables analysts to compare the variability of two data sets that are measured on different scales. The coefficient of variation (CV) itself does not have a unit of measure. Larger values of CV indicate greater variability or spread. The coefficient of variation is given as

$$\text{CV} = \frac{\text{standard deviation}}{\text{mean}} \cdot 100\%$$

Use this measure of variability for Exercises 65 and 66.

65. Coefficient of Variation for Cylinders, Engine Size, and City MPG. Refer to Table 3.5 on page 101.

   a. Calculate the coefficient of variation for the following variables: *cylinders*, *engine size*, and *city mpg*.

   b. According to the coefficient of variation, which variable has the greatest spread? The least variability?

66. Coefficient of Variation for the SAT Scores. Refer to Table 3.7 on page 101.

   a. Calculate the coefficient of variation for the SAT Mathematics, the SAT Reading, and the SAT Writing tests.

   b. According to the coefficient of variation, which test data has the greatest spread?

Mean Absolute Deviation. Recall that the variance and standard deviation use squared deviations because the mean deviation for any data set is zero. Another way to avoid negative deviations offsetting positive ones is to use the absolute value of the deviations. The *mean absolute deviation (MAD)* is a measure of spread that looks at the average of the absolute values of the deviations:

$$\text{MAD} = \frac{\sum |x_i - \bar{x}|}{n}$$

Use this measure of variability for Exercises 67 and 68.

67. Mean Absolute Deviation for the Fuel Economy Data. Refer to Table 3.5 on page 101.

   a. Find the mean absolute deviation for *cylinders*, *engine size*, and *city mpg*.

   b. According to the mean absolute deviation, which variable has the greatest variability? The least variability?

68. Mean Absolute Deviation for the SAT Scores. Refer to Table 3.7 on page 101.

   a. Calculate the mean absolute deviation for the SAT Mathematics, the SAT Reading, and the SAT Writing tests.

   b. According to the mean absolute deviation, which test data has the greatest spread?

Coefficient of Skewness. The coefficient of skewness quantifies the skewness of a distribution. It is defined as

$$\text{skewness} = \frac{3(\text{mean} - \text{median})}{\text{standard deviation}}$$

Most skewness values lie between −3 and 3. Negative values of skewness are associated with left-skewed distributions, while positive values are associated with right-skewed distributions. Values close to zero indicate symmetric distributions. Use this information for Exercises 69–71.

69. Coefficient of Skewness. For the following distributions, compute the coefficient of skewness and comment on the skewness of the distribution.

   a. Mean = 0, Median = 0, Standard deviation = 1

   b. Mean = 1, Median = 0, Standard deviation = 1

   c. Mean = 0, Median = 1, Standard deviation = 1

   d. Mean = 75, Median = 80, Standard deviation = 10

   e. Mean = 100, Median = 100, Standard deviation = 15

   f. Mean = 3.2, Median = 3.0, Standard deviation = 1.0

70. What is the coefficient of skewness for any distribution where the mean equals the median, regardless of the value of the standard deviation?

71. Coefficient of Skewness for the Case Study Data. The median price change for the Professional analysts is 9.60, the median for the Darts is 3.25, and the median for the DJIA is 7.00. Use this information, along with the information in Figure 3.15 on page 114 to answer the following.

   a. Calculate the coefficient of skewness for each of the Pros, the Darts, and the DJIA.

   b. Comment on the skewness of each distribution.

BRINGING IT ALL TOGETHER

72. Fuel Economy Data. You calculated the range, variance, and standard deviation for this data in Exercises 37–39. You calculated the coefficient of variation in Exercise 65 and the mean absolute deviation in Exercise 67. Use this information to do the following.

   a. Construct a table of the five measures of dispersion (range, sample variance, sample standard deviation, coefficient of variation, and mean absolute deviation) for the number of cylinders, the engine size, and the city mpg.

b. Which measures of dispersion suggest that the *city mpg* is the most dispersed variable? *Engine size? Number of cylinders?*

73. SAT Scores Data. You calculated the range and variance for this data in Exercise 56. You calculated the coefficient of variation in Exercise 66 and the mean absolute deviation in Exercise 68. Use this information to do the following.

  a. Using the variance, calculate the standard deviation for the SAT Mathematics, the SAT Reading, and the SAT Writing tests.

  b. Construct a table of the five measures of spread (range, sample variance, sample standard deviation, coefficient of variation, and mean absolute deviation) for the SAT Mathematics, the SAT Reading, and the SAT Writing tests.

  c. Do the measures of spread agree on which distribution has the greatest variability?

  d. Bringing together all your statistics about measures of spread, what is your conclusion about the variability in the SAT Mathematics test, compared to the other two tests?

CONSTRUCT YOUR OWN DATA SETS

74. Construct two data sets, A and B, that you make up on your own, so that the range of A is greater than the range of B. Verify this.

75. Construct two data sets, A and B, that you make up on your own, so that the standard deviation of A is greater than the range of B. Verify this.

76. Construct two data sets, A and B, that you make up on your own, so that the mean of A is greater than the mean of B, but the standard deviation of B is greater than that of A. Verify this.

77. Construct two data sets, A and B, that you make up on your own, so that the mean of A is greater than the mean of B, and the standard deviation of A is greater than that of B. Verify this.

78. Construct two data sets, A and B, that you make up on your own, so that the range of A is greater than the range of B, but the standard deviation of B is greater than that of A. Verify this. (*Hint:* Remember the sensitivity of the standard deviation to extreme values.)

3.3 Working with Grouped Data

OBJECTIVES By the end of this section, I will be able to . . .

1   Calculate the weighted mean.

2   Estimate the mean for grouped data.

3   Estimate the variance and standard deviation for grouped data.

1 The Weighted Mean

Note: Before tackling this section, you may wish to review Section 2.2, "Graphs and Tables for Quantitative Data" (page 54).

Sometimes not all the data values in a data set are of equal importance. Certain data values may be assigned greater weight than others when calculating the mean. For example, have you ever figured out what your final grade for a course was based on the percentages listed in the syllabus? What you actually found was the **weighted mean** of your grades.

> **Weighted Mean**
>
> To find the **weighted mean:**
>
> 1. Multiply each data point x_i by its respective weight w_i.
> 2. Sum these products.
> 3. Divide the result by the sum of the weights:
>
> $$\bar{x}_w = \frac{\sum w_i x_i}{\sum w_i} = \frac{w_1 x_1 + w_2 x_2 + \cdots + w_n x_n}{w_1 + w_2 + \cdots + w_n}$$

Example 3.18 Weighted mean of course grades

The syllabus for the Introduction to Management course at a local college specifies that the midterm exam is worth 30%, the term paper is worth 20%, and the final exam is worth 50% of your course grade. Now, say you did not get serious about the course until Halloween, so that you got a 40 on the midterm. You then began working harder, and got a 70 on the term paper. Finally, you remembered that you had to pay for the course again if you did not pass and had to retake it, and so you worked really hard for the last month of the course and got a 90 on the final exam. Calculate your course average, that is, the weighted mean of your grades.

Solution

Note: The weights w_i do not have to be percentages that add up to 1.

The data values are $x_1 = 40$, $x_2 = 70$, and $x_3 = 90$. The weights are $w_1 = 0.30$, $w_2 = 0.20$, and $w_3 = 0.50$. Your course weighted mean is then calculated as follows:

$$\bar{x}_w = \frac{\sum w_i x_i}{\sum w_i} = \frac{w_1 x_1 + w_2 x_2 + w_3 x_3}{w_1 + w_2 + w_3} = \frac{(0.30)(40) + (0.20)(70) + (0.50)(90)}{0.30 + 0.20 + 0.50} = \frac{71}{1.0} = 71$$

Now You Can Do
Exercises 4–8.

Because the final exam had the most weight, you were able to raise your course weighted mean to 71, and pass the course. ∎

2 Estimating the Mean for Grouped Data

Thus far in Chapter 3, we have computed measures of center and spread from a raw data set. However, data are often reported using frequency distributions. Without the original data, we cannot calculate the exact values of the measures of center and spread. The remainder of this section examines methods for approximating the mean, variance, and standard deviation of *grouped data*—that is, population data summarized using frequency distributions.

For each class in the frequency distribution, we estimate the class mean using the class *midpoint*. The class midpoint is defined as the mean of two adjoining lower class limits. The midpoint for the *i*th class is denoted m_i.

Example 3.19 | Finding the class midpoints

There were 1150 children adopted in the state of Georgia in 2006, according to the Administration for Children and Families.[5] The frequency distribution of the ages of the children at adoption is shown in Table 3.16. Find the class midpoints.

Table 3.16 Frequency distribution of children adopted in Georgia, by age

Class: age	Midpoint m_i	Frequency f_i
0–0.99	0.5	12
1–5.99	3.5	611
6–10.99	8.5	320
11–15.99	13.5	161
16–17.99	17.0	46

Solution

The midpoint for the first class (ages 0–0.99) is the mean of the lower class limits for this class (0) and the adjoining class (1). That is, the midpoint is $(0 + 1)/2 = 0.5$.

Now You Can Do
Exercises 9 and 10.

Similarly, the midpoint for the second class (ages 1–5.99) is $(1 + 6)/2 = 3.5$. The remainder of the class midpoints are shown in Table 3.16. ∎

The product of the class frequency f_i and class midpoint m_i is used as an estimate of the sum of the data values within that class. Summing these products across all classes and dividing by the total population size thus provides us with an **estimated mean for data grouped into a frequency distribution.**

Note: Notice the difference between $\hat{\mu}$ and $\bar{x}$. The estimated mean $\hat{\mu}$ is used only when the data are grouped into a frequency distribution. The sample mean $\bar{x}$ is used when all the data values in the sample are known. Both $\hat{\mu}$ and $\bar{x}$ are used to estimate the population mean μ.

> **Estimated Mean for Data Grouped into a Frequency Distribution**
>
> Given a frequency distribution with k classes, the **estimated mean** for the variable is given by
>
> $$\hat{\mu} = \frac{\sum m_i f_i}{N} = \frac{m_1 f_1 + m_2 f_2 + \cdots + m_k f_k}{N}$$
>
> where m_i and f_i represent the midpoint and frequency of the ith class, respectively, and N represents the total population size, which is the sum of the class frequencies: $N = \sum f_i$. The "hat" notation for $\hat{\mu}$, called "mu-hat," indicates that $\hat{\mu}$ is an estimate and not the exact value of the mean.

Example 3.20   Calculating the estimated mean for grouped data

Calculate the estimated mean age of the adopted children in Table 3.16.

Solution

The midpoints m_i and frequencies f_i are provided in Table 3.16. For example, $m_1 = 0.5$ and $f_1 = 12$. We thus calculate the sum of the products as follows:

$$\sum m_i f_i = (0.5)(12) + (3.5)(611) + (8.5)(320) + (13.5)(161) + (17)(46)$$
$$= 6 + 2138.5 + 2720 + 2173.5 + 782 = 7820$$

Next we calculate the total population size:

$$N = \sum f_i = 12 + 611 + 320 + 161 + 46 = 1150$$

The estimated mean is therefore

Now You Can Do
Exercises 11, 12, and 15b.

$$\hat{\mu} = \frac{\sum m_i f_i}{N} = \frac{7820}{1150} = 6.8$$

The estimated mean age of the children adopted in Georgia in 2006 is 6.8 years. ∎

3 Estimating the Variance and Standard Deviation for Grouped Data

We also use class midpoints and class frequencies to calculate the **estimated variance for data grouped into a frequency distribution** and the **estimated standard deviation for data grouped into a frequency distribution.**

Note: Notice the difference between $\hat{\sigma}$ and s. The estimated standard deviation $\hat{\sigma}$ is used only when the data are grouped into a frequency distribution. The sample standard deviation s is used when all the data values in the sample are known. Both $\hat{\sigma}$ and s are used to estimate the population standard deviation σ.

> **Estimated Variance and Standard Deviation for Data Grouped into a Frequency Distribution**
>
> Given a frequency distribution with k classes, the estimated variance for the variable is given by
>
> $$\hat{\sigma}^2 = \frac{\sum (m_i - \hat{\mu})^2 \cdot f_i}{N}$$
>
> and the estimated standard deviation is given by
>
> $$\hat{\sigma} = \sqrt{\hat{\sigma}^2} = \sqrt{\frac{\sum (m_i - \hat{\mu})^2 \cdot f_i}{N}}$$
>
> where m_i and f_i represent the midpoint and frequency of the ith class, respectively, and N represents the total population size, which is the sum of the class frequencies: $N = \sum f_i$. The "hat" notation for $\hat{\sigma}$, called "sigma-hat," indicates that $\hat{\sigma}$ is an estimate and not the exact value of the standard deviation.

You should carry as many decimal places as you can for the value of $\hat{\mu}$ when calculating $\hat{\sigma}^2$, and for $\hat{\sigma}^2$ when calculating $\hat{\sigma}$.

Example 3.21 | Calculating the estimated variance and standard deviation for grouped data

Calculate the estimated variance and standard deviation of the ages of the adopted children in Table 3.16.

Solution

Table 3.17 contains the calculations required for finding $\sum(m_i - \hat{\mu})^2 \cdot f_i = 20{,}068$. The variance is therefore estimated as

$$\hat{\sigma}^2 = \frac{\sum(m_i - \hat{\mu})^2 \cdot f_i}{N} = \frac{20{,}068}{1150}$$

and the standard deviation is estimated as

$$\hat{\sigma} = \sqrt{\hat{\sigma}^2} = \sqrt{\frac{20{,}068}{1150}} \approx 4.177371755 \approx 4.2$$

Table 3.17 Calculating $\sum(m_i - \hat{\mu})^2 \cdot f_i$

Class: age	Midpoint m_i	Frequency f_i	$\hat{\mu}$	$m_i - \hat{\mu}$	$(m_i - \hat{\mu})^2 \cdot f_i$
0–0.99	0.5	12	6.8	−6.3	476.28
1–5.99	3.5	611	6.8	−3.3	6653.79
6–10.99	8.5	320	6.8	1.7	924.8
11–15.99	13.5	161	6.8	6.7	7227.29
16–17.99	17.0	46	6.8	10.2	4785.84

$$\sum(m_i - \hat{\mu})^2 \cdot f_i = 20{,}068$$

Now You Can Do
Exercises 13 and 14.

In other words, the age of the adopted children typically differs from the mean age of 6.8 years by about 4.2 years. ■

Example 3.22 | Using technology to find the estimated mean, variance, and standard deviation for grouped data

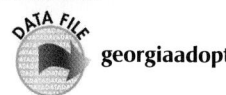
georgiaadopt

Use the TI-83/84 calculator to find the estimated mean, variance, and standard deviation for the frequency distribution in Table 3.17.

Solution

Following the instructions in the Step-by-Step Technology Guide, we get the estimated mean $\hat{\mu}$ (shown in the output as $\bar{x}$) = 6.8, the estimated standard deviation $\hat{\sigma}$ (shown in the output as σx) = 4.177371755, and the estimated variance to be $(4.177371755)^2 = 17.45$. ■

STEP-BY-STEP TECHNOLOGY GUIDE: Estimating the Mean, Variance, and Standard Deviation for Grouped Data

TI-83/84

Step 1 Press **STAT** and select **1:Edit**. Enter the class midpoints in **L1** and the frequencies or relative frequencies in **L2**.
Step 2 Press **STAT**, select the **CALC** menu, and choose **1: 1-Var Stats**.

Step 3 Press **2nd 1 Comma 2nd 2**, so that the following appears on the home screen: **1-Var Stats L1, L2**.
Step 4 Press **ENTER**.

Section 3.3 Summary

1 The weighted mean is the sum of the products of the data points with their respective weights, divided by the sum of the weights.

2 Since we do not have access to the original raw data, it is not possible to find exact values for the mean, variance, and standard deviation of data that have been grouped into a

frequency distribution. The estimated mean $\hat{\mu}$ in this case is the sum of the products of the class frequencies f_i and class midpoints m_i, divided by the total sample size N.

3 Class midpoints and class frequencies are also used to find the estimated variance $\hat{\sigma}^2$ and estimated standard deviation $\hat{\sigma}$ of grouped data.

Section 3.3 Exercises

CLARIFYING THE CONCEPTS

1. Explain why the formula for the mean of grouped data will provide an estimate only and not the exact value of the mean if the data were not grouped.
2. Explain what the "hat" notation indicates for $\hat{\mu}$ and $\hat{\sigma}$.
3. What quantity do both $\hat{\mu}$ and $\bar{x}$ estimate?

PRACTICING THE TECHNIQUES

For Exercises 4–8, the data values and weights are provided. Find the weighted mean.

4. $x_1 = 50, x_2 = 60; x_3 = 70; w_1 = 0.25, w_2 = 0.50,$ $w_3 = 0.25.$
5. $x_1 = 50, x_2 = 80, x_3 = 70; w_1 = 0.25, w_2 = 0.40,$ $w_3 = 0.35.$
6. $x_1 = 100, x_2 = 120, x_3 = 150; w_1 = 10, w_2 = 20,$ $w_3 = 5.$
7. $x_1 = 3.0, x_2 = 2.5, x_3 = 3.5, x_4 = 4.0, x_5 = 3.0;$ $w_1 = w_2 = w_3 = w_4 = 3, w_5 = 4.$
8. $x_1 = 70, x_2 = 80, x_3 = 85, x_4 = 95; w_1 = 0.20,$ $w_2 = 0.30, w_3 = 0.25, w_4 = 0.25.$

For Exercises 9 and 10, the class limits are provided. Find the class midpoints.

9.

0–1.99	6–7.99
2–3.99	8–9.99
4–5.99	

10.

0–4.99	20–29.99
5–9.99	30–49.99
10–14.99	50–99.99
15–19.99	100–199.99

For Exercises 11 and 12, find the estimated mean for the frequency distribution.

11.

Midpoint m_i	Frequency f_i
5	10
10	20
15	20
20	10
25	10

12.

Midpoint m_i	Frequency f_i
−10	3
−5	2
0	5
5	12
10	8
15	10

For Exercises 13 and 14, find the estimated variance and standard deviation

13. For the frequency distribution in Exercise 11.
14. For the frequency distribution in Exercise 12.

APPLYING THE CONCEPTS

15. **Dupage County Age Groups.** The Census Bureau reports the following frequency distribution of population by age group for Dupage County, Illinois, residents less than 65 years old. 📊 dupageage

Age	Residents
0–4.99	63,422
5–17.99	240,629
18–64.99	540,949

a. Find the class midpoints.
b. Find the estimated mean age of residents of Dupage County.
c. Find the estimated variance and standard deviation of ages.

16. **Capacity of Lakes and Reservoirs.** The National Water and Climate Center tracks the percentage capacity of lakes and reservoirs (how full the lake or reservoir is). The table below contains the percentage capacity for a random sample of lakes and reservoirs in Arizona, California, and Colorado.[6] Find the weighted mean percentage capacity.

Arizona	California	Colorado
$n = 4$	$n = 6$	$n = 5$
$\bar{x} = 48.5$	$\bar{x} = 81$	$\bar{x} = 47$

17. **Broward County House Values.** Table 3.18 gives the frequency distribution of the dollar value of the owner-occupied housing units in Broward County, Florida. 📊 browardhouse

TABLE 3.18   Broward County house values

Dollar value	Housing units
0–49,999	5,430
50,000–99,999	90,605
100,000–149,999	90,620
150,000–199,999	54,295
200,000–299,999	34,835
300,000–499,999	15,770
500,000–999,999	5,595

Source: U.S. Census Bureau.

a. Find the class midpoints.
b. Find the estimated mean dollar value for housing units in Broward County.
c. Find the estimated variance and standard deviation of the dollar value.

18. **Lightning Deaths.** Table 3.19 gives the frequency distribution of the number of deaths due to lightning nationwide over a 67-year period. Find the estimated mean and standard deviation of the number of lightning deaths per year. **lightningdeath**

TABLE 3.19   Lightning deaths

Deaths	Years
20–59.99	13
60–99.99	21
100–139.99	10
140–179.99	6
180–259.99	10
260–459.99	7

Source: National Oceanic and Atmospheric Administration.

19. **Calculating a Course Grade.** An introductory statistics syllabus has the following grading system. The weekly quizzes are worth a total of 25% toward the final course grade. The midterm exam is worth 32%; the final exam is worth 33%; and attendance/participation is worth 10% toward the final course grade. Anthony's weekly quiz average is 70. He got an 80 on the midterm and a 90 on the final exam. He got 100 for attendance/participation. Calculate Anthony's final course grade.

20. **Wages for Computer Managers.** The U.S. Bureau of Labor Statistics (BLS) publishes wage information for various occupations. For the occupation "computer and information systems management," Table 3.20 gives the wages reported by the BLS for the top-paying states. Find the weighted mean wage across all five states, using the employment figures as weights. **compwage**

TABLE 3.20   Wages for computer managers

State	Employment	Hourly mean wage
New Jersey	12,380	$60.32
New York	18,580	$60.25
Virginia	9,540	$59.39
California	35,550	$57.98
Massachusetts	10,130	$55.95

21. **Salaries of Scientists and Engineers.** The National Science Foundation compiles statistics on the annual salaries of full-time employed doctoral scientists and engineers in universities and four-year colleges. The mean annual salary for the fields of science, engineering, and health are $67,000, $82,200, and $70,000, respectively. Suppose we have a sample of 10 professors, 5 of whom are in science, 2 in engineering, and 3 in health, and each of whom is making the mean salary for his or her field. Find the weighted mean salary of these 10 professors.

22. **Challenge Exercise.** Assign the weights w_i to show that the formula for the sample mean from Section 3.1 $\bar{x} = \sum x_i / n$ is a special case of the formula for the weighted mean $\bar{x}_w = \sum w_i x_i / \sum w_i$.

3.4   Measures of Position and Outliers

OBJECTIVES By the end of this section, I will be able to . . .

1   Calculate z-scores, and explain why we use them.

2   Detect outliers using the z-score method.

3   Find percentiles and percentile ranks for both small and large data sets.

4   Compute quartiles and the interquartile range.

In this section we learn about *measures of position,* which tell us the position that a particular data value has relative to the rest of the data set. For example, a prestigious nursing school may grant admission to only the top 10% of applicants. How high a score would you need to enter? This is one type of question we will answer in this section.

1 z-Scores

Our first measure of position is the z-score. Recall that the standard deviation is a common measure of the variability, or spread, of a data set. The value of the standard deviation is interpreted as a typical deviation from the mean. Many students take the Scholastic Aptitude Test (SAT) when preparing to apply for college. The SAT is designed so that the distribution of scores is bell-shaped with a mean of 500 and a standard deviation of 100. Note in Figure 3.16 that we can measure the distance from a particular SAT score to the mean in terms of standard deviations. For example, an SAT score of 600 lies 1 standard deviation above the mean, while an SAT score of 300 lies 2 standard deviations below the mean.

The term **z-score** indicates how many standard deviations a particular data value is from the mean. If the z-score is positive, then the data value is above the mean. If the z-score is negative, then the data value is below the mean.

FIGURE 3.16 The distribution of SAT scores.

Recall that the standard deviation is a common measure of the variability, or spread, of a data set, and its value is interpreted as a typical deviation from the mean.

---

z-Score

The **z-score** for a particular data value from a *sample* is

$$z\text{-score} = \frac{\text{data value} - \text{mean}}{\text{standard deviation}} = \frac{x - \bar{x}}{s}$$

where $\bar{x}$ is the sample mean, and s is the sample standard deviation.

The z-score for a particular data value from a *population* is

$$z\text{-score} = \frac{\text{data value} - \text{mean}}{\text{standard deviation}} = \frac{x - \mu}{\sigma}$$

where μ is the population mean, and σ is the population standard deviation.

In this section, we will use the sample z-score unless otherwise indicated.

Example 3.23 Meaning of a z-score

Suppose the mean score on the Math SAT is $\mu = 500$, with a standard deviation of $\sigma = 100$ points. Suppose Jasmine's Math SAT score is 650. How many standard deviations is Jasmine's score from the mean? Note that here we have population values.

Solution

Here $\mu = 500$, $\sigma = 100$, and Jasmine's score is $x = 650$. Her z-score is

$$z\text{-score} = \frac{\text{data value} - \text{mean}}{\text{standard deviation}} = \frac{x - \mu}{\sigma} = \frac{650 - 500}{100} = 1.5$$

Jasmine's z-score of 1.5 indicates that her Math SAT is 1.5 standard deviations from the mean of 500. Z-scores can be positive or negative. Jasmine's z-score is positive (1.5), which means that her Math SAT score falls above the mean. Bright lady! Consider Figure 3.17, which shows the distribution of SAT scores, with a mean of 500 and a standard deviation of 100. The arrows represent "units" of 1 standard deviation each, that is, each arrow is 100 SAT points long. Counting the arrows as you go above or below the mean is thus the same as counting the number of standard deviations above or below the mean. Jasmine's SAT score lies between 600 and 700, an area with z-scores ranging from 1 to 2. ■

FIGURE 3.17
Jasmine's z-score of 1.5 places her 1.5 standard deviations above the mean.

Jasmine's SAT score of 650 has a z-score of 1.5.

In Example 3.23, since the standard deviation equals 100, the *z*-score represents units of 100. That is, a *z*-score of 1 represents 1 standard deviation above the mean, which is 100 points above the mean. Thus, the *scale* of the *z*-scores for the SAT scores in Figure 3.17 is in units of 100, since the standard deviation equals 100. However, if the standard deviation was, say, $\sigma = 50$, then the scale would be different.

Example 3.24   Calculating z-scores given data values

Note: This use of "μ" for "micro" in the measure "micrograms per deciliter" is not related to our use of μ as the population mean.

A study of workers who were exposed to lead at their jobs found that their mean blood lead level was 31.4 μg/dl (micrograms per deciliter) with a standard deviation of 14.2 μg/dl.[7]
a. If we calculate *z*-scores, what is the scale?
b. Calculate the *z*-scores for the following workers:
   i. Ryan, with a blood lead level of 78.26 μg/dl
   ii. Megan, with a blood lead level of 1.58 μg/dl
   iii. Kyle, with a blood lead level of 55.54 μg/dl
c. For each worker, interpret the value of the *z*-score.

Solution
a. If we calculate *z*-scores for the workers' lead levels, the scale of the *z*-scores will be 14.2 μg/dl, since that is the value of the standard deviation.
b. Here are the workers' lead levels.
   i. Ryan:

$$z\text{-score} = \frac{x - \bar{x}}{s} = \frac{78.26 - 31.4}{14.2} = \frac{46.86}{14.2} = 3.3$$

   ii. Megan:

$$z\text{-score} = \frac{x - \bar{x}}{s} = \frac{1.58 - 31.4}{14.2} = \frac{-29.82}{14.2} = -2.1$$

   iii. Kyle:

$$z\text{-score} = \frac{x - \bar{x}}{s} = \frac{55.54 - 31.4}{14.2} = \frac{24.14}{14.2} = 1.7$$

c. Ryan's lead level lies 3.3 standard deviations above the mean; Megan's lead level lies 2.1 standard deviations below the mean; and Kyle's lead level lies 1.7 standard deviations above the mean. ■

Now You Can Do
Exercises 12–15.

Alternatively, we may be given a *z*-score, and asked to find its associated data value *x*. To do so, use the following formulas.

> Given a z-score, to find its associated data value x:
>
> $$\text{For a sample:} \qquad x = z\text{-score} \cdot s + \bar{x}$$
> $$\text{For a population:} \quad x = z\text{-score} \cdot \sigma + \mu$$
>
> where μ is the population mean, $\bar{x}$ is the sample mean, σ is the population standard deviation, and s is the sample standard deviation.

The next example shows us how to compute a data value for a given z-score.

Example 3.25   Finding data values given z-scores

Continuing with the blood lead level data from Example 3.24, find the blood lead levels associated with the following z-scores:

    a. −1   **b.** 0   **c.** 3

Solution

We have $\bar{x} = 31.4 \ \mu\text{g/dl}$ and $s = 14.2 \ \mu\text{g/dl}$.

a. For a z-score of -1, we have

$$x = z\text{-score} \cdot s + \bar{x} = (-1) \cdot 14.2 + 31.4 = 17.2 \ \mu\text{g/dl}.$$

A blood lead level of 17.2 μg/dl lies 1 standard deviation below the mean.

b. For a z-score of 0, we have

$$x = z\text{-score} \cdot s + \bar{x} = (0) \cdot 14.2 + 31.4 = 14.2 \ \mu\text{g/dl}.$$

A blood lead level of 14.2 μg/dl lies exactly on the mean.

c. For a z-score of 3, we have

$$x = z\text{-score} \cdot s + \bar{x} = (3) \cdot 14.2 + 31.4 = 74 \ \mu\text{g/dl}.$$

Now You Can Do
Exercises 16 and 17.

A blood lead level of 74 μg/dl lies 3 standard deviations above the mean. ■

Example 3.26   Using the z-score to compare data from different data sets

Andrew is bragging to his friend Brittany that he did better than she did on the last statistics test. Andrew got a 90 while Brittany got an 80. Andrew's class mean was 80 with a standard deviation of 10. Brittany's class mean was 60 with a standard deviation of 10. The professors in both classes grade "on a curve" using z-scores. Who did better relative to his or her class?

Solution

Brittany can use z-scores to show that she did better *relative to her class*. Figure 3.18 shows comparative dotplots of the scores in the two classes. The red dots represent Brittany's and Andrew's scores. Brittany found her z-score by subtracting her class mean from her score of 80 and then dividing by the standard deviation $s = 10$:

$$z\text{-score}_{\text{Brittany}} = \frac{x - \bar{x}}{s} = \frac{80 - 60}{10} = 2$$

z-Scores enable the data analyst to compare data values from two different distributions.

FIGURE 3.18 Brittany actually did better relative to her class.

Brittany's z-score is 2. What does that mean? It means that *Brittany scored 2 standard deviations above the mean* of 60. Brittany then found the z-score for Andrew:

$$z\text{-score}_{\text{Andrew}} = \frac{x - \bar{x}}{s} = \frac{90 - 80}{10} = 1$$

Andrew's z-score was 1, which means that Andrew scored 1 standard deviation above the mean. From Figure 3.18 we can observe that Andrew's exam score of 90 lies closer to the mean exam score of 80 for his class. That is, the arrow is shorter for Andrew than for Brittany. Finally, note that 10 of the 100 students who took the exam in his class did better than he did, whereas only 2 did better than Brittany in her class. So, relative to her class, Brittany did better than Andrew, even though Andrew got a higher score. The z-scores allowed her to compare their grades, even though they were in different classes. ∎

Now You Can Do
Exercises 18 and 19.

2 Detecting Outliers Using the z-Score Method

An **outlier** is an extremely large or extremely small data value relative to the rest of the data set. It may represent a data entry error, or it may be genuine data. One way of identifying an outlier is to determine whether it is farther than 3 standard deviations from the mean, that is, its z-score is less than −3 or greater than 3. Figure 3.19 illustrates the following guidelines for identifying outliers using z-scores.

Guidelines for Identifying Outliers

Note: If an outlier is detected, it does not automatically follow that it should be discarded. Outliers often indicate the presence of something interesting going on in the data that would call for further investigation. On the other hand, it could simply be a typo. The analyst should check with the data source.

1. A data value whose z-score lies in the following range is not considered to be unusual:
$$-2 < z\text{-score} < 2$$

2. A data value whose z-score lies in either of the following ranges may be considered moderately unusual:
$$-3 < z\text{-score} \leq -2 \quad \text{or} \quad 2 \leq z\text{-score} < 3$$

3. A data value whose z-score lies in either of the following ranges may be considered an outlier:
$$z\text{-score} \leq -3 \quad \text{or} \quad z\text{-score} \geq 3$$

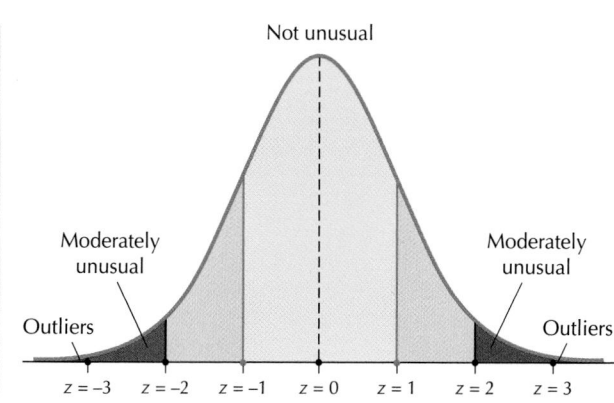

FIGURE 3.19
z-Scores help to identify outliers.

Example 3.27 Detecting outliers using the z-score method

For the three workers in Example 3.24 on page 125, determine whether each of their blood lead levels represents an outlier.

Solution

Ryan's z-score is 3.3, which is greater than 3. Thus, Ryan's lead level of 78.26 μg/dl represents an outlier. Megan's z-score is −2.1, which lies between −3 and −2. Hence, Megan's lead level of 1.58 μg/dl may be considered moderately unusual but is not an outlier. Kyle's z-score is 1.7, which lies between −2 and 2. Thus, Kyle's lead level of 55.54 is not considered unusual. ∎

Now You Can Do
Exercises 20–23.

In Section 3.5 we will learn about the IQR method of detecting outliers.

3 Percentiles and Percentile Ranks

Some instructors prefer to define the *p*th percentile to be the data value at which at least *p* percent of the values in the data set are less than or equal to this value, *and* at least $(1 - p)$ percent of the values are greater than or equal to this value.

The next measure of position we consider is the **percentile,** which shows the location of a data value relative to the other values in the data set.

> **Percentile**
> Let *p* be any integer between 0 and 100. The *p*th **percentile** of a data set is the data value at which *p* percent of the values in the data set are less than or equal to this value.

Example 3.28   Meaning of a percentile

After taking the SAT, students receive test results that include not only their score, but also the percentile that this score represents. Jasmine's Math SAT score was 650, which represents the 90th percentile. What does "90th percentile" mean?

Solution

To say that 650 is the 90th percentile means that 90% of all scores on the Math SAT fell at or below Jasmine's score of 650. We call the percentile a *measure of position* since it indicates the position of Jasmine's Math SAT score relative to all other Math SAT scores. Clearly, Jasmine is good at math. Figure 3.20 indicates the position of Jasmine's score relative to the rest of the test takers. ∎

90% of SAT scores are less than or equal to 650.

Only 10% of SAT scores are greater than 650.

FIGURE 3.20
The 90th percentile is the score with 90% of the data values at or below its value.

SAT scores   Jasmine's SAT score of 650 represents the 90th percentile.

For large data sets, calculation of the percentiles is best left to computers. However, for small data sets, we can use the following step-by-step method to calculate the position of any percentile.

Step 1 Sort the data into ascending order (from smallest to largest).

Step 2 Calculate

 These steps do not give the value of the pth percentile itself, but rather the position *of the pth percentile in the data set when the data set is in ascending order.*

$$i = \left(\frac{p}{100}\right)n$$

where *p* is the particular percentile you wish to calculate, and *n* is the sample size.

Step 3 **a.** If *i* is an integer (a whole number with no decimal part), the *p*th percentile is the mean of the data values in positions *i* and $i + 1$.   **b.** If *i* is not an integer, round up to the next integer and use the value in this position.

Example 3.29 Finding percentiles

dancescore

Yolanda would like to go to a prestigious graduate school of the arts. She knows that this school accepts only those students who score at the 75th percentile or higher in a grueling dance audition. The following data represent the dance audition scores of Yolanda's group. Yolanda scored 85. Find the 75th percentile of the data set. Will Yolanda be accepted at the prestigious graduate school of the arts?

| 78 | 56 | 89 | 44 | 65 | 94 | 81 | 62 | 75 | 85 | 30 | 68 |

Solution

Step 1 Sort the data into ascending order:

| 30 | 44 | 56 | 62 | 65 | 68 | 75 | 78 | 81 | 85 | 89 | 94 |

Step 2 The particular percentile we wish to calculate is the 75th percentile, so $p = 75$. There are 12 scores in our data set, so $n = 12$. Calculate

$$i = \left(\frac{p}{100}\right)n = \left(\frac{75}{100}\right)12 = 9$$

So, $i = 9$.

Step 3 Here, since i is an integer, the 75th percentile is the mean of the data values in positions 9 and 10.

(81 + 85)/2 = 83

Counting from left to right, the data value in the ninth position is 81, and the data value in the tenth position is 85. The mean of these two values is 83. Thus, the 75th percentile is 83. Yolanda's dance score of 85 is therefore above the 75th percentile. She will be accepted to the prestigious graduate school. ∎

Now You Can Do
Exercises 24–29.

Remember: A percentile is a data value, while a percentile rank is a percentage.

The **percentile rank** of a data value x equals the percentage of values in the data set that are less than or equal to x. In other words:

$$\text{percentile rank of data value } x = \frac{\text{number of values in data set} \le x}{\text{total number of values in data set}} \cdot 100$$

Example 3.30 Finding percentile ranks

missingchild

In Example 2.7 (page 54), we were introduced to a data set of 50 missing and exploited children in California. Table 3.21 shows the ages of those children, sorted into ascending order. Find the percentile ranks for the following ages:
a. 2 years old and
b. 5 years old

Table 3.21 Ages of 50 missing and exploited children in California

| 1 | 1 | 1 | 2 | 2 | 2 | 3 | 3 | 4 | 4 | 4 | 4 | 4 | 4 | 4 | 5 | 5 | 5 | 5 | 5 | 5 | 5 | 5 | 5 |
| 6 | 6 | 6 | 6 | 6 | 6 | 6 | 6 | 6 | 6 | 7 | 7 | 7 | 7 | 7 | 7 | 8 | 8 | 8 | 8 | 8 | 8 | 9 | 9 | 9 |

Solution

a. Here $x = 2$. There are 3 two-year old children and 3 one-year old children, so the percentile rank of two-year old children is

$$\text{percentile rank of } (x = 2) = \frac{\text{number of values in data set} \leq 2}{\text{total number of values in data set}} \cdot 100$$

$$= \frac{6}{50} \cdot 100 = 12\%$$

b. Here $x = 5$. There are 9 five-year old children, and 16 children less than five years old.

$$\text{percentile rank of } (x = 5) = \frac{\text{number of values in data set} \leq 5}{\text{total number of values in data set}} \cdot 100$$

$$= \frac{25}{50} \cdot 100 = 50\% \ \blacksquare$$

Now You Can Do
Exercises 30–35.

4 Quartiles and the Interquartile Range

Just as the median divides the data set into halves, the **quartiles** are the percentiles that divide the data set into quarters (Figure 3.21).

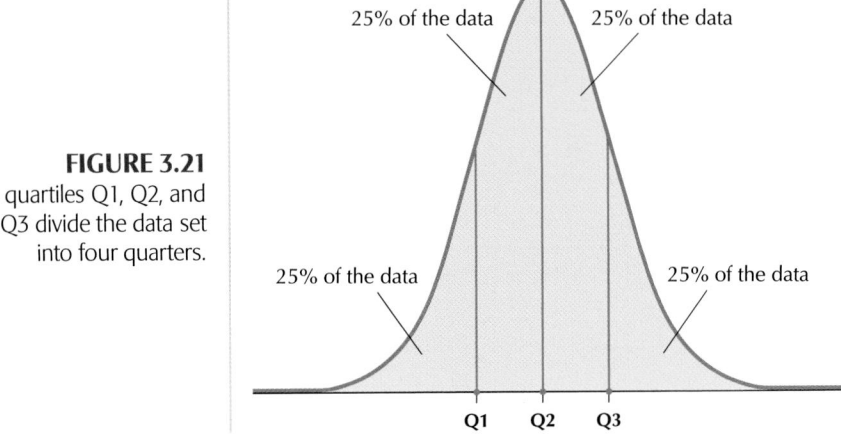

25% of the data   25% of the data

25% of the data   25% of the data

Q1   Q2   Q3

FIGURE 3.21
The quartiles Q1, Q2, and
Q3 divide the data set
into four quarters.

Note: It may be helpful to note that the phrase *third quartile* is akin to the phrase *three quarters,* which is 75%, representing the 75th percentile. Also, the phrase *first quartile* is akin to the phrase *one quarter,* which is 25%, representing the 25th percentile.

The Quartiles
The **quartiles** of a data set divide the data set into four parts, each containing 25% of the data.
- The *first quartile* (Q1) is the 25th percentile.
- The *second quartile* (Q2) is the 50th percentile, that is, the median.
- The *third quartile* (Q3) is the 75th percentile.
For small data sets, the division may be into four parts of only approximately equal size.

Example 3.31 Finding the quartiles for a small data set

In Example 3.29 (page 129), we examined the dance scores of 12 students auditioning for admission into a prestigious graduate school of the arts. Recall that we found the 75th percentile of the dance audition scores to be 83. By definition, the 75th percentile is the third quartile Q3. Therefore, this score of 83 is also the third quartile (Q3) of the audition scores. Now we will find the first quartile and the median (second quartile).

Solution

To find the quartiles, we use the steps for finding percentiles (page 129). First, arrange the data set in ascending order, as follows:

30   44   56   62   65   68   75   78   81   85   89   94

Here, $n = 12$. To find Q1, plug $p = 25$ into the equation $i = \left(\dfrac{p}{100}\right)n$, where $n = 12$. We get $i = \left(\dfrac{p}{100}\right)n = \left(\dfrac{25}{100}\right)12 = 3$. Since 3 is an integer, we know that the 25th percentile is the mean of the dance scores in the 3rd and 4th positions. The score of 56 is in the 3rd position, while 62 is in the 4th position. Since $(56 + 62)\,/\,2 = 59$, we get the 25th percentile of the dance scores to be 59 (Figure 3.22).

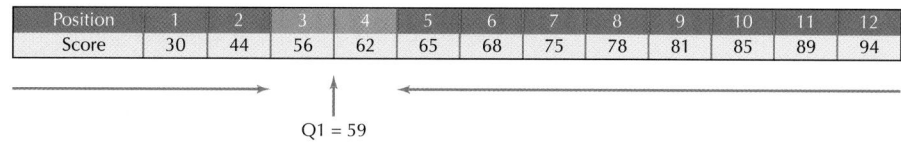

FIGURE 3.22 The 25th percentile splits the difference between 56 and 62.

To find the median (the second quartile, Q2), plug $p = 50$ into your steps for finding the percentiles: $i = \left(\dfrac{p}{100}\right)n = \left(\dfrac{50}{100}\right)12 = 6$. Since 6 is an integer, we know that the 50th percentile is the mean of the dance scores in the 6th and 7th positions, that is, 68 and 75. Since $(68 + 75)/2 = 71.5$, the 50th percentile of the dance scores is 71.5 (Figure 3.23). This agrees with the method we learned for finding the median, on page 94.

FIGURE 3.23 The 50th percentile splits the difference between 68 and 75.

In Example 3.29, we determined that the 75th percentile was 83. Therefore, the quartiles for the dance score data set are Q1 = 59, median = Q2 = 71.5, and Q3 = 83. Note that these quartiles divide the data set into four equal sections, of 3 observations each (Figure 3.24). ∎

The quartiles may be found on the TI-83/84 by using the instructions for descriptive statistics shown on page 99.

Position	1	2	3	4	5	6	7	8	9	10	11	12
Score	30	44	56	62	65	68	75	78	81	85	89	94

Q1 = 59   Median = Q2 = 71.5   Q3 = 83

FIGURE 3.24 The quartiles for the dance audition data.

Now You Can Do
Exercises 36–38.

Of course, for small data sets, the division into quarters is not always exact. For example, what if one dancer had sprained her ankle that morning and could not make the audition? Then there would have been only 11 dance scores, which cannot be divided equally into four quarters. In this case, therefore, the quartiles would divide the data set up into four sections of approximately equal size. However, for large data sets, which the data analyst most often encounters, this becomes less of an issue.

Example 3.32   Finding quartiles of a large data set: cholesterol levels in food

Nutrition

The U.S. Department of Agriculture recommends a diet low in cholesterol, to reduce the risk of heart disease. The data set **Nutrition** contains information on the cholesterol content (in milligrams) of 961 different foods. Find the mean, standard deviation, and quartiles.

Solution

The Minitab descriptive statistics for the cholesterol data are shown in Figure 3.25. Note that the mean cholesterol content is 32.55 mg and that the standard deviation is about 120 mg. Recall that a standard deviation that is much larger than the mean may be associated with strongly skewed distributions. Compare the value for the mean with the values for the quartiles.

- Q1, the first quartile, or 25th percentile, is 0 mg of cholesterol.
- The median, or Q2, the second quartile (50th percentile), is also 0 mg of cholesterol.
- Q3, the third quartile, or 75th percentile, is 20 mg of cholesterol. ▪

Note: Minitab uses a different way to calculate the quartiles than the way we have learned, which results in different values than our hand-calculation methods. However, for large data sets, the difference is minimal.

Variable	N	Mean	StDev	Min	Q1	Median	Q3	Max
Cholesterol	961	32.55	119.96	0	0	0	20	2053

FIGURE 3.25 Descriptive statistics for the cholesterol data.

Figure 3.26 shows that the data distribution is extremely right-skewed. There are only a few foods with over 1000 mg cholesterol, and another handful with over 500 (see data on disk). Therefore, it appears that we have outliers in this data set. What is the effect of these outliers on the mean and standard deviation? Does the mean represent a truly typical cholesterol content level for the data set, or is its value unduly increased by the outliers? Let's find out.

FIGURE 3.26
Cholesterol content (mg) of 961 foods.

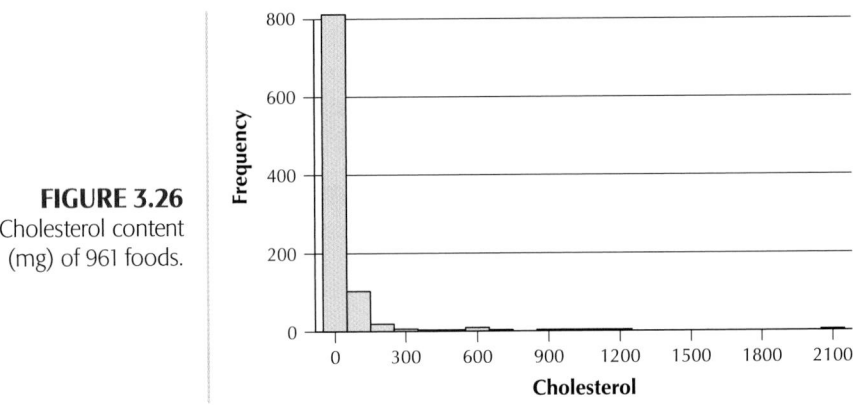

Developing Your Statistical Sense

The Mean Is Not Always Representative

Note that the median is 0 mg of cholesterol, meaning that at least half of the food items tested by the USDA in this data set had no cholesterol at all. We are intrigued by this result and ask Minitab to provide us with a frequency distribution for the cholesterol content, along with the cumulative percentages ("CumPct"). Figure 3.27 provides a portion of this frequency distribution, with the following results:

- 61.91% of the food items have no cholesterol at all, which explains why Q1 and the median are both zero.
- The 75th percentile, Q3, is verified to be 20 mg cholesterol.
- The 81st percentile of the data set is 32 mg cholesterol.

	Chol	Count	CumPct		Chol	Count	CumPct	
61.91% of food	0	595	61.91		20	5	75.23	75th percentile
items had zero	1	12	63.16		21	5	75.75	(Q3) = 20 mg
cholesterol.	2	8	64.00		22	6	76.38	cholesterol
Thus, Q1 = 0 and	3	7	64.72		23	3	76.69	
median = 0.	4	11	65.87		24	4	77.11	
	5	10	66.91		25	3	77.42	
	6	6	67.53		26	4	77.84	
	7	5	68.05		27	9	78.77	
	8	7	68.78		28	3	79.08	
	9	4	69.20		29	4	79.50	
	10	8	70.03		30	3	79.81	
	11	3	70.34		31	6	80.44	
	12	4	70.76		32	5	80.96	81st percentile
	13	4	71.18		33	3	81.27	is 32 mg.
	14	5	71.70		34	4	81.69	The mean is
	15	7	72.42		35	2	81.89	32.55 mg.
	16	5	72.94		36	1	82.00	
	17	6	73.57		37	4	82.41	
	18	7	74.30		38	1	82.52	
	19	4	74.71		40	1	82.62	

FIGURE 3.27 Partial frequency distribution of cholesterol content.

Think about these results for a moment. We found that the 81st percentile is 32 mg cholesterol. In other words, 81% of the food items have a cholesterol content of 32 mg or less. And yet, this 32 mg is still *less than the mean* cholesterol content, reported by Minitab to be 32.55 mg. In other words, the mean of this data set is larger than 81% of the data values in the data set.

It seems clear, then, that *the mean 32.55 mg cannot be considered as typical or representative* of the data set. Its value has been exaggerated by the presence of the outliers, to such an extent that it is now larger than 81% of the data. We need another, more *robust* measure of center, one that is *resistant* to the undue influence of outliers, such as the median. Here, the value of the median is 0 mg cholesterol. An argument may certainly be made that this is indeed typical and representative of the data set, since 61.91% of the food items have no cholesterol content at all. ◢

Recall from Section 3.2 that the variance and standard deviation are measures of spread that are sensitive to the presence of extreme values. A more robust (less sensitive) measure of variability is the **interquartile range,** or **IQR.**

Interquartile Range

The **interquartile range (IQR)** is a robust measure of variability. It is calculated as

$$IQR = Q3 - Q1$$

The interquartile range is interpreted to be the spread of the middle 50% of the data.

The Latin word *inter* means "between," so the *inter*quartile range is the *difference between* the quartiles Q3 and Q1. The IQR represents how spread out the "middle half" of the data set is. A larger IQR implies a greater degree of variability, or spread, in the data set. Since the IQR ignores both the highest 25% and the lowest 25% of the data set, it is completely unaffected by outliers and is thus quite robust.

Example 3.33   Finding the interquartile range

In Example 3.31, we found that, for the dance audition score data, Q1 = 59 and Q3 = 83. Find the IQR for the dance score data and explain what it means.

Solution

Since Q1 = 59 and Q3 = 83, the IQR is IQR = Q3 − Q1 = 83 − 59 = 24. We would say that the middle 50%, or middle half, of the dance audition scores ranged over 24 points (see Figure 3.28).

FIGURE 3.28 The interquartile range for the dance audition data.

Now You Can Do
Exercise 39.

What would happen if we introduced an outlier into this data set? For example, what if we changed the lowest score from 30 to 3? The IQR would remain completely unaffected, as it would even if we changed the 44 to a 4. However, if we changed the 56, then the IQR would be affected, since Q1 would then change. ■

STEP-BY-STEP TECHNOLOGY GUIDE: Percentiles

EXCEL
Step 1   Enter the data into column **A**.
Step 2   Select **Data . . . Data Analysis**.
Step 3   Select **Rank and Percentile** and click **OK**.

Step 4   Click in the **Input Range** cell. Then highlight the data in column A. Click **OK**.

CRUNCHIT!
We will use the data from Example 3.29 (page 129).

Step 1   Click **File . . .** then highlight **Load from Larose2e . . . Chapter 3 . . .** and click on **Example 3.29**.
Step 2   Click **Statistics** and select **Descriptive statistics**. For **Data**, select **Scores**.

Step 3   In the **Percentiles (comma-separated)** cell, enter the percentiles that you would like to find. For example, to find the 5th and 95th percentiles, enter **5, 95**.
Step 4   Click **Calculate**.

Section 3.4 Summary

1 In this section, we learned about measures of position, which tell us the position that a particular data value holds relative to the rest of the data set. The z-score indicates how many standard deviations a particular data value is from the mean. The z-score equals the data value minus the mean, divided by the standard deviation. We may also calculate a data value, given its z-score.

2 An outlier is an extremely large or extremely small data value relative to the rest of the data set. An outlier can be identified when its z-score is less than -3 or greater than 3.

3 The pth percentile of a data set is the value at which p percent of the values in the data set are less than or equal to this value. The percentile rank of a data value equals the percentage of values in the data set that are less than or equal to that value.

4 Quartiles divide the data set into approximately equal quarters. The interquartile range (IQR) is a measure of spread found by subtracting the first quartile from the third quartile.

Section 3.4 Exercises

CLARIFYING THE CONCEPTS
1. What does it mean for a z-score to be positive? Negative? Zero?
2. Explain in your own words why z-scores are useful.
3. Explain in your own words what the 95th percentile of a data set means.
4. Why doesn't it make sense for there to be a 120th percentile of a data set?
5. Is it possible for the 1st percentile of a data set to equal the 99th percentile? Explain when this would happen.

6. Explain the difference between a percentile and a percentile rank.
7. True or false: The IQR is sensitive to the presence of outliers.

For Exercises 8–11, consider whether the scenarios are possible. If it is possible, then clearly describe what the data set would look like. If it is not possible, why not?
8. A scenario where the first and second quartiles of a data set are equal

9. A scenario where the mean of a data set is larger than Q3

10. A scenario where the median of a data set is smaller than Q1

11. A scenario where the IQR is negative

Use the following information for Exercises 12–17. Suppose the mean blood sugar level is 100 mg/dl (milligrams per deciliter), with a standard deviation of 10 mg/dl.

12. Alyssa has a blood sugar level of 90 mg/dl. How many standard deviations is Alyssa's blood sugar level below the mean?

13. Benjamin has a blood sugar level of 135 mg/dl. How many standard deviations is Benjamin's blood sugar level above the mean?

14. Chelsea has a blood sugar level of 125 mg/dl.
   a. If we calculate Chelsea's z-score, what is the scale?
   b. Calculate Chelsea's z-score.
   c. Interpret her z-score.

15. David has a blood sugar level of 85 mg/dl.
   a. Calculate David's z-score.
   b. Interpret his z-score.

16. Find the blood sugar level associated with a z-score of 1.

17. Find the blood sugar level associated with a z-score of −2.

18. Elizabeth's statistics class had a mean quiz score of 70 with a standard deviation of 15. Fiona's statistics class had a mean quiz score of 75 with a standard deviation of 5. Both Elizabeth and Fiona got an 85 on the quiz. Who did better relative to her class?

19. Juan's business class had a mean quiz score of 60 with a standard deviation of 15. Luis's business class had a mean quiz score of 70 with a standard deviation of 5. Both Juan and Luis got a 75 on the quiz. Who did better relative to his class?

For Exercises 20–23, determine whether the person's blood sugar level represents an outlier, using the z-score method.

20. Alyssa from Exercise 12

21. Benjamin from Exercise 13

22. Chelsea from Exercise 14

23. David from Exercise 15

Use the following set of stock prices (in dollars) for Exercises 24–39.

   10   7   20   12   5   15   9   18   4   12   8   14

For Exercises 24–29, find the stock price representing the indicated percentiles.

24. 50th   **25.** 75th   **26.** 25th
27. 10th   **28.** 5th   **29.** 95th

For Exercises 30–35, calculate the percentile rank for the indicated stock price.

30. $12   **31.** $20   **32.** $7
33. $4   **34.** $18   **35.** $5

36. Find Q1, the first quartile.

37. Calculate Q2, the second quartile.

38. Compute Q3, the third quartile.

39. Calculate the IQR.

APPLYING THE CONCEPTS

Twitter Followers. Refer to the following table for Exercises 40–47. 🐦 **twitterceleb**

Celebrity	Twitter followers (millions)
Lady Gaga	6.6
Britney Spears	6.1
Ashton Kutcher	5.9
Justin Bieber	5.6
Ellen DeGeneres	5.3
Kim Kardashian	5.0

40. Find the z-scores for the number of Twitter followers for the following celebrities.
   a. Kim Kardashian   **b.** Lady Gaga   **c.** Justin Bieber

41. Find the number of followers indicated by the following z-scores.
   a. −2   **b.** 1   **c.** 3

42. Determine whether the number of followers for any of the celebrities represents an outlier.

43. If the number of followers for Lady Gaga and Kim Kardashian do not represent outliers, explain why we need not check whether the numbers of followers for the other celebrities are outliers.

44. Find the indicated percentiles.
   a. 50th   **b.** 75th   **c.** 25th

45. Calculate the percentile rank for the following.
   a. 5.0 million followers
   b. 5.3 million followers
   c. 6.6 million followers

46. Find the following for the number of followers.
   a. Q1   **b.** Q2   **c.** Q3   **d.** IQR

47. Interpret the IQR value from Exercise 46(**d**) so that a nonspecialist could understand it.

Breakfast Calories. Refer to Table 3.22 for Exercises 48–55. 📊 **breakfastcal**

TABLE 3.22   Calories in 12 breakfast cereals

Cereal	Calories
Apple Jacks	110
Basic 4	130
Bran Chex	90
Bran Flakes	90
Cap'n Crunch	120
Cheerios	110
Cinammon Toast Crunch	120
Cocoa Puffs	110
Corn Chex	110
Corn Flakes	100
Corn Pops	110
Count Chocula	110

48. Find the z-scores for the calories for the following cereals.
   a. Corn Flakes   **b.** Basic 4
   c. Bran Flakes   **d.** Cap'n Crunch

49. Find the number of calories associated with the following z-scores:
  a. 0 **b.** 1 **c.** −1 **d.** 0.5

50. Determine whether any of the cereals is an outlier.

51. Find the following percentiles:
  a. 25th **b.** 50th **c.** 75th **d.** 95th

52. Find the percentile rank for each of the following:
  a. 90 calories   **b.** 120 calories
  c. 110 calories   **d.** 100 calories

53. Find the following:
  a. Q1 **b.** Q2 **c.** Q3 **d.** IQR

54. Explain what the IQR value from Exercise 53(**d**) means.

55. Suppose that a weight-control organization recommended eating breakfast cereals with the lowest 10% of calories.
  a. How many calories does this cutoff represent?
  b. Which cereals are recommended?

Dietary Supplements. Refer to Table 3.23 for Exercises 56–63. The table gives the number of American adults who have used the indicated "nonvitamin, nonmineral, natural products." 🌿 **dietarysupp**

TABLE 3.23   Use of dietary supplements

Product	Usage (in millions)	Product	Usage (in millions)
Echinacea	14.7	Ginger	3.8
Ginseng	8.8	Soy	3.5
Ginkgo biloba	7.7	Chamomile	3.1
Garlic	7.1	Bee pollen	2.8
Glucosamine	5.2	Kava kava	2.4
St. John's wort	4.4	Valerian	2.1
Peppermint	4.3	Saw palmetto	2.0
Fish oil	4.2		

Source: Centers for Disease Control and Prevention, Vital and Health Statistics, 2004.

56. Find the z-scores for usage for the following products:
  a. Echinacea   **b.** Saw palmetto
  c. Valerian   **d.** Ginseng

57. Find the usage associated with each of the following z-scores.
  a. 0 **b.** 3 **c.** −3 **d.** 1

58. Identify any outliers in the data set.

59. Find the following percentiles:
  a. 10th **b.** 90th **c.** 5th **d.** 95th

60. Find the percentile rank for each of the following usages:
  a. 14.7 million   **b.** 2.0 million
  c. 8.8 million   **d.** 2.1 million

61. Find the following:
  a. Q1 **b.** Q2 **c.** Q3 **d.** IQR

62. Interpret the IQR value from Exercise 61(**d**) so that a nonspecialist could understand it.

63. Suppose an advertising agency is interested in the top 15% of supplements.
  a. What usage does this represent?
  b. Which supplements would be of interest?

64. Female SAT Performance. Females tend to perform well on the Writing SAT. The College Board reported that the mean score on the Writing SAT for females in 2010 was 498. Assume that the standard deviation is 100 and that we do not know the distribution. Brandy scored in the 50th percentile on the Writing SAT.
  a. Draw a distribution curve where the 50th percentile is above the mean.
  b. Draw a distribution curve where the 50th percentile is below the mean.
  c. If the data distribution is bell-shaped, what was Brandy's score?

65. Expenditure per Pupil. The 5th percentile expenditure per pupil nationwide in 2005 was $6381, the 50th percentile was $8998, and the 95th percentile was 17,188.[8]
  a. Determine whether the distribution of expenditures is symmetric, left-skewed, or right-skewed.
  b. Would we expect the mean expenditure per pupil to be less than, equal to, or greater than $8998? Explain.
  c. Draw a distribution curve that matches this information.

3.5   Five-Number Summary and Boxplots

OBJECTIVES By the end of this section, I will be able to . . .

  1   Calculate the five-number summary of a data set.

  2   Construct and interpret a boxplot for a given data set.

  3   Detect outliers using the IQR method.

1 The Five-Number Summary

Because the mean and the standard deviation are sensitive to the presence of outliers, data analysts sometimes prefer a less sensitive set of statistics to summarize a data set.

One robust (or resistant) method of summarizing data that is used widely is called the **five-number summary**. The set consists of five measures we have already seen.

Which parts of the five-number summary are less robust than others? Since the minimum and maximum are the most extreme values, these are clearly very sensitive to outliers. However, Q1, the median, and Q3 are very resistant to the influence of outliers.

> The **five-number summary** consists of the following set of statistics, which together constitute a robust summarization of a data set:
> 1. Minimum; the smallest value in the data set
> 2. First quartile, Q1
> 3. Median, Q2
> 4. Third quartile, Q3
> 5. Maximum; the largest value in the data set

Example 3.34 The five-number summary for a small data set: the dance audition scores

 dancescore

Find the five-number summary for the dance audition data from Example 3.31 on page 130.

Solution

Examining Figure 3.29, we can without difficulty find the five-number summary for the dance audition data.

Position	1	2	3	4	5	6	7	8	9	10	11	12
Score	30	44	56	62	65	68	75	78	81	85	89	94

Q1 = 59   Q2 = 71.5   Q3 = 83

FIGURE 3.29 The quartiles for the dance audition data.

1. Minimum = 30
2. First quartile, Q1 = 59
3. Median = Q2 = 71.5
4. Third quartile, Q3 = 83
5. Maximum = 94

Now You Can Do
Exercises 9, 15, and 21.

More succinctly, the five-number summary is often reported as Min = 30, Q1 = 59, Med = 71.5, Q3 = 83, Max = 94. ∎

Example 3.35 The five-number summary for a large data set: cholesterol levels in food

 Nutrition

Find the five-number summary for the cholesterol data from Example 3.32 on page 131.

Solution

Minitab's reporting of the descriptive statistics makes it particularly straightforward to report the five-number summary, as here in Figure 3.30 (repeated from page 132) for the cholesterol data.

Variable	N	Mean	StDev	Min	Q1	Median	Q3	Max
Cholesterol	961	32.55	119.96	0	0	0	20	2053

FIGURE 3.30 Descriptive statistics for the cholesterol data.

The five-number summary for the cholesterol data set is

1. Smallest value in the data set = Min = 0
2. First quartile, Q1 = 0

   3. Median = 0
   4. Third quartile, Q3 = 20
   5. Largest value in the data set = Max = 2053

   Or, simply, Min = 0, Q1 = 0, Med = 0, Q3 = 20, Max = 2053. ■

   The five-number summary is associated with a certain type of graphical summary of data, called a *boxplot*, which we examine next.

2 The Boxplot

The **boxplot** is a convenient graphical display of the five-number summary of a data set. The boxplot allows the data analyst to evaluate the symmetry or skewness of a data set.

Example 3.36   The characteristics of a boxplot

Interpret the boxplot for the audition scores in Figure 3.31.

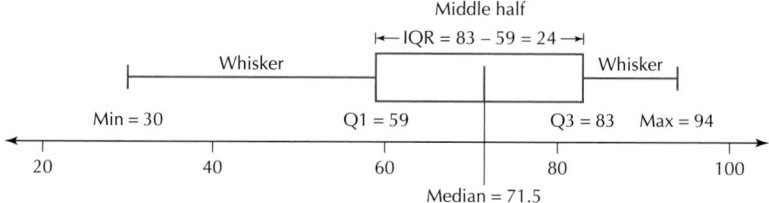

FIGURE 3.31 Boxplot of the dance score data.

Solution

Let's examine this boxplot carefully. The horizontal axis represents the dance scores. The red box itself represents the middle half of the data set. The right-hand side of the box, called the *upper hinge,* is located at Q3, which is 83. The left-hand side of the box, called the *lower hinge,* is located at Q1, which is 59. The solid vertical line inside the box is located at the median, which is 71.5. The horizontal lines emanating from the left and right of the box are called the *whiskers*. If there are no outliers, the whiskers extend as far as the maximum and minimum values of the data set, which are represented by the vertical lines at Max = 94 and Min = 30.

   On page 143, we demonstrate how to create a boxplot using technology. ■

Constructing a Boxplot by Hand

   1. Determine the lower and upper fences:
      a. Lower fence = Q1 − 1.5(IQR)
      b. Upper fence = Q3 + 1.5(IQR), where IQR = Q3 − Q1

   2. Draw a horizontal number line that encompasses the range of your data, including the fences. Above the number line, draw vertical lines at Q1, the median, and Q3. Connect the lines for Q1 and Q3 to each other so as to form a box.

   3. Temporarily indicate the fences as brackets ([and]) above the number line.

   4. Draw a horizontal line from Q1 to the smallest data value greater than the lower fence. This is the lower whisker. Draw a horizontal line from Q3 to the largest data value smaller than the upper fence. This is the upper whisker.

   5. Indicate any data values smaller than the lower fence or larger than the upper fence using an asterisk (*). These data values are outliers. Remove the temporary brackets.

Example 3.37   Constructing a boxplot by hand

Construct a boxplot for the dance score data.

Solution

From Example 3.36, the five-number summary for the dance score data is Min = 30, Q1 = 59, Med = 71.5, Q3 = 83, Max = 94. The interquartile range for the dance score data is IQR = Q3 − Q1 = 83 − 59 = 24.

Step 1   Determine the lower and upper fences:
  a. Lower fence = Q1 − 1.5(IQR) = 59 − 1.5(24) = 59 − 36 = 23
  b. Upper fence = Q3 + 1.5(IQR) = 83 + 1.5(24) = 83 + 36 = 119

Step 2   Draw a horizontal number line that encompasses the range of your data, including the fences. Above the number line, draw vertical lines at Q1 = 59, median = 71.5, and Q3 = 83. Connect the lines for Q1 and Q3 to each other so as to form a box, as shown in Figure 3.32a.

FIGURE 3.32a   Constructing a boxplot by hand: Steps 1 and 2.

Step 3   Temporarily indicate the fences (lower fence = 23 and upper fence = 119) as brackets above the number line. (See Figure 3.32b.)

FIGURE 3.32b   Constructing a boxplot by hand: Step 3.

Step 4   Draw a horizontal line from Q1 = 59 to the smallest data value greater than the lower fence. The lowest data value is Min = 30. This is greater than the lower fence = 23. So draw the line from 59 to 30. Draw a horizontal line from Q3 = 83 to the largest data value smaller than the upper fence. The largest data value is Max = 94, which is smaller than the upper fence. So draw the line from 83 to 94. (See Figure 3.32c.)

FIGURE 3.32c   Constructing a boxplot by hand: Step 4.

Step 5   There are no data values lower than the lower fence or greater than the upper fence. Thus, there are no outliers in this data set. Therefore, simply remove the temporary brackets, and the boxplot is complete, as shown in Figure 3.32d. ■

Now You Can Do
Exercises 12, 18, and 24.

FIGURE 3.32d   The completed boxplot.

The next examples show how to recognize when boxplots indicate that a data set is right-skewed, left-skewed, or symmetric.

Example 3.38 Boxplot for right-skewed data

The number of strikeouts per player in the 2007 American League season is a right-skewed distribution, as shown in histogram of the data in Figure 3.33. The five-number summary is Min = 0, Q1 = 9, Med = 21, Q3 = 47, and Max = 111. How is this skewness reflected in a boxplot (Figure 3.34)? Well, in right-skewed data, the median is closer to Q1 than to Q3, and the lowest non-outlier is closer to Q1 than the highest non-outlier is to Q3. This means that the median is closer to the lower hinge than the upper hinge, and the upper whisker is much longer than the lower whisker. This combination of characteristics indicates a right-skewed data set.

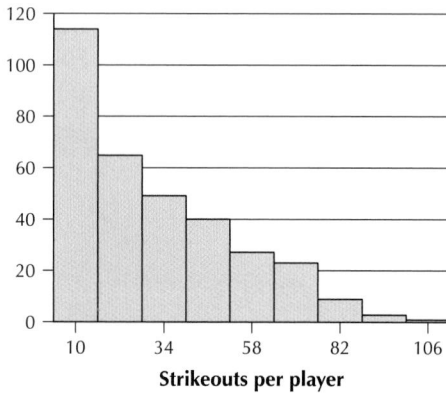

FIGURE 3.33 Strikeouts are right-skewed.

FIGURE 3.34 TI-83/84 boxplot of strikeouts: right-skewed.

The two little boxes at the right represent outliers. (The TI-83/84 uses little boxes rather than asterisks.) These players are David Ortiz of the Boston Red Sox, who led the league that year with 111 strikeouts, and Jack Cust of the Oakland Athletics, with 105 strikeouts. When there are no outliers, the whiskers extend as far as the minimum and maximum values. However, when there are outliers, the whiskers extend only as far as the most extreme data value that is not an outlier. ∎

Example 3.39 Boxplot for left-skewed data

Figure 3.35 is a histogram of 650 exam scores. Clearly, the data are left-skewed, with many students getting scores in the 90s, and fewer getting grades in the 70s or 80s. Now, with right-skewed data, remember that the median was closer to Q1 than to Q3. What do you think will happen for left-skewed data?

FIGURE 3.35 Histogram of exam scores.

FIGURE 3.36 TI-83/84 boxplot of the exam scores.

Solution

The five-number summary is Min = 70, Q1 = 86, Med = 94, Q3 = 98, and Max = 100. So, this time, with left-skewed data, the median is closer to Q3 than to Q1. Bet you guessed it!

In the boxplot (Figure 3.36), notice that the median (94) is closer to the upper hinge (Q3, 98) than to the lower hinge (Q1, 86), and the lower whisker is much longer than the upper whisker. This combination of characteristics indicates a left-skewed data set. ■

What Result Might We Expect?

Symmetric Data and Boxplots

So, can you now predict how a boxplot of *symmetric* data will look? The median will be about the same distance from Q1 (lower hinge) and Q3 (upper hinge). And the upper and lower whiskers will be about the same length. An example of a box-plot of symmetric data is shown in Figure 3.37 ◢

Now You Can Do
Exercises 25–28.

FIGURE 3.37 Boxplot of symmetric data.

3 Detecting Outliers Using the IQR Method

When using the mean and standard deviation as your summary measures, in most cases outliers occur more than 3 standard deviations from the mean. However, due to the sensitivity of these measures to the outliers themselves, we often use a more robust method of detecting outliers. Earlier we mentioned that, when constructing a boxplot, data values lower than the lower fence and higher than the upper fence are considered outliers. We can use this method to detect outliers without constructing a boxplot.

> **IQR Method to Detect Outliers**
>
> A data value is an outlier if
> a. it is located 1.5(IQR) or more below Q1, or
> b. it is located 1.5(IQR) or more above Q3.

Example 3.40 **IQR method for detecting outliers**

Determine if there are any outliers in the dance score data.

Solution

Recall for the dance score data set that IQR = 24, Q1 = 59, and Q3 = 83. So we have 1.5(IQR) = 1.5(24) = 36. The first step is to find the two quantities Q1 − 1.5(IQR) and Q3 + 1.5(IQR):

$$Q1 - 1.5(IQR) = Q1 - 36 = 59 - 36 = 23$$

$$Q3 + 1.5(IQR) = Q3 + 36 = 83 + 36 = 119$$

Now You Can Do
Exercises 10, 11, 16, 17 and 22, and 23.

Thus, for this data set, a data value would be an outlier if it were 23 or less or 119 or more. Since there are no data values that are 23 or less or 119 or more in the data set, no outliers are identified by the IQR method. ■

IQR Method for Outlier Detection

What if the minimum dance score of 30 is changed to 23. Based on Example 3.40, this new value should be detected as an outlier. Note that changing the minimum value does not affect the calculation of Q1, Q3, the IQR, or the thresholds for outlier detection.

Figure 3.38 shows that the box, hinges, and whiskers are all located at precisely the same spots as in the boxplot of the original dance score data. However, the software has calculated, using the robust detection method, that the new data value of 23 is an outlier and indicates it as such with a blue dot. Comparing this boxplot to the earlier one (see Figure 3.31), we notice that the lower whisker is shorter. In Figure 3.38, the whisker terminates at the dance score of 44 instead of 30.

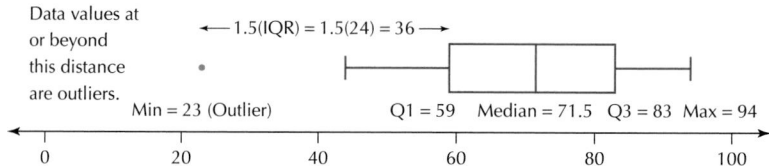

FIGURE 3.38 Boxplot of dance score data showing presence of outlier, after change.

The next example shows how comparison boxplots may be used to compare two data sets side-by-side.

Example 3.41	Comparison boxplots: comparing body temperatures for women and men

bodytemp

Determine whether the body temperatures of women or men exhibit greater variability.

Solution

Consider the comparison boxplots in Figure 3.39. The box for females (on top) lies slightly to the right of that for the males, meaning that the first quartile, the median, and the third quartile are each higher for the women than the men. Therefore, the middle 50% of the body temperatures is higher for women than men.

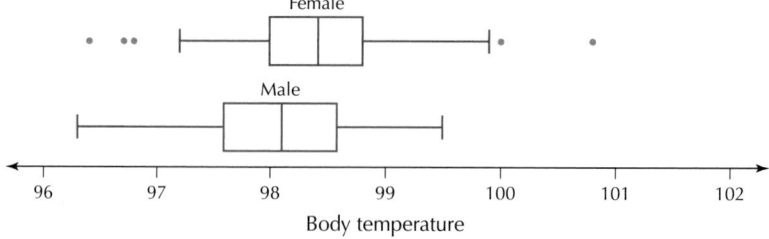

FIGURE 3.39 Comparison of boxplots of female and male body temperatures.

This figure seems to offer some evidence that the mean body temperature for women may be higher than that for men. The location of the box is an indication of the center of the data. But where would we look for a difference in the variability of body temperatures between women and men? From Figure 3.40, for the females we have

$$IQR = Q3 - Q1 = 98.8 - 98.0 = 0.8$$

For the males we have

$$IQR = Q3 - Q1 = 98.6 - 97.6 = 1.0$$

We will formally test whether there is a difference in the true mean body temperature between women and men in Chapter 10.

So the IQR for males is greater.

Let's determine which data set has greater variability based on the three different measures of spread that we have learned: the range, the standard deviation, and the IQR.

Gender	N	Mean	Median	StDev	Min	Max	Q1	Q3
female	65	98.394	98.4	0.743	96.4	100.8	98.0	98.8
male	65	98.105	98.1	0.699	96.3	99.5	97.6	98.6

FIGURE 3.40 Descriptive statistics for body temperature, by gender.

Now You Can Do
Exercises 29 and 30.

Range for women = $100.8 - 96.4 = 4.4$ Range for men = $99.5 - 96.3 = 3.2$
Standard deviation for women = 0.743   Standard deviation for men = 0.699
IQR for women = 0.8   IQR for men = 1.0 ∎

Developing Your
Statistical Sense

When Measures of Spread Disagree

Two measures of spread that are sensitive to the presence of extreme values—range and standard deviation—find that the female body temperatures are more variable. The measure of spread that is resistant to the effects of extreme values—IQR—finds that the male body temperatures are more variable. How do we resolve this apparent inconsistency? What appears to be happening is that, for the middle 50% of each data set, the men are more variable, but as we move toward the tails, the women are more spread out.

Note that there are outliers for the women but not for the men. In part, this may be because the IQR for the women is smaller, and thus the distance 1.5(IQR) is smaller as well. For example, the woman whose body temperature is 100 degrees is identified as an outlier because 100 is the same as the outlier threshold Q3 + 1.5(IQR) = 98.8 + 1.5(0.8) = 100. *The same temperature in a man would not be classified as an outlier, even though the male temperatures are lower overall* (and Q3, specifically, is lower). This is because the temperature of 100 is not higher than Q3 + 1.5(IQR) = 98.6 + 1.5(1.0) = 100.1, the male outlier threshold. Thus, the measures of spread that are sensitive to outliers indicate that women have greater variability, while the measure of spread that is not sensitive to outliers indicates that men have greater variability. ◢

STEP-BY-STEP TECHNOLOGY GUIDE: Boxplots

We will make boxplots for the data in Example 3.36 (page 138).

TI-83/84

Step 1 Enter the data in list **L1**.
Step 2 Press **2nd Y=**, and choose 1: **Plot 1**.
Step 3 Turn plots **On**. Highlight the boxplot icon, as shown in Figure 3.41.
Step 4 Press **ZOOM**, and choose **9: ZoomStat**.
A boxplot similar to Figure 3.31 in Example 3.36 is then produced.

FIGURE 3.41

MINITAB

Step 1 Enter the data in column **C1**, and name your data *Scores*.

Step 2 Click **Graph** > **Boxplot**.

Step 3 Select **Simple** and click **OK**.

Step 4 Select the variable *Scores*, and click **OK**, as shown in Figure 3.42. A boxplot similar to Figure 3.31 in Example 3.36 is then produced.

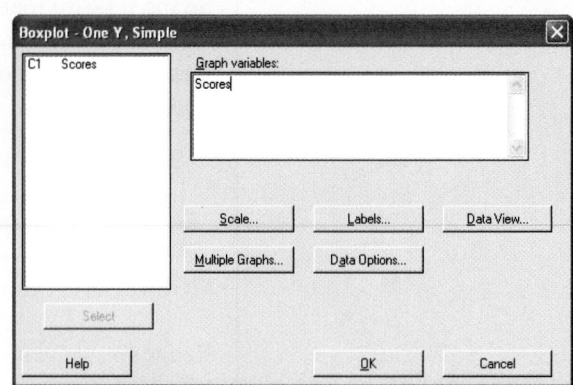

FIGURE 3.42

CRUNCHIT!

Step 1 Click **File . . .** then highlight **Load from Larose2e . . . Chapter 3 . . .** and click on **Example 3.34**.

Step 2 Click **Graphics** and select **Box plot**. For **Data** select **Scores**. Click **Calculate**.

Section 3.5 Summary

1 The five-number summary is a robust alternative to the usual mean-and-standard-deviation method of summarizing a data set. It consists of simply reporting the minimum, first quartile, median, third quartile, and maximum of the data set.

2 A boxplot is a graphical representation of the five-number summary and is useful for investigating skewness and the presence of outliers.

3 The IQR method of detecting outliers is to consider a data value an outlier if it is located 1.5(IQR) or more below Q1, or it is located 1.5(IQR) or more above Q3.

Section 3.5 Exercises

CLARIFYING THE CONCEPTS

1. True or false: The five-number summary consists of the minimum, Q1, Mean, Q3, Maximum.

2. Explain what we mean when we say that the five-number summary is associated with the boxplot.

3. Explain how we can use a boxplot to recognize the following:
    a. Symmetric distribution
    b. Right-skewed distribution
    c. Left-skewed distribution

4. When is it possible for outliers to be found inside the box of a boxplot?

5. Explain the IQR method for detecting outliers.

6. Why do we need the IQR method for detecting outliers when we already have the *z*-score method?

PRACTICING THE TECHNIQUES

Use the following set of 10 student heights (in inches) to answer Exercises 7–12.

    64 64 65 66 68 68 70 70 71 78

7. Find the quartiles.

8. Calculate the interquartile range.

9. Compute the five-number summary.

10. Use the IQR method to determine whether 71 inches is an outlier.

11. Use the IQR method to determine whether 78 inches is an outlier.

12. Construct a boxplot for student height.

Use the following data, the commuting times (in minutes) for 12 community college students, to answer Exercises 13–18.

    10 15 10 20 15 15 25 50 15 20 25 15

13. Find the quartiles.

14. Calculate the interquartile range.

15. Compute the five-number summary.

16. Use the IQR method to determine whether 10 minutes is an outlier.

17. Use the IQR method to determine whether 50 minutes is an outlier.

18. Construct a boxplot for commuting time.

Here are the final-exam scores for 20 psychology students. Use this data set to answer Exercises 19–24.

```
75  81  82  70  60  59  94  77  68  98
86  68  85  72  70  91  78  86  41  67
```

19. Find the quartiles.
20. Calculate the interquartile range.
21. Compute the five-number summary.
22. Use the IQR method to determine whether a score of 41 is an outlier.
23. Use the IQR method to determine whether a score of 98 is an outlier.
24. Construct a boxplot for final-exam score.

For Exercises 25 and 26, do the following:
  a. Identify the shape of the distribution.
  b. Use the boxplot to find the five-number summary.

25.

26.
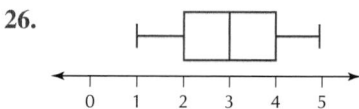

Use the comparison boxplots shown to answer Exercises 27–30.

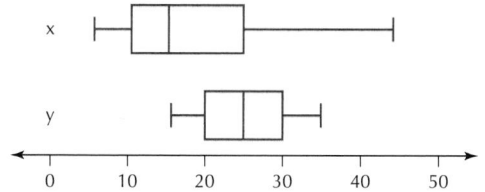

27. For the variable *x*:
  a. Identify the shape of the distribution.
  b. Use the boxplot to find the five-number summary.
28. For the variable *y*:
  a. Identify the shape of the distribution.
  b. Use the boxplot to find the five-number summary.
29. Which variable has greater variability, according to the IQR?
30. Which variable has greater variability, according to the range?

APPLYING THE CONCEPTS
Women's Volleyball Team Heights. Refer to Table 3.9 (page 104) for Exercises 31–33. **volleyball**
31. Find five-number summaries for the volleyball team heights for WMU and NCU. Comment on whether one should use a five-number summary for data sets of size 5.
32. Find the interquartile range for each team. Interpret what this value actually means, so that a nonspecialist could understand it.
33. By hand, construct a boxplot for each team. Comment on why your boxplots look unusual.

Most Active Stocks. Use Table 3.24 for Exercises 34–41. These companies represent the 11 most actively traded

stocks on the New York Stock Exchange for February 5, 2007. Variables include the stock price and the net change in stock price, with both variables in dollars. **nysestock**

TABLE 3.24 The most active stocks on the NYSE

Company	Price	Change
Pfizer Inc.	26.88	+0.08
Slm Corp.	42.37	−4.09
Ford Motor Co.	8.33	+0.10
General Electric Co.	36.37	+0.10
Equity Office Properties Trust	55.46	+0.08
AT&T Inc.	37.79	−0.33
EMC Corp.	13.69	−0.05
LSI Logic Corp.	9.14	−0.14
Motorola, Inc.	19.87	+0.02
Advanced Micro Devices	15.60	−0.09

34. Find the five-number summary for *price*.
35. Find the interquartile range for *price*. Interpret what this value actually means, so that a nonspecialist could understand it.
36. Use the IQR method to investigate the presence of outliers in *price*.
37. Construct a boxplot for *price*.
38. Find the five-number summary for *change*.
39. Find the interquartile range for *change*. Interpret what this value actually means, so that a nonspecialist could understand it.
40. Use the IQR method to investigate the presence of outliers in *change*.
41. Construct a boxplot for *change*.

Dietary Supplements. Refer to Table 3.23 (page 136) for Exercises 42–47. **dietarysupp**
42. Find the five-number summary for *usage*.
43. Find the interquartile range for *usage*. Interpret what this value actually means, so that a nonspecialist could understand it.
44. Use the IQR method to investigate the presence of outliers in *usage*.
45. Construct a boxplot for *usage*.
46. Calculate the mean and standard deviation of *usage*.
47. Find the *z*-score for echinacea, and use it to determine whether the product is an outlier. Compare the result with that from the IQR method.

BRINGING IT ALL TOGETHER
Zooplankton and Phytoplankton. For Exercises 48–56, refer to the zooplankton and phytoplankton meta-analysis effect size data from the Section 3.2 exercises (page 116). **plankton**
48. Compute the five-number summary for each of the zooplankton and phytoplankton data.
49. Construct comparison boxplots for the zooplankton and phytoplankton data.
50. Describe the shapes of the distribution for the zooplankton and phytoplankton data.

51. Based on your descriptions in the previous exercise, would you expect the mean to be larger or smaller or about the same as the median for the zooplankton data? The phytoplankton data?

52. Calculate the mean for the zooplankton data and the phytoplankton data. Do they concur with your expectations from the previous exercise?

53. Describe the difference between the effect sizes between the zooplankton and phytoplankton, in terms of the location of the box. Which type of plankton seems to have the greater overall effect sizes? Does this agree with what a comparison of the means from the previous exercise is telling you?

54. Describe the difference between the effect sizes between the zooplankton and phytoplankton, in terms of the IQR measure of spread. Which type of plankton has greater variability?

55. Identify any outliers for the zooplankton data and the phytoplankton data, using the IQR method.

56. Challenge Exercise. Identify any outliers for the phytoplankton data using the z-score method. Compare the outliers identified using the IQR method and the z-score method. Clearly explain why the two methods disagree.

Nutrition. Use the data set **Nutrition** for Exercises 57–60.

🐾 **Nutrition**

57. Open the data set **Nutrition.**
   a. How many observations are in the data set?
   b. How many variables?

58. Use a statistical computing package (like Minitab) to explore the variable *iron.*
   a. Find the mean and standard deviation for the amount of iron in the food.
   b. Find the five-number summary, the range, and the interquartile range.

59. Which food item has the maximum amount of iron? Does this surprise you?

60. Use the computer to generate a boxplot. Also, comment on the symmetry or the skewness of the boxplot.

3.6 Chebyshev's Rule and the Empirical Rule

OBJECTIVES By the end of this section, I will be able to . . .

1   Calculate percentages using Chebyshev's Rule.

2   Find percentages and data values using the Empirical Rule.

1 Chebyshev's Rule

Portrait of Pafnuty Tchebyshev-Yaroslav Sergeyevich (1899–1978)/State Central Artillery Museum, St. Petersburg, Russia/The Bridgeman Art Library

P. L. Chebyshev (1821–94, Russia) derived a result, called **Chebyshev's Rule,** that can be applied to any continuous data set whatsoever.

> **Chebyshev's Rule**
>
> The proportion of values from a data set that will fall within k standard deviations of the mean will be *at least*
>
> $$\left(1 - \frac{1}{k^2}\right)100\%,$$
>
> where $k > 1$. Chebyshev's Rule may be applied to either samples or populations. For example:
> - $k = 2$. At least 3/4 (or 75%) of the data values will fall within 2 standard deviations of the mean.
> - $k = 3$. At least 8/9 (or 88.89%) of the data values will fall within 3 standard deviations of the mean.

Example 3.42 Finding the scores within 3 standard deviations of the mean

An instructor giving an exam expects that the mean will be 75 and the standard deviation will be 5. What exam scores represent the scores within 3 standard deviations of the mean exam score?

Solution

We have $\bar{x} = 75$ and $s = 5$. The instructor is interested in estimating the proportion *within 3 standard deviations,* so that $k = 3$. In general, "within 3 standard deviations of the mean" means

a.   the mean minus 3 standard deviations $(\bar{x} - 3s)$, up to

b.   the mean plus 3 standard deviations $(\bar{x} + 3s)$, as shown in Figure 3.43.

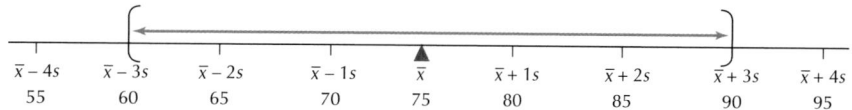

| $\bar{x} - 4s$ | $\bar{x} - 3s$ | $\bar{x} - 2s$ | $\bar{x} - 1s$ | $\bar{x}$ | $\bar{x} + 1s$ | $\bar{x} + 2s$ | $\bar{x} + 3s$ | $\bar{x} + 4s$ |
| 55 | 60 | 65 | 70 | 75 | 80 | 85 | 90 | 95 |

FIGURE 3.43 Within 3 standard deviations of the mean.

Since $\bar{x} = 75$ and $s = 5$, "within 3 standard deviations of the mean" means from $75 - 3(5) = 60$ to $75 + 3(5) = 90$. ■

A key to solving a Chebyshev-type problem lies in finding the value of k, the number of standard deviations that a data value lies from the mean. The following example demonstrates how to find the value of k, as well as how to calculate the lower bound.

Example 3.43   Finding k and calculating the Chebyshev lower bound

Continuing the previous example, find the Chebyshev lower bound on the percentage of students who will score between 60 and 90 on the upcoming exam.

Solution

First, we need to find k. This is done as follows:

> You may have noticed that the k is found in a manner similar to finding the z-score. What is the difference, then, between k and a z-score? The difference is that z-scores are always associated with an existing data value, whereas k need not be.

$$k = \left| \frac{\text{numerical value} - \text{mean}}{\text{standard deviation}} \right| = \left| \frac{60 - 75}{5} \right| = |-3.0| = 3$$

$$k = \left| \frac{\text{numerical value} - \text{mean}}{\text{standard deviation}} \right| = \left| \frac{90 - 75}{5} \right| = |3.0| = 3$$

Thus, $k = 3$.

Once you have found the value of k, plug it into the *at least* $\left(1 - \frac{1}{k^2}\right)100\%$ formula from Chebyshev's Rule to solve the problem, as follows:

$$at\ least\left(1 - \frac{1}{k^2}\right)100\% = at\ least\left(1 - \frac{1}{3^2}\right)100\% = at\ least\left(1 - \frac{1}{9}\right)100\%$$

$$= at\ least\left(\frac{8}{9}\right)100\% \approx at\ least\ 88.8889\% \approx at\ least\ 88.9\%$$

That is, at least 88.9% of the students will score between 60 and 90 on the upcoming exam. Note that you were told nothing about the shape of the distribution. Chebyshev's Rule can be applied to distributions of any shape, even unknown distributions, as long as the data are continuous. ■

Now You Can Do
Exercises 5 and 9.

Developing Your
Statistical Sense

The "At Least" Is Not Optional

Chebyshev's Rule states that *at least* a certain percentage of the distribution lies between these two numbers. Data analysts say that Chebyshev's Rule gives a *lower bound* to this percentage, since it uses the phrase "at least." When giving percentages using Chebyshev, make sure you use the words "at least." There is a big difference between "about 88.9%" and "at least 88.9%." "At least 88.9%" could mean 100%, 95%, 88.9%, or anything in between. It is rather imprecise. ◢

2 The Empirical Rule

Metaphorically, the **Empirical Rule** is a high-performance Porsche compared to Chebyshev's Rule, which is a go-anywhere ATV (all-terrain vehicle). If your path calls for dirt roads and mud, you wouldn't use the Porsche but would hop in the ATV. Similarly, if you have a skewed data distribution or an unknown distribution, use Chebyshev's Rule. However, in the right circumstances, you should use the Empirical Rule. What are those circumstances? *Use the Empirical Rule when you know that your distribution is bell-shaped (normal).* On the autobahn, the Porsche would leave the ATV in the dust. Thus, when the data distribution is bell-shaped, the Empirical Rule outperforms Chebyshev. The more information you have, the more precise and powerful your statistical analysis will be.

> **The Empirical Rule**
> If the data distribution is bell-shaped:
>
> - About 68% of the data values will fall within 1 standard deviation of the mean.
> - About 95% of the data values will fall within 2 standard deviations of the mean.
> - About 99.7% of the data values will fall within 3 standard deviations of the mean.
>
> Stated in terms of z-scores:
>
> - About 68% of the data values will have z-scores between 1 and -1.
> - About 95% of the data values will have z-scores between 2 and -2.
> - About 99.7% of the data values will have z-scores between 3 and -3.

The Empirical Rule applies only to the z-scores 1, 2, and 3. For example, we won't learn until Chapter 6 how to calculate the percentage of values that fall within 1.5 standard deviations of the mean for bell-shaped data.

How do we arrive at the percentages shown in Figure 3.44? Subtracting the 68% from the 95% leaves 27% with z-scores between 1 and 2 and between -1 and -2, combined. By symmetry, this leaves about 13.5% (half of 27%) of z-scores between 1 and 2. Similar arithmetic leads to the other percentages shown in Figure 3.44. Although Figure 3.44 is for z-scores, the percentages are approximately correct for any data set that has a bell-shaped distribution.

FIGURE 3.44
Distribution of the z-scores for bell-shaped data.

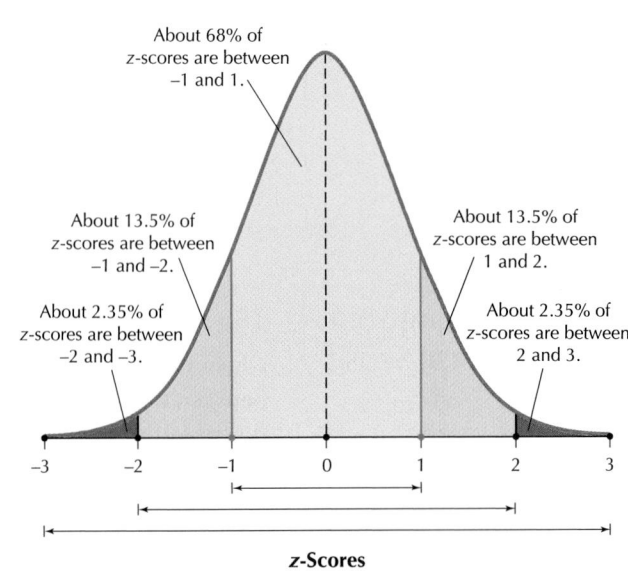

About 68% of z-scores are between -1 and 1.

About 13.5% of z-scores are between -1 and -2.

About 13.5% of z-scores are between 1 and 2.

About 2.35% of z-scores are between -2 and -3.

About 2.35% of z-scores are between 2 and 3.

z-Scores

Example 3.44   Using the Empirical Rule to find percentages

Suppose we know that student grade point averages (GPAs) are bell-shaped with a mean of 2.5 and a standard deviation of 0.5.
a.   Find the proportion of GPAs between 2.0 and 3.0.
b.   Find the proportion of GPAs that lie either above 3.5 or below 1.5.

Solution

a.   Again, the key is finding k, just as we did for Chebyshev's Rule:

$$k = \left| \frac{\text{numerical value } - \text{ mean}}{\text{standard deviation}} \right| = \left| \frac{2.0 - 2.5}{0.5} \right| = |-1| = 1$$

$$k = \left| \frac{\text{numerical value } - \text{ mean}}{\text{standard deviation}} \right| = \left| \frac{3.0 - 2.5}{0.5} \right| = |1| = 1$$

Remember: That word "about" is not optional; it is required. The Empirical Rule is an approximation of normal distribution probabilities that we will examine more closely in Chapter 6.

So, $k = 1$. We are interested in finding the proportion of GPAs within 1 standard deviation of the mean. We are told that the data are bell-shaped; therefore, we may use the Empirical Rule. Since k represents the number of standard deviations between the data value and the mean, $k = 1$ represents "within 1 standard deviation of the mean." Thus, according to the Empirical Rule, about 68% of the GPAs lie between 2.0 and 3.0.
b.   Again start by finding k:

$$k = \left| \frac{\text{numerical value } - \text{ mean}}{\text{standard deviation}} \right| = \left| \frac{1.5 - 2.5}{0.5} \right| = |-2| = 2$$

$$k = \left| \frac{\text{numerical value } - \text{ mean}}{\text{standard deviation}} \right| = \left| \frac{3.5 - 2.5}{0.5} \right| = |2| = 2$$

So, $k = 2$. We are interested in what proportion lies above 3.5 or below 1.5, that is, what proportion lies 2 or more standard deviations away from the mean. From Figure 3.45, we know from the Empirical Rule that about 95% of the GPAs lie within 2 standard deviations of the mean, so that about 95% of the GPAs lie between 1.5 and 3.5.

About 68% of GPAs are between 2.0 and 3.0.

About 2.5% of GPAs are less than 1.5.

About 2.5% of GPAs are greater than 3.5.

FIGURE 3.45
Distribution of grade point average.

Grade point average

Since the bell-shaped curve is symmetrical about the mean, half of the left-over 5% is above 3.5 and half is below 1.5.

The left-over area in the two tails in Figure 3.45 is the proportion of GPAs above 3.5 or below 1.5. To find the percentage in the left-over area, we subtract 100% − 95% = 5%. Thus, *about 5% of the GPAs lie either above 3.5 or below 1.5.* ■

Now You Can Do
Exercises 6 and 11.

Example 3.45   Using the Empirical Rule to find data values

So far we have given values for the GPAs and asked for relevant proportions. We can turn this around and ask which GPAs are associated with various proportions. Suppose the college is interested in identifying extreme outlier GPAs. Assuming the distribution

If we know that the distribution is bell-shaped, may we still apply Chebyshev's Rule? Yes, Chebyshev applies to any continuous distribution.

Now You Can Do
Exercises 7 and 8.

of GPAs is bell-shaped, find the range of GPAs that define the middle 99.7% (approximately) of all GPAs.

Solution

Here we have to work backward. According to the Empirical Rule, 99.7% is associated with $k = 3$. So, about 99.7% of the GPAs lie within $k = 3$ standard deviations of the mean. The mean plus 3 standard deviations is $2.5 + 3(0.5) = 4.0$, and the mean minus 3 standard deviations is $2.5 - 3(0.5) = 1.0$. Therefore, 99.7% of all GPAs lie between 1.0 and 4.0. ∎

We will wrap up this section with an example that brings together the notions of *percentile, z-score, Chebyshev's Rule,* and the *Empirical Rule.*

Example 3.46   Bringing it all together

Matthew and Ashley just completed their English test. Matthew's score was at the 80th percentile. Ashley's *z*-score was 1. Who did better and why?

Solution

Well, Matthew's score was at the 80th percentile, so 80% of the test scores were at or below Matthew's test score. If more than 80% of scores were below Ashley's test score, she wins. However, we are not told that the scores are bell-shaped, so we can't use the Empirical Rule and must use Chebyshev. Ashley's *z*-score was 1, which is $k = 1$ standard deviation above the mean. But Chebyshev's Rule does not apply either, because k must be greater than 1. So the answer is, *we don't know who did better.*

Now, say we add the extra knowledge that the English test scores were *bell-shaped.* Bell-shaped means that we can use the Empirical Rule. Again, 80% of the scores were at or below Matthew's score. This time we know that Ashley's *z*-score of 1 indicates that, not only is she above the "middle" 68% (from the Empirical Rule), but she is also above half of the remaining 32% (Figure 3.46). So Ashley's test score beat about 68% plus about 16% = about 84%. Therefore, Ashley did better than Matthew. ∎

FIGURE 3.46
Sketch of the Matthew and Ashley problem, assuming a bell-shaped distribution.

Section 3.6 Summary

1 Chebyshev's Rule allows us to set a lower bound on the proportion of data values that lie within a certain interval for continuous distributions. Chebyshev's Rule states that the proportion of values from a data set that will fall within k standard deviations of the mean will be at least $[1 - (1/k)^2]$ 100%, where $k > 1$.

2 For bell-shaped distributions, the Empirical Rule may be applied, which is more precise than Chebyshev's Rule. The Empirical Rule states that, for bell-shaped distributions, about 68%, 95%, and 99.7% of the data values will fall within 1, 2, and 3 standard deviations of the mean, respectively.

Section 3.6 Exercises

CLARIFYING THE CONCEPTS

1. When may Chebyshev's Rule not be used? (*Hint:* Use k in your answer.)

2. Explain what the following phrase means: "within 2 standard deviations of the mean."

3. True or false: The Empirical Rule is more precise than Chebyshev's Rule.

4. When may the Empirical Rule be used?

PRACTICING THE TECHNIQUES

5. A data distribution has a mean of 100 and a standard deviation of 10. Suppose we do not know whether the distribution is bell-shaped.
   a. Estimate the proportion of the data that falls between 80 and 120.
   b. Estimate the proportion of the data that falls between 70 and 130.

6. A data distribution has a mean of 100 and a standard deviation of 10. Assume that the distribution is bell-shaped.
   a. Estimate the proportion of the data that falls between 80 and 120.
   b. Estimate the proportion of the data that falls between 70 and 130.

7. A data distribution has a mean of 100 and a standard deviation of 10. Assume that the distribution is bell-shaped.
   a. Find the range of data values that define the middle 95% of the data. (*Hint:* See Example 3.44.)
   b. Find the 97.5th percentile of the data. (*Hint:* Draw a picture.)
   c. Find the 2.5th percentile of the data.

8. A data distribution has a mean of 500 and a standard deviation of 100. Assume that the distribution is bell-shaped.
   a. Find the range of data values that define the middle 68% of the data. (*Hint:* See Example 3.44.)
   b. Find the data value that lies above 84% of the data. (*Hint:* Draw a picture.)
   c. Find the data value that lies below 84% of the data.

APPLYING THE CONCEPTS

9. **Heating Degree-Days.** The National Climate Data Center reports that the mean annual heating degree-days (an index of energy usage) for the period 1949–2006 was 4500 with a standard deviation of 200. Suppose we do not know the shape of the data distribution. If possible, find the percentage of years with heating degree-days within the following ranges. If not possible, explain why.
   a. Between 4100 and 4900 heating degree-days
   b. Between 3900 and 5100 heating degree-days
   c. Between 4300 and 4700 heating degree-days

10. **Solar Power Production.** The U.S. Department of Energy reports that the mean annual production of solar power in the United States for the years 1989–2006 was 66 trillion Btu (British thermal units) with a standard deviation of 4 trillion Btu. Suppose we do not know the shape of the data distribution. If possible, find the

percentage of years with solar power production within the following ranges. If not possible, explain why.
   a. Between 62 trillion and 70 trillion Btu
   b. Between 60 trillion and 72 trillion Btu
   c. Above 72 trillion Btu

11. Refer to Exercise 9. Suppose that we know now that the distribution of heating degree-days is bell-shaped. If possible, recalculate the three percentages in Exercise 9, with this added knowledge.

12. Refer to Exercise 10. Suppose that we know now that the distribution of solar power production is bell-shaped. If possible, recalculate the three percentages in Exercise 10, with this added knowledge.

13. **Shares Traded on the NYSE.** The *Statistical Abstract of the United States* reports that the mean daily number of shares traded on the New York Stock Exchange in 2005 was 1602 (in millions). Let the standard deviation equal 500 million shares.
   a. A broker said that one particular day was very slow on the NYSE. He said it was so slow that the z-score for the number of shares traded was -3.
      i. Find the number of shares traded that has a z-score of -3.
      ii. Comment on the truthfulness of the broker.
   b. Assume that the number of shares traded is bell-shaped. Which day had more shares traded: a day with a z-score of -1 or a day that was at the 25th percentile?
   c. Assume we don't know the distribution of shares traded. What is the percentage of days in which between 602 million and 2602 million shares are traded?

14. **Life Expectancy.** The U.S. National Center for Health Statistics reported that the mean life expectancy for 20-year-old males was 75.5 years. Assume that the standard deviation is 5 years.
   a. Assuming that the distribution is bell-shaped, obtain a lower and upper bound that captures 95% of the life expectancies of 20-year-old males.
   b. Suppose we don't know the shape of the distribution. Redo (a) without the benefit of the bell-shaped assumption. Comment on the relative precision of the two methods.

BRINGING IT ALL TOGETHER

Grade Inflation. Use the following information for Exercises 15–19. Many educators are concerned about grade inflation. A study found that one low-performing high school (with mean combined SAT score of 750) had a higher mean grade point average (mean GPA = 3.6) than a high-performing school (with mean combined SAT score of 1050), which had mean GPA = 2.6.[9] Assume that GPA at the high-performing school has standard deviation $\sigma = 0.5$.

15. Suppose we do not know the shape of the distribution of GPA at the high-performing school.
    a. Find the proportion of students with a GPA between 2.1 and 3.1.
    b. Find the proportion of students with a GPA between 1.6 and 3.6.
    c. If possible, find the proportion of students with a GPA greater than 3.6. If not possible, clearly explain why not.
16. Now assume that the distribution of GPA at the high-performing school is bell-shaped.
    a. Find the proportion of students with a GPA between 2.1 and 3.1.
    b. Find the proportion of students with a GPA between 1.6 and 3.6.

c. If possible, find the proportion of students with a GPA greater than 3.6. If not possible, clearly explain why not.
17. Compare your responses to (a) and (b) in the previous two exercises. Which answer is more precise? What extra information accounts for this increased precision?
18. Suppose the mean GPA at the low-performing school was $\mu = 3.6$ with standard deviation $\sigma = 0.5$, and that the maximum GPA is 4.0. Does it make sense to assume that the distribution of GPA at this school is bell-shaped? Draw a graph to support your finding.
19. The maximum GPA at these schools is 4.0. Compare whether it is unusual for a student to get a 4.0 at each school.

Chapter 3 Formulas and Vocabulary

SECTION 3.1
- **Mean** (p. 90)
- **Measure of center** (p. 90)
- **Median** (p. 93)
- **Mode** (p. 95)
- **Population mean** (p. 92). $\mu = \sum x / N$.
- **Population size** (p. 92). Denoted by N.
- **Sample mean** (p. 91). $\bar{x} = \sum x / n$.
- **Sample size** (p. 90). Denoted by n.

SECTION 3.2
- **Deviation** (p. 105). $x - \bar{x}$.
- **Measure of variability (measure of spread, measure of dispersion)** (p. 104)
- **Population standard deviation** (p. 109).

$$\text{Definition formula: } \sigma = \sqrt{\frac{\sum(x - \mu)^2}{N}}$$

$$\text{Computational formula: } \sigma = \sqrt{\frac{\sum x^2 - \left(\sum x\right)^2 / N}{N}}$$

- **Population variance** (p. 108).

$$\text{Definition formula: } \sigma^2 = \frac{\sum(x - \mu)^2}{N}$$

$$\text{Computational formula: } \sigma^2 = \frac{\sum x^2 - \left(\sum x\right)^2 / N}{N}$$

- **Range** (p. 105)
- **Sample standard deviation** (p. 110).

$$\text{Definition formula: } s = \sqrt{\frac{\sum(x - \bar{x})^2}{n - 1}}$$

$$\text{Computational formula: } s = \sqrt{\frac{\sum x^2 - \left(\sum x\right)^2 / n}{n - 1}}$$

- **Sample variance** (p. 110).

$$\text{Definition formula: } s^2 = \frac{\sum(x - \bar{x})^2}{n - 1}$$

$$\text{Computational formula: } s^2 = \frac{\sum x^2 - \left(\sum x\right)^2 / n}{n - 1}$$

- **Standard deviation** (p. 105)

SECTION 3.3
- **Estimated mean for data grouped into a frequency distribution** (p. 119).

$$\hat{\mu} = \frac{\sum m_i f_i}{N} = \frac{m_1 f_1 + m_2 f_2 + \cdots + m_k f_k}{N}$$

- **Estimated standard deviation for data grouped into a frequency distribution** (p. 120).

$$\hat{\sigma} = \sqrt{\hat{\sigma}^2} = \sqrt{\frac{\sum(m_i - \hat{\mu})^2 \cdot f_i}{N}}$$

- **Estimated variance for data grouped into a frequency distribution** (p. 120).

$$\hat{\sigma}^2 = \frac{\sum(m_i - \hat{\mu})^2 \cdot f_i}{N}$$

- **Weighted mean** (p. 118).

$$\hat{x}_w = \frac{\sum w_i x_i}{\sum w_i} = \frac{w_1 x_1 + w_2 x_2 + \cdots + w_n x_n}{w_1 + w_2 + \cdots + w_n}$$

SECTION 3.4
- **Interquartile range (IQR)** (p. 133).

$$\text{IQR} = Q3 - Q1$$

- **Outlier** (p. 127)
- **Percentile** (p. 128)
- **Percentile rank** (p. 129)

- **Quartiles** (p. 130)
- **z-Score** (p. 124)
  - **a.** The z-score for a particular data value from a *sample* is
  $$z\text{-score} = \frac{\text{data value} - \text{mean}}{\text{standard deviation}} = \frac{x - \bar{x}}{s}$$
  - **b.** The z-score for a particular data value from a *population* is
  $$z\text{-score} = \frac{\text{data value} - \text{mean}}{\text{standard deviation}} = \frac{x - \mu}{\sigma}$$

SECTION 3.5
- **Boxplot** (p. 138)
- **Five-number summary** (p. 137)
- **IQR method of detecting outliers** (p. 141)

SECTION 3.6
- **Chebyshev's Rule** (p. 146). The proportion of values from a data set that will fall within k standard deviations of the mean will be *at least* $\left(1 - \frac{1}{k^2}\right)100\%$, where $k > 1$.
- **Empirical Rule** (p. 148). If the data distribution is bell-shaped:
  About 68% of the data values will fall within 1 standard deviation of the mean.
  About 95% of the data values will fall within 2 standard deviations of the mean.
  About 99.7% of the data values will fall within 3 standard deviations of the mean.

Chapter 3 Review Exercises

SECTION 3.1
Phytoplankton. Refer to the phytoplankton data from Exercise 51 in Section 3.2 (page 116) for Exercises 1–3.
1. Find the mean.
2. Find the median.
3. Find the mode, if any.

Calories in Cereal. For Exercises 4–6, refer to the calories in breakfast cereals gives in Table 3.22 (page 135).
4. Which is the largest, the mean, median, or mode? How do you know?
5. If we eliminated the cereals with 90 or less calories from the sample, which measure would not be affected at all? Why?
6. If we added 10 calories to each cereal, how would that affect the mean, median, and mode? Would it affect each of the measures equally?

SECTION 3.2
Common Syllables in English. Refer to the following table of some common syllables in English for Exercises 7–10. 🔊 **syllables**

Syllable	Frequency
an	462
bi	621
sit	104
ed	907
its	293
est	186
wil	470
tiv	136
en	675
biz	114

7. Find the mean and the range of the syllable frequencies.
8. Would you say that a typical distance from the mean for the frequencies is about 900, about 500, about 300, or about 100?
9. What is your best guesstimate of the value of a typical distance from the mean for the syllable frequencies?

10. Find the sample variance and the sample standard deviation of syllable frequencies.
   - **a.** How far is it from your estimate of the typical deviation earlier?
   - **b.** Interpret the meaning of this value for the standard deviation so that someone who has never studied statistics would understand it.

SECTION 3.3
11. **Calculating a Grade Point Average.** At a certain college in Texas, student grade point averages are calculated as follows. For each credit hour, an A is worth 4.0 quality points, an A− is worth 3.7 quality points, a B+ is worth 3.3 quality points, a B is worth 3.0, a B− is worth 2.7, a C+ is worth 2.3, and so on. To find the grade point average, the number of credits for each course is multiplied by the quality points earned for that course; the results are added together; and the sum is divided by the number of credits. This semester, Angelita's grades are as follows. She got an A in her four-credit honors biology course, an A− in her three-credit calculus course, a B+ in her three-credit English course, a B− in her three-credit anthropology course, and a C+ in her two-credit physical education course. Calculate Angelita's grade point average for this semester.
12. **AIDS Cases by Age.** The National Center for Health Statistics reported the number of cases of acquired immunodeficiency syndrome (AIDS) by age of patient in 2004.[10] Find the estimated mean and standard deviation of the age of AIDS patients. 🔊 **aidsbyage**

Class: age	Frequency f_i
0–12.99	48
13–14.99	60
15–24.99	2,114
25–34.99	9,361
35–44.99	16,778
45–54.99	10,178
55–64.99	3,075
65–74.99	901

SECTION 3.4

NASCAR. Use the NASCAR winners data in Table 3.6 (page 101) for Exercises 13–22.

Find the following percentiles of total wins.
13. 10th percentile
14. 50th percentile
15. 90th percentile

For Exercises 16–18, find the *z*-scores for the following drivers for the number of total wins.
16. Richard Petty
17. Darrell Waltrip
18. Mark Martin
19. Identify any outliers or moderately unusual observations in the number of short tracks wins.

For Exercises 20–22, find the percentile rank for the given number of total wins.
20. 35
21. 55
22. 84

Ragweed Pollen. Use the table of ragweed pollen index in New York localities for Exercises 23–25. Do you suffer from ragweed pollen? You are not alone. The American Academy of Allergy maintains the ragweed pollen index, which details the severity of the pollen problem for hundreds of communities across the nation. The following table contains the ragweed pollen index on a particular day for 10 localities in New York State. 🌾 **ragweed**

Locality	Ragweed pollen index
Albany	48
Binghamton	31
Buffalo	59
Elmira	43
Manhattan	25
Rochester	60
Syracuse	25
Tupper Lake	8
Utica	26
Yonkers	38

23. Find the first, second, and third quartiles of the ragweed pollen index.
24. Find the interquartile range. Interpret what this value actually means, so that a nonspecialist could understand it.
25. Detect any outliers using the *z*-score method.

SECTION 3.5

26. Let's draw a boxplot of the ragweed pollen index.
   a. What is the five-number summary?
   b. By hand, draw a boxplot.
   c. Is the data set left-skewed, right-skewed, or symmetric?
   d. What should the symmetry or skewness mean in terms of the relative values of the mean and median?
   e. Find the mean and standard deviation. Is your prediction in **(d)** supported?
27. Detect any outliers using the IQR method. Compare with Exercise 25. Do the two methods concur or disagree?
28. Suppose the ragweed pollen index in Rochester were 600 instead of 60. How would this outlier affect the quartiles and the IQR? What property of these measures is this behavior an example of?

SECTION 3.6

Use the following information for Exercises 29–31. The vehicles on Interstate 95 have a mean speed of 70 miles per hour with a standard deviation of 5 miles per hour.
29. If the distribution of vehicle speeds is unknown, find the proportion of vehicles traveling between 60 and 80 miles per hour.
30. If the distribution of vehicle speeds is bell-shaped, find the proportion of vehicles traveling between 60 and 80 miles per hour.
31. If the distribution of vehicle speeds is bell-shaped, find an approximation of the 84th percentile.

Chapter 3 QUIZ

TRUE OR FALSE

1. True or false: If two data sets have the same mean, median, and mode, then the two data sets are identical.
2. True or false: The variance is the square root of the standard deviation.
3. True or false: The Empirical Rule applies for any data set.

FILL IN THE BLANK

4. An _____ is an extremely large or extremely small data value relative to the rest of the data set.
5. The mean can be viewed as the _____ point of the data.
6. The measure of center that is sensitive to the presence of extreme values is the _____.

SHORT ANSWER

7. What do we call summary descriptive measures that are not sensitive to the presence of outliers?
8. Which of the mean, median, and mode may be used for categorical data?
9. For any data set, what is the average of the deviations?
10. What do we use to estimate the mean for each class in a frequency distribution?

CALCULATIONS AND INTERPRETATIONS

Airline Passengers. Refer to the following table for Exercises 11 and 12. 🐦 **portlandair**

Passengers arriving at Portland International Airport, January–April 2007, by airline

Airline	Passengers
Alaska Airlines	98,008
Delta Air Lines	31,054
Horizon Air	117,964
Southwest Airlines	106,178
United Airlines	84,059

11. Calculate the following:
    a. Sample mean
    b. Sample median
12. Calculate the following:
    a. Range
    b. Sample standard deviation
13. **Deaths Due to Heat.** The following frequency distribution contains the numbers of deaths due to heat, by age group, as reported by the National Weather Service for 2006. Find the estimated mean and standard deviation of age. 🐦 **heatdeath**

Age	Deaths due to heat
0–39.99	22
40–49.99	31
50–59.99	51
60–69.99	47
70–79.99	44
80–89.99	44

14. The Department of Agriculture reports that the mean consumption of carbonated beverages per year per American is greater than 52 gallons. A sample of 30 Americans yielded a sample mean of 60 gallons. Assume the standard deviation is 40 gallons. Find the z-scores for the following amounts of carbonated beverage consumption.
    a. 120 gallons
    b. 20 gallons
    c. 100 gallons
    d. 0 gallons
    e. 60 gallons
15. Refer to the information in Exercise 14. Assume the distribution is bell-shaped. (*Note:* Use your knowledge about the Empirical Rule to give a range for the proportions in parts (**b**) and (**d**)).
    a. Find the 50th percentile.
    b. Estimate the proportion of Americans who drink between 29 and 109 gallons per year.
    c. Discuss whether we could find the estimate in (**b**) without assuming that the distribution is bell-shaped.
    d. Estimate the proportion of Americans who drink more than 109 gallons per year.

Use the information in the following table for Exercises 16–20. 🐦 **satmath**

SAT scores for the states with the highest participation rate

State	SAT 1 Math
New York	510
Connecticut	515
Massachusetts	523
New Jersey	514
New Hampshire	521
Maine	501
Pennsylvania	502
Delaware	499

16. Find the following quartiles for SAT 1 Math score:
    a. Q1
    b. Q2
    c. Q3
17. Find the interquartile range of SAT 1 Math score.
18. Find the five-number summary for SAT 1 Math score.
19. Use robust methods to investigate the presence of outliers.
20. Construct a boxplot for SAT 1 Math score.

4

Correlation and Regression

Introduction

In Chapter 4, students learn to examine the relationship between two quantitative variables. Section 4.1 discusses the naturally related topics of scatterplots and correlation. Section 4.2 introduces us to linear regression, while Section 4.3 provides further methods for regression analysis. Both correlation and regression quantify the linear relationship between two quantitative variables.

From the Author

- **Section 4.1 Scatterplots and Correlation**
  - We moved crosstabs and clustered bar graphs from Chapter 4 to Chapter 2. This allows instructors to concentrate on a related set of topics in this chapter: scatterplots, correlation, and regression.
  - Note that we avoid the terminology "independent variable" and "dependent variable" for the x and y variables. This avoids confusion with the notions of independence that we will learn in Chapter 5, "Probability," and Chapter 11, "Categorical Data Analysis."
  - The properties of the correlation coefficient r on page 163 are meant to be viewed simultaneously with the illustrative graphics in Figure 4.6 on page 164.
  - Note the new topic: *Test for Linear Correlation.* The threshold for determining whether x and y are correlated depends on the sample size, so no absolute rule of thumb is correct for all sample sizes. We provide a simple test, using a new table in the Appendix, Table G, for determining whether x and y are indeed correlated. The old rule of thumb was therefore omitted, since it did not allow for difference in sample sizes.

- **Section 4.2 Introduction to Regression**
  - Note that we have changed the form of the regression equation from $\hat{y} = b_0 + b_1 x$ to $\hat{y} = b_1 x + b_0$. This is so instructors who also teach algebra may be comfortable moving from the $y = mx + b$ notation.
  - The temperature example has been reworked to provide nice round numbers for the values of the slope and y intercept of the regression line. We thought it more important for students to concentrate on the new concepts rather than worry about extra decimal places. The bonus is that this percolates throughout the remainder of the chapter, as we calculate the estimated value $\hat{y}$ and the prediction error $y - \hat{y}$.

- **Section 4.3 Further Topics in Regression Analysis**
  - Instructors who prefer not to spend too much time on regression early in the course may decide to delay or omit Section 4.3, "Further Topics in Regression Analysis."
  - Note that our extended example in Section 4.4 also provide nice round numbers for several statistics, including SSE, SST, and SSR.
  - We now provide two ways to calculate SST, (a) the usual method summing the $(y - \bar{y})^2$, and (b) a nice new method, using the fact that the SST is proportional to the variance of the y data. This underscores the method that SST measures the variability in y.

Teaching Tips

Stress the idea that, in this chapter, every element has two variable values associated with it. For example, for each student, there is a height and a weight associated with that student. There must therefore be the same number of x-values as y-values. Clustered bar graphs fit well with crosstabulations but may be omitted if time is short.

In-Class Activities

1. For Sections 4.2 and 4.3, construct a scatterplot and calculate the correlation coefficient and the regression equation for the same data set. One possible example is to use high school GPA (x) and college GPA (y).

2. For each student in the class, obtain the following information: the distance (in miles) his or her (off-campus) home is from the statistics classroom and the time (in minutes) it takes to commute that distance. If the class is large, take a random sample of the students in the class using either (a) technology, or (b) the *Random Sample* applet.

   a. Discuss which variable is the predictor (x) variable, and which variable is the response (y) variable.

   b. Construct a scatterplot of time versus distance.

   c. Is there a positive relationship? Negative relationship? No apparent relationship?

   d. Estimate the value of the correlation coefficient. Will it be positive or negative?

   e. Calculate the correlation coefficient.

   f. Interpret the correlation coefficient.

g. Next, consider the regression of time on distance. Will the slope be positive or negative?

h. Using the scatterplot, visually estimate the slope and *y* intercept of the regression line.

i. Calculate the actual values of the slope and *y* intercept.

j. Carefully interpret the meaning of the value for the slope, using words that someone who has not taken statistics would understand.

k. Interpret the meaning of the *y* intercept.

l. For the person who lives farthest from campus, use the regression equation to estimate the time it takes him or her to get to class.

m. Calculate the prediction error for this student (the difference between the actual commuting time and the estimated commuting time).

n. Can you estimate commuting time for a new student who lives farther away than any other student in the class? If not, clearly explain why not.

Supplements

- StatTutor 4.0–4.5, 5.1–5.4, 5.7, 5.8
- Stats@Work Simulation
  - Picture This, Scatterplots and Correlation; Jan Pepperoni
- EESEE case studies for describing data numerically
  - Visibility of Highway Signs (Question 6(a) on regression)
  - The State of SAT (Questions 6, 7, and 8 on scatterplots, correlation, and regression)
  - Meddling with Olympic Medals (Questions 2, 4, and 6 on scatterplots)
  - Blood Alcohol Content (Questions 1–10 on scatterplots and regression)
  - Is Old Faithful Faithful? (Questions 3 and 4 on scatterplots and regression)

Applets

The *Correlation and Regression* applet is referenced in Chapter 4 to compute correlations and to perform regression analysis. It is used for Exercises 64–66 in Section 4.1, Exercises 77 and 78 in Section 4.2, and Exercises 70–72 in Section 4.3.

Activities and applets that relate to correlation and regression can be found at **http:// mathforum.org/mathtools/sitemap2/ps/**.

The site Online Statistics: An Interactive Multimedia Course of Study has the *Prediction* applet that deals with correlation and regression: **http://onlinestatbook.com/index.html**.

Videos

- *Against All Odds*: **www.learner.org/resources/series65.html**
  - Program 7: Models for Growth
  - Program 8: Describing Relationships
  - Program 9: Correlation

Web Sites

- This site has a collection of 20 class projects, at least one of which deals with the topics of this chapter: **www.amstat.org/publications/jse/v6n3/smith.html**.
- This Texas Instruments Web site has a host of TI-83/84 statistics activities: **http://education.ti.com/educationportal/sites/US/nonProductSingle/activitybook_83_statistics.html**.
- This site lists other sites that do statistical calculations: **http://statpages.org/**.

ImagesBazaar/Getty Images

OVERVIEW

4

Correlation and Regression

CASE STUDY

Female Literacy and Fertility Worldwide

The United Nations estimates that world population levels will continue to increase, to as high as 10 billion people by 2050. These 10 billion people will strain the finite resources of planet Earth and contribute to environmental degradation around the world. Most of this increase will occur in developing countries, which are least equipped to handle and care for the additional population. It is therefore useful to ask, "What policies might governments adopt to help alleviate overpopulation in developing countries?"

One encouraging trend is that fertility rates tend to decrease as the quality of life improves. As developing countries begin to educate girls as well as boys—that is, as the female literacy rate increases—fertility rates tend to come down. In Section 4.2, we examine details of the relationship between these two quantitative variables.

The Big Picture

Where we are coming from, and where we are headed . . .

- Chapter 3 showed us methods for summarizing data using descriptive statistics, but only one variable at a time.

- In Chapter 4, we learn how to analyze the relationship between two quantitative variables using scatterplots, correlation, and regression.

- In Chapter 5, we will learn about probability, which we will need in order to perform statistical inference.

4.1 Scatterplots and Correlation

OBJECTIVES By the end of this section, I will be able to . . .

1   Construct and interpret scatterplots for two quantitative variables.

2   Calculate and interpret the correlation coefficient.

3   Determine whether a linear correlation exists between two variables.

So far, most of our work has looked at ways to describe only one quantitative variable at a time. But there may exist a relationship between two quantitative variables, say, *height* and *weight*, that we would like to graph or quantify. We may also want to use the value of one variable, say, *height,* to predict the value of the other variable, *weight.* In Section 4.1 we explore scatterplots, which are graphs of the relationship between two quantitative variables, and we learn about correlation, which quantifies this relationship.

1 Scatterplots

Whenever you are examining the relationship between two quantitative variables, your best bet is to start with a scatterplot. A **scatterplot** is used to summarize the relationship between two quantitative variables that have been measured on the same element. An example of a scatterplot is given in Figure 4.1.

> A **scatterplot** is a graph of points (x, y), each of which represents one observation from the data set. One of the variables is measured along the horizontal axis and is called the *x variable.* The other variable is measured along the vertical axis and is called the *y variable.*

Often, the value of the *x* variable can be used to predict or estimate the value of the *y* variable. For this reason, the *x* variable is referred to as the *predictor* variable, and the *y* variable is called the *response* variable.

Example 4.1 Constructing a scatterplot

sqrfootsale

Suppose you are interested in moving to Glen Ellyn, Illinois, and would like to purchase a lot upon which to build a new house. Table 4.1 contains a random sample of eight lots for sale in Glen Ellyn, with their square footage and prices. Identify the predictor variable and the response variable, and construct a scatterplot.

Note: The square footage is expressed in 100s of square feet, so that "90" represents 90 × 100 = 9000 square feet. Similarly, the sales price is expressed in $1000s, so that "200" = 200 × 1000 = $200,000.

Table 4.1 Lot square footage and sales price

Lot	x = square footage (100s of sq. ft.)	y = sales price ($1000s)
Harding St.	75	155
Newton Ave.	125	210
Stacy Ct.	125	290
Eastern Ave.	175	360
Second St.	175	250
Sunnybrook Rd.	225	450
Ahlstrand Rd.	225	530
Eastern Ave.	275	635

Note: The predictor variable and response variable are sometimes referred to as the independent variable and dependent variable, respectively. This textbook avoids this terminology, since it may be confused with the definition of independent and dependent events and variables in probability (Chapter 5) and categorical data analysis (Chapter 11).

Solution

It is reasonable to expect that the price of a new lot depends in part on how large the lot is. Thus, we define our predictor variable *x* to be *x = square footage* and our response variable *y* to be *y = sales price.* Next we construct the scatterplot using the data from Table 4.1. Draw the horizontal axis so that it can contain all the values of the predictor (*x*) variable, and similarly for the vertical axis. Then, at each data point (*x, y*), draw a dot. For example, for the Harding Street lot, move along the *x* axis to 75, then go up until you reach a spot level with *y* = 155, at which point you draw a dot. Proceed similarly for all eight properties. The result should look similar to the scatterplot in Figure 4.1.

FIGURE 4.1
Scatterplot of sales price versus square footage.

From this scatterplot, we can see that there is a tendency for larger lots to have higher prices. This is not the case for each observation. For example, the Second Street property is larger than the Stacy Court property but has a lower price. Nevertheless, the overall tendency remains. ■

Now You Can Do
Exercises 9–12.

Developing Your
Statistical Sense

Scatterplot Terminology

Note the terminology in the caption to Figure 4.1. When describing a scatterplot, always indicate the *y* variable first and use the term *versus* (*vs.*) or *against* the *x* variable. This terminology reinforces the notion that the *y* variable depends on the *x* variable. ◢

The relationship between two quantitative variables can take many different forms. Four of the most common relationships are shown in Figures 4.2a–4.2d.

Note the phrase, "as *x* increases in value . . ." When interpreting scatterplots, we always move from left to right.

- **Positive linear relationship** between *x* and *y* (Figure 4.2a): Smaller values of the *x* variable are associated with smaller values of the *y* variable; larger values of *x* are associated with larger values of *y*. In other words, as *x* increases, *y* also tends to increase.

- **Negative linear relationship** between *x* and *y* (Figure 4.2b): Smaller values of the *x* variable are associated with larger values of the *y* variable; larger values of *x* are associated with smaller values of *y*. In other words, as *x* increases, *y* tends to decrease.

- **No apparent relationship** (Figure 4.2c): The values of the *x* variable are not associated with any particular range of values of the *y* variable. In other words, as *x* increases, *y* tends to remain unchanged.

- **Nonlinear relationship** (Figure 4.2d): The *x* variable and the *y* variable are related, but not in a way that can be approximated using a straight line.

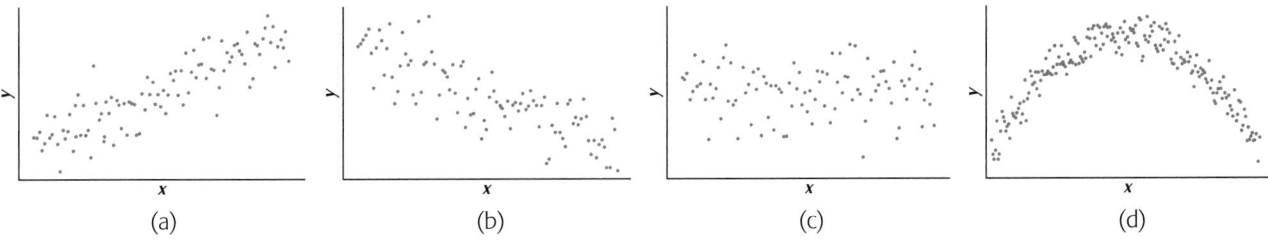

FIGURE 4.2 Scatterplots of (a) a positive relationship; (b) a negative relationship; (c) no apparent relationship; (d) a nonlinear relationship.

Example 4.2 Characterize the relationship between two variables using a scatterplot

Using Figure 4.1, characterize the relationship between lot square footage and lot price.

Solution

The scatterplot in Figure 4.1 most resembles Figure 4.2a, where a positive relationship exists between the variables. Thus, smaller lot sizes tend to be associated with lower prices, and larger lot sizes tend to be associated with higher prices. Put another way, as the lot size increases, the lot price tends to increase as well. ■

Now You Can Do
Exercises 13–20.

2 Correlation Coefficient

Scatterplots provide a visual description of the relationship between two quantitative variables. The *correlation coefficient* is a numerical measure for quantifying the linear relationship between two quantitative variables. Table 4.2 contains the low and high temperatures in degrees Fahrenheit (°F) for 10 American cities on a particular winter day. The variables are $x = $ *low temperature* and $y = $ *high temperature*. Applying what we have just learned, we construct a scatterplot of the data set, which is presented in Figure 4.3.

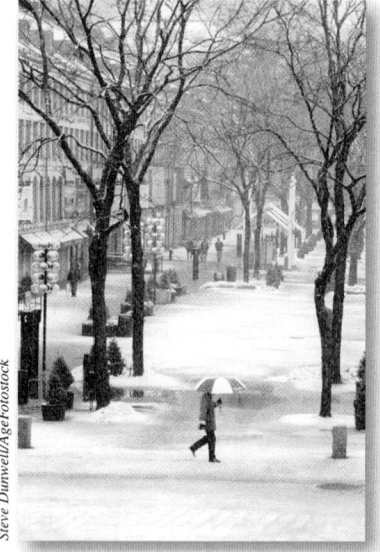

Steve Dunwell/AgeFotostock

Table 4.2 Low and high temperatures, in degrees Fahrenheit, of 10 American cities

City	$x = $ low temp.	$y = $ high temp.	City	$x = $ low temp.	$y = $ high temp.
Minneapolis	10	29	Washington, DC	40	50
Boston	20	37	Las Vegas	40	58
Chicago	20	43	Memphis	50	64
Philadelphia	30	41	Dallas	50	70
Cincinnati	30	49	Miami	60	74

FIGURE 4.3
Scatterplot of high versus low temperatures for 10 American cities.

Figure 4.3 shows us that there is a positive relationship between the high temperature and the low temperature of a city. That is, colder low temperatures are associated with colder high temperatures. Warmer low temperatures are associated with warmer high

temperatures. In this section we seek to *quantify this relationship* between two numerical variables, using the **correlation coefficient r.** The correlation coefficient r (sometimes known as the *Pearson product moment correlation coefficient*) measures the strength and direction of the linear relationship between two variables. By *linear,* we mean *straight line.* The correlation coefficient does not measure the strength of a curved relationship between two variables.

The **correlation coefficient r** measures the strength and direction of the linear relationship between two variables. The correlation coefficient r is

$$r = \frac{\sum(x - \bar{x})(y - \bar{y})}{(n - 1)s_x s_y}$$

where s_x is the sample standard deviation of the x data values, and s_y is the sample standard deviation of the y data values.

Example 4.3 Calculating the correlation coefficient r

highlowtemp

Find the value of the correlation coefficient r for the temperature data in Table 4.2.

Solution

We will outline the steps used in calculating the value of r using the temperature data.

Step 1 Calculate the respective sample means, $\bar{x}$ and $\bar{y}$.

$$\bar{x} = \frac{\sum x}{n} = \frac{10 + 20 + 20 + 30 + 30 + 40 + 40 + 50 + 50 + 60}{10} = \frac{350}{10} = 35.0$$

$$\bar{y} = \frac{\sum y}{n} = \frac{29 + 37 + 43 + 41 + 49 + 50 + 58 + 64 + 70 + 74}{10} = \frac{515}{10} = 51.5$$

Step 2 Construct a table, as shown here in Table 4.3.

Table 4.3 Calculation table for the correlation coefficient r

City	x	y	$(x - \bar{x}) =$ $(x - 35)$	$(x - \bar{x})^2 =$ $(x - 35)^2$	$(y - \bar{y}) =$ $(y - 51.5)$	$(y - \bar{y})^2 =$ $(y - 51.5)^2$	$(x - \bar{x})(y - \bar{y}) =$ $(x - 35)(y - 51.5)$
Minneapolis	10	29	−25	625	−22.5	506.25	562.5
Boston	20	37	−15	225	−14.5	210.25	217.5
Chicago	20	43	−15	225	−8.5	72.25	127.5
Philadelphia	30	41	−5	25	−10.5	110.25	52.5
Cincinnati	30	49	−5	25	−2.5	6.25	12.5
Washington, DC	40	50	5	25	−1.5	2.25	−7.5
Las Vegas	40	58	5	25	6.5	42.25	32.5
Memphis	50	64	15	225	12.5	156.25	187.5
Dallas	50	70	15	225	18.5	342.25	277.5
Miami	60	74	25	625	22.5	506.25	562.5
				$\sum(x - \bar{x})^2$ $= 2250$		$\sum(y - \bar{y})^2$ $= 1954.5$	$\sum(x - \bar{x})(y - \bar{y})$ $= 2025$

Note on Rounding: Whenever you calculate a quantity that will be needed for later calculations, do not round. Round only when you arrive at the final answer. Here, since the quantities s_x and s_y are used to calculate the correlation coefficient r, neither of them is rounded until the end of the calculation.

Step 3 Calculate the respective sample standard deviations s_x and s_y. Using the sums calculated from Table 4.3, we have

$$s_x = \sqrt{\frac{\sum(x-\bar{x})^2}{n-1}} = \sqrt{\frac{2250}{10-1}} \approx 15.8113883 \qquad \text{and}$$

$$s_y = \sqrt{\frac{\sum(y-\bar{y})^2}{n-1}} = \sqrt{\frac{1954.5}{10-1}} \approx 14.73657581$$

Step 4 Put these values all together in the formula for the correlation coefficient r:

$$r = \frac{\sum(x-\bar{x})(y-\bar{y})}{(n-1)s_x s_y} = \frac{2025}{(9)(15.8113883)(14.73657581)} \approx 0.9656$$

The correlation coefficient r for the high and low temperatures is 0.9656. ∎

Now You Can Do
Exercises 21–24.

What Does This Formula Mean?

The Correlation Coefficient r

Let's analyze the definition formula for the correlation coefficient r. When would r be positive, and when would it be negative? We see that the formula

$$r = \frac{\sum(x-\bar{x})(y-\bar{y})}{(n-1)s_x s_y}$$

consists of a ratio. Note that the denominator can never be negative, since it is the product of three non-negative values (standard deviations can never be negative). Therefore, the numerator determines whether r will be positive or negative. We know that $x-\bar{x}$ is positive whenever the data value x is greater than $\bar{x}$, and negative when x is less than $\bar{x}$. Similarly for $y-\bar{y}$. The numerator of r is the sum of the products $(x-\bar{x}) \cdot (y-\bar{y})$. There are four cases (or regions, illustrated in Figure 4.4) that describe when the product $(x-\bar{x})(y-\bar{y})$ will be positive or negative. Note that Figure 4.4 is centered at the point $(\bar{x}, \bar{y})$.

FIGURE 4.4
The four regions for determining whether r will tend to be positive or negative.

Region 2	Region 1
$(x-\bar{x})<0$	$(x-\bar{x})>0$
$(y-\bar{y})>0$	$(y-\bar{y})>0$
$(x-\bar{x})(y-\bar{y})<0$	$(x-\bar{x})(y-\bar{y})>0$
$r<0$	$r>0$
point $(\bar{x}, \bar{y})$	line $y=\bar{y}$
Region 3	Region 4
$(x-\bar{x})<0$	$(x-\bar{x})>0$
$(y-\bar{y})<0$	$(y-\bar{y})<0$
$(x-\bar{x})(y-\bar{y})>0$	$(x-\bar{x})(y-\bar{y})<0$
$r>0$	$r<0$
line $x=\bar{x}$	

Data values that fall in Regions 1 and 3 will tend to make the value of r positive, while data values that fall in Regions 2 and 4 will tend to make the value of r negative. The summation in the numerator of r acts as a blender, combining the contributions of all the various data values falling in all the various regions.

- If most of the data values fall in Regions 1 and 3, then r will tend to be positive.
- If most of the data values fall in Regions 2 and 4, then r will tend to be negative.
- If the four regions share the data values more or less equally, then r will be near zero. ◢

Let's explore how our high and low temperature data fit into the above framework. The mean low temperature is $\bar{x} = 35°F$, while the mean high temperature is $\bar{y} = 51.5°F$. We find the point $(\bar{x}, \bar{y}) = (35, 51.5)$ in our scatterplot of the high and low temperatures, draw the lines $x = \bar{x} = 35$ and $y = \bar{y} = 51.5$, and mark out our four regions, as shown in Figure 4.5. Note that nine of the ten data points fall in Regions 1 and 3. Therefore, we expect the value of r for this data set to be positive, which is indeed the case, since we observed $r = 0.9656$ in Example 4.3.

FIGURE 4.5
Nearly all of the temperature data points lie in Regions 1 and 3, making r positive.

Next we outline the properties of the correlation coefficient r.

1. The correlation coefficient r always takes on values between -1 and 1, inclusive. That is, $-1 \leq r \leq 1$.

2. When $r = +1$, a perfect positive relationship exists between x and y. See Figure 4.6a.

3. Values of r near $+1$ indicate a positive relationship between x and y (Figures 4.6b and 4.6c):
   - The closer r gets to $+1$, the stronger the evidence for a positive relationship.
   - The variables are said to be **positively correlated.**
   - As x increases, y tends to increase.

4. When $r = -1$, a perfect negative relationship exists between x and y. See Figure 4.6d.

5. Values of r near -1 indicate a negative relationship between x and y (Figures 4.6e and 4.6f):
   - The closer r gets to -1, the stronger the evidence for a negative relationship.
   - The variables are said to be **negatively correlated.**
   - As x increases, y tends to decrease.

6. Values of r near 0 indicate there is no linear relationship between x and y (Figure 4.6g):
   - The closer r gets to 0, the weaker the evidence for a linear relationship.
   - The variables are **not linearly correlated.**
   - A *nonlinear* relationship may exist between x and y. See Figure 4.6h.

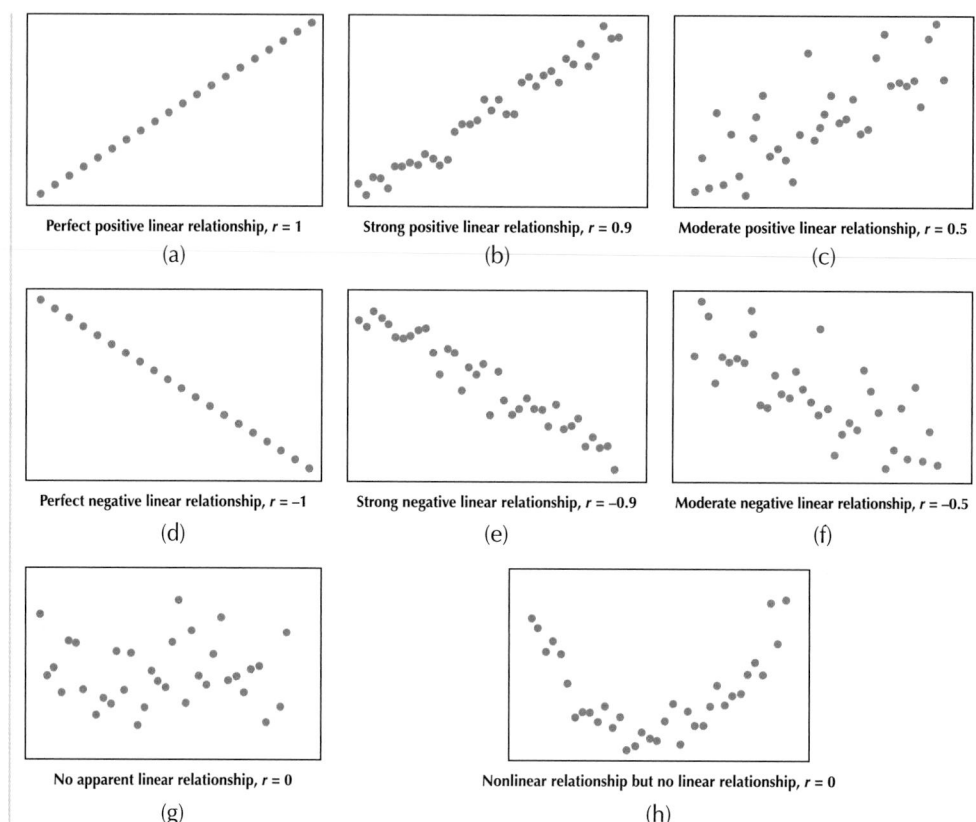

FIGURE 4.6
Scatterplots and correlation coefficients of the various types of relationships between x and y.

Developing Your Statistical Sense

Correlation Is Not Causation

If we conclude that two variables are correlated, it does not necessarily follow that one variable *causes* the other to occur. For example, in the late 1940s, prior to the development of a vaccine for the disease polio, analysts noticed a strong correlation between the amount of ice cream consumed nationwide and higher levels of the onset of polio. Some doctors went on to recommend eliminating ice cream as a way to fight polio. But did ice cream really *cause* polio? No. Ice cream consumption and polio outbreaks both peaked in the hot summer months, and so were *correlated* seasonally. Ice cream did not cause polio. After the development of the polio vaccine by Jonas Salk in the 1950s, the disease disappeared from most countries in the world. ◢

Example 4.4 Interpreting the correlation coefficient

Interpret the correlation coefficient found in Example 4.3.

Here we have made a judgment that 0.9656 is close to 1. Later in this section, we will learn a more precise method for making such decisions.

Now You Can Do
Exercises 25–28.

Solution

In Example 4.3, we found the correlation coefficient for the relationship between high and low temperatures to be $r = 0.9656$. This value of r is very close to the maximum value $r = 1$. We would therefore say that high and low temperatures for these ten American cities are positively correlated. As low temperature increases, high temperatures also tend to increase. ■

The following computational formula may be used as an equivalent of the definition formula for the correlation coefficient r.

> **Equivalent Computational Formula for Calculating the Correlation Coefficient r**
>
> $$r = \frac{\sum xy - \left(\sum x \sum y\right)/n}{\sqrt{\left[\sum x^2 - \left(\sum x\right)^2/n\right]\left[\sum y^2 - \left(\sum y\right)^2/n\right]}}$$

Example 4.5 — Using the computational formula to calculate r

Use the computational formula to calculate the correlation coefficient r for the relationship between square footage and sales price of the eight home lots for sale in Glen Ellyn from Example 4.1 (page 158).

Table 4.4 Calculation table for using the computation formula for r

x = square footage	y = sales price	x^2	y^2	xy
75	155	5625	24,025	11,625
125	210	15,625	44,100	26,250
125	290	15,625	84,100	36,250
175	360	30,625	129,600	63,000
175	250	30,625	62,500	43,750
225	450	50,625	202,500	101,250
225	530	50,625	280,900	119,250
275	635	75,625	403,225	174,625
$\sum x = 1400$	$\sum y = 2880$	$\sum x^2 = 275{,}000$	$\sum y^2 = 1{,}230{,}950$	$\sum xy = 576{,}000$

From Table 4.4 we have $n = 8$ and the following summations:

$$\sum x = 1400, \quad \sum y = 2880, \quad \sum x^2 = 275{,}000, \quad \sum y^2 = 1{,}230{,}950, \quad \sum xy = 576{,}000.$$

Substituting into the computational formula, we have

(margin note) Note that this numerator of r equals 72,000. We shall use this fact for Example 4.9 in Section 4.2.

$$r = \frac{576{,}000 - (1400)(2880)/8}{\sqrt{[275{,}000 - (1400)^2/8][1{,}230{,}950 - (2880)^2/8]}} \approx 0.9434$$

The value of r is close to 1, so it appears that square footage and sales price are positively correlated. But we need the next topic, the *comparison test,* to determine this conclusively. ■

3 Test for Linear Correlation

We have seen that values of the correlation coefficient r that are close to $+1$ indicate a positive linear relationship between x and y. However, what do we mean by "close to $+1$"? There is a simple comparison test that will tell us whether or not a positive correlation exists between the variables. In general, the comparison test will help us determine whether the correlation coefficient is strong enough to conclude that the variables are correlated.

> **Comparison Test for Linear Correlation**
>
> 1. Find the absolute value of the correlation coefficient r, denoted as $|r|$. For example, $|0.5| = 0.5$ and $|-0.4| = 0.4$.
>
> 2. Turn to the Table of Critical Values for the Correlation Coefficient (Table G in the Appendix), and select the row corresponding to the sample size n.
>
> 3. Compare the absolute value of your correlation coefficient $|r|$ from Step 1 to the critical value from the table from Step 2,
>
>   a. If $|r|$ is greater than the critical value, then you can conclude that x and y are **linearly correlated.**
>
>   i. If $r > 0$, then x and y are **positively correlated.**
>
>   ii. If $r < 0$, then x and y are **negatively correlated.**
>
>   b. If $|r|$ is not greater than the critical value, then x and y are **not linearly correlated.**

Example 4.6 Determining whether x and y are correlated, and interpreting the results

For the following scenarios, determine whether x and y are correlated, and interpret the results.

a. $r = -0.4$, $n = 25$
b. $r = -0.4$, $n = 24$
c. The temperature data from Example 4.3
d. The square footage and sales price data from Example 4.5

Solution

a. $\boxed{\text{Step 1}}$ $|r| = |-0.4| = 0.4$.

$\boxed{\text{Step 2}}$ From Table G in the Appendix, the critical value for $n = 25$ is 0.396.

$\boxed{\text{Step 3}}$ 0.4 is > 0.396, so we conclude that x and y are correlated. Since $r < 0$, we can state that x and y are negatively correlated. As x increases, y tends to decrease.

b. $\boxed{\text{Step 1}}$ $|r| = |-0.4| = 0.4$.

$\boxed{\text{Step 2}}$ From Table G in the Appendix, the critical value for $n = 24$ is 0.404.

$\boxed{\text{Step 3}}$ 0.4 is not > 0.404, so we conclude that x and y are not linearly correlated.

c. From Example 4.3, we have $r = 0.9656$ and $n = 10$.

$\boxed{\text{Step 1}}$ $|r| = |0.9656| = 0.9656$.

$\boxed{\text{Step 2}}$ From Table G in the Appendix, the critical value for $n = 10$ is 0.632.

$\boxed{\text{Step 3}}$ 0.9656 is > 0.632, so we conclude that low temperature and high temperature are correlated. Since $r > 0$, we can state that low temperature and high temperature are positively correlated. As low temperatures increase, high temperatures tend to increase.

d. From Example 4.5, we have $r = 0.9434$ and $n = 8$.

$\boxed{\text{Step 1}}$ $|r| = |0.9434| = 0.9434$.

$\boxed{\text{Step 2}}$ From Table G in the Appendix, the critical value for $n = 8$ is 0.707.

$\boxed{\text{Step 3}}$ 0.9434 is > 0.707, so we conclude that square footage and sales price are correlated. Since $r > 0$, we can state that square footage and sales price are positively correlated. As square footage increases, sales price tends to increase. ■

Now You Can Do
Exercises 29–32.

The *Correlation and Regression* applet allows you to insert your own data values and see how the value of the correlation coefficient changes.

STEP-BY-STEP TECHNOLOGY GUIDE: Tables and Graphs for Two Variables sqrfootsale

TI-83/84

Constructing a Scatterplot for Data in Table 4.1 (page 158)
Step 1   Enter the *x* variable (square footage) into **L1** and the
y variable (sales price) into **L2**.
Step 2   Press **2nd**, then **Y=** for the STAT PLOTS menu.
Step 3   Select **1**, and press **ENTER**. Select **ON**, and press
ENTER.
Step 4   Select the scatterplots icon (see Figure 4.7), and press
ENTER.
Step 5   Select **L1** for **Xlist**, and **L2** for **Ylist**.

Step 6   Press **ZOOM**, choose **9: ZoomStat**, and press **ENTER**.
The scatterplot is shown in Figure 4.8.

FIGURE 4.7   **FIGURE 4.8**

Correlation Coefficient *r*
Step 1   Turn on the diagnostics, as follows. Press **2nd 0**
(catalog). Then scroll down and select **DiagnosticOn**. Press
ENTER twice to turn the diagnostics on. This will give you
more output results for regression and correlation.

Step 2   Enter your *x* data into **L1** and your *y* data into **L2**.
Step 3   Press **STAT**, select **CALC**, and select **LinReg (ax+b)**.
Press **ENTER** twice to get the results. The correlation coefficient
r is given, among other statistics used in regression.

EXCEL
Scatterplots
Step 1   Enter your *x* variable and your *y* variable in two
neighboring columns, with the *x* variable on the left. Make sure
the first entry in each column is the variable name. Select the
two columns.
Step 2   Click **Insert > Scatter** (in **Chart** section). See
Figure 4.9.

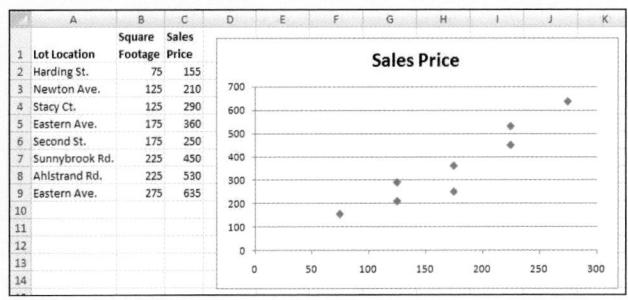

FIGURE 4.9   Excel scatterplot.

Correlation Coefficient *r*
Step 1   Make sure the Data Analysis add-in is activated. Click
on the **Data** tab, then the **Data Analysis** package, then select
Correlation and click **OK**.

Step 2   Click on the box next to **Input Range**, then highlight
the data, and click **OK**.

MINITAB
Scatterplots
Step 1   Enter the data into two columns.
Step 2   Click **Graph > Scatterplot**.

Step 3   Click on the cell under **Y**, and double-click on your
y variable; then click on the cell under **X**, and double-click on
your *x* variable. Then click **OK**.

Correlation Coefficient *r*
Step 1   Enter your *x* data into column **C1** and your *y* data into
column **C2**.
Step 2   Click on **Stat**, highlight **Basic Statistics,** and select
Correlation.

Step 3   Choose the variables you wish to analyze and
click **OK**.

CRUNCHIT!
We will use the data from Example 4.1 (page 158).

Scatterplots
Step 1   Click **File . . .** then highlight **Load from Larose2e . . .**
Chapter 4 . . . and click on **Example 4.1**.

Step 2   Click **Graphics** and select **Scatterplot**. For **X** select
the predictor (*x*) variable **Square feet**. For **Y** select the response
(*y*) variable **Price**. Then click **Calculate**.

Correlation Coefficient *r*
Step 1   Click **File . . .** then highlight **Load from Larose2e . . .**
Chapter 4 . . . and click on **Example 4.1**.

Step 2   Click **Statistics** and select **Correlation**.
Step 3   Click the boxes next to **Square feet** and **Price**. Then
click **Calculate**.

Section 4.1 Summary

1 For two quantitative variables, scatterplots summarize the relationship by plotting all the (x, y) points.

2 The correlation coefficient r is a measure of the strength of linear association between two numeric variables. Values of r close to 1 indicate that the variables are positively correlated. Values of r close to -1 indicate that the variables are negatively correlated. Values of r close to 0 indicate that the variables are not correlated.

3 A comparison test may be used to determine whether the value of the correlation coefficient r is strong enough to conclude that x and y are correlated.

Section 4.1 Exercises

CLARIFYING THE CONCEPTS

1. When investigating the relationship between two quantitative variables, what graph should you use first?
2. In your own words, explain what the correlation coefficient measures. What is the symbol that we use for the correlation coefficient?
3. What is the range of values the correlation coefficient can take?
4. What do the following values of r indicate about the relationship between two variables? What can we say about the variables?
   a. A value of r close to 1
   b. A value of r close to -1
   c. A value of r close to 0
5. Why do we call x the predictor variable?
6. Suppose two quantitative variables have a positive relationship. What can we say about the values of the y variable as the x variable increases?
7. Suppose two quantitative variables have a negative relationship. What can we say about the values of the y variable as the x variable increases?
8. Suppose that the correlation coefficient r equals 0. Does this mean that x and y have no relationship? Explain.

PRACTICING THE TECHNIQUES
For Exercises 9–12, construct a scatterplot of the relationship between x and y.

9.

x	y
1	2
2	2
3	3
4	4
5	4

10.

x	y
10	10
20	9
30	8
40	8
50	7

11.

x	y
-3	-5
-1	-15
3	-20
4	-25
5	-30

12.

x	y
0	11
20	11
40	16
60	21
80	26

For Exercises 13–20, do the following:
   a. Characterize the relationship between x and y.
   b. State what happens to the values of the y variable as the x-values increase.

13.

14.

15.

16.

17.

18.

19.

20.

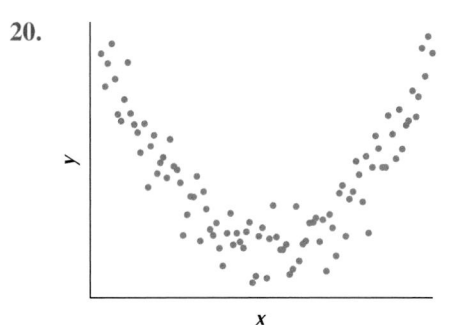

For Exercises 21–24, calculate the correlation coefficient *r* for the indicated data.

21. The data from Exercise 9
22. The data from Exercise 10
23. The data from Exercise 11
24. The data from Exercise 12

For Exercises 25–28, interpret the value of the correlation coefficient *r* in the indicated exercise.

25. From Exercise 21
26. From Exercise 22
27. From Exercise 23
28. From Exercise 24

For Exercises 29–32, use the comparison test to determine whether *x* and *y* are correlated, using the data and the value of *r* from the indicated exercises.

29. The data from Exercise 9 and the value of *r* from Exercise 21
30. The data from Exercise 10 and the value of *r* from Exercise 22
31. The data from Exercise 11 and the value of *r* from Exercise 23
32. The data from Exercise 12 and the value of *r* from Exercise 24

APPLYING THE CONCEPTS

For Exercises 33–36, identify which of the scatterplots in **i–iv** represents the data set with the following correlation coefficients:

i.

ii.

iii.

iv.

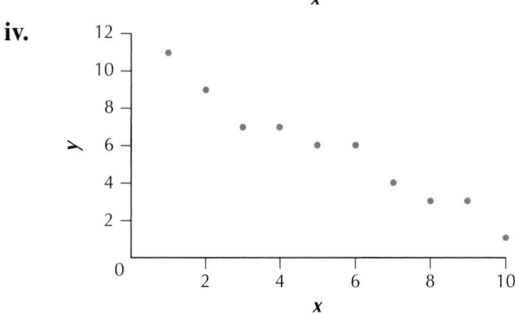

33. Near 1
34. Near zero
35. Near −0.5
36. Near −1

In Exercises 37–40, the values for *x* and *y* in each scatterplot are integer-valued. For each scatterplot, (a) reconstruct the original data set, and (b) calculate the correlation coefficient for the data.

37. The data in scatterplot i
38. The data in scatterplot ii
39. The data in scatterplot iii
40. The data in scatterplot iv

For Exercises 41–44, determine whether the correlation coefficient *r* is strong enough to conclude that *x* and *y* are correlated for the indicated data.

41. The data in scatterplot i
42. The data in scatterplot ii
43. The data in scatterplot iii
44. The data in scatterplot iv

Education and Unemployment. Does it pay to stay in school? Use the table of U.S. Census Bureau data for Exercises 45–48. 🖱 **edunemploy**

x = years of education	*y* = unemployment rate
5	16.8
7.5	17.1
8	15.3
10	20.6
12	11.7
14	8.1
16	3.8

45. Do the following.
  a. Construct a scatterplot of the relationship between *x* and *y*.
  b. Describe the relationship between *x* and *y*.
46. Calculate and interpret the correlation coefficient for *x* and *y*.
47. Determine whether we can conclude that years of education and unemployment rate are linearly correlated.
48. Based on your work in Exercises 45–47, in general, does it pay to stay in school? State your evidence.

Brain and Body Weight. A study compared the body weight (in kilograms) and brain weight (in grams) for a sample of mammals, with the results shown in the following table. Use the following data for Exercises 49–51. 🖱 **brainbody**

x = body weight (kg)	*y* = brain weight (g)
52.16	440
60	81
27.66	115
85	325
36.33	119.5
100	157
35	56
62	1320
83	98.2
55.5	175

49. Construct a scatterplot of the data. Describe the apparent relationship, if any, between the variables. Based on the scatterplot alone, would you say that *x* and *y* are positively correlated, negatively correlated, or not correlated?
50. Calculate and interpret the value of the correlation coefficient *r*.
51. Does this agree with your judgment from Exercise 49? Determine whether we can conclude that body weight and brain weight are correlated.

Batting Average and Age. For Exercises 52 and 53, refer to the following scatterplot of batting average against player age.

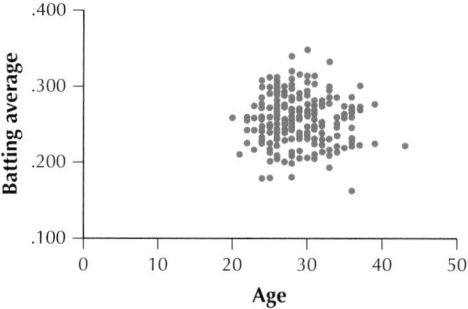

52. Estimate the correlation coefficient *r*. Is the correlation coefficient positive, negative, or near zero?
53. Interpret the estimated value of *r* for this data set.

BRINGING IT ALL TOGETHER
Country and Hip-Hop CDs. Use the information in the table for Exercises 54–58. The table contains the number of country music CDs and the number of hip-hop CDs owned by six randomly selected students. 🖱 **countryhip**

	Student					
	1	2	3	4	5	6
Hip-hop CDs owned (*y*)	10	12	1	3	6	1
Country CDs owned (*x*)	1	3	11	8	5	27

54. Investigate the relationship.
  a. Construct a scatterplot of the variables. Make sure the *y* variable goes on the *y* axis.
  b. What type of relationship do these variables have: positive, negative, or no apparent linear relationship?
  c. Will the correlation coefficient be positive, negative, or near zero?
55. Calculate and interpret the correlation coefficient.
  a. Compute the value of the correlation coefficient.
  b. Does this value for *r* concur with your judgment in part **(a)** of the previous exercise?
  c. Interpret the meaning of this value of the correlation coefficient.
56. Determine whether we can conclude that *x* and *y* are correlated.

57. Transformation. Add 5 to each value for *y*.
  a. Redraw the scatterplot. Comment on the similarity or difference from the scatterplot in Exercise 54**(a)**.
  b. Recalculate the correlation coefficient.
  c. Compare your answers from Exercise 57**(b)** and Exercise 55**(a)**.
  d. Compose a rule that states the behavior of the correlation coefficient *r* when a constant is added to each *y* data value.

58. Suppose that, starting with the original data in the table, we added a certain unknown constant amount to each value for *x*.
  a. *Without redrawing the scatterplot,* describe how this change would affect the scatterplot you drew in Exercise 54**(a)**.
  b. *Without recalculating the correlation coefficient,* state what you think the effect of this change would be on the correlation coefficient. Why do you think that?
  c. Compose a rule that states the behavior of the correlation coefficient *r* when a constant is added to each *x* data value.

Refer to the following table for Exercises 59–61. **statesat**

Mean SAT scores for the five states with the best participation rate

State	SAT Reading	SAT Math
New York	497	510
Connecticut	515	515
Massachusetts	518	523
New Jersey	501	514
New Hampshire	522	521

59. Construct a scatterplot of the data, with *x* = SAT Reading and *y* = SAT Math. Describe the apparent relationship, if any, between the variables. Based on the scatterplot, would you say that *x* and *y* are positively correlated, negatively correlated, or not correlated?
60. Calculate the value of the correlation coefficient, using the following steps.
  a. Calculate the respective sample means $\bar{x}$ and $\bar{y}$.
  b. Construct a table like Table 4.3, as follows.
  i. For each observation, calculate the deviations $(x - \bar{x})$ and $(y - \bar{y})$.
  ii. For each observation, calculate $(x - \bar{x})^2$, $(y - \bar{y})^2$, and $(x - \bar{x})(y - \bar{y})$.
  iii. Calculate the following sums: $\Sigma(x - \bar{x})^2$, $\Sigma(y - \bar{y})^2$, and $\Sigma(x - \bar{x})(y - \bar{y})$.
  c. Calculate the respective sample standard deviations s_x and s_y.
  d. Put these all together in the formula for the correlation coefficient *r*.
  e. Using technology, confirm the value you calculated in **(d)**.

61. Interpret the meaning of the correlation coefficient you found in Exercise 60, using at least two sentences. Does this agree with your judgment from Exercise 59?

CONSTRUCT YOUR OWN DATA SETS
62. Describe two variables from real life that would have a value of *r* close to 1. Explain why they are positively correlated.
63. Create a sample of five observations from each of your variables in the previous exercise, and put them into a table similar to Table 4.2 (page 160). Next, construct a scatterplot of the variables. Finally, draw a single straight line through the data points in the plot in a manner that you think best approximates the relationship between the variables.

APPLET Use the *Correlation and Regression* applet for Exercises 64–66.

64. Create a set of *n* = 10 points such that the correlation coefficient *r* takes approximately the following values. Note that you can drag points up or down to adjust your value of *r*.
  a. *r* = 0.90
  b. *r* = −0.90
  c. *r* = 0.00
65. Describe the relationship between the variables for each of the sets of points in the previous exercise.
66. Select "Show mean X and mean Y lines." Create a set of *n* = 4 points such that the correlation coefficient *r* takes approximately the following values. Note that you can drag points up or down to adjust your value of *r*.
  a. *r* = 0.70
  b. *r* = −0.70
  c. *r* = 0.00

4.2 Introduction to Regression

OBJECTIVES By the end of this section, I will be able to . . .

1 Calculate the value and understand the meaning of the slope and the *y* intercept of the regression line.

2 Predict values of *y* for given values of *x*, and calculate the prediction error for a given prediction.

1 The Regression Line

Table 4.2 Temperature data

City	x = low temp.	y = high temp.
Minneapolis	10	29
Boston	20	37
Chicago	20	43
Philadelphia	30	41
Cincinnati	30	49
Wash., DC	40	50
Las Vegas	40	58
Memphis	50	64
Dallas	50	70
Miami	60	74

In Section 4.1 we learned about the *correlation coefficient*. Here, in Section 4.2, we will learn how to approximate the linear relationship between two numerical variables using the regression line and the regression equation. For convenience, we repeat Table 4.2 here.

Consider again Figure 4.3 (page 160), the scatterplot of the high and low temperatures for ten American cities, from Table 4.2. The data points generally seem to follow a roughly linear path. We may in fact draw a straight line from the lower left to the upper right to approximate this relatively linear path. Such a straight line, called a **regression line,** is shown in Figure 4.10.

FIGURE 4.10 Scatterplot of high versus low temperatures, with regression line.

As you may recall from high school algebra, the equation of a straight line may be written as $y = mx + b$. We will write the **equation of the regression line** similarly as $\hat{y} = b_1 x + b_0$.

The "hat" over the y (pronounced "y-hat") indicates that this is an estimate of y and not necessarily an actual value of y.

Equation of the Regression Line

The **equation of the regression line** that approximates the relationship between x and y is

$$\hat{y} = b_1 x + b_0$$

where the *regression coefficients* are the **slope,** b_1, and the **y intercept,** b_0. Do not let $\hat{y}$ and $\bar{y}$ be confused. $\hat{y}$ is the predicted value of y from the regression equation. $\bar{y}$ represents the mean of the y values in the data set. The equations of these coefficients are

$$b_1 = \frac{\sum(x - \bar{x})(y - \bar{y})}{\sum(x - \bar{x})^2} \qquad\qquad b_0 = \bar{y} - (b_1 \cdot \bar{x})$$

Note that all of the quantities needed to calculate b_0 and b_1 have already been computed in the formula for r. In particular, the numerators for b_1 and r are exactly the same.

There are an infinite number of different straight lines that could approximate the relationship between high and low temperatures. Why did we choose this one? Because this is the *least-squares* regression line, which is the most widely used linear approximation for bivariate relationships. We will learn more about least squares in Section 4.3.

Example 4.7 Calculating the regression coefficients b_0 and b_1

The scatterplot is shown in Figure 4.10 on p. 172.

Find the value of the regression coefficients b_0 and b_1 for the temperature data in Table 4.2.

Solution

We will outline the steps used in calculating the value of b_1 using the temperature data.

Step 1 Calculate the respective sample means $\bar{x}$ and $\bar{y}$. We have already done this in Example 4.3: $\bar{x} = 35$ and $\bar{y} = 51.5$.

Step 2 Construct a table like Table 4.3, except that the $(y - \bar{y})^2$ column is not needed. Write down the values of $\sum(x - \bar{x})^2$ and $\sum(x - \bar{x})(y - \bar{y})$. We have already done this in Example 4.3, and we have

$$\sum(x - \bar{x})^2 = 2250 \text{ and } \sum(x - \bar{x})(y - \bar{y}) = 2025$$

Step 3 Use the statistics from Steps 1 and 2 to calculate b_1:

$$b_1 = \frac{\sum(x - \bar{x})(y - \bar{y})}{\sum(x - \bar{x})^2} = \frac{2025}{2250} = 0.9$$

Step 4 Use the statistics from Steps 1–3 to calculate b_0:

$$b_0 = \bar{y} - (b_1 \cdot \bar{x}) = 51.5 - (0.9)(35) = 20$$

Thus, the equation of the regression line for the temperature data is

$$\hat{y} = 0.9x + 20$$

Since y and x represent high and low temperatures, respectively, this equation is read as follows: "The estimated high temperature for an American city is 0.9 times the low temperature for that city plus 20 degrees Fahrenheit." ∎

Now You Can Do
Exercises 13–20.

What Do These Numbers Mean?

Interpreting the Slope and the y Intercept

- In statistics, we interpret the slope of the regression line as the *estimated change in y per unit increase in x.*
- In our temperature example, the units are degrees Fahrenheit, so we interpret our value $b_1 = 0.9$ as follows:
  - "For each increase of 1°F in low temperature, the estimated high temperature increases by 0.9°F."
- The y intercept is interpreted as the *estimated value of y when x equals zero.*
- Here, we interpret our value $b_0 = 20$ as follows:
  - "When the low temperature is 0°F, the estimated high temperature is 20°F." ◢

Now You Can Do
Exercises 21–28.

Recall from Section 4.1 that the correlation coefficient for the temperature data is $r = 0.9656$. Is it a coincidence that both the slope and the correlation coefficient are positive? Not at all.

Relationship Between Slope and Correlation Coefficient

The slope b_1 of the regression line and the correlation coefficient r always have the same sign.

- b_1 is positive if and only if r is positive.
- b_1 is negative if and only if r is negative.

Hence, when we found in Section 4.1 that the correlation coefficient between high and low temperatures was positive, we could have immediately concluded that the slope of the regression line was also positive.

Example 4.8 Correlation and regression using technology

Other ways to describe regression include

- "Perform a regression of the *y* variable versus the *x* variable."
- "Regress the *y* variable on the *x* variable."

Note that the first variable is always the *y* variable and the second variable is always the *x* variable. For example, in Example 4.8 we could write, "Perform a regression of high temperature against low temperature."

Use technology to find the correlation coefficient r and the regression coefficients b_1 and b_0 for the temperature data in Example 4.3.

Solution

The instructions for using technology for correlation and regression are provided in the Step-by-Step Technology Guide at the end of this section (page 180). The TI-83/84 scatterplot is shown in Figure 4.11, and the TI-83/84 results are shown in Figure 4.12. (Note that the TI-83/84 indicates the slope b_1 as a, and the y intercept b_0 as b.) Figures 4.13a and 4.13b show the Excel results, with the y intercept ("Intercept") and the slope ("Low") highlighted. Figure 4.14 shows the Minitab results, with the y intercept ("Constant") and the slope ("Low") highlighted. ■

highlowtemp

FIGURE 4.11 TI-83/84 scatterplot.

FIGURE 4.12 TI-83/84 correlation and regression results.

	Low	High
Low	1	
High	0.965642	1

FIGURE 4.13a Excel correlation results.

	Coefficients	Standard error	t stat	P-value
Intercept	20	3.260879227	6.133315161	0.000279056
Low	0.9	0.085634884	10.50973575	5.84917E-06

FIGURE 4.13b Excel regression results.

Correlations: Low, High
Pearson correlation of Low and High = 0.966
P-Value = 0.000

Regression Analysis: High versus Low
The regression equation is High = 20.0 + 0.900 Low

Predictor	Coef	SE Coef	T	P
Constant	20.000	3.261	6.13	0.000
Low	0.90000	0.08563	10.51	0.000

FIGURE 4.14 Minitab correlation and regression results.

The following computational formula is equivalent to the definition formula for the slope b_1.

Equivalent Computational Formula for Calculating the Slope b_1

$$b_1 = \frac{\sum xy - \left(\sum x \sum y\right)/n}{\sum x^2 - \left(\sum x\right)^2/n}$$

Example 4.9 Using the computational formula to calculate the slope b_1

Use the computational formula to calculate the slope b_1 for the relationship between square footage and sales price of the eight home lots for sale in Glen Ellyn from Example 4.1 in Section 4.1. Then find the y intercept b_0 and the regression equation.

Solution

From Example 4.5 (page 165), we have $n = 8$ and the following summations: $\Sigma x = 1400$, $\Sigma y = 2880$, $\Sigma xy = 576,000$, and $\Sigma x^2 = 275,000$. Substituting into the computational formula, we have

$$b_1 = \frac{576,000 - (1400)(2880)/8}{275,000 - 1400^2/8} = \frac{72,000}{30,000} = 2.4$$

To find b_0, we first calculate

$$\bar{y} = \frac{\Sigma y}{n} = \frac{2880}{8} = 360 \text{ and } \bar{x} = \frac{\Sigma x}{n} = \frac{1400}{8} = 175$$

Then

$$b_0 = \bar{y} - (b_1 \cdot \bar{x}) = 360 - (2.4)(175) = -60$$

This gives us the following regression equation:

$$\hat{y} = b_1 x + b_0 = 2.4x - 60$$

To save time, we could have remembered that the numerator for the computational formula for r from Example 4.5 is 72,000.

The Sensitivity of the Regression Line to Extreme Values

What if the sales price of the largest lot for sale (27,500 square feet) was not $635,000 but $120,000. What would happen to the slope and the y intercept of the regression line?

Solution

The correlation coefficient and the regression line are both sensitive to extreme values. As shown in Figure 4.15, the change to a much lower price for the largest lot acts as a weight pulling down on the upper (right-hand) end of the regression line. The slope decreases from $b_1 = 2.4$ to $b_1 = 0.683$.

FIGURE 4.15
Regression line is sensitive to extreme values.

Consequently, the y intercept increases from $b_0 = -60$ to $b_0 = 176$, giving us the new regression equation:

$$\hat{y} = 0.683x + 176$$

Also, the correlation coefficient falls from $r = 0.9434$ to $r = 0.3130$.

2 Predictions and Prediction Error

We can use the regression equation to make estimates or predictions. For any particular value of x, the predicted value for y lies on the regression line.

Example 4.10 Using the regression equation to make a prediction

Suppose we are moving to a city that has a low temperature of 50°F on this particular winter's day. Use the regression equation in Example 4.7 to find the predicted high temperature for this city.

Solution

To generate an estimate of the high temperature, we plug in the value of 50°F for the x variable *low*:

$$\hat{y} = 0.9(low) + 20 = 0.9(50) + 20 = 65$$

Now You Can Do
Exercises 29–36.

We would say, "The estimated high temperature for an American city with a low temperature of 50°F is 65°F." ■

---

iStockphoto

Dallas, Texas

Developing Your
Statistical Sense

Actual Data versus Predicted (Estimated) Data

We have two cities in our data table (Table 4.2) whose low temperature is 50°F: Dallas, Texas, and Memphis, Tennessee. For simplicity, we will illustrate using Dallas only. The actual high temperature for Dallas is 70°F, but our predicted high temperature is $\hat{y} = 65$°F. The actual high temperature in Dallas is an established fact: real, observed data. On the other hand, our prediction $\hat{y}$ is just an estimate based on a formula, the regression equation. ◢

Prediction Error

The actual data point for Dallas is shown circled in the scatterplot in Figure 4.16. The predicted high temperature $\hat{y} = 65$°F is the y-value of the point on the regression line where it intersects $x = 50$. Notice that the point with the predicted high temperature value $\hat{y}$ lies directly on the regression line vertically below the Dallas data point. This is true for all values of $\hat{y}$:

All values of $\hat{y}$ (the predicted values of y) lie on the regression line.

FIGURE 4.16
Prediction error for
Dallas high
temperature.

Our prediction's position in the graph is at $(x, \hat{y}) = (50, 65)$, compared to $(x, y) = (50, 70)$ for Dallas. Our prediction for Dallas was too low by

$$y - \hat{y} = 70 - 65 = 5°F$$

The difference $y - \hat{y}$ is the vertical difference from the Dallas data point to the regression line. This difference is called the *prediction error*.

The **prediction error** or **residual** $(y - \hat{y})$ measures how far the predicted value $\hat{y}$ is from the actual value of y observed in the data set. The prediction error may be positive or negative.

- Positive prediction error: The data value lies *above* the regression line, so the observed value of y is greater than predicted for the given value of x.

- Negative prediction error: The data value lies *below* the regression line, so the observed value of y is lower than predicted for the given value of x.

- Prediction error equal to zero: The data value lies *directly on* the regression line, so the observed value of y is exactly equal to what is predicted for the given value of x.

Of course, we need not restrict our predictions to values of x (low temperature) that are in our data set (though see the warning on extrapolation below). For example, the estimated high temperature for a city in which $low = 25°F$ is

$$\hat{y} = 0.9(low) + 20 = 0.9(25) + 20 = 42.5°F$$

Note that we cannot calculate the prediction error for this estimate, since we do not have a city with a low temperature of 25°F to which to compare it.

Example 4.11 Calculating and interpreting prediction errors (residuals)

Use the regression equation from Example 4.10 to calculate and interpret the prediction error (residual) for the following cities.
a. Cincinnati: Low = 30, high = 49
b. Philadelphia: Low = 30, high = 41

Solution

a. The actual high temperature in Cincinnati that day was $y = 49$. Using the regression equation, the predicted high temperature is $\hat{y} = 0.9(30) + 20 = 47$. So the prediction error is $y - \hat{y} = 49 - 47 = 2°F$. The data point lies above the regression line, so that its actual high temperature of 49°F is greater than predicted given its low temperature of 30°F.
b. Philadelphia: Actual high = $y = 41$. Predicted high = $\hat{y} = 0.9(30) + 20 = 47$. So the residual is $y - \hat{y} = 41 - 47 = -6°F$. Philadelphia's data point lies below the regression line, so that its actual high temperature of 41°F is lower than predicted given its low temperature of 30°F. ∎

Now You Can Do
Exercises 37–42.

Extrapolation

The y intercept b_0 is the estimated value for y when x equals zero. However, in many regression problems, a value of zero for the x variable would not make sense. For example, a lot for sale of $x = 0$ square feet does not make sense, so the y intercept would not be meaningful. On the other hand, a value of zero for the low temperature does make sense. Therefore, we would be tempted to predict $\hat{y} = 0.9(0) + 20 = 20°F$ as the high temperature for a city with a low of zero degrees. However, $low = 0°F$ is not within the range of the data set. Making predictions based on x-values that are beyond the range of the x-values in our data set is called *extrapolation*. It may be misleading and should be avoided.

> **Extrapolation** consists of using the regression equation to make estimates or predictions based on x-values that are outside the range of the x-values in the data set.

Extrapolation should be avoided, if possible, because the relationship between the variables may no longer be linear outside the range of x. A regression line based solely on the available data (white background) and ignoring the hidden data (gray background) is shown in Figure 4.17. Since the regression line is based on incomplete data, in this case, predicting y at the point $x = a$ resulted in a large difference between the predicted value $\hat{y}$ and the actual value y, called the *prediction error*, or *residual*.

FIGURE 4.17
Dangers of extrapolation.

Example 4.12 Identifying when extrapolation occurs

Using the regression equation from Example 4.10, estimate the high temperature for the following low temperatures. If the estimate represents extrapolation, indicate so.
a. 60°F
b. 70°F

Solution
From Table 4.2, the smallest value of x is 10°F and the largest is 60°F, so estimates for any value of x between 10°F and 60°F, inclusive, would not represent extrapolation.
a. $\hat{y} = 0.9(60) + 20 = 74°F$. Since $x = 60°F$ lies between 10°F and 60°F, inclusive, this estimate does not represent extrapolation.
b. $\hat{y} = 0.9(70) + 20 = 83°F$. Since $x = 70°F$ does not lie between 10°F and 60°F, this estimate represents extrapolation. ∎

Now You Can Do
Exercises 43–50.

ImagesBazaar/Getty Images

CASE STUDY

Female Literacy and Fertility Worldwide

Overpopulation is a serious concern for planet Earth in the twenty-first century. However, there are some encouraging signs of how to combat overpopulation, especially in developing countries. Figure 4.18 shows a scatterplot of the fertility rate versus the female literacy rate in 204 countries around the world.[1] The fertility rate is the mean number of children born to a typical woman in the country, and the female literacy rate is the percentage of women at least 15 years old who can read and write.

FIGURE 4.18
Scatterplot of fertility rate versus female literacy rate for 204 countries.

Based on the scatterplot in Figure 4.18, we can state that there is a *negative* relationship between female literacy and fertility. That is, as female literacy increases, fertility tends to decrease. Since the relationship is negative, the correlation coefficient r must therefore be negative, $-1 < r < 0$. Excel provides the correlation coefficient in Figure 4.19, $r = -0.7962$.

As expected, the correlation coefficient is negative. For a sample size of 204, the critical value from Table G in the Appendix is 0.361. Since $|r| = |-0.7962| = 0.7962 > 0.361$, we can conclude that fertility and female literacy are negatively correlated. An increase in female literacy is associated with a decrease in fertility. The y intercept and slope of the regression line are shown in the Excel output in Figure 4.20, giving us the regression line

$$\hat{y} = -0.05495(\text{female literacy}) + 7.37969$$

The estimated fertility rate is negative 0.05495 times the female literacy rate plus 7.37969 children. We interpret the slope b_1 as follows: an increase of 1% in the female literacy rate is associated with a decrease of 0.05495 children in the fertility rate. Thus, for example, an increase of 20% in the female literacy rate is associated with a decrease in the estimated number of births per woman of 20(0.05495) = 1.099 children. The y intercept is interpreted as follows: when the female literacy rate is zero percent, the estimated fertility rate equals $b_0 = 7.37969$ children.

	Female literacy	Fertility
Female literacy	1	
Fertility	–0.7962	1

FIGURE 4.19 Excel correlation results.

	Coefficients	
Intercept	7.37969	y intercept
Female literacy	–0.05495	slope

FIGURE 4.20 Excel regression results.

For a country with a 50% literacy rate, the estimated number of births per woman is

$$\hat{y} = 0.05495(50) + 7.37969 \approx 4.6$$

Note the two countries singled out in Figure 4.18. The Republic of Congo has a relatively high female literacy rate, so one would expect the fertility rate to be low. But the fertility rate in the Republic of Congo is 6.45 births per woman, which is higher than expected. Bangladesh has a relatively low female literacy rate, so one would expect the fertility rate to be high. But the fertility rate in Bangladesh is 3.11 births per woman, which is lower than expected. Note that the data points for both Congo and Bangladesh lie far from the regression line. In general, unusual observations in a linear regression problem are points that lie at an unusually large vertical distance from the regression line. ■

 The *Correlation and Regression* applet allows you to insert your own data values and see how the regression line changes.

STEP-BY-STEP TECHNOLOGY GUIDE: Regression

We illustrate using Example 4.3, the temperature data (pages 160–161).

TI-83/84

Step 1 Turn diagnostics on as follows. Press **2nd 0**. Scroll down and select **DiagnosticOn** (Figure 4.21). Press **ENTER** twice to turn diagnostics on.

Step 2 **Enter** the **X (Low Temp)** data in **L1**, and the **Y (High Temp)** data in **L2**.

Step 3 Press **STAT** and highlight **CALC**.

Step 4 Select **LinReg(ax+b)**.

Step 5 On the home screen, **LinReg(ax+b)** appears. Press **ENTER**.

```
CATALOG        ▣
  DependAsk
  DependAuto
  det(
  DiagnosticOff
▶ DiagnosticOn
  dim(
  Disp
```

FIGURE 4.21

EXCEL

Step 1 Enter the *x* variable in column **A** and the *y* variable in column **B**.

Step 2 Click on **Data > Data Analysis > Regression** and click **OK**.

Step 3 For **Input Y Range**, select cells **B1–B10**. For **Input X Range**, select cells **A1–A10**. Click **OK**.

MINITAB

Regression

Step 1 Enter the *x* variable in **C1** and the *y* variable in **C2**.

Step 2 Click on **Stat > Regression > Regression**.

Step 3 Select the *y* variable for the **Response Variable** and the *x* variable for the **Predictor Variable**. Click **OK**.

CRUNCHIT!

Step 1 Click **File** . . . then highlight **Load from Larose2e** . . . **Chapter 4** . . . and click on **Example 4.3**.

Step 2 Click **Statistics** . . . **Regression** . . . **Simple linear regression**.

Step 3 For **Response variable y** select **High temp**. For **Predictor variable x** select **Low Temp**.

Step 4 For **Display** make sure **Numerical results** is selected. Then click **Calculate**.

Section 4.2 Summary

1 Section 4.2 introduces regression, where the linear relationship between two numerical variables is approximated using a straight line, called the regression line. The equation of the regression line is written as $\hat{y} = b_1 x + b_0$, where the regression coefficients are the *y* intercept, b_0, and the slope, b_1.

2 The regression equation can be used to make predictions about values of *y* for particular values of *x*.

Section 4.2 Exercises

CLARIFYING THE CONCEPTS

1. What is the objective of regression analysis?
2. What is the regression equation?
3. Describe how we use the regression equation to make predictions.
4. Explain the difference between y and $\hat{y}$.
5. Describe what is meant by extrapolation.
6. What is the relationship between the slope of the regression line and the correlation coefficient?

PRACTICING THE TECHNIQUES

Exercises 7–12 refer to scatterplots in the Section 4.1 exercises. For each indicated scatterplot, state whether the slope b_1 of the regression line would be positive, negative, or near zero.

7. Exercise 13
8. Exercise 14
9. Exercise 15
10. Exercise 16
11. Exercise 17
12. Exercise 18

For Exercises 13–20, do the following:
  a. Calculate the slope b_1 of the regression line.
  b. Calculate the y intercept b_0 of the regression line.
  c. Write the regression equation.

13.

x	1	2	3	4
y	2	5	9	12

14.

x	0	2	4	6
y	5	6	5	4

15.

x	−5	−4	−3	−2	−1
y	0	8	8	16	16

16.

x	−3	−1	1	3	5
y	−5	−15	−20	−25	−30

17.

x	5	10	15	20	25	30
y	2	3	3	3	2	3

18.

x	6	7	8	9	11	13
y	4	4	4	4	4	4

19.

x	0	10	20	30	40	50	60	70
y	5	10	15	20	25	30	35	40

20.

x	−30	−23	−15	−12	−1	5	14	29
y	93	78	66	52	44	37	20	10

For Exercises 21–28, do the following for the indicated data:
  a. Interpret the value for the slope b_1 of the regression line.
  b. Interpret the value for the y intercept b_0 of the regression line.

21. Data from Exercise 13
22. Data from Exercise 14
23. Data from Exercise 15
24. Data from Exercise 16
25. Data from Exercise 17
26. Data from Exercise 18
27. Data from Exercise 19
28. Data from Exercise 20

For Exercises 29–36, predict the value of y for the given value of x for the indicated data.

29. Data from Exercise 13; $x = 3$
30. Data from Exercise 14; $x = 0$
31. Data from Exercise 15; $x = -2$
32. Data from Exercise 16; $x = 8$
33. Data from Exercise 17; $x = 10$
34. Data from Exercise 18; $x = 4$
35. Data from Exercise 19; $x = 0$
36. Data from Exercise 20; $x = 40$

For Exercises 37–42, do the following:
  a. Calculate the prediction error.
  b. Interpret the prediction error.

37. Prediction from Exercise 29
38. Prediction from Exercise 30
39. Prediction from Exercise 31
40. Prediction from Exercise 33
41. Prediction from Exercise 34
42. Prediction from Exercise 35

For Exercises 43–50, for the prediction from the indicated exercise, state whether or not the prediction represents extrapolation.

43. Prediction from Exercise 29
44. Prediction from Exercise 30
45. Prediction from Exercise 31
46. Prediction from Exercise 32
47. Prediction from Exercise 33
48. Prediction from Exercise 34
49. Prediction from Exercise 35
50. Prediction from Exercise 36

APPLYING THE CONCEPTS

For Exercises 51–54, do the following
  a. Calculate the slope b_1 and the y intercept b_0 of the regression line.
  b. State the regression equation in words that a non-specialist would understand, as shown at the end of Example 4.7.
  c. Interpret the value for the slope b_1 of the regression line, in terms of the variables from the particular exercise.
  d. Interpret the value for the y intercept b_0 of the regression line, in terms of the variables from the particular exercise.

51. **Education and Unemployment.** The U.S. Census Bureau published the following data (see the table on the next page) on years of education and unemployment rate. Use your calculations from Exercise 46 in Section 4.1.
🐦 **edunemploy**

x = years of education	y = unemployment rate
5	16.8
7.5	17.1
8	15.3
10	20.6
12	11.7
14	8.1
16	3.8

52. NASCAR Wins. Refer to the following table of NASCAR wins in super speedway races and short track races. 🏁 **nascar**

Driver	x = short track wins	y = super speedway wins
Darrell Waltrip	47	18
Dale Earnhardt	27	29
Jeff Gordon	15	15
Cale Yarborough	29	15
Richard Petty	23	19

53. SAT Scores. Refer to the following table of SAT Reading scores and SAT Math scores. 🏁 **satesat**

State	x = mean SAT Reading score	y = mean SAT Math score
New York	497	510
Connecticut	515	515
Massachusetts	518	523
New Jersey	501	514
New Hampshire	522	521

54. Brain and Body Weight. Refer to the following table of brain and body weight for a sample of mammals. Use your calculations from Exercise 50 in Section 4.1. 🏁 **brainbody**

x = body weight (kg)	y = brain weight (g)
52.16	440
60	81
27.66	115
85	325
36.33	119.5
100	157
35	56
62	1320
83	98.2
55.5	175

55. Education and Unemployment. Refer to your work from Exercise 51. For parts (a)–(c), if appropriate, use your regression equation to estimate the unemployment for individuals with the following years of education. If it is not appropriate, clearly state why not.
a. 10 years   b. 15 years   c. 20 years
d. What is the distinction between your result from part (a) and the actual unemployment rate of 20.6 for individuals with 10 years of education?

e. Calculate the prediction error for your prediction in part (a). Does this data point lie above or below the regression line, and what does that mean?

56. NASCAR Wins. Refer to your work from Exercise 52. For parts (a)–(c), if appropriate, use your regression equation to estimate the number of super speedway wins for drivers with the following numbers of short track wins. If it is not appropriate, clearly state why not.
a. 30 short track wins
b. 47 short track wins
c. 50 short track wins
d. Explain so that a nonspecialist would understand, the distinction between your result from part (b) and the number of super speedway wins for Darrell Waltrip.
e. Calculate the prediction error for your prediction in part (b). Does this data point lie above or below the regression line, and what does that mean?

57. SAT Scores. Refer to your work from Exercise 53.
a. Estimate the mean SAT Math score for a state with a mean SAT Reading score of 501.
b. Is the interpretation of the y intercept from Exercise 53 useful? Explain.
c. Is it OK, or is it misleading to use the regression equation to predict the mean SAT Math score for a state with a mean SAT Reading score of 400? Explain.
d. What is the distinction between your result from part (a) and the mean SAT Math score for New Jersey?
e. Calculate and interpret the prediction error for your prediction in part (a).

58. Brain and Body Weight. Refer to your work from Exercise 54.
a. Estimate the brain weight for a mammal with a body weight of 100 kilograms.
b. Is the interpretation of the y intercept from Exercise 54 useful? Explain.
c. Is it OK, or is it misleading to use the regression equation to predict the brain weight for a mammal with body weight of 10 kg? Explain.
d. Explain the distinction between your result from part (a) and the actual brain weight of 157 grams for the mammal from the data table.
e. Calculate and interpret the prediction error for your prediction in part (a).

Scrabble. Use the information in the following table and scatterplot for Exercises 59–61. Scrabble® (www.hasbro.com/scrabble/home.cfm) is one of the most popular games in the world. We are interested in approximating the relationship between the frequency (x) of the letter tiles in the game and their point value (y). The scatterplot shows the point value versus the letter frequency, along with the regression line, as plotted by Minitab. 🏁 **scrabble**

Letter	Freq.	Points	Letter	Freq.	Points
A	9	1	N	6	1
B	2	3	O	8	1
C	2	3	P	2	3
D	4	2	Q	1	10
E	12	1	R	6	1
F	2	4	S	4	1
G	3	2	T	6	1
H	2	4	U	4	1
I	9	1	V	2	4
J	1	8	W	2	4
K	1	5	X	1	8
L	4	1	Y	2	4
M	2	3	Z	1	10

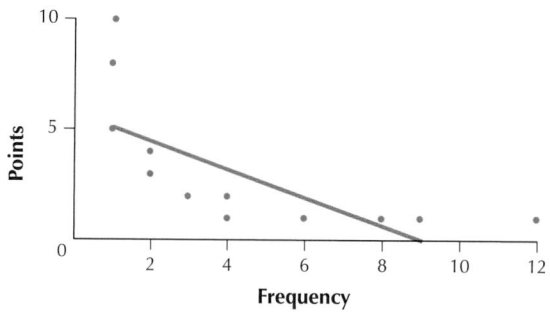

Scatterplot of Scrabble® point value versus letter frequency, with regression line.

59. Does the relationship between frequency and points seem to be positive or negative?

60. Does the relationship between frequency and points seem to be a straight-line relationship or a curved relationship?

61. Do you think that we should use a regression line to approximate the relationship between frequency and points? If not, explain clearly what you think is wrong.

DC Households. Use the following information for Exercises 62–64. The data set **Households,** located on your CD and companion Web site, contains information on the number and type of households in the fifty states and the District of Columbia. For each state, there are seven variables. Two of these variables are the percentage of households headed by women (y = HHLD_WOMEN) and the total number of households in the state (x = TOT_HHLD). Minitab provides the following regression equation: 🐾 **Households**

Regression Analysis
The regression equation is
HHLD_Women = 10.5 + 2.82E-07 TOT_HHLD

Note: Minitab shows its regression equations as $y = b_0 + b_1x$ rather than $\hat{y} = b_1 x + b_0$. Also, the notation 2.82E-07 refers to the scientific notation method of writing numbers. Often, software and calculators will present you with this type of notation, so you need to know how to read it. The number 2.82E-07 represents 2.82 times 10^{-7}, or 0.000000282.

62. In this exercise, we explore the regression coefficients and the regression equation.
   a. Find and interpret the meaning of the value for the y intercept. Does it make sense?
   b. Would the estimate in **(a)** be considered extrapolation? Why or why not?
   c. Find and interpret the meaning of the slope coefficient as the total number of households in the state increases.
   d. Write the regression equation. Now state in words what the regression equation means.
   e. Is the correlation coefficient positive or negative? How do you know?

63. Estimate the increase or decrease in the percentage of households headed by women, using a sentence, for the following situations.
   a. Suppose State A has 1 million more households than State B.
   b. Suppose State C has 5 million fewer households than State D.

64. The number of households per state ranges from about 170,000 to about 10 million.
   a. Estimate the percentage of households headed by women for a state with 7 million households, if appropriate.
   b. Estimate the percentage of households headed by women for a state with 100,000 households, if appropriate.

Chapter 3 Case Study (Continued). Use the following information for Exercises 65–68. Shown here is the regression equation for the linear relationship between the randomly selected Darts portfolio and the Dow Jones Industrial Average (DJIA), from the Chapter 3 Case Study.

Regression Analysis
The regression equation is
Darts = -2.49 + 1.032 DJIA

65. In this exercise, we examine the y intercept.
   a. Which variable is the x variable and which is the y variable? Work by analogy with the previous exercises.
   b. What is the value of the y intercept?
   c. Interpret the meaning of this value for the y intercept. Does it make sense?
   d. Would the estimate in **(c)** be considered extrapolation? Why or why not?

66. In this exercise, we look at the slope and the regression equation.
   a. Find and interpret the meaning of the value of the slope coefficient, as the DJIA increases.
   b. Write the regression equation. Now state in words what the regression equation means.
   c. Is the correlation coefficient positive or negative? How do we know?

67. Estimate the increase or decrease in the net price of the Darts portfolio, using a sentence, for the following situations.

a. Suppose that for Contest A the DJIA increased by 10% more than for Contest B.

b. Suppose that for Contest C the DJIA decreased by 5% more than for Contest D.

68. The net change in the DJIA ranged from –13.1% to 22.5%.

a. Estimate the net price change for the Darts portfolio when the DJIA is up by 22%, if appropriate.

b. Estimate the net price change for the Darts portfolio when the DJIA is down by 10%, if appropriate.

c. Estimate the net price change for the Darts portfolio when the DJIA is down by 22%, if appropriate.

WHAT IF?

? 69. Consider again the temperature data in Example 4.7. *What if* there was a typo, and all the low temperatures in the data set needed to be adjusted downward by the same amount. Explain how this change would affect the following, and why. Increase, decrease, or no change?

a. $\bar{x}$

b. $\bar{y}$

c. y intercept b_0

d. Slope b_1

e. Correlation coefficient r

BRINGING IT ALL TOGETHER

Fuel Economy. Refer to the following table of fuel economy data for a sample of 10 vehicles for Exercises 70–74. The predictor variable is x = engine size, expressed in liters; the response variable is y = combined (city/highway) gas mileage, expressed in miles per gallon (mpg). **enginempg**

Vehicle	x = engine size (liters)	y = combined mpg
Mini Cooper	1.6	31
Ford Focus	2.0	28
Toyota Camry	2.5	26
Subaru Forester	2.5	23
Honda Accord	2.4	26
Toyota Highlander	2.7	22
Chevrolet Equinox	3.0	19
Ford Taurus	3.5	20
Dodgo Nitro	4.0	17
Cadillac Limousine	4.6	14

70. **Exploring the Data.**

a. Look at the data table. As the engine size values increase, what seems to be happening to the combined mpg?

b. Construct a scatterplot of the data.

c. Interpret the scatterplot. Is your insight from part (a) supported?

71. **What Results Do You Expect?** Based on your scatterplot in Exercise 70, answer the following.

a. Will the correlation coefficient be positive or negative?

b. Do you expect that the correlation will be closer to −0.9 or −0.5? Why?

c. Would you predict that our comparison test will allow us to conclude that engine size is correlated with combined mpg?

d. Do you think that the slope b_1 will be positive or negative? Why?

72. **Correlation.** Do the following.

a. Calculate the correlation coefficient r. Does this concur with your predictions from Exercises 71(a) and 71(b)?

b. Test whether we may conclude that engine size is correlated with combined mpg. Does this agree with your prediction from Exercise 71(c)?

c. Interpret the correlation between engine size and combined mpg.

73. **Regression.** Answer the following.

a. Calculate the slope b_1 of the regression equation. Does the sign of b_1 agree with your prediction from Exercise 71(d)?

b. Calculate the y intercept b_0.

c. Interpret the values you calculated in parts (a) and (b) so that a nonstatistician would understand them.

74. **Making Predictions.** Answer the following.

a. Predict the combined mpg for a vehicle with an engine size of 3 liters.

b. Is your prediction error positive or negative? Hence, does the data value lie above or below the regression line? What does this mean?

c. Explain the distinction between your result from part (a) and the actual combined mpg obtained by the Chevrolet Equinox.

d. We are interested in the combined mpg for a Chevrolet Suburban, which has an engine size of 6 liters. Would you recommend using the regression equation to predict the combined mpg for the Chevrolet Suburban? Clearly explain why or why not.

CONSTRUCT YOUR OWN DATA SETS

75. Describe two variables from real life whose regression line would have a positive slope b_1.

a. Explain why the y variable depends on the x variable.

b. Explain why the slope is positive.

76. Create a sample of five observations from each of your variables from Exercise 75, and put them into a table similar to Table 4.1 in Section 4.1.

a. Construct a scatterplot of the variables.

b. Draw a single straight line through the data points in the plot in a manner that you think best approximates the relationship between the variables.

c. Using your regression line from (b), estimate the slope b_1 and the y intercept b_0.

d. Write your results from (c) in the form of a regression equation.

APPLET

Use the *Correlation and Regression* applet for Exercises 77 and 78.

77. Create a set of n = 10 points such that the slope of the regression line has the following characteristic. (Note that you can drag points up or down to adjust your regression line.)

a. The slope is positive.

b. The slope is negative.

c. The slope is neither positive nor negative.

78. Describe the relationship between the variables for each of the sets of points in the previous exercise.

4.3 Further Topics in Regression Analysis

OBJECTIVES By the end of this section, I will be able to . . .

1   Calculate the sum of squares error (SSE), and use the standard error of the estimate s as a measure of a typical prediction error.

2   Describe how total variability, prediction error, and improvement are measured by the total sum of squares (SST), the sum of squares error (SSE), and the sum of squares regression (SSR).

3   Explain the meaning of the coefficient of determination r^2 as a measure of the usefulness of the regression.

In Section 4.2, we were introduced to regression analysis, which uses an equation to approximate the linear relationship between two quantitative variables. Here in Section 4.3, we learn some further topics that will enable us to better apply the tools of regression analysis for a deeper understanding of our data.

1 Sum of Squares Error (SSE) and Standard Error of the Estimate *s*

Copyright David Young-Wolff/Photo Edit

Table 4.5 shows the results for ten student subjects who were given a set of short-term memory tasks to perform within a certain amount of time. These tasks included memorizing nonsense words and random patterns. Later, the students were asked to repeat the words and patterns, and the students were scored according to the number of words and patterns memorized and the quality of the memory. Partially remembered words and patterns were given partial credit, so the score was a continuous variable. Figure 4.22 displays the scatterplot of y = score versus x = time, together with the regression line $\hat{y} = 7 + 2x$ (that is, $\hat{y} = 2x + 7$), as calculated by Minitab.

Table 4.5 Results of short-term memory test

Student	Time to memorize (in minutes) (x)	Short-term memory score (y)
1	1	9
2	1	10
3	2	11
4	3	12
5	3	13
6	4	14
7	5	19
8	6	17
9	7	21
10	8	24

FIGURE 4.22
Scatterplot with regression line.

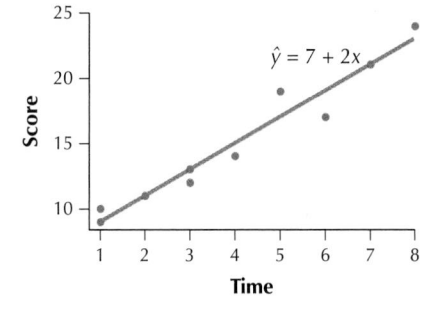

```
The regression equation is
Score = 7.00 + 2.00 Time
```

Minitab regression results (excerpt).

In Section 4.2, we learned that the difference $y - \hat{y}$ represented the prediction error or residual between the actual data value y and the predicted value $\hat{y}$. For example, for a student who is given $x = 5$ minutes to study, the predicted score is $\hat{y} = 2\,(time) + 7 = 17$. For Student 7, who was given 5 minutes to study and got a score of 19, the prediction error is $y - \hat{y} = 19 - 17 = 2$.

We can calculate the prediction errors for every student who was tested. If we wish to use the regression to make useful predictions, we would like to keep all our prediction errors small. To measure the prediction errors, we calculate the sum of squared prediction errors, or more simply, the **sum of squares error (SSE):**

Sum of Squares Error (SSE)

$$\text{SSE} = \sum(y - \hat{y})^2 = \sum(\text{residual})^2 = \sum(\text{prediction error})^2$$

Since we want our prediction errors to be small, it follows that we want SSE to be as small as possible.

Least-Squares Criterion

The least-squares criterion states that the regression line will be the *line for which the SSE is minimized.* That is, out of all possible straight lines, the least-squares criterion chooses the line with the smallest SSE to be the regression line.

Example 4.13 | Calculating SSE, the sum of squares error

 shortmemory

a. Construct a scatterplot of the memory score data, indicating each residual.
b. Calculate the sum of squares error (SSE) for the memory score data.

Solution

a. The brackets (}) in the scatterplot in Figure 4.23 indicate the residual for each student's score. The quantities represented by these brackets are the residuals $y - \hat{y}$.

b. Table 4.6 shows the $\hat{y}$-values and residuals for the data in Table 4.5. The sum of squares error is then found by squaring each residual and taking the sum. Thus

$$\text{SSE} = \sum(y - \hat{y})^2 = 12$$

Now You Can Do
Exercises 11–16.

Since we know that $\hat{y} = 2x + 7$ is the regression line, according to the least-squares criterion, no other possible straight line would result in a smaller SSE. ∎

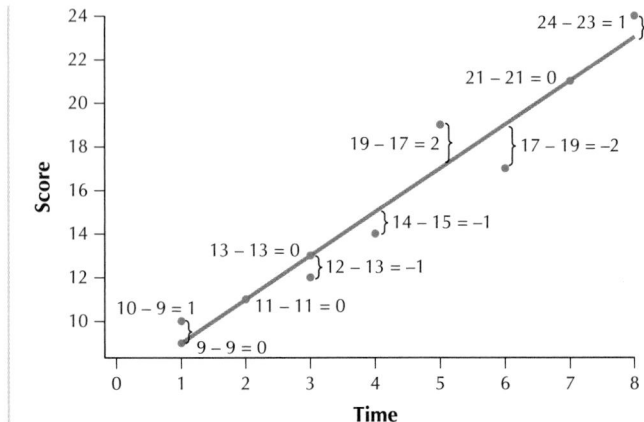

FIGURE 4.23 Scatterplot showing the prediction errors or residuals $y - \hat{y}$.

Table 4.6 Calculation of the SSE for the short-term memory test example

Student	Time (x)	Actual score (y)	Predicted score $(\hat{y} = 2x + 7)$	Residual $(y - \hat{y})$	$(\text{Residual})^2$ $(y - \hat{y})^2$
1	1	9	9	0	0
2	1	10	9	1	1
3	2	11	11	0	0
4	3	12	13	−1	1
5	3	13	13	0	0
6	4	14	15	−1	1
7	5	19	17	2	4
8	6	17	19	−2	4
9	7	21	21	0	0
10	8	24	23	1	1

$$\text{SSE} = \Sigma(y - \hat{y})^2 = 12$$

A useful interpretive statistic is s, the **standard error of the estimate.** The formula for s follows.

 CAUTION Don't confuse this use of the s notation for the standard error of the estimate with the use of the s notation for the sample standard deviation.

Standard Error of the Estimate s

$$s = \sqrt{\frac{\text{SSE}}{n - 2}}$$

The standard error of the estimate gives a measure of the typical residual. That is, s is a measure of the size of the *typical prediction error,* the typical difference between the predicted value of y and the actual observed value of y. If the typical prediction error is large, then the regression line may not be useful.

Example 4.14 Calculating and interpreting s, the standard error of the estimate

Calculate and interpret the standard error of the estimate s for the memory score data.

Solution

SSE = 12 and $n = 10$, so

Note: Here we are rounding $s = 1.2247$ for reporting purposes. However, when we use s for calculating other quantities later, we will not round until the last calculation.

$$s = \sqrt{\frac{\text{SSE}}{n - 2}} = \sqrt{\frac{12}{8}} \approx 1.2247$$

Thus, the typical error in prediction is 1.2247 points. In other words, if we know the amount of time (x) a given student spent memorizing, then our estimate of the student's score on the short-term memory test will typically differ from the student's actual score by only 1.2247 points. ■

Now You Can Do
Exercises 17–22.

2 SST, SSR, and SSE

The coefficient of determination r^2 depends on the values of two new statistics, SST and SSR, which we learn next. The least-squares criterion guarantees that the value of SSE = 12 that we found in Example 4.13 is the smallest possible value for SSE, given the data in Table 4.5. However, this guarantee in itself does not tell us that the regression is useful. For the regression to be useful, the prediction error (and therefore SSE) must be small. But, we cannot yet tell whether the value of SSE = 12 is indeed small, since we have nothing to compare it against.

Suppose for a moment that we want to estimate short-term memory scores but have no knowledge of the amount of time (x) for memorizing. Then the best estimate for y is simply $\bar{y} = 15$, the mean of the sample of short-term memory test scores. The graph of $\bar{y} = 15$ is the horizontal line in Figure 4.24.

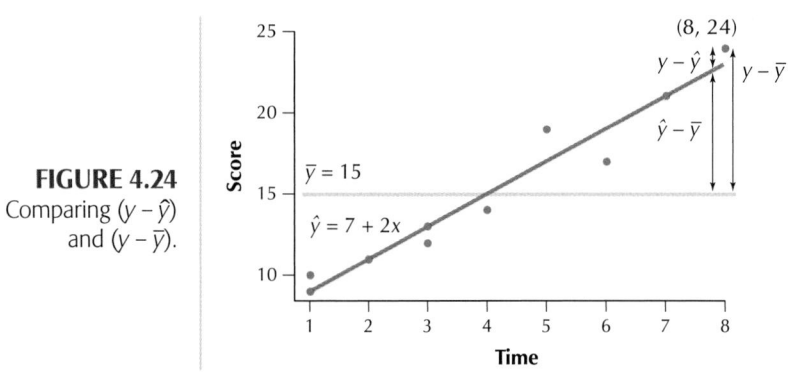

FIGURE 4.24
Comparing $(y - \hat{y})$
and $(y - \bar{y})$.

In general, the data points are closer to the regression line than they are to the horizontal line $\bar{y} = 15$, indicating that the errors in prediction are smaller when using the regression equation. Consider Student 10, who had a short-term memory score of $y = 24$ after memorizing for $x = 8$ minutes. Using $\bar{y} = 15$ as the estimate, the error for Student 10 is

$$(y - \bar{y}) = 24 - 15 = 9$$

This error is shown in Figure 4.24 as the vertical distance $(y - \bar{y})$.

Suppose we found this value $(y - \bar{y})$ for every student in the data set and summed the squared $(y - \bar{y})$, just as we did for the $(y - \hat{y})$ when finding SSE. The resulting statistic is called the **total sum of squares (SST)** and is a measure of the total variability in the values of the y variable:

$$\text{SST} = \sum(y - \bar{y})^2$$

Developing Your Statistical Sense

Relationship Between SST and the Variance of the y's

Note that SST ignores the presence of the x information; it is simply a measure of the variability in y. Recall (see page 110) that the *variance* of a sample of y-values is given by $s^2 = \sum(y - \bar{y})^2/(n - 1)$. Thus

$$\text{SST} = (n - 1)\, s^2$$

Hence, SST is proportional to the variance of the y's and, as such, is a measure of the variability in the y data. ◢

Example 4.15   Calculating SST, the total sum of squares, in two ways

Calculate SST, the total sum of squares, for the memory score data in two ways:
a.   By using Table 4.7
b.   By using the fact that the sample variance of the score data (the y values) equals $25\frac{1}{3}$.

Solution

a.   Table 4.7 shows the values for $(y - \bar{y}) = (y - 15)$ for the data in Table 4.5. Thus, SST $= \Sigma(y - \bar{y})^2 = 228$.

Table 4.7 Calculation of SST

Student	Score (y)	($y - \bar{y}$)	($y - \bar{y}$)^2
1	9	-6	36
2	10	-5	25
3	11	-4	16
4	12	-3	9
5	13	-2	4
6	14	-1	1
7	19	4	16
8	17	2	4
9	21	6	36
10	24	9	81

$$\mathbf{SST = \Sigma(y - \bar{y})^2 = 228}$$

b.   When we are given the variance of y, we may calculate SST as follows:

$$\text{SST} = (n - 1)s^2 = (10 - 1)(25\tfrac{1}{3}) = 228$$

Now You Can Do
Exercises 23a, b–28a, b.

Consider Figure 4.24 once again. For Student 10, note that the error in prediction when ignoring the x data is $(y - \bar{y}) = 9$, while the error in prediction when using the regression equation is $(y - \hat{y}) = 1$. (Recall that $\hat{y} = 2(8) + 7 = 23$, since Student 10's time is $x = 8$.) The amount of improvement (that is, the amount by which the prediction error is diminished) is the difference between $\hat{y}$ and $\bar{y}$:

$$(\hat{y} - \bar{y}) = 23 - 15 = 8$$

Once again, we can find $(\hat{y} - \bar{y})$ for each observation in the data set, square them, and sum the squared results to obtain $\Sigma(\hat{y} - \bar{y})^2$. The resulting statistic is **SSR, the sum of squares regression.**

$$\text{SSR} = \Sigma(\hat{y} - \bar{y})^2$$

SSR measures the amount of *improvement* in the accuracy of our estimates when using the regression equation compared with relying only on the y-values and ignoring the x information. Note in Figure 4.24 that the distance $(y - \bar{y})$ is the same as the sum of the distances $(\hat{y} - \bar{y})$ and $(y - \hat{y})$. It can be shown, using algebra, that the following also holds true.

Note: None of these sums of squares can ever be negative.

Relationship Among SST, SSR, and SSE

$$\text{SST} = \text{SSR} + \text{SSE}$$

If any two of these sums of squares are known, the third can be calculated as well, as shown in the following example.

Example 4.16   Using SST and SSE to find SSR

Use SST and SSE to find the value of SSR for the data from Example 4.15.

Solution

From Example 4.13, we have SSE = 12, and from Example 4.15, we have SST = 228. That leaves us with just one unknown in the equation SST = SSR + SSE, so we can solve for the unknown SSR:

$$SSR = SST - SSE = 228 - 12 = 216$$

Now You Can Do
Exercises 23c–28c.

---

3 Coefficient of Determination r^2

SSR represents the amount of variability in the response variable that is accounted for by the regression equation, that is, by the linear relationship between y and x. SSE represents the amount of variability in the y that is left unexplained after accounting for the relationship between x and y (including random error). Since we know that SST represents the sum of SSR and SSE, it makes sense to consider the *ratio* of SSR and SST, called the **coefficient of determination r^2.**

> The **coefficient of determination r^2** = SSR/SST measures the goodness of fit of the regression equation to the data. We interpret r^2 as the proportion of the variability in y that is accounted for by the linear relationship between y and x. The values that r^2 can take are $0 \leq r^2 \leq 1$.

Example 4.17   Calculating and interpreting the coefficient of determination r^2

Calculate and interpret the value of the coefficient of determination r^2 for the memory score data.

Solution

From Example 4.15 we have SST = 228, and from Example 4.16 we have SSR = 216. Hence,

$$r^2 = \frac{SSR}{SST} = \frac{216}{228} \approx 0.9474$$

Now You Can Do
Exercises 29a, b–34a, b.

Thus, 94.74% of the variability in the memory test score (y) is accounted for by the linear relationship between score (y) and the time given for study (x). ∎

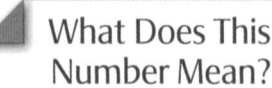
What Does This Number Mean?

What does the value of $r^2 \approx 0.9474$ mean? Consider that the memory test scores have a certain amount of variability: some scores are higher than others. In addition to the amount of time (x) given for memorizing, there may be several other factors that might account for variability in the scores, such as the memorizing ability of the students, how much sleep the students had, and so on. However, $r^2 \approx 0.9474$ indicates that 94.74% of this variability in memory scores (y) is explained by the single factor "amount of time given for study" (x). All other factors (including factors like amount of sleep) account for only 100% − 94.74% = 5.26% of the variability in the memory test scores. ◢

Suppose that the regression equation was a perfect fit to the data, so that every observation lay exactly on the regression line. Since there would be no errors in prediction, SSE would equal 0, which would imply that

$$SST = SSR + 0 = SSR$$

Since in this case SST = SSR, then

$$r^2 = \frac{SSR}{SST} = \frac{SST}{SST} = 1$$

Conversely, if SSR = 0, then *no improvement at all* is gained by using the regression equation. That is, the regression equation accounts for no variability at all, and $r^2 = 0/SST = 0$.

The closer the value of r^2 is to 1, the better the fit of the regression equation to the data set. A value near 1 indicates that the regression equation fits the data extremely well. A value near 0 indicates that the regression equation fits the data extremely poorly.

Here are the alternate computational formulas for finding SST and SSR.

Note that the formula for SSR is the same as the computational formula for the slope b_1 of the regression equation, except that the numerator is squared.

Computational Formulas for SST and SSR

$$SST = \sum y^2 - \left(\sum y\right)^2/n \qquad SSR = \frac{\left[\sum xy - \left(\sum x\right)\left(\sum y\right)/n\right]^2}{\sum x^2 - \left(\sum x\right)^2/n}$$

Example 4.18 Calculating SSR and SST using the computational formulas

Use the computational formulas to find SSR and SST for the memory score data. Assume we have the following summary statistics: $\sum x = 40$, $\sum y = 150$, $\sum xy = 708$, $\sum x^2 = 214$, $\sum y^2 = 2478$.

Solution

$$SST = \sum y^2 - \left(\sum y\right)^2/n = 2478 - (150)^2/10 = 228$$

$$SSR = \frac{\left[\sum xy - \left(\sum x\right)\left(\sum y\right)/n\right]^2}{\sum x^2 - \left(\sum x\right)^2/n} = \frac{[708 - (40)(150)/10]^2}{214 - (40)^2/10} = [108]^2/54 = 216$$

Then SSE = SST − SSR = 228 − 216 = 12. This value SSE = 12 agrees with the value we calculated earlier using Table 4.6. ∎

Recall from Section 4.1 that the correlation coefficient r is given by

$$r = \frac{\sum (x - \bar{x})(y - \bar{y})}{(n - 1) s_x s_y}$$

where s_x and s_y represent the sample standard deviation of the x data and the y data, respectively. We can express the correlation coefficient r as

$$r = \pm\sqrt{r^2}$$

where r^2 is the coefficient of determination. The correlation coefficient r takes the same sign as the slope b_1. If the slope b_1 of the regression equation is positive, then $r = \sqrt{r^2}$; if the slope b_1 of the regression equation is negative, then $r = -\sqrt{r^2}$.

Example 4.19 Calculate and evaluate the correlation coefficient using r^2

a. Use r^2 to calculate the value of the correlation coefficient r for the memory score data.
b. Perform the comparison test to determine whether x and y are correlated.

Solution

a. The slope $b_1 = 2$, which is positive, tells us that the sign of the correlation coefficient r is positive. Hence

$$r = \sqrt{r^2} = \sqrt{0.9474} \approx 0.9733$$

b. From Table G in the Appendix, the critical value for the correlation coefficient for $n = 10$ is 0.632. We have $r \approx 0.9733$, which is greater than 0.632.

Now You Can Do
Exercises 29c–34c.

Thus, student scores on the short-term memory test are strongly positively correlated with the amount of time allowed for memorization. ∎

Section 4.3 Summary

1 The sum of squared prediction errors is referred to as the sum of squares error, SSE $= \Sigma(y - \hat{y})^2$. The standard error of the estimate, $s = \sqrt{\dfrac{SSE}{n-2}}$, is an indicator of the precision of the estimates derived from the regression equation, since it provides a measure of the typical residual or prediction error.

2 The total variability in the y variable is measured by the total sum of squares, SST $= \Sigma(y - \bar{y})^2$, and may be divided into the sum of squares regression, SSR $= \Sigma(\hat{y} - \bar{y})^2$, and the

sum of squares error, SSE $= \Sigma(y - \hat{y})^2$. SSR measures the amount of improvement in the accuracy of estimates when using the regression equation compared with ignoring the x information.

3 The coefficient of determination, $r^2 = SSR/SST$, measures the goodness of fit of the regression equation as an approximation of the relationship between x and y. Finally, the correlation coefficient r may be expressed as $r = \pm\sqrt{r^2}$, taking the positive or negative sign of the slope b_1.

Section 4.3 Exercises

CLARIFYING THE CONCEPTS

1. What does s measure? Would we want s to be large or small? Why?

2. How does the least-squares criterion choose the "best" line to approximate the relationship between x and y?

3. What does SSE measure? Would we want SSE to be large or small? Why?

4. What does SSR measure? Would we want SSR to be large or small? Why?

5. What does SST measure? What statistic is it proportional to?

6. What does it mean when r^2 is close to 1? How about when it is close to 0?

7. Do the values of x affect SST at all?

8. Suppose we performed a regression analysis that resulted in $r^2 = 0.64$. Without further information, would it be possible to calculate the correlation coefficient r? Explain.

9. Suppose we performed a regression analysis on a data set that resulted in $r^2 = 0.64$. Interpret this statistic in terms of the amount of variance in y explained by the linear relationship between x and y.

10. True or false: When the prediction errors are too small, the sum of squared error SSE can be negative.

PRACTICING THE TECHNIQUES
For Exercises 11–16, use the regression equations you calculated in Exercises 13–18 in Section 4.2. Do the following.
   a. Construct a table like Table 4.6, and calculate the following quantity for each observation.
      i. $\hat{y}$, the estimated value of y
      ii. $y - \hat{y}$, the prediction error or residual
      iii. $(y - \hat{y})^2$, the squared residual
   b. Calculate SSE, the sum of squares error.

11.

x	1	2	3	4
y	2	5	9	12

12.

x	0	2	4	6
y	5	6	5	4

13.

x	−5	−4	−3	−2	−1
y	0	8	8	16	16

14.

x	−3	−1	1	3	5
y	−5	−15	−20	−25	−30

15.

x	5	10	15	20	25	30
y	2	3	3	3	2	3

16.

x	6	7	8	9	11	13
y	4	4	4	4	4	4

For Exercises 17–22, calculate the standard error of the estimate, s, for the indicated data.
17. Data from Exercise 11
18. Data from Exercise 12
19. Data from Exercise 13
20. Data from Exercise 14
21. Data from Exercise 15
22. Data from Exercise 16

For Exercises 23–28, follow these steps.
   a. Compute the sample variance of the y data, $s^2 = \sum(y - \bar{y})^2/(n - 1)$.
   b. Use s^2 to calculate the total sum of squares, $SST = (n - 1)s^2$.
   c. Then use the relationship between the three sums of squares to find SSR, based on part **(b)** and your work in Exercises 11**(b)**–16**(b)**.
23. Data in Exercise 11
24. Data in Exercise 12
25. Data in Exercise 13
26. Data in Exercise 14
27. Data in Exercise 15
28. Data in Exercise 16

For Exercises 29–34, do the following.
   a. Using the results from Exercises 23**(b, c)**–28**(b, c)**, calculate the coefficient of determination, r^2.
   b. Interpret r^2 in terms of the proportion of variance in y accounted for by the linear regression between x and y.

   c. Use your work from part **(a)** and from Exercises 13**(a)**–18**(a)** of Section 4.2 to calculate the correlation coefficient, r.
29. Data in Exercise 11
30. Data in Exercise 12
31. Data in Exercise 13
32. Data in Exercise 14
33. Data in Exercise 15
34. Data in Exercise 16

APPLYING THE CONCEPTS
For Exercises 35–38, follow these steps. You have already calculated the regression equation in Exercises 51–54 in Section 4.2.
   a. Compute the residual for each data value. Form a table similar to Table 4.6 of the residuals and squared residuals. Sum the squared residuals to get SSE.
   b. Calculate and interpret s, the standard error of the estimate.
35. Education and Unemployment. Refer to the education and unemployment data from Exercise 51 in Section 4.2.
36. NASCAR Wins. Refer to the NASCAR data from Exercise 52 in Section 4.2.
37. SAT Scores. Refer to the SAT data from Exercise 53 in Section 4.2.
38. Brain and Body Weight. Refer to the brain and body weight data from Exercise 54 in Section 4.2.

For Exercises 39–42, follow these steps. Use your calculations from Exercises 35–38.
   a. Calculate the sample variance of the y data, s^2. Then use s^2 to calculate SST.
   b. Use SST and SSE to find SSR.
   c. Calculate and interpret the coefficient of determination r^2.
   d. Use r^2 and b_1 to find the correlation coefficient r.
39. Education and Unemployment. Refer to your calculations in Exercise 35 above and Exercise 46 in Section 4.1.
40. NASCAR Wins. Refer to your calculations in Exercise 36 above.
41. SAT Scores. Refer to your calculations in Exercise 37 above.
42. Brain and Body Weight. Refer to your calculations in Exercise 38 above and Exercise 50 in Section 4.1.

For Exercises 43–48 the regression equation is provided. Follow these steps.
   a. Compute the residual for each data value. Form a table similar to Table 4.6 of the residuals and squared residuals. Sum the squared residuals to get SSE.
   b. Calculate and interpret s, the standard error of the estimate.

c. Calculate the sample variance of the y data, s^2. Then use s^2 to calculate SST.

d. Use SST and SSE to find SSR.

e. Calculate and interpret the coefficient of determination, r^2.

f. Use r^2 and b_1 to find the correlation coefficient r.

43. Volume and Weight. The table contains the volume. (x, in cubic meters) and weight (y, in kilograms) of 5 randomly chosen packages shipped to a local village. The regression equation is $\hat{y} = 1.6x + 4$. 🐢 **volweight**

Volume (x)	Weight (y)
4	10
8	16
12	25
16	30
20	35

44. World Temperatures. Listed in the table are the low (x) and high (y) temperatures for a particular day in 2006, measured in degrees Fahrenheit, for a random sample of cities worldwide. The regression equation is $\hat{y} = 1.05x + 11.9$. 🐢 **worldtemp**

City	Low (x)	High (y)
Kolkata, India	57	77
London, England	36	45
Montreal, Quebec	7	21
Rome, Italy	39	55
San Juan, Puerto Rico	70	83
Shanghai, China	34	45

45. NCAA Power Ratings. For the NCAA basketball power ratings, is there a relationship between a school's winning percentage and the power rating? The table shows each team's winning percentage (x) and power rating (y) for the 2004 NCAA Basketball Tournament, according to **www.teamrankings.com**. The regression equation is $\hat{y} = 0.117x + 85$. 🐢 **ncaarate**

School	Win % (x)	Rating (y)
Duke	84	96.0
St. Joseph's	94	95.5
Connecticut	85	95.5
Oklahoma State	88	95.3
Pittsburgh	86	94.5
Georgia Tech	74	93.1

46. Teenage Birth Rate. The National Center for Health Statistics publishes data on state birth rates. The table contains the overall birth rate and the teenage birth rate for ten randomly chosen states. The overall birth rate is defined by the NCHS as "live births per 1000 women," and the teenage birth rate is defined as "live births per 1000 women aged 15–19." The regression equation is $\hat{y} = 5.39x - 34.3$. 🐢 **teenbirth**

State	x = overall birth rate	y = teenage birth rate
California	15.2	39.5
Florida	12.5	42.4
Georgia	15.7	53.4
New York	13.0	26.9
Ohio	13.0	38.5
Pennsylvania	11.7	30.5
Texas	17.0	62.6
Virginia	13.9	35.2

47. Height and Weight. The university medical unit is collecting data on the heights (in inches) and weights (in pounds) of the female students on campus. A random sample of ten female students showed the following heights and weights. The regression equation is $\hat{y} = 4.99x - 189$. 🐢 **studenthw**

Student	Height (x)	Weight (y)
1	60	100
2	60	115
3	62	110
4	63	125
5	63	135
6	64	145
7	66	140
8	67	145
9	68	150
10	70	155

48. Stock Prices. Would you expect there to be a relationship between the price (x) of a stock and its change (y) in price on a particular day? The table provides stock price and stock price change for August 2, 2004, for a random sample of ten stocks listed on the New York Stock Exchange. The regression equation is $\hat{y} = 0.01x - 0.112$. 🐢 **stockprice**

Stock	Price (x)	Change (y)
Nortel Networks	3.86	+0.04
Qwest Communications	3.41	−0.56
Lucent Technologies	3.04	−0.03
Tenet Healthcare	10.36	−0.82
Select Medical Group	14.74	+1.62
Cox Communications	33.19	+0.03
Verizon Communications	39.15	+0.46
General Electric	33.05	−0.21

Education and Unemployment. Refer to your work in Exercise 35 for Exercises 49 and 50.

49. Answer the following.
    a. Which data value has the largest residual? Describe what is unusual about this observation.
    b. Suppose a public figure stated that 50% of the variability in the unemployment rate was due to competition from abroad. How would you use the regression results to respond to this claim?
    c. Suppose a politician claimed that using the years of education alone could allow us to predict the unemployment rate to within 1%. How would you use the regression results to respond to this claim?
    d. Suppose a newspaper claimed that each additional year of education brought down the unemployment rate by "more than 1%." How would you use the regression results to either support or refute this claim?

50. *What if* the unemployment rate for those with 5 years of education was not 16.8% but a much higher percentage. Describe how this would affect the slope and y intercept of the regression line. Explain your reasoning. (*Hint:* Consult the What If Scenario in Section 4.2, page 175.)

SAT Scores. Look at your results from Exercise 37 for support in answering Exercises 51–53.

51. Answer the following.
    a. Which state has the largest positive residual? Describe what this means.
    b. Which state has the largest negative residual? Describe what this means.
    c. There is no zero score for the SAT Reading test. Does the y intercept make sense for this data set? Explain.

52. Use the regression results to either support or refute the indicated claim.
    a. Suppose someone said that for every additional point increase in the mean SAT Reading score, you could expect a 1-point increase in the mean SAT Math score.
    b. Suppose someone claimed that there was no correlation at all between the mean SAT Reading score and the mean SAT Math score.
    c. Suppose someone claimed that one could predict the mean SAT Math score to within 3 points, using the mean SAT Reading score alone.
    d. Suppose a newspaper said that the mean SAT Reading score explained over half of the variability in the mean SAT Math score.

53. *What if* the mean SAT Math score for New York was much higher than 510. Describe what would happen to the slope and y intercept of the regression line, and why.

Brain and Body Weight. Refer to your results from Exercise 38 for help in answering Exercises 54–57.

54. Use the regression results to either support or refute the indicated claim.
    a. Suppose a scientist said that body weight and brain weight were positively correlated.
    b. Suppose a biologist claimed that we could use body weight alone to predict brain weight to within about 402 grams.
    c. Suppose a scientist stated that, for every 1-kg increase in body weight, the brain weight increased by 5 grams.
    d. Suppose someone said that our results were crazy because they predict the brain weight of a mammal which weighed nothing at all to be 194 grams.

55. Which observation has the largest residual? Explain why this mammal is unusual. Can you tell which mammal this is?

56. Recalculate the regression results, after omitting the observation identified in Exercise 55.
    a. Describe whether the following statistics increase or decrease: b_1, b_0, s, r^2, r.
    b. Are brain weight and body weight positively correlated now?

57. Put the omitted observation back in the data set. Now *what if* we added a certain (unknown) amount to each mammal's brain weight. State how this would affect each of the following statistics, and why: b_1, b_0, s, r^2, r.

BRINGING IT ALL TOGETHER

Fuel Economy. For Exercises 58–65, refer to the table of fuel economy data from Exercises 70–74 in Section 4.2. The predictor variable is x = engine size, expressed in liters; the response variable is y = combined (city/highway) gas mileage, expressed in miles per gallon (mpg).

58. **Calculating and interpreting the residuals and SSE and s.**
    a. Compute the residual for each data value. Form a table similar to Table 4.6 of the residuals and squared residuals. Sum the squared residuals to get SSE.
    b. What is it that SSE is measuring? At this point, do we know whether SSE is large or small? Why or why not?
    c. Which vehicle has the largest absolute residual? Clearly explain why this vehicle is unusual.
    d. Suppose Subaru claimed that its combined mpg was higher than expected for the Subaru Forester, given its engine size. Do your regression results contain evidence in support of or against this claim?

59. **Calculating and Interpreting s.**
    a. Calculate the value of s, the standard error of the estimate.
    b. Interpret the value of s so that a nonstatistician could understand it.
    c. Suppose *Car and Driver* magazine claimed that, using engine size alone, we could predict the

combined mpg of a vehicle to within 2 miles per gallon. Support or refute this claim using your regression results.

60. **Computing and Interpreting SST, SSR, and r^2.**
    a. Calculate the sample variance of the y data, s^2. Then use s^2 to calculate SST.
    b. Use SSE and SST to find SSR. Explain clearly what it is that SSR is measuring.
    c. Calculate and interpret the coefficient of determination, r^2.
    d. Suppose *Consumer Reports* stated that over 90% of the variability in combined mpg could be explained by the size of the engine alone. Support or refute this claim using your regression results.

61. **Correlation.** Do the following.
    a. Use r^2 and b_1 to find the correlation coefficient r.
    b. Use the comparison test to determine whether we may conclude that engine size is correlated with combined mpg. Interpret the correlation between engine size and combined mpg.
    c. Suppose that a magazine claimed that engine size and combined mpg were correlated. How could you use your regression results to support or refute this claim?

62. *What if* we added one new vehicle to the data set, and its value was exactly $(\bar{x}, \bar{y})$. How would this affect the slope and the y intercept?

63. Refer to the previous exercise. *What if* we added an unknown amount to the engine size of the new vehicle. Describe how this change would affect the slope and the y intercept.

64. **Challenge Exercise.** Suppose we increased the combined mpg for the Cadillac Limousine so that the slope of the regression line would be exactly zero. What would the combined mpg for the Cadillac Limousine have to be to accomplish this?

65. **Challenge Exercise.** Refer to the previous exercise. Describe how this change to the fuel economy of the Cadillac Limousine would affect each of the following, and why: SSE, SSR, SST, s, r^2, r.

Calories and Fat Content. Use the following information for Exercises 66 and 67: Minitab calculated the regression equation, shown here, for the linear relationship between the number of calories (y) and the fat content in grams (x) in a sample of breakfast cereals.

```
Regression Analysis
The regression equation is
Calories = 97.1 + 9.65 Fat
```

66. The regression coefficients and the regression equation.
    a. What is the value of the y intercept?

b. Interpret the meaning of this value for the y intercept. Does it make sense?
    c. In view of the fact that there are many cereals in the data set with zero fat content, would the value for the y intercept in (b) be considered extrapolation? Why or why not?
    d. Interpret the meaning of the slope coefficient $b_1 = 9.65$ as fat content increases.
    e. Write the regression equation. Now state in words what the regression equation means.
    f. Is the correlation coefficient positive or negative? How do you know?

67. **Challenge Exercise.** Estimate the increase or decrease in calories, using a sentence, for the following situations.
    a. Suppose Cereal A has two more grams of fat than Cereal B.
    b. Suppose Cereal C has three fewer grams of fat than Cereal D.

For Exercises 68–70, use Minitab or Excel and follow steps **(a)–(e)**.
    a. Construct the scatterplot.
    b. Compute and interpret the regression equation.
    c. Calculate and interpret the coefficient of determination, r^2.
    d. Compute and interpret s, the standard error of the estimate.
    e. Find r, using r^2.

68. Open the **darts** data set, which we used for the Chapter 3 Case Study. Let $x =$ the Dow Jones Industrial Average, and let $y =$ the pros' performance. **darts**

69. Open the **Nutrition** data set. Let $x =$ the amount of fat per gram, and let $y =$ the number of calories per gram. **Nutrition**

70. Open the **pulse and temp** data set. Let $x =$ heart rate, and let $y =$ body temperature. **pulseandtemp**

CONSTRUCT YOUR OWN DATA SETS

Suppose we have a tiny data set with the following (x, y) pairs.

x	y
1	?
2	?
3	?

For Exercises 71–75, create a set of y-values that would fulfill each specification.

71. The slope of the line is positive.
72. The slope of the line is negative.
73. The slope of the line is 0.
74. The slope of the line is equal to 2.
75. The slope of the line is equal to -3.

Use the *Correlation and Regression* applet for Exercises 76–78.

76. In these applet exercises, use the "thermometer" above the graph (where it says "Sum of squares =") to help find the least-squares regression line interactively.

   a. Select 5 points so that the correlation coefficient is about 0.8. Then select "Draw line."

   b. Make your best guess about where the least-squares regression line should be, and draw the line there.

77. The blue section of the thermometer is a measure of the sum of squares error, the total squared vertical distance from the data points to the actual regression line. Recall that the least-squares regression line minimizes this distance. The green section of the thermometer tells you how much "extra" squared error you get from using the line you constructed in Exercise 76(a).

   a. Adjust the line you drew in Exercise 76(a) by clicking and dragging on the points until the green section of the thermometer has disappeared.

   b. What does the disappearance of the green part tell you about the adjusted line you constructed?

   c. Will the line now coincide with the least-squares regression line?

78. Verify that your adjusted line from Exercise 77 coincides with the least-squares regression line by selecting "Show least-squares line."

Chapter 4 Formulas and Vocabulary

SECTION 4.1
- **Comparison test for linear correlation** (p. 166)
- **Correlation coefficient *r*** (p. 161).

Definition formula:

$$r = \frac{\sum(x - \bar{x})(y - \bar{y})}{(n - 1)s_x s_y}$$

Computational formula:

$$r = \frac{\sum xy - \left(\sum x \sum y\right)/n}{\sqrt{\left[\sum x^2 - \left(\sum x\right)^2/n\right]\left[\sum y^2 - \left(\sum y\right)^2/n\right]}}$$

- **Positive and negative correlation** (p. 163)
- **Scatterplot** (p. 158)

SECTION 4.2
- **Extrapolation** (p. 178)
- **Prediction error, or residual** (p. 177).

$$(y - \hat{y})$$

- **Regression equation (regression line)** (p. 172).

$$\hat{y} = b_1 x + b_0$$

- **Slope of the regression line** (p. 172).

Definition formula:

$$b_1 = \frac{\sum(x - \bar{x})(y - \bar{y})}{\sum(x - \bar{x})^2}$$

Computational formula (p. 174):

$$b_1 = \frac{\sum xy - \left(\sum x \sum y\right)/n}{\sum x^2 - \left(\sum x\right)^2/n}$$

- **y Intercept of the regression line** (p. 172).

$$b_0 = \bar{y} - (b_1 \cdot \bar{x})$$

SECTION 4.3
- **Coefficient of determination *r²*** (p. 190).

$$r^2 = \text{SSR/SST}$$

- **Least-squares criterion** (p. 186)
- **SSE, sum of squares error** (p. 186).

$$\text{SSE} = \sum(y - \hat{y})^2$$

- **Standard error of the estimate *s*** (p. 187).

$$s = \sqrt{\frac{\text{SSE}}{n - 2}}$$

- **SSR, sum of squares regression** (p. 189).

Definition formula:

$$\text{SSR} = \sum(\hat{y} - \bar{y})^2$$

Computational formula (p. 191):

$$\text{SSR} = \frac{\left[\sum xy - \left(\sum x\right)\left(\sum y\right)/n\right]^2}{\sum x^2 - \left(\sum x\right)^2/n}$$

- **SST, total sum of squares** (p. 188).

Definition formula:

$$\text{SST} = \sum(y - \bar{y})^2$$

Computational formula (p. 191):

$$\text{SST} = \sum y^2 - \left(\sum y\right)^2/n$$

Chapter 4 Review Exercises

SECTION 4.1

Midterm Exams and Overall Grade. Use the data in the following table to answer Exercises 1–5. Can you predict how you will do in a course based on the result of the midterm exam only? The midterm exam score and the overall grade were recorded for a random sample of 12 students in an elementary statistics course. The results are shown in the following table. 🖐 **midexam**

Midterm exams and overall grades

Student	Midterm exam score (x)	Overall grade (y)
1	50	65
2	90	80
3	70	75
4	80	75
5	60	45
6	90	95
7	90	85
8	80	80
9	70	65
10	70	70
11	60	65
12	50	55

1. Construct a scatterplot of overall grade versus midterm exam score.
2. Refer to your scatterplot from Exercise 1.
   a. Characterize the relationship as positive, negative, or not apparent.
   b. Write a sentence that describes the behavior of the overall grade as the midterm exam score increases.
3. Calculate the value of the correlation coefficient r between midterm exam scores and overall grades.
4. Use the comparison test to determine whether we may conclude x and y are correlated.
5. Interpret the value for r.

Income and Hours Worked. Use the following information for Exercises 6–8. The table contains the weekly gross income (y) and the number of hours worked (x) for a random selection of 5 fast-food workers. 🖐 **fastfoodhrs**

Gross income (in dollars) and hours worked for five fast-food workers

	Fast-food worker				
	1	2	3	4	5
Gross income: y	80	120	160	200	240
Hours worked: x	10	15	20	25	30

6. Construct a scatterplot of the variables.
7. What type of relationship do these variables have: positive, negative, or no apparent linear relationship?
8. Calculating and interpreting the correlation coefficient.
   a. Before calculating the value of the correlation coefficient, try to guess what it might be, based on your scatterplot.
   b. Compute the value of the correlation coefficient.
   c. Does this value for r agree with your earlier estimate?
   d. Determine whether x and y are correlated.
   e. Interpret in two different ways the meaning of this value of the correlation coefficient.

SECTION 4.2

For Exercises 9–15, refer to the table of midterm exams (x) and overall grades (y).
9. Calculate the regression coefficients b_0 and b_1, and write the regression equation.
10. State the regression equation in words, as shown at the end of Example 4.7 (page 173).
11. Interpret the value of the slope b_1.
12. Interpret the value of the y-intercept b_0.
13. Use the regression equation to predict the overall grades for the following midterm exam scores.
    a. $x = 50$ b. $x = 100$
14. Calculate and interpret the prediction error for each prediction in Exercise 13.
15. For each prediction in Exercise 13, state whether the prediction represents extrapolation.

SECTION 4.3

Refer to the midterm exam and overall grade data, to answer Exercises 16–20.
16. Calculate SSE.
17. Calculate s, the standard error of the estimate. What does this number mean?
18. Calculate SST. Then use SSE and SST to find SSR.
19. Calculate r^2, the coefficient of determination. Comment on how useful midterm exam scores are for predicting overall grades.
20. Use r^2 to calculate the correlation coefficient. Comment on the relationship between midterm exam scores and overall grades.

Chapter 4 QUIZ

TRUE OR FALSE

 1. True or false: Scatterplots are constructed with the y variable on the horizontal axis and the x variable on the vertical axis.

 2. True or false: The y intercept measures the strength of the linear relationship between two numerical variables.

FILL IN THE BLANK

 3. The "hat" over the y in $\hat{y}$ indicates that it is an _____ of y.

 4. We interpret the slope of the regression line as the estimated change in y per _____ increase in x.

SHORT ANSWER

 5. Making predictions based on x-values that are beyond the range of the x-values in our data set is called what?

 6. Values of r close to -1 indicate what type of relationship between the two variables?

CALCULATIONS AND INTERPRETATIONS

Violent Crime. Use the following information for Exercises 7–14. The Federal Bureau of Investigation publishes crime statistics, including those in the following table, which shows the percentage of violent crime committed per month nationwide for the years 2002 and 2004.[2] **violentcrime**

Month	2002	2004
January	7.9	7.8
February	6.8	7.0
March	7.9	8.3
April	8.1	8.2
May	8.7	9.0
June	8.8	8.6
July	9.3	9.2
August	9.3	9.0
September	9.2	8.5
October	8.6	8.6
November	7.7	7.8
December	7.7	7.9

 7. Construct a scatterplot of 2004 monthly crime versus 2002 monthly crime.

 8. Based on your scatterplot, would you characterize the linear relationship, if any, as positive or negative?

 9. Compute the regression equation.

 10. Calculate the three sums of squares: SSR, SST, and SSE.

 11. Calculate s, the standard error of the estimate. What does this number mean?

 12. Calculate r^2. Comment on how useful the 2002 percentages are in predicting the 2004 percentages.

 13. Use r^2 to calculate and interpret the correlation coefficient.

 14. Find the prediction error for the following percentages:
   a. 7.9   **b.** 9.3   **c.** 8.1

5

Probability

Introduction

Chapter 5 explains the tools of probability, which enable data analysts to quantify the level of uncertainty in statistical inference.

Section 5.1 introduces experiments, outcomes, events, and sample spaces. The classical method, the relative frequency method, and the subjective method of assigning probabilities are introduced, as well as the Law of Large Numbers.

In Section 5.2, students learn about combining events using the concepts of union, intersection, and complement. Section 5.3 examines conditional probability, independent events, and sampling with and without replacement. In Section 5.4, counting methods are used to find the number of combinations and permutations of a set of objects.

From the Author

- **Section 5.1 Introducing Probability**

  - You may wish to stress the "difference in perspective" of this chapter from previous chapters. See the feature on page 202.

  - The probability chapter offers many opportunities to increase student motivation by talking about the application of probability to games of chance. For example, many students enjoy working with the two-dice sample space, or the deck of cards sample space.

- **Section 5.2 Combining Events**

  - Students who have trouble with the concept of intersection may benefit from a look at Figure 5.13 on page 219. Consider the row to be a "street" and the column to be a different street. Then the ace of heart lies in the *intersection* of these two streets. You can do something similar with Table 5.5 on page 220.

- **Section 5.3 Conditional Probability**

  - In conditional probability, students often confuse "B given A" with "B and A." Stress the Caution at the top of page 228, along with Figure 5.16 on page 227 to help dispel this confusion.

  - The 1% Guideline on page 233 has been added to clarify when successive draws from a population may be considered independent.

  - It may save your gambling students a lot of money if you discuss the Gambler's Fallacy on page 229.

- **Section 5.4 Counting Methods**

  - Many business and engineering students may need to learn quality control methods. *Acceptance sampling* on page 250 is a widespread method for businesses to track quality across their enterprise.

Teaching Tips

In Chapters 1–4, the students used statistics, tables, and graphs to describe a data set. This is descriptive statistics. However, here in Chapter 5, we need to shift our point of view. No longer are we given a data set to describe. Instead, we are presented with an experiment, with certain outcomes and events defined. We need to find probabilities of these outcomes and events. This is the tri-class activities realm of probability, which has a different perspective from descriptive statistics.

In-Class Activities

1. To explain the difference between the classical method and the relative frequency method of assigning probabilities, first ask students, "What is the probability of an event that uses the classical method of probability, such as rolling a 72 with a 100-sided die?" Then ask, "What is the probability of an event that uses the relative frequency method, such as selecting a student at random from a college in your state?" and "What is the probability that the student is enrolled in an elementary statistics class that semester?" Students will be able to find the first probability even if they have never rolled a 100-sided die before, but they won't be able to find the second probability without knowing the number of students enrolled at a college in their state and the number of students enrolled in an elementary statistics class.

2. To explain the counting rules, ask students to think about how they would perform the task. Suppose you wanted to line up 6 people. Ask them how many ways there are to select a first person in line. Have them select a first person. Now ask them how many ways there are to select a second person in line. Have them select a second person. Continue this process until all 6 people are lined up. Then show that there are $6 \cdot 5 \cdot 4 \cdot 3 \cdot 2 \cdot 1 = 720$ ways to line up 6 people.

3. To illustrate the Law of Large Numbers, have students do an experiment in class such as flipping a coin or rolling a die. Divide them into groups of 2 or 3 and perform the experiment 50 times. Ask students to keep track of the number of heads and tails if they flip coins or the number of 1s, 2s, . . . 6s if they roll a die. Pool all the results and have students calculate the relative frequencies. Ask them to compare the relative frequencies to the theoretical probabilities.

4. Have you ever taken a multiple-choice test where you couldn't decide between the alternatives and wished you could flip a coin or roll a die to decide? Suppose you are facing a four-question multiple-choice exam, with three alternatives (A, B, or C) for each question, and you have no clue as to what the right answers are. In this activity you will calculate the probability of getting one or more answers right.

    a. Why does it make sense to use the classical method?

    b. Draw a tree diagram for this four-question test—the experiment.

    c. What is the probability that you will answer a particular question correctly?

    d. What is the probability that you will answer two questions correctly?

    e. What is the probability that you will answer three questions correctly?

    f. What is the probability that you will answer all four questions correctly?

    g. Suppose that you need to answer at least three out of the four questions correctly to pass. What is the probability that you will pass?

5. We use simulation to estimate the probabilities we calculated in activity 1. We use a single fair die to determine our responses.

    a. How should we "code" the die results so that there is an even chance of choosing A, B, or C?

    b. Your answer to each exam question will be either right or wrong. Why not use a coin toss rather than a die roll for this simulation?

    c. We need to code the probability of getting a correct answer. For each question, A, B, or C is correct. We want to simulate the probability of guessing correctly, which is 1/3. How do you code the die roll so that the probability of guessing correctly is 1/3?

    d. Perform 20 trials of the experiment. Rolling the die one time is considered to be answering one test question. So rolling the die four times is considered to be one "trial" of the experiment (taking the test). For each trial, keep track of the number of "right" and "wrong" guesses. Answer questions (e)–(h) using your simulation results.

    e. Estimate the probability that you will answer exactly one particular question correctly.

    f. Estimate the probability that you will answer exactly two questions correctly.

    g. Estimate the probability that you will answer exactly three questions correctly.

    h. Estimate the probability that you will answer all four questions correctly.

    i. Estimate the probability that you will pass.

Supplements

- StatTutor 6.1, 6.2, 10.1–10.3, 12.1–12.6

Applets

The *Law of Large Numbers for Proportion* applet is referenced in Chapter 5 to compute relative frequencies for experiments and for Exercises 96 and 97 in Section 5.1.

    Activities on probability simulation can be found at **http://mathforum.org/mathtools/ sitemap2/ps/**.

    The site Online Statistics: An Interactive Multimedia Course of Study has a *Probability* applet that demonstrates several simulations: **http://onlinestatbook.com/index.html**.

Videos

- *Against All Odds*: **www.learner.org/resources/series65.html**
  - Program 15: What Is Probability?
  - Program 16: Random Variables

Web Sites

- This Web site has a collection of 20 class projects: **www.amstat.org/publications/jse/v6n3/ smith.html**.
- This Texas Instruments Web site has a host of TI-83/84 statistics activities: **http://education .ti.com/educationportal/sites/US/nonProductSingle/activitybook_83_statistics.html**.
- This Web site lists other sites that do statistical calculations: **http://statpages.org/**.
- This Web site lists numerous activities on all topics: **http://mathforum.org/mathtools/ sitemap2/ps/**.

Martin Heitner/Stock Connection/Glow Images

OVERVIEW

5

Probability

CASE STUDY

The ELISA Test for the Presence of HIV

If someone suspects that he or she is at increased risk of HIV infection, then he or she might be interested in going for an HIV ELISA test. The ELISA test is used to screen blood for the presence of HIV. Sometimes called an HIV enzyme immunoassay (EIA), an HIV ELISA is the most basic test for finding out if an individual is carrying a particular pathogen, such as HIV.

Like most diagnostic procedures, the ELISA test is not foolproof. In this chapter's Case Study we study the types of errors the ELISA test can make and what this means for those who carry the HIV virus and for those who do not. For example, did you know that if your ELISA test comes back positive, then the chances are eight out of ten that you do *not* carry the virus?

The Big Picture

Where we are coming from, and where we are headed . . .

- Chapters 1–4 dealt with descriptive statistics that summarize data. In later chapters, we will learn inferential statistics, which generalize from a sample to a population. But generalizing involves *uncertainty*.

- Chapter 5 teaches us the language of uncertainty: **probability.** We will learn how to quantify uncertainty, using experiments, events, outcomes, rules for combining events, conditional probability, and counting methods.

- In Chapter 6, "Probability Distributions," we learn about the two most important probability distributions, the normal and the binomial, which will be our companions for the remainder of the text.

5.1 Introducing Probability

OBJECTIVES By the end of this section, I will be able to . . .

1 Understand the meaning of an experiment, an outcome, an event, and a sample space.

2 Describe the classical method of assigning probability.

3 Explain the Law of Large Numbers and the relative frequency method of assigning probability.

Imagine you are striding down the midway of your local town fair, when a particular game of chance catches your eye. The object of this game is to roll a 6 on a single roll of a single fair die. If you do so, you win $5. It costs $1 to play the game. What is the likelihood of winning?

To show how to solve this problem, we must first introduce the building blocks of probability.

1 Building Blocks of Probability

Our daily lives are filled with *uncertainty,* seemingly governed by *chance.* We try to cope with uncertainty by estimating the *chances* that a particular event will occur. We are daily called on to make intelligent decisions about probabilities. Consider the following scenarios, and think about how the italicized words all refer to uncertainty.

- What is the *chance* that there will be a speed trap on this stretch of I-95 on a particular day?

- What is the *likelihood* that this lottery ticket will make me rich?

- What is the *probability* that this throw of the dice will come up a seven?

Sometimes, the amount of uncertainty in our daily lives is so great that there appears to be no order to the world whatsoever. However, if you look closely, there are *patterns in randomness.* In this chapter, we learn to become better decision makers by becoming acquainted with the tools of probability in order to quantify many of the uncertainties of everyday life.

Developing Your Statistical Sense	**A Different Perspective**

A Different Perspective

As you read this chapter, notice that the perspective differs from that in previous chapters. Earlier, we were looking at a data set and trying to describe it graphically and numerically. Now, instead of trying to describe a data set, we are faced with an experimental situation, and our task is to calculate probabilities associated with various outcomes in the experiment. ◢

The **probability** of an outcome is defined as the long-term proportion of times the outcome occurs.

We discuss what we mean by "long-term proportion" later in this section. But first we acquaint ourselves with the building blocks of probability, starting with the concept of an experiment. In probability, an **experiment** is any activity for which the outcome is uncertain. Consider the stock market, for example. Suppose you own 100 shares of Consolidated Widgets and are interested in what the share price will be at the end of trading tomorrow. Will the share price increase or decrease? The actual result is uncertain, so this is an example of an experiment. Each of the possible results of the experiment is called an **outcome.** Another example of an experiment is when you toss a coin. In the coin-toss experiment, the result may be heads or it may be tails. The collection of all possible outcomes is called the **sample space.** The sample space for the coin-toss experiment is {heads, tails} or {H, T}. Following are some common experiments, together with their sample spaces.

We use braces, [ ], to enclose a set of outcomes.

Experiment	Sample space
Roll a single six-sided die	{1, 2, 3, 4, 5, 6}
Toss two coins	{HH, HT, TH, TT}
Play a video game	{win, lose}

We use the building blocks of probability to investigate the likelihood of an outcome or **event.**

> **Building Blocks of Probability**
>
> An **experiment** is any activity for which the outcome is uncertain.
>
> An **outcome** is the result of a single performance of an experiment.
>
> The collection of all possible outcomes is called the **sample space.** We denote the sample space S.
>
> An **event** is a collection of outcomes from the sample space. To find the probability of an event, add up the probabilities of all the outcomes in the event.

When we talk about the probability of some outcome, we are referring to a number that indicates how likely the particular outcome is. The notation $P(A)$ stands for "the probability that outcome A occurred." Say we define outcome W to be $W =$ "you win the video game." Then "the probability that you win the video game" can be denoted as $P(W)$. Probabilities abide by the following rules.

> **Rules of Probability**
> 1. The probability $P(E)$ for any event E is always between 0 and 1, inclusive. That is, $0 \leq P(E) \leq 1$.
> 2. **Law of Total Probability:** For any experiment, the sum of all the outcome probabilities in the sample space must equal 1.

CAUTION If the probability that you calculated is negative or greater than 1, then you should try again.

Now You Can Do
Exercises 11–16.

From the definition, the probability of an event is a proportion, so the probability cannot be negative because proportions cannot be negative and it cannot be greater than 1 (100%) because an event cannot occur more than 100% of the time. A **probability model** is a table or listing of all the possible outcomes of an experiment, together with the probability of each outcome. A probability model must follow the Rules of Probability.

Throughout the remainder of this book, you will often be asked to calculate the probability of various events. Following are the meanings of some probabilities.

Probability value	Meaning
Near 0	Outcome or event is very unlikely.
Equal to 0	Outcome or event cannot occur.
Near 1	Outcome or event is nearly certain to occur.
Equal to 1	Outcome or event is certain to occur. It's "a sure thing."
Low	Outcome or event is unusual.
High	Outcome or event is not unusual.

The threshold of an unusual event depends on the specific experiment; the 0.05 is not set in stone.

Higher probability values are associated with higher likelihood of occurrence. An outcome with probability 0.5 will happen about half of the time. An outcome with probability 0.95 is very likely. We say that an outcome or event is *unusual* if its probability is below a certain threshold, say, 0.05. When we perform an experiment, it is a "sure thing" that one of the outcomes in the sample space will occur. For example, when you toss a coin, you know that it will be either heads or tails. Put into probability terms, the sum of the probabilities of all the individual outcomes must equal 1, the **Law of Total Probability.**

The following table shows some typical events for the experiments in the table on page 202.

Experiment	Sample space	Typical events
Roll a single die	{1, 2, 3, 4, 5, 6}	E: roll an even number = {2, 4, 6} L: roll a 4 or larger = {4, 5, 6}
Toss two coins	{HH, HT, TH, TT}	H: exactly one head = {HT, TH} T: at most one tail = {HH, HT, TH}
Play a video game	{win, lose}	W: win = {win} L: lose = {lose}

2 Classical Method of Assigning Probability

Many people have a certain degree of intuition when it comes to assigning probabilities. For example, when asked what the chances are of rolling a 6 on a single toss of a fair die, many people would quite correctly answer 1/6. However, intuition can often let us down. For example, when asked what the chances are of observing two heads when you toss a fair coin twice, many people would incorrectly respond 1/3 ("Well, it's either both heads or both tails or one of each." The correct answer is in fact 1/4.) In this section, we learn how to quantify our methods of assigning probabilities so that we don't have to depend on intuition alone.

There are three methods for assigning probabilities:

- Classical method
- Relative frequency method
- Subjective method

We first take a close look at the classical method. Later in this section, we will examine the relative frequency method and the subjective method.

Many experiments are structured so that each experimental outcome is equally likely. *Equally likely outcomes* are outcomes that have the same probability of occurring. For example, if you toss a fair coin, the probability of observing either of the outcomes heads or tails is the same. The **classical method of assigning probabilities** is used when an experiment has equally likely outcomes.

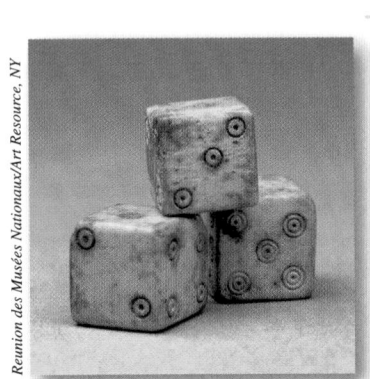

Did you know? People have been tossing dice for a long time. Archaeologists have dug up dice from Roman ruins looking just the same as ours. These three dice were uncovered from the ruins of Pompeii buried by the eruption of Mount Vesuvius in the first century A.D.

Classical Method of Assigning Probabilities

Let $N(E)$ and $N(S)$ denote the number of outcomes in event E and the sample space S, respectively. If the experiment has equally likely outcomes, then the probability of event E is

$$P(E) = \frac{\text{number of outcomes in } E}{\text{number of outcomes in sample space}} = \frac{N(E)}{N(S)}$$

Example 5.1   Probability of drawing an ace

Find the probability of drawing an ace when drawing a single card at random from a deck of cards.

Solution

The sample space for the experiment where a subject chooses a single card at random from a deck of cards is given in Figure 5.1. If the card is chosen truly at random, then it is

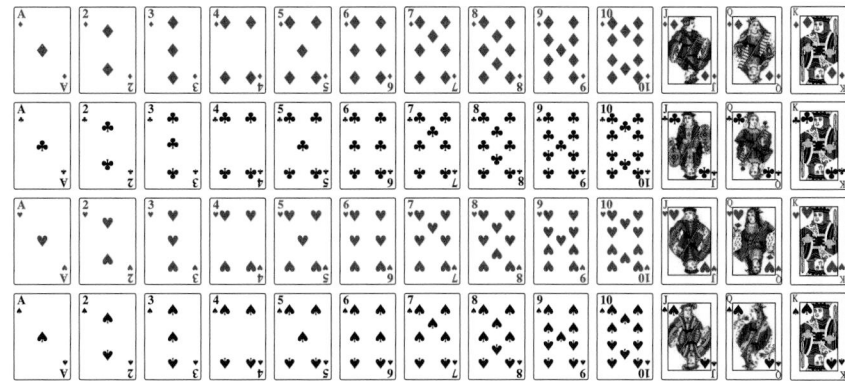

FIGURE 5.1 Sample space for drawing a card at random from a deck of cards.

reasonable to assume that each card has the same chance of being drawn. Since each card is equally likely to be drawn, we can use the classical method to assign probabilities.

There are 52 outcomes in this sample space, so $N(S) = 52$. Let E be the event that an ace is drawn. Event E consists of the four aces $\{A\heartsuit, A\diamondsuit, A\clubsuit, A\spadesuit\}$, so $N(E) = 4$. Therefore, the probability of drawing an ace is

Now You Can Do
Exercises 17–20.

$$P(E) = \frac{N(E)}{N(S)} = \frac{4}{52} = \frac{1}{13}$$ ∎

Example 5.2 Fair die toss outcomes are equally likely

Recall the town fair example (at the top of page 202). In the game, you win if you roll a 6 on a single roll of a single fair die. Find the probability of winning the game.

Solution

The sample space for a single die toss consists of six outcomes, $\{1, 2, 3, 4, 5, 6\}$. When the six outcomes are equally likely, we say that the die is *fair*. If the outcomes are not equally likely, then the die is *loaded* or defective. If we assume the die is fair, then, since the sum of the probabilities of the $n = 6$ outcomes must equal 1, the probability of any particular outcome must equal 1/6, using the classical method. We write

Now You Can Do
Exercises 21–26.

probability of winning $= P(W) = 1/6$ ∎

Tree Diagrams

A **tree diagram** is a graphical display that allows us to list all the outcomes in the sample space of a multistage experiment. The next example shows how to construct a tree diagram.

Example 5.3 List all outcomes in a sample space using a tree diagram

Suppose our experiment is to toss a fair coin twice.
a. Construct a tree diagram.
b. Use the tree diagram to list all the outcomes in the sample space.

Solution

a. Think of this experiment as a two-stage process:
- Stage 1: Toss the coin the first time.
- Stage 2: Toss the coin the second time.

Figure 5.2 shows the tree diagram for the experiment of tossing a fair coin twice. Note the branches for Stage 1: the first time the coin is tossed, it can come up heads or tails. At Stage 2, the tree diagram again has branches for either heads or tails.

b. The sample space for the experiment of tossing a coin twice is {HH, HT, TH, TT}. There are $N(S) = 4$ outcomes in the sample space. ■

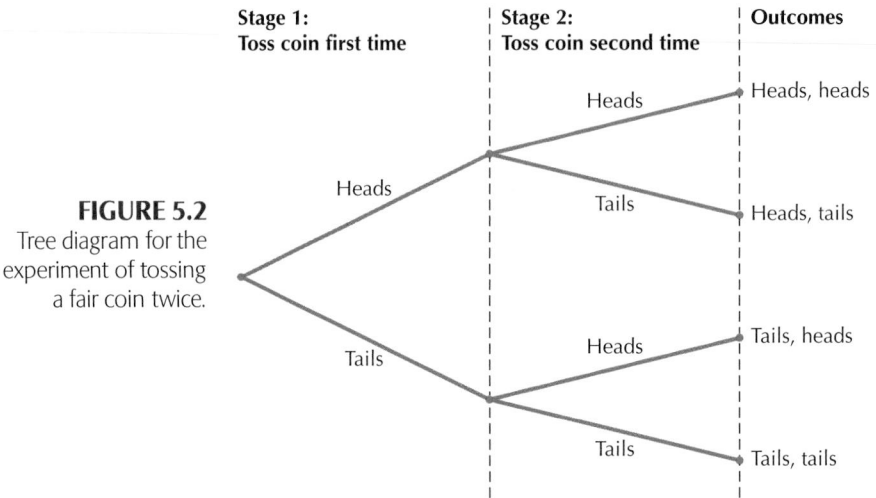

FIGURE 5.2
Tree diagram for the experiment of tossing a fair coin twice.

Now You Can Do
Exercises 29 and 30.

Note that there are two possible outcomes at Stage 1 of this two-stage experiment and two possible outcomes when flipping the coin at Stage 2. To determine how many outcomes there are in the entire experiment, the *counting rule* is simply to multiply the number of possible outcomes at each stage. In this two-stage experiment, 2 times 2 equals 4 possible outcomes, which is the number of outcomes we see in the sample space.

Example 5.4   Finding probabilities for the experiment of tossing a coin twice

Find the probability of obtaining one heads and one tails when a fair coin is tossed twice.

Solution

It is reasonable to assume that the $N(S) = 4$ outcomes in the sample space {HH, HT, TH, TT} are equally likely. The coin doesn't remember what occurred at Stage 1, so the probabilities at Stage 2 are precisely the same as at Stage 1. Also, recall from the Law of Total Probability that the sum of the probabilities of all the outcomes in the sample space must equal 1. Thus, each of the four outcomes must have probability 1/4. Let E be the event that one heads and one tails is obtained. Then $E = $ {HT, TH}, so $N(E) = 2$. Thus,

Now You Can Do
Exercises 31–33.

$$P(E) = \frac{\text{number of outcomes in } E}{\text{number of outcomes in sample space}} = \frac{N(E)}{N(S)} = \frac{2}{4} = \frac{1}{2}$$ ■

Example 5.5   Finding probabilities for the experiment of tossing two fair dice

Imagine that you are playing Monopoly with your dormitory roommate, and the loser has to do the laundry for both of you for the rest of the semester. You have a hotel on Boardwalk, and if your roommate lands on it, you will surely win. Right now your roommate's piece is on Short Line: if he or she rolls a 4, you will win and get your laundry done free for the remainder of the semester. Put into statistical terms, the experiment is to toss two fair dice and observe the sum of the two dice. Find the probability of rolling a sum of 4 when tossing two fair dice.

Solution

It is reasonable to assume that each of these $N(S) = 36$ outcomes in the sample space (Figure 5.3) is equally likely. The experiment of tossing two dice can be viewed as a two-stage experiment, where we add the result from the first die to the result from the second die. If a 5 appears on the first (say, dark green) die, and a 3 appears on the second (light green) die, the overall outcome is (5,3), with the resulting sum equal to 8. Note that the outcome (5,3) is not the same as the outcome (3,5), where the dark green die comes up 3 and the light green die comes up 5.

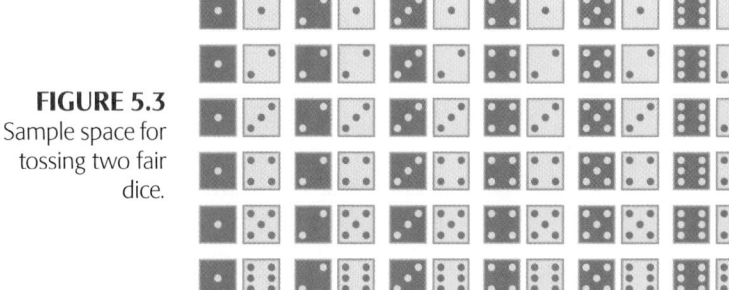

FIGURE 5.3
Sample space for tossing two fair dice.

Let E denote the event that your roommate rolls a sum equal to 4. Then the outcomes that belong in this event are E: {(3,1) (2,2) (1,3)}, so $N(E) = 3$. Since the outcomes are equally likely, we can use the classical method for finding probabilities of events.

$$P(E) = \frac{\text{number of outcomes in } E}{\text{number of outcomes in sample space}} = \frac{N(E)}{N(S)} = \frac{3}{36} = \frac{1}{12}$$

The probability that your roommate will land on Boardwalk on this throw of the dice is 1/12. ∎

Now You Can Do
Exercises 49–53.

Example 5.6 Inappropriate use of the classical method

A recent study[1] showed that 59% of teenagers owned a computer (either a desktop or a laptop). Suppose we choose one teenager at random. Define the following events:

  C: The randomly chosen teenager owns a computer.
  D: The randomly chosen teenager does not own a computer.

Determine whether the classical method can be used to assign probability to events C and D.

Solution

Because more than half of teenagers own a computer, if we choose a teenager at random, we are more likely to select a teenager who owns a computer than to select one who does not. Therefore, the events C and D are not equally likely. It would be inappropriate to use the classical method of assigning probabilities for this experiment because the classical method can be used only when all the outcomes of an experiment are equally likely. ∎

The proper method for solving this problem is the relative frequency method, which we discuss next.

3 Relative Frequency Method

In Example 5.2, we need the classical method to find that the probability of rolling a 6 with a fair die is 1/6. What does this probability mean? Remember that the definition of *probability* included the phrase "long-term proportion." The next example demonstrates what we mean by "long-term."

Example 5.7 | Simulating the long-term proportion of 6s in a fair die roll

Suppose we would like to investigate the proportion of 6s we observe if we roll a fair die 100 times. We can use technology, such as the TI-83/84 used here, to help us simulate rolling a fair die a large number of times. A **simulation** uses methods such as rolling dice or computer generation of random numbers to generate results from an experiment. The actual die rolls from our simulation are shown here, in order, with the 6s in boldface.

1 4 4 **6** 2 4 3 2 1 3 4 3 3 4 3 3 **6** 3 5 5 1 5 3 5 5 2 1 3 1 1 1 5 5 **6** 3 **6** 2 1 **6** 5 5 4 4 **6** 5 4 1 1 4 **6**
4 2 2 2 **6** 3 2 5 5 **6** 1 1 3 1 **6** 5 4 **6** **6** 5 5 5 2 5 5 3 4 2 4 **6** 4 5 5 1 **6** 3 1 1 1 3 5 4 2 3 3 3 **6** 2 5 3

Thus, the first die roll was a 1, so the proportion of 6s was 0/1. The second and third die rolls were 4s, so the proportion of 6s after 3 rolls was 0/3. On the fourth roll a 6 appeared, so the proportion of 6s after the fourth roll was 1/4. Figure 5.4 provides a graph of the proportion of 6s in this simulation as the number of die rolls increased. Note that as the number of die rolls increases, the proportion of 6s tends to get closer to the horizontal line, $0.1667 \approx 1/6$.

The simulation was rerun, this time with 1000 die rolls. The resulting graph of the proportion of 6s is provided in Figure 5.5. Note that as the number of die rolls increases, the proportion of 6s approaches the line $0.1667 \approx 1/6$, and the fit is tighter with 1000 die rolls than with 100. This is what we mean by "long-term proportion." ∎

FIGURE 5.4 Proportion of 6s, 100 die rolls.   **FIGURE 5.5** Proportion of 6s, 1000 die rolls.

This example leads directly to the following law.

Law of Large Numbers

As the number of times that an experiment is repeated increases, the relative frequency (proportion) of a particular outcome tends to approach the *probability* of the outcome.

- For quantitative data, as the number of times that an experiment is repeated increases, the mean of the outcomes tends to approach the population mean.
- For categorical (qualitative) data, as the number of times that an experiment is repeated increases, the proportion of times a particular outcome occurs tends to approach the population proportion.

The *Law of Large Numbers for Proportions* applet allows you to simulate coin tossing and observe the proportion of heads as the number of tosses increases.

Relative Frequency Method

If we can't use the classical method for assigning probabilities, then the **Law of Large Numbers** gives us a hint about how we can estimate the probability of an event. It often happens that previous information is available about the relative frequency of an event. Relative frequency information can be used to estimate the probability of the event.

Note: Tree diagrams can be used for the relative frequency method as well as the classical method of assigning probability.

> **Relative Frequency Method of Assigning Probabilities**
>
> The probability of event E is approximately equal to the relative frequency of event E. That is,
>
> $$P(E) \approx \text{relative frequency of } E = \frac{\text{frequency of } E}{\text{number of trials of experiment}}$$
>
> The relative frequency method is also known as the **empirical method.**

Example 5.8 Relative frequency method: teen bloggers

A recent study found that 35% of all online teen girls are bloggers, compared to 20% of online teen boys. Suppose that the 35% came from a random sample of 100 teen girls who use the Internet, 35 of whom are bloggers. If we choose one teen girl at random, find the probability that she is a blogger.

Solution

Define the event.

    B: The online girl is a blogger.

We use the relative frequency method to find the probability of event B:

Now You Can Do
Exercises 57–60.

$$P(B) \approx \text{relative frequency of } B = \frac{\text{frequency of } B}{\text{number of trials in experiment}} = \frac{35}{100} = 0.35 \ \blacksquare$$

We can also use the relative frequency method to build a probability model with data that have been summarized in a table.

Example 5.9 Probability models based on frequency tables

Table 5.1 Employment types

Employment type	Count
Private company	597
Federal government	141
Self-employed	97
Private nonprofit	92
Local government	59
State government	12
Other	2

Table 5.1 contains the employment type for a sample of 1000 employed citizens of Fairfax County, Virginia.[2] Use the data to construct the probability model by generating the relative frequencies and using the relative frequencies to estimate the probabilities for each employment type.

Solution

We calculate the relative frequencies of each employment group by dividing the count (frequency) for each group by the sample size 1000. For example, the relative frequency for "Private Company" is $\frac{597}{1000} = 0.597$. The relative frequency is then used to estimate the probability of selecting citizens who work at private companies in Fairfax County, Virginia. Filling in the remaining calculations produces the *probability model* in Table 5.2. Note that the table follows the Rules of Probability in that (a) each outcome has probability between 0 and 1 and (b) the sum of the probabilities of all the outcomes equals 1.0. ■

fairfaxemploy

Table 5.2 Probability model	
Employment type	**Probability**
Private company	0.597
Federal government	0.141
Self-employed	0.097
Private nonprofit	0.092
Local government	0.059
State government	0.012
Other	0.002

Now You Can Do
Exercises 67 and 68.

Exercises 67 and 68.

Example 5.10 Random draws using a probability model

Suppose we consider the probabilities in Table 5.2 as population values. Use technology to simulate random draws using the probability model in Table 5.2.

Solution

Using the Step-by-Step Technology Guide on the next page, we drew samples of sizes 10, 100, 1000, and 10,000 from the probability model in Table 5.2. The results are shown in Table 5.3.

Table 5.3 Relative frequencies from random draws of different sizes

Employment type	Rel freq $n = 10$	Rel freq $n = 100$	Rel freq $n = 1000$	Rel freq $n = 10,000$
Private company	0.60	0.62	0.566	0.596
Federal government	0.20	0.15	0.15	0.143
Self-employed	0.10	0.11	0.109	0.991
Private nonprofit	0.10	0.07	0.106	0.914
Local government	0.00	0.04	0.055	0.056
State government	0.00	0.01	0.012	0.012
Other	0.00	0.00	0.002	0.002

Note that each relative frequency tends to approach its respective probability as the sample sizes grow larger. ■

Subjective Method

There are cases where the outcomes are not equally likely (so the classical method does not apply) and there has been no previous research (so the relative frequency approach does not apply). For example, what is the probability that the Dow Jones Industrial Average will decrease today? In cases like this, there is no absolutely correct probability. Reasonable people can disagree reasonably over these probabilities. The idea is to consider all available information, tempered by our experience and intuition, and then assign a probability value that expresses our estimate of the likelihood that the outcome will occur. For example, we might say, "The Chairman of the Federal Reserve warned against inflation in a major speech yesterday, so we expect that the probability that the Dow Jones Industrial Average will go down today is about 90%." Finally, it should be noted that the subjective method should be used when the event is not (even theoretically) repeatable.

Now You Can Do
Exercise 74.

> **Subjective probability** refers to the assignment of a probability value to an outcome based on personal judgment.

STEP-BY-STEP TECHNOLOGY GUIDE: Probability Simulations Using Technology

TI-83/84

Simulating 100 Die Rolls

Step 1 Set the random number seed as follows. (The random number seed is a number that the calculator uses to generate random numbers.) Enter any number on the home screen. Press **STO→**, then **MATH**, highlight **PRB**, select **1: rand**, and press **ENTER**. On the home screen press **ENTER**.

Step 2 Press **MATH**, highlight **PRB**, select **5: randInt(**, and press **ENTER**.

Step 3 Enter **1**, comma, **6**, comma, **100**, close parenthesis (Figure 5.6).

Step 4 Store the data in list **L1** as follows. Press **STO→**, then **2nd**, then **1**, then press **ENTER**.

Step 5 To examine the die rolls, press **STAT**, select **1: EDIT**, and press **ENTER** (Figure 5.7).

FIGURE 5.6

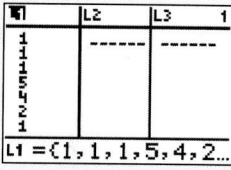

FIGURE 5.7

Simulating Coin Flips

You can simulate coin flips instead of die rolls by coding "heads" as 1 and "tails" as 0. Use the instructions for simulating 100 die rolls with the following changes: Enter **0**, comma, **1**, comma, **100**, close parenthesis, so that the home screen shows **randInt(0, 1, 100)**.

EXCEL

Simulating 100 Die Rolls

Step 1 Select cell **A1**. Click the **Insert Function** icon f_x.

Step 2 For **Search for a Function**, type **randbetween** and click **OK**.

Step 3 For **Bottom**, enter **1**. For **Top**, enter **6** (Figure 5.8). Click **OK**. Cell **A1** now contains a simulated random die roll.

Step 4 Select cell **A1**, copy it, and paste the contents into cells **A2** through **A100**.

FIGURE 5.8 Random die rolls in Excel.

Simulating the Sum of Two Dice

Step 1 Generate 100 die rolls in column A and another 100 die rolls in column B.

Step 2 Select cell **C1**. Enter **= (A1+B1)**, and press **ENTER**.

Step 3 Select cell **C1**, copy it, and paste the contents into cells **C2** through **C100**. Column C then represents 100 randomly generated sums of two dice.

Simulating Random Draws from a Probability Table

We illustrate using Example 5.10 (page 210). Excel and Minitab both require that the categories in the probability model be coded as numeric. We therefore code "Private company" as 1, "Federal government" as 2, and so on.

Step 1 Type the model categories (for example, "Employment type") in column A, their numeric codes in column B, and the respective probabilities in column C.

Step 2 Click **Data > Data Analysis > Random Number Generation**, then **OK**.

Step 3 For **Number of Variables**, enter **1**.

Step 4 For **Number of Random Numbers**, enter the desired sample size.

Step 5 For **Distribution**, select **Discrete**.

Step 6 For **Value & Prob. Input Range**, click and drag to select the coded categories and their probabilities, for example, **B1:C7**.

Repeat Steps 1–6 for increasing sample sizes.

Simulating Coin Flips Using Technology

You can simulate coin flips instead of die rolls by coding "heads" as 1 and "tails" as 0. Use the die roll instructions with the following changes: For **Bottom**, enter **0**. For **Top**, enter **1**.

(Continued)

MINITAB

Simulating 100 Die Rolls
Step 1 Click on **Calc > Random Data > Integer**.
Step 2 For **Generate ___ rows of data**, enter **100**.
Step 3 For **Store in column(s)**, select **C1**.
Step 4 For **Minimum value**, enter **1**. For **Maximum value**, enter **6**.
Step 5 Click **OK**.

Simulating the Sum of Two Dice
Step 1 Generate 100 die rolls in **C1** and another 100 die rolls in **C2**.
Step 2 Click **Calc > Calculator**. For **Store result in variable**, enter **C3**. For **Expression**, enter **C1 + C2**. Click **OK**. Column **C3** then represents 100 randomly generated sums of two dice.

Simulating Random Draws from a Probability Table
Step 1 Type the model categories in **C1**, their numeric codes in **C2**, and the respective probabilities in **C3** (Figure 5.9).
Step 2 Click on **Calc > Random Data > Discrete**.
Step 3 For **Generate ___ rows of data**, enter the desired sample size.
Step 4 For **Store in column(s)**, select the next available column, such as **C4**.
Step 5 For **Values in**, enter the column with the numerically coded categories, such as **C2**.

	C1-T	C2	C3	C4	C5	C6	C7
↓	Type	Type-N	Prob	10	100	1000	10000
1	Private Company	1	0.597	1	3	1	1
2	Federal Government	2	0.141	1	5	1	4
3	Self-Employed	3	0.097	1	1	1	2
4	Private Nonprofit	4	0.092	1	1	4	4
5	Local Government	5	0.059	1	1	1	1
6	State Government	6	0.012	3	1	2	3
7	Other	7	0.002	4	1	1	2
8				2	1	1	1
9				2	1	3	1
10				1	4	1	6
11					1	1	5
12					1	3	1
13					4	1	3

FIGURE 5.9 Random draws in Minitab.

Step 6 For **Probabilities in**, enter the column with the probabilities, such as **C3**.
Step 7 Click **OK**.

Repeat Steps 1–7 for increasing sample sizes, as shown in Figure 5.9.

Simulating Coin Flips
You can simulate coin flips instead of die rolls by coding "heads" as 1 and "tails" as 0. Use the die roll instructions with the following changes: For **Minimum value**, enter **0**. For **Maximum value**, enter **1**.

Section 5.1 Summary

1 Section 5.1 introduces the building blocks of probability, including the concepts of probability, outcome, experiment, and sample space. Probabilities always take values between 0 and 1, where 0 means that the outcome cannot occur and 1 means that the outcome is certain.

2 The classical method of assigning probability is used if all outcomes are equally likely. The classical method states that the probability of an event *A* equals the number of outcomes in *A* divided by the number of outcomes in the sample space.

3 The Law of Large Numbers states that, as an experiment is repeated many times, the relative frequency (proportion) of a particular outcome tends to approach the probability of the outcome. The relative frequency method of assigning probability uses prior knowledge about the relative frequency of an outcome. The subjective method of assigning probability is used when the other methods are not applicable.

Section 5.1 Exercises

CLARIFYING THE CONCEPTS

1. Describe in your own words how chance and uncertainty affect you in your life. List some synonyms that we use in everyday life for the word *probability*.

2. Why do you think we use numerical values for probability rather than only qualitative terms such as "likely" or "impossible"?

3. Give three examples from your own life of experiments, as the term is used in this chapter.
   a. For each experiment, what are some of the outcomes?
   b. Write out the sample space of one of these experiments.
   c. Describe how the Law of Total Probability applies to the sample.

4. List the three methods for assigning probabilities.

5. What assumption do we need to make to use the classical method?

6. When can we use the relative frequency method?

7. If we can't use either the classical method or the relative frequency method, explain how we go about using the subjective method.

8. The experiment is to toss 10 fair coins 25 times each. Which methods can we use to assign probabilities?

9. How would you find the probability that a randomly chosen student at your college likes hip-hop music? What method would you use?

10. Describe the meaning of the following probabilities.
  a. Near 0
  b. 0
  c. Near 1
  d. 1

PRACTICING THE TECHNIQUES

Determine whether each table in Exercises 11–16 is a probability model. If not, clearly explain why it is not a probability model.

11. Customers at a clothing store at the mall

Gender	Probability
Females	1.5
Males	0.2

12. Singers in the church choir

Voice	Probability
Soprano	0.25
Alto	0.25
Tenor	−0.25
Bass	0.50

13. Voters at a town meeting

Party	Probability
Democrat	0.3
Republican	0.25
Independent	0.25
Green	0.1
Libertarian	0.1
Other	0.1

14. Majors of students taking introductory statistics

Major	Probability
Business	0.75
Nursing	0.25
Social sciences	0.20
Science	0.20
Math	0.10

15. Students taking undergraduate introductory statistics

Class	Probability
Freshmen	0.15
Sophomores	0.25
Juniors	0.40
Seniors	0.20

16. Reasons why Hurricane Katrina survivors did not evacuate

Reason	Probability
I did not have a car or a way to leave	0.36
I thought the storm and its aftermath would not be as bad as they were	0.29
I just didn't want to leave	0.10
I had to care for someone who was physically unable to leave	0.07
All other reasons	0.18

For Exercises 17–20, the experiment is to draw a card at random from a shuffled deck of 52 cards. Find the following probabilities.

17. Drawing a king
18. Drawing a heart
19. Drawing the king of hearts
20. Drawing a black card

For Exercises 21–26, the experiment is to roll a fair die once. Find the following probabilities.

21. Observing a 3
22. Observing an even number
23. Observing a number greater than 3
24. Observing a number less than 3
25. Observing a 3 or a 5
26. Observing a 3 and a 5

For Exercises 27 and 28, refer to Exercises 21–26.

27. For each of Exercises 21–26, was the probability you found for an event or an outcome?

28. Explain in your own words why the probability of observing a 3 cannot be more than the probability of observing a 3 or a 5.

For Exercises 29–34, consider the experiment of tossing a fair die two times, with the outcomes being observing either an even number or an odd number.

29. Construct a tree diagram for the experiment.
30. Construct the sample space for the experiment.
31. Find the probability of observing zero even numbers.
32. Find the probability of observing one even number and one odd number.
33. Find the probability of observing two even numbers.
34. Use your results from Exercises 31–33 to construct the probability model for the number of even numbers observed.

For Exercises 35–38, let the experiment be tossing a fair die two times, with the outcomes being observing either a number less than 4 or a number greater than or equal to 4.

35. Construct a tree diagram for the experiment.
36. Construct the sample space for the experiment.
37. What is the probability of observing both outcomes being less than 4?

38. What is the probability of observing both outcomes being 4 or greater?

For Exercises 39–48, consider the experiment of tossing a fair coin three times, and observing either heads or tails.
39. Construct a tree diagram for the experiment.
40. Construct the sample space for the experiment.
41. How does the tree diagram help to construct the sample space?
42. How do we find each outcome using the tree diagram?
43. Find the probability of zero heads.
44. What is the probability of exactly one head.
45. Calculate the probability of exactly two heads.
46. Find the probability of exactly three heads.
47. Use your results from Exercises 43–46 to construct a probability model for the number of heads observed.
48. For Exercises 43–46, which method of assigning probability are you using?

For Exercises 49–56, consider the experiment of tossing two fair dice, and observing the sum of the two dice. (*Hint:* Use the sample space in Figure 5.3 on page 207.)
49. What is the probability that the sum of the dice equals 5?
50. Find the probability that the dark green die equals 5.
51. Calculate the probability that the sum of the dice equals 12.
52. Find the probability that the light green die equals 6.
53. What is the probability that the sum of the dice equals 1?
54. Construct the probability model for the sum of the dice.
55. Use the probability model to find which event has the greatest probability.
56. Which events have the lowest probability?

For Exercises 57–62, suppose that, in a sample of 100 students who drink hot caffeinated beverages, 40 preferred regular coffee, 25 preferred latte, 20 preferred cappuccino, and 15 preferred tea. Find the probability that a randomly selected student prefers the following.
57. Regular coffee
58. Latte
59. Cappuccino
60. Tea
61. For Exercises 57–60, which method of assigning probability are you using?
62. Construct the probability model for hot caffeinated beverages.

For Exercises 63–66, suppose that, in a sample of 200 college students, 100 live on campus, 60 live with family off campus, and 40 live in an apartment off campus. Find the probability that a randomly selected student lives in the following places.
63. On campus
64. With family off campus
65. In an apartment off campus

66. Construct the probability model for where these students live.
67. Use the following frequency table to estimate the probabilities for each color and construct the probability model. A sample of 100 students were asked to name their favorite color.

Favorite color	Frequency
Red	30
Blue	25
Green	20
Black	10
Violet	10
Yellow	5

68. Use the following frequency table to estimate the probabilities for each season and construct the probability model. A sample of 200 students were asked to name their favorite season.

Favorite season	Frequency
Summer	80
Spring	60
Autumn	40
Winter	20

APPLYING THE CONCEPTS

69. Picnic Lunch. Picnickers at the Fourth of July Fair have the following preferences for grilled lunch: cheeseburger 50%, hot dog 25%, veggieburger 25%. Consider the experiment of two picnickers chosen at random choosing their preferred lunch.
    a. Construct the tree diagram for the experiment.
    b. What is the sample space?
70. Video Games. The following percentages of students at a local high school express preference for the following game consoles: PlayStation 3, 40%; Xbox 360, 35%; Wii, 25%. Consider the experiment of choosing three students at random.
    a. Construct the tree diagram for the experiment.
    b. What is the sample space?
71. Rainy Days. Students at the local middle school have been keeping track of the number of days it has rained. In the past 100 days, it rained on 33 days.
    a. What is the probability that it rains on a randomly chosen day?
    b. What is the probability that it doesn't rain on a randomly chosen day?
    c. Which method of assigning probability did you use?
72. Illegal Parking. Suppose you find that 10 out of 50 cars parked in handicapped zones are parked there illegally.
    a. You would like to find the probability that a car parked in the handicapped zone is parked illegally. Explain whether or not you can use the classical method of assigning probability and why.

b. Find the probability that a car parked in a handicapped zone is illegally parked. Which method did you use?

73. Cutting Classes. Over her college career, a student has cut 25 of the total 1000 class periods in all her courses.

    a. Find the probability that the student cuts a particular class.

    b. Which method did you use?

    c. Does it make sense to use the classical method? Why or why not?

74. Basketball. Your college's basketball team is playing a game next week.

    a. What is the probability that the team will win the game?

    b. What reasoning went into your probability assessment?

    c. Which method did you use?

75. Brisbane Babies. The table shows the births of babies at a Brisbane, Australia, hospital on a particular day.

Girl	Girl	Boy	Boy	Boy	Girl	Girl	Boy	Boy
Boy	Boy	Boy	Girl	Girl	Boy	Girl	Girl	Boy
Boy	Boy	Boy	Girl	Girl	Girl	Girl	Boy	Boy
Boy	Girl	Boy	Girl	Boy	Boy	Boy	Boy	Boy
Girl	Boy	Boy	Boy	Boy	Girl	Girl	Girl	

    a. Construct a relative frequency distribution of the numbers of girls and boys born.

    b. Use the relative frequencies to construct a probability model.

    c. Confirm that your probability model follows the Rules of Probability.

Mozart Effect. Use this information for Exercises 76 and 77. The Mozart effect refers to the hypothesis that listening to a piano sonata by the great Austrian master improves cognitive performance. Assume that we have an experiment where two children have each listened to Mozart's Sonata for Two Pianos in D Major (K 448). The children's cognitive skills are then tested. Assume that for each child, there are three possible outcomes: cognitive performance increased, cognitive performance decreased, and cognitive performance remained unchanged.

76. a. Construct a tree diagram for the experiment.

    b. Construct the sample space for the experiment.

    c. For how many outcomes do both children improve their cognitive performance?

    d. Explain why it is not appropriate to use the classical method to assign probabilities for the Mozart experiment.

77. Challenge Exercise. Using your own subjective probabilities, find the probability that both children in the Mozart experiment will improve their cognitive performance.

Letters in English. Use Table 5.4 for Exercises 78 and 79 (it is the frequency distribution of letters in the English alphabet that we used in the Chapter 2 Case Study, "The Caesar Cipher").

Imagine yourself on the television game show *Wheel of Fortune,* where contestants guess the letters contained in a hidden phrase. You would like to ask for the letters that have the greatest chance of occurring, so you want to know the various probabilities of the letters in the English alphabet.

The experiment is to choose one letter at random from a sample of 1000 letters. The sample space is the 26 letters of the alphabet. Since the total sample size is 1000, you can find the relative frequencies of the letters in English simply by dividing each frequency by the total sample size (remember this from Chapter 2?).

TABLE 5.4   Frequency distribution of English letters

A	B	C	D	E	F	G
73	9	30	44	130	28	16
H	**I**	**J**	**K**	**L**	**M**	**N**
35	74	2	3	35	25	78
O	**P**	**Q**	**R**	**S**	**T**	**U**
74	27	3	77	63	93	27
V	**W**	**X**	**Y**	**Z**		
13	16	5	19	1		

78. Answer the following questions using Table 5.4.

    a. Choosing one letter at random, which is more likely, a consonant or a vowel?

    b. Of the sample of 1000 letters, what proportion are vowels?

    c. Of the 8 letters with the highest frequencies, what proportion are vowels?

79. Answer the following questions using Table 5.4.

    a. Compare your answers to Exercise 78(**b**) and (**c**), and explain why *Wheel of Fortune* contestants are not allowed to guess vowels (they have to buy them).

    b. If you were a contestant on *Wheel of Fortune* and had no money to buy a vowel, what would be your first five letter choices?

80. Draw an Ace. If you draw the ace of spades from a deck of cards, you win $100.

    a. What is the probability of winning this game?

    b. What would be a fair price for playing this game? (*Hint:* A fair price might be determined by balancing out the winnings and the price in the long run.)

81. A Bazaar Game. Lenny has gone to the church bazaar with his family. In one of the games at the bazaar, if Lenny rolls two dice and gets a sum of at least 9, he wins $5; otherwise, he wins nothing.

    a. Find the probability of winning $5.

    b. Find the probability of winning nothing.

    c. What would you suggest would be a fair (break-even) price for playing this game?

Teenagers' Music and Lifestyle. Every year, *USA Weekend* conducts a survey of the nation's teenagers, asking them various questions about lifestyle and music. Nearly 60,000 teenagers responded to the survey, conducted in part through a Web site. Use this information for Exercises 82 and 83.

82. One *USA Weekend* survey question asked teenagers, "Do you listen to music while you are . . . ?" and listed several options. The most common responses are shown in the table. Respondents could choose more than one response. Explain why you cannot construct a probability model with these percentages.

Doing chores	79%
On the computer	73%
Doing homework	72%
Eating meals at home	33%
In the classroom	18%

83. Another survey question asked by *USA Weekend* was "If you had to choose just one type of music to listen to exclusively, which would it be?" The results are shown in the table. **teenmusic**

Hip-hop/rap	27%
Pop	23%
Rock/punk	17%
Alternative	7%
Christian/gospel	6%
R&B	6%
Country	5%
Techno/house	4%
Jazz	1%
Other	4%

  a. Construct a probability model.
  b. Is it unusual for a respondent to prefer jazz?
  c. Use technology to draw random samples of sizes 10, 100, 1000, and 10,000 from your probability model.
  d. What can you conclude about the relative frequencies as the sample size increases?

84. Fairfax County Income. The following table contains a probability model for the distribution of income in Fairfax County, Virginia. **fairfaxincome**

Annual income	Probability
Under $25,000	0.083
$25,000 to $49,999	0.166
$50,000 to $74,999	0.169
$75,000 to $99,999	0.160
$100,000 to $149,999	0.200
$150,000 or more	0.222

  a. Use technology to draw random samples of sizes 10, 100, 1000, and 10,000 from this probability model.
  b. What can you conclude about the relative frequencies as the sample size increases?

85. Paul the Predicting Octopus. During the 2010 World Cup, Paul the Octopus picked the correct outcome of each soccer match that Germany was involved in, and then continued his winning streak right to the end, picking champion Spain in the final match. Paul indicated his choice by swimming over and choosing one of two containers of mussels (his favorite food). Each container had the flag of a country in the day's match. Paul predicted the outcome correctly eight times in a row.
  a. Find the probability of Paul predicting all eight matches correctly, assuming a success probability of 50% for each match. Express this answer in the form $(1/2)^k$, where k is the number of matches.
  b. Say Paul had predicted nine matches in a row correctly. Find the probability of doing so, assuming 50% probability of success for each match. Express this answer in the form $(1/2)^k$.
  c. What is the ratio of your results from **(b)** to your results from **(a)**?
  d. Use your results from **(a)**–**(c)** to form a general rule for the probability of correctly predicting k matches in a row when the probability of success for each match is 50%.

86. Refer to the previous exercise. *What if* the probability of Paul predicting correctly was larger than 50%. Would your answers to the following be greater or less than what you calculated in the previous exercise?
  a. The probability of Paul predicting all eight matches in a row correctly
  b. The probability of Paul predicting nine matches in a row correctly

87. Refer to the previous two exercises. Suppose that the probability of Paul predicting correctly is not 50% but some unknown probability p. What is the probability that Paul will predict k matches in a row correctly?

BRINGING IT ALL TOGETHER
Use the following information for Exercises 88–95. Consider the experiment where a fair die is rolled twice. Define the following events for each roll: low = {1, 2}, medium = {3, 4}, high = {5, 6}, odd = {1, 3, 5}, even = {2, 4, 6}.

88. Construct a tree diagram for this experiment. Make sure you use the outcomes and not the events.

89. Use the tree diagram to construct the sample space. Which sample space discussed in Section 5.1 is the sample space for this experiment similar to? Explain why this is so.

90. The sample space is the collection of all possible outcomes of an experiment. Explain why the sample space is not defined as the collection of all possible events.

91. Find the probability of observing a 1, followed by another 1. What method of assigning probability are you using? Why?

92. Find the probability of observing two high die rolls. What method of assigning probability are you using? Why?

93. What is the probability of observing an odd die roll followed by an even die roll?

94. What is the probability of observing an odd die roll and an even die roll in no particular order? Why is this different from your result from the previous exercise?

95. Find the following probabilities.
 a. Two high die results
 b. Exactly one medium die result
 c. No low die results
 d. At least one high die result
 e. At most one medium die result

Use the *Law of Large Numbers for Proportions* applet for Exercises 96 and 97.

96. Set the probability of heads to 0.5 and the number of tosses to 40. Click **Toss.**

 a. Record the proportion of heads observed.
 b. Without pressing **Reset,** continue to click **Toss** until the total number of tosses is 120. Again record the proportion of heads.
 c. Without pressing **Reset,** continue to click **Toss** until the total number of tosses is 240. Again record the proportion of heads.
 d. Without pressing **Reset,** continue to click **Toss** until the total number of tosses is 480. Again record the proportion of heads.

97. The proportions you recorded in Exercise 96 are relative frequencies of heads. What can you conclude about the relative frequencies as the sample size increases?

5.2 Combining Events

OBJECTIVES By the end of this section, I will be able to . . .

1 Understand how to combine events using complement, union, and intersection.

2 Apply the Addition Rule to events in general and to mutually exclusive events in particular.

1 Complement, Union, and Intersection

In Example 5.5, if your roommate rolled a 4, then your roommate was to do your laundry for the rest of the semester. Your roommate is keenly interested in *not* rolling a 4. If *A* is an event, then the collection of outcomes not in event *A* is called the **complement of *A*,** denoted A^C. The term *complement* comes from the word "to complete," meaning that any event and its complement together make up the complete sample space.

Example 5.11 Finding the probability of the complement of an event

If *A* is the event "observing a sum of 4 when the two fair dice are rolled," then your roommate is interested in the probability of A^C, the event that a 4 is not rolled. Find the probability that your roommate does not roll a 4.

Solution

Which outcomes belong to A^C? By the definition, A^C is all the outcomes in the sample space that do not belong in *A*. There are the following outcomes in *A*: {(3,1), (2,2), (1,3)}.

Figure 5.10 shows all the outcomes except the outcomes from *A* in the two-dice sample space. There are 33 outcomes in A^C and 36 outcomes in the sample space. The classical probability method then gives the probability of not rolling a 4 to be

$$P(A^C) = \frac{N(A^C)}{N(S)} = \frac{33}{36} = \frac{11}{12}$$

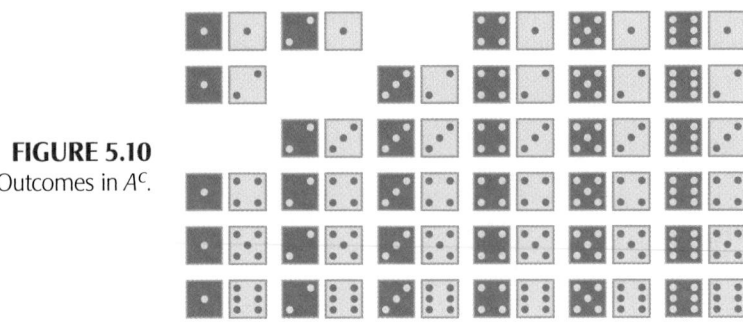

FIGURE 5.10
Outcomes in A^c.

Now You Can Do
Exercises 9–11.

The probability is high that, on this roll at least, your roommate will not land on Boardwalk. ■

For event A in Example 5.11, note that

$$P(A) + P(A^C) = \frac{1}{12} + \frac{11}{12} = 1$$

Is this a coincidence, or does the sum of the probabilities of an event and its complement always add to 1? Recall the Law of Total Probability (Section 5.1), which states that the sum of all the outcome probabilities in the sample space must be equal to 1. Since any event A and its complement A^C together make up the entire sample space, then it always happens that $P(A) + P(A^C) = 1$.

Probabilities for Complements

For any event A and its complement A^c, $P(A) + P(A^C) = 1$. Applying a touch of algebra gives the following:

- $P(A) = 1 - P(A^C)$
- $P(A^C) = 1 - P(A)$

Sometimes we need to find the probability of a combination of events. For example, consider the casino game of craps where you roll two dice. One way of winning is by rolling the sum 7 or 11. We can find the probability of the following two events: the sum is 7 or the sum is 11. First, we need some tools for finding the probability of a combination of events.

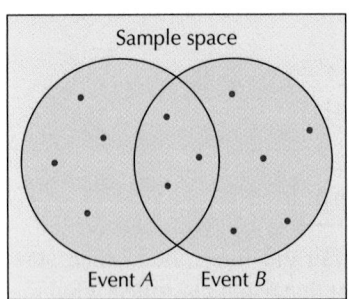

FIGURE 5.11 Union of events A, B.

Union and Intersection of Events

The **union** of two events A and B is the event representing all the outcomes that belong to A or B or both. The union of A and B is denoted as $A \cup B$ and is associated with "or."

The **intersection** of two events A and B is the event representing all the outcomes that belong to both A and B. The intersection of A and B is denoted as $A \cap B$ and is associated with "and."

If you are asked to find the probability of "A or B," you should find the probability of $A \cup B$. Figure 5.11 shows the union of two events, with the red dots indicating the outcomes. Note from Figure 5.11 that the union of the events A and B refers to all outcomes in A or B or both. Figure 5.12 shows that the intersection of the two events is the part where A and B overlap. Both union and intersection are commutative. That is, $A \cup B = B \cup A$ and $A \cap B = B \cap A$.

FIGURE 5.12 Intersection of events A, B.

Example 5.12 Union and intersection

Let our experiment be to draw a single card at random from a deck of cards. Define the following events:

    A: The card drawn is an ace.
    H: The card drawn is a heart.

a. Find $A \cup H$.
b. Find $A \cap H$.

Solution

a. The union of *A* and *H* is the event containing all the outcomes that are either aces or hearts or both (the ace of hearts). That is, the event $A \cup H$ consists of the set of outcomes (the cards) shown in Figure 5.13.

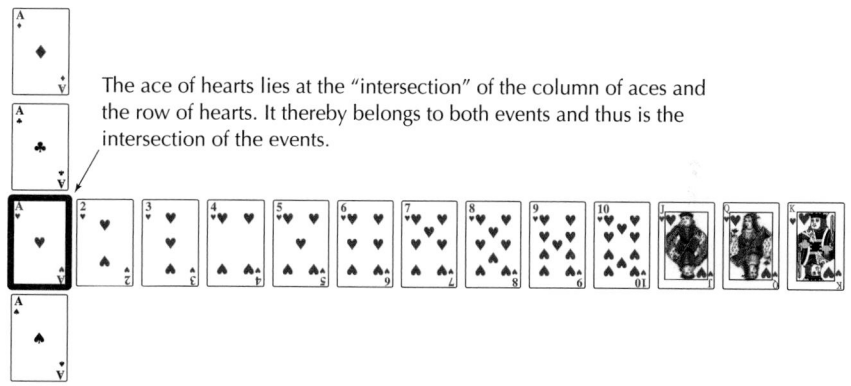

The ace of hearts lies at the "intersection" of the column of aces and the row of hearts. It thereby belongs to both events and thus is the intersection of the events.

FIGURE 5.13 The ace of hearts is the intersection of the events "ace" and "hearts."

Now You Can Do
Exercises 13–18.

b. The intersection of *A* and *H* is the event containing the outcomes that are common to both *A* and *H*. There is only one such outcome: the ace of hearts (see Figure 5.13). ∎

2 Addition Rule

We are often interested in finding the probability that either one event *or* another event may occur. The formula for finding these kinds of probabilities is called the **Addition Rule.**

> **Addition Rule**
>
> $$P(A \text{ or } B) = P(A \cup B) = P(A) + P(B) - P(A \cap B)$$

What Does the Addition Rule Mean?

We can use Figure 5.11 to understand the Addition Rule. We are trying to find the probability of all the outcomes in *A* or *B* or both. The first part of the formula says to add the probabilities of the outcomes in *A* to those of the outcomes in *B*. But what about the overlap between *A* and *B*, outcomes that belong to both events? To avoid counting the outcomes in the overlap (intersection) twice, we have to subtract the probability of the intersection, $P(A \cap B)$. ◢

Example 5.13 Addition Rule applied to a deck of cards

Suppose you pay \$1 to play the following game. You choose one card at random from a deck of 52 cards, and you will win \$3 if the card is either an ace *or* a heart. Find the probability of winning this game.

Solution

Using the same events defined in Example 5.12, we find $P(A \text{ or } H) = P(A \cup H)$. By the Addition Rule, we know that

$$P(A \cup H) = P(A) + P(H) - P(A \cap H)$$

There are 4 aces in a deck of 52 cards, so by the classical method (equally likely outcomes), $P(A) = 4/52$. There are 13 hearts in a deck of 52 cards, so $P(H) = 13/52$. From Example 5.12, we know that $A \cap H$ represents the ace of hearts. Since each card is equally likely to be drawn, then $P(\text{ace of hearts}) = P(A \cap H) = 1/52$. Thus,

$$P(A \cup H) = P(A) + P(H) - P(A \cap H)$$
$$= \frac{4}{52} + \frac{13}{52} - \frac{1}{52} = \frac{16}{52} = \frac{4}{13}$$

Now You Can Do
Exercises 19–24.

The intersection of two events may be represented by the intersection of a row and a column in a two-way table. Recall from Section 2.1 (pages 42–43) that a *two-way table* (also known as a *crosstabulation* or a *contingency table*) is a tabular summary of the relationship between two categorical variables.

Example 5.14 Addition Rule applied to a two-way table

A study of online dating behavior found that users of a particular online dating service self-reported their physical appearance according to the counts given in Table 5.5.[3]

Table 5.5 Gender and self-reported physical appearance

	Physical Appearance				
Gender	Very attractive	Attractive	Average	Prefer not to answer	Total
Female	3113	16,181	6,093	3478	28,865
Male	1415	12,454	7,274	2809	23,952
Total	4528	28,635	13,367	6287	52,817

Using this information, find the probability that a randomly chosen online dater has the following characteristics.
a. Is female
b. Self-reported as attractive
c. Is a female who self-reported as attractive
d. Is a female *or* self-reported as attractive

Solution

a. There are a total of $N(S) = 52{,}817$ online daters in the entire data set. Of these, 28,865 are female, denoted as event F. Therefore,

$$P(F) = P(\text{Female}) = \frac{N(\text{Female})}{N(S)} = \frac{N(F)}{N(S)} = \frac{28{,}865}{52{,}817} \approx 0.5465$$

b. There are 28,635 people who self-reported their physical appearance as attractive, denoted as event A. Therefore,

$$P(A) = P(\text{Self-reported attractive}) = \frac{N(\text{Self-reported attractive})}{N(S)} = \frac{N(A)}{N(S)}$$
$$= \frac{28{,}635}{52{,}817} \approx 0.5422$$

c. The online daters who are both female and self-reported as attractive are shown in the highlighted cell in Table 5.5. This cell is located at the *intersection* of the row of females and the column of people who self-reported as attractive. Therefore, this cell reports the frequency of people who belong to both events. Thus,

$$P(F \text{ and } A) = P(F \cap A) = P(\text{Female and self-reported attractive}) = \frac{N(F \cap A)}{N(S)}$$

$$= \frac{16{,}181}{52{,}817} \approx 0.3064$$

d. Here we seek $P(F \text{ or } A) = P(F \cup A)$. By the Addition Rule,

$$P(F \cup A) = P(F) + P(A) - P(F \cap A) = 0.5465 + 0.5422 - 0.3064 = 0.7823 \ \blacksquare$$

Now You Can Do
Exercises 25–32.

Mutually Exclusive Events

When drawing a card at random from a deck of 52 cards, the events "a heart is drawn" and "a diamond is drawn" have no outcomes in common. That is, no card is both a heart and a diamond. We say that these two events are **mutually exclusive.**

> Two events are said to be **mutually exclusive,** or **disjoint,** if they have no outcomes in common.

Note that any event and its complement are always mutually exclusive. Other examples of mutually exclusive events are given in Table 5.6.

Table 5.6 Examples of mutually exclusive events

Experiment	Mutually exclusive events
Toss fair coin	Observe heads; observe tails
Draw a single card from a deck of 52 cards	Card is red; card is a spade
Select a student at random	Student is female; student is male
Choose a digit at random	Digit is even; digit is odd

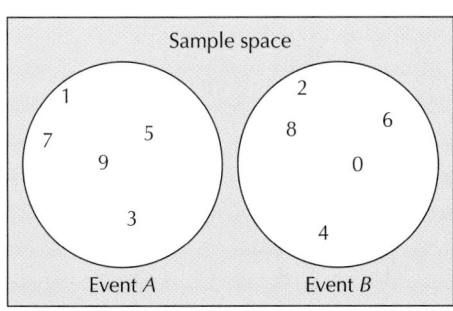

FIGURE 5.14 Even and odd digits are mutually exclusive.

Figure 5.14 shows how mutually exclusive events are represented graphically. It shows the events

$$A = \{1, 3, 5, 7, 9\} \quad \text{and} \quad B = \{0, 2, 4, 6, 8\}$$

Note that there is no overlap between the two events. When two events are mutually exclusive, they share no outcomes, and therefore the intersection of mutually exclusive events is empty. Since the intersection $(A \cap B)$ is empty, then for mutually exclusive events, $P(A \cap B) = 0$. Therefore, we can formulate a special case of the **Addition Rule for Mutually Exclusive Events** A and B:

$$P(A \cup B) = P(A) + P(B) - P(A \cap B) = P(A) + P(B) - 0 = P(A) + P(B)$$

> **Addition Rule for Mutually Exclusive Events**
> If A and B are mutually exclusive events, $P(A \cup B) = P(A) + P(B)$.

Example 5.15 Addition Rule for Mutually Exclusive Events

Using Table 5.5 from Example 5.14, find the probability that a randomly chosen online dater self-reported as either attractive or very attractive.

Solution

From Table 5.5, there are 28,635 online daters who self-reported as attractive and 4528 who self-reported as very attractive, yielding the following probabilities:

$$P(A) = P(\text{Self-reported attractive}) = \frac{N(A)}{N(S)} = \frac{28{,}635}{52{,}817} \approx 0.5422$$

$$P(V) = P(\text{Self-reported very attractive}) = \frac{N(V)}{N(S)} = \frac{4528}{52{,}817} \approx 0.08573$$

Since no online daters self-reported as both attractive and very attractive, the two groups are mutually exclusive. Thus, by the Addition Rule for Mutually Exclusive Events,

Now You Can Do
Exercises 33–34.

$$P(A \cup V) = P(A) + P(V) = 0.5422 + 0.08573 = 0.62793 \qquad \blacksquare$$

Section 5.2 Summary

1 Combinations of events may be formed using the concepts of complement, union, and intersection.

2 The Addition Rule provides the probability of event A or event B to be the sum of their two probabilities minus the probability of their intersection. Mutually exclusive events have no outcomes in common.

Section 5.2 Exercises

CLARIFYING THE CONCEPTS

1. Describe in your own words what it means for two events to be mutually exclusive.

2. Describe the intersection of two mutually exclusive events.

3. Describe the union of two mutually exclusive events.

4. Is it true that the union of two events always contains at least as many outcomes as the intersection of two events? Use Figures 5.11 and 5.12 to help you visualize this problem.

5. If we choose a student at random from your college or university, is it more likely that we choose a male or a male football player? Why?

6. What is your personal estimate of the probability that it will rain on any given day? How about the probability that it won't rain? Why do these numbers have to add up to 1 (or 100%)?

PRACTICING THE TECHNIQUES

For Exercises 7–12, consider the experiment of rolling a fair die once. Find the indicated probabilities.

7. Observing a number that is not 4

8. Observing some other number than 5

9. The complement of the event E, where E: $\{2, 4, 6\}$

10. L^C, where L: $\{1, 2\}$

11. E^C, where E: $\{2, 4, 6\}$

12. Not rolling an odd number

For Exercises 13–18, consider the experiment of drawing a single card at random from a deck of cards. Define the following events. Find the indicated unions and intersections.

K: The card is a king.
R: The card is a red suit.
H: The card is a heart.

13. $K \cup R$ **15.** $R \cup H$ **17.** $K \cap H$
14. $K \cup H$ **16.** $K \cap R$ **18.** $R \cap H$

For Exercises 19–24, consider the experiment of drawing a single card at random from a deck of cards. Define the following events. Find the indicated probabilities.

K: The card is a king.
R: The card is a red suit.
H: The card is a heart.

19. $P(K \cup R)$ **21.** $P(R \cup H)$ **23.** $P(K \cap H)$
20. $P(K \cup H)$ **22.** $P(K \cap R)$ **24.** $P(R \cap H)$

For Exercises 25–32, refer to Table 5.5 in Example 5.14 on page 220. Find the probability that a randomly chosen dater has the following characteristics.

25. Is male
26. Self-reported as average
27. Is a male who self-reported as average
28. Is a male or self-reported as average
29. Self-reported as very attractive
30. Is a female who self-reported as very attractive
31. Is a male who self-reported as very attractive
32. Self-reported as prefer not to answer

For Exercises 33–44, consider the experiment of rolling a single die once. Define the following events: L: {1, 2, 3}, H: {4, 5, 6}, E: {2, 4, 6}, O: {1, 3, 5}. Find the following probabilities.

33. $P(L \cup H)$
34. $P(E$ or $O)$
35. $P(L$ or $E)$
36. $P(L \cup O)$
37. $P(H \cup E)$
38. $P(H$ or $O)$
39. $P(L$ and $H)$
40. $P(E \cap O)$
41. $P(L \cap E)$
42. $P(L$ and $O)$
43. $P(H$ and $E)$
44. $P(H \cap O)$

For Exercises 45–50, consider the experiment of rolling a fair die twice. Find the indicated probabilities.

45. Exactly one of the dice is a 4
46. Neither die is a 4
47. Sum of the two dice equals 3
48. Sum of the two dice equals 3 and one of the dice is a 4
49. Sum of the two dice equals 3 or one of the dice is a 4
50. Sum of the two dice equals 3 or neither of the dice is a 4

For Exercises 51–56, consider the experiment of drawing a card at random from a shuffled deck of 52 cards. Find the indicated probabilities.

51. Drawing a king and a black card
52. Drawing a king or a black card
53. Drawing a card that is neither a king nor a black card
54. Drawing a heart or a spade
55. Drawing a heart and a spade
56. Drawing a card that is not the king of hearts

For Exercises 57–62, consider the experiment of drawing a card at random from a shuffled deck of 52 cards. Find the indicated probabilities.

57. Drawing a face card (king, queen, or jack)
58. Drawing a card that is not red
59. Drawing a card that is not a face card
60. Drawing a face card that is not a diamond
61. Drawing a face card or a diamond
62. Drawing a face card and a diamond

For Exercises 63–66, consider the experiment of tossing a fair coin three times. Find the indicated probabilities. (*Hint:* Use a tree diagram similar to the one in Figure 5.2 in Section 5.1 [page 206] but adding one more stage.)

63. Observing 3 heads
64. Not observing 3 heads
65. Observing 2 tails
66. Not observing 2 tails

For Exercises 67–72, imagine that your sister is going to have triplets. Assume that the probability of a baby boy or a baby girl is equally likely. (In fact, it is not quite.)

67. Construct the sample space.
68. Find the probability of 1 girl and 2 boys.
69. Find the probability of 1 boy and 2 girls.
70. Find the probability of 2 of one gender and 1 of the other gender.
71. Find the probability of 1 girl or 1 boy.
72. Find the probability of getting 3 girls.

APPLYING THE CONCEPTS

73. **Game of Craps.** You win the casino game of craps if you roll a 7 or 11. Find the probability of rolling a sum of 7 or 11 when two dice are rolled.

74. **Acing College Courses.** Jessica has gotten A's in 10 of her 30 college courses.
    a. Find the probability that Jessica gets an A in a randomly chosen college course.
    b. Find the probability that Jessica gets a grade other than an A in a randomly chosen college course.

Trout Fishing. Use the following information for Exercises 75 and 76. Of the 20 fish Brent has caught at his favorite fishing spot this season, 5 have been trout and 7 have been bass.

75. Find the following probabilities.
    a. Catching a trout
    b. Catching a bass
76. Find the following probabilities.
    a. Catching a trout or a bass
    b. Catching a fish that is not a trout
    c. Catching a fish that is neither a trout nor a bass

77. **Traffic Lights.** Let A be the event that you encounter a green light at your next traffic light.
    a. What outcomes make up A^C?
    b. What is the probability of A? Which method did you use?
    c. What is the probability of A^C?

78. **Monopoly.** You are playing Monopoly with your roommate (the loser does laundry for both for the rest of the semester). Your piece is sitting on Water Works, and you are about to roll your two fair dice. Your opponent has hotels on Park Place and Boardwalk, and if you land on either one, you will lose. Park Place lies 9 spaces away and Boardwalk lies 11 spaces away.
    a. What is the probability that you will land on Park Place and get stuck with laundry duty?
    b. What is the probability that you will land on Boardwalk and still get stuck with laundry duty?
    c. What is the probability that you will lose the game on this roll?

79. Monopoly. As well as the conditions in Exercise 78, you have hotels on the green properties (Pacific, North Carolina, and Pennsylvania Avenues), and if your roommate lands on one of them, your roommate will be sorting your laundry starting tonight. Your roommate's piece is on B & O Railroad.

    a. What is the probability that your roommate will land on Pacific Avenue, 6 spaces away?

    b. What is the probability that your roommate will land on North Carolina Avenue, 7 spaces away?

    c. What is the probability that your roommate will land on Pennsylvania Avenue, 9 spaces away?

    d. What is the probability that your roommate will lose the game on this roll?

80. High School Students. In a local high school of 500 students, there are 200 females, 100 sophomores, and 50 female sophomores.

    a. If we choose a student at random, what is the probability that we choose a female or a sophomore?

    b. Find the probability that a randomly chosen student is a male or a sophomore.

    c. Find the probability that a randomly chosen student is a female or is not a sophomore.

81. Halloween Candy. At Halloween, the accent is on taste—taste of candy, that is. In a sample of 100 children, 70 like chocolate bars, 60 like peanut butter cups, and 50 like both.

    a. If we choose one child at random, find the probability that the child likes either chocolate bars or peanut butter cups.

    b. In (a), suppose you forgot to subtract the probability of the intersection. How would you know that your answer is wrong?

82. Pick a Card. If we draw a single card at random from a deck of 52 playing cards, find the probability that the card is

    a. a heart or a diamond.

    b. a red card or a jack.

    c. a club or a face card (king, queen, jack).

    d. a heart and a diamond.

    e. not a spade.

83. A New Sonata. Music researchers have discovered a new sonata from the classical period of the late eighteenth century. The probability that the sonata was written by the following composers is as follows: Mozart 35%, Haydn 50%, Beethoven 15%. It is known that the sonata composers are mutually exclusive, meaning that no sonata was written by more than one of these composers. Find the following probabilities.

    a. The sonata was written by either Mozart or Haydn.

    b. The sonata was written by either Mozart or Beethoven.

    c. The sonata was written by either Haydn or Beethoven.

    d. The sonata was written by both Mozart and Haydn.

84. Cheeseburger or Chicken? The college football team (60 players) stopped off at a hamburger joint on the way home from a big road win. Thirty players ordered a bacon cheeseburger. Twenty players ordered a chicken deluxe. No player ordered both.

    a. Find the probability that a randomly chosen player ordered either a bacon cheeseburger or a chicken deluxe.

    b. Suppose we didn't know that no player ordered both. Would we have been able to answer (a)? Why or why not?

85. Baseball Strategy. Earnshaw Cook analyzed 20,000 baseball games and used the relative frequency method to assign the following probabilities.[4] The probability of scoring a run with a runner on first and no outs is 0.43. The probability of scoring a run with a runner on second and one out is 0.45. Actually, considering all the bunting and sacrifice fly strategies used by baseball managers to get from the first situation to the second, it seems hardly worth it, increasing the probability of scoring by only 0.02. Using these probabilities, answer the following questions.

    a. If there is a runner on first with no outs, what is the probability of not scoring?

    b. If there is a runner of second with one out, what is the probability of not scoring?

86. Online Dating Data. Refer to Table 5.5 (page 220). Find the probability that a randomly selected online dater has the following characteristics.

    a. Prefers not to describe physical appearance

    b. Is male and prefers not to describe physical appearance

    c. Is male or prefers not to describe physical appearance

87. Social Networking Apps. The Nielsen Apps Playbook was a survey taken in 2010 of 3692 males and females on the use of social networking apps (mobile software applications). The results are shown in the following table.

	Has downloaded a social networking app in the last 30 days	
	Yes	No
Male	884	841
Female	1220	746

Source: Kristen Purcell, Roger Entner, and Nichole Henderson, *The Rise of Apps Culture,* Internet and American Life Project, Pew Research Center, September 15, 2010.

Find the probability that a randomly chosen person has the following characteristics.

    a. Is female

    b. Has downloaded a social networking app in the last 30 days

    c. Is a female who has downloaded a social networking app in the last 30 days

    d. Is a female *or* has downloaded a social networking app in the last 30 days

Causes of Death. Refer to Table 5.7 for Exercises 88–90.

TABLE 5.7   Causes of death

Cause of death	Deaths
Heart disease	654,092
Cancer	550,270
All other causes	1,194,003
Total	2,398,365

Source: Centers for Disease Control and Prevention.

88. Find the following probabilities.
   a. The cause of death was heart disease.
   b. The cause of death was not heart disease.
89. Find the following probabilities.
   a. The cause of death was heart disease and cancer.
   b. The cause of death was heart disease or cancer.
90. Are the causes of death mutually exclusive?

BRINGING IT ALL TOGETHER
Don't Mess with Texas. Don't Mess with Texas (dontmesswithtexas.org) is a Texas statewide antilittering organization. Its 2005 report, *Visible Litter Study 2005*, identified paper, plastic, metal, and glass as the top four categories of litter by composition. The report also identified tobacco, household/personal, food, and beverages as the top four categories of litter by use. Assume that a sample of 12 items of litter had the following characteristics. Use Table 5.8 for Exercises 91–93.

TABLE 5.8   Litter composition and use

Litter item	Composition	Use
1	Paper	Tobacco
2	Plastic	Household/personal
3	Glass	Beverages
4	Paper	Tobacco
5	Metal	Household/personal
6	Plastic	Food
7	Glass	Beverages
8	Paper	Household/personal
9	Metal	Household/personal
10	Plastic	Beverages
11	Paper	Tobacco
12	Plastic	Food

91. A litter item is chosen at random.
   a. Find the probability that the composition of the item is paper.
   b. Find the probability that the composition of the item is not paper. Calculate this probability in two different ways.
92. A litter item is chosen at random.
   a. Find the probability that the use of the item is tobacco.
   b. Find the probability that the use of the item is not tobacco. Calculate this probability in two different ways.
93. A litter item is chosen at random.
   a. Find the probability that the composition of the item is paper *and* its use is tobacco.
   b. Find the probability that the composition of the item is paper *or* its use is tobacco.

5.3   Conditional Probability

OBJECTIVES By the end of this section, I will be able to . . .

1   Calculate conditional probabilities.

2   Explain independent and dependent events.

3   Solve problems using the Multiplication Rule and recognize the difference between sampling with replacement and sampling without replacement.

4   Approximate probabilities for dependent events.

1 Introduction to Conditional Probability

As we progress through this book, you will notice a recurring theme: *the more information available, the better.* Very often, when we are investigating the probability of a certain event *A,* we learn that another event *B* has occurred. If events *A* and *B* are related, then the occurrence of event *B* often influences the probability that event *A* will occur.

Example 5.16 | Having more information often affects the probability of an event

In Section 5.1, we found that the probability of rolling a sum of 4 when tossing two dice is 3/36 ≈ 0.0833. But what if we were told that at least one of the dice shows a 1. How does this extra information affect the probability of rolling a 4?

Solution

Figure 5.15 shows the 11 outcomes from the two-dice sample space in which at least one die shows a 1. The extra information reduces the number of possible outcomes in the sample space from 36 to 11. We see that two of these outcomes have a sum equal to 4. Thus, the probability of observing a sum of 4, *given that* at least one of the dice shows a 1, is 2/11 ≈ 0.1818. ∎

FIGURE 5.15
Using the extra knowledge changes the probability.

The extra information about a related event changed the probability of the event of interest. This type of probability is an example of what is called **conditional probability.**

> For two related events A and B, the probability of B given A is called a **conditional probability** and denoted $P(B|A)$.

Thus, if we let A represent the event that one of the dice shows a 1, and let B represent the event that the sum of the two dice equals 4, then

$$P(B) = \frac{3}{36} \approx 0.0833 \qquad \text{but} \qquad P(B|A) = \frac{2}{11} \approx 0.1818$$

Figure 5.16 can help us visualize how conditional probability works. The idea is that, *once event A has occurred*, the only chance for event B to occur is in the overlap, the intersection $A \cap B$. Therefore, the conditional probability that B will occur, given that event A has already taken place, is found by taking the ratio $P(A \cap B)/P(A)$.

FIGURE 5.16
How conditional probability works.

(a)

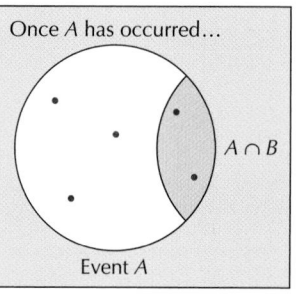

(b)

> **Calculating Conditional Probability**
> The conditional probability that B will occur, given that event A has already taken place, equals
> $$P(B|A) = \frac{P(A \cap B)}{P(A)} = \frac{N(A \cap B)}{N(A)}$$

Example 5.17 | Calculating conditional probability

Punchstock/Photodisc

Table 5.9 is adapted from a study on direct mail marketing. It contains the numbers of customers who either responded or did not respond to a direct mail marketing campaign, along with whether they had a credit card on file with the company. The two events are

   R: Responded to direct mail marketing campaign
   C: Has a credit card on file

Table 5.9 Credit card status and marketing response

Response	Credit Card on File?		Total
	No	**Yes**	
Did not respond	161	79	240
Did respond	17	31	48
Total	178	110	288

Source: Daniel Larose, *Data Mining Methods and Models* (Wiley Interscience, 2006).

a. Find the probability that a randomly chosen customer responded to the marketing campaign.

b. Find the conditional probability that a randomly selected customer responded, given that the customer has a credit card on file.

Solution

a. $P(R) = \dfrac{N(R)}{N(S)}$. There are $N(R) = 48$ customers who did respond, and there are $N(S) = 288$ customers in this experiment. Thus,

$$P(R) = \frac{N(R)}{N(S)} = \frac{48}{288} \approx 0.1667$$

b. We will use $P(R|C) = N(R \cap C)/N(C)$ because in this example it is easier to work directly with the numbers of outcomes rather than the probabilities. Now, $R \cap C$ represents customers who did respond and had a credit card on file. From Table 5.9, there are $N(R \cap C) = 31$ such customers. Also, there are $N(C) = 110$ customers total who had a credit card on file. Therefore,

$$P(R|C) = \frac{N(R \cap C)}{N(C)} = \frac{31}{110} \approx 0.2818$$

Now You Can Do
Exercises 9–24.

That is, the probability that a randomly chosen customer responded to the direct mail marketing campaign, given that the customer had a credit card on file, is 0.2818. ∎

◢ **What Do These Numbers Mean?**

Conditional Probability

Conditional probabilities can often be interpreted as percentages of some *subset* of a population. For example, the conditional probability that a customer responded, given that the customer has a credit card on file, may be interpreted as the percentage of customers with credit cards who responded. ◢

Students sometimes confuse the meanings of $P(B \cap A)$ and $P(B|A)$. For $P(B|A)$, we *assume that the event A has occurred* and now need to find the probability of event B, given event A. On the other hand, for $P(B \cap A)$, we do not assume that event A has occurred and instead need to determine the probability that both events occurred.

2 Independent Events

Since having a credit card on file increased the probability of a customer responding from 0.1667 to 0.2818, we can therefore say that the probability of responding *depends* in part on whether the customer has a credit card on file. In other words, the events R and C are *dependent events*.

On the other hand, if the probability of responding had been unaffected by whether the customer had a credit card on file, then we would have said that R and C were **independent events.** That is, R and C would have been independent events had $P(R|C)$ equaled $P(R)$. In general, if the occurrence of an event does not affect the probability of a second event, then the two events are independent.

Events A and B are **independent** if

$$P(A|B) = P(A) \quad \text{or if} \quad P(B|A) = P(B)$$

Otherwise the events are said to be **dependent.**

Alternatively, in Step 1 you can find $P(A)$ and in Step 2 you can find $P(A|B)$. Then compare these two quantities for Step 3.

Strategy for Determining Whether Two Events Are Independent

1. Find $P(B)$.
2. Find $P(B|A)$.
3. Compare the two probabilities. If they are equal, then A and B are independent events. Otherwise, A and B are dependent events.

Example 5.18 Determining whether two events are independent

Suppose our experiment is to toss two fair dice, so that our sample space is given in Figure 5.3 on page 207. Define the following events.

X: Roll a sum equal to 7.
Y: Roll a sum equal to 6.
Z: Dark green die equals 1.

a. Determine whether events X and Z are independent.
b. Determine whether events Y and Z are independent.

Solution

For both (a) and (b) we use the strategy for determining whether two events are independent.

a. [Step 1] Find $P(\text{Rolling a sum equal to } 7) = P(X)$. There are 36 outcomes in the sample space, 6 of which have a sum equal to 7. Thus, $P(X) = 6/36 = 1/6$.

[Step 2] We need to find $P(X|Z)$, which is the probability that the sum equals 7, given that the dark green die equals 1. Figure 5.17 shows how the sample space is reduced when we know that Z has occurred (dark green die equals 1). There are 6 outcomes where the dark green die equals 1, of which 1 has a sum equal to 7. Thus, $P(X|Z) = 1/6$.

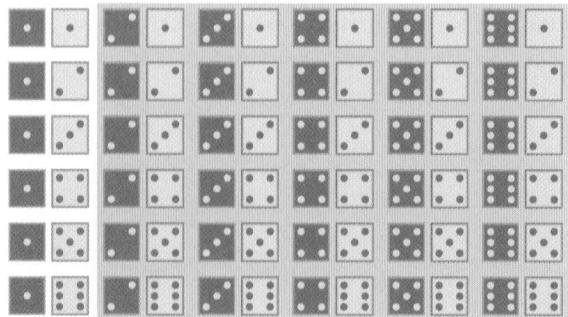

FIGURE 5.17 When we know the dark green die equals 1, the sample space is reduced.

Step 3 Since $P(X) = P(X|Z)$, we conclude that X and Z are independent events.

b. **Step 1** Find P(Rolling a sum equal to 6) = $P(Y)$. There are 36 outcomes in the sample space, 5 of which have a sum equal to 6. Thus, $P(Y) = 5/36$.

Step 2 There are 6 outcomes where the dark green die equals 1, of which 1 has a sum equal to 6. Thus, $P(Y|Z) = 1/6$.

Step 3 From Step 1, $P(Y) = 5/36$. From Step 2, $P(Y|Z) = 1/6$. Since $P(Y) \neq P(Y|Z)$, we conclude that X and Z are dependent events. ∎

Now You Can Do
Exercises 29–34.

Developing Your Statistical Sense

Don't Confuse Independent Events and Mutually Exclusive Events

It is important to stress the difference between independent events and mutually exclusive events. Mutually exclusive events have no outcomes in common. For two events to be independent means that the occurrence of one does not affect the probability of the other. The concepts are different. ◢

Example 5.19 Gambler's Fallacy

Suppose we have tossed a fair coin ten times and have observed heads come up every time. Find the probability of tails on the next toss.

Solution

Since we have observed an unusual number of heads, we might think that the probability of tails on the next toss is increased. However, the short answer is "Not so." Successive tosses of a fair coin are independent because the coin has no memory of its previous tosses. Thus, what happened on the first ten tosses has no effect on the next toss. Probability theory tells us that, in the long run, the proportion of heads and tails will eventually even out if the coin is fair. Therefore, the probability of tails on the next toss is 0.5. This is an example of the Gambler's Fallacy. ∎

3 Multiplication Rule

Just as the Addition Rule is used to find probabilities of unions of events, the **Multiplication Rule** is used to find probabilities of intersections of events. Recall the formula for the conditional probability of event B given event A:

$$P(B|A) = \frac{P(A \cap B)}{P(A)}$$

We solve for $P(A \cap B)$ by multiplying each side by $P(A)$:

$$P(A \cap B) = P(A)\,P(B|A)$$

Similarly, consider the conditional probability of event A given event B:

$$P(A|B) = \frac{P(A \cap B)}{P(B)}$$

Solving for $P(A \cap B)$ gives us a second equation for $P(A \cap B)$:

$$P(A \cap B) = P(B)\,P(A|B)$$

The two equations for $P(A \cap B)$ lead directly to the Multiplication Rule.

> **Multiplication Rule**
>
> $$P(A \cap B) = P(A)\, P(B|A) \qquad \text{or equivalently} \qquad P(A \cap B) = P(B)\, P(A|B)$$

Example 5.20 Multiplication Rule

Bambu Productions/Getty Images

According to the Pew Internet and American Life Project,[5] 35% of American adults have cell phones with apps, but only 68% of those who have apps on their cell phones actually use the apps. Define the following events:

    A: American adult has a cell phone with apps.
    U: American adult uses the apps on his or her cell phone.

a. Find $P(A)$.
b. Find $P(U|A)$, the probability that an American adult uses the apps, given that he or she has a cell phone with apps.
c. Use the Multiplication Rule to calculate $P(A \text{ and } U)$, the probability that an American adult has a cell phone with apps *and* uses the apps on his or her cell phone.

Solution

a. According to the study, 35% of American adults have a cell phone with apps. So $P(A) = 0.35$.
b. The research says that 68% of those who have apps actually use them, so $P(U|A) = 0.68$.
c. Using the Multiplication Rule, we have

$$P(A \text{ and } U) = P(A \cap U) = P(A)P(U|A) = 0.35(0.68) = 0.238$$

Now You Can Do
Exercises 35–38

The probability that an American adult has a cell phone with apps *and* uses them is 0.238. ∎

When events A and B are independent, $P(A|B) = P(A)$ or $P(B|A) = P(B)$. Using these identities, we can formulate a special case of the Multiplication Rule. Using $P(A|B) = P(A)$, we can write the Multiplication Rule as

$$P(A \cap B) = P(B)\, P(A|B) = P(B)\, P(A) = P(A)\, P(B)$$

Equivalently, the Multiplication Rule also states that $P(A \cap B) = P(A)\, P(B|A)$, but if A and B are independent, $P(B|A) = P(B)$, so, again, $P(A \cap B) = P(A)\, P(B)$.

> **Multiplication Rule for Two Independent Events**
> If A and B are any two independent events, $P(A \cap B) = P(A)\, P(B)$.

Example 5.21 Multiplication Rule for Two Independent Events

Suppose the experiment is to toss a fair die twice. If you roll a 6 on both tosses, you will win $18.

a. What is the probability that you will win this game?
b. What is a "fair price" to play this game? A fair price might be determined by balancing out the winnings and the price in the long run.

Solution

a. Define the following events:

  A: Roll a 6 on the first toss.
  B: Roll a 6 on the second toss.

From Example 5.2, $P(A) = P(B) = 1/6$. It is reasonable to assume that successive die rolls are independent, since the die has no memory of its previous tosses. Then, from the Multiplication Rule for Two Independent Events:

$$P(\text{Winning}) = P(A \text{ and } B) = P(A \cap B) = P(A)\,P(B) = \left(\frac{1}{6}\right)\left(\frac{1}{6}\right) = \left(\frac{1}{36}\right)$$

b. In the long run, you would win $18 on average once every 36 games, so your long-run average winnings would be $\left(\frac{1}{36}\right)(\$18) = \$0.50$. Thus, a fair price to play this game would be 50 cents. ■

We investigate this idea of a fair price, known as your *expected winnings*, much more in Chapter 6.

Now You Can Do
Exercises 39–44.

Sampling With and Without Replacement

The relationship between two events can be determined by the way the samples are chosen. Two methods of choosing samples are *sampling with replacement* and *sampling without replacement*.

> In **sampling with replacement,** the randomly selected unit is returned to the population after being selected. When sampling with replacement, it is possible for the same unit to be sampled more than once.
>
> In **sampling without replacement,** the randomly selected unit is not returned to the population after being selected. When sampling without replacement, it is not possible for the same unit to be sampled more than once.

Example 5.22 Sampling with replacement

We draw a card at random from a shuffled deck, observe the card, and return it to the deck. The deck is then reshuffled, and we draw another card at random. What is the probability that both cards we select will be aces?

Solution

Define the following events:

  A: Observe an ace on the first draw.
  B: Observe an ace on the second draw.

We want to find $P(A \cap B)$, the probability of observing an ace on the first draw *and* an ace on the second draw. From the Multiplication Rule, $P(A \cap B) = P(A)\,P(B|A)$. To find $P(A)$, recall that there are 4 aces in the deck of 52 cards. It is reasonable to assume that all cards are equally likely to be selected, so using the classical method, $P(A) = 4/52$. Similarly, $P(B) = 4/52$.

Next we need to find $P(B|A)$, the probability of observing an ace on the second draw, given that we observe an ace on the first draw. Since *the deck of 52 cards has not changed* (except for shuffling), there are still 52 cards, 4 of which are aces. Therefore, $P(B|A) = 4/52$. Thus, the probability that both cards we select will be aces is $P(A \cap B) = P(A)P(B|A) = (4/52)(4/52) \approx 0.0059$.

Note that $P(B|A) = P(B) = 4/52$. Thus, by the alternative method for determining independence, *A* and *B* are independent events when sampling with replacement. ■

Now You Can Do
Exercises 45 and 46.

We can generalize this result as follows.

> When sampling with replacement, successive draws can be considered **independent.**

Example 5.23 | Sampling without replacement

Punchstock/Charles Sturge

Suppose we alter the experiment in Example 5.22 as follows: We draw a card at random from a shuffled deck, hold onto the card (do not replace it) while the deck is reshuffled, and then select another card at random. What is the probability that both cards we select will be aces?

Solution

Define events A and B as in Example 5.22. Again we use the Multiplication Rule to find $P(A \cap B)$. The difference in this experiment comes when finding $P(B|A)$, the probability of observing an ace on the second draw given an ace on the first draw. Once we select the first ace, we do not replace it in the deck. Therefore, when the deck is reshuffled, it has only 51 cards left, only 3 of which are aces. The classical method then gives the probability of observing an ace on the second draw:

$$P(B|A) = \frac{\text{number of aces in the deck}}{\text{number of cards in the deck}} = \frac{3}{51}$$

Thus, the probability that both cards we select will be aces is

$$P(A \cap B) = P(A)P(B|A) = \frac{4}{52} \cdot \frac{3}{51} = \frac{12}{2652} \approx 0.0045$$

This probability is somewhat less than the probability that both cards will be aces when sampling with replacement. Note that here we found that $P(B|A)$ was not equal to $P(B)$. Thus, by the alternative method for determining independence, A and B are not independent events; they are dependent events. ∎

Now You Can Do
Exercises 47 and 48.

We can generalize this result as follows.

> When sampling without replacement, successive draws should be considered **dependent.**

4 Approximating Probabilities for Dependent Events

In some instances we can estimate the probability of a dependent event as if it were independent. The next example shows this can be done.

Example 5.24 | Approximating probabilities for dependent events

Imagine that we are fraud investigators sifting through a database (population) of 1 million financial transactions. Suppose we know that 100 of these transactions are fraudulent. We select two transactions without replacement, so that the successive draws are dependent.
a. Find the probability that both transactions are fraudulent.
b. Approximate this probability, on the assumption that the successive draws are independent, and compute the approximation error.
c. Draw a conclusion about the relationship between sample size and the size of the error using this approximation.

Solution

a. Define the following events:

A: First transaction is fraudulent.
B: Second transaction is fraudulent.

Then, $P(A) = \dfrac{100}{1{,}000{,}000}$ and $P(B|A) = \dfrac{99}{999{,}999}$. Thus, similar to Example 5.23, we have

$$P(\text{both fraudulent}) = \frac{100}{1{,}000{,}000} \cdot \frac{99}{999{,}999} = 0.0000000099$$

b. Suppose that we estimate this probability using the assumption that the successive draws were independent. Then

$$P(\text{both fraudulent}) = \frac{100}{1{,}000{,}000} \cdot \frac{100}{1{,}000{,}000} = 0.00000001$$

The approximation error is the difference between these two probabilities, which is very small:

$$0.00000001 - 0.0000000099 = 0.0000000001$$

This means that our approximation is rather good.

c. Our sample size is small (2) compared to our population (1,000,000). Thus, the error in using the independence assumption to approximate dependent successive draws is very small. ■

The question is: How small is a small sample? We shall use the following *1% Guideline*.

The 1% Guideline

Suppose successive draws, such as those for a random sample, are being made from a population. If the sample size is no larger than 1% of the size of the population, then the probability of dependent successive draws from the population may be approximated using the assumption that the draws are independent.

Example 5.25 Applying the 1% Guideline

Metropolitan Washington, D.C., has the highest proportion of female top-level executives in the United States: 27%.[6] Suppose there are 1000 top-level executives in the area, and we take a random sample of size 2. Approximate the probability that both top-level executives are female, using the 1% Guideline.

Solution

Define the following events:

A: First top-level executive is female.
B: Second top-level executive is female.

The sample of size 2 represents $\dfrac{2}{1000} = 0.002 = 0.2\%$ of the population. Thus, the 1% Guideline applies, and we may treat the successive draws as independent. Thus, we can use the Multiplication Rule for Independent Events to solve this problem.

$$P(A \cap B) = P(A)P(B) = (0.27)(0.27) = 0.0729 \qquad ■$$

The 1% Guideline is also helpful when we do not know the size of the population, but may presume that the population is very large compared to the sample size.

Now You Can Do
Exercises 49–52.

Note that the Multiplication Rule for Independent Events provides us with an alternative method for determining whether two events are indeed independent.

> **Alternative Method for Determining Independence**
> If $P(A)\,P(B) = P(A \cap B)$, then events A and B are **independent**.
> If $P(A)\,P(B) \neq P(A \cap B)$, then events A and B are **dependent**.

Example 5.26 Determining independence using the alternative method

We return to the direct mail marketing data from Example 5.16, reproduced here in Table 5.9. Use the alternative method for determining independence to determine whether the following two events are independent.

    R: Responded to direct mail marketing campaign.
    C: Has a credit card on file.

Table 5.9 Credit card status and marketing response

Response	Credit Card on File? No	Yes	Total
Did not respond	161	79	240
Did respond	17	31	48
Total	178	110	288

Source: Daniel Larose, *Data Mining Methods and Models* (Wiley Interscience, 2006).

Solution

Using Table 5.9, we may find the following probabilities:

$$P(R) = \frac{48}{288} \quad P(C) = \frac{110}{288} \quad P(R \cap C) = \frac{31}{288} \approx 0.1076$$

$$P(R)P(C) = \frac{48}{288} \cdot \frac{110}{288} \approx 0.0637$$

Since $0.0637 \neq 0.1076$, we have $P(R)P(C) \neq P(R \cap C)$, and therefore, R and C are dependent. ■

Now You Can Do
Exercises 53–56.

Example 5.27 Conditional probability for mutually exclusive events

Suppose two events A and B are mutually exclusive, with $P(A) > 0$ and $P(B) > 0$.
a. Find $P(B|A)$.
b. Are events A and B independent or dependent?

Solution

a. Since A and B are mutually exclusive, $P(A \cap B) = 0$. Then

$$P(B|A) = \frac{P(A \cap B)}{P(A)} = 0$$

That is, *if event A has occurred, then event B cannot occur*. This is a natural consequence of events A and B being mutually exclusive.

> ### What Results Might We Expect?
>
> Two events are independent if the occurrence of one does not affect the probability that the other will occur. However, as we saw in (a), if event A occurs, then the probability that event B will occur is 0. Thus, we would expect events A and B to be dependent. ◢

In other words, if two events are mutually exclusive, then they are dependent.

Now You Can Do
Exercises 57–60.

b. We are given that $P(A) > 0$ and $P(B) > 0$. Hence the product $P(A)\,P(B)$ is also greater than 0. However, from (a), $P(A \cap B) = 0$. Thus, $P(A)\,P(B) \neq P(A \cap B)$, and from the alternative method for determining independence, we conclude that events A and B are dependent. ■

We can extend the Multiplication Rule to cover n independent events.

Multiplication Rule for *n* Independent Events

If $A, B, C, \ldots$ are independent events, then $P(A \cap B \cap C \cap \ldots) = P(A)\,P(B)\,P(C)\ldots$

Example 5.28   Multiplication Rule for *n* Independent Events

According to the National Health Interview Survey, 24% of Americans aged 18–44 smoke tobacco.
a. In a random sample of $n = 3$ Americans aged 18–44, find the probability that all 3 smoke.
b. In a random sample of $n = 10$ Americans aged 18–44, find the probability that all 10 smoke.

Solution

Since we are taking random samples, it is reasonable to assume that the events are independent. Let S_i denote the event that the ith American aged 18–44 smokes.
a. $P(S_1) = P(S_2) = P(S_3) = 0.24$. Then, using the Multiplication Rule for n Independent Events,

$$P(S_1 \cap S_2 \cap S_3) = P(S_1) \cdot P(S_2) \cdot P(S_3) = (0.24)(0.24)(0.24) = (0.24)^3 = 0.013824$$

b. $P(S_1) = P(S_2) = \cdots = P(S_{10}) = 0.24$. Then, using the Multiplication Rule for Independent Events,

Now You Can Do
Exercises 61–64.

$$P(S_1 \cap S_2 \cap \ldots \cap S_{10}) = P(S_1) \cdot P(S_2) \cdot \ldots \cdot P(S_{10}) = (0.24)^{10} \approx 0.0000006 \quad ■$$

Example 5.29   Solving an "at least" problem

Using information in Example 5.28, find the probability that, in a random sample of three Americans aged 18–44, at least one of them smokes.

Solution

The phrase "at least" means that one or more of the three Americans smoke. Using the complement, the probability for this event may be written

$$P(\text{At least one of the three Americans smokes})$$

$$= P(\text{One or more of the three Americans smoke})$$

$$= 1 - P(\text{None of the three Americans smokes})$$

The probability of not smoking for the first American is

$$P(N_1) = 1 - P(S_1) = 1 - 0.24 = 0.76$$

and similarly for each American in the sample. Thus,

$$P(\text{None of the three Americans smokes}) = P(N_1) \cdot P(N_2) \cdot P(N_3) = (0.76)^3 = 0.438976$$

Hence, the probability that at least one of the three Americans smokes is

Now You Can Do
Exercises 65–68.

$$1 - P(\text{None of the three Americans smokes}) = 1 - 0.438976 = 0.561024 \quad \blacksquare$$

Give the Calculator a Rest

Suppose that the percentage of Americans aged 18–44 who smoke tobacco this year has decreased to less than 24%, though we are not sure how much less. Determine whether the following quantities will increase or decrease from the values calculated in Examples 5.28 and 5.29.

    a. In a random sample of $n = 3$ Americans aged 18–44, the probability that all 3 smoke

    b. In a random sample of $n = 3$ Americans aged 18–44, the probability that none of them smokes

Solution

    a. Let $P(S_1^*) < 0.24$ represent the revised probability that an American aged 18–44 smokes. Then

$$P(S_1^* \cap S_2^* \cap S_3^*) = P(S_1^*) \cdot P(S_2^*) \cdot P(S_3^*)$$

$$< P(S_1) \cdot P(S_2) \cdot P(S_3) = P(S_1 \cap S_2 \cap S_3)$$

Thus, the probability that all three will smoke will decrease.

    b. If $P(S_1^*) < 0.24$, then $P(N_1^*) = 1 - P(S_1^*) > 1 - 0.24 = P(N_1)$; that is, the probability that an American aged 18–44 doesn't smoke has increased. Thus,

$$P(\text{None of the three Americans smokes}) = P(N_1^*) \cdot P(N_2^*) \cdot P(N_3^*) > (0.76)^3 = 0.438976.$$

Therefore, the probability that none of the three Americans aged 18–44 smokes will increase.

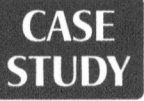

The ELISA Test for the Presence of HIV

The ELISA test is used to screen blood for the presence of HIV. Like most diagnostic procedures, the test is not foolproof.

● When a blood sample contains HIV, the ELISA test will give a positive result 99.6% of the time. That is, the *false-negative rate,* the percentage of tests returning a negative result when the HIV virus is actually present, is $1 - 0.996 = 0.004$.

● When the blood does not contain HIV, the ELISA test will give a negative result 98% of the time. That is, the *false-positive rate,* the percentage of tests returning a positive result when the HIV virus is not actually present, is $1 - 0.98 = 0.02$.

    A positive result means that the test says that the person has the HIV infection. A negative result means that the test says that the person does not have the HIV virus. The *prevalence rate* for HIV in the general population is 0.5%. That is, 5 of 1000 persons in the general population have HIV.

Suppose we have samples of blood from 100,000 randomly chosen people.

Problem 1. How many people in the sample of 100,000 have HIV? How many do not?

Solution

The prevalence rate of 0.5% means that 0.005 (100,000) = 500 people in the sample have HIV. The remainder—99,500—do not.

Problem 2. A positive result is given 99.6% of the time for blood containing HIV. For the 500 people with HIV, how many positive results will the ELISA test return? How many of the 500 people with HIV will receive a negative result?

Solution

The ELISA test will return a positive result for 0.996 (500) = 498 of the 500 people. Thus, two people who actually have HIV will receive a test result indicating that they do not have the virus.

Problem 3. A negative result is given 98% of the time for blood without HIV. For the 99,500 people without HIV, how many negative results will the ELISA test return? Positive results?

Solution

The ELISA test will return a negative result for 0.98 (99,500) = 97,510 of the 99,500 people without HIV. The remaining 2%, or 1990 people, will receive positive ELISA test results, even though they do not have the virus.

We can use the counts we found to fill in the following table.

ELISA test results	In Reality		Total
	Person has HIV	**Person does not have HIV**	
Positive	498	1,990	2,488
Negative	2	97,510	97,512
Total	500	99,500	100,000

We will use the information in the ELISA test contingency table to solve Problems 4 and 5. If a person is chosen at random from the sample of 100,000, define the following events:

A: Person has HIV.
A^C: Person does not have HIV.
Pos: ELISA test returned positive results.
Neg: ELISA test returned negative results.

Problem 4. What is the probability that a randomly chosen person actually does have HIV, given that the ELISA results are negative? In other words, find $P(A \mid \text{Neg})$.

Solution

$$P(A \mid \text{Neg}) = \frac{N(A \cap \text{Neg})}{N(\text{Neg})} = \frac{2}{97,512} \approx 0.0000205$$

Problem 5. What is the probability that a randomly chosen person actually does not have HIV, given that the ELISA test results are positive? In other words, find $P(A^C \mid \text{Pos})$.

Solution

$$P(A^C \mid \text{Pos}) = \frac{N(A^C \cap \text{Pos})}{N(\text{Pos})} = \frac{1990}{2488} \approx 0.7998 \approx 0.80$$

Developing Your Statistical Sense

Which Error Is More Dangerous?

In Problems 4 and 5, we examined the probabilities of the two ways that the ELISA test can be wrong. Which error do you think is more dangerous? $P(A|\text{Neg})$ represents the probability that HIV is present, even though the ELISA test says otherwise. $P(A^C|\text{Pos})$ represents the probability that HIV is not present, even though the ELISA test says it is present. The designers of the ELISA test worked hard to reduce the false-negative rate $P(A|\text{Neg})$ to as low a level as possible. They rightly considered that it is the more dangerous type of error because of the epidemic nature of the illness. A person who receives a false-negative ELISA result could spread the infection further. Therefore, the designers tried to keep this probability as low as they could.

There is a price to be paid, however, which is the high false-positive rate, $P(A^C|\text{Pos})$, a very high 80%. Thus, if a random person receives a positive ELISA test result, the probability that the person does *not* have HIV is 80%. When the ELISA test comes back positive, a second batch of tests that have a more reasonable false-positive rate is usually administered. ◢

Section 5.3 Summary

1 Section 5.3 discusses conditional probability $P(B|A)$, the probability of an event B given that an event A has occurred.

2 We can compare $P(B|A)$ to $P(B)$ to determine whether the events A and B are independent. Events are independent if the occurrence of one event does not affect the probability that the other event will occur.

3 The Multiplication Rule for Independent Events is the product of the individual probabilities. Sampling with replacement is associated with independence, while sampling without replacement means that the events are not independent.

4 We can use the 1% Guideline for approximating probabilities of dependent events.

Section 5.3 Exercises

CLARIFYING THE CONCEPTS

1. Suppose you are the coach of a football team, and your star quarterback is injured.
  a. Does the injury affect the chances that your team will win the big game this weekend?
  b. How would you describe this situation in the terminology presented in this section?

2. Write a sentence or two about a situation in your life similar to Exercise 1, where the probability of some event was affected by whether or not some other event occurred.

3. Explain clearly the difference between $P(A \cap B)$ and $P(A|B)$.

4. Give an example from your own experience of two events that are independent. Describe how they are independent.

5. Picture yourself explaining to your friends about the Gambler's Fallacy. How would you explain the Gambler's Fallacy in your own words?

6. Explain why two events A and B cannot have the following characteristics: $P(A) = 0.25$, $P(B) = 0.25$, and $P(A \cap B) = 0.30$. (*Hint*: Figure 5.16b might help.)

7. Explain why each of the following events is either dependent or independent.
  a. Drawing a ball from a box, replacing it, and then drawing a second ball
  b. Drawing a ball from a box, not replacing it, and then drawing a second ball

8. Explain why the following events are either dependent or independent, and provide support for your assertion.
  a. Tossing a coin and drawing a card from a deck of playing cards
  b. Drawing a card from a deck, not replacing it, and drawing another card

PRACTICING THE TECHNIQUES

A sample of 200 students was asked to state whether they prefer the color pink or blue. Define the following events: P: Prefers pink, B: Prefers blue, F: Female, M: Male. Use the results compiled in Table 5.10 to find the probabilities indicated in Exercises 9–24.

TABLE 5.10 Color preference and gender

Gender	Pink	Blue
Female	40	60
Male	10	90

9. $P(P)$
10. $P(B)$
11. $P(F)$
12. $P(M)$
13. $P(P \text{ and } F)$
14. $P(P \text{ and } M)$
15. $P(B \text{ and } F)$
16. $P(B \text{ and } M)$
17. $P(P \mid F)$
18. $P(P \mid M)$
19. $P(B \mid F)$
20. $P(B \mid M)$
21. $P(F \mid P)$
22. $P(M \mid P)$
23. $P(F \mid B)$
24. $P(M \mid B)$

For Exercises 25–28, refer to Table 5.9 on page 234 to find the probability that a randomly selected customer had the following characteristics.

25. Did not have a credit card on file
26. Did not respond to the direct mail marketing
27. Did not respond, given that he or she did not have a credit card on file
28. Did not have a credit card on file, given that he or she did not respond to the direct mail marketing

For Exercises 29–34, let the experiment be to toss two fair dice. Use the sample space in Figure 5.3 on page 207. Define the following events.

X: Roll a sum equal to 7.
Y: Roll a sum equal to 6.
Z: Roll doubles, where the dark green die equals the light green die.
W: Light green die equals 6.

Use the strategy for determining whether two events are independent (page 228) to determine whether the following pairs of events are independent.

29. *X* and *Z*
30. *Y* and *Z*
31. *X* and *W*
32. *Y* and *W*
33. *X* and *Y*
34. *Z* and *W*

For Exercises 35–38, use the Multiplication Rule to find the indicated probability.

35. Thirty percent of students at a particular college take statistics. Ninety percent of students taking statistics at the college pass the course. What is the probability that a student will take statistics and pass the course?
36. Fifty percent of students at a particular college are commuters. Of those, 10% bike to school. Find the probability that a student is a commuter and bikes to school.
37. Twenty-five percent of the nursing students at a particular college are male. Of these, 50% are taking a biology course this semester. Calculate the probability that a nursing student is a male and is taking a biology course this semester.
38. Thirty percent of the statistics students at a particular college have taken advantage of the college tutoring program. After doing so, 80% of them received a higher score on the next exam. Find the probability that a statistics student has taken advantage of the college tutoring program and has received a higher score on the next exam.

For Exercises 39–44, let *A*, *B*, *C*, and *D* be independent events such that $P(A) = 0.5$, $P(B) = 0.4$, $P(C) = 0.2$, and $P(D) = 0.1$. Use the Multiplication Rule for Two Independent Events to find the following probabilities.

39. $P(A \text{ and } B)$
40. $P(A \cap C)$
41. $P(A \cap D)$
42. $P(B \text{ and } C)$
43. $P(B \text{ and } D)$
44. $P(C \cap D)$

For Exercises 45 and 46, suppose we sample two cards at random and with replacement from a deck of cards. Define the following events. *R*1: Red card observed on the first draw, *R*2: Red card observed on the second draw, *H*1: Heart observed on the first draw, *H*2: Heart observed on the second draw.

45. Find $P(R1 \text{ and } R2)$.
46. Find $P(H1 \cap H2)$.

For Exercises 47 and 48, suppose we sample two cards at random and without replacement from a deck of cards. Define the same events as for Exercises 45 and 46.

47. Find $P(R1 \text{ and } R2)$.
48. Find $P(H1 \cap H2)$.

Use the following information for Exercises 49–52. Suppose 25% of the 2000 students at a local college use Gmail as their primary email account.

49. If we take a sample of 2 students, verify that the 1% Guideline applies.
50. If we take a sample of 2 students, use the 1% Guideline to approximate the probability that both students use Gmail as their primary email account.
51. If we take a sample of 3 students, approximate the probability that all 3 students use Gmail as their primary email account.
52. If we take a sample of 4 students, approximate the probability that all 4 students use Gmail as their primary email account.

For Exercises 53–56, use Table 5.10 and the alternative method for determining independence (page 234) to determine whether the following pairs of events are independent.

53. *P* and *F*
54. *P* and *M*
55. *B* and *F*
56. *B* and *M*
57. Suppose $P(X \text{ and } Y) = 0$, for events *X* and *Y*. State whether *X* and *Y* are independent.
58. Define the following events. *A* = salary $50,000 or more, *B* = salary less than $50,000. Are *A* and *B* independent? Why?
59. The intersection between events *W* and *Z* is empty. Then is it true or not true that $P(W \text{ and } Z) = P(W) \cdot P(Z)$? Explain.
60. Define event *W*: team wins. Are *W* and W^c independent? Why?

For Exercises 61–64, use the Multiplication Rule for *n* Independent Events to find the probabilities. Define *L*: observe either a 1 or a 2 on a toss of a fair die.

61. *L* occurs on three successive tosses.
62. *L* occurs on four successive tosses.
63. *L* occurs on five successive tosses.
64. *L* occurs on ten successive tosses.

For Exercises 65–68, define *H*: observe a number greater than 2 on a toss of a fair die. Find the following probabilities.

65. That *H* occurs at least once in three tosses
66. That *H* occurs at least once in four tosses
67. That *H* occurs at least once in five tosses
68. That *H* occurs at least once in ten tosses
69. Calculate the probability of observing tails on each of five successive tosses of a fair coin.
70. Compute the probability of observing tails on each of ten successive tosses of a fair coin.

For Exercises 71–74, let *A* and *B* be two independent events, with $P(A) = 0.6$ and $P(B) = 0.4$. Find the indicated probabilities.

71. $P(A \cap B)$
72. $P(A|B)$
73. $P(B|A)$
74. $P(A \cup B)$

For Exercises 75–78, let *A* and *B* be two independent events, with $P(A) = 0.5$ and $P(B) = 0.2$. Find the indicated probabilities.

75. $P(A \cap B)$
76. $P(A|B)$
77. $P(B|A)$
78. $P(A \cup B)$
79. Suppose that *A* and *B* are two events with $P(A) = 0.3$ and $P(A \cap B) = 0.05$. Find $P(B|A)$.
80. Suppose that *A* and *B* are two events, with $P(A) = 0.9$ and $P(B|A) = 0.6$. Find $P(A \cap B)$.

For Exercises 81–86, let *A* and *B* be independent events such that $P(A) = 0.4$ and $P(B) = 0.5$. Find the indicated probabilities.

81. $P(A \text{ and } B)$
82. $P(A|B)$
83. $P(B|A)$
84. $P(A \text{ or } B)$
85. $P(A \text{ and } B)^C$
86. $P(A \text{ or } B)^C$

For Exercises 87–90, let *C* and *D* be events such that $P(C) = 0.7$, $P(D) = 0.3$, and $P(C \text{ and } D) = 0.21$.

87. Find $P(C|D)$.
88. Find $P(D|C)$.
89. Are events *C* and *D* independent? How can you tell?
90. Are events *C* and *D* mutually exclusive? How can you tell?

For Exercises 91 and 92, let *E* and *F* be events such that $P(E) = 0.5$ and $P(F) = 0.6$.

91. What further information do we need to know to determine whether events *E* and *F* are independent?
92. What further information do we need to know to determine whether events *E* and *F* are mutually exclusive?

For Exercises 93–96, a single fair die is rolled twice in succession. Find the indicated probabilities.

93. Observe a 1 on the second roll
94. Observe an even number on the second roll
95. Observe an even number on the second roll, given that you observe an even number on the first roll
96. Based on the probabilities in Exercises 93–95, what can you say about the dependence or independence of successive rolls of a single fair die?

APPLYING THE CONCEPTS

97. Teen Birth Rate. The Federal Interagency Forum on Child and Family Statistics (**www.childstats.gov**) reported that the teenage birth rate in 2010 was 0.04.
  a. Find the probability that two randomly selected births are to teenagers.
  b. Find the probability that five randomly selected births are to teenagers.
  c. Find the probability that at least one of four randomly selected births is to a teenager.

98. Fair Die Experiment. The experiment is to roll a fair die once.
  a. What is the probability of rolling a 6 with a fair die?
  b. What if we are told that the number rolled is an even number? How does this knowledge affect the probability of rolling a 6?
  c. We saw that the probability of rolling a 6 increased when we were told that an even number was observed. Does this always happen? Can you think of an example where the probability of an event decreases given the occurrence of another event?

99. Balls in a Box. A box contains four blue balls and three red balls. If we select two balls at random, what is the probability that both balls will be blue if
  a. we sample with replacement.
  b. we sample without replacement.

100. Acceptance Sampling. You are in charge of purchasing for a large computer retailer. Your wholesaler delivers computers to you in batches of 100. You either accept or reject an entire batch based on a random sample of two computers: if both computers you sample are defective, then you reject the entire batch. Suppose that (unknown to you, of course) there are 10 defective computers in the batch of 100 computers.
  a. Should you conduct your sampling with or without replacement? Why?
  b. What is the probability that the first computer you select is defective?
  c. What is the probability that the second computer you select is defective, given that the first was defective, if you sample without replacement?

d. What is the probability that you will accept the batch?

e. What is the probability that you will reject the batch?

f. Usually you accept each batch of computers from this wholesaler. Do you think that is a wise move, considering that 10% of their product is defective? How could you make your test stricter so that there is a smaller chance of accepting a batch with 10% defectives?

101. 9/11 Information. Within two weeks of the terrorist attacks of September 11, 2001, the Pew Internet and American Life Project conducted a survey, asking, among other things, from which medium the respondent received most of his/her information regarding these events. The results indicated that 1.9% of Americans received most of their information about September 11 from the Internet. Assuming independence, find the following probabilities.

a. 2 randomly selected people both received most of their information from the Internet

b. 2 randomly selected people both received most of their information from sources other than the Internet

c. 5 randomly selected people received most of their information from sources other than the Internet

d. At least 1 of 3 randomly selected people received most information from the Internet

102. Treasury Bonds. One of the most important tasks for economists is to make forecasts for the performance (up or down) of investments such as 30-year Treasury bonds. *The Journal of Investing* (Vol. 6, No. 2, page 8, 1997) reports that, in a sample of 30 six-month surveys, the consensus estimate of performance for the 30-year Treasury bond has been wrong 20 out of the 30 times!

a. Find the probability that two randomly selected consensus estimates were correct.

b. Find the probability that three randomly selected consensus estimates were wrong.

c. If we choose two consensus estimates and if we sample with replacement, find the probability that the second consensus estimate was right, given that the first consensus estimate was right. Are the successive draws independent? Why or why not?

d. Repeat **(c)**, this time sampling without replacement. Are the successive draws independent? Why or why not?

103. Female Students. At Northern Connecticut University, 55% of the students are female. Of these, 10% are business majors. Find the following probabilities, assuming sampling with replacement.

a. A randomly chosen student is a female business major.

b. Two randomly selected students are females.

c. The second of two randomly selected students is a female, given that the first is a female.

d. The second of two randomly selected students is a female, given that the first is a male.

e. Two randomly selected students are female business majors.

f. If possible, find the probability that two randomly selected students are business majors. If not possible, explicitly explain why not.

104. Adjustable Rate Mortgages. Half of the 20 mortgages provided by a certain mortgage lending company last week are adjustable rate mortgages (ARMs). Suppose we sample three mortgages without replacement. Find the following probabilities.

a. The first mortgage is an ARM.

b. The second mortgage is an ARM, given that the first mortgage is an ARM.

c. The third mortgage is an ARM, given that the first two mortgages are ARMs.

105. Sampling Songs. Juan is sampling music at his local CD store. Suppose Juan is sampling one particular CD, and on this CD are ten songs, of which Juan would like six. Juan will sample only two songs. If he likes both songs, he will purchase the CD. Assuming that the songs are sampled without replacement, find the following probabilities.

a. Juan will like the first song he hears.

b. Juan will not like the first song he hears.

c. Juan will like both the first and the second songs he hears.

d. Juan will like the second song, given that he liked the first song.

e. Juan will purchase the CD.

9/11 and Pearl Harbor. What were the feelings of Americans in the days immediately following the events of September 11, 2001? In an NBC News Terrorism Poll, the following question was asked: "Would you say that Tuesday's attacks are more serious than, equal to, or not as serious as the Japanese attack on Pearl Harbor?" This poll was conducted on September 12, 2001. Use the following crosstabulation of the poll results for Exercises 106–109.

	SEX		Total
	Male	Female	
More serious than Pearl Harbor	200	212	412
Equal to Pearl Harbor	70	84	154
Not as serious as Pearl Harbor	23	6	29
Not sure	11	12	23
	304	314	618

106. Find the probabilities that a randomly chosen person has the following characteristics.

a. Is female, $P(F)$

b. Is male, $P(M)$

c. Believes September 11 is more serious than Pearl Harbor, $P(\text{More})$

107. Find the probability that a randomly chosen person has the following characteristics.

a. Is female and believes September 11 is more serious than Pearl Harbor, $P(F \cap \text{More})$

b. Is male and believes September 11 is more serious than Pearl Harbor, $P(M \cap \text{More})$

108. Find the following conditional probabilities for a randomly chosen person.

   a. Given that the person is female, believes September 11 is more serious than Pearl Harbor, $P(\text{More} \mid F)$

   b. Given that the person is male, believes September 11 is more serious than Pearl Harbor, $P(\text{More} \mid M)$

109. Are gender and the belief whether September 11 was more or less serious than Pearl Harbor independent? Why or why not?

BRINGING IT ALL TOGETHER

Gender and Pet Preference. Use Table 5.11 for Exercises 110–114. Do you think your gender affects what type of pet you own?

TABLE 5.11   Pet preference

Gender	Cats	Dogs	Other pets	Total
Female	100	50	30	180
Male	50	50	20	120
Total	150	100	50	300

110. Find the probabilities that a randomly chosen person has the following characteristics.

   a. Is female, $P(F)$

   b. Is male, $P(M)$

   c. Owns a cat, $P(C)$

   d. Owns some other kind of pet, $P(O)$

111. Find the probability that a randomly chosen person has the following characteristics.

   a. Is female and owns a cat, $P(F \cap C)$

   b. Is female and owns some other kind of pet, $P(F \cap O)$

   c. Is male and owns a cat, $P(M \cap C)$

   d. Is male and owns some other kind of pet, $P(M \cap O)$

112. Find the following conditional probabilities for a randomly chosen person.

   a. Owns a cat, given that the person is female, $P(C \mid F)$

   b. Owns a cat, given that the person is male, $P(C \mid M)$

   c. Owns some other kind of pet, given that the person is female, $P(O \mid F)$

   d. Owns some other kind of pet, given that the person is male, $P(O \mid M)$

113. Are gender and pet preference independent? Why or why not?

114. If you were a cat-food manufacturer, would you advertise more in men's magazines or women's magazines? Why? Cite your evidence.

5.4   Counting Methods

OBJECTIVES By the end of this section, I will be able to . . .

1   Apply the Multiplication Rule for Counting to solve certain counting problems.

2   Use permutations and combinations to solve certain counting problems.

3   Compute probabilities using combinations.

Counting methods allow us to solve a range of problems, including how to compute certain probabilities.

1 Multiplication Rule for Counting

Let us begin with an example illustrating a general rule of counting.

Example 5.30   Design your own T-shirt

A store at the local mall allows customers to design their own T-shirts. The store offers the following options to its customers:

   • **Sleeve type:** Long-sleeve or short-sleeve
   • **Color:** White, black, or red
   • **Image:** Stock picture or uploaded photo

List the possible T-shirt options.

Solution

Figure 5.18 is a tree diagram that shows all the different T-shirts that can be designed. There are two choices for type of sleeve. For each sleeve type, there are three choices for color. For each color, there are two choices of image: stock picture or uploaded photo. All together, customers have a choice from among

$$2 \cdot 3 \cdot 2 = 12$$

different T-shirt options.

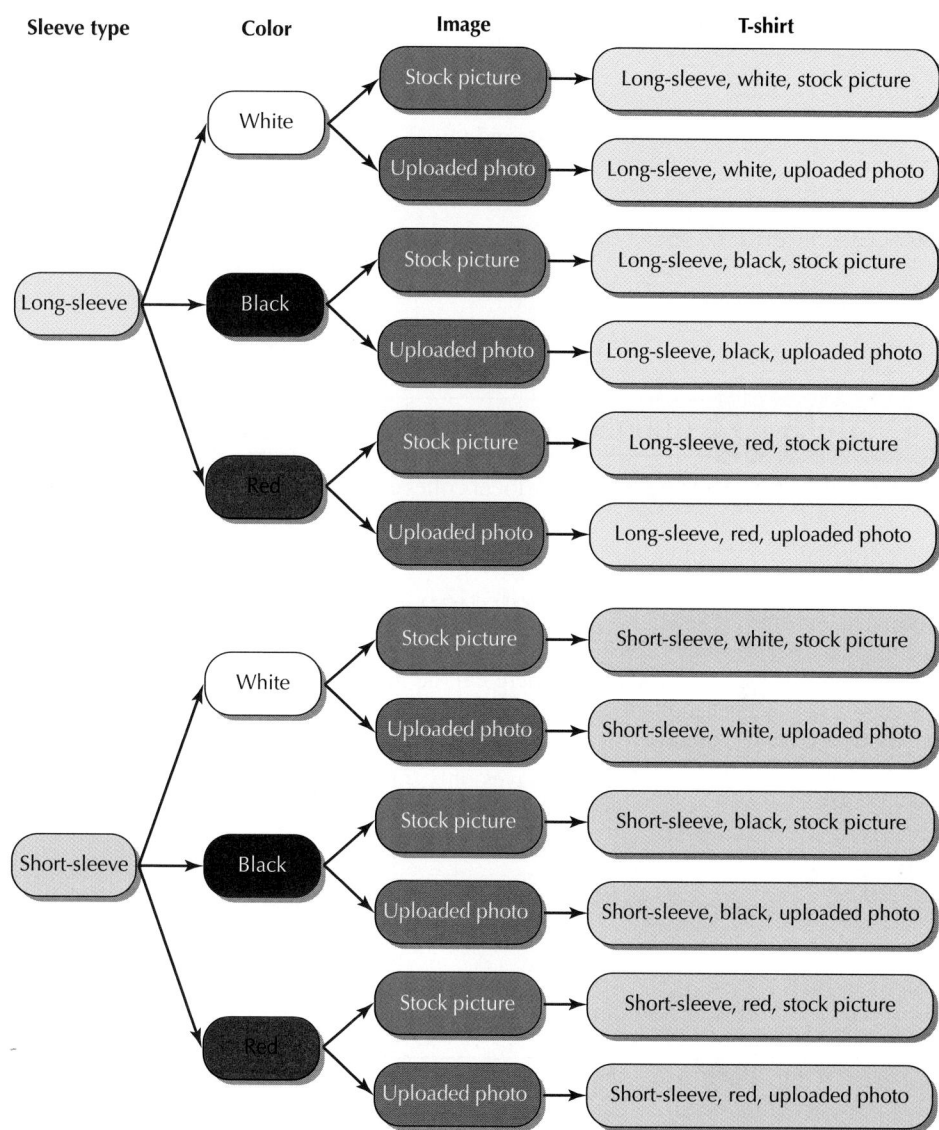

Sleeve type	Color	Image	T-shirt

FIGURE 5.18 Tree diagram for the different T-shirt options.

Now You Can Do
Exercises 7–10.

We can generalize the result as the **Multiplication Rule for Counting.**

Multiplication Rule for Counting

Suppose an activity consists of a series of events in which there are *a* possible outcomes for the first event, *b* possible outcomes for the second event, *c* possible outcomes for the third event, and so on. Then the total number of different possible outcomes for the series of events is

$$a \cdot b \cdot c \cdot \ldots$$

Example 5.31 — Counting with repetition: famous initials

Some Americans in history are uniquely identified by their initials. For example, "JFK" stands for John Fitzgerald Kennedy, and "FDR" stands for Franklin Delano Roosevelt. How many different possible sets of initials are there for people with a first, middle, and last name?

Solution

Let us consider the three initials as an activity consisting of three events. Note that a particular letter may be repeated, as in "AAM" for A. A. Milne, author of *Winnie the Pooh*. Then there are $a = 26$ ways to choose the first initial, $b = 26$ ways to choose the second initial, and $c = 26$ ways to choose the third initial. Thus, by the Multiplication Rule for Counting, the total number of different sets of initials is

$$26 \cdot 26 \cdot 26 = 17{,}576$$

Now You Can Do
Exercises 11 and 12.

Example 5.32 — Counting without repetition: intramural singles tennis

A local college has an intramural singles tennis league with five players, Ryan, Megan, Nicole, Justin, and Kyle. The college presents a trophy to the top three players in the league. How many different possible sets of three trophy winners are there?

Solution

The major difference between Examples 5.31 and this example is that in Example 5.31 there can be no repetition. Ryan cannot finish in first place *and* second place. So we proceed as follows. Five possible players could finish in first place, so $a = 5$. Now there are only four players left, one of whom will finish in second place, so $b = 4$. That leaves only three players, one of whom will finish in third place, giving $c = 3$. Thus, by the Multiplication Rule for Counting, the number of different possible sets of trophy winners is

$$5 \cdot 4 \cdot 3 = 60$$

Note: To summarize the key difference between Examples 5.31 and 5.32: If repetitions are allowed, then $a = b = c$. If repetitions are not allowed, then the numbers being multiplied decrease by one from left to right.

Now You Can Do
Exercises 13 and 14.

Example 5.33 — Traveling salesman problem

A Southeast regional salesman has eight destinations that he must travel to this month: Atlanta, Raleigh, Charleston, Nashville, Jacksonville, Richmond, Mobile, and Jackson. How many different possible routes could he take?

Solution

The salesman has $a = 8$ different choices for where to go first. Once the first destination has been chosen, there are only $b = 7$ choices for where to go second. And once the first two destinations have been chosen, there are only $c = 6$ choices for where to go third. And so on. Thus, by the Multiplication Law for Counting, the number of different possible routes for the salesman is

$$a \cdot b \cdot c \cdot d \cdot e \cdot f \cdot g \cdot h = 8 \cdot 7 \cdot 6 \cdot 5 \cdot 4 \cdot 3 \cdot 2 \cdot 1 = 40{,}320$$

Now You Can Do
Exercises 15 and 16.

The calculation in Example 5.33 leads us to introduce the **factorial symbol,** which is used for the counting rules we will learn in the remainder of this section.

> For any integer $n \geq 0$, the **factorial symbol $n!$** is defined as follows:
> - $0! = 1$
> - $1! = 1$
> - $n! = n(n - 1)(n - 2) \cdots 3 \cdot 2 \cdot 1$

For example:

$$2! = 2 \cdot 1 = 2$$
$$3! = 3 \cdot 2 \cdot 1 = 6$$
$$4! = 4 \cdot 3 \cdot 2 \cdot 1 = 24$$
$$5! = 5 \cdot 4 \cdot 3 \cdot 2 \cdot 1 = 120$$
$$6! = 6 \cdot 5 \cdot 4 \cdot 3 \cdot 2 \cdot 1 = 720$$
$$7! = 7 \cdot 6 \cdot 5 \cdot 4 \cdot 3 \cdot 2 \cdot 1 = 5040$$
$$8! = 8 \cdot 7 \cdot 6 \cdot 5 \cdot 4 \cdot 3 \cdot 2 \cdot 1 = 40{,}320, \text{ as in Example 5.33}$$

Now You Can Do
Exercises 17–22.

2 Permutations and Combinations

Example 5.34   Traveling to some but not all of the cities

Example 5.33 calculated the number of possible routes for traveling to $n = 8$ cities. However suppose we are interested in traveling to *some but not all* of the cities? For example, suppose that the salesman is traveling to three of the eight cities. Find the number of possible routes.

Solution

There are eight choices for the first city, seven choices for the second city, and six choices for the third city. Since the salesman is traveling to three cities only, the number of possible routes is thus

$$8 \cdot 7 \cdot 6 = 336$$

This result may be rewritten using factorial notation, as follows:

Now You Can Do
Exercises 23 and 24.

$$8 \cdot 7 \cdot 6 = \frac{8 \cdot 7 \cdot 6 \cdot (5 \cdot 4 \cdot 3 \cdot 2 \cdot 1)}{(5 \cdot 4 \cdot 3 \cdot 2 \cdot 1)} = \frac{8!}{5!} = \frac{8!}{(8 - 3)!}$$

Example 5.34 leads us to the following definition.

> **Permutations**
>
> A **permutation** is an arrangement of items, such that
> - r items are chosen at a time from n distinct items.
> - repetition of items is not allowed.
> - the order of the items is important.
>
> The number of permutations of n items chosen r at a time is denoted as $_nP_r$ and given by the formula
>
> $$_nP_r = \frac{n!}{(n - r)!}$$

In Example 5.34, we are looking for the number of permutations of 8 cities taken 3 at a time. We have $n = 8$, $r = 3$:

$$_nP_r = {_8P_3} = \frac{n!}{(n-r)!} = \frac{8!}{(8-3)!} = \frac{8!}{5!} = 8 \cdot 7 \cdot 6 = 336$$

Example 5.35 Calculating numbers of permutations

Find the following numbers of permutations.

a. $_5P_2$ **b.** $_6P_2$ **c.** $_6P_6$

Solution

a. $_5P_2 = \dfrac{5!}{(5-2)!} = \dfrac{5 \cdot 4 \cdot 3!}{3!} = 20$

b. $_6P_2 = \dfrac{6!}{(6-2)!} = \dfrac{6 \cdot 5 \cdot 4!}{4!} = 30$

Now You Can Do
Exercises 25–32.

c. $_6P_6 = \dfrac{6!}{(6-6)!} = \dfrac{6 \cdot 5 \cdot 4 \cdot 3 \cdot 2 \cdot 1}{0!} = 720$

Example 5.36 Counting permutations: Secret Santas

"Secret Santa" refers to a method whereby each member of a group anonymously buys a holiday gift for another member of the group. Each person is secretly assigned to buy a gift for another randomly chosen person in the group. Suppose Jessica, Laverne, Samantha, and Luisa share a dorm suite and would like to do Secret Santa this holiday season.

a. Verify that in this instance one woman purchasing a gift for another woman represents a permutation.

b. Calculate how many possible different permutations of gift buying there are for the four women.

Solution

a. • There are $n = 4$ women, and $r = 2$ people are associated with each gift, the giver and the receiver.
   • Each person can buy only one gift, so repetition is not allowed.
   • Finally, there is a difference between Jessica buying for Laverne and Laverne buying for Jessica. Thus, order is important, and thus, buying a gift represents a permutation.

b. The number of permutations is calculated as follows:

$$_nP_r = {_4P_2} = \frac{4!}{(4-2)!} = \frac{4 \cdot 3 \cdot 2!}{2!} = 12$$

In a permutation, order is important. For example, in Example 5.36, there was a difference between Jessica buying a gift for Laverne and Laverne buying one for Jessica. However, what if we consider shaking hands instead? Then Jessica shaking hands with Laverne is considered the same as Laverne shaking hands with Jessica. Hence, sometimes order is not important. What is important here is the **combination** of Jessica and Laverne.

> **Combinations**
>
> A **combination** is an arrangement of items in which
> - r items are chosen from n distinct items.
> - repetition of items is not allowed.
> - the order of the items is not important.
>
> The number of combinations of r items chosen from n different items is denoted as
>
> $$_nC_r$$

Example 5.37 How many combinations in the intramural tennis league?

We return to the intramural singles tennis league at the local college. There are five players: Ryan, Megan, Nicole, Justin, and Kyle. Each player must play each other once.

a. Confirm that a match between two players represents a combination.
b. How many matches will be held?

Solution

a. Let {Ryan, Megan} denote a tennis match between Ryan and Megan. *Note:*
- There are $r = 2$ players chosen from $n = 5$ players.
- Each player plays each other player once, so repetition is not allowed.
- There is no difference between {Ryan, Megan} and {Megan, Ryan}, so order is not important.

Thus, a tennis match between two players represents a combination.

b. The list of all matches is as follows.

{Ryan, Megan}	{Megan, Nicole}	{Nicole, Justin}
{Ryan, Nicole}	{Megan, Justin}	{Nicole, Kyle}
{Ryan, Justin}	{Megan, Kyle}	{Justin, Kyle}
{Ryan, Kyle}		

Thus there are $_5C_2 = 10$ possible matches of $r = 2$ players chosen from $n = 5$ players. ∎

We saw in Example 5.35 that $_5P_2 = 20$ and in Example 5.37 that $_5C_2 = 10$. Permutations and combinations differ only in that ordering is ignored for combinations. To calculate the number of combinations $_nC_r$, we simply do not count however many rearrangements there are of the same items. For example, in Example 5.37, there are $r! = 2! = 2$ rearrangements of the same players, such as {Ryan, Megan} and {Megan, Ryan}. Thus,

$$_5C_2 = \frac{_5P_2}{2!} = \frac{20}{2} = 10$$

In general, the *number of combinations* can be computed as the number of permutations divided by the factorial of the number of items chosen.

Note: Following are some special combinations you may find useful. For any integer n:

$$_nC_n = 1$$
$$_nC_0 = 1$$
$$_nC_1 = n$$
$$_nC_{n-1} = n$$

> **Formula for the Number of Combinations**
>
> The number of combinations of r items chosen from n different items is given by
>
> $$_nC_r = \frac{n!}{r!(n-r)!}$$

For instance, in Example 5.37, the formula for the number of combinations is

$$_5C_2 = \frac{5!}{2!(5-2)!} = \frac{5!}{2!\,3!} = \frac{5 \cdot 4 \cdot 3!}{2 \cdot 1 \cdot 3!} = \frac{20}{2} = 10$$

Thus the relation: $_5C_2 = \,_5P_2/2!$ is verified.

Example 5.38   Calculating numbers of combinations

Find the following numbers of combinations.
a. $_6C_2$ b. $_6C_3$ c. $_6C_4$

Solution

a. $_6C_2 = \dfrac{6!}{2!(6-2)!} = \dfrac{6 \cdot 5 \cdot 4!}{2 \cdot 1 \cdot 4!} = \dfrac{30}{2} = 15$

b. $_6C_3 = \dfrac{6!}{3!(6-3)!} = \dfrac{6 \cdot 5 \cdot 4 \cdot 3!}{3 \cdot 2 \cdot 1 \cdot 3!} = \dfrac{120}{6} = 20$

c. $_6C_4 = \dfrac{6!}{4!(6-4)!} = \dfrac{6!}{(6-4)!\,4!} = \dfrac{6 \cdot 5 \cdot 4!}{2 \cdot 1 \cdot 4!} = \dfrac{30}{2} = 15$

Now You Can Do
Exercises 33–40.

Note that in (c) we used the commutative property of multiplication ($a \cdot b = b \cdot a$) and found that $_6C_4 = \,_6C_2 = 15$. In general, $_nC_r = \,_nC_{n-r}$ for this reason. ■

Example 5.39   Calculating the number of permutations and combinations using technology

Use the TI-83/84 and Excel to calculate the following.
a. $_9P_6$ b. $_{10}C_7$

Solution

We use the instructions provided in the Step-by-Step Technology Guide at the end of this section (page 252).

a. From Figures 5.19 and 5.20, we find that $_9P_6 = 60,480$.

FIGURE 5.19 TI-83/84 permutation results.   FIGURE 5.20 Excel permutation results.

b. From Figures 5.21 and 5.22, we find that $_{10}C_7 = 120$. ■

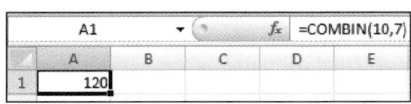

FIGURE 5.21 TI-83/84 combination results.   FIGURE 5.22 Excel combination results.

Sometimes we wish to find the number of permutations of items where some of the items are not distinct.

Example 5.40 Permutations with nondistinct items

How many distinct strings of letters can we make by using all the letters in the word STATISTICS?

Solution

Each string will be 10 letters long and include 3 S's, 3 T's, 2 I's, 1 A, and 1 C. The 10 positions shown here need to be filled.

$$\underline{\quad}\ \underline{\quad}\ \underline{\quad}\ \underline{\quad}\ \underline{\quad}\ \underline{\quad}\ \underline{\quad}\ \underline{\quad}\ \underline{\quad}\ \underline{\quad}$$
$$\quad 1\quad 2\quad 3\quad 4\quad 5\quad 6\quad 7\quad 8\quad 9\quad 10$$

The string-forming process is as follows:

[Step 1] Choose the positions for the three S's.

[Step 2] Choose the positions for the three T's.

[Step 3] Choose the positions for the two I's.

[Step 4] Choose the position for the one A.

[Step 5] Choose the position for the one C.

There are $_{10}C_3$ ways to place the three S's in Step 1. Once Step 1 is done, there are seven slots left, leaving $_7C_3$ positions for the three T's. Once Step 2 is done, there are four slots left, so there are $_4C_2$ ways to place the two I's. Once Step 3 is done, there are only 2 slots left, so there are only $_2C_1$ ways to position the A. Finally, there is only $_1C_1$ way to place the C.

Putting Steps 1–5 together, we calculate the number of distinct letter strings as

$$_{10}C_3 \cdot {}_7C_3 \cdot {}_4C_2 \cdot {}_2C_1 \cdot {}_1C_1 = \frac{10!}{3!\,\cancel{7!}} \cdot \frac{\cancel{7!}}{3!\,\cancel{4!}} \cdot \frac{\cancel{4!}}{2!\,2!} \cdot \frac{2!}{1!\,\cancel{1!}} \cdot \frac{\cancel{1!}}{1!\,0!}$$

$$= \frac{10!}{3!\,3!\,2!\,1!\,1!} = \frac{3,628,800}{72}$$

$$= 50,400$$

There are 50,400 distinct strings of letters that can be made using the letters in the word STATISTICS. ∎

This example can be generalized in the following result.

Permutations of Nondistinct Items

The number of permutations of n items of which n_1 are of the first kind, n_2 are of the second kind, ..., and n_k are of the kth kind is calculated as

$$\frac{n!}{n_1! \cdot n_2! \cdot \ldots \cdot n_k!}$$

where $n = n_1 + n_2 + \cdots + n_k$.

Example 5.41 Number of permutations of nondistinct items

Brandon brings a healthy snack to school each day, consisting of 5 carrot sticks, 4 celery sticks, and 2 cherry tomatoes. If Brandon eats one item at a time, in how many different ways can he eat his snack?

Solution

We are seeking the number of permutations of $n = 11$ items, of which $n_1 = 5$ are carrot sticks, $n_2 = 4$ are celery sticks, and $n_3 = 2$ are cherry tomatoes. Using the formula for the number of permutations of nondistinct items,

$$\frac{n!}{n_1! \cdot n_2! \cdot n_3!} = \frac{11!}{5! \cdot 4! \cdot 2!} = \frac{39,916,800}{120 \cdot 24 \cdot 2} = 6930$$

Now You Can Do
Exercises 41 and 42.

There are 6930 distinct ways in which Brandon can eat his snack. ∎

Acceptance sampling refers to the process of (1) selecting a random sample from a batch of items, (2) evaluating the sample for defectives, and (3) either accepting or rejecting the entire batch based on the evaluation of the sample.

Example 5.42 Acceptance sampling uses combinations

Suppose we have a batch of 20 cell phones, of which, unknown to us, 3 are defective and 17 are nondefective. We will take a random sample of size 2 and evaluate both items once.
a. Are the arrangements in acceptance sampling permutations or combinations?
b. Find the number of ways that both sampled cell phones are defective.

Solution

a. Both permutations and combinations require the following:
  • r items are chosen from n distinct items. Here we are selecting $r = 2$ phones from a batch of $n = 20$.
  • Repetition of the items is not allowed. Each item is evaluated only once.
The difference between permutations and combinations is that, for permutations order is important while for combinations order is not important. In acceptance sampling, the order of the items is not important. Thus, acceptance sampling uses combinations.
b. The number of ways of choosing 2 of the 3 defectives is

$$_3C_2 = \frac{3!}{2!(3-2)!} = \frac{3 \cdot 2!}{2! \cdot 1!} = 3$$

Selecting 2 defectives means that we are choosing 0 of the 17 nondefectives. The number of ways this can happen is

$$_{17}C_0 = \frac{17!}{0!(17-0)!} = \frac{17!}{1 \cdot 17!} = 1$$

By the Multiplication Rule for Counting, the number of ways that both sampled cell phones are defective is

$$_3C_2 \cdot {}_{17}C_0 = 3 \cdot 1 = 3$$ ∎

3 Computing Probabilities Using Combinations

The counting methods we have learned in this section may be used to compute probabilities. We assume that each possible outcome in a random sample is *equally likely,* and thus we use the classical method for assigning the probability of an event E:

$$P(E) = \frac{\text{number of outcomes in } E}{\text{number of outcomes in sample space}} = \frac{N(E)}{N(S)}$$

Example 5.43 Probability using combinations: acceptance sampling

Continuing with Example 5.42, if both cell phones in the sample of size 2 are defective, we will reject the batch and cancel our contract with the supplier.
a. What is the number of ways that both cell phones will be defective?
b. What is the number of outcomes in this sample space?
c. What is the probability that both cell phones will be defective?

Solution

a. From Example 5.42, the number of ways that both cell phones will be defective is

$$_3C_2 \cdot {}_{17}C_0 = 3 \cdot 1 = 3$$

b. The number of outcomes in the sample space is given by the number of ways of selecting 2 cell phones out of a batch of 20, that is,

$$N(S) = {}_{20}C_2 = \frac{20!}{2!(20-2)!} = \frac{20 \cdot 19 \cdot 18!}{2! \cdot 18!} = \frac{380}{2} = 190$$

c. Therefore, the probability that both cell phones will be defective is given by

$$P(\text{Both defective}) = \frac{\text{number of ways both defective}}{\text{number of outcomes in sample space}} = \frac{3}{190} \approx 0.01579 \quad \blacksquare$$

Example 5.44 Florida Lotto

You can win the jackpot in the Florida Lotto by correctly choosing all 6 winning numbers out of the numbers 1–53.
a. What is the number of ways of winning the jackpot by choosing all 6 winning numbers?
b. What is the number of outcomes in this sample space?
c. If you buy a single ticket for $1, what is your probability of winning the jackpot?
d. If you mortgage your house and buy 500,000 tickets, what is your probability of winning the jackpot (assuming that all the tickets are different)?

Solution

a. The number of ways of winning the jackpot by correctly choosing all 6 of the winning numbers and none of the losing numbers is

$$N(\text{Jackpot}) = {}_6C_6 \cdot {}_{47}C_0 = 1 \cdot 1 = 1$$

b. The size of the sample space is

$$N(S) = {}_{53}C_6 = \frac{53!}{6!(53-6)!} = \frac{53 \cdot 52 \cdot 51 \cdot 50 \cdot 49 \cdot 48 \cdot 47!}{6! \cdot 47!}$$

$$= \frac{16,529,385,600}{720} = 22,957,480$$

c. Therefore, if you buy a single ticket for $1, your probability of winning the jackpot is given by

$$P(\text{Jackpot}) = \frac{1}{22,957,480} \approx 0.00000004356$$

d. If you buy 500,000 tickets and they are all unique, then your probability of winning becomes

$$P(\text{Jackpot}) = \frac{500,000}{22,957,480} \approx 0.02178$$

This is because the unique tickets are mutually exclusive, and the Addition Rule for Mutually Exclusive Events allows us to add the probabilities of the 500,000 tickets. After mortgaging your $500,000 house and buying lottery tickets with the proceeds, there is a better than 97% probability that you will *not* win the lottery. ■

STEP-BY-STEP TECHNOLOGY GUIDE: Factorials, Permutations, and Combinations

TI-83/84

Factorials *n*!
Step 1   On the home screen, enter the value of *n*.
Step 2   Press **MATH**, highlight **PRB**, and select **4: !** (Figure 5.23).
Step 3   Press **ENTER**.

FIGURE 5.23

Permutations $_nP_r$ and Combinations $_nC_r$
Step 1   On the home screen, enter the value of *n*.
Step 2   **a.** For permutations, press **MATH**, highlight **PRB**, and select **2:nPr**.
    b. For combinations, press **MATH**, highlight **PRB**, and select **3:nCr**.
Step 3   On the home screen, enter the value of *r*.
Step 4   Press **ENTER** (see Figure 5.19 and Figure 5.21 in Example 5.39 [page 248]).

EXCEL

Factorials *n*!
Calculate *9!*
Step 1   Select an empty cell, and type = **FACT(9)**.
Step 2   Press **ENTER**.

Permutations $_nP_r$
We illustrate Example 5.39a (page 248): $_9P_6$.
Step 1   Select an empty cell and type = **PERMUT(9,6)**.
Step 2   Press **ENTER**. See Figure 5.20 in Example 5.39 for the result.

Combinations $_nC_r$
We illustrate Example 5.39b (page 248): $_{10}C_7$.
Step 1   Select an empty cell and type =**COMBIN(10,7)**.
Step 2   Press **ENTER**. See Figure 5.22 in Example 5.39 for the result.

Section 5.4 Summary

1 The Multiplication Rule for Counting provides the total number of different possible outcomes for a series of events.

2 A permutation $_nP_r$ is an arrangement in which
- *r* items are chosen from *n* distinct items.
- repetition of items is not allowed.
- the order of the items is important.

In a permutation, order is important. In a combination, order does not matter. A combination $_nC_r$ is an arrangement in which
- *r* items are chosen from *n* distinct items.
- repetition of items is not allowed.
- the order of the items is not important.

3 Combinations may be used to calculate certain probabilities. For such problems, use the following steps.

Step 1   Confirm that the desired probability involves a combination.
Step 2   Find $N(E)$, the number of outcomes in event E.
Step 3   Find $N(S)$, the number of outcomes in the sample space.
Step 4   Assuming that each possible combination is equally likely, find the probability of event E as follows:

$$P(E) = \frac{N(E)}{N(S)}$$

Section 5.4 Exercises

CLARIFYING THE CONCEPTS

1. What type of diagram is helpful in itemizing the possible outcomes of a series of events?

2. Explain in words how 5! is calculated.

3. What is the difference between a permutation and a combination?

4. Does $_8P_9$ make sense? Explain why or why not.

5. Describe in your own words what is meant by acceptance sampling.

6. The counting methods that we have learned in this section may be used to compute probabilities.

    a. For assigning probability, which method is used: classical, relative frequency, or subjective?

    b. Referring to part **(a)**, what assumption must be made to apply the method?

PRACTICING THE TECHNIQUES

7. A pizza store offers the following options to its customers. Use a tree diagram to list all the possible options that a customer may choose from.

    • Cheese: no cheese, regular cheese, double cheese

    • Pepperoni: no pepperoni, regular pepperoni, double pepperoni

8. An ice cream shop offers the following options to its customers. Use a tree diagram to list all the possible options that a customer may choose from.

    • Ice cream: vanilla, chocolate, mint chocolate chip

    • Toppings: hot fudge, butterscotch, sprinkles

9. A particular baseball pitcher has to choose from the following options on each pitch. Use a tree diagram to list all the possible options.

    • Type of pitch: fastball, curve, slider

    • Horizontal position: inside corner, over the plate, outside corner

    • Vertical position: high, low

10. A women's clothing store tracks its sales transactions according to the following options. Use a tree diagram to list all the possible options.

    • Payment method: credit card, debit card, check, cash

    • Size category: Juniors, Misses, Women's

    • Type of clothing: top, pants

11. Our 41st president, George Herbert Walker Bush, had four names, with initials GHWB. How many different possible sets of initials are there for people with four names?

12. NCAA ice hockey games can have the following outcomes: win (W), lose (L), or tie (T). In a tournament of five games, how many different possible sets of outcomes are there? (*Hint:* LLTWW is one possible set.)

13. A college dining service conducted a survey in which it asked students to select their first and second favorite flavors of ice cream from a list of five flavors: vanilla, chocolate, mint chocolate chip, strawberry, maple walnut. How many different possible sets of two favorites are there?

14. A town library is considering loaning video games, and surveyed its membership to ask their four favorite PlayStation 3 games from among the following six games: Gran Turismo, Call of Duty 4, Metal Gear Solid 4, Little Big Planet, Grand Theft Auto IV, and Final Fantasy XIII. How many different possible sets of four favorites are there?

15. A woman is considering four sororities to rush this year. How many possible orderings are there?

16. Students working for the college newspaper have six drop locations around campus at which they must drop off newspapers. How many different possible routes are there for the students to do so?

For Exercises 17–22, find the value of each factorial.

17. 6!   **19.** 0!   **21.** 1!

18. 9!   **20.** 11!   **22.** 15!

23. A woman is considering four sororities to rush this year, but only has time to rush two. How many possible orderings are there?

24. Students working for the college newspaper have six drop locations around campus at which they must drop off newspapers, but they only have enough time to get to four locations. How many different possible routes are there for the students to do so?

For Exercises 25–32, find the value of each permutation $_nP_r$.

25. $_7P_3$ **28.** $_8P_3$ **31.** $_{100}P_{100}$

26. $_7P_4$ **29.** $_{100}P_1$ **32.** $_{100}P_{99}$

27. $_8P_5$ **30.** $_{100}P_0$

For Exercises 33–40, find the value of each combination $_nC_r$. Then answer Exercises 43 and 44.

33. $_7C_3$ **36.** $_{11}C_9$ **39.** $_{100}C_0$

34. $_7C_4$ **37.** $_{11}C_{10}$ **40.** $_{100}C_1$

35. $_{11}C_8$ **38.** $_{11}C_{11}$

41. How many distinct strings of letters can we make by using all the letters in the word PIZZA?

42. How many distinct strings of letters can we make by using all the letters in the word PEPPERONI?

43. Explain why the answers to Exercises 33 and 34 are equal. Use the commutative property of multiplication (for example, $2 \cdot 7 = 7 \cdot 2$) in your answer.

44. Use the idea behind your answer to Exercise 43 to find a combination that is equal to $_{11}C_8$. Verify your answer.

45. List all the permutations of the following people taken three at a time: Amy, Bob, Chris, Danielle. What is $_4P_3$?

46. List all the combinations of the following people taken three at a time: Amy, Bob, Chris, Danielle. What is $_4C_3$?

47. Explain in your own words why $_4P_3$ is larger than $_4C_3$.

48. What quantity do we divide $_4P_3$ by to get $_4C_3$? Express this quantity as a factorial. (*Hint:* For example, if the quantity were 120, we would express it as 5!)

49. In general, what do we divide $_nP_r$ by to get $_nC_r$?

APPLYING THE CONCEPTS

50. Fast Food. A fast-food restaurant has three types of sandwiches: chicken sandwich, fish sandwich, and beef burger. The restaurant has two types of side dishes: French fries and salad.

    a. Draw a tree diagram to find all the different meals a customer can order at this restaurant.

    b. How many different meals can a customer order at this restaurant?

51. What to Eat? A sit-down restaurant has two types of appetizers: garden salad and buffalo wings. It has three entrees: spaghetti, steak, and chicken. And it offers three kinds of desserts: ice cream, cake, and pie.

    a. Draw a tree diagram to find all the different meals a customer can order at this restaurant.

    b. How many different meals can a customer order at this restaurant?

52. Greek Alphabet. The ancient Greek alphabet had 24 letters. How many different possible initials are there for people with a first and last name?

53. Baseball Lineup. A baseball manager has to submit to the umpire the ordering of his lineup of nine players. How many ways can the manager arrange the nine players?

54. Facebook Friends. A student has 10 friends on her Facebook page. How many ways can she arrange her 10 friends top to bottom?

55. Document Delivery. A document delivery person must deliver documents to five different destinations within a particular city. How many different routes are possible?

56. Country Music Mix. Madison has just burned 15 songs onto a country music–mix CD. She chooses "random" on the CD player when she listens to the CD. How many different orderings of the 15 songs are there?

57. Traveler Fellow. A corporate sales executive must travel to the following countries this quarter: China, Russia, Germany, Brazil, India, and Nigeria. How many different routes are possible?

58. Sales Traveler. A corporate sales executive has the choice of traveling to four of the following six countries this quarter: China, Russia, Germany, Brazil, India, and Nigeria. How many different routes are possible?

59. Playing Catch. Five children are playing catch with a ball. How many different ways can one child throw a ball to another child once?

60. Chimp Grooming. Six chimpanzees are grooming each other at the city zoo. In how many different ways can one chimp groom another?

61. Shake Hands. In an ice-breaker exercise, each of 25 students is asked to shake hands with each of the other students. How many handshakes will there be in all?

62. Statistics Competition. Three students from the Honors Statistics class of 15 students will be chosen to represent the school at the state statistics competition. How many different possible groupings of 3 students are there?

63. How many random samples of size 1 can be chosen from a population of size 20?

64. How many random samples of size 20 can be chosen from a population of size 20?

65. How many random samples of size 10 can be chosen from a population of size 20?

66. How many distinct strings of letters can be made using all the letters in the word MATHEMATICS?

67. How many distinct strings of letters can be made using all the letters in the word BUSINESS?

68. CD Burning. You would like to use your new CD burner to make two new music-mix CDs. Your box of discs contains 14 CDs and 7 DVDs. If you choose 2 at random, find the number of ways that both discs will be CDs.

69. Grocery Produce Manager. A grocery produce manager inspects the corn supplied by a nearby farm. In a bushel of 30 ears of corn, the manager inspects 3 ears of corn. If 2 or more of the ears of corn are defective, the entire bushel is rejected. In this bushel, 5 ears of corn are defective.

    a. Explain whether the grocery produce manager is using a permutation or a combination.

    b. Find the number of ways that 2 or more ears of corn will be found defective by the produce manager.

    c. Find the probability that the bushel will be rejected.

70. Acceptance Sampling. A shipment of 25 personal digital assistants (PDAs) contains 3 that are defective. A quality control specialist inspects 2 of the 25 PDAs. If both are defective, then the shipment is rejected.

    a. Explain whether a permutation or a combination is being used.

    b. Find the number of ways that both PDAs will be defective.

    c. Find the probability of rejecting the shipment.

71. Downloading Music. You have just downloaded a new album of 12 songs from an online music retailer and made a playlist of the 12 songs. It turns out that you like 7 of the songs. Setting the playlist to random mode, find the probability that, of the first 5 songs you hear,

    a. you like all of them.

    b. you like none of them.

    c. you like exactly 2 of them.

    d. you like exactly 3 of them.

Chapter 5 Formulas and Vocabulary

SECTION 5.1

- **Classical method of assigning probabilities** (p. 204).

$$P(E) = \frac{\text{number of outcomes in } E}{\text{number of outcomes in sample space}} = \frac{N(E)}{N(S)}$$

- **Event** (p. 203)

- **Experiment** (p. 203)
- **Law of Large Numbers** (p. 208)
- **Law of Total Probability** (p. 203)
- **Outcome** (p. 203)
- **Probability** (p. 202)
- **Probability model** (p. 203)

- **Tree diagram** (p. 205)
- **Relative frequency method of assigning probabilities** (Also known as the **empirical method**) (p. 209).

$$P(E) \approx \frac{\text{frequency of } E}{\text{number of trials of experiment}}$$

- **Sample space** (p. 203)
- **Simulation** (p. 208)
- **Subjective probability** (p. 211)

SECTION 5.2
- **Addition Rule** (p. 219).
$P(A \text{ or } B) = P(A \cup B) = P(A) + P(B) - P(A \cap B)$
- **Addition Rule for Mutually Exclusive Events** (p. 221). If A and B are mutually exclusive, then $P(A \cup B) = P(A) + P(B)$.
- **Complement of an event** A (p. 217). Denoted as A^c.
- **Intersection of two events** A and B (p. 218). Denoted as $A \cap B$ or as "A and B."
- **Mutually exclusive (disjoint) events** (p. 221)
- **Probabilities for complements** (p. 218).
$P(A) + P(A^C) = 1$, $P(A) = 1 - P(A^C)$, and $P(A^C) = 1 - P(A)$
- **Union of two events** A and B (p. 218). Denoted as $A \cup B$ or as "A or B."

SECTION 5.3
- **Conditional probability** (p. 226).

$$P(B|A) = \frac{P(A \cap B)}{P(A)} = \frac{N(A \cap B)}{N(A)}$$

- **Independent events** (p. 228). Events A and B are *independent* if $P(A|B) = P(A)$ or if $P(B|A) = P(B)$.
- **Multiplication Rule** (p. 230). $P(A \cap B) = P(B) P(A|B)$ or, equivalently, $P(A \cap B) = P(A) P(B|A)$.
- **Multiplication Rule for Independent Events** (p. 230). If events A and B are independent, then $P(A \cap B) = P(A) P(B)$.
- **Multiplication Rule for n Independent Events** (p. 235). If A, B, C, ... are independent events, then $P(A \cap B \cap C \cap \ldots) = P(A) P(B) P(C) \ldots$.
- **Sampling with replacement** (p. 231)
- **Sampling without replacement** (p. 231)

SECTION 5.4
- **Acceptance sampling** (p. 250)
- **Combination** (p. 247).

$$_nC_r = \frac{n!}{r!(n-r)!}$$

- **Factorial symbol** $n!$ (p. 245). $0! = 1$; $1! = 1$; $n! = n(n-1)(n-2) \ldots 3 \cdot 2 \cdot 1$
- **Multiplication Rule for Counting** (p. 243)
- **Permutation** (p. 245).

$$_nP_r = \frac{n!}{(n-r)!}$$

- **Permutations of nondistinct items** (p. 249).

$$\frac{n!}{n_1! \cdot n_2! \cdot \ldots \cdot n_k!}$$

Chapter 5 Review Exercises

SECTION 5.1
For Exercises 1–5, consider the experiment of tossing a fair coin three times and find the probabilities.

1. 2 heads
2. At least 2 heads
3. 4 heads
4. 2 tails
5. At most 1 tail
6. **A New Sonnet.** Literature researchers have unearthed a sonnet that they know to be by either William Shakespeare or Christopher Marlowe. The probability that the sonnet is by Marlowe is 25%.
   a. What is the probability that the sonnet is by Shakespeare?
   b. What method of assigning probability do you think was used here? Why was this method used, and not the others?

SECTION 5.2
7. **Farmworkers' Educational Level.** The U.S. Department of Agriculture reports on the demographics of hired farmworkers.[7] An excerpt of the results is provided in the table, showing the percentage of noncitizen and citizen farmworkers who attained various educational levels. The educational levels are mutually exclusive. Find the following probabilities.
   a. The probability that a noncitizen farmworker is a high school graduate or has some college
   b. The probability that a citizen farmworker is a high school graduate or has some college
   c. The probability that a noncitizen farmworker has less than a ninth-grade education and has some college

	Noncitizens	Citizens
Less than 9th grade	238,008	61,776
9th–12th grade (no diploma)	57,904	152,880
High school graduate	59,784	222,144
Some college	20,304	187,200

Ecstasy and Methamphetamine Use. The following table contains the numbers of 12th-grade students who said that they had used Ecstasy (MDMA) or methamphetamine in the past 30 days for data collected in 2006 and 2007, as reported by the National Institute on Drug

Abuse (www.drugabuse.gov). Use the table to answer Exercises 8–10.

Drug	2006	2007
Ecstasy	185	232
Methamphetamine	128	87
Sample size	14,200	14,500

8. Find the indicated probabilities.
    a. A randomly selected 12th-grader in 2006 used Ecstasy in the past 30 days.
    b. A randomly selected 12th-grader in 2006 used methamphetamine in the past 30 days.
    c. A randomly selected 12th-grader in 2007 used Ecstasy in the past 30 days.
    d. A randomly selected 12th-grader in 2007 used methamphetamine in the past 30 days.
9. Assume that no student in the samples repeated 12th grade. Answer the following questions.
    a. Are these two events mutually exclusive: $A =$ 12th-grader in 2006 used Ecstasy and $B =$ 12th-grader in 2007 used Ecstasy? Explain why or why not.
    b. Find the probability that a randomly selected 12th-grader in 2006 used Ecstasy or a randomly selected 12th-grader in 2007 used Ecstasy.
    c. Find the probability that a randomly selected 12th-grader in 2006 used methamphetamine or a randomly selected 12th-grader in 2007 used methamphetamine.
10. Answer the following questions.
    a. Are these two events mutually exclusive: $C =$ used Ecstasy in the past 30 days and $D =$ used methamphetamine in the past 30 days? Explain why or why not.
    b. Discuss why we cannot find the probability that a randomly chosen 2006 12th-grader used both Ecstasy and methamphetamine in the past 30 days. What extra information do we need?

SECTION 5.3

11. **Drug Research Studies.** The *Annals of Internal Medicine* reported that 39 of the 40 research studies sponsored by a drug company had outcomes favoring a certain drug. Find the following probabilities, assuming independence.
    a. Three randomly selected research studies all favor this drug.
    b. None of the three randomly selected research studies favors this drug.
    c. At least one of three randomly selected research studies favors this drug.
12. **Gun Control.** A Harris Poll of 2408 American adults found 52% who supported tighter gun control. Find the following probabilities.
    a. Two randomly selected respondents both supported tighter gun control.

    b. At least two of three randomly selected respondents supported tighter gun control.
    c. At most one of three randomly selected respondents did not support tighter gun control.
13. **Politics of Gay Marriage.** The Pew Research Center for the People and the Press (http://people-press.org) reported that 322 out of 1149 people surveyed would not vote for a political candidate who disagreed with their views on gay marriage. Find the probabilities. Assume independence.
    a. Three out of three randomly selected respondents would vote for a political candidate who disagreed with his or her views on gay marriage.
    b. At least one of three randomly selected respondents would not vote for a political candidate who disagreed with his or her views on gay marriage.
14. **Drug Research Studies.** Use the information in Exercise 11. Suppose we sample two research studies without replacement. Find the probability that the second study does not favor this drug given that the first study does not favor this drug.

Gender and Pet Preference. Do you think your gender affects what type of pet you own? For Exercises 15–18, use the following table, showing preferences for various pets by owner gender.

Gender of owner	Cats	Dogs	Other pets	Total
Female	100	50	30	180
Male	50	50	20	120
Total	150	100	50	300

15. Find the probability that a randomly chosen person has the following characteristics.
    a. Owns a cat, $P(C)$ b. Owns a dog, $P(D)$
16. Find the probability that a randomly chosen person has the following characteristics.
    a. Is female and owns a dog, $P(F \cap D)$
    b. Is male and owns a dog, $P(M \cap D)$
17. Find the following conditional probabilities for a randomly chosen person.
    a. Owns a dog, given that the person is female, $P(D|F)$
    b. Owns a dog, given that the person is male, $P(D|M)$
18. If you were a dog-food manufacturer, would you advertise more on a men's TV channel or a women's TV channel? Why? Cite your evidence.

SECTION 5.4

19. How many distinguishable strings of letters can be made using all the letters in the word MISSISSIPPI?
20. **Statistics Quiz.** On a statistics quiz, there are five true/false questions, four fill-in-the-blank questions, and three short-answer questions. How many different ways are there of taking this quiz?

21. Inspection Time. A U.S. Army drill instructor will perform inspection on 2 soldiers in a squad of 18 soldiers. If both soldiers fail the inspection because their rifles are not clean, the entire squad will have to run a five-mile course in full gear. Three of the 18 soldiers have rifles that are not clean.

a. Explain whether the drill instructor is using a permutation or a combination.
b. Find the number of ways that both soldiers will fail the inspection.
c. Find the probability that the entire squad will have to run a five-mile course in full gear.

Chapter 5 QUIZ

TRUE OR FALSE

1. True or false: An outcome is a collection of a series of events from the sample space of an experiment.
2. True or false: For any event A (even events like A: the moon is made of green cheese) the probability of A plus the probability of A^c always add up to 1.

FILL IN THE BLANK

3. The minimum value that a probability can take is _____ and the maximum value is _____.
4. The union of two events is associated with the English word _____, and the intersection of two events is associated with the English word _____.
5. Someone has told you that there is a 50-50 chance of rain tomorrow. This means that the probability of rain tomorrow equals _____.

SHORT ANSWER

6. For any experiment, what is the sum of all the outcome probabilities in the sample space?
7. For which type of sampling are consecutive draws independent?
8. For two events A and B, what do we call the event containing only those outcomes that belong to both A and B?

CALCULATIONS AND INTERPRETATIONS

9. Consider the experiment of rolling a fair die twice. Find the following probabilities.
   a. Sum of the two dice equals 5.
   b. Sum of the two dice does not equal 5.
   c. One of the dice shows 2.
   d. Sum of the two dice equals 5 and one of the dice shows 2.
   e. Sum of the two dice equals 5 or one of the dice shows 2.
10. Suppose that A and B are any two events, with $P(B) = 0.75$ and $P(A \cap B) = 0.15$. Find $P(A|B)$.
11. Suppose that A and B are any two events, with $P(B) = 0.85$ and $P(A|B) = 0.25$. Find $P(A \cap B)$.
12. **Pick a Card.** Consider the experiment of drawing a single card from a deck of 52 cards. Find the probability of observing the following events.

a. Heart
b. Face card (king, queen, or jack)
c. Seven
d. Red card
e. Seven of hearts
f. Red queen

Happiness in Marriage. The General Social Survey tracks trends in American society through annual surveys. The married respondents were asked to characterize their feelings about being married. The results, crosstabulated with gender, are shown in the following figure. Use this information for Exercises 13–15.

		HAPPINESS OF MARRIAGE			
		VERY HAPPY	PRETTY HAPPY	NOT TOO HAPPY	Total
SEX	MALE	242	115	9	366
	FEMALE	257	149	17	423
Total		499	264	26	789

13. Find the probabilities that a randomly chosen person has the following characteristics.
   a. Is female, $P(F)$
   b. Is male, $P(M)$
   c. Is not too happily married, $P(\text{Not})$
14. Find the probabilities that a randomly chosen person has the following characteristics.
   a. Is female and not too happily married, $P(F \cap \text{Not})$
   b. Is male and not too happily married, $P(M \cap \text{Not})$
15. Are gender and being not too happily married independent? Why or why not?
16. **Football Teams.** The four teams in the AFC South division of the National Football League are Indianapolis Colts, Jacksonville Jaguars, Tennessee Titans, and Houston Texans. Suppose the top three teams in the division this year will make the playoffs. How many different sets of teams making the playoffs are there?
17. **State Lottery.** In a state lottery, balls numbered 1 to 20 are placed in an urn. To win, you must choose numbers that match the three balls chosen in the order that they're chosen.
   a. Explain whether a permutation or a combination is being used.
   b. How many possible outcomes are there?
   c. Find the probability of winning this lottery if your ticket contains a single ordering of three numbers.

6

Probability Distributions

Introduction

In Chapter 5, students were introduced to probability. In Chapter 6, students encounter *random variables* and *probability distributions*. With these new tools, they can increase the efficiency of their decision making. Sections 6.1–6.3 introduce discrete random variables, including the binomial random variable and the Poisson random variable. In Section 6.4, students learn about continuous random variables, including the normal random variable. Section 6.5 covers the special case of the standard normal distribution, and Section 6.6 provides some applications of the normal distribution to everyday problems. Finally, Section 6.7 covers the normal approximation to the binomial distribution.

From the Author

- **Section 6.1 Discrete Random Variables**
  - Section 6.1 was substantially rewritten, and greatly streamlined, to convey more information in less space.
  - Sometimes students have a hard time moving from Chapter 5 to Chapter 6. Example 6.1 will help them express the concepts they learned in Chapter 5 using the language of Chapter 6.
  - Students who need practice in recognizing valid discrete probability distributions may benefit from the new Example 6.4.
  - Your more eager students may enjoy learning that the formula for the mean of a discrete random variable is a special case of a weighted mean (page 265).
  - Note that the mean as the balance point applies to probability distributions just as it did for the graphs in Chapter 3.
  - A new example (6.9) shows how to find the most likely value of a discrete random variable.
  - The examples for calculating the variance and standard deviation of X now provide a whole-number answer for both. This topic is a computational challenge to many students, and they don't need lots of decimals getting in the way of the concepts.
  - Students may wonder why we go to the trouble of calculating the standard deviation of a discrete random variable X. Example 6.12 on page 269 shows that we can then use it to determine an unusual result.
  - Students may appreciate the new Step-by-Step Technology Guide for this section.
- **Section 6.2 Binomial Probability Distribution**
  - Instructors may wish to stress that the key to a binomial distribution is knowing the sample size n and the probability of success p. When faced with a word problem, students should find the values of these quantities. Then find the values of X that the problem is asking about.

- Because students sometimes need clarification on the meaning of these measures, we added a new feature, *What Do the Value for the Mean and Standard Deviation Mean?*
- A new example shows how to find the *mode* of a binomial distribution.
- A new Applying the Concepts exercise explores when the mean, median, and mode of a binomial random variable are equal.
- Note that new topics in the Section 6.2 exercises are (a) *geometric probability distribution,* (b) *negative binomial probability distribution.* (c) *hypergeometric probability distribution,* and (d) *multinomial distribution.*

- **Section 6.3 Poisson Probability Distribution**
  - Some instructors may find that they do not have time to cover Section 6.3.

- **Section 6.4 Continuous Random Variables and the Normal Probability Distribution**
  - New topic: the *Uniform Probability Distribution.* The uniform distribution makes it easy to introduce how to find probabilities as areas.

- **Section 6.5 Standard Normal Distribution**
  - Instructors who will be covering the *p*-value method in later chapters should make sure the students understand how to calculate the areas in Table 6.6.

- **Section 6.6 Applications of the Normal Distribution**
  - The Normal Approximation to the Binomial Distribution was moved its own section, 6.7.
  - The Chapter Case Study was updated using the latest NFL salaries data. With the possibility of a lockout or strike never for away, this may appear especially relevant for some students.

- **Section 6.7 Normal Approximation to the Binomial Probability Distribution**
  - Moved to its own section, with a rewritten introduction to quickly review the binomial distribution.

Teaching Tips

Describing the number of students in class today is a way to convey the meaning of a discrete variable. For example, there are either 20 or 21 students in class but nothing in between (there are not 20½ students or 20.23 students in the class, for instance). A continuous variable can be explained by using an example of distance. How far can someone throw an eraser in the room? It is possible to throw an eraser anywhere from 0 feet to the back of the room. For instance, it is possible to throw the eraser 10 and one-half feet or 8.645 feet. Another example of a continuous variable is time. If students have ever competed in a timed event or watched the timed events at the Olympics, they can see that once the clock starts it can stop at any time.

In this chapter we are working with probability distributions. This means that, as in Chapter 5, we are not given a data set to describe; instead, we are provided with a probability distribution, with a known population mean and known population standard deviation, and asked to find certain probabilities.

We use the cumulative normal distribution table, which may be new to some instructors. The author finds that it is easier to use because the students don't have to remember to add or subtract 0.5.

You may want to make sure that your students are expert at finding the tail area probability under a standard normal curve. This skill is needed for finding p-values for Z tests in later chapters.

In-Class Activities

1. Elicit the heights (in inches) of all the students in the class.

   a. Would you expect the distribution of heights to be normal? Why or why not?

   b. Construct a graph (dotplot, histogram, or stem-and-leaf display) of student heights. Is your expectation in (a) supported?

   c. Next consider the heights of only the males in the class. Might this distribution be more normally distributed than the heights of all the students? Why or why not?

   d. Construct a graph (dotplot, histogram, or stem-and-leaf display) of male student heights. Is your expectation in (c) supported?

   e. If desired, repeat (c) and (d) for the females in the class.

2. Go to **http://lib.stat.cmu.edu/DASL/Stories/ChestsizesofMilitiamen.html** and download the Scottish Militiamen chest size data set. Ask students to construct histograms with different numbers of classes and discuss their observations. Also, students can display the data using a scatterplot. In addition, they can compute descriptive statistics for the mean, median, and mode and compare their values. Discussions may be focused on the shape of the distribution and the measures of central tendencies.

Probability Distributions and a Deck of Cards

3. Bring in a deck of cards and perform the following experiment.

   a. Take out the 12 face cards (kings, queens, and jacks).

   b. Construct the probability distribution of the face value of the remaining cards (ace $\rightarrow X = 1$, deuce $\rightarrow X = 2$, and so on).

   c. Find the population mean μ and standard deviation σ of this probability distribution.

   d. Designate one student as shuffler, another student as selector. Have the selector draw one card at random from the abridged deck, observe it, record the value of X, and replace it.

   e. The shuffler then shuffles the cards. The selector then selects another card at random, until 20 cards have been sampled with replacement.

   f. Using the relative frequencies from (e), construct a relative frequency distribution of your observed face values. Is it very different from the population distribution from (b)?

   g. Calculate the mean and standard deviation of your relative frequency distribution. Are they very different from the population values calculated in (c)? How would you define "very different"?

A Binomial Probability Activity

4. There is a famous problem in binomial probability. Which parents would wind up with the greater proportion of boy babies: the parents who simply stopped having babies after a certain number of babies or the parents who had babies until they had a boy? It might seem that the answer is that the parents who stopped after the first boy would have more boys, but the answer is that both sets of parents could expect to have the same proportion of boys. You will use simulation to try to confirm this. Assume that the probability that a randomly chosen newborn is a boy is 50%. Then, clearly, the parents who simply stopped having babies after a certain number of babies could

expect to have the same proportion (long-run probability!) of boys and girls. Now, take a single die and define the results of your rolls as follows: an odd-number result will represent a boy, and an even-number result will represent a girl.

    a. Have your group roll the die. If you get a girl the first time, record it and roll again. Continue rolling and recording until you get a boy. That ends that particular trial.

    b. Repeat until you have a large number (say, 30) of trials.

    c. Then find the proportions of boys and girls in your 30 trials (representing 30 reproducing families). Your results shouldn't be too far away from a 50-50 split between boys and girls.

Supplements

- StatTutor 3.1–3.8, 10.2, 10.4–10.6, 13.1–13.6
- EESEE case studies
  - Is Caffeine Dependence Real? (Questions 1, 2, 3, 4, and 5(a) on probability)

Applets

The *Normal Density Curve* applet is referenced in Chapter 6 to compute normal probabilities for Exercises 81 and 82 in Section 6.5 and Exercises 45 and 46 in Section 6.6. The *Normal Approximation to the Binomial Distribution* applet is used for Exercises 35 and 36 in Section 6.7.

Videos

- *Against All Odds* **www.learner.org/resources/series65.html**
  - Program 16: Random Variables
  - Program 4: Normal Distributions
  - Program 5: Normal Calculations
  - Program 17: Binomial Distributions

Web Sites

- This Texas Instruments Web site has a host of TI-83/84 statistics activities: **http:// education.ti.com/educationportal/sites/US/nonProductSingle/activitybook_83_statistics .html**.
- This Web site lists other sites that do statistical calculations: **http://statpages.org/**.
- This Web site lists numerous activities on all topics: **http://mathforum.org/mathtools/ sitemap2/ps/**.
- This site has several activities using Excel and Minitab: **www.mathspace.com/NSF_ProbStat/ Teaching_Materials/Primarily_Statistics.htm**.
- The site Online Statistics: An Interactive Multimedia Course of Study has a *Normal Distribution* applet that demonstrates simulations and computes normal probabilities, and it has a link to the Rice Virtual Lab in Statistics with numerous simulation demonstrations along with other topics related to statistics: **http://onlinestatbook.com/index.html**.

AP Photo/David Stluka

OVERVIEW

6

Probability Distributions

| CASE STUDY | Be Careful What You Assume: National Football League Salaries |

Many fans of the National Football League (NFL) are concerned about the continuing increase in player salaries, making a trip to the stadium an expensive family outing. In this Case Study, we consider a scenario where the NFL owners wish to "cap" a team's top salary, with the owners suggesting the 75th percentile of all salaries. In our scenario, the players' union states that they will agree to the salary cap only if the owners add a bonus to the salaries of the lowest-paid players, as measured by the 10th percentile. We will find out what happens on page 320.

The Big Picture

Where we are coming from, and where we are headed . . .

- In Chapter 5, we learned about *probability*, which allows us to quantify the uncertainty involved in performing statistical inference in later chapters.

- However, we first need a new set of tools in our probability toolbox: *random variables* and *probability distributions*. Here, in Chapter 6, we learn these new tools, including the binomial distribution and the normal distribution.

- Chapter 7, "Sampling Distributions," is a pivotal chapter where we learn that statistics have predictable behavior, which allows us to perform the statistical inference we learn in the remainder of the book.

6.1 Discrete Random Variables

OBJECTIVES By the end of this section, I will be able to . . .

1 Identify random variables.

2 Explain what a discrete probability distribution is and construct probability distribution tables and graphs.

3 Calculate the mean, variance, and standard deviation of a discrete random variable.

1 Random Variables

In Chapter 5, we calculated the probabilities of outcomes from experiments. If the experiment is tossing a fair coin twice, the outcomes are HH, HT, TH, and TT. The probability of observing exactly one head in two tosses is the probability of the event $A = \{HT, TH\}$. Since the outcomes are equally likely, we used the classical method of assigning probability. The probability of $\{HT, TH\}$ is $N(A)/N(S) = 2/4 = 0.5$, where S is the sample space.

In this chapter, we develop a different approach that analyzes probability problems more efficiently. Recall from Chapter 1 that a *variable* is a characteristic that can assume different values. Suppose we define a variable $X =$ number of heads observed when 2 fair coins are tossed. In this experiment we may observe zero heads, one head, or two heads, so that the possible values of X are 0, 1, and 2. Clearly, before we conduct our experiment, we do not know how many heads we will observe. Thus, randomness plays a role in the value of the variable X, and so we call X a *random variable*.

> A **random variable** is a variable that takes on quantitative values representing the results of a probability experiment, and thus its values are determined by chance. We denote random variables using capital letters such as X, Y, or Z.

In Chapter 5 (page 206), we found that the probability of observing exactly $X =$ one head was 0.5. We denote this probability using the notation

$$P(X = 1) = 0.5$$

Similarly, the probability of observing zero heads is $P(X = 0) = 0.25$, and the probability of two heads is $P(X = 2) = 0.25$.

Developing Your Statistical Sense

Random Variables Must Be Random!

The role of chance in the definition of a random variable is crucial. For example, is your age a random variable? If we are just talking about you and no one else, and we know your age, then there is no chance involved. In that case, your age is not a random variable. On the other hand, what if we select students *at random* by picking names from a hat? Then the age of the person drawn is a random variable because its value depends at least partly on chance (on which name is drawn at random). ◢

Let's start with an example aimed at helping you move from the language of probability (experiments and outcomes) to the language of random variables.

Example 6.1 Notation for random variables

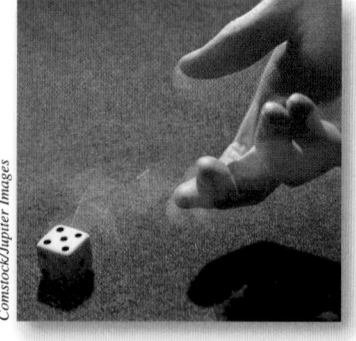

Comstock/Jupiter Images

Suppose our experiment is to toss a single fair die, and we are interested in the number rolled. We define our random variable X to be the outcome of a single die roll.
a. Why is the variable X a random variable?
b. What are the possible values that the random variable X can take?
c. What is the notation used for rolling a 5?
d. Use random variable notation to express the probability of rolling a 5.

Solution

a. We don't know the value of X before we toss the die, which introduces an element of chance into the experiment, thereby making X a random variable.
b. The possible values for X are 1, 2, 3, 4, 5, and 6.

c. When a 5 is rolled, then *X* equals the outcome 5, and we write *X* = 5.
d. Recall from Section 5.1 that the probability of rolling a 5 for a fair die is 1/6. In random variable notation, we denote this as $P(X = 5) = 1/6$. ∎

There are two main types of random variables: **discrete random variables** and **continuous random variables.** The difference between the two types relates to the possible values that each type of random variable can assume.

Discrete and Continuous Random Variables

-   A **discrete random variable** can take either a finite or a countable number of values. Since these values may be written as a list of numbers, each value can be graphed as a separate point on a number line, with space between each point. (See Figure 6.1a.)

FIGURE 6.1a

-   A **continuous random variable** can take infinitely many values. Because there are infinitely many values, the values of a continuous random variable form an interval on the number line. (See Figure 6.1b.)

FIGURE 6.1b

Discrete random variables usually need to be counted, like 1, 2, 3, and so forth. Continuous random variables usually need to be measured, not counted, such as measuring the amount of gasoline purchased.

Examples of discrete random variables include the number of children a randomly selected person has and the number of times a randomly chosen student has been pulled over for speeding on the interstate. Continuous random variables often need to be measured, not counted. For example, the temperature in Atlanta, Georgia, at noon today may be reported as 77 degrees, but this value represents actual temperatures that may lie anywhere between 76.5 degrees and 77.5 degrees.

Example 6.2 | Identifying discrete and continuous random variables

For the following random variables, (i) determine whether they are discrete or continuous, and (ii) indicate the possible values they can take.
a. The number of automobiles owned by a family
b. The width of your desk in this classroom
c. The number of games played in the next World Series
d. The weight of model year 2011 SUVs

Solution

a. Since the possible number of automobiles owned by a family is finite and may be written as a list of numbers, it represents a discrete random variable. The possible values are {0, 1, 2, 3, 4, . . .}.
b. Width is something that must be measured, not counted. Width can take infinitely many different possible values, with these values forming an interval on the number line. Thus, the width of your desk is a continuous random variable. The possible values might be 1 ft ≤ *W* ≤ 10 ft.
c. The number of games played in the next World Series can be counted and thus represents a discrete random variable. The possible values are finite and may be written as a list of numbers: {4, 5, 6, 7}.
d. The weight of model year 2011 SUVs must be measured, not counted, and so represents a continuous random variable. Weight can take infinitely many different possible values, with these values forming an interval on the number line: 2500 lb ≤ *Y* ≤ 7000 lb. ∎

Now You Can Do
Exercises 7–16.

We will return to continuous random variables in Section 6.4; Sections 6.1–6.3 concentrate on discrete random variables.

2 Discrete Probability Distributions

For every random variable, there is a probability distribution that allows us to view all possible values of the random variable at a glance. Discrete probability distributions show the probabilities associated with the various values that the discrete random variable can take.

> A **probability distribution of a discrete random variable** provides all the possible values that the random variable can assume, together with the probability associated with each value. The probability distribution can take the form of a table, graph, or formula. Probability distributions describe populations, not samples.

When constructing the tabular form of a **probability distribution of a discrete random variable,** create a table with two rows:

- The top row will contain all the possible values of X.
- The bottom row will contain the probability associated with each value of X.

Example 6.3 Probability distribution table

Construct the probability distribution table of the number of heads observed when tossing a fair coin twice.

Solution

The probability distribution table given in Table 6.1 uses the probabilities we found on page 260. ∎

The probabilities in Table 6.1 were assigned using the classical method, since we assumed that tossing a fair coin would result in equally likely outcomes.

Now You Can Do
Exercises 17–20.

Table 6.1 Probability distribution table of the number of heads on two fair coin tosses

X = number of heads observed	0	1	2
$P(X)$ = probability of observing that many heads	1/4	1/2	1/4

Note that the probabilities in the bottom row of Table 6.1 add up to 1. This is no coincidence. According to the Law of Total Probability from Chapter 5, the sum of the probabilities of all the outcomes in the sample space must equal 1. Put into the language of random variables, this means that the sum of the probabilities of all the possible values of a discrete random variable X must equal 1. This requirement is written as $\sum P(X) = 1$. Also, since each value in the bottom row is a probability, each value must be between 0 and 1, inclusive, that is, $0 \leq P(X) \leq 1$. There are no such restrictions on the values that X can take except that they be countable.

> **Rules for a Discrete Probability Distribution**
> - The sum of the probabilities of all the possible values of a discrete random variable must equal 1. That is, $\sum P(X) = 1$.
> - The probability of each value of X must be between 0 and 1, inclusive. That is, $0 \leq P(X) \leq 1$.

Example 6.4 Recognizing valid discrete probability distributions

Identify which of the following is a valid discrete probability distribution.
a.

X	1	10	100	1000
$P(X)$	0.2	0.4	0.3	0.2

b.

X	−10	0	10	20
P(X)	0.5	0.3	0.4	−0.2

c.

X	Red	Green	Blue	Yellow
P(X)	0.1	0.3	0.4	0.2

d.

X	−5	0	5	10
P(X)	0.1	0.3	0.4	0.2

Solution

a. This is not a valid probability distribution, because the probabilities add up to 1.1, which is greater than 1.

b. This is not a valid probability distribution, because $P(X = 20)$ is negative.

c. This is not a valid probability distribution for a discrete random variable because the values of X are not quantitative.

Now You Can Do
Exercises 21–24.

d. This is a valid probability distribution, since the probabilities sum to 1, and each probability $P(X)$ takes a value between 0 and 1. ∎

Probability distributions can also take the form of a probability distribution graph.

Example 6.5 Discrete probability distribution as a graph

The number of points a soccer team gets for a game is a random variable, because it is not certain, prior to the game, how many points the team will get.

Jamie Sabau/Getty Images

The probabilities were assigned to the random variable X using the relative frequency (empirical) method.

In Major League Soccer (MLS), teams are awarded 3 points in the standings for a win, 1 point for a tie, and 0 points for a loss. In the 30-game 2010 MLS season, the New York Red Bulls had 15 wins, 9 losses, and 6 ties.

a. Construct a probability distribution table of the number of points per game, based on the team's performance during the 2010 MLS season.

b. Construct a probability distribution graph of the number of points per game.

Solution

a. Let X = points awarded. Then the probability distribution table is given in Table 6.2.

Table 6.2 Probability distribution table of points awarded for New York Red Bulls

X = points	0	1	3
P(X)	9/30 = 0.3	6/30 = 0.2	15/30 = 0.5

b. The probability distribution graph is given in Figure 6.2.
  - The horizontal axis is the usual x axis (the number line), and shows all the possible values that the random variable X can take, such as X = 0, 1, or 3. The horizontal axis gives the same information as the top row of the table.
  - The vertical axis represents probability, and is the information in the bottom row in the table. A vertical bar is drawn at each value of X, with the height representing the probability of that value of X. For example, the bar of probability at X = 0 goes up to 0.3 and represents the probability that the New York Red Bulls will lose a game. ∎

Given a graph of a probability distribution, you should know how to construct the probability distribution table, and vice versa.

FIGURE 6.2
Probability distribution graph of points awarded for New York Red Bulls.

Now You Can Do
Exercises 25–28.

We may use probability distributions to calculate probabilities for multiple values of X. In discrete probability distributions, the outcomes are always mutually exclusive. For example, it is not possible to observe both zero heads ($X = 0$) and two heads ($X = 2$) when tossing two fair coins. Thus, we always use the Addition Rule for Mutually Exclusive Events to find the probability of two or more outcomes for a discrete random variable. For example, $P(X = 0 \text{ or } 2) = P(X = 0) + P(X = 2)$.

Example 6.6 | Calculating probabilities for multiple values of X

Use the probability distribution from Example 6.5 to find the following probabilities.
a. Probability that the New York Red Bulls are awarded either 0 or 3 points in a game
b. Probability that the New York Red Bulls are awarded both 0 and 3 points in a game
c. Probability that the New York Red Bulls are awarded at least 1 point in a game
d. Probability that the New York Red Bulls are awarded at most 1 point in a game

Solution
a. $P(X = 0 \text{ points } or \text{ 3 points}) = P(X = 0) + P(X = 3) = 0.3 + 0.5 = 0.8$. For a randomly selected game, the probability that the Red Bulls either lose the game or win the game is 0.8.
b. The outcomes $X = 0$ and $X = 3$ are mutually exclusive. Therefore, $P(X = 0 \text{ points } and \text{ 3 points}) = 0$.
c. The phrase *at least* means "that many or more." Thus we need to find: $P(X \geq 1) = P(X = 1 \text{ point } or \text{ 3 points}) = P(X = 1) + P(X = 3) = 0.2 + 0.5 = 0.7$.

Now You Can Do
Exercises 29–32.

d. The phrase *at most* means "that many or fewer." Hence: $P(X \leq 1) = P(X = 1 \text{ point } or \text{ 0 points}) = P(X = 1) + P(X = 0) = 0.2 + 0.3 = 0.5$. ∎

3 Mean and Variability of a Discrete Random Variable

Just as we can compute the mean and standard deviation of quantitative data, we can calculate the mean and standard deviation of a random variable X.

The **mean μ of a discrete random variable** X represents the mean result when the experiment is repeated an indefinitely large number of times.

Finding the Mean of a Discrete Random Variable X

The mean μ of a discrete random variable X is found as follows:

1. Multiply each possible value of X by its probability.
2. Add the resulting products.

This procedure is denoted as

$$\mu = \sum [X \cdot P(X)]$$

Example 6.7 Calculating the mean of a discrete probability distribution

Note: These 250,000 teenagers constitute a population, not a sample, so the mean is μ, not $\bar{x}$.

The U.S. Department of Health and Human Services reports that there were 250,000 babies born to teenagers aged 15–18 in 2004. Of these 250,000 births, 7% were to 15-year-olds, 17% were to 16-year-olds, 29% were to 17-year-olds, and 47% were to 18-year-olds.
a. Construct the probability distribution table for X = age.
b. Calculate the mean age μ.

Solution

a. The following table contains the probability distribution of the random variable X = age.

X = age	$P(X)$
15	0.07
16	0.17
17	0.29
18	0.47

b. To find the mean μ, we first need to multiply each possible outcome (value of X) by its probability $P(X)$. We multiply the value $X = 15$ by its probability $P(X) = 0.07$, the value $X = 16$ by its probability $P(X) = 0.17$, and so on. Then we add these four products to find the mean:

$$\mu = 15(0.07) + 16(0.17) + 17(0.29) + 18(0.47) = 17.16$$

The mean age of the mother for the babies born to teenagers aged 15–18 is 17.16 years. ■

What Does This Number Mean?

What does it mean to say that $\mu = 17.16$ is the mean of the random variable X = age? First of all, the mean of the random variable X is definitely not the same as the mean of a sample of teenage mothers. The latter is a sample mean. For example, suppose that, for a certain hospital, the teenage mothers' ages for the last 5 such births were 16, 18, 18, 17, 18. The mean of this sample of 5 births is $\bar{x} = 17.4$. However, if we were to consider an *infinite number* of births to mothers aged 15–18, then the mean of this very large sample would converge to $\mu = 17.16$. So the mean μ of a discrete random variable is interpreted as the mean of the results from the *population* of all possible repetitions of the experiment, which is why we denote the mean of a random variable as μ. ◢

Note: The population mean μ need not equal any values of X, nor need it be an integer.

Developing Your Statistical Sense

Why Does This Formula Work?

The formula for the mean of a discrete random variable works because it is a special case of the weighted mean (page 118). Of the population of 250,000 babies, 7%, or 17,500, were born to 15-year-olds. Thus, $w_1 = 17,500$. Similarly, we can find, $w_2 = (0.17)(250,000) = 42,500$, $w_3 = (0.29)(250,000) = 72,500$, and $w_4 = (0.47)(250,000) = 117,500$. Thus, the population weighted mean is

$$\mu = \frac{\sum w_i x_i}{\sum w_i} = \frac{(17,500)(15) + (42,500)(16) + (72,500)(17) + (117,500)(18)}{250,000}$$

Dividing through and rearranging terms give us

$$\mu = (15)(0.07) + (16)(0.17) + (17)(0.29) + (18)(0.47) = \sum [X \cdot P(X)] \quad ◢$$

We may also interpret the mean μ as the *balance point* of the distribution.

Example 6.8 Mean μ as balance point of the distribution

Graph the probability distribution of the random variable X = age, and insert a fulcrum at the value of the mean, $\mu = 17.16$.

Solution

The probability distribution graph of X = age is given in Figure 6.3. Note that the distribution is balanced at the point $\mu = 17.16$. ■

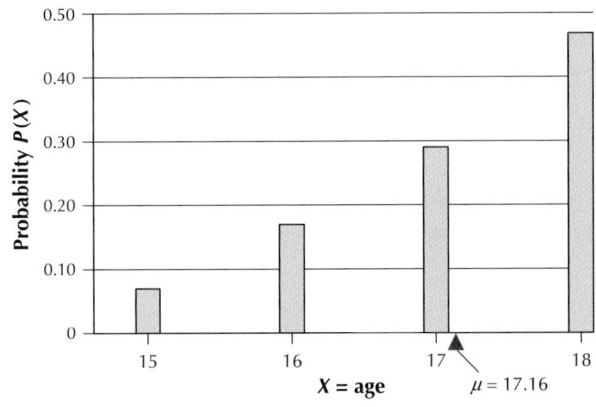

FIGURE 6.3 Probability distribution graph balances at $\mu = 17.16$.

In certain situations, we may need to identify the most likely or the least likely value of the random variable X.

Example 6.9 Identifying the most likely or least likely value of a discrete random variable

Note: When we ask for the *least likely value* of a discrete random variable X, we implicitly mean *of the values of X that have nonzero probability.*

If one of the teenagers represented in the table in Example 6.7 is chosen at random, find the following.
a. What is the most likely age of that teenager when her baby was born?
b. What is the least likely age of that teenager when her baby was born?

Solution

a. Since the largest probability in the probability table is $P(X = 18)$, and the longest bar in the probability graph is for $X = 18$, then 18 is the most likely age.

b. Because the smallest probability in the probability table is $P(X = 15)$, and the shortest bar in the probability graph is for $X = 15$, then 15 is the least likely age. ■

Now You Can Do
Exercises 45–47.

The mean μ of a random variable is also called the **expected value** or the **expectation of the random variable X.** It does not necessarily follow that the expected value of X is the most likely value of X (although it does follow if the distribution is symmetric with a single mode). However, the expected value of X (that is, the mean μ) is often a good indication of the center of the distribution of the random variable.

> The **expected value, or expectation, of a random variable X** is the mean μ of X. It is denoted as $E(X)$. This definition holds for both discrete and continuous random variables.

Example 6.10 Expected value of a discrete random variable X

Find the expected value $E(X)$ of the following discrete random variables.
a. X = number of heads in Example 6.3.
b. X = number of points awarded in Example 6.5.
c. X = age of teenage birth mothers in Example 6.7.

Solution

a. Using the probabilities in Table 6.1, we have

$$E(X) = \mu = \sum[X \cdot P(X)] = 0(0.25) + 1(0.5) + 2(0.25) = 1$$

The expected number of heads is 1

b. Using Table 6.2, we have

$$E(X) = \mu = \sum[X \cdot P(X)] = 0(0.3) + 1(0.2) + 3(0.5) = 1.7$$

The expected number of points is 1.7.

Now You Can Do
Exercises 49–52.

c. From Example 6.7, $E(X) = \mu = 17.16$. The expected age of teenage mothers is 17.16 years. ■

Note from Example 6.10(b) and 6.10(c) that the mean or expected value of a random variable need not be a particular value of X. Rather, it is the mean of a very large number of repetitions of the experiment.

Variability of a Discrete Random Variable

Since a discrete random variable takes on quantitative values, we use the **variance** or **standard deviation of a random variable** X to help us determine whether a particular value of that random variable is unusual. Just as a random variable X has a mean (μ), which is a measure of center, so a random variable X also has a standard deviation (σ) and variance (σ^2), which are measures of spread. The variance of a discrete random variable is given by

$$\sigma^2 = \sum[(X - \mu)^2 \cdot P(X)]$$

Notice that this formula includes μ as one of its terms, so that you must first find the mean of a discrete random variable before you find the variance (or standard deviation). Recall from Chapter 3 that the standard deviation is simply the square root of the variance. The definition and computational formulas for the standard deviation of a discrete random variable are the square roots of the formulas for the variance. The definition formula for the variance can sometimes be tedious since you must find each of the deviations $(X - \mu)$. There is a computational formula for the variance of a discrete random variable that is equivalent to the definition formula but sometimes is computationally simpler.

| **Formulas for the Variance and Standard Deviation of a Discrete Random Variable** ||
Definition Formulas	**Computational Formulas**
$\sigma^2 = \sum[(X - \mu)^2 \cdot P(X)]$	$\sigma^2 = \sum[X^2 \cdot P(X)] - \mu^2$
$\sigma = \sqrt{\sum[(X - \mu)^2 \cdot P(X)]}$	$\sigma = \sqrt{\sum[X^2 \cdot P(X)] - \mu^2}$

Example 6.11	Calculating the variance and standard deviation of a discrete random variable

X = number of credits taken	P(X)
12	0.1
13	0.1
14	0.1
15	0.5
16	0.1
20	0.1

 credits

Carla has 10 friends in school. She took a census of all 10 friends, asking each how many credits they had registered for that semester. Five of her friends were taking 15 credits, with one each taking 12, 13, 14, 16, and 20 credits. The resulting probability distribution table is shown here.

a. Find the mean μ number of credits taken.
b. Calculate the variance and standard deviation using the definition formula.
c. Calculate the variance and standard deviation using the computational formula.

Solution

a. $\mu = \Sigma[X \cdot P(X)] = 12(0.1) + 13(0.1) + 14(0.1) + 15(0.5) + 16(0.1) + 20(0.1) = 15$. The mean number of credits taken this semester among Carla's friends is $\mu = 15$.

b. Refer to Table 6.3. The first two columns correspond to the probability distribution of $X =$ number of credits taken. The third column represents the calculations needed to find $(X - \mu)^2 \cdot P(X)$. Summing the values in the rightmost column provides the variance $\sigma^2 = 4$. Taking the square root of the variance gives us the standard deviation $\sigma = \sqrt{\sigma^2} = \sqrt{4} = 2$.

Table 6.3 Calculating σ^2 and σ using the definition formula

X	P(X)	$(X - \mu)^2 \cdot P(X)$
12	0.1	$(12 - 15)^2 \cdot 0.1 = 0.9$
13	0.1	$(13 - 15)^2 \cdot 0.1 = 0.4$
14	0.1	$(14 - 15)^2 \cdot 0.1 = 0.1$
15	0.5	$(15 - 15)^2 \cdot 0.5 = 0.0$
16	0.1	$(16 - 15)^2 \cdot 0.1 = 0.1$
20	0.1	$(20 - 15)^2 \cdot 0.1 = 2.5$
		$\sigma^2 = \Sigma(X - \mu)^2 \cdot P(X) = 4$

c. Refer to Table 6.4. The rightmost column contains the values $X^2 \cdot P(X)$. Summing the values in the rightmost column provides $\Sigma[X^2 \cdot P(X)] = 229$. To find the variance σ^2, we must subtract the square of the mean μ^2:

$$\sigma^2 = \Sigma[X^2 \cdot P(X)] - \mu^2 = 229 - 15^2 = 4$$

Taking the square root of the variance gives us the standard deviation $\sigma = \sqrt{\sigma^2} = \sqrt{4} = 2$. ∎

Table 6.4 Calculating σ^2 and σ using the computational formula

X	P(X)	$X^2 \cdot P(X)$
12	0.1	$(12)^2 \cdot 0.1 = 14.4$
13	0.1	$(13)^2 \cdot 0.1 = 16.9$
14	0.1	$(14)^2 \cdot 0.1 = 19.6$
15	0.5	$(15)^2 \cdot 0.5 = 112.5$
16	0.1	$(16)^2 \cdot 0.1 = 25.6$
20	0.1	$(20)^2 \cdot 0.1 = 40$
		$\Sigma X^2 \cdot P(X) = 229$

Now You Can Do
Exercises 53–56.

Now that we have calculated the standard deviation σ, we may use it to determine whether values of X are outliers or moderately unusual, using the Z-score method.

Example 6.12 Z-score method for determining an unusual result

a. Using the information from Example 6.11, determine whether $X = 20$ is an unusual number of credits to register for this semester.
b. Construct a probability distribution graph of X.

Solution

a. Recall from Section 3.4 (page 127) that a data value with a Z-score between 2 and 3 may be considered moderately unusual. The Z-score for $X = 20$ credits is

$$Z = \frac{X - \mu}{\sigma} = \frac{20 - 15}{2} = 2.5$$

Thus, among Carla's friends, it would be considered moderately unusual to take 20 credits this semester.

b. Figure 6.4 shows the probability distribution graph of X = number of credits. The mean $\mu = 15$ is indicated, along with the distances $\mu \pm 1\sigma$, $\mu \pm 2\sigma$, and $\mu \pm 3\sigma$. ∎

Now You Can Do
Exercises 57–60.

FIGURE 6.4 $X = 20$ credits is moderately unusual because it lies $Z = 2.5$ standard deviations above the mean.

Example 6.13 Compute the mean and standard deviation of a discrete random variable using technology

FIGURE 6.5 TI-83/84 results for mean and standard deviation of a discrete random variable.

Compute the mean and standard deviation of the probability distribution given in Example 6.11 using the TI-83/84 graphing calculator.

Solution

We use the instructions provided in the following Step-by-Step Technology Guide. The results are shown in Figure 6.5. Be careful! The calculator indicates that the mean is $\bar{x}$. It is not $\bar{x}$ but μ. ∎

STEP-BY-STEP TECHNOLOGY GUIDE: Mean and Standard Deviation of a Discrete Random Variable

We illustrate using the data from Example 6.11.

TI-83/84

Step 1 Enter the X values in list **L1**, and the corresponding P(X) values in list **L2**. See Figure 6.6a.
Step 2 Press **STAT**, highlight **CALC**, and select **1-Var Stats**.
Step 3 Type **L1** followed by a comma, followed by **L2**, as shown in Figure 6.6b. Press **ENTER**. The results are shown in Figure 6.5 (page 269).

FIGURE 6.6a   **FIGURE 6.6b**

Section 6.1 Summary

1 Section 6.1 introduces the idea of random variables, which are variables whose value is determined at least partly by chance. Discrete random variables take values that are either finite or countable and may be put in a list. Continuous random variables take an infinite number of possible values, represented by an interval on the number line.

2 Discrete random variables can be described using a probability distribution, which specifies the probability of observing each value of the random variable. Such a distribution can take the form of a table, graph, or formula. Probability distributions describe populations, not samples.

3 We can calculate and interpret the mean μ, standard deviation σ, and variance σ^2 of a discrete random variable using formulas.

Section 6.1 Exercises

CLARIFYING THE CONCEPTS

1. Explain in your own words what a random variable is. Give an example of a random variable from your own life experience.
2. Is your height a random variable? Under what circumstances would your height be considered a random variable? Under what circumstance would your height not be considered a random variable?
3. What is the difference between a discrete random variable and a continuous random variable?
4. What is the difference between a discrete random variable and a discrete probability distribution?
5. What are the two rules for a discrete probability distribution?
6. Explain the difference between $\bar{x}$ from Section 3.1 and the mean of a discrete random variable.

PRACTICING THE TECHNIQUES

For Exercises 7–12, indicate whether the variable is a discrete or continuous random variable.

7. Number of siblings a randomly chosen person has
8. How long you will wait in your next checkout line
9. How much coffee there is in your next cup of coffee
10. How hot it will be the next time you visit the beach
11. The number of correct answers on your next multiple-choice quiz
12. How many songs you download this month

For Exercises 13–16, write down the possible values of the discrete random variables.
13. The number of students in a classroom where the maximum class size is 15
14. How many different fingers you will get paper cuts on next week
15. The number of games that the California Angels will win the next time they are in the World Series (maximum = 4)
16. The number of Donald Duck's three nephews, Huey, Dewey, and Louie, who will get into trouble in their next cartoon adventure

For Exercises 17–20, use the given information to construct a probability distribution table.
17. Shirelle enjoys listening to CDs while doing her homework. The probabilities that she will listen to X = 0, 1, 2, 3, or 4 CDs tonight are 6%, 24%, 38%, 22%, and 10%, respectively.
18. Josefina loves to score goals for her college soccer team. The probabilities that she will score X = 0, 1, 2, or 3 goals tonight are 0.25, 0.35, 0.25, and 0.15.
19. Joshua is going to make it big on Wall Street, if only he can graduate from college first. Joshua has invested money in a high-risk mutual fund, and has figured his probability of losing $10,000 to be one-third, his probability of gaining $10,000 to be one-half, and his probability of gaining $50,000 to be one-sixth. Let X = money gained.

20. Chelsea is looking for a roommate, and would prefer a roommate who had either one or two pets. Of the 10 possible roommates who answered Chelsea's ad, 5 have no pets, 3 have one pet, 1 has two pets, and 1 has three pets.

For Exercises 21–24, determine whether the distribution represents a valid probability distribution. If it does not, explain why.

21.

X	−10	0	10
P(X)	1/5	1/2	1/5

22.

X	15	16	17	20
P(X)	0.98	0.005	0.005	0.01

23.

X	1	2	3	4	5
P(X)	−0.5	0.5	0.7	0.1	0.2

24.

X	−100,000	50,000	100,000
P(X)	0.5	0.1	1.1

For Exercises 25–28, construct a probability distribution graph for the indicated discrete random variable X.
25. The number of CDs from Exercise 17
26. The number of goals from Exercise 18
27. The amount of money gained from Exercise 19
28. The number of pets from Exercise 20

For Exercises 29–32, refer to the probability distribution from Exercise 17. Find the probability that Shirelle will listen to the indicated numbers of CDs.
29. At least 3 CDs
30. At most 1 CD
31. Exactly 5 CDs
32. At least 1 CD

For Exercises 33–36, refer to the probability distribution from Exercise 18. Find the probability that Josefina will score the following numbers of goals.
33. At least 2 goals
34. At most 1 goal
35. Exactly 4 goals
36. At least 1 goal

For Exercises 37–40, refer to the probability distribution from Exercise 19. Calculate the following probabilities.
37. That Joshua will gain money on his investment
38. That Joshua will lose money
39. That Joshua will neither gain nor lose money
40. That Joshua will gain $100,000

For Exercises 41–44, refer to the probability distribution from Exercise 20. Calculate the following probabilities.
41. That the roommate has at least 1 pet
42. That the roommate has at most 1 pet
43. That the roommate has at least 2 pets
44. That the roommate has the number of pets that Chelsea prefers

For Exercises 45–48, identify (**a**) the most likely value of X, and (**b**) the least likely value of X, for the indicated random variables.

45. The number of CDs from Exercise 17
46. The number of goals from Exercise 18
47. The amount of money gained from Exercise 19
48. The number of pets from Exercise 20

For Exercises 49–52, find the expected value of the indicated random variable X.
49. The number of CDs from Exercise 17
50. The number of goals from Exercise 18
51. The amount of money gained from Exercise 19
52. The number of pets from Exercise 20

For Exercises 53–56, compute the variance and standard deviation of the indicated random variable X.
53. The number of CDs from Exercise 17
54. The number of goals from Exercise 18
55. The amount of money gained from Exercise 19
56. The number of pets from Exercise 20

For Exercises 57–60, use the Z-score method to determine whether there are any outliers or unusual data values.
57. The number of CDs from Exercise 17
58. The number of goals from Exercise 18
59. The amount of money gained from Exercise 19
60. The number of pets from Exercise 20

APPLYING THE CONCEPTS
61. Stanley Cup Finals. The National Hockey League championship is decided by a best-of-seven playoff called the Stanley Cup Finals. The following table shows the possible values of X = number of games in the series, and the frequency of each value of X, for the Stanley Cup Finals between 1990 and 2010. **stanleycup**

X = games	Frequency
4	5
5	4
6	5
7	6

a. Explain why the number of games is a random variable.
b. Explain why the number of games is a discrete and not a continuous random variable.
c. Construct a probability distribution table for X.
d. Construct a probability distribution graph for X.
e. Find P(X ≤ 5).
f. Identify the most likely and the least likely values of X.

62. Florida Vehicle Ownership. The following table provides the probability distribution for X = number of vehicles owned by residents of Florida.[1] **floridacar**

X = vehicles	P(X)
0	0.08
1	0.42
2	0.38
3	0.12

a. Explain why the number of vehicles owned is a random variable.

b. Explain why the number of vehicles owned is a discrete, and not a continuous, random variable.

c. Construct a probability distribution graph for X.

d. Find $P(X \leq 2)$.

e. Identify the most likely and the least likely values of X.

63. Number of Courses Taught. The table provides the probability distribution for X = number of courses taught by faculty at all degree-granting institutions of higher learning in the United States in the fall 2010 semester.[2] 🎓 **coursestaught**

X = courses taught	$P(X)$
1	0.23
2	0.34
3	0.24
4	0.12
5	0.07

a. Construct a probability distribution graph for X.

b. Find $P(X \geq 3)$.

c. Compute $P(X > 3)$.

d. What is the difference between your answers to (b) and (c)?

e. Identify the most likely and the least likely values of X.

64. Teenage Smokers. The National Survey on Drug Use and Health (2005) reported that 5 million young people aged 12–18 had tried tobacco products in the previous month. The table contains the proportions of the 5 million who had done so, at each age level. Let X = age of the person who had tried tobacco products in the previous month. 🚬 **teensmoker**

X = age	$P(X)$
12	0.01
13	0.04
14	0.07
15	0.13
16	0.18
17	0.23
18	0.34

a. Construct a probability distribution graph for X.

b. Find $P(X \leq 16)$.

c. Compute $P(X < 16)$.

d. What is the difference between your answers to (b) and (c)?

e. Identify the most likely and the least likely values of X.

65. Stanley Cup Finals. Refer to Exercise 61.

a. Calculate and interpret the mean number of games.

b. Compute the variance and standard deviation of the number of games.

c. Use the Z-score method to determine whether it is unusual for the Stanley Cup Finals to be a sweep ($X = 4$ games).

66. Florida Vehicle Ownership. Refer to Exercise 62.

a. Find and interpret the mean number of vehicles owned.

b. Compute the variance and standard deviation of the number of vehicles owned.

c. Use the Z-score method to determine whether it is unusual to own zero vehicles.

67. Number of Courses Taught. Refer to Exercise 63.

a. Find and interpret the expected number of courses.

b. Calculate the variance and standard deviation of the number of courses taught.

c. Use the Z-score method to determine whether it is unusual to teach 5 courses.

68. Teenage Smokers. Refer to Exercise 64.

a. Calculate and interpret the expected value of the variable *age*.

b. Calculate the variance and standard deviation of the variable *age*.

c. Determine whether a 12-year-old who had tried tobacco products in the previous month would be considered unusual. How about a 13-year-old?

69. Age at First Marriage. Five U.S. states have a median age at first marriage for women of 28 years old. For 10 states the median is 27, for 22 states the median is 26, for 10 states the median is 10, and for 4 states the median age at first marriage for women is 25.[3] (*Note*: Washington, DC, is included.)

a. Construct a probability distribution table of X = median age at first marriage.

b. If we choose a state at random, find the probability that the median age will be at most 25.

c. What is the most likely and least likely value of X?

d. Calculate and interpret the mean μ.

e. Construct a probability distribution graph for X, and indicate the value of μ on the graph.

70. Challenge Exercise. Refer to part (d) of the previous exercise. Explain clearly what it means to say that μ is the mean of the median age at first marriage.

71. Goals Scored in the NHL. The following table represents the numbers of goals scored per game in each game played during the 2009–2010 National Hockey League season. 🏒 **nhlgoals**

Goals	0	1	2	3	4	5	6	7	8	9
Games	161	407	602	603	455	249	108	40	11	2

a. Construct a probability distribution table for X = goals per game.

b. What is the probability that a team was shut out (got zero goals)?

c. What is the most likely number of goals scored? Least likely?

d. Construct a probability distribution graph for X, and indicate the value of μ on the graph.

e. Compute the standard deviation of the number of goals scored.

f. Identify which values of X would be considered outliers or moderately unusual.

BRINGING IT ALL TOGETHER
The Two-Dice Experiment. Use the following information for Exercises 72–75. Your experiment is to toss a pair of fair dice and find X = sum of the two dice.

72. Recall the sample space for the two-dice experiment from Figure 5.3 in Section 5.1 (page 207).
   a. Construct the probability distribution table of X.
   b. Graph the probability distribution of X, estimating the mean μ using the balance point method.
   c. Calculate the mean μ, and compare the result with your estimate from part (**b**). Interpret the value of μ so that a nonspecialist would understand it.
   d. Compute the standard deviation σ of X.
   e. In your probability distribution graph from part (**b**), label the mean μ, and indicate the size of the standard deviation σ, similar to Figure 6.4 on page 269.

73. Determine whether snake eyes ($X = 2$) is an unusual result. By symmetry, apply your finding to another value of X.

74. Note that the mean of X also happens to be the most likely value of X.
   a. Does it always happen that the mean of a discrete random variable is the same as the most likely value of that variable? If not, give a counterexample.
   b. Specify the conditions when it is true that the mean of X equals the most likely value of X.

75. **Linear Transformation.** *What if* we add the same unknown amount k to each value of X. Describe what would happen to the following, and why.
   a. The mean of X
   b. The standard deviation of X

6.2 Binomial Probability Distribution

OBJECTIVES By the end of this section, I will be able to . . .

1 Explain what constitutes a binomial experiment.

2 Compute probabilities using the binomial probability formula.

3 Find probabilities using the binomial tables.

4 Calculate the mean, variance, and standard deviation of the binomial random variable and find the mode of the distribution.

1 Binomial Experiment

There are many different types of discrete probability distributions. Perhaps the most important is the *binomial* distribution, which we will learn about in this section. Life is full of situations where there are *only two possible outcomes* to a process.

- A baby is about to be born. Will it be a boy or a girl?

- A basketball player is about to attempt a free throw. Will she make it or miss?

- A friend of yours is also taking statistics. Will he pass or fail?

Because situations where there are only two possible outcomes are so widespread, methods have been developed to make it more convenient to analyze them. These methods begin with the definition of a **binomial experiment.**

Binomial Experiment

A probability experiment that satisfies the following four requirements is said to be a **binomial experiment:**

1. Each trial of the experiment has only *two possible mutually exclusive outcomes* (or is defined in such a way that the number of outcomes is reduced to two). One outcome is denoted a *success* and the other a *failure*.

2. There is a *fixed number of trials*, known in advance of the experiment.

3. The experimental outcomes are *independent* of each other.

4. The *probability* of observing a success remains the same from trial to trial.

Let's take a moment to discuss what these requirements really mean.

1. A *success* denotes simply the outcome we are interested in, without necessarily implying that the outcome is desirable. For example, for a researcher investigating college dropout rates, a dropout would be considered a success in the context of a binomial experiment.

2. Tossing a coin 10 times is a binomial experiment because we know the *fixed number of trials*. A salesman contacting customers one-by-one until he makes a sale is not a binomial experiment because he doesn't know how many customers he will have to contact.

3. Sampling without replacement would technically violate the *independence* requirement. However, recall that we may apply the 1% Guideline from Section 5.3, so that when the sample is small compared to the population, successive trials can be considered to be independent. Also, surveying an employer and an employee is a violation of independence, since the employee may be influenced by the employer's response.

4. Suppose four friends are wondering how many of them will get an A in statistics. This is not a binomial experiment because the four friends presumably do not all have the same probability of success.

Many experiments having more than two outcomes can often be defined so that there are only two outcomes. For example, the answer to a multiple-choice question that has five answer choices may be recorded as either correct or incorrect.

The outcomes of a binomial experiment, together with their probabilities, generate a special discrete probability distribution called the **binomial probability distribution.** For binomial probability distributions, there are always only two outcomes, and each outcome has a probability associated with it. The *binomial random variable,* denoted by X, represents the number of successes observed in the n trials. Note that $0 \leq X \leq n$.

Example 6.14   Recognizing binomial experiments

Determine whether each of the following experiments fulfills the conditions for a binomial experiment. If the experiment is binomial, identify the random variable X, the number of trials, the probability of success, and the probability of failure. If the experiment is not binomial, explain why not.

a. A fisherman is going fishing and will continue to fish until he catches a rainbow trout.
b. We flip a fair coin three times and observe the number of heads.
c. A market researcher at a shopping mall is asking consumers whether they use Fib detergent. She asks a sample of 4 men, one of whom is clearly the employer of the other 3.
d. The National Burglar and Fire Alarm Association reports that 34% of burglars get in through the front door. A random sample of 36 burglaries is taken, and the number of entries through the front door is noted.

Solution

a. This is not a binomial experiment because since you don't know how many fish he will catch before the rainbow trout shows up, there is not a fixed number of trials known in advance.
b. This is a binomial experiment because it fulfills the requirements:
    i.   There are only two possible outcomes on each trial, with heads defined as success and tails as failure.
    ii. We know in advance that we are tossing the coin three times.
    iii. The coin doesn't remember its result from toss to toss, and so the trials are independent.
    iv. The coin is fair on each toss, and so the probability of observing heads is the same on each toss.

The binomial random variable X is the number of heads observed on the three trials; since the coin is fair, the probability of success is 0.5 and the probability of failure is 0.5. The possible values for X are 0, 1, 2, or 3.

c. This is not a binomial experiment, because the responses are not independent. The response given by the employer is likely to affect the employees' responses.

d. This is a binomial experiment because it fulfills the requirements:
   i. There are only two possible outcomes on each trial: entering through the front door or not entering through the front door.
   ii. We know in advance that the size of the random sample is 36 burglaries.
   iii. Since the sample is random, the trials are independent.
   iv. Since the sample is quite small compared to the size of the population, the probability of entering through the front door remains the same from burglary to burglary.

The binomial random variable X is the number of front-door-entry burglaries noted for the 36 break-ins; the probability of success is 0.34 and the probability of failure is $1 - 0.34 = 0.66$. ∎

Now You Can Do
Exercises 5–14.

Table 6.5 gives some notation regarding binomial experiments and the binomial distribution.

Table 6.5 Notation for binomial experiments and the binomial distribution

Symbol	Meaning
S	The outcome denoted as a success
F	The outcome denoted as a failure
$P(\text{Success}) = P(S) = p$	The probability of observing a success
$P(\text{Failure}) = P(F) = 1 - p$	The probability of observing a failure
n	The number of trials

Using this notation in the experiment in Example 6.14(d), we have

$$S = \text{burglary through front door, and } F = \text{burglary not through front door}$$
$$P(S) = p = 0.34, \text{ and } P(F) = 1 - p = 1 - 0.34 = 0.66$$

2 Binomial Probability Distribution Formula

Before we examine the binomial probability distribution formula, let us recall from Section 5.4 (page 247) the formula for the **number of combinations.**

Note: In Section 5.4, we used $_nC_r$ to indicate the number of combinations. Now that we have learned about random variables, which can be denoted X, we use $_nC_X$ to represent the number of combinations.

The **number of combinations** of X items chosen from n different items is given by

$$_nC_X = \frac{n!}{X!\,(n - X)!}$$

where $n!$ represents n **factorial,** which equals $n(n - 1)(n - 2) \cdots (2)(1)$, and 0! is defined to be 1.

Example 6.15 How many team combinations in the intramural volleyball league?

Jeffrey is in charge of drawing up a schedule for his college's intramural volleyball league. This year five teams have been fielded, and they must play each other once. How many games will be held?

Note: You may find the following special combinations useful. For any integer *n*:

$$_nC_n = 1 \quad _nC_0 = 1$$
$$_nC_1 = n \quad _nC_{n-1} = n$$

Solution

The number of combinations of $n = 5$ volleyball teams taken $x = 2$ at a time is

$$_5C_2 = \frac{5!}{2!(5-2)!} = \frac{5 \cdot 4 \cdot 3 \cdot 2 \cdot 1}{(2 \cdot 1)(3 \cdot 2 \cdot 1)} = \frac{120}{(2)(6)} = 10$$

Ten games will be held. ■

We are often interested in finding probabilities associated with a binomial experiment. For example, out of five randomly selected cars on the highway, what is the probability that four out of five drivers are obeying the speed limit if we assume that there is a 50% chance that a driver is obeying the speed limit? Pretty small, you think? Example 6.16 shows how to solve a problem like this.

Example 6.16 | Constructing a binomial probability distribution

A recent study reported that about 40% of online dating-survey respondents are "hoping to start a long-term relationship" (LTR).[4] Consider the experiment of choosing three online daters at random, and let

$$X = \text{the number of "LTRers"}$$

so that a success is defined as choosing someone hoping to start a long-term relationship.
a. Construct a tree diagram for this experiment.
b. Suppose that we are interested in finding the probability that exactly two of the three online daters would be LTRers, $P(X = 2)$. In the tree diagram, highlight in blue the outcomes where exactly two of the three online daters are LTRers. Find the probability for each outcome, and use these to find $P(X = 2)$.
c. Suppose that we are interested in finding $P(X = 1)$. In the tree diagram, highlight in red the outcomes where exactly one of the three online daters is an LTRer. Find the probability for each outcome, and use these to find $P(X = 1)$.

Solution

a. Figure 6.7 shows the tree diagram for this experiment.

1st Trial	2nd Trial	3rd Trial	Outcome	Number of successes, X	Probability of outcome
		S	S, S, S	3	$(0.4) \cdot (0.4) \cdot (0.4) = 0.064$
	S	F	S, S, F	2	$(0.4) \cdot (0.4) \cdot (0.6) = 0.096$
S		S	S, F, S	2	$(0.4) \cdot (0.6) \cdot (0.4) = 0.096$
	F	F	S, F, F	1	$(0.4) \cdot (0.6) \cdot (0.6) = 0.144$
		S	F, S, S	2	$(0.6) \cdot (0.4) \cdot (0.4) = 0.096$
	S	F	F, S, F	1	$(0.6) \cdot (0.4) \cdot (0.6) = 0.144$
F		S	F, F, S	1	$(0.6) \cdot (0.6) \cdot (0.4) = 0.144$
	F	F	F, F, F	0	$(0.6) \cdot (0.6) \cdot (0.6) = 0.216$

FIGURE 6.7 Tree diagram and binomial probabilities.

b. As we can see from Figure 6.7, there are $(_nC_X) = (_3C_2) = 3$ different ways that exactly two of the three online daters could be LTRers (highlighted in blue).

For each of these three outcomes, the probability that $X = 2$ is $(0.4)^2(0.6) = 0.096$.

- The outcome S, S, F (second row in Figure 6.7) has probability $(P)(P)(1 - P) = (0.4)(0.4)(0.6) = 0.096$.
- The outcome S, F, S has probability $(p)(1 - p)(p) = (0.4)(0.6)(0.4) = 0.096$.
- The outcome F, S, S has probability $(1 - p)(p)(p) = (0.6)(0.4)(0.4) = 0.096$.

Note that each of these products equals $(p)^2 (1 - p)$, with p having exponent $X = 2$, and $(1 - p)$ having exponent $n - X = 3 - 2 = 1$. Thus,

$$P(X = 2) = (_3C_2)(0.4)^2(0.6)$$
$$= 3(0.096)$$
$$= 0.288$$

c. Similarly, suppose that we are interested in whether exactly one ($X = 1$) of the three online daters is an LTRer. Then, Figure 6.7 shows us, highlighted in red, that there are $(_nC_X) = (_3C_1) = 3$ different ways this could happen. Each of these outcomes has probability $(p)(1 - p)^2 = (0.4)(0.6)^2 = 0.144$, where p has exponent $X = 1$, and $(1 - p)$ has exponent $n - X = 3 - 1 = 2$. Thus,

$$P(X = 1) = (_3C_1)(0.4)(0.6)^2$$
$$= 3(0.144)$$
$$= 0.432$$

Remember: $p(S) = p, p(F) = 1 - p.$

We can generalize these procedures and use the **binomial probability distribution formula** to find probabilities for the number of successes for any binomial experiment.

> **The Binomial Probability Distribution Formula**
>
> The probability of observing exactly X successes in n trials of a binomial experiment is
>
> $$P(X) = (_nC_X) p^X (1 - p)^{n-X}$$
>
> we often call this the binomial probability formula.

In other words, the binomial probability formula is
$P(X) = (_nC_X) P(\text{Success})^{\text{number of successes}} \cdot P(\text{Failure})^{\text{number of failures}}$

Developing Your Statistical Sense

Steps for Solving Binomial Probability Problems

To solve a binomial probability distribution problem, follow these steps:

Step 1. Find the number of trials n, and the probability of success on a given trial p.

Step 2. Find the number of successes X that the question is asking about.

Step 3. Using the values from Steps 1 and 2, find the required probabilities using either the binomial probability formula, the binomial tables (which we learn below), or technology.

Example 6.17 Applying the binomial probability distribution formula

Android Market is an online software store where owners of Android devices, such as cell phones, can buy mobile software applications called apps. According to a report by security vendor SMobile Systems,[5] 20% of Android apps available at Android Market threaten user privacy. Joshua received a random sample of 4 apps from the Android Market when he bought his cell phone. Find the probability that the number of these apps that threaten user privacy equaled the following:

a. None
b. At least 1
c. Between 1 and 3, inclusive
d. 5

Solution

We apply the steps for solving binomial probability problems.

$\boxed{\text{Step 1}}$ We have a random sample of four apps, so the number of trials is $n = 4$. "Success" is denoted as a particular app threatening user privacy. The report states that 20% of such apps from Android Market do so, so $p = 0.2$.

$\boxed{\text{Step 2}}$ For (a), $X = 0$. For (b), $X \geq 1$, that is, $X = 1, 2, 3,$ or 4. For (c), $1 \leq X \leq 3$, that is, $X = 1, 2,$ or 3. For (d), $X = 5$.

$\boxed{\text{Step 3}}$ We apply Step 3 for each of (a)–(d) as follows:

a. **Step 3**   To find the probability that none $(X = 0)$ of the apps threaten user privacy, we use the binomial probability formula:

$$P(X = 0) = (_4C_0)(0.2)^0 (1 - 0.2)^{4-0} = (1)(1)(0.4096) = 0.4096$$

So the probability that none of the apps Joshua received threaten user privacy is 0.4096.

b. **Step 3**   Note that "at least 1" includes all possible values of X except $X = 0$. In other words, the two events $(X = 0)$ and $(X \geq 1)$ are complements of each other. Therefore, from the formula for the probability for complements in Section 5.2 (page 218), we have

$$P(X \geq 1) = 1 - P(X = 0) = 1 - 0.4096 = 0.5904$$

The probability that at least one of the apps will threaten user privacy is 0.5904.

c. **Step 3**   We need to find the probability that either $X = 1$ or $X = 2$ or $X = 3$ of the apps that threaten user privacy. Since these three values of X are mutually exclusive, we find the required probability by using the Addition Rule for Mutually Exclusive Events.

$$P(1 \leq X \leq 3) = P(X = 1 \text{ or } X = 2 \text{ or } X = 3)$$
$$= P(X = 1) + P(X = 2) + P(X = 3)$$

So we calculate the following:

$$P(X = 1) = (_4C_1)(0.2)^1 (1 - 0.2)^{4-1} = (4)(0.2)(0.512) = 0.4096$$
$$P(X = 2) = (_4C_2)(0.2)^2 (1 - 0.2)^{4-2} = (6)(0.04)(0.64) = 0.1536$$
$$P(X = 3) = (_4C_3)(0.2)^3 (1 - 0.2)^{4-3} = (4)(0.008)(0.8) = 0.0256$$

Hence, $P(1 \leq X \leq 3) = 0.4096 + 0.1536 + 0.0256 = 0.5888$. The probability is 0.5888 that between 1 and 3, inclusive, of Joshua's apps will threaten user privacy.

d. **Step 3**   In a binomial experiment, the number of successes X can never exceed the number of trials n. In other words, $X \leq n$, always. So, if Joshua has only $n = 4$ apps, $P(X = 5) = 0$. It is not possible that Joshua has 5 apps that threaten user privacy. ∎

Now You Can Do
Exercises 15–22.

3 Binomial Distribution Tables

As you can imagine, calculations involving binomial probabilities can sometimes get tedious. For example, to find the probability of observing at least 60 heads on 100 tosses of a fair coin, we would have to use the binomial formula for $X = 60, X = 61,$

$X = 62$, and so on, right up to $X = 100$. For this type of problem, you can use Table B, Binomial Distribution, in the Appendix. If you are trying to answer a question involving unusual values of n, such as 103, or unusual values of p, such as 0.47, then you can use technology instead.

Example 6.18   Finding probabilities using the binomial table

Use the binomial table and the binomial distribution from Example 6.17 to find the following probabilities:
a. None of Joshua's apps will threaten user privacy.
b. At least one of Joshua's apps will threaten user privacy.

Solution

a. From Example 6.17, we have a binomial distribution with $n = 4$ and $p = 0.2$. We next find n and p in the binomial table. In Figure 6.8:
  - Look under the n column until you find $n = 4$. That is the portion of the table you will use.
  - Then go across the top of the table until you get to $p = 0.2$.
  - For part **(a)**, $X = 0$, so go down the X column until you see 0 under the X column on the left (and in the subgroup with $n = 4$).
  - The number in the p column is 0.4096 (see Figure 6.8), which is the same answer we calculated in Example 6.17(a).

					p	
n	X	**0.10**	**0.15**	**0.20**	**0.25**	**0.30**
2	0	0.8100	0.7225	0.6400	0.5625	0.4900
	1	0.1800	0.2550	0.3200	0.3750	0.4200
	2	0.0100	0.0225	0.0400	0.0625	0.0900
3	0	0.7290	0.6141	0.5120	0.4219	0.3430
	1	0.2430	0.3251	0.3840	0.4219	0.4410
	2	0.0270	0.0574	0.0960	0.1406	0.1890
	3	0.0010	0.0034	0.0080	0.0156	0.0270
4	0	0.6561	0.5220	0.4096	0.3164	0.2401
	1	0.2916	0.3685	0.4096	0.4219	0.4116
	2	0.0486	0.0975	0.1536	0.2109	0.2646
	3	0.0036	0.0115	0.0256	0.0469	0.0756
	4	0.0001	0.0005	0.0016	0.0039	0.0081

FIGURE 6.8 Excerpt from the binomial tables.

b. In this case, "at least 1" means 1 or 2 or 3 or 4. So, by the Addition Rule for Mutually Exclusive Events, find the probabilities for $X = 1$, $X = 2$, $X = 3$, and $X = 4$, and add them up. Using the same column with column head 0.20 in the table as in part (a), we add up the four probabilities.

$$P(X \geq 1) = P(X = 1) + P(X = 2) + P(X = 3) + P(X = 4)$$
$$= 0.4096 + 0.1536 + 0.0256 + 0.0016 = 0.5904$$

This is the same answer we calculated in Example 6.17(b), but arrived at in a different way. ∎

Now You Can Do
Exercises 23–28.

Next, a word about *cumulative probability*. Cumulative probability refers to the probability of *at most* a particular value of X. For example, what is the probability that at most X = 2 of Joshua's apps threaten user privacy? This is the cumulative probability that X = 0, X = 1, or X = 2. Statistical software and the TI-83/84 graphing calculator each have a function that will find cumulative binomial probabilities for you.

Example 6.19 Using technology to find binomial probabilities

Using the binomial distribution from Example 6.17, use the TI-83/84 to find the following probabilities:
a. $P(X = 4)$, the probability that all 4 apps will threaten user privacy
b. $P(X \le 2)$, the (cumulative) probability that *at most* 2 apps will threaten user privacy

Solution

We use the instructions in the Step-by-Step Technology Guide at the end of this section (page 282).
a. Figure 6.9 shows that we use the function **binompdf** with $n = 4$, $p = 0.2$, and $X = 4$. Figure 6.10 shows the result, $P(X = 4) = 0.0016$.

FIGURE 6.9   **FIGURE 6.10**   **FIGURE 6.11**

b. We use the function **binomcdf** with $n = 4$, $p = 0.2$, and $X = 2$. Figure 6.11 shows the result, $P(X \le 2) = 0.9728$. ∎

4 Binomial Mean, Variance, Standard Deviation, and Mode

In Section 6.1, we examined the mean, variance, and standard deviation of a discrete random variable. Since the binomial random variable X is discrete, it also has a **mean, variance,** and **standard deviation,** shown here.

Mean, Variance, and Standard Deviation of a Binomial Random Variable X

- Mean (or expected value): $\mu = n \cdot p$
- Variance: $\sigma^2 = n \cdot p \cdot (1 - p)$
- Standard deviation: $\sigma = \sqrt{n \cdot p \cdot (1 - p)}$

Example 6.20 Calculating mean, variance, and standard deviation of a binomial random variable

Suppose we know that the population proportion p of left-handed students is 0.10, and that we have a random sample of $n = 100$ students.
a. Find the mean or expected number of left-handed students.
b. Calculate the variance and standard deviation of the number of left-handed students.
c. Would 22 left-handed students out of 100 be considered an outlier?

Solution

The binomial random variable here is X = the number of left-handed students, with $n = 100$ and $p = 0.10$.

a.   The mean or expected number of left-handed students is $\mu = E(X) = n \cdot p = (100)(0.10) = 10$.

b. $\sigma^2 = n \cdot p \cdot (1 - p) = (100)(0.10)(0.90) = 9$. The variance of the number of left-handed students equals 9, expressed in "students squared." Then, $\sigma = \sqrt{\sigma^2} = \sqrt{9} = 3$ students.

c.   We use the Z-score method (Section 6.1, page 269) to determine whether 22 left-handed students out of 100 would be unusual. The Z-score for 22 left-handers is

$$Z = \frac{X - \mu}{\sigma} = \frac{22 - 10}{3} = 4$$

Now You Can Do
Exercises 49–52.

According to the Z-score method of identifying outliers, $X = 22$ left-handed students out of 100 would be considered an outlier, because $Z \geq 3$. ∎

What Do μ and σ Mean?

The value $\mu = 10$ is the "long-run" mean and the value $\sigma = 3$ is the "long-run" standard deviation. That is, if we repeat this experiment an infinite number of times, record the number of left-handed students in each sample, and take the mean and standard deviation of each of these samples, they will equal $\mu = 10$ and $\sigma = 3$. ◢

Next we consider the mode of a binomial distribution.

The *mode* of a binomial distribution is the most likely outcome of the binomial experiment for the given values of n, p, and X, that is, the outcome with the largest probability.

The next example shows how to find the mode for a binomial distribution.

Example 6.21   Finding the most likely outcome of a binomial experiment

Sixty percent of American adults access the Internet wirelessly, according to a 2010 report by the Pew Research Center's Internet and American Life Project. Suppose we take a random sample of $n = 3$ American adults.

a.   Calculate the mean number μ of American adults who access the Internet wirelessly.

b.   Use the binomial table to construct a probability distribution graph of the random variable X = the number of Americans who access the Internet wirelessly.

c.   Use the binomial table or the probability distribution graph to find the most likely number of American adults who access the Internet wirelessly. Note that this represents the *mode* of the distribution.

Solution

Example 6.5 (page 263) shows how to construct a probability distribution graph.

a. $\mu = n \cdot p = (3)(0.6) = 1.8$.

b.   Figure 6.12 is an excerpt from the binomial table, highlighting the probabilities for $X = 0, 1, 2$, and 3, for $n = 3$ and $p = 0.6$. We use these probabilities to construct the probability distribution graph shown in Figure 6.13.

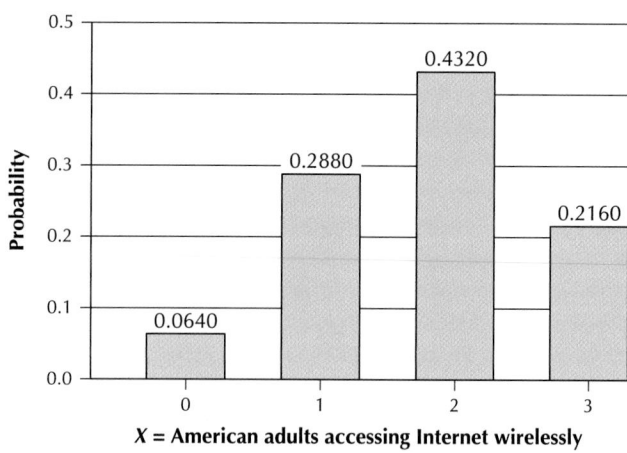

n	*x*	**0.55**	**0.60**
2	0	0.2025	0.1600
	1	0.4950	0.4800
	2	0.3025	0.3600
③	0	0.0911	0.0640
	1	0.3341	0.2880
	2	0.4084	0.4320
	3	0.1664	0.2160

FIGURE 6.12 Probabilities for $X = 0, 1, 2, 3$.

FIGURE 6.13 Probability distribution graph of X.

Now You Can Do
Exercises 53–56.

c. The most likely number of Americans accessing the Internet is associated with the largest probability in the highlighted section of Figure 6.12, 0.4320, which is $P(X = 2)$. Note from Figure 6.13 that $X = 2$ has the longest bar of probability. Thus, $X = 2$ is the most likely number of American adults accessing the Internet wirelessly. We say that $X = 2$ is the *mode* of the distribution of X. ∎

STEP-BY-STEP TECHNOLOGY GUIDE: Finding Binomial Probabilities

For Example 6.19 (page 280).

TI-83/84

Step 1 Press **2ⁿᵈ > DISTR** (the **VARS** key).
Step 2 Do one of **(a)** or **(b)**:
a. For individual binomial probabilities, highlight **binompdf(** and press **ENTER**. (See Figure 6.9 on page 280.)

b. For cumulative binomial probabilities, highlight **binomcdf(** and press **ENTER**.
Step 3 Enter the values for *n*, *p*, and *K*, separated by commas.
Step 4 Press **ENTER**. (See Figures 6.10 and 6.11 on page 280.)

EXCEL

Step 1 Select cell **A1**. Click the **Insert Function** icon f_x.
Step 2 In the **Search for a function** area, type **BINOMDIST**, and click **OK**.
Step 3 For **Number_s**, enter the number of successes, *K*. For **Trials**, enter the sample size, **n**. For **Probability_s**, enter the probability of success, **p**.
Step 4 Do one of **(a)** or **(b)**:

a. For individual binomial probabilities, next to **Cumulative**, enter **false**.
b. For cumulative binomial probabilities, next to **Cumulative**, enter **true**.
Step 5 Click **OK**. See Figures 6.14 and 6.15 for illustrations using Example 6.19.

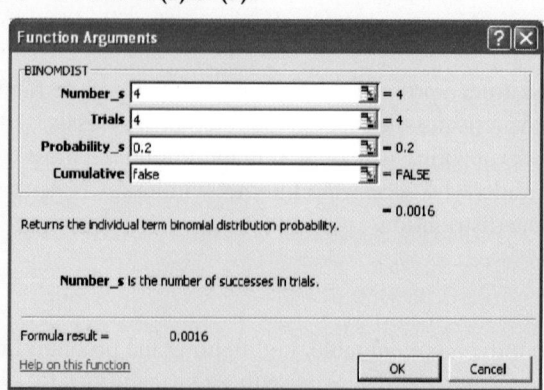

FIGURE 6.14 Example 6.19(a) using Excel.

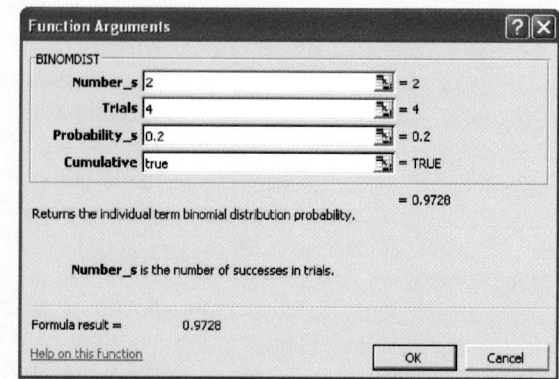

FIGURE 6.15 Example 6.19(b) using Excel.

MINITAB

Step 1   Click **Calc > Probability Distributions > Binomial**.
Step 2   Do one of **(a)** or **(b)**:
a. For individual binomial probabilities, select **Probability** and enter the number of trials **n** and probability of success **p**.

b. For cumulative binomial probabilities, select **Cumulative Probability** and enter the number of trials **n** and probability of success **p**.
Step 3   Select **Input Constant**, enter *K* and click **OK**.

CRUNCHIT!

We will use the data from Example 6.18.

Step 1   Click **Distribution calculator . . . Binomial**.
Step 2   For *n* enter **4**. For *p* enter **0.2**.

Step 3   For part **(a)** select = and enter **4**. For part **(b)** select ≤ and enter **2**.
Step 4   Click **Calculate**.

Section 6.2 Summary

1 The most important discrete distribution is the binomial distribution, where there are two possible outcomes, each with probability of success *p*, and *n* independent trials.

2 The probability of observing a particular number of successes can be calculated using the binomial probability distribution formula.

3 Binomial probabilities can also be found using the binomial tables or using technology.

4 There are formulas for finding the mean, variance, and standard deviation of a binomial random variable, *X*. The mode is the value of *X* with the largest probability.

Section 6.2 Exercises

CLARIFYING THE CONCEPTS

1. State the four requirements for a binomial experiment.
2. What is meant by a "success" in a binomial experiment? Is a success always a good thing?
3. In a binomial experiment, explain why it is not possible for *X* to exceed *n*.
4. Restate the binomial probability distribution formula using the following terms: ($_nC_X$), the probability of success, the number of successes, the probability of failure, the number of failures.

PRACTICING THE TECHNIQUES

For Exercises 5–14, determine whether the experiment is binomial or not. If the experiment is binomial, identify the random variable *X*, the number of trials *n*, the probability of success *p*, and the probability of failure $1 - p$. If the experiment is not binomial, explain why not.

5. Ask ten of your friends to come to your party (remember the independence assumption).
6. Toss a fair die three times, and note the total number of spots.
7. Answer a random sample of 8 multiple-choice questions either correctly or incorrectly by random guessing. There are 4 choices, (a)–(d), for each question.
8. Toss a fair die three times, and note the number of 6s.
9. Select a student at random in the class until you come across a left-handed student.
10. Four cards are selected at random with replacement from a deck of cards, and the number of queens is observed.

11. Four cards are selected at random without replacement from a deck of cards, and the number of queens is observed.
12. Four cards are selected at random with replacement from a deck of cards, and the total number of blackjack-style points (number cards = number of points; face cards = 10 points; aces = either 1 or 11) is calculated.
13. Bob has paid to play two games at a carnival. The probability that he wins a particular game is 0.25.
14. Bob is playing a game at a carnival where he gets to play until he loses. The probability that he wins a particular game is 0.25.

For Exercises 15–28, calculate the probability of *X* successes for the binomial experiments with the following characteristics.
15. $n = 5, p = 0.25, X = 1$
16. $n = 5, p = 0.25, X = 0$
17. $n = 10, p = 0.5, X = 7$
18. $n = 10, p = 0.5, X = 8$
19. $n = 12, p = 0.9, X = 10$
20. $n = 12, p = 0.9, X = 11$
21. $n = 5, p = 0.25, X \le 1$
22. $n = 5, p = 0.25, X \ge 1$
23. $n = 10, p = 0.5, X = 7$ or $X = 8$
24. $n = 10, p = 0.5, X = 7$ and $X = 8$
25. $n = 12, p = 0.9, X \ge 10$
26. $n = 12, p = 0.9, X < 10$ (*Hint:* Use the result from Exercise 25.)

27. $n = 12, p = 0.9, 9 \leq X \leq 12$
28. $n = 12, p = 0.9, 8 \leq X \leq 12$

For Exercises 29–34, the binomial experiment is to toss a fair coin three times. Find the indicated probabilities.
29. Observe no heads
30. Observe one head
31. Observe two heads
32. Observe at most two heads
33. Observe at least one head
34. Observe between zero and two heads, inclusive

For Exercises 35–40, the binomial experiment is to roll a pair of dice four times, and observe the number of doubles that you roll. (*Hint: P*(Doubles) = 1/6.) Find the following probabilities.
35. Observe doubles on three of the rolls
36. Observe doubles on at least three of the rolls
37. Observe no doubles
38. Observe doubles on at most one of the rolls
39. Observe between one and four doubles, inclusive
40. Observe five doubles

For Exercises 41–44, the binomial experiment is to take a random sample of 5 vehicles on the interstate highway, and observe the number of vehicles obeying the speed limit. Assume that the probability that a vehicle obeys the speed limit is 0.4. Find the indicated probabilities.
41. None of the vehicles obey the speed limit.
42. At least 1 of the vehicles obeys the speed limit.
43. At most 2 of the vehicles obey the speed limit.
44. Between 1 and 3 of the vehicles obey the speed limit, inclusive.

For Exercises 45–48, conduct a survey of a random sample of 6 voters, asking each voter whether they would support an Independent for president in the next election. Assume that 15% of voters would support an Independent for president. Find the following probabilities of voters who would support an Independent for president.
45. All of the voters
46. At most 5 voters
47. At least 4 voters
48. Between 3 and 5 voters, inclusive

For each of the following binomial experiments, do the following.
    a. Find and interpret the mean μ of X.
    b. Calculate the variance σ^2 of X.
    c. Compute the standard deviation σ of X.
49. The binomial experiment in Exercises 29–34
50. The binomial experiment in Exercises 35–40
51. The binomial experiment in Exercises 41–44
52. The binomial experiment in Exercises 45–48

For each of the following binomial experiments, do the following.
    a. Construct the probability distribution graph of X.
    b. Identify the mode of X.

53. The binomial experiment in Exercises 29–34
54. The binomial experiment in Exercises 35–40
55. The binomial experiment in Exercises 41–44
56. The binomial experiment in Exercises 45–48

APPLYING THE CONCEPTS

57. Random Guessing on a Quiz. Suppose that you are taking a quiz of 5 multiple-choice questions (the instructor chose the questions randomly), each question having 4 possible responses. You did not study at all for the quiz and will randomly guess the correct response for each question. The random variable X is the number of correct responses.
    a. If there are 4 possible responses to each question, why is this a valid binomial experiment?
    b. State the values of n and p.
    c. Calculate the probability that you will pass this quiz by correctly responding to at least 3 of the 5 questions. Is this good news for you?
    d. Use your answer to (c) to find the probability that you will not pass the quiz.

58. Abandoning Landlines. The National Health Interview Survey reports that 25% of telephone users no longer use landlines, and have switched completely to cell phone use.[6] Suppose we take a random sample of 12 telephone users.
    a. Find the probability that the sample contains exactly 3 users who have abandoned their landlines.
    b. Find the probability that the sample contains at most 3 users who have abandoned their landlines.
    c. Use either the binomial table or technology to determine the most likely number of users in the sample who have abandoned their landlines.
    d. Compute the probability that the sample contains the mode number of users who have abandoned their landlines.

59. Vowels. Did you know that 37.8% of the letters in the written English language are vowels? Suppose we select 15 letters at random.
    a. Explain why we cannot use the binomial table to solve probability problems for this binomial experiment.
    b. Find the probability that the sample contains exactly 2 vowels.
    c. Find the probability that the sample contains at most 2 vowels.

60. Women in Management. According to the U.S. Government Accountability Office, women hold 40% of the management positions in the United States.[7] Suppose we take a random sample of 20 people in management positions.
    a. Find the probability that the sample contains exactly 10 women.
    b. Find the probability that the sample contains at most 1 woman.
    c. Find the probability that the sample contains between 8 and 10 women, inclusive.

61. Random Guessing on a Quiz. Refer to Exercise 57.
 a. Compute the mean, variance, and standard deviation of X. Interpret the mean.
 b. Use the Z-score method to determine which numbers of correct responses should be considered outliers.
 c. Use the binomial table to construct a probability distribution graph of X. Then state the mode of X, that is, the most likely number of correct responses.

62. Abandoning Landlines. Refer to Exercise 58.
 a. Calculate the mean, variance, and standard deviation of the number of users in the sample who have abandoned their landlines. Interpret the mean.
 b. Suppose the sample contains no users who have abandoned their landlines. Is this outcome unusual or an outlier? Use the Z-score method to find out.

63. Vowels. Refer to Exercise 59.
 a. Find the mean, variance, and standard deviation of the number of vowels.
 b. Suppose that the sample contains only 3 vowels. Use the Z-score method to determine whether this outcome is unusual or not.

64. Women in Management. Refer to Exercise 60.
 a. Find the mean, variance, and standard deviation of the number of women in management positions.
 b. Suppose that the sample contains 6 women in management positions. Use the Z-score method to determine whether this outcome is unusual or not.

65. Spinal Cord Injuries. The National Spinal Cord Injury Statistical Center reports that 46.9% of all spinal cord injuries are caused by vehicle crashes. Suppose that we choose 1000 spinal cord injuries at random. Let X be the number of spinal cord injuries caused by vehicle crashes.
 a. Find the expected number of X. Interpret this number.
 b. Find the probability that X equals the expected value of X.
 c. Find the standard deviation of X.
 d. Suppose that the sample contains 520 spinal cord injuries caused by vehicle crashes. Use the Z-score method to determine whether this number is an outlier.
 e. Refer to part (d). *Without performing any calculations*, state whether 521 spinal cord injuries is an outlier. What is your reasoning?

66. What Women Want. In its study *What Women Want: Five Secrets to Better Ratings*, the Arbitron Company reported that "Music I Like" is the biggest factor in deciding which radio station to tune to, and that women chose this reason 87% of the time. Suppose a random sample of 4 women is taken. Let X be the number of women reporting "Music I Like" as the biggest factor in deciding which radio station to tune to.
 a. Find the expected value of X. Interpret this number.
 b. If possible, find the probability that X equals the expected value of X. If not possible, explain why it is not possible to do so.
 c. Construct the probability distribution graph of X.

 d. Identify the mode of X.
 e. Find the probability that X equals the mode of X.

67. Small Business Jobs. According to the U.S. Small Business Administration, small businesses provide 75% of the net new jobs added to the economy. Consider a random sample of 3 new jobs. Let X represent the number of new jobs added to the economy that are provided by small businesses.
 a. Find and interpret the mean μ of X.
 b. If possible, find the probability that X equals μ. If not possible, explain why it is not possible to do so.
 c. Construct the probability distribution graph of X.
 d. Identify the mode of X.
 e. Find the probability that X equals the mode of X.

68. AIDS and Drug Use. The Centers for Disease Control and Prevention reported that, in 2008, 13% of males living with AIDS contracted it through intravenous drug use. A random sample of 120 males living with AIDS is obtained. Let X represent the number of males living with AIDS who contracted it through intravenous drug use.
 a. Find and interpret the mean μ of X.
 b. If possible, find the probability that X equals μ. If not possible, explain why not.
 c. Calculate the variance and standard deviation of X.
 d. Suppose the sample contains 12 males living with AIDS who contracted it through intravenous drug use. Use the Z-score method to determine whether this value of X is an outlier.
 e. Refer to (d). *Without performing any calculations*, state whether $X = 13$ is an outlier. Explain your reasoning.
 f. Suppose that a new sample of 120 males living with AIDS taken this year showed 25 who contracted it through intravenous drug use. What might you conclude has happened to the value of p since 2008?

69. Women and Depression. According to the National Institute for Mental Health, nearly twice the proportion of women (12%) as men (6.6%) are affected by a depressive disorder each year. Suppose that random samples of 5 women and 5 men are taken. Let X represent the number of women affected by a depressive disorder.
 a. Find and interpret the mean of X.
 b. If possible, find the probability that X equals the mean of X. If not possible, explain why it is not possible to do so.
 c. Construct the probability distribution graph of X, and identify the mode of X.
 d. Find the probability that X equals the mode of X.

70. Men and Depression. Refer to Exercise 69. Let Y represent the number of men affected by a depressive disorder.
 a. Find and interpret the mean of Y.
 b. If possible, find the probability that Y equals the mean of Y. If it is not possible, explain why not.
 c. Construct the probability distribution graph of Y, and identify the mode of Y.
 d. Find the probability that Y equals the mode of Y.

71. Downloading Music. The Pew Internet and American Life Project reported in 2004 that "17% of current music downloaders say they are using paid services." Consider a random sample of 400 music downloaders.

    a. Calculate the mean, variance, and standard deviation of the number of music downloaders who are using paid services.

    b. Compute the probability that X equals the mean of X.

    c. Suppose that the sample contains 40 music downloaders who are using paid services. Is this an outlier?

    d. Suppose that a new sample of 400 current music downloaders taken this year showed 150 who were using paid services. What might you conclude has happened to the value of p since 2004?

72. Mean, Median, Mode. For a binomial distribution, if the mean $\mu = n \cdot p$ is a whole number, then

    mean of X = median of X = mode of X

Use this equation to answer the following questions.

    a. Find the median of X for the binomial distribution in Example 6.20.

    b. Find the mode of X for the binomial distribution in Example 6.20.

    c. What is the most likely value of X for the binomial distribution in Example 6.20?

73. Geometric Probability Distribution. Refer to Example 6.14(a), where a fisherman is going fishing and will continue to fish until he catches a rainbow trout. This is an example of the *geometric probability distribution*, which has the same requirements as the binomial distribution, except that there is not a fixed number of trials n. Instead, the geometric random variable X represents the number of trials until a success is observed. The geometric probability distribution formula is

$$P(X) = p(1 - p)^{X-1}$$

where p represents the probability of success. The possible values of X are $X = 1, 2, 3, \ldots$. The U.S. Census Bureau reported in 2010 that 30% of U.S. households have no access at all to the Internet. A random sample is taken of U.S. households. Let the random variable X represent the number of trials until a household is found that has access to the Internet.

    a. Find the probability that $X = 1$, that is, the first household sampled has access to the Internet.

    b. Find the probability that $X = 2$, that is, the first household sampled does not have access but the second household sampled does have access to the Internet.

    c. Find the probability that $X = 3$, that is, the first two households sampled do not have access but the third household sampled does have access to the Internet.

74. Geometric Probability Distribution. Refer to Exercise 73.

    a. The mean of the geometric distribution is $1/p$, and the variance of the geometric distribution is $(1 - p)/p^2$. Calculate the mean, variance, and standard deviation for the random variable $X =$ number of trials until a household is found that has access to the Internet. Interpret the mean.

    b. Suppose that the first 11 households sampled do not have access but the 12th household does have access to the Internet. Is this outcome an outlier? Support your claim.

    c. Without performing any calculations, state whether $X = 13$ is an outlier. Explain your reasoning.

    d. Explain why, unlike the binomial distribution, the geometric random variable X cannot equal zero.

75. Negative Binomial Probability Distribution. The *negative binomial probability distribution* is similar to the geometric distribution, except that, instead of X being the number of trials until the first success is observed, the negative binomial X equals the number of trials until the rth success is observed. The probability distribution formula is

$$P(X) = (_{X-1}C_{r-1})\, p^r\, (1 - p)^{X-r}$$

where p represents the probability of success. The possible values of X are $X = r, r + 1, r + 2, r + 3, \ldots$. The journal *Pediatrics* reports that 70% of child car safety seats are improperly installed.[8] A random sample of car safety seats is obtained. Let X represent the number of car safety seats sampled before finding the rth incorrectly installed one.

    a. Find the probability that it takes $X = 1$ trials to find the first ($r = 1$) car safety seat to be incorrectly installed.

    b. Find the probability that it takes $X = 2$ trials to find the first ($r = 1$) car safety seat to be incorrectly installed.

    c. Find the probability that it takes $X = 2$ trials to find the second ($r = 2$) car safety seat to be incorrectly installed.

    d. The mean of the negative binomial distribution is r/p, and the variance of the negative binomial distribution is $r(1 - p)/p^2$. Calculate the mean, variance, and standard deviation for the random variable $X =$ number of trials it takes to find the second car safety seat to be incorrectly installed ($r = 2$). Interpret the mean.

    e. Suppose that the second car safety seat to be incorrectly installed is found on the 6th trial. Is this outcome an outlier? What is your evidence?

    f. Explain why X cannot be less than r.

76. Hypergeometric Probability Distribution. If samples are drawn from a relatively small finite population, and the sample size is larger than 1% of the population, so that the 1% Guideline (page 233) does not apply, we should not use the binomial distribution, because the samples are not independent. Instead, if we are sampling without replacement, and there are two mutually exclusive categories, then you should use the *hypergeometric probability distribution*. Suppose that N_1 objects belong to the first category ("successes"), and N_2 objects belong to the second category ("failures"). Then the probability of getting X successes and $n - X$ failures is given by the hypergeometric probability distribution formula:

$$P(X) = \frac{\left({}_{N_1}C_X\right)\left({}_{N_2}C_{n-X}\right)}{\left({}_{N}C_n\right)}$$

where $N_1 + N_2 = N$, N is the population size, and n is the sample size. You are dealt 5 cards at random from a deck of 52 cards.

    a. Find the probability that all 5 cards are spades.
    b. Find the probability that exactly 4 cards are spades.
    c. Find the probability that at least 4 cards are spades.
    d. Find the probability that exactly 3 cards are spades.
    e. Find the probability that at most 2 cards are spades.

77. Multinomial Distribution. The *multinomial probability distribution* is similar to the binomial distribution, except that the binomial involves only two categories, while the multinomial involves more than two categories. Suppose we have three mutually exclusive outcomes, A, B, and C, where and $p_A = P(A)$, $p_B = P(B)$, and $p_C = P(C)$. If we have a sample of n independent trials, then the probability that we get X_A outcomes of category A, X_B outcomes of category B, and X_C outcomes of category C is given by the following formula:

$$P(X_A, X_B, X_C) = \frac{n!}{X_A! \, X_B! \, X_C!} \cdot p_A^{X_A} \cdot p_B^{X_B} \cdot p_C^{X_C}$$

Suppose that 30% of students on a particular college campus are Democrats, 30% are Republicans, and 40% are Independents. Suppose we take a random sample of 10 students.

    a. Find the probability that 3 are Democrat, 3 are Republican, and 4 are Independent.
    b. Find the probability that 3 are Democrat, 4 are Republican, and 3 are Independent.
    c. Find the probability that 4 are Democrat, 3 are Republican, and 3 are Independent.

6.3   Poisson Probability Distribution

OBJECTIVES By the end of this section, I will be able to . . .

  1   Explain the requirements for the Poisson probability distribution.

  2   Compute probabilities for a Poisson random variable.

  3   Calculate the mean, variance, and standard deviation of a Poisson random variable.

  4   Use the Poisson distribution to approximate the binomial distribution.

1 Requirements for the Poisson Distribution

The Poisson distribution was developed in 1838 by Siméon Denis Poisson (1781–1840), a French mathematician and physicist, who published more than 300 works in mathematical physics.

The Poisson distribution, like the binomial distribution, is a discrete probability distribution. The Poisson probability distribution is used when we wish to find the probability of observing a certain number of occurrences (X) of a particular event within a fixed interval of space or time. For example, the number of calls X per hour to a 911 emergency center follows a Poisson distribution, as does the number of typographical errors X per chapter in a book.

> **Poisson Probability Distribution**
>
> The **Poisson probability distribution** is a discrete probability distribution that is used when observing the number of occurrences of an event within a fixed interval of space or time. The random variable X represents the number of occurrences of the event in the interval.
>
> **Requirements for the Poisson Probability Distribution**
>
>   1. The occurrences must be random.
>   2. Each occurrence must be independent.
>   3. The occurrences must be uniformly distributed over the given interval.

For a binomial random variable, the maximum number of successes X is the number of trials n. But for the Poisson random variable, there is no upper limit to the number of occurrences X. For example, there is no upper limit to the number of calls X per hour to a 911 emergency center.

Example 6.22 Recognizing when to use the Poisson distribution

For each of the following situations, state whether or not the random variable X follows a Poisson probability distribution. If not, state why not.

a. X is the number of telephone poles along a particular one-mile stretch of highway.
b. X is the number of rabbits living in a particular five-acre plot of land scheduled for development.
c. X is the number of calls to a radio station phone line in the hour following the announcement of a two-free-ticket giveaway to a sold-out concert.
d. X is the number of customers who purchase gasoline at a particular filling station from 2 P.M. to 2:15 P.M.

Solution

a. X does not follow a Poisson distribution. Telephone poles are spaced equidistantly from each other. Knowing the distance between the first two poles gives us the distance to each of the succeeding poles. This violates the requirement that the occurrences be random.
b. X does not follow a Poisson distribution. Related rabbits live together in warrens or dens. Thus, if there is one rabbit living within the specified area, there is probably more than one. This violates the independence requirement.
c. X does not follow a Poisson distribution. Presumably, the radio station would be inundated with calls within the first few minutes of the announcement. Later, there would be fewer calls to the station. This violates the requirement that the occurrences be uniformly distributed throughout the interval.
d. X does follow a Poisson distribution. The customers are random, independent, and occur uniformly over the 15-minute period. ∎

Now You Can Do
Exercises 5–8.

2 Computing Probabilities for a Poisson Random Variable

In Section 6.2 we used the binomial probability distribution formula to compute binomial probabilities. Similarly, we may use the following formula for calculating probabilities for a Poisson random variable X.

Poisson Probability Distribution Formula

If the requirements are met, the probability that a particular event occurs X times within a given interval is

$$P(X) = \frac{\mu^X \cdot e^{-\mu}}{X!}$$

where

μ = the mean of the Poisson probability distribution

e = a constant approximately equal to 2.718281828

X = the number of occurrences of the event within the interval

Example 6.23 Number of cardiac arrests per week in a hospital

A study was done of the number of cardiac arrests to occur per week in a particular hospital of 850 beds over a period of five years.[9] The number of cardiac arrests fulfills the requirements for the Poisson probability distribution and has a mean of $\mu = 1.09$ cardiac arrests per week. Calculate the following probabilities.

a. The probability of 2 cardiac arrests in a given week
b. The probability of fewer than 2 cardiac arrests in a week
c. The probability of at most 2 cardiac arrests in a week
d. The probability of more than 2 cardiac arrests in a week
e. The probability of at least 3 cardiac arrests in a week

Solution

Since the number of cardiac arrests fulfills the requirements for the Poisson probability distribution, we may use the Poisson probability distribution formula to calculate the desired probabilities. To use this formula, we must determine the values of μ and X. For each of (a)–(e), we have $\mu = 1.09$. The Poisson distribution with $\mu = 1.09$ for $x = 1 \ldots 6$ is shown in Figure 6.16.

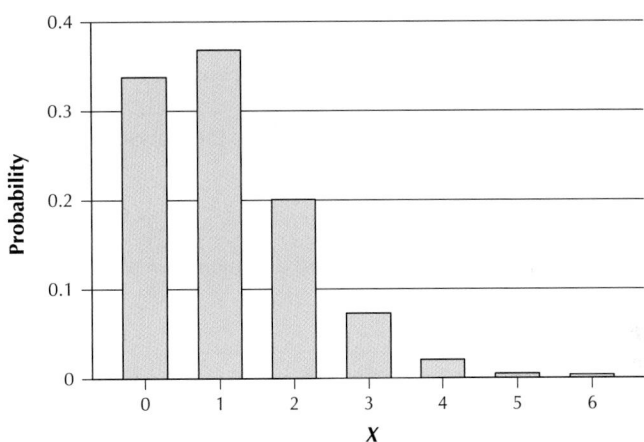

FIGURE 6.16 The Poisson distribution for $\mu = 1.09$. (Note that there is no upper limit to the value X may take but that the probabilities for $X \geq 6$ are very small.)

a. Here $X = 2$, so the probability that $X = 2$ is

$$P(2) = \frac{1.09^2 \cdot e^{-1.09}}{2!} \approx 0.1997$$

b. The Poisson distribution is a discrete distribution, so that "fewer than 2" means $X = 0$ or $X = 1$. We thus find $P(0)$ and $P(1)$ and add the resulting probabilities to arrive at the answer.

$$P(0) = \frac{1.09^0 \cdot e^{-1.09}}{0!} \approx 0.3362 \qquad P(1) = \frac{1.09^1 \cdot e^{-1.09}}{1!} \approx 0.3365$$

So the probability of fewer than 2 cardiac arrests in a week equals $0.3362 + 0.3365 = 0.6727$.

c. The phrase "at most 2" means $X = 0$ or $X = 1$ or $X = 2$. We thus find $P(0)$, $P(1)$, and $P(2)$ and add the resulting probabilities to arrive at the answer.

We have already found $P(0)$ and $P(1)$ from part **(b)** and have found $P(2)$ from part **(a)**. Thus, the probability of at most 2 cardiac arrests in a week equals

$$P(X \le 2) = P(0) + P(1) + P(2) = 0.3362 + 0.3665 + 0.1997 = 0.9024$$

d. The phrase "more than 2" means $X = 3$, $X = 4$, and so on to infinity. In Figure 6.16, these probabilities are represented by the rectangles for $X = 3$, $X = 4$, and so on. Now the Law of Total Probability says that the sum of the probabilities of all values of X equals 1. Thus, the probabilities represented by the rectangles for $X = 3$, $X = 4$, and so on equal 1 minus the sum of the rectangles for $X = 0$, $X = 1$, and $X = 2$. In other words, $P(X > 2) = 1 - P(X \le 2)$. We found $P(X \le 2) = 0.9024$ in part **(c)**. Thus, $P(X > 2) = 1 - 0.9024 = 0.0976$.

e. The phrase "at least 3" means $X = 3$, $X = 4$, and so on to infinity. These are the same X-values represented in part **(d)** by the phrase "more than 2." Thus, $P(X \ge 3) = P(X > 2) = 0.0976$. ∎

Now You Can Do
Exercises 9–14.

3 The Mean, Variance, and Standard Deviation for a Poisson Distribution

Just as the binomial distribution has a mean, variance, and standard deviation, we can calculate these quantities for a Poisson probability distribution. The mean, variance, and standard deviation for a Poisson distribution are as follows.

Parameters of the Poisson Distribution

Mean $= \mu$

Variance $= \sigma^2 = \mu$

Standard deviation $= \sigma = \sqrt{\mu}$

Example 6.24   Home sales in Silicon Valley

The number of homes sold in a month in Los Gatos, a town in California's Silicon Valley, in February 2009 was 21, according to **MercuryNews.com**.[10] Suppose that the number of homes sold in Los Gatos meets the requirements for the Poisson probability distribution, with mean $\mu = 21$.

a. Calculate the mean, variance, and standard deviation of the number of homes sold in a month in Los Gatos.

b. Determine which values of $X =$ the number of homes sold in a month in Los Gatos would be considered unusual.

Solution

a. Mean $= \mu = 21$. Variance $= \sigma^2 = \mu = 21$. Standard deviation $= \sigma = \sqrt{\mu} = \sqrt{21} \approx 4.5826$.

b. Recall from Section 3.4 (page 127) that a data value farther than 2 standard deviations from the mean is considered moderately unusual. The numbers of homes that lie 2 standard deviations above and below the mean are calculated as follows:

$$\mu + 2\sigma \approx 21 + (2)4.5826 = 30.1653$$
$$\mu - 2\sigma \approx 21 - (2)4.5826 = 11.8348$$

Thus, if 11 or fewer homes were sold in Los Gatos in one month, this would be considered moderately unusual. Similarly, it would be moderately unusual if 30 or more homes were sold. ∎

Now You Can Do
Exercises 15–18.

4 Using the Poisson Distribution to Approximate the Binomial Distribution

We can use the Poisson distribution to approximate the binomial distribution when the number of trials n is large and the probability of successes p is small, as measured by the following requirements.

> **Requirements for Using the Poisson Distribution to Approximate the Binomial Distribution**
>
> $$n \geq 100 \quad \text{and} \quad np \leq 10$$
>
> where n is the number of trials and p is the probability of success for the binomial distribution.

If the requirements are met, then the mean of the Poisson distribution used to approximate the binomial distribution is given as

$$\mu = np$$

Example 6.25 Fraudulent online e-commerce transactions

Two percent of online e-commerce transactions are fraudulent.[11] (a) In a sample of 100 online e-commerce transactions, approximate the probability that there are 3 fraudulent transactions. (b) Measure the accuracy of the approximation.

Solution

a. We first verify that the requirements are met. The number of trials is $n = 100 \geq 100$. The probability of "success" (that is, fraud) on any particular transaction is $p = 0.02$, so that $np = (100)(0.02) = 2 \leq 10$. The requirements are met. Next we find the mean of the Poisson distribution used to approximate the binomial distribution: $\mu = np = (100)(0.02) = 2$. Then the probability that there are $X = 3$ fraudulent transactions is

$$P(3) = \frac{\mu^X \cdot e^{-\mu}}{X!} = \frac{2^3 \cdot e^{-2}}{2!} \approx 0.1804$$

The probability is 0.1804 that there are 3 fraudulent transactions in the sample of 100 online e-commerce transactions.

b. How good an approximation is this? Using the more accurate binomial distribution, we get $P(3) = 0.1823$, meaning that the Poisson approximation is accurate in this instance to within $|0.1823 - 0.1804| = 0.0019$ of the binomial probability. ∎

Now You Can Do
Exercises 19–22.

STEP-BY-STEP TECHNOLOGY GUIDE: Poisson Distribution

TI-83/84

Step 1 Press **2nd DISTR**, select **poissonpdf(**, and **press ENTER**.

Step 2 Enter the value of the mean μ, then a comma, then the number of occurrences X, and then). Press **ENTER**.

EXCEL

Step 1 Click **fx** on the menu bar. For "Search for a function," type **Poisson** and click **Go**.
Step 2 For "Select a function," select **POISSON** and click **OK**.

Step 3 For **X**, enter the number of occurrences X; for **Mean**, enter the value of the mean μ; and for **Cumulative**, type **false**.

MINITAB

Step 1 Click **Calc > Probability Distributions > Poisson**.
Step 2 Select **Probability**. For **Mean**, enter the value of the mean μ. Select **Input constant** and enter the number of occurrences X.

Step 3 Click **OK**.

Section 6.3 Summary

1 The Poisson probability distribution is a discrete probability distribution that is used when observing the number of occurrences of an event within a fixed interval of space or time. The random variable X represents the number of occurrences of the event in the interval. The requirements for the Poisson probability distribution are that the occurrences be (a) random, (b) independent of each other, and (c) uniformly distributed over the given interval.

2 The Poisson probability distribution formula is used for calculating probabilities for a Poisson random variable X:

$$P(X) = \frac{\mu^{X} \cdot e^{-\mu}}{X!}$$

3 For a Poisson random variable, the mean is μ, the variance is $\sigma^2 = \mu$, and the standard deviation is $\sigma = \sqrt{\mu}$.

4 The Poisson distribution may be used to approximate the binomial distribution when the number of trials n is large and the probability of success p is small.

Section 6.3 Exercises

CLARIFYING THE CONCEPTS

1. Describe when the Poisson probability distribution is used.

2. For a Poisson random variable X, what does X refer to?

3. Explain the requirements for the Poisson probability distribution.

4. What are the conditions for using the Poisson distribution to approximate the binomial distribution?

PRACTICING THE TECHNIQUES

For each of the following situations, state whether or not the random variable X follows a Poisson probability distribution. If not, state why not.

5. X is the number of sheep in an area of land that is part pasture and part forest.

6. X is the number of fraternity members on a certain campus who will consume alcoholic beverages this weekend.

7. X is the number of vehicles to pass by a certain point on a rural stretch of road between 11 P.M. and midnight.

8. X is the number of soldiers marching in a one-mile-long parade.

For each of the following situations, assume that the requirements for the Poisson probability distribution are met. Use the given mean to find the indicated probability.

9. $\mu = 10$; find the probability that X equals 8.

10. $\mu = 10$; find the probability that X equals 9.

11. $\mu = 3$; find the probability that X is at most 3.

12. $\mu = 3$; find the probability that X is greater than 3. (*Hint:* First find $P(X \leq 3)$.)

13. $\mu = 4$; find the probability that X is at most 2.

14. $\mu = 4$; find the probability that X is greater than 2. (*Hint:* First find $P(X \leq 2)$.)

For each of the following situations, assume that the requirements for the Poisson probability distribution are met and do the following.

a. Calculate the standard deviation.

b. Find the values of X that would be considered moderately unusual.

15. $\mu = 20$

16. $\mu = 25$

17. $\mu = 10$

18. $\mu = 2$

For each of the following situations, do the following.

a. Verify that the requirements are met for using the Poisson approximation for the binomial distribution.

b. Use the Poisson approximation for the binomial distribution to approximate the indicated probability.

19. $n = 200$, $p = 0.05$. Approximate the probability that $X = 12$.

20. $n = 120$, $p = 0.03$. Approximate the probability that $X = 4$.

21. $n = 200$, $p = 0.04$. Approximate the probability that $X = 10$.

22. $n = 120$, $p = 0.05$. Approximate the probability that $X = 5$.

APPLYING THE CONCEPTS

Assume that the requirements for the Poisson probability distribution are met for Exercises 23–31. Also, when asked to approximate a probability, use the Poisson approximation for the binomial distribution.

23. Trees per Acre. The mean number of trees per acre (after thinning) in the Lassen National Forest in California was $\mu = 100$ trees.[12] Let X refer to the number of trees (after thinning in the Lassen National Forest in California). Find the following probabilities.
- **a.** Probability that $X = 100$
- **b.** $P(X = 95)$
- **c.** $P(X = 101)$

24. Clickstream Analysis. "Clickstream analysis" refers to the analysis of the sequence of Web page clicks by users of a particular Web site. The mean number of page hits on the Web site of the Environmental Protection Agency (EPA) was $\mu = 7.9$ page hits per visitor.[13] Let X refer to the number of page hits on the EPA Web site. Find the following probabilities.
- **a.** Probability that $X = 10$
- **b.** $P(X = 9)$
- **c.** $P(X = 2)$
- **d.** Probability that X is less than 2
- **e.** Probability that X is greater than 2. (*Hint:* Use the answers to **(c)** and **(d)**.)

25. DNA Mutation Rate. The mutation rate for human DNA is 0.0000000214 per base pair per generation.[14] Suppose that we examine the 247 million base pairs in human chromosome 1 (the largest of the 23 human chromosomes). Do the following.
- **a.** Verify that the requirements are met for using the Poisson distribution to approximate the binomial distribution.
- **b.** Find the mean of the Poisson distribution used to approximate the binomial distribution.
- **c.** Approximate the probability that chromosome 1 will have $X = 0$ mutations.
- **d.** Approximate the probability that chromosome 1 will have at least 1 mutation.
- **e.** Approximate the probability that chromosome 1 will have at most 2 mutations.

26. Due-Date Babies. Only 4% of babies are born on their due date.[15] Massachusetts General Hospital in Boston assists in the delivery of 142 babies per two-week period.[16] Do the following.
- **a.** Verify that the requirements are met for using the Poisson distribution to approximate the binomial distribution.
- **b.** Find the mean of the Poisson distribution used to approximate the binomial distribution.
- **c.** Approximate the probability that $X = 2$ babies will be born on their due date during a two-week period.
- **d.** Approximate the probability that at least 1 baby will be born on its due date during a two-week period.

27. Rangers Runs. In 2008, the Texas Rangers led all Major League Baseball teams with a mean number of runs per game of $\mu = 5.5617$.[17] Let X refer to the number of runs per game for the Texas Rangers. Find the following probabilities.
- **a.** Probability that $X = 5$
- **b.** $P(X = 4)$
- **c.** Probability that the Rangers get shut out (score zero runs)
- **d.** Probability that $X = \mu$

28. Broward Burglaries. The mean number of burglaries taking place at the Central Campus of Broward Community College in Davie, Florida, is $\mu = 23.3$ per year.[18] Let X refer to the number of burglaries taking place on that campus in a year. Find the following probabilities.
- **a.** Probability that $X = 23$
- **b.** Probability that X is either 23 or 24
- **c.** Probability that there are no burglaries
- **d.** Probability that $X = \mu$

29. Football Fatalities. The mean number of fatalities from playing high school football in the United States is 3.8.[19] Let X refer to the number of fatalities from playing high school football in one year. Find the following probabilities.
- **a.** Probability that $X = 3$
- **b.** $P(X = 2)$
- **c.** Probability that there are no fatalities in a year
- **d.** Probability that $X > 3$

30. Russians on Facebook. Only 0.05% of people living in Russia are using the social networking site Facebook.[20] Suppose that we take a sample of 100 people living in Russia. Do the following.
- **a.** Verify that the requirements are met for using the Poisson distribution to approximate the binomial distribution.
- **b.** Find the mean of the Poisson distribution used to approximate the binomial distribution.
- **c.** Approximate the probability that $X = 1$ person is using Facebook.
- **d.** Approximate the probability that at least 1 person in the sample is using Facebook.

31. Teens in Virtual Worlds. According to a 2008 study, 10% of teenagers participate in online virtual worlds such as Second Life, Gaia, or Habbo Hotel.[21] Suppose that we take a sample of 100 teenagers. Do the following.
- **a.** Verify that the requirements are met for using the Poisson distribution to approximate the binomial distribution.

b. Find the mean of the Poisson distribution used to approximate the binomial distribution.

c. Approximate the probability that $X = 10$ teenagers participate in such online virtual worlds.

d. Approximate the probability that either 10, 11, or 12 teenagers participate in such online virtual worlds.

32. Challenge Exercise. For the given exercise, identify the values of X that would be considered (**i**) moderately unusual, (**ii**) outliers.

    a. Exercise 27

    b. Exercise 28

    c. Exercise 29

    d. Exercise 30

6.4 Continuous Random Variables and the Normal Probability Distribution

OBJECTIVES By the end of this section, I will be able to . . .

1   Identify a continuous probability distribution and state the requirements.

2   Calculate probabilities for the uniform probability distribution.

3   Explain the properties of the normal probability distribution.

Sections 6.1–6.3 dealt with discrete random variables, such as the binomial and Poisson random variables. Next we turn to continuous random variables.

1 Continuous Probability Distributions

Continuous random variables assume infinitely many possible values, with no gap between the values. For example, the height of a randomly chosen classmate of yours is a continuous random variable because it can take an infinite number of possible values.

For a given continuous random variable X, we are not interested in whether X equals any particular value. Rather, we are interested in whether X is

- greater than a particular value, or
- less than a particular value, or
- between two particular values.

That is, we are interested in whether X is located in an *interval*.

We are not interested in the probability that X equals some particular value, because this probability *always equals zero*. If this sounds crazy, then consider the following example. How much soda does a "12-ounce can" of soda actually contain? Are you sure it's 12 ounces and not 11.99999999 ounces? Or could it contain 12.00000001 ounces? In fact, the can could contain any of the infinite number of possible amounts of soda, say between 11.9 and 12.1 ounces (see Figure 6.17). Thus, any given weight of soda in the can is so unlikely that the probability that you will get exactly 12.00000000 ounces of soda in your 12-ounce can is zero.

In contrast to the graph for a discrete distribution, the graph for a continuous probability distribution is "smooth" because it represents probability at infinitely many points along an interval.

FIGURE 6.17
X = amount of soda is a continuous random variable with a continuous probability distribution.

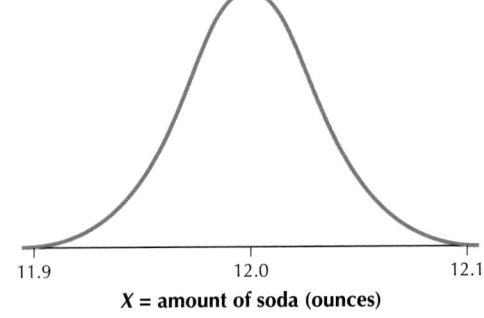

X = amount of soda (ounces)

The graph in Figure 6.17 is called a **continuous probability distribution,** defined as follows.

Continuous Probability Distribution

A **continuous probability distribution** is a graph that indicates on the horizontal axis the range of values that the continuous random variable X can take, and above which is drawn a curve, called the **density curve.** A continuous probability distribution must meet the following requirements.

Requirements for a Continuous Probability Distribution
1. The total area under the density curve must equal 1 (this is the **Law of Total Probability for Continuous Random Variables**).
2. The vertical height of the density curve can never be negative. That is, the density curve never goes below the horizontal axis.

---

2 Calculating Probabilities for the Uniform Probability Distribution

To learn how to calculate probabilities for continuous random variables, we turn to the **uniform probability distribution.**

The **uniform probability distribution** is a continuous distribution that has constant probability from left endpoint a to right endpoint b. Its curve is a flat, straight line, so that the shape of the uniform distribution is a rectangle.

For example, suppose the waiting time X for the campus shuttle bus follows a uniform distribution, with waiting times ranging from $a = 0$ minutes to $b = 10$ minutes. Then the uniform probability distribution is given in Figure 6.18.

FIGURE 6.18
Waiting time X has a rectangular shape.

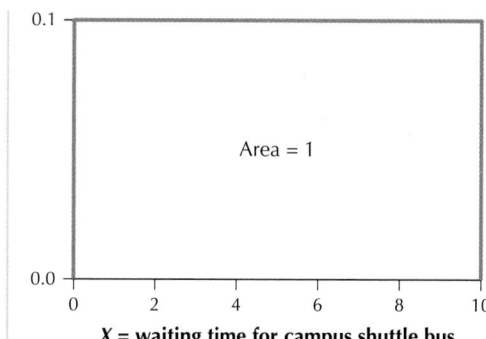

X = waiting time for campus shuttle bus

Note that the width of the rectangle in Figure 6.18 is $b - a = 10 - 0 = 10$. Since the total area under the density curve must equal 1 by the Law of Total Probability for Continuous Distributions, the height of the rectangle must therefore equal $1/10 = 0.1$.

So how do we represent probability for the uniform distribution, or for continuous distributions in general?

Probability for Continuous Distributions

The probability that a continuous random variable X takes a value in an interval is equal to the *area under the density curve above that interval.*

Example 6.26   Probability is represented by area

Find the probability that you will wait between 2 and 4 minutes for the campus shuttle bus.

Solution

We are interested in the interval between $X = 2$ and $X = 4$ minutes. The area above this interval forms a rectangle, shown in Figure 6.19. This area of this green rectangle represents the probability that X is between 2 and 4 minutes. The base of the rectangle equals $b - a = 4 - 2 = 2$. Since the height of the rectangle equals 0.1, we find that the area of this rectangle is

$$\text{area} = \text{base} \times \text{height} = 2 \times 0.1 = 0.2$$

Since area represents probability, we conclude that the probability is 0.2 that you will wait between 2 and 4 minutes for the campus shuttle bus. ▦

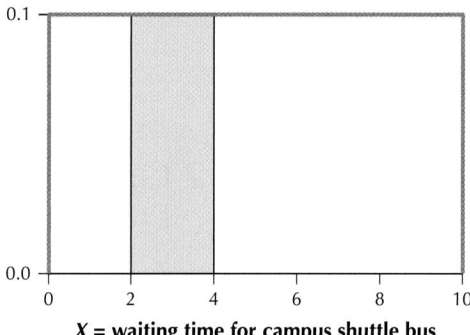

FIGURE 6.19
Probability X between 2 and 4 equals the area of the green rectangle.

X = waiting time for campus shuttle bus

Now You Can Do
Exercises 7–16.

Notice from Example 6.26 that $0.2 = \dfrac{4 - 2}{10 - 0}$. We generalize this as follows:

> The probability that a uniform random variable with left endpoint a and right endpoint b takes a value in the interval $[c, d]$ is given by
> $$P(c \le X \le d) = \frac{d - c}{b - a}$$

For example, the probability that you would wait between $c = 0$ and $d = 5$ minutes for the campus shuttle bus is

$$P(0 \le X \le 5) = \frac{5 - 0}{10 - 0} = 0.5$$

Now, because X is a continuous random variable, $P(X = 0) = 0$ and $P(X = 5) = 0$. Thus, $P(0 \le X \le 5) = P(0 < X < 5)$. In fact, for any continuous random variable, the inequalities $\le$ and $<$ are interchangeable, as are $\ge$ and $>$.

3 Introduction to Normal Probability Distribution

We now turn to what is considered to be the most important probability distribution in the world: the **normal probability distribution.** Sometimes referred to as the bell-shaped curve (Chapter 3), the normal distribution is a continuous distribution that has been found to model accurately such phenomena as

- the amount of rainfall in Imperial Valley, California;

- the heights and weights of high-risk infants in New York City; and

- the errors in manufacturing machine bolts in a Pennsylvania factory.

Like a discrete random variable, a continuous random variable has a mean and a standard deviation. The parameters of the normal distribution are the mean μ, which determines the center of the distribution on the number line, and the standard deviation σ, which determines the spread or shape of the distribution curve. The mean μ can be positive, negative, or zero; the standard deviation σ can never be negative.

From Figure 6.20 we can see that the normal distribution curve is symmetric about μ. If you slice the curve neatly in half at the mean μ, the result will be two pieces that are perfect mirror images of each other, as in Figure 6.20.

Remember that, like all probability distributions, we are dealing with a population of data values.

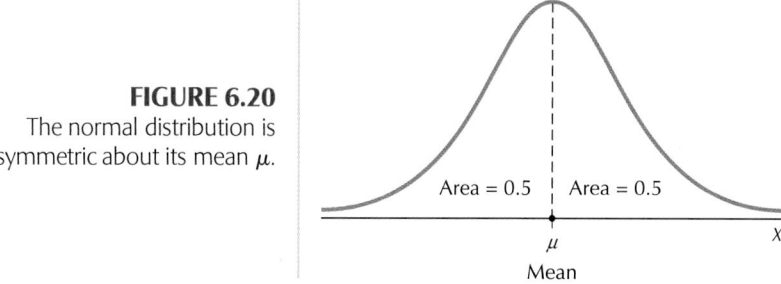

FIGURE 6.20
The normal distribution is symmetric about its mean μ.

Properties of the Normal Density Curve (Normal Curve)

1. It is symmetric about the mean μ.
2. The highest point occurs at $X = \mu$, because symmetry implies that the mean equals the median, which equals the mode of the distribution.
3. The total area under the curve equals 1.
4. Symmetry also implies that the area under the curve to the left of μ and the area under the curve to the right of μ are both equal to 0.5 (Figure 6.20).
5. The normal distribution is defined for values of X extending indefinitely in both the positive and negative directions. As X moves farther from the mean, the curve approaches but never quite touches the horizontal axis.
6. Values of X are always found on the horizontal axis. Probabilities are represented by areas under the curve.

Figure 6.21 shows two normal density curves, with different means but the same standard deviation. Note that the two curves have precisely the same spread or shape, because each distribution has the same standard deviation, $\sigma = 2$. However, because the mean of the curve on the right is $\mu = 6$ while the mean of the curve on the left in $\mu = 2$, the curve on the right is shifted four units to the right.

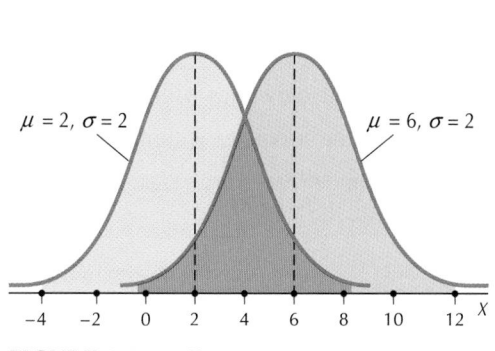

FIGURE 6.21 Different μ, same σ.

FIGURE 6.22 Same μ, different σ.

Since σ is a measure of spread, the larger the value of σ, the more spread out the distribution of X will be. This is illustrated in Figure 6.22. The normal distribution with the smaller standard deviation ($\sigma = 1$) has a curve with a higher peak in the center and thinner "tails" than the distribution with a larger standard deviation ($\sigma = 2$).

Now You Can Do
Exercises 33 and 34.

Example 6.27 Properties of the normal curve

A statistical study found that when nurses made home visits to pregnant teenagers to provide support services, discourage smoking, and otherwise provide care, the mean birth weight of the babies was higher for this treatment group (3285 grams) than for a control group of teenagers who were not visited (2922 grams), when the visits began before midgestation.[22] The birth weights of babies are known to follow a normal distribution.[23]

Suppose the birth weights for the babies whose mothers were visited by the nurses (treatment group) also follow a normal distribution. Then our random variable is

$$X = \text{birth weight of babies in the treatment group}$$

The mean is $\mu = 3285$ grams. Assume that the standard deviation is $\sigma = 500$ grams. Graph the normal curve of $X =$ birth weights and describe some properties of this distribution.

Solution

Figure 6.23 shows the probability graph of $X =$ birth weights. Note that the curve has the following properties:

1. It is symmetric about the mean $\mu = 3285$ grams.
2. The highest point occurs at $\mu = 3285$ grams, which is also the median and the mode.
3. The total area under the curve equals 1.
4. The area under the curve to the left of $\mu = 3285$ equals 0.5, as does the area under the curve to the right of $\mu = 3285$. ■

Hint: Draw a bell-shaped curve with center at $\mu = 3285$. Label the horizontal axis in increments equal to the standard deviation $\sigma = 500$. Make sure the areas to the left and right of μ are equal.

FIGURE 6.23
The normal curve of $X =$ birth weights is symmetric about its mean $\mu = 3285$.

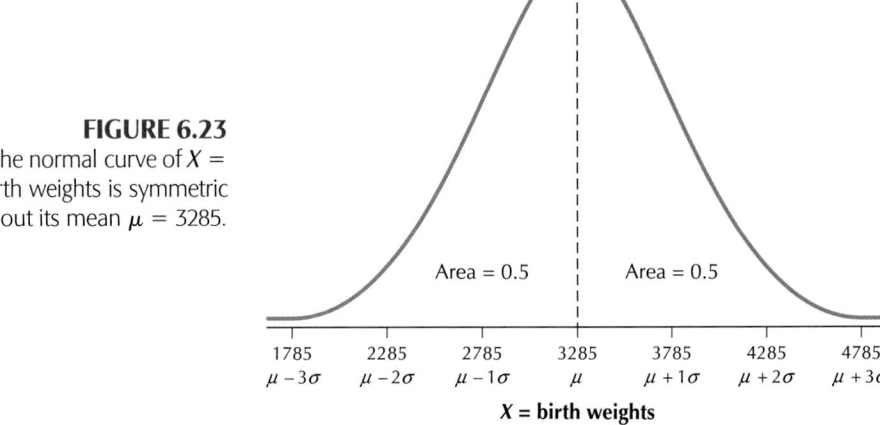

In Chapter 3, we learned that according to the Empirical Rule the area under the normal curve has the following properties (see Figure 6.24).

1. About 68% of the area under the curve lies within 1 standard deviation of the mean.

2. About 95% of the area under the curve lies within 2 standard deviations of the mean.

3. About 99.7% of the area under the curve lies within 3 standard deviations of the mean.

FIGURE 6.24
The Empirical Rule.

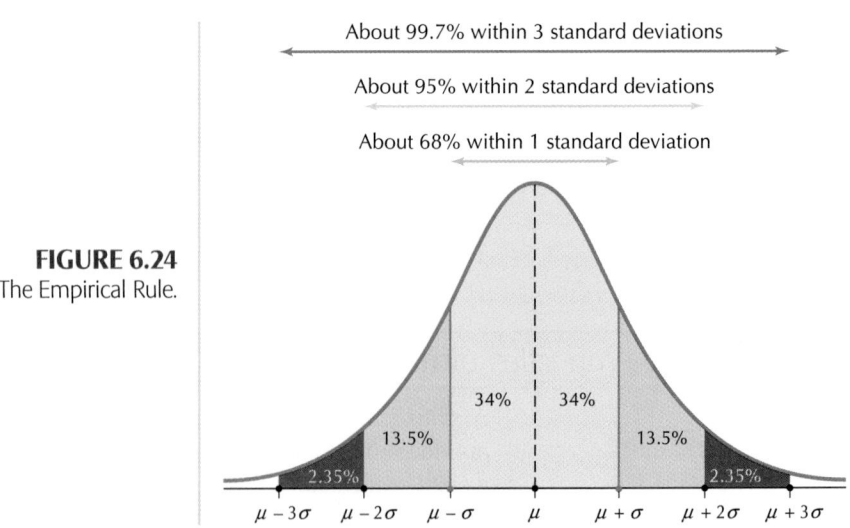

We will verify the Empirical Rule in Section 6.5.

Example 6.28 | Empirical Rule

Recall the distribution of birth weights from Example 6.27.
a. What is the probability that a randomly chosen baby from the treatment group has a birth weight between 3785 grams and 4285 grams?
b. Find the probability that a randomly chosen baby from the treatment group has a birth weight greater than 425 grams.

Solution

a. Figure 6.25 shows the distribution of X = birth weights of babies from the treatment group. The area under the curve between 3785 and 4285 represents the area between $\mu + \sigma$ and $\mu + 2\sigma$. Courtesy of the Empirical Rule, Figure 6.25 tells us that the area between $\mu + \sigma$ and $\mu + 2\sigma$ is about 13.5% of the area under the curve.

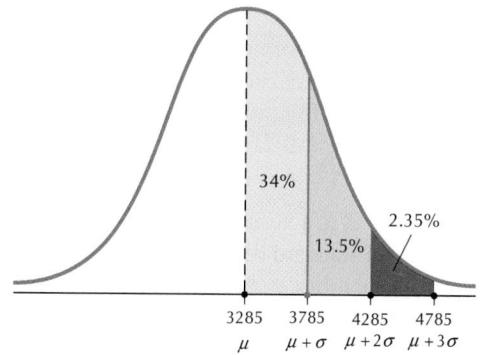

3285	3785	4285	4785
μ	$\mu + \sigma$	$\mu + 2\sigma$	$\mu + 3\sigma$

FIGURE 6.25 Some Empirical Rule probabilities for X = birth weights.

We may use the *probability* of a birth weight greater than 4285 grams to represent the *percentage* or the *proportion* of birth weights greater than 4285.

Therefore, the probability that a randomly chosen baby from the treatment group has a birth weight between 3785 grams and 4285 grams is about 0.135.

b. The area to the right of $\mu = 3285$ equals 0.5, or 50%, of the area under the curve. To find the area to the right of $X = 4285$, we need to subtract the yellow area (34%) and the light green area (13.5%) from 50%: $50\% - 34\% - 13.5\% = 2.5\%$. Therefore, the probability that a randomly chosen baby from the treatment group has a birth weight greater than 4285 grams is about 0.025. ■

Now You Can Do
Exercises 25–32.

Section 6.4 Summary

1 Continuous random variables assume infinitely many possible values, with no gap between the values. Probability for continuous random variables consists of the area above an interval on the number line and under the distribution curve.

2 The uniform probability distribution has constant probability from its left to its right endpoints and is therefore shaped like a rectangle.

3 The normal distribution is the most important continuous probability distribution. It is symmetric about its mean μ and has standard deviation σ.

Section 6.4 Exercises

CLARIFYING THE CONCEPTS

1. For a continuous random variable X, why are we not interested in whether X equals some particular value?

2. In the graph of a probability distribution, what is represented on the number line?

3. How is probability represented in the graph of a continuous probability distribution?

4. What are the possible values for the mean of a normal distribution? For the standard deviation?

5. True or false: The graph of the uniform distribution is always shaped like a square.

6. For continuous probability distributions, what is the difference between $P(X > 1)$ and $P(X \geq 1)$?

PRACTICING THE TECHNIQUES

For Exercises 7–12, assume that X is a uniform random variable, with left endpoint 0 and right endpoint 100. Find the following probabilities.

7. $P(50 < X < 100)$ **10.** $P(15 \leq X \leq 35)$
8. $P(50 \leq X \leq 100)$ **11.** $P(24 < X < 25)$
9. $P(25 < X < 90)$ **12.** $P(25 < X < 25)$

For Exercises 13–16, assume that X is a uniform random variable, with left endpoint -5 and right endpoint 5. Compute the following probabilities.

13. $P(0 \leq X \leq 5)$ **15.** $P(-5 \leq X \leq -4)$
14. $P(-5 \leq X \leq 5)$ **16.** $P(-1 \leq X \leq 5)$

For Exercises 17–20, assume that X is a normal random variable, with mean $\mu = 4$ and standard deviation $\sigma = 2$. Use the Empirical Rule to approximate the following probabilities.

17. $P(2 \leq X \leq 6)$ **19.** $P(X \leq 0)$
18. $P(0 \leq X \leq 8)$ **20.** $P(X \geq 6)$

For Exercises 21–24, assume that X is a normal random variable, with mean $\mu = 100$ and standard deviation $\sigma = 15$. Approximate the following probabilities.

21. $P(55 \leq X \leq 145)$ **23.** $P(55 \leq X \leq 70)$
22. $P(0 \leq X \leq 130)$ **24.** $P(X \leq 85)$

Use the normal distribution from Example 6.27 for Exercises 25–32. Birth weights are normally distributed with a mean weight of $\mu = 3285$ grams and a standard deviation of $\sigma = 500$ grams.

25. What is the probability of a birth weight equal to 3285 grams?

26. What is the probability of a birth weight more than 3285 grams?

27. What is the probability of a birth weight of at least 3285 grams?

28. Is the area to the right of $X = 4285$ grams greater than or less than 0.5? How do you know this?

29. Is the area to the left of $X = 4285$ grams greater than or less than 0.5? How do you know this?

30. What is the probability of a birth weight between 2785 and 3785 grams?

31. What is the probability of a birth weight between 1785 and 4785 grams?

32. What is the probability of a birth weight between 785 and 5785 grams?

33. The two normal distributions in the accompanying figure have the same standard deviation of 5 but different means. Which normal distribution has mean 10 and which has mean 25? Explain how you know this.

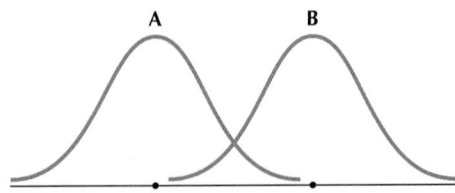

34. The two normal distributions in the figure below have the same mean of 100 but different standard deviations. Which normal distribution has standard deviation 3 and which has standard deviation 6? Explain how you know this.

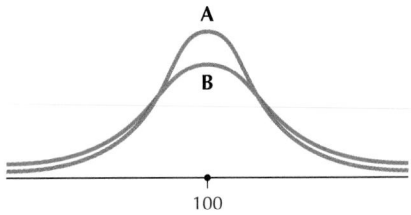

For Exercises 35–42, use the graph of the normal distribution to determine the mean and standard deviation. (*Hint:* The distance between dotted lines in the figures represents 1 standard deviation.)

35.

36.

37.

38.

39.

40.

41.

42.

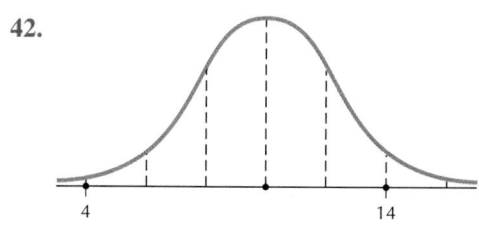

APPLYING THE CONCEPTS

43. Uniform Distribution: Web Page Loading Time.
Suppose that the Web page loading time for a particular home network is uniform, with left endpoint 1 second and right endpoint 5 seconds.

  a. What is the probability that a randomly selected Web page will take between 3 seconds and 4 seconds to load?

  b. Find the probability that a randomly selected Web page will take between 1 second and 2 seconds to load.

  c. How often does it take less than 1 second for a Web page to load?

44. Uniform Distribution: Random Number Generation.
Computers and calculators use the uniform distribution to generate random numbers. Suppose we have a calculator that randomly generates numbers between 0 and 1 so that they form a uniform distribution.

  a. What is the probability that a random number is generated which is less than 0.3?

  b. Find the probability that a random number is generated that is between 0.27 and 0.92.

  c. What is the probability that a random number greater than 1 is generated?

For Exercises 45–49, sketch the distribution, showing μ, $\mu + \sigma$, $\mu + 2\sigma$, $\mu + 3\sigma$, $\mu - \sigma$, $\mu - 2\sigma$, and $\mu - 3\sigma$. Then answer the questions.

45. Windy Frisco. The average wind speed in San Francisco in July is 13.6 miles per hour (mph), according to the U.S. National Oceanic and Atmospheric Administration. Suppose that the distribution of the wind speed in July in San Francisco is normal with mean $\mu = 13.6$ mph and standard deviation $\sigma = 4$ mph.

  a. Shade the region that represents wind speeds between 9.6 and 17.6 mph.

  b. What is the proportion of wind speeds between 9.6 and 17.6? (*Hint:* See Figure 6.24 (page 298).)

46. Viewers of *60 Minutes*. Nielsen Media Research reported that, for the week of October 18, 2010, 16 million viewers watched the television show *60 Minutes*. Suppose that the distribution of viewers of *60 Minutes* is normal with mean $\mu = 16$ million and standard deviation $\sigma = 4$ million.

  a. Shade the region that represents fewer than 8 million viewers.

  b. What is the probability that fewer than 8 million viewers will watch *60 Minutes*?

47. Math Scores. The National Center for Education Statistics reports that in 2005 the mean score on the standardized mathematics test for eighth-graders increased by 7 points from 2000. The mean score in 2005 was $\mu = 273$; assume a standard deviation of $\sigma = 7$.

  a. Shade the region that represents scores between 266 and 273.

  b. What is the probability that a student scored between 266 and 273 on the test?

48. Los Angeles Temperature. The U.S. Department of Commerce reports that the mean temperature in downtown Los Angeles is 66.2 degrees Fahrenheit (°F). Assume that the distribution of temperature in Los Angeles is normal with mean $\mu = 66.2$°F and standard deviation $\sigma = 8$°F. What is the probability that the temperature in Los Angeles is between 50.2°F and 82.2°F?

49. Hospital Patient Length of Stays. A study of Pennsylvania hospitals showed that the mean patient length of stay was 4.87 days with a standard deviation of 0.97 day.[24] Assume that the distribution of patient length of stays is normal. Find the probability that a randomly selected patient has a length of stay of less than 3.9 days.

50. Engineers' Salaries. According to the U.S. Census Bureau, students in their first year after graduating with bachelor's degrees in engineering earned an average salary of $3189 per month. Assume that this distribution is normal with mean $\mu = 3189$ and standard deviation $\sigma = 600$.

  a. What proportion of salaries lies between $3789 and $4389?

  b. What proportion of salaries is greater than $2589?

51. Tobacco-Related Deaths. The World Health Organization states that tobacco is the second leading cause of death in the world. Every year, an average of 5 million people die of tobacco-related causes. Assume that the distribution is normal with mean $\mu = 5$ (in millions) and standard deviation $\sigma = 1$ (in millions).

  a. What is the probability of between 4 million and 7 million deaths?

  b. What is the probability of more than 6 million deaths?

52. Median Household Income. The Census Bureau reports that the median household income was $48,201 in 2006. Assume that the distribution of income is normal with mean $\mu = \$48,201$ and standard deviation $\sigma = \$16,000$.

    a. Find the probability that a randomly selected household has an income of greater than $80,201.

    b. What proportion of household incomes lie between $32,201 and $64,201?

53. Refer to Exercise 52. *What if* the mean μ was not $48,201 but some unknown value greater than $48,201? Describe whether the following probabilities you calculated in Exercise 52 would increase or decrease. Explain your reasoning.

    a. $P(X > \$80,201)$

    b. $P(X < \$32,201)$

    c. Challenge Exercise. $P(\$32,201 < X < \$64,201)$

54. Percentiles of the Uniform Distribution. The pth *percentile* of a continuous distribution is the value of X that is greater than or equal to $p\%$ of the values of X. Find the following percentiles of the uniform distribution in Example 6.26.

    a. 95th   **d.** 5th

    b. 90th   **e.** 10th

    c. 97.5th   **f.** 2.5th

55. Mean of the Uniform Distribution. Explain two ways that you could find the mean of the uniform distribution.

    a. Use the balance point method.

    b. Find the median (50th percentile), and argue that, since the distribution is rectangle shaped, the mean equals the median.

6.5 Standard Normal Distribution

OBJECTIVES By the end of this section, I will be able to . . .

  1 Find areas under the standard normal curve, given a Z-value.

  2 Find the standard normal Z-value, given an area.

1 Finding Areas Under the Standard Normal Curve for a Given Z-Value

Note: Understanding the techniques explained in this section will allow you to analyze a whole world of data sets, even those that are not themselves normally distributed (see the Central Limit Theorem in the next chapter). Beyond this chapter, these techniques help you to calculate and understand *p*-values in Chapters 9–13.

There are many populations in the world that are normally distributed, from test scores to student heights. But there is one very special normal distribution called the **standard normal distribution.** The mean and standard deviation of the standard normal distribution make it unique.

> The **standard normal (Z) distribution** is a normal distribution with
> - mean $\mu = 0$ and
> - standard deviation $\sigma = 1$.

Because of its importance, the standard normal random variable is always denoted as a capital Z. The graph of the standard normal random variable Z is given in Figure 6.26. The standard normal curve is symmetric about its mean $\mu = 0$.

FIGURE 6.26
Z is symmetric about its mean $\mu = 0$.

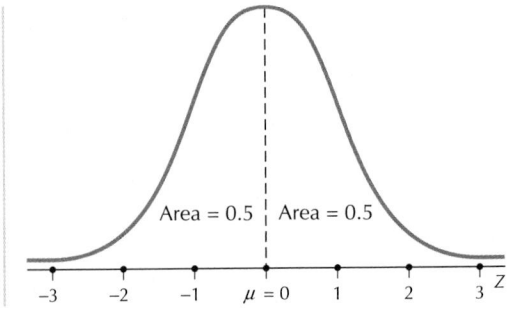

We will discuss two methods for finding probabilities associated with Z, using (a) the table for finding standard normal probabilities, called the **Z table,** and (b) technology. For the Z table, see Table C in the Appendix. *The Z table provides areas under the standard normal curve* <u>*to the left*</u> *of a specified value of Z, denoted as* Z_1 (see Figure 6.27).

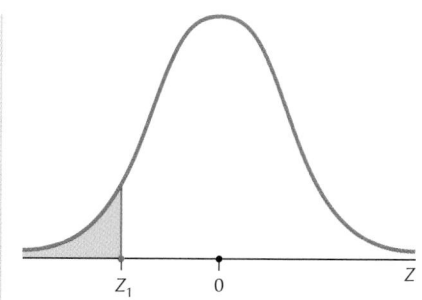

FIGURE 6.27
The Z table provides areas under the curve to the left of a specified value Z_1.

Note: Although your Z table contains only values between $Z = -3.49$ and $Z = 3.49$, there is no upper or lower limit to the values that Z may take. The curve essentially goes on forever in both the positive and the negative directions, always getting closer and closer to the horizontal axis but never quite touching it (there's a great plot for a love story in there somewhere).

Let's get acquainted with the Z table (see excerpt in Figure 6.29). Along the left side and across the top of the Z table are possible values of Z. These numbers, which in the table run from -3.49 to 3.49, are the values of Z found on the number line when you draw a graph. Down the left are the ones and tenths digits of the Z-value, and across the top is the hundredths digit. The body of the Z table contains areas (probabilities). These numbers, which run from 0.0002 to 0.9998, are areas under the standard normal curve that represent probabilities *to the left* of the specified value of Z. Table 6.6 shows the steps for finding areas under the standard normal curve, that is, for finding probabilities for specified values of Z.

Table 6.6 Steps for finding areas under the standard normal curve

Case 1	**Case 2**	**Case 3**
Find the area to the left of Z_1.	**Find the area to the right of Z_1.**	**Find the area between Z_1 and Z_2.**
Step 1 Draw the standard normal curve. Label the Z-value Z_1.	*Step 1* Draw the standard normal curve. Label the Z-value Z_1.	*Step 1* Draw the standard normal curve. Label the Z-values Z_1 and Z_2.
Step 2 Shade in the area to the left of Z_1.	*Step 2* Shade in the area to the right of Z_1.	*Step 2* Shade in the area between Z_1 and Z_2.
		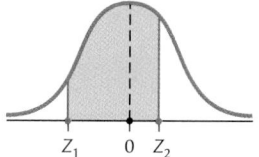
Step 3 Use the Z table to find the area to the left of Z_1.	*Step 3* Use the Z table to find the area to the left of Z_1. The area to the right of Z_1 is then equal to 1 − (area to the left of Z_1).	*Step 3* Use the Z table to find the area to the left of Z_1 and the area to the left of Z_2. The area between Z_1 and Z_2 is then equal to (area to the left of Z_2) − (area to the left of Z_1).

Example 6.29 Case 1: find the area to the left of a value of Z

Find the area to the left of $Z = 0.57$.

Solution

Step 1 First draw the standard normal curve and label $Z = 0.57$.

Step 2 Shade the area to the left of 0.57, as shown in Figure 6.28.

Step 3 Now, $Z = 0.57 = 0.5 + 0.07$. In the Z table, excerpted here as Figure 6.29, go down the left-hand column to 0.5 and select that row. Then go across the top row to 0.07 and select that column. The quantity at the intersection of this row and column represents the area to the left of $Z = 0.57$. That is, the area to the left of $Z = 0.57$ is 0.7157. ■

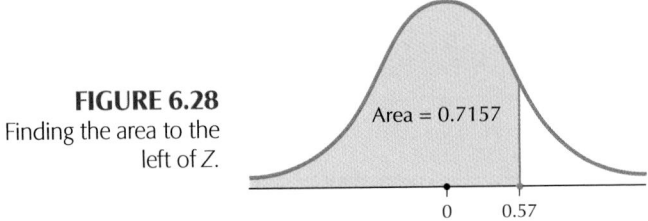

FIGURE 6.28
Finding the area to the left of Z.

Now You Can Do
Exercises 17–24.

Standard Normal Distribution

Z	0.00	0.01	0.02	0.03	0.04	0.05	0.06	0.07	0.08	0.09
0.0	0.5000	0.5040	0.5080	0.5120	0.5160	0.5199	0.5239	0.5279	0.5319	0.5359
0.1	0.5398	0.5438	0.5478	0.5517	0.5557	0.5596	0.5636	0.5675	0.5714	0.5753
0.2	0.5793	0.5832	0.5871	0.5910	0.5948	0.5987	0.6026	0.6064	0.6103	0.6141
0.3	0.6179	0.6217	0.6255	0.6293	0.6331	0.6368	0.6406	0.6443	0.6480	0.6517
0.4	0.6554	0.6591	0.6628	0.6664	0.6700	0.6736	0.6772	0.6808	0.6844	0.6879
0.5	0.6915	0.6950	0.6985	0.7019	0.7054	0.7088	0.7123	0.7157	0.7190	0.7224
0.6	0.7257	0.7291	0.7324	0.7357	0.7389	0.7422	0.7454	0.7486	0.7517	0.7549

FIGURE 6.29 Using the Z table to find the area to the left of Z.

Example 6.30 Case 2: find the area to the right of a value of Z

Find the area to the right of $Z = -1.25$.

Solution

Step 1 First draw the standard normal curve and label $Z = -1.25$.

Step 2 Shade the area to the right of -1.25, as shown in Figure 6.30.

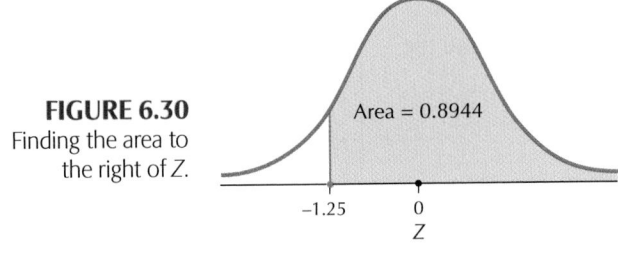

FIGURE 6.30
Finding the area to the right of Z.

Now You Can Do
Exercises 25–28.

Step 3 In the Z table, excerpted here as Figure 6.31, go down the left-hand column to -1.2 and select that row. Then go across the top row to 0.05 and select that column. The area to the left of $Z = -1.25$ is therefore 0.1056. From Case 2 in Table 6.6, the area to the right of -1.25 is then

$$1 - (\text{area to the left of } -1.25) = 1 - 0.1056 = 0.8944$$ ∎

Standard Normal Distribution

Z	0.00	0.01	0.02	0.03	0.04	0.05	0.06	0.07	0.08	0.09
-3.4	0.0003	0.0003	0.0003	0.0003	0.0003	0.0003	0.0003	0.0003	0.0003	0.0002
-3.3	0.0005	0.0005	0.0005	0.0004	0.0004	0.0004	0.0004	0.0004	0.0004	0.0003
-3.2	0.0007	0.0007	0.0006	0.0006	0.0006	0.0006	0.0006	0.0005	0.0005	0.0005
-3.1	0.0010	0.0009	0.0009	0.0009	0.0008	0.0008	0.0008	0.0008	0.0007	0.0007
-3.0	0.0013	0.0013	0.0013	0.0012	0.0012	0.0011	0.0011	0.0011	0.0010	0.0010
-1.4	0.0808	0.0793	0.0778	0.0764	0.0749	0.0735	0.0721	0.0708	0.0694	0.0681
-1.3	0.0968	0.0951	0.0934	0.0918	0.0901	0.0885	0.0869	0.0853	0.0838	0.0823
-1.2	0.1151	0.1131	0.1112	0.1093	0.1075	0.1056	0.1038	0.1020	0.1003	0.0985
-1.1	0.1357	0.1335	0.1314	0.1292	0.1271	0.1251	0.1230	0.1210	0.1190	0.1170
-1.0	0.1587	0.1562	0.1539	0.1515	0.1492	0.1469	0.1446	0.1423	0.1401	0.1379

FIGURE 6.31 Using the Z table to find the area to the right of Z.

 CAUTION Remember that, although values of Z can be negative, *probabilities (or areas) can never be negative.*

Developing Your Statistical Sense

Checking That Your Answer Makes Sense

As you are finding probabilities for values of Z, you should always be checking to see that your answer makes sense. For instance, in Example 6.30, what if we had added the table area to 1 rather than subtracted the table area from 1? We would know that this answer is incorrect because the resulting probability would then have exceeded 1, and no probability can ever exceed 1. ◢

Example 6.31 | Case 3: find the area between two Z-values (checking the accuracy of the Empirical Rule)

Recall that the Empirical Rule (page 148) states that about 68% of the area under the curve lies within 1 standard deviation of the mean, that is, between $\mu - \sigma$ and $\mu + \sigma$. Check this result for the standard normal distribution by using the Z table.

Solution

For the standard normal random variable Z, $\mu = 0$ and $\sigma = 1$, so that $\mu - \sigma = 0 - 1 = -1$ and $\mu + \sigma = 0 + 1 = 1$. Thus, using Case 3, we have $Z_1 = -1$ and $Z_2 = 1$.

Step 1 Draw the standard normal curve. Label the Z-values $Z_1 = -1$ and $Z_2 = 1$.

Step 2 Shade the area between -1 and 1, as shown in Figure 6.32a.

[Step 3] Find the area to the left of $Z_1 = -1$ and the area to the left of $Z_2 = 1$. The Z table gives these areas as follows: area to the left of $Z_1 = -1$ is 0.1587, and area to the left of $Z_2 = 1$ is 0.8413. We subtract the smaller area from the larger to give us the area between -1 and 1, as shown in Figures 6.32a–c.

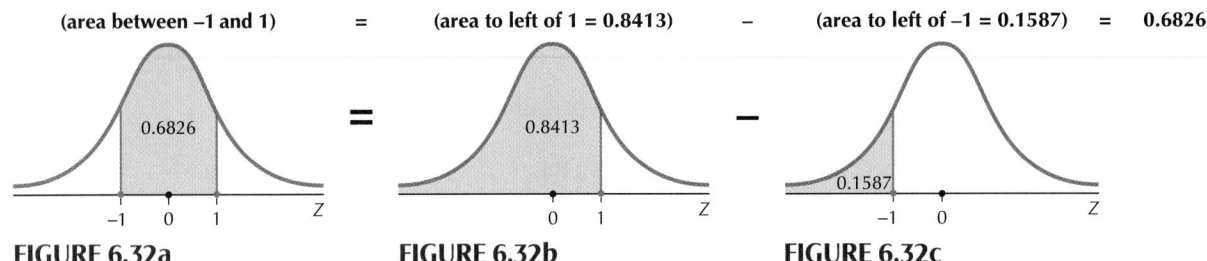

FIGURE 6.32a FIGURE 6.32b FIGURE 6.32c

Now You Can Do
Exercises 29–38.

Thus, the area under the Z curve within 1 standard deviation of the mean equals 0.6826. The Empirical Rule does very well for an approximation, missing the actual area by only 0.0026. Checking the accuracy of the Empirical Rule for other values of Z is left as an exercise. ■

Example 6.32 Using technology to find the area under a standard normal curve

In Example 6.29, we found the area under the standard normal curve to the left of $Z = 0.57$ to be 0.7157. Confirm this result using technology.

Solution

We follow the instructions in the Step-by-Step Technology Guide at the end of Section 6.6 (page 321). Figures 6.33a–c show the results from TI-83/84, Excel, and Minitab, respectively.

```
normalcdf(-1E99,
0.57,0,1)
        .7156611917
```

=NORMDIST(0.57,0,1,TRUE)

D	E	F
0.7156612		

Cumulative Distribution Function

Normal with mean = 0 and standard deviation = 1

```
  x    P( X <= x )
0.57     0.715661
```

FIGURE 6.33a TI-83/84 results.   FIGURE 6.33b Excel results.   FIGURE 6.33c Minitab results.

The word "cumulative" in the Minitab output means "less than or equal to." Each of these results provides the area under the standard normal curve for values of Z that are less than or equal to 0.57. Each technology rounds to a different number of decimal places. ■

Note that the areas we have been finding in this section may also be expressed as probabilities. For continuous distributions probabilities are represented by areas under the curve above an interval. Specifically, for the standard normal distribution, probability is represented as the area above an interval under the standard normal curve. For instance, in Example 6.29, we found that the area under the standard normal curve to the left of $Z = 0.57$ is 0.7157. This may be reexpressed as follows:

"The probability that Z is less than 0.57 is 0.7157"

or

$$P(Z < 0.57) = 0.7157$$

Example 6.33 | Expressing areas under the standard normal curve as probabilities

Reexpress the following areas as probabilities.
a. In Example 6.30, we found the area under the standard normal curve to the right of $Z = -1.25$ to be 0.8944.
b. In Example 6.31, we found the area under the standard normal curve between $Z = -1$ and $Z = 1$ to be 0.6826.

Solution
a. The probability that Z is greater than -1.25 is 0.8944. That is, $P(Z > -1.25) = 0.8944$.
b. The probability that Z is between -1 and 1 is 0.6826. That is, $P(-1 < Z < 1) = 0.6826$. ■

Now You Can Do
Exercises 39–50.

 The *Normal Density Curve* applet allows you to find areas associated with various values of Z.

2 Finding Standard Normal Z-Values for a Given Area

In previous examples, we were given a Z-value and asked to find an area or probability. What if we turned this around, so that we are given an area, and asked to find its associated Z-value? We may call these "backwards" problems because we would need to use the Z table in reverse (unless we are using technology to solve the problem). Let's check out an example.

Example 6.34 | Finding the Z-value with given area to its left

Find the Z-value with area 0.90 to its left.

Solution

[Step 1] Draw the standard normal curve. Label the Z-value Z_1.

[Step 2] Shade the area to the left of Z_1. Remember that *we are given an area and are looking for a value of Z.* Label the area to the left of Z_1 with the given area (0.90), as shown in Figure 6.34.

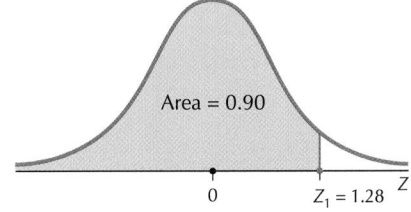

Area = 0.90

0 $Z_1 = 1.28$ Z

FIGURE 6.34 $Z_1 = 1.28$ is the value of Z with area 0.90 to the left of it.

Recall that the *rth percentile* is the value in the data set such that *r* percent of the data values fall at or below that value. Thus, $Z = 1.28$ represents the 90th percentile of the Z distribution, since it is greater than 90% of Z-values.

Now You Can Do
Exercises 51–58.

[Step 3] Look for 0.90 on the inside of the Z table (that is, in the body of the table), since the values *inside the table* represent areas. Because there is no 0.90 inside the table, by convention we take the area that is closest to 0.90, which is 0.8997. Next comes the trick of the backward problems, and the reason for that name. Move from 0.8997 to the left until you reach 1.2 in the first column, and then move up from 0.8997 until you get to 0.08 (see Figure 6.35). Putting these values together, we get $Z = 1.2 + 0.08 = 1.28$. ■

Standard Normal Distribution

Z	0.00	0.01	0.02	0.03	0.04	0.05	0.06	0.07	(0.08)	0.09
0.0	0.5000	0.5040	0.5080	0.5120	0.5160	0.5199	0.5239	0.5279	0.5319	0.5359
0.1	0.5398	0.5438	0.5478	0.5517	0.5557	0.5596	0.5636	0.5675	0.5714	0.5753
0.2	0.5793	0.5832	0.5871	0.5910	0.5948	0.5987	0.6026	0.6064	0.6103	0.6141
0.3	0.6179	0.6217	0.6255	0.6293	0.6331	0.6368	0.6406	0.6443	0.6480	0.6517
0.4	0.6554	0.6591	0.6628	0.6664	0.6700	0.6736	0.6772	0.6808	0.6844	0.6879
0.5	0.6915	0.6950	0.6985	0.7019	0.7054	0.7088	0.7123	0.7157	0.7190	0.7224
0.6	0.7257	0.7291	0.7324	0.7357	0.7389	0.7422	0.7454	0.7486	0.7517	0.7549
0.7	0.7580	0.7611	0.7642	0.7673	0.7704	0.7734	0.7764	0.7794	0.7823	0.7852
0.8	0.7881	0.7910	0.7939	0.7967	0.7995	0.8023	0.8051	0.8078	0.8106	0.8133
0.9	0.8159	0.8186	0.8212	0.8238	0.8264	0.8289	0.8315	0.8340	0.8365	0.8389
1.0	0.8413	0.8438	0.8461	0.8485	0.8508	0.8531	0.8554	0.8577	0.8599	0.8621
1.1	0.8643	0.8665	0.8686	0.8708	0.8729	0.8749	0.8770	0.8790	0.8810	0.8830
(1.2)	0.8849	0.8869	0.8888	0.8907	0.8925	0.8944	0.8962	0.8980	(0.8997)	0.9015
1.3	0.9032	0.9049	0.9066	0.9082	0.9099	0.9115	0.9131	0.9147	0.9162	0.9177

FIGURE 6.35 Using the Z table to find a value of Z for a given area.

Example 6.35 | Find the Z-value with given area to its right

Find the standard normal Z-value that has area 0.03 to the right of it.

Solution

Step 1 Draw the standard normal curve. Label the Z-value Z_1. Shade the area to the right of it with the given area, as shown in Figure 6.36.

Step 2 Since the Z table contains areas to the left of values of Z, we must find the area to the left of the specific value Z_1, as follows:

$$\text{area to left of } Z_1 = 1 - \text{area to right of } Z_1$$

So the area to the left of Z_1 is $1 - 0.03 = 0.97$.

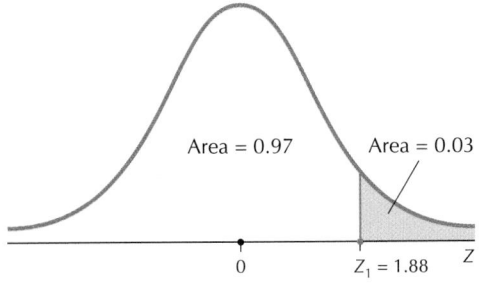

FIGURE 6.36 $Z_1 = 1.88$ has an area 0.03 to the right of it.

Now You Can Do
Now You Can Do
Exercises 59–66.

Step 3 Look up 0.97 on the inside of the Z table. The closest area is 0.9699. Move from 0.9699 to the left until you reach 1.8, and then move up from 0.9699 until you get to 0.08 (see Figure 6.37). Putting these values together, we get $Z = 1.8 + 0.08 = 1.88$. In other words, the Z-value with area 0.03 to its right is $Z = 1.88$. ∎

Standard Normal Distribution

Z	0.00	0.01	0.02	0.03	0.04	0.05	0.06	0.07	(0.08)	0.09
0.0	0.5000	0.5040	0.5080	0.5120	0.5160	0.5199	0.5239	0.5279	0.5319	0.5359
0.1	0.5398	0.5438	0.5478	0.5517	0.5557	0.5596	0.5636	0.5675	0.5714	0.5753
0.2	0.5793	0.5832	0.5871	0.5910	0.5948	0.5987	0.6026	0.6064	0.6103	0.6141
1.6	0.9452	0.9463	0.9474	0.9484	0.9495	0.9505	0.9515	0.9525	0.9535	0.9545
1.7	0.9554	0.9564	0.9573	0.9582	0.9591	0.9599	0.9608	0.9616	0.9625	0.9633
(1.8)	◀0.9641	0.9649	0.9656	0.9664	0.9671	0.9678	0.9686	0.9693	(0.9699)	0.9706
1.9	0.9713	0.9719	0.9726	0.9732	0.9738	0.9744	0.9750	0.9756	0.9761	0.9767

FIGURE 6.37 Using the Z table to find a value of Z for a given area.

When we learn statistical inference in later chapters, we will need to identify which Z-values divide the middle 90%, 95%, or 99% of the area under the standard normal curve from the tail area.

Example 6.36 Find the values of Z that mark the boundaries of the middle 95% of the area

Find the two values of Z that mark the boundaries of the middle 95% of the area under the standard normal curve.

Solution

Step 1 Draw the standard normal curve, showing the desired middle area (95%) with boundaries labeled as Z_1 and Z_2, as shown in Figure 6.38. By symmetry, there is area $= (1 - 0.95)/2 = 0.025$ in each tail.

Step 2 Look up 0.025 on the inside of the Z table. Find Z_1 by moving to the left and up from 0.025 in the Z table, giving us $Z_1 = -1.96$.

Step 3 Since the area in the right tail is 0.025 as well, the area to the left of Z_2 is $1 - 0.025 = 0.975$. Looking up 0.975 in the Z table gives us $Z_2 = 1.96$.

Note: Is it a coincidence that the two values of Z that determine the middle 95% of the area under the standard normal curve are 1.96 and −1.96? Not at all. Since the standard normal curve is symmetric about the mean 0, the values −1.96 and 1.96 that form the boundaries of the middle 95% must be *equidistant from zero.*

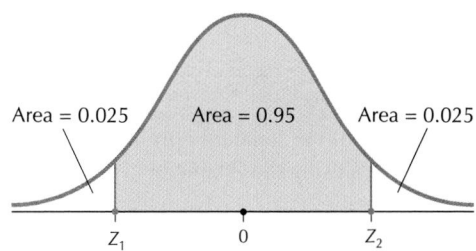

FIGURE 6.38 Z_1 and Z_2 mark the middle 95% of the Z distribution.

Now You Can Do
Exercises 67–70.

Thus, the two Z-values that mark the boundaries of the middle 95% of the area under the standard normal curve are −1.96 and 1.96. ∎

Example 6.37 Using technology to find values of *Z*, given an area

In Example 6.34, we found that the value of *Z* with area 0.90 to its left is $Z = 1.28$. Confirm this result using technology.

Solution

We follow the instructions in the Step-by-Step Technology Guide at the end of Section 6.6 (page 321). Figures 6.39a–c show the results from TI-83/84, Excel, and Minitab, respectively. ∎

FIGURE 6.39a TI-83/84 results.

=NORMINV(0.9,0,1)

D	E
1.2815516	

FIGURE 6.39b Excel results.

```
Inverse Cumulative
Distribution Function

Normal with mean = 0 and
standard deviation = 1

P( X <= x )          x
       0.9  1.28155
```

FIGURE 6.39c Minitab results.

Section 6.5 Summary

1 The standard normal distribution has mean $\mu = 0$ and standard deviation $\sigma = 1$. This distribution is often called the *Z* distribution. The *Z* table and technology can be used to find areas under the standard normal curve. In the *Z* table, the numbers on the outside are values of *Z*, and the numbers inside are areas to the left of values of *Z*.

2 The *Z* table and technology can also be used to find a value of *Z*, given a probability or an area under the curve.

Section 6.5 Exercises

CLARIFYING THE CONCEPTS
1. What is the value for the mean of the standard normal distribution?
2. What is the value for the standard deviation of the standard normal distribution?
3. True or false: The area under the *Z* curve to the right of $Z = 0$ is 0.5.
4. True or false: $P(Z = 0) = 0$.

PRACTICING THE TECHNIQUES
For Exercises 5–16, use the graph of the standard normal distribution to find the shaded area using the *Z* table or technology.

5.

6.

7.

8.

9.

10.

11.

12.

13.

14.

15.

16.

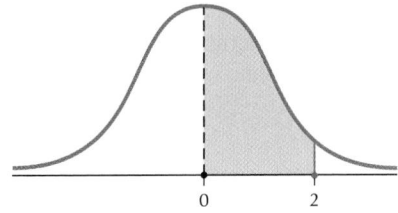

For Exercises 17–38,
  a. draw the graph.
  b. find the area using the Z table or technology.

Find the area under the standard normal curve that lies to the left of the following.

17. $Z = 1$
18. $Z = 2$
19. $Z = 3$
20. $Z = 0.5$
21. $Z = -2.7$
22. $Z = -0.9$
23. $Z = -0.2$
24. $Z = -1.2$

Find the area under the standard normal curve that lies to the right of the following.

25. $Z = 1.27$
26. $Z = 2.12$
27. $Z = -3.01$
28. $Z = -0.69$

Find the area under the standard normal curve that lies between the following.

29. $Z = 0$ and $Z = 1$
30. $Z = 1$ and $Z = 2$
31. $Z = 2$ and $Z = 3$
32. $Z = 1.28$ and $Z = 1.96$
33. $Z = -1$ and $Z = 0$
34. $Z = -2$ and $Z = -1$
35. $Z = -3$ and $Z = -2$
36. $Z = -1.96$ and $Z = -1.28$
37. $Z = -1.28$ and $Z = 1.28$
38. $Z = -2.01$ and $Z = 2.37$

For Exercises 39–50, find the indicated probability for the standard normal Z.
  a. Draw the graph.
  b. Find the area using the Z table or technology.

39. $P(Z = 0)$
40. $P(Z < 0)$
41. $P(Z < 10)$
42. $P(Z > 1.29)$
43. $P(Z < -2.17)$
44. $P(Z < 0.57)$
45. $P(-1.96 < Z < 1.96)$
46. $P(-2.07 < Z < 0.46)$
47. $P(-3.05 < Z < -0.94)$
48. $P(1.54 < Z < 2.20)$
49. $P(-100 < Z < 0)$
50. $P(-1.72 < Z < -1.57)$

For Exercises 51–58, find the Z-value with the following areas under the standard normal curve to its left. Draw the graph, then find the Z-value.

51. 0.3336
52. 0.4602
53. 0.3264
54. 0.4247
55. 0.95
56. 0.975
57. 0.98
58. 0.99

For Exercises 59–66, find the Z-value with the following areas under the standard normal curve to its right. Draw the graph, then find the Z-value.

59. 0.8078
60. 0.3085
61. 0.9788
62. 0.5120
63. 0.90
64. 0.975
65. 0.9988
66. 0.9998

For Exercises 67–70, find the values of Z that mark the boundaries of the indicated areas.

67. The middle 80%
68. The middle 95%
69. The middle 98%
70. The middle 85%
71. Find the 50th percentile of the Z distribution. (*Hint*: See margin note on page 307.)
72. Find the 75th percentile of the Z distribution.
73. Find the value of Z that is larger than 99.5% of all values of Z.
74. Find the value of Z that is smaller than 99.5% of all values of Z.

APPLYING THE CONCEPTS

75. **Checking the Empirical Rule.** Check the accuracy of the Empirical Rule for $Z = 2$. That is, find the area between $Z = -2$ and $Z = 2$ using the techniques of this section. Then compare your finding with the results for $Z = 2$ using the Empirical Rule.

76. **Checking the Empirical Rule.** Check the accuracy of the Empirical Rule for $Z = 3$. That is, find the area between $Z = -3$ and $Z = 3$ using the techniques of this section. Then compare your finding with the results for $Z = 3$ using the Empirical Rule.

77. **Without Tables or Technology.** Find the following areas *without* using the Z table or technology. The area to the left of $Z = -1.5$ is 0.0668.
 a. Find the area to the right of $Z = 1.5$.
 b. Find the area to the right of $Z = -1.5$.
 c. Find the area between $Z = -1.5$ and $Z = 1.5$.

78. **Without Tables or Technology.** Find the following areas *without* using the Z table or technology. The area to the right of $Z = 2.7$ is 0.0035.
 a. Find the area to the left of $Z = 2.7$.
 b. Find the area to the left of $Z = -2.7$.
 c. Find the area between $Z = -2.7$ and $Z = 2.7$.

79. **Values of Z That Mark the Middle 99%.** Find the two values of Z that contain the middle 99% of the area under the standard normal curve.

80. **Values of Z That Mark the Middle 90%.** Find the two values of Z that contain the middle 90% of the area under the standard normal curve.

Use the *Normal Density Curve* applet for Exercises 81 and 82.

81. Find the quartiles of the standard normal distribution. That is, find the 25th, 50th, and 75th percentiles of the standard normal distribution.

82. Use the applet to find the answers to the following exercises from this section.
 a. Exercise 6
 b. Exercise 7
 c. Exercise 17
 d. Exercise 18
 e. Exercise 28
 f. Exercise 29

6.6 Applications of the Normal Distribution

OBJECTIVES By the end of this section, I will be able to . . .

1 Compute probabilities for a given value of any normal random variable.

2 Find the appropriate value of any normal random variable, given an area or probability.

1 Finding Probabilities for Any Normal Distribution

The data in problems that we face in the real world do not usually follow the standard normal distribution, Z. Instead, a problem may be stated in terms of some normal random variable X that has a mean other than 0 or a standard deviation other than 1. In cases like these, X needs to be standardized to Z so that we can use the Section 6.5 techniques.

Standardizing X to Z

To standardize a normal random variable X, we *transform* that normal random variable X into the standard normal random variable Z.

Suppose that X is a normal random variable with population mean μ and population standard deviation σ. We standardize X by subtracting the mean μ and dividing by the standard deviation σ. The result of this transformation is the familiar **standard normal random variable Z.**

> **Standardizing a Normal Random Variable**
>
> Any normal random variable X can be transformed into the standard normal random variable Z by *standardizing X* using the formula
>
> $$Z = \frac{X - \mu}{\sigma}$$

To *standardize* things means to make them all the same. For example, college applicants take standardized tests so that the admissions officers can compare students according to a uniform assessment tool. Here, we standardize many different normal random variables X into the same standard normal Z.

The key here is the following: *for a given area of interest for a normal random variable X, the corresponding area after the transformation to Z is exactly the same.* For any normal random variable X

the area between a and b

is exactly the same as

the area between $\quad Z_a = \dfrac{(a - \mu)}{\sigma} \quad$ and $\quad Z_b = \dfrac{(b - \mu)}{\sigma} \quad$ (see Figure 6.40)

So we can solve problems about areas under the nonstandard normal X curve by using the corresponding area under the Z curve.

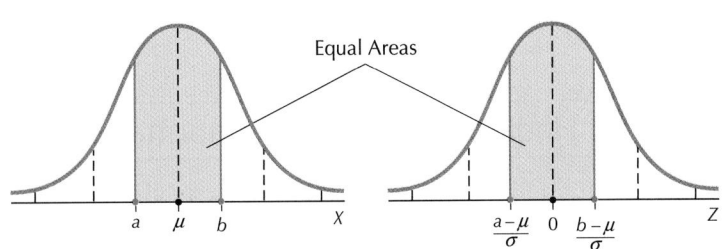

FIGURE 6.40 Corresponding areas are equal.

Example 6.38 April in Georgia

The state of Georgia reports that the average temperature statewide for the month of April from 1949 to 2010 was $\mu = 61.5°F$. Assume that the standard deviation is $\sigma = 8°F$ and that temperature in Georgia in April is normally distributed. Draw the normal curve for temperatures between 45.5°F and 77.5°F, and the corresponding Z curve. Find the probability that the temperature is between 45.5°F and 77.5°F in April in Georgia.

Solution

Here we have $a = 45.5$ and $b = 77.5$, giving us

$$Z_a = \frac{a - \mu}{\sigma} = \frac{45.5 - 61.5}{8} = -2 \quad \text{and} \quad Z_b = \frac{b - \mu}{\sigma} = \frac{77.5 - 61.5}{8} = 2$$

In Figure 6.41, the area between 45.5°F and 77.5°F is the same as between $Z = -2$ and $Z = 2$. In other words

$$P(45.5 < X < 77.5) = P(-2 < Z < 2)$$

FIGURE 6.41
Find the area under the Z curve and we have found the area under the X curve.

This is a Case 3 problem from Table 6.6. The Z table tells us that the area to the left of $Z_1 = -2$ is 0.0228, and the area to the left of $Z_2 = 2$ is 0.9772. The area between -2 and 2 is then equal to $0.9772 - 0.0228 = 0.9544$. The probability that temperature is between 45.5°F and 77.5°F in April in Georgia is 0.9544. ∎

Finding Probabilities for Any Normal Distribution

Step 1 Determine the random variable X, the mean μ, and the standard deviation σ. Draw the normal curve for X, and shade the desired area.

Step 2 Standardize by using the formula $Z = (X - \mu)/\sigma$ to find the values of Z corresponding to the X-values.

Step 3 Draw the standard normal curve and shade the area corresponding to the shaded area in the graph of X.

Step 4 Find the area under the standard normal curve using either the Z table or technology. This area is equal to the area under the normal curve for X drawn in Step 1.

Example 6.39 Finding probability for a normal random variable X

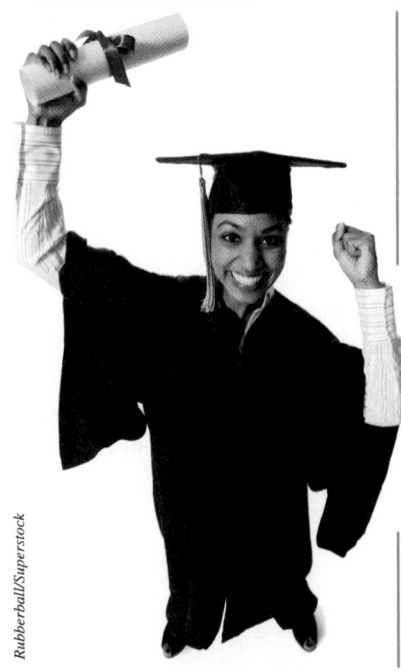

Suppose that you are in charge of ordering caps and gowns for senior graduation in May. You know that the heights of the population of students at your college are normally distributed with a mean of 68 inches (5 feet 8 inches) and a standard deviation of 3 inches. The gown manufacturer wants to know how many students will need to special-order their gowns because they are very tall. Find the proportion of students who are above 74 inches tall (6 feet 2 inches).

Solution

Step 1 **Determine X, μ, and σ.** We are given that the normal random variable $X =$ heights of students has mean $\mu = 68$ inches and standard deviation $\sigma = 3$ inches. In the center of the number line, mark the mean μ. Also mark on the number line the value of X that the problem is asking about. Figure 6.42 shows the graph of X (the heights of students) with the mean of 68 inches and the height of 74 inches marked.

Since you need to know the proportion of students taller than 74 inches, shade the area under the curve to the right of 74 inches. We can express this proportion as a probability, the probability that a randomly chosen student will be taller than 74 inches, or $P(X > 74)$. Just by looking at Figure 6.42 you should be able to get a rough idea of what the proportion of students taller than 74 inches will be. Certainly this proportion will be less than 50%, and probably pretty small. If you get an answer like "60%" for your proportion, you would surely know that it is wrong.

Remember that you may solve problems asking for proportions or percentages by finding the appropriate probability.

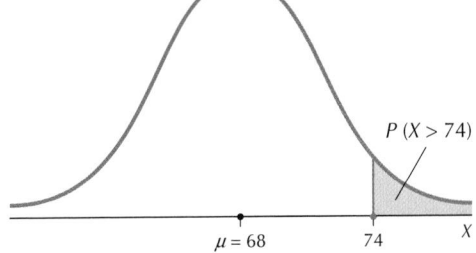

FIGURE 6.42
Graph of proportion of college students taller than 74 inches.

$P(X > 74)$

$\mu = 68$ 74 X

Step 2 **Standardize.** Now standardize the random variable X to the standard normal Z:

$$Z = \frac{X - \mu}{\sigma} = \frac{X - 68}{3}$$

Find the Z-value corresponding to the height of 74 inches:

$$\frac{74 - \mu}{\sigma} = \frac{74 - 68}{3} = 2$$

So the Z-value associated with 74 inches is 2, which indicates that the height of 74 inches is 2 standard deviations above the mean of 68 inches.

Step 3 **Draw the standard normal curve.** Heights above 74 inches are more than 2 standard deviations above the mean, so shade the area to the right of 2 in Figure 6.43. Now find the area to the right of $Z = 2$ using the methods of Section 6.5.

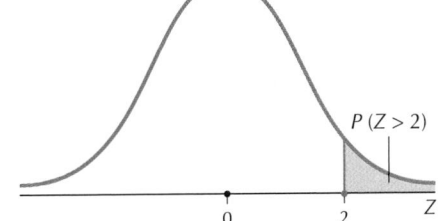

FIGURE 6.43
Graph of $P(Z > 2)$.

$P(Z > 2)$

0   2 Z

Step 4 **Find the area under the standard normal curve.** Figure 6.43 represents a Case 2 problem from Table 6.6 (page 303). The Z table tells us that the area to the left of $Z = 2.00$ is 0.9772. Thus, the area to the right is

$$P(Z > 2) = 1 - 0.9772 = 0.0228$$

The proportion of students taller than 74 inches is 0.0228, or 2.28%. Note that this value for $P(X > 74)$ agrees with our earlier intuition that the proportion was surely less than 50% and most likely very small. ∎

Now You Can Do
Exercises 3–9.

Example 6.40 Finding probability that X lies between two given values

Continuing the cap-and-gown problem, what percentage of students are between 60 and 70 inches tall?

Solution

Step 1 **Determine X, μ, and σ.** We have already seen that X = heights of students, $\mu = 68$ inches, and $\sigma = 3$ inches. Once again, draw a graph of the distribution of heights X, with the mean 68 inches in the middle, the height 60 inches to the left of the mean, and the height 70 inches to the right of the mean, as in Figure 6.44.

Step 2 **Standardize.** This is a "between" example, where two values of X are given, and we are asked to find the area between them. In this case, just standardize both of these values of X to get a Z-value for each:

$$Z = \frac{60 - \mu}{\sigma} = \frac{60 - 68}{3} \approx -2.67 \quad \text{and} \quad Z = \frac{70 - \mu}{\sigma} = \frac{70 - 68}{3} \approx 0.67$$

FIGURE 6.44
Graph of percentage of students between 60 and 70 inches tall.

$P(60 < X < 70)$

Step 3 **Draw the standard normal curve.** Draw a graph of Z, shading the area between $Z = -2.67$ and $Z = 0.67$, as shown in Figure 6.45. Again, the key is that the area between $Z = -2.67$ and $Z = 0.67$ is exactly the same as the area between $X = 60$ inches and $X = 70$ inches.

FIGURE 6.45
Graph of percentage of Z-values between -2.67 and 0.67.

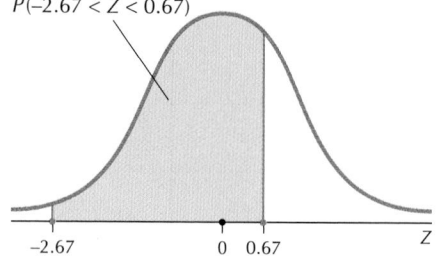

$P(-2.67 < Z < 0.67)$

Step 4 **Find area under the standard normal curve.** Figure 6.45 is a Case 3 problem from Table 6.6. Find the area to the left of 0.67, which is 0.7486, and the area to the left of -2.67, which is 0.0038. Subtracting the smaller from the larger gives us

$$P(-2.67 < Z < 0.67) = 0.7486 - 0.0038 = 0.7448$$

Thus, the percentage of students who are between 60 and 70 inches tall is 74.48%. ■

Now You Can Do
Exercises 10–14.

Check Your Answer! According to the Empirical Rule, almost all Z-values lie between -3 and 3, so it is unlikely that a randomly selected value of Z lies outside this range. You should remember this when you are doing your calculations. If you are standardizing a normal random variable X and get a very large Z-value (such as, say, 50), you should recheck your calculations because the probability that Z takes such a large value is very small.

2 Finding a Normal Data Value for a Given Area of Probability

Sometimes we are given a probability (or proportion or area), and we are asked to find the associated value of X. Questions like these are similar to the "backward" problems of Section 6.5, so called because we must use the Z table backward. Since the formula for standardizing X gives the value for Z, we need to use our algebra skills to find the equation for X: Start with the standard normal formula $Z = (X - \mu)/\sigma$. Multiply both sides by σ to get $Z\sigma = X - \mu$. Then add μ to both sides, giving us $X = Z\sigma + \mu$.

> **Finding Normal Data Values for a Given Area or Probability**
>
> *Step 1* **Determine X, μ, and σ, and draw the normal curve for X.** Shade the desired area. Mark the position of X_1, the unknown value of X.
>
> *Step 2* **Find the Z-value corresponding to the desired area.** Look up the area you identified in Step 1 on the *inside* of the Z table. If you do not find the exact value of your area, by convention choose the area that is closest.
>
> *Step 3* **Transform this value of Z into a value of X, which is the solution.** Use the formula $X_1 = Z\sigma + \mu$.

Example 6.41 | Finding a normal data value for a given area

Suppose that we wanted only the tallest 1% of our students to have to special-order gowns. What is the height at which tall students will have to special-order their gowns?

Solution

Notice that we are not asked to find a probability (or proportion or area). Instead, we are given a percentage (1%) and asked to find the value of X (the height) that is associated with this 1%.

[Step 1] **Determine X, μ, and σ, and draw the normal curve for X.** We already know that X = heights of students, μ = 68 inches, and σ = 3 inches. The value of X we are interested in refers to very tall students, so that X_1 will be at the far right of the distribution of X. Only 1% of students will be taller than this height, so the area to the right of X_1 is 0.01, as shown in Figure 6.46.

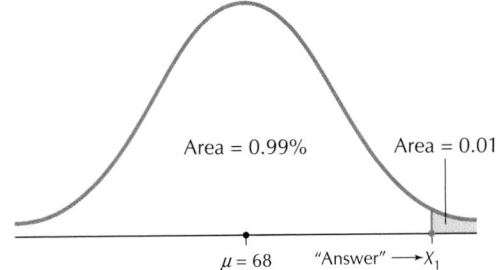

FIGURE 6.46
X_1 is the cutoff value (or critical value) of X, at which graduates will need to special-order their gowns.

Area = 0.99%   Area = 0.01

μ = 68   "Answer" →X_1

[Step 2] **Find the Z-value corresponding to the desired area.** The area to the right of X_1 equals 0.01, so that the area to the left of X_1 equals $1 - 0.01 = 0.99$. Looking up 0.99 on the inside of the Z table gives us Z = 2.33.

[Step 3] **Transform using the formula $X_1 = Z\sigma + \mu$.** We calculate

$$X_1 = Z\sigma + \mu = (2.33)(3) + 68 = 74.99$$

Now You Can Do
Exercises 15–22.

If we want only the tallest 1% of our students to have to special-order their gowns, the height at which tall students will have to special-order their gowns is 74.99 inches. ■

Example 6.42 | Finding the X-values that mark the boundaries of the middle 95% of X-values

Edmunds.com reported that the average amount that people were paying for a 2007 Toyota Camry XLE was $23,400. Let X = price, and assume that price follows a normal distribution with μ = $23,400 and σ = $1000. Find the prices that separate the middle 95% of 2007 Toyota Camry XLE prices from the bottom 2.5% and the top 2.5%.

Solution

Step 1   **Determine X, μ, and σ, and draw the normal curve for X.** Let X = price, μ = \$23,400, and σ = \$1000. The middle 95% of prices are delimited by X_1 and X_2, as shown in Figure 6.47.

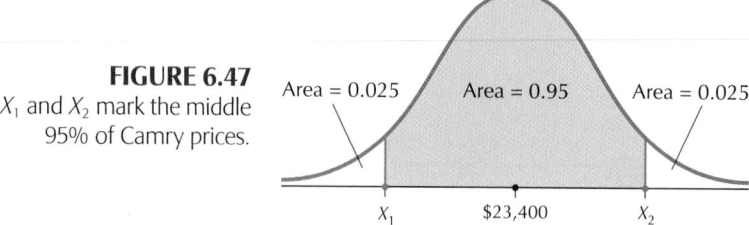

FIGURE 6.47
X_1 and X_2 mark the middle 95% of Camry prices.

Area = 0.025   Area = 0.95   Area = 0.025

X_1 \$23,400 X_2

Step 2   **Find the Z-values corresponding to the desired area.** The area to the left of X_1 equals 0.025, and the area to the left of X_2 equals 0.975. Looking up area 0.025 on the inside of the Z table gives us $Z_1 = -1.96$. Looking up area 0.975 on the inside of the Z table gives us $Z_2 = 1.96$.

Step 3   **Transform using the formula $X_1 = Z\sigma + \mu$.** We calculate

$$X_1 = Z_1\sigma + \mu = (-1.96)(1000) + 23{,}400 = 21{,}440$$

$$X_2 = Z_2\sigma + \mu = (1.96)(1000) + 23{,}400 = 25{,}360$$

Now You Can Do
Exercises 23–26.

The prices that separate the middle 95% of 2007 Toyota Camry XLE prices from the bottom 2.5% of prices and the top 2.5% of prices are \$21,440 and \$25,360. ■

 WHAT IF?

How Change in Spread Affects Camry Prices

In Example 6.42, *what if* we ask the same question again, but this time the standard deviation σ of 2007 Toyota Camry XLE prices is not \$1000 but some value less than \$1000. How and why would this affect the following?

a.   The values Z_1 and Z_2 found in Step 2

b.   The value X_1 separating the middle 95% of prices from the bottom 2.5%

c.   The value X_2 separating the middle 95% of prices from the top 2.5%

Solution

Figure 6.48 illustrates the distribution of 2007 Toyota Camry XLE prices, where everything is the same as in Figure 6.47 except that the standard deviation of the prices is smaller by an unknown amount. Thus, the spread of the distribution is smaller.

a.   Since we are still asking for the middle 95% of prices, the Z-values remain the same, -1.96 and 1.96.

b.   Reexpress the formula $X_1 = Z_1\sigma + \mu$ as $X_1 = \$23{,}400 - 1.96 \cdot \sigma$. If σ is smaller than \$1000, then the quantity $1.96 \cdot \sigma$, which represents the difference between the mean price and X_1, will also be smaller.

Since X_1 is less than the mean $\mu = \$23{,}400$, the smaller difference between the mean price and X_1 leads us to conclude that X_1 will be *larger* than in Example 6.42. For example, if the new standard deviation is $\sigma = \$500$, then $X_1 = \$23{,}400 - 1.96 \cdot 500 = \$22{,}420$, which is larger than the \$21,440 in Example 6.42.

c.   Similarly, a smaller σ means a smaller quantity $1.96 \cdot \sigma$, which means that $X_2 = \$23{,}400 + 1.96 \cdot \sigma$ will be closer to the mean $\mu = \$23{,}400$. Since X_2 is larger than the mean, the new value for X_2 will be *smaller* than in Example 6.42.

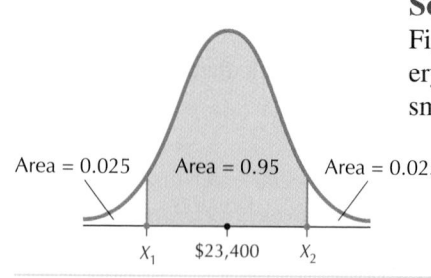

Area = 0.025   Area = 0.95   Area = 0.025

X_1 \$23,400 X_2

FIGURE 6.48 The middle 95% of prices now has less spread.

The *Normal Density Curve* applet allows you to find areas associated with various values of any normal random variable.

Example 6.43   Normal probabilities and percentiles using technology

Applying the information on Toyota Camry prices from Example 6.42, use the TI-83/84, Excel, or Minitab to find the following.

a. The proportion of 2007 Camry XLEs costing between $22,000 and $24,000, $P(22{,}000 \le X \le 24{,}000)$

b. The 99th percentile of Camry XLE prices, that is, find the value of X, namely, X_1, such that $P(X \le X_1) = 0.99$

Solution

The instructions for finding these quantities are given in the Step-by-Step Technology Guide at the end of this section (page 321).

TI-83/84

a. Figure 6.49 shows that $P(22{,}000 \le X \le 24{,}000) = 0.6449902243 \approx 0.6450$.

b. Figure 6.50 shows that the value for X_1 such that $P(X \le X_1) = 0.99$ is given by $X_1 = \$25{,}726.34788 \approx \$25{,}726.35$.

FIGURE 6.49 TI-83/84: Finding a probability.

FIGURE 6.50 TI-83/84: Finding a value of X.

Excel

a. Excel provides the cumulative probabilities $P(X \le 22{,}000)$ in Figure 6.51 and $P(X \le 24{,}000)$ in Figure 6.52. To find $P(22{,}000 \le X \le 24{,}000)$, we subtract $P(X \le 22{,}000)$ from $P(X \le 24{,}000)$:

$$P(22{,}000 \le X \le 24{,}000) = 0.725746882 - 0.080756659 = 0.644990223$$

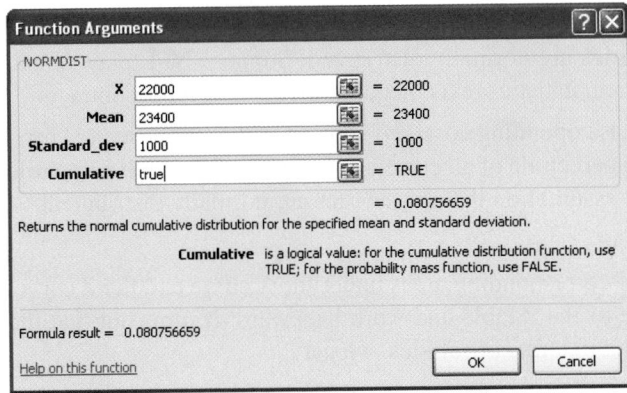

FIGURE 6.51 Excel: $P(x \le 22{,}000)$.

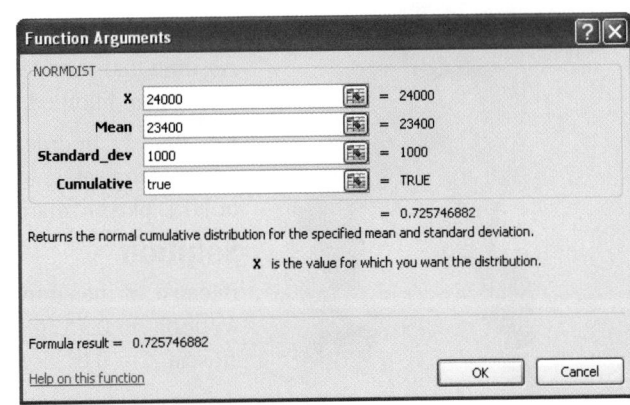

FIGURE 6.52 Excel: $P(x \le 24{,}000)$.

b. Excel provides the result shown in Figure 6.53, $X_1 = \$25{,}726.34787 \approx \$25{,}726.35$.

FIGURE 6.53 Excel: Finding a value of X.

Minitab

a. Like Excel, Minitab asks you to take the difference of two cumulative probabilities, $P(X \leq 22{,}000)$ in Figure 6.54 and $P(X \leq 24{,}000)$ in Figure 6.55:

$$P(22{,}000 \leq X \leq 24{,}000) = 0.725747 - 0.0807567 = 0.6449903 \approx 0.6450$$

```
Cumulative Distribution Function
Normal with mean = 23400 and standard deviation = 1000

    x    P( X <= x )
22000    0.0807567
```

FIGURE 6.54 Minitab: $P(x \leq 22{,}000)$.

```
Cumulative Distribution Function
Normal with mean = 23400 and standard deviation = 1000

    x    P( X <= x )
24000    0.725747
```

FIGURE 6.55 Minitab: $P(x \leq 24{,}000)$.

b. The results are given in Figure 6.56; $X_1 = \$25{,}726.30$. ∎

```
Inverse Cumulative Distribution Function
Normal with mean = 23400 and standard deviation = 1000

P( X <= x )        x
       0.99   25726.3
```

FIGURE 6.56 Minitab: Finding a value of X.

CASE STUDY

Be Careful What You Assume: National Football League Salaries

The following are the summary characteristics for the population of all NFL salaries, as of the 2009 season:

$$\text{population mean salary } \mu = \$1{,}858{,}000$$
$$\text{population standard deviation of salary } \sigma = \$2{,}580{,}000$$

Assume that the football salaries are normally distributed. Suppose NFL players and owners are huddled around their statistics texts, negotiating the new NFL contract.

Problem 1. In order to decrease operating costs, NFL owners have proposed to "cap" a team's top salary at the 75th percentile of all current salaries. Find the 75th percentile of NFL player salaries on the assumption that the salaries are normally distributed.

Solution

Because of the equivalence of corresponding areas under the X curve and the Z curve, we look up 0.75 in the inside of the Z table and work backward. It turns out that the closest $Z = 0.67$. Reexpressing in terms of salaries, we get

$$X_1 = Z\sigma + \mu = (0.67)(2{,}580{,}000) + 1{,}858{,}000 \approx \$3{,}586{,}600$$

The owners feel that approximately $3.6 million per year is plenty of compensation to play football.

Problem 2. The players' union states that they will agree to the cap in Problem 1 only if the owners add a bonus to the salaries of the lowest-paid players, as measured by the 10th percentile. Find the 10th percentile of the NFL player salaries on the assumption that the salaries are normally distributed.

Solution

To find the 10th percentile, we look up 0.10 in the inside of the Z table and work backward. Here we get $Z = -1.28$. Reexpressing in terms of salaries we get

$$X_1 = Z\sigma + \mu = (-1.28)(2{,}580{,}000) + 1{,}858{,}000 \approx -\$1{,}444{,}400$$

What went wrong? How could a salary be negative? Figure 6.57 provides a histogram (in green) of the distribution of actual player salaries, overlaid with the assumed normal distribution (in orange) of player salaries. Both are centered at $1,858,000 (triangle), and both have standard deviation $2,580,000, but that is about all the two distributions have in common. Clearly, we cannot assume that the salaries are normally distributed.

The salaries are in fact quite right-skewed and decidedly non-normal. Our finding that the 10th percentile salary is negative is a direct result of the inappropriate assumption of normality. *Be careful what you assume.* We provide methods for assessing the normality of a data set in Chapter 7. ∎

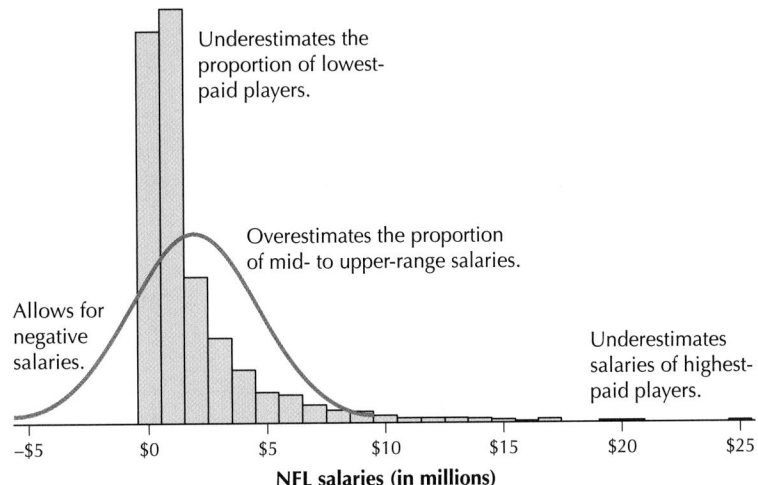

FIGURE 6.57 The assumption of normality is not appropriate here and leads to the errors shown in the graph.

STEP-BY-STEP TECHNOLOGY GUIDE: Finding Areas, Probabilities, and Percentiles for Any Normal Distribution

TI-83/84

Finding Areas or Probabilities for Any Normal Distribution
Step 1 Press **2ⁿᵈ**, then **DISTR** (the **VARS** key).
Step 2 Press **2** to choose **normalcdf(**.
Step 3 On the home screen, enter the smaller value of X, comma, the larger value of X, comma, the mean of X, comma, the standard deviation of X, then close parenthesis. See Figure 6.49 (page 319).
Step 4 Press **ENTER**.

Note: When finding the area to the right of a value of X, use **1E99** as the larger value. When finding the area to the left of a value of X, use **-1E99** as the smaller value. Also, the shortcut for using the standard normal distribution is to specify only the lower and higher values of X. If you enter only two values, the calculator assumes you want the standard normal distribution.

Finding Percentiles for Any Normal Distribution
Step 1   Press **2ⁿᵈ**, then **DISTR** (the **VARS** key).
Step 2   Press **3** to choose **invNorm(.**
Step 3   On the home screen, enter the probability value or area, then the mean of X, then the standard deviation of X, then close parenthesis. See Figure 6.50 (see page 319).
Step 4   Press **ENTER.**

Note: A shortcut for finding standard normal percentiles is to enter only the value of X for this function, in which case the calculator assumes you want the standard normal distribution.

Note: Not all TI-83/84's have the **invNorm** function.

EXCEL

Finding Areas or Probabilities for Any Normal Distribution
Step 1   Select cell **A1** and click the **Insert Function** icon F_x.
Step 2   In the **Search for a function**, type **NORMDIST**, click **GO**, then **OK**.
Step 3   For **X**, enter the X-value that you want to find the probability for. For **Mean,** enter the value of μ. For **Standard_ dev**, enter the value of σ. For **Cumulative**, always enter **true**. Click **OK**. See Figure 6.51 (page 319).
Step 4   Excel provides the cumulative probability, $P(X \leq X_1)$ (see Example 6.43). If you need to find $P(X > X_1)$, subtract the result from 1. If you need to find $P(X_1 \leq X \leq X_2)$, find the two

cumulative probabilities, and subtract the lesser from the greater, as in Example 6.43.

Finding Percentiles for Any Normal Distribution
Step 1   Select cell **A1** and click the **Insert Function** icon f_x.
Step 2   In the **Search for a function**, type **NORMINV**, click **GO**, then **OK**.
Step 3   For **Probability**, enter the desired percentile in decimal form (for example, 0.99). For **Mean,** enter the value of μ. For **Standard_dev**, enter the value of σ. Click **OK**. See Figure 6.53 (page 320).

MINITAB

Finding Areas or Probabilities for Any Normal Distribution
Step 1   Click **Calc > Probability Distributions > Normal**.
Step 2   Select **Cumulative Probability**, enter the mean μ and standard deviation σ.
Step 3   Select **Input Constant**, enter the X-value that you want to find the probability for.
Step 4   Minitab provides the cumulative probability, $P(X \leq X_1)$ (see Figure 6.54 on page 320). If you need to find $P(X > X_1)$, subtract the result from 1. If you need to find $P(X_1 \leq X \leq X_2)$,

find the two cumulative probabilities, and subtract the lesser from the greater, as in Example 6.43.

Finding Percentiles for Any Normal Distribution
Step 1   Click **Calc > Probability Distributions > Normal**.
Step 2   Select **Inverse Cumulative Probability**, and enter the mean μ and standard deviation σ.
Step 3   Select **Input Constant**. For the constant, enter the desired percentile in decimal form (for example, 0.99). See Figure 6.56 (page 320).

CRUNCHIT!

We will use the Toyota Camry data from Example 6.43 (page 319).

The answer will then be 0.7257468822 − 0.0807566592 = 0.644990223.

Finding Areas or Probabilities for Any Normal Distribution
Step 1   Click **Distribution calculator . . . Normal**.
Step 2   For **mean** enter **23400**. For **sd** enter the standard deviation **1000**.
Step 3   Select ≤ and enter **24000**. Click **Calculate**. The result shown is $P(X \leq 24{,}000) = 0.7257468822$.
Step 4   Delete **24000** and enter **22000**. Click **Calculate**. The result shown is $P(X \leq 22{,}000) = 0.0807566592$.

Finding Percentiles for Any Normal Distribution
Step 1   Click **Distribution calculator . . . Normal**.
Step 2   For **mean** enter **23400**. For **sd** enter the standard deviation **1000**.
Step 3   Select **Quantile**. Enter the desired percentile in decimal form. For the 99ᵗʰ percentile, enter **0.99** and click **Calculate**.

Section 6.6 Summary

1 Section 6.6 showed how to solve normal probability problems for any conceivable normal random variable by first standardizing X into Z and then using the methods of Section 6.5. Methods for finding probabilities for a given value of the normal random variable X were discussed.

2 For any normal probability distribution, values of X can be found for given probabilities using the formula $X_1 = Z\sigma + \mu$.

Section 6.6 Exercises

CLARIFYING THE CONCEPTS

1. What does the word *standardize* mean? Explain how we use standardization in solving normal probability problems.

2. When finding a data value for a specified probability, explain why we can't just report the Z-value but must transform back to the original normal distribution.

PRACTICING THE TECHNIQUES

For Exercises 3–14, assume that the random variable X is normally distributed with mean $\mu = 70$ and standard deviation $\sigma = 10$. Draw a graph of the normal curve with the desired probability and value of X indicated. Find the indicated probabilities by standardizing X to Z.

3. $P(X > 70)$
4. $P(X > 80)$
5. $P(X < 80)$
6. $P(X > 95)$
7. $P(X \geq 95)$
8. $P(X \geq 60)$
9. $P(X \geq 55)$
10. $P(60 < X < 100)$
11. $P(60 \leq X \leq 100)$
12. $P(90 \leq X \leq 100)$
13. $P(90 \leq X \leq 91)$
14. $P(60 \leq X \leq 70)$

For Exercises 15–26, assume that the random variable X is normally distributed with mean $\mu = 70$ and standard deviation $\sigma = 10$. Draw a graph of the normal curve with the desired probability and value of X indicated. Find the indicated values of X using the formula $X_1 = Z\sigma + \mu$.

15. The value of X larger than 95% of all X-values (that is, the 95th percentile)
16. The value of X smaller than 95% of all X-values
17. The value of X larger than 97.5% of all X-values
18. The value of X smaller than 97.5% of all X-values
19. The 1st percentile
20. The 99th percentile (note that the 1st and 99th percentiles are symmetric values of X that contain the central 98% of the area under the curve between them)
21. The 0.5th percentile
22. The 99.5th percentile
23. The two symmetric values of X that contain the central 90% of X-values between them
24. The two symmetric values of X that contain the central 95% of X-values between them
25. The two symmetric values of X that contain the central 98% of X-values between them
26. The two symmetric values of X that contain the central 99% of X-values between them

APPLYING THE CONCEPTS

27. **Hungry Babies.** Six-week-old babies consume a mean of $\mu = 15$ ounces of milk per day, with a standard deviation σ of 2 ounces. Assume that the distribution is normal. Find the probability that a randomly chosen baby consumes the following amounts of milk per day.
    a. Less than 15 ounces
    b. More than 17 ounces
    c. Between 17 and 19 ounces

28. **Trading Volume.** The Associated Press reports that the mean trading volume for equity and index options contracts was 3.6 million in July 2007. Assume that the distribution is normal with mean $\mu = 3.6$ (in millions) and standard deviation $\sigma = 0.5$ (in millions). Find the probability that a randomly selected day of trading has the following volume.
    a. More than 4.1 million contracts
    b. Less than 4.1 million contracts
    c. Between 3.6 million and 4.1 million contracts

29. **Windy Frisco.** The mean wind speed in San Francisco is 13.6 mph in July, according to the U.S. National Oceanic and Atmospheric Administration. Suppose that the distribution of the wind speed in July in San Francisco is normal with mean $\mu = 13.6$ mph and standard deviation $\sigma = 6$ mph. Find the probability that a randomly chosen day in July has the following wind speeds.
    a. 7.2 mph or less
    b. Greater than 20 mph
    c. Between 15 and 20 mph
    d. Tours to Alcatraz Island are canceled if the day is too windy, specifically if the wind speed is higher than 99% of all other wind speeds in July. Find the cutoff wind speed.
    e. Suppose that a particular day in July has no wind at all. Should this be considered unusual? On what do you base your answer?

30. **Viewers of *60 Minutes*.** Nielsen Media Research reported that, for the week ending October 18, 2010, 16 million viewers watched the television show *60 Minutes*. Suppose that the distribution of viewers of *60 Minutes* is normal with mean $\mu = 12$ million and standard deviation $\sigma = 4$ million. Find the probability that the following numbers of people will watch *60 Minutes*.
    a. Fewer than 10 million people
    b. Between 10 million and 11 million people
    c. More than 11 million people
    d. Find the number of viewers that represents the 75th percentile.
    e. On one particular night, 28 million people watched *60 Minutes*. Is this unusual? On what do you base your answer?

31. **Hungry Babies.** Refer to Exercise 27
    a. Find the amount of milk X greater than 95% of all values of X.

b. Find the amount of milk X less than 95% of all values of X.

c. Compute the two symmetric amounts of milk X_1 and X_2 that contain the central 90% of X-values between them.

32. Trading Volume. Refer to Exercise 28.

a. Calculate the trading volume X greater than 99% of all values of X.

b. Compute the trading volume X less than 99% of all values of X.

c. Find the two symmetric trading volumes X_1 and X_2 that contain the central 98% of X-values between them.

33. Windy Frisco. Refer to Exercise 29.

a. Tours to Alcatraz Island are canceled if the day is too windy, specifically if the wind speed is higher than 90% of all other wind speeds in July. Find the cutoff wind speed.

b. Find the 10th percentile of wind speeds.

c. Calculate the two symmetric wind speeds X_1 and X_2 that contain the central 80% of X-values between them.

d. Suppose that a particular day in July has no wind at all. Should this be considered unusual? Use the Z-score method for outliers to determine the answer.

34. Viewers of *60 Minutes*. Refer to Exercise 30.

a. A sponsor will withdraw its support if the number of viewers falls below the 5th percentile. Find the 5th percentile.

b. Suppose the network can charge more for advertising if the number of viewers is greater than the 95th percentile. Compute the 95th percentile.

c. Calculate the two symmetric numbers of viewers X_1 and X_2 that contain the central 90% of X-values between them.

d. On one particular night, 24 million people watched *60 Minutes*. Is this unusual? Use the Z-score method for outliers to determine the answer.

35. Math Scores. The National Center for Education Statistics reports that mean scores on the standardized math test for eighth-graders in 2009 increased slightly from those for previous years. The mean score in 2009 was $\mu = 283$. Assume $\sigma = 10$.

a. Find the probability that the test score of a randomly selected eighth-grader was greater than 290.

b. What proportion of test scores was between 295 and 300?

c. Suppose students who scored at the 5th percentile or lower could not graduate. Find the 5th percentile test score.

d. Suppose you know someone who scored 258 on the test. Is this unusual? On what do you base your answer?

36. Long-Lived Tortoise. The Philadelphia Zoo reports that the mean life span of a Galápagos tortoise is 100 years. Assume that their life span follows a normal distribution with mean $\mu = 100$ years and standard deviation $\sigma = 15$ years.

a. Find the probability that a randomly chosen tortoise will live longer than 70 years.

b. What percentage of tortoises live longer than 125 years?

c. Suppose that a particular zoo claims to have a tortoise older than 99% of all such tortoises. Find the age of this tortoise.

d. A particular tortoise is 150 years old. Is this unusual? On what do you base your answer?

37. Hospital Patient Length of Stays. A study of Pennsylvania hospitals showed that the mean patient length of stay in 2001 was 4.87 days with a standard deviation of 0.97 day. Assume that the distribution of patient length of stays is normal.

a. Find the probability that a randomly selected patient has a length of stay of greater than 7 days.

b. What proportion of patient lengths of stay are between 3 and 5 days?

c. Find the 50th percentile of patient lengths of stay. What is the relationship between the mean and the median for normal distributions?

d. A particular patient had a length of stay of 8 days. Determine whether this is unusual.

38. Tobacco-Related Deaths. The World Health Organization states that tobacco is the second leading cause of death in the world. Every year, a mean of 5 million people die of tobacco-related causes. Assume that the distribution is normal with $\mu = 5$ million and $\sigma = 2$ million.

a. Find the probability that more than 4 million people will die of tobacco-related causes in a particular year.

b. Find the 25th percentile of the distribution of tobacco-related deaths.

c. Is there a way you can use symmetry and your answer to part **(c)** to find the 75th percentile of the distribution of tobacco-related deaths?

d. In one particular year, 8 million people died from tobacco-related causes. Determine whether this is unusual.

39. Grade Inflation. Many educators are concerned about grade inflation. One study showed that one low-SAT-score high school (with mean combined SAT score = 750) had a higher mean grade point average (mean GPA = 3.6) than a high-SAT-score school (with mean combined SAT score = 1050 and mean GPA = 2.6).[25] Assume that GPA at the high-SAT-score school is normally distributed with mean $\mu = 2.6$ and standard deviation $\sigma = 0.5$.

a. What is the probability that a randomly selected student at the high-SAT-score school has a GPA of 3.6 or higher?

b. What percentage of students at the school have a GPA of 3.0 or higher?

c. Suppose that students with the lowest 5% of GPAs get put on academic probation. Find the cutoff grade.

d. One particular student had a GPA of 4.0. Is this unusual? Explain your answer.

40. Patriots Passing. ESPN reports that the 2009 New England Patriots football team had a mean of 5.9 yards passing per passing play. Assume that the distribution of yards passing per play is normal with $\mu = 5.9$ yards and $\sigma = 6$ yards.

a. What is the probability that a randomly chosen passing play loses yardage?

b. What proportion of passing plays gain between 5 and 10 yards?

c. Between which two yardage amounts do the central 95% of passing plays fall?

d. Determine whether a passing play that went for 30 yards is unusual.

41. Stock Shares Traded. The mean number of shares traded on the New York Stock Exchange in March 2010 was 2.1 billion per day. Assume that the distribution of shares traded is normal with $\mu = 2.1$ and $\sigma = 0.6$ (both in billions of shares).

a. Find the probability that the number of shares traded on a randomly selected day falls below 0.3 billion.

b. What proportion of days finds the volume of shares traded between 1 billion and 2 billion?

c. A slow trading day has fewer shares traded than 99% of all other days. Find the number of shares traded that represents this amount.

d. Determine whether 27 billion shares traded is unusual.

42. Sociology Salaries. Sociology graduates, upon entering the workforce, earn a mean salary of $30,000 with a standard deviation of $4000.

a. Jessica is an honors sociology student. Upon graduation she would like to take a job that starts at $40,000. What is the probability that a randomly chosen salary exceeds $40,000?

b. Jeremy squeezed through his sociology major with a C– average. He would take any job he could lay his hands on, as long as it wasn't tossing fries, which he had been doing for four years. What is the probability that a randomly chosen salary is less than $22,000?

c. Jolene would like to earn between $27,000 and $38,000 when she graduates. What is the probability that a randomly chosen salary lies within this range?

d. Josefina didn't pull those all-nighters for nothing. She would like to make between $32,000 and $39,000. What is the probability that a randomly chosen salary lies within this range?

e. Jamal looks forward to spending that big salary after graduation. Anything over $27,000 would do just fine. What is the probability that a randomly chosen salary exceeds $27,000?

f. Jillian struggled through college, having to care for her children while holding down a full-time job. She hopes that her salary is at least at the 10th percentile. Find the 10th percentile of sociology salaries.

g. Jung is not sure how much he will make upon graduation. He would be happy if his salary was in the middle 60% of salaries. Find the two salaries that are the cutoff values for the middle 60% of salaries.

43. Emotional Maturity. An emotional maturity test was administered at a local university hospital. The scores are normally distributed with a mean of 100 and a standard deviation of 10.

a. Find the probability that a randomly chosen subject scored better than average.

b. Find the probability that a randomly chosen subject scored lower than 72.

c. Find the probability that a randomly chosen subject scored between 95 and 101.

d. Find the scores that mark off the middle 95% of scores.

44. Calories per Gram. The histogram shows the number of calories per gram for 961 food items. Assume that the population mean calories per gram is 2.25 with a standard deviation of 2.

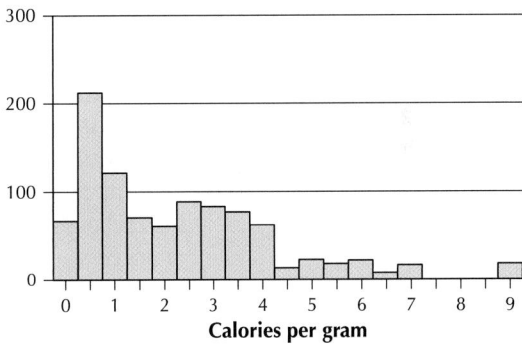

a. Assuming that the data follow a normal distribution, what is the 5th percentile of calories per gram?

b. Comment on whether your answer from **(a)** makes any sense.

c. The actual 5th percentile for this data set is 0.2 calorie per gram. Looking at the histogram, does this make more sense than your answer from **(a)**?

d. Why is your answer in **(a)** wrong?

Use the *Normal Density Curve* applet for Exercises 45 and 46.

45. Use the applet to find the answers to the following exercises from this section.

a. Exercise 42(a)

b. Exercise 42(b)

c. Exercise 42(c)

d. Exercise 42(d)

46. Use the applet to find the answers to the following exercises from this section.

a. Exercise 43(b)

b. Exercise 43(c)

c. Exercise 43(d)

6.7 Normal Approximation to the Binomial Probability Distribution

OBJECTIVE By the end of this section, I will be able to . . .

1 Use the normal distribution to approximate probabilities of the binomial distribution.

1 Using the Normal Distribution to Approximate Probabilities of the Binomial Distribution

Recall from Section 6.2 that a binomial experiment satisfies the following four requirements: (1) Each trial must have two possible outcomes. (2) There is a fixed number of trials, n. (3) The experimental outcomes are independent. (4) The probability of observing a success is the same from trial to trial.

For certain values of n and p, it may be inconvenient to calculate probabilities for the binomial distribution. For example, if $n = 100$ and $p = 0.5$, it may be tedious to calculate $P(X \geq 57)$, which, in the absence of technology, would involve 44 applications of the binomial probability formula. Fortunately, if the requirements are met, we may use the normal distribution to approximate such probabilities.

The binomial random variable X represents the number of successes in n trials and thus depends on the sample size n and the probability of success p. For a given probability of success p, if the sample size n gets large enough, the binomial distribution begins to resemble the normal distribution. Figure 6.58 shows the binomial probability distribution for Example 6.17 (page 277), where 20% ($p = 0.2$) of apps at Android Market threatened user privacy and Joshua received $n = 4$ apps with his new cell phone. The distribution of $X =$ the number of apps that threaten user privacy in Figure 6.58 is clearly not normal.

FIGURE 6.58
Binomial distribution:
$n = 4, p = 0.2$.

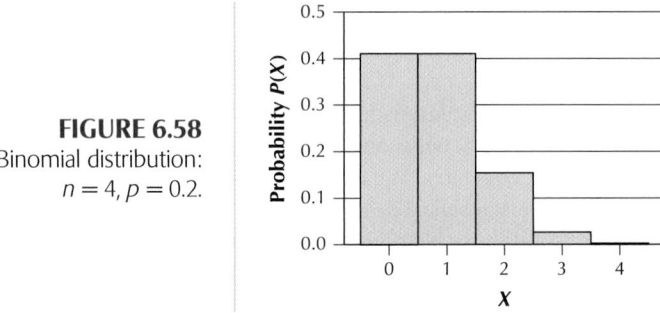

If we increase the sample size to $n = 64$ (Figure 6.59), the binomial distribution of X for $n = 64$ and $p = 0.2$, which is discrete, looks like it can be nicely approximated by the normal distribution, which is continuous.

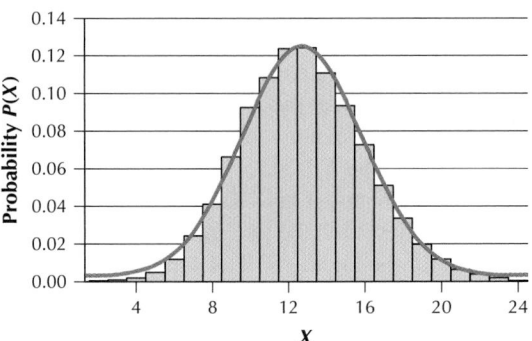

FIGURE 6.59 Binomial distribution: $n = 64, p = 0.2$.

We generalize this behavior as follows.

> **The Normal Approximation to the Binomial Probability Distribution**
>
> For the binomial random variable X with probability of success p and number of trials n: if $n \cdot p \geq 5$ and $n \cdot (1 - p) \geq 5$, the binomial distribution may be approximated by a normal distribution with mean $\mu_x = np$ and standard deviation $\sigma_x = \sqrt{np(1 - p)}$.

Example 6.44 The normal approximation to the binomial distribution

Punchstock/Blend

Now You Can Do
Exercises 3–8.

The Centers for Disease Control and Prevention reported that 20% of preschool children lack required immunizations, thereby putting themselves and their classmates at risk. For a group of $n = 64$ children with $p = 0.2$, the binomial probability distribution is shown in Figure 6.59.
a.   Verify that this distribution can be approximated by a normal distribution.
b.   Find the mean and standard deviation of this normal distribution.

Solution

a.   The normal approximation is valid if $n \cdot p \geq 5$ and $n \cdot (1 - p) \geq 5$. Substituting $n = 64$ and $p = 0.2$, we get

$$n \cdot p = (64)(0.2) = 12.8 \geq 5 \quad \text{and} \quad n \cdot (1 - p) = (64)(0.8) = 51.2 \geq 5$$

Thus, the normal approximation is valid.
b.   The mean and standard deviation of the normal distribution are

$$\mu_x = np = (64)(0.2) = 12.8$$
$$\sigma_x = \sqrt{np(1 - p)} = \sqrt{(64)(0.2)(0.8)} = 3.2$$

Figure 6.60 reproduces Figure 6.59, with the rectangle for $X = 12$ highlighted. The height of the rectangle represents the binomial probability that exactly 12 of the 64 children lack the required immunizations, that is, $P(X = 12)$. Since the width of the rectangle equals $12.5 - 11.5 = 1$, it follows that the area of the rectangle also represents the binomial probability that $X = 12$. Now, the area under the normal curve

FIGURE 6.60
Normal curve approximates binomial distribution.

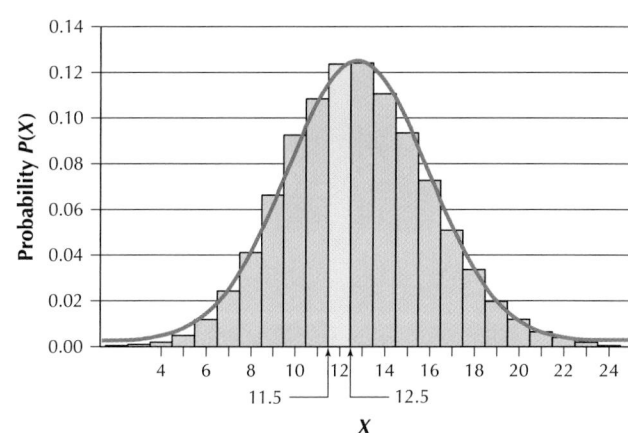

between 11.5 and 12.5 is approximately equal to this rectangle, which is $P(X = 12)$ for the binomial random variable X, with $n = 64$ and $p = 0.2$. That is

$$P(X_{\text{binomial}} = 12) \approx P(11.5 \leq Y_{\text{normal}} \leq 12.5)$$

where Y_{normal} is the normal random variable from Example 6.44(b), with mean $\mu_X = 12.8$ and standard deviation $\sigma_X = 3.2$.

The 0.5 that we add and subtract from 12 when approximating the binomial distribution with the normal distribution is called the *continuity correction,* since it is an adjustment for approximating a discrete probability with a continuous one. When using the normal approximation to the binomial, the analyst must determine which binomial rectangles are included and apply the continuity correction accordingly. This is shown in Table 6.7, which provides a listing of several types of binomial probabilities and their normal probability approximations.

Table 6.7 Binomial probabilities and approximate normal probabilities

Exact binomial probability	Approximate normal probability
$P(X_{\text{binomial}} = a)$	$P(a - 0.5 \leq Y_{\text{normal}} \leq a + 0.5)$
$P(X_{\text{binomial}} \leq a)$	$P(Y_{\text{normal}} \leq a + 0.5)$
$P(X_{\text{binomial}} \geq a)$	$P(Y_{\text{normal}} \geq a - 0.5)$
$P(X_{\text{binomial}} < a)$	$P(Y_{\text{normal}} < a - 0.5)$
$P(X_{\text{binomial}} > a)$	$P(Y_{\text{normal}} > a + 0.5)$
$P(a \leq X_{\text{binomial}} \leq b)$	$P(a - 0.5 < Y_{\text{normal}} \leq b + 0.5)$
$P(a < X_{\text{binomial}} < b)$	$P(a + 0.5 < Y_{\text{normal}} \leq b - 0.5)$

Example 6.45 Performing the normal approximation to the binomial probability distribution

For a group of $n = 64$ pre-schoolchildren with probability of lack of immunization $p = 0.2$, perform the following approximations.
a. Approximate the probability that there are at most 12 children without immunization.
b. Approximate the probability that there are more than 12 children without immunization.

Solution

Once again we have a binomial experiment with $n = 64$ and $p = 0.2$.
a. "At most" 12 children means 12 or fewer children. That is, $X = 12$ and $X = 11$ and $X = 10$, and so on; that is, $P(X_{\text{binomial}} \leq 12)$. In this case, we see that $X = 12$ is included in the probability we seek, as shown in Figure 6.61. From Table 6.7, we see that $P(X_{\text{binomial}} \leq 12)$ is of the form $P(X_{\text{binomial}} \leq a)$. Thus, our continuity correction takes the form $P(Y_{\text{normal}} \leq a + 0.5)$, where we add 0.5 to 12, so that

$$P(X_{\text{binomial}} \leq 12) \approx P(Y_{\text{normal}} \leq 12.5)$$

Recall that $\mu_X = 12.8$ and $\sigma_X = 3.2$. We use the TI-83/84, as shown in Figures 6.62 and 6.63, and find that the probability that at most 12 children lack immunization is $0.4626221269 \approx 0.4626$.

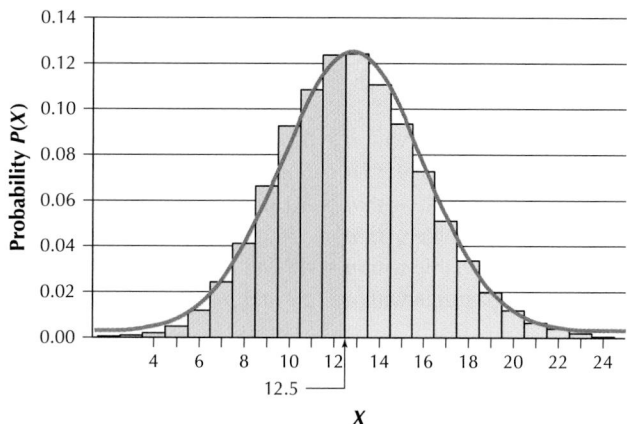

FIGURE 6.61 Approximately a binomial probability with a normal probability.

FIGURE 6.62 TI-83/84. **FIGURE 6.63** TI-83/84 results.

b. "More than" 12 children means $X = 13$ and $X = 14$, and so on. In other words, $X = 12$ is not included. That is, we want $P(X_{binomial} > 12)$. From Table 6.7, we see that $P(X_{binomial} > 12)$ is of the form $P(X_{binomial} > a)$. Thus, our continuity correction takes the form $P(Y_{normal} > a + 0.5)$, where we add 0.5 to 12, so that

$$P(X_{binomial} > 12) \approx P(Y_{normal} > 12.5)$$

Since the desired area is the complement of the green area in Figure 6.61, we can find the answer like this:

$$P(X_{binomial} > 12) \approx P(Y_{normal} > 12.5) = 1 - P(Y_{normal} \leq 12.5) = 1 - 0.4626 = 0.5374$$

Now You Can Do
Exercises 9–24.

The probability that more than 12 pre-schoolchildren will not have the required immunizations is 0.5374. ■

The *Normal Approximation to the Binomial* applet allows you to choose your own values of *n* and *p* and see how changes in these values affect the normal approximation to the binomial distribution.

Section 6.7 Summary

1 For certain values of *n*, *p*, and *X*, it may be inconvenient to calculate probabilities for the binomial distribution. The normal distribution can be used to approximate binomial probabilities when $np \geq 5$ and $np(1 - p) \geq 5$.

Section 6.7 Exercises

CLARIFYING THE CONCEPTS

1. Provide an example of why we would need to use the normal approximation to the binomial distribution.

2. What are the requirements for using the normal approximation to the binomial distribution?

PRACTICING THE TECHNIQUES

For Exercises 3–8, determine whether the requirements are met for using the normal approximation to the binomial probability distribution.

3. X is a binomial random variable with $n = 10$ and $p = 0.5$
4. X is a binomial random variable with $n = 8$ and $p = 0.5$
5. X is a binomial random variable with $n = 10$ and $p = 0.4$
6. X is a binomial random variable with $n = 13$ and $p = 0.4$
7. X is a binomial random variable with $n = 45$ and $p = 0.1$
8. X is a binomial random variable with $n = 50$ and $p = 0.1$

For Exercises 9–16, let X be a binomial random variable with $n = 40$ and $p = 0.5$. Use the normal approximation to find the following probabilities.

9. $P(X = 20)$
10. $P(X \geq 20)$
11. $P(X > 20)$
12. $P(X \leq 20)$
13. $P(X < 20)$
14. $P(18 \leq X \leq 22)$
15. $P(18 < X < 22)$
16. $P(18 \leq X < 22)$

For Exercises 17–24, let X be a binomial random variable with $n = 120$ and $p = 0.1$. Use the normal approximation to find the following probabilities.

17. $P(X = 10)$
18. $P(X \geq 10)$
19. $P(X > 10)$
20. $P(X \leq 8)$
21. $P(X < 8)$
22. $P(9 \leq X \leq 11)$
23. $P(9 < X < 11)$
24. $P(9 < X \leq 11)$

APPLYING THE CONCEPTS

25. Gas Tax. A *New York Times*/CBS News Poll conducted in April 2007 reported that 64% of Americans would favor an increased federal tax on gasoline if it would reduce dependence on foreign oil. For a sample of 200 Americans, approximate the following probabilities.
  a. Exactly 128 would favor such a tax.
  b. At least 128 would favor such a tax.

26. Dress Casual. A survey conducted in 2007 by the Society for Human Resource Management found that the number of businesses allowing employees to "dress casually" every day dropped from 53% in 2002 to 38% in 2007. Suppose we have a sample of 50 businesses from 2002 and a sample of 50 businesses from 2007. Approximate the following probabilities.
  a. At least 25 businesses allowed casual dress every day in 2002.
  b. At least 25 businesses allowed casual dress every day in 2007.

27. Hurricane Response. A survey found that 19% of respondents in New Orleans rated the overall response by

government and volunteer agencies to major hurricanes in the past three years as good or excellent, while 57% of those living in other areas did so.[26] Suppose that we have a sample of 100 people living in New Orleans and 100 people living in other areas. Approximate the following probabilities.
  a. At least 30 of the respondents living in New Orleans rated the response as good or excellent.
  b. At least 30 of the respondents living in other areas rated the response as good or excellent.

28. Disease Outbreak. A survey found that only 9% of Americans were "very confident" that the U.S. government is prepared to handle a major outbreak of an infectious disease.[27] Suppose that we have a sample of 100 Americans. Approximate the following probabilities.
  a. Exactly 9 Americans are very confident.
  b. At least 9 Americans are very confident.

29. Terrorism Concerns. A September 2006 *New York Times*/CBS News Poll found that 69% of New York City residents were personally very concerned about a terrorist attack occurring in the area in which they live, compared with 22% of Americans as a whole. Suppose we have a sample of 100 New York City residents and 100 non–New Yorkers. Approximate the following probabilities.
  a. More than 50 New Yorkers are so concerned.
  b. More than 50 non–New Yorkers are so concerned.

30. Gas Tax. Refer to Exercise 25. Approximate the following probabilities.
  a. More than 128 would favor such a tax.
  b. Between 120 and 130 would favor such a tax.

31. Dress Casual. Refer to Exercise 26. Approximate the following probabilities.
  a. Fewer than 15 businesses allowed casual dress every day in 2002.
  b. Fewer than 15 businesses allowed casual dress every day in 2007.

32. Hurricane Response. Refer to Exercise 27. Approximate the following probabilities.
  a. Fewer than 20 of the respondents living in New Orleans rated the response as good or excellent.
  b. Fewer than 20 of the respondents living in other areas rated the response as good or excellent.

33. Disease Outbreak. Refer to Exercise 28. Approximate the following probabilities.
  a. More than 9 Americans are very confident.
  b. At most 9 Americans are very confident.
  c. Fewer than 9 Americans are very confident.

34. Terrorism Concerns. Refer to Exercise 29. Approximate the following probabilities.
  a. Fewer than 25 New Yorkers are so concerned.
  b. Fewer than 25 non–New Yorkers are so concerned.

 Use the *Normal Approximation to the Binomial Distribution* applet for Exercises 35 and 36.

35. Select n (trials) = 10 and p (probability) = 0.2. The rectangles represent the binomial probabilities and the area under the curve represents the normal probabilities.

   a. For $n = 10$ and $p = 0.2$, is there a tight fit between the rectangles and the curve?

   b. What does this mean for whether the normal approximation should be used for a binomial distribution with $n = 10$ and $p = 0.2$?

   c. Verify whether the conditions are met for applying the normal approximation.

36. Select n (trials) = 63 and p (probability) = 0.2. The rectangles represent the binomial probabilities and the area under the curve represents the normal probabilities.

   a. For $n = 63$ and $p = 0.2$, is there a tight fit between the rectangles and the curve?

   b. What does this mean for whether the normal approximation should be used for a binomial distribution with $n = 63$ and $p = 0.2$?

   c. Verify whether the conditions are met for applying the normal approximation.

Chapter 6 Formulas and Vocabulary

SECTION 6.1

- **Continuous random variable** (p. 261)
- **Discrete random variable** (p. 261)
- **Expected value, or expectation, of a random variable** X (p. 266). Denoted $E(X)$
- **Mean** μ **of a discrete random variable** (p. 264). $\mu = \Sigma[X \cdot P(X)]$
- **Probability distribution of a discrete random variable** (p. 262)
- **Random variable** (p. 260)
- **Rules for a discrete probability distribution** (p. 262). $\Sigma P(X) = 1$ and $0 \le P(X) \le 1$
- **Variance and standard deviation of a discrete random variable** (p. 267).

   Definition formulas:

   $$\sigma^2 = \sum[(X - \mu)^2 \cdot P(X)]$$

   $$\sigma = \sqrt{\sum[(X - \mu)^2 \cdot P(X)]}$$

   Computational formulas:

   $$\sigma^2 = \sum[X^2 \cdot P(X)] - \mu^2$$

   $$\sigma = \sqrt{\sum[X^2 \cdot P(X)] - \mu^2}$$

SECTION 6.2

- **Binomial experiment** (p. 273)
- **Binomial probability distribution formula** (p. 277). $P(X) = (_nC_X)\, p^X\,(1 - p)^{n-X}$
- **Factorial (!)** (p. 275). $n! = n(n - 1)(n - 2) \ldots (2)(1)$
- **Mean, variance, and standard deviation of a binomial random variable** X (p. 280).

Mean (or expected value):	$\mu = n \cdot p$
Variance:	$\sigma^2 = n \cdot p \cdot (1 - p)$
Standard deviation:	$\sigma = \sqrt{n \cdot p \cdot (1 - p)}$

- **Number of combinations** (p. 275). $_nC_X = \dfrac{n!}{X!(n - X)!}$

SECTION 6.3

- **Mean, variance, and standard deviation for a Poisson random variable** X (p. 290). Mean = μ, Variance = $\sigma^2 = \mu$, Standard deviation = $\sigma = \sqrt{\mu}$.
- **Poisson probability distribution formula** (p. 288).

   $$P(x) = \frac{\mu^X \cdot e^{-\mu}}{X!}$$

SECTION 6.4

- **Continuous probability distribution** (p. 295)
- **Density curve** (p. 295)
- **Law of Total Probability for Continuous Random Variables** (p. 295)
- **Probability for continuous distributions** (p. 295)
- **Properties of the normal density curve (normal curve)** (p. 297)
- **Requirements for a continuous probability distribution** (p. 295)
- **Uniform probability distribution** (p. 295)

SECTION 6.5

- **Standard normal (Z) distribution** (p. 302)
- **Z table for the standard normal random variable Z** (p. 303)

SECTION 6.6

- **Finding normal data values for specified probabilities** (p. 317)
- **Finding probabilities for any normal distribution** (p. 314)
- **Standardizing a normal random variable** (p. 313).

   $$Z = \frac{X - \mu}{\sigma}$$

SECTION 6.7

- **Normal approximation to the binomial probability distribution** (p. 327)

Chapter 6 Review Exercises

SECTION 6.1

For Exercises 1 and 2, use the given information to construct a probability distribution table and a probability distribution graph. Then answer the questions.

1. Take Me to the Ball Game. Andrew loves to go to the ballpark to watch Major League Baseball games. If this year is like most years, there is only a 5% chance that he will not catch a single game, 20% that he will see one game,

35% that he will see two games, 25% that he will see three games, and 15% that he will see four games.

a. What is the probability that Andrew will see at least one game this year?

b. What is the most likely number of games that Andrew will see?

c. What is the probability that Andrew will see at most two games this year?

2. Early Lunch. Chad has gotten to lunch early and is waiting for his friends to catch up. He figures that the probability that one friend shows up is 25%; two friends, 35%; three friends, 20%; and more than three friends, 5%.

a. What is the probability that no friends show up?

b. What is the probability that more than one friend shows up?

c. What is the least likely outcome?

3. Investment Profits. Chang is looking forward to a profitable career as a day trader on Wall Street, after he has completed college. His present investments have the following probability distribution, with X = profit.

X	$-10,000$	5000	10,000
$P(X)$	0.3	0.5	0.2

a. Find the mean, variance, and standard deviation of X.

b. Draw a probability distribution graph.

c. Plot the mean of the random variable on the graph from **(b)**. Does this value for the mean make sense as the point where the distribution balances?

4. Connecticut Lotto. The Connecticut Lottery Corporation runs a game called Connecticut Classic Lotto. The player picks six different numbers from 1 to 44 and pays $1 to play.

- If your picks match 3 of the 6 numbers chosen (probability 0.02381), you win $2.
- If you match 4 out of 6 (probability 0.001495), you win $50.
- If you match 5 out of 6 (probability 0.0000323), you win $2000.
- If you match all 6 numbers (probability 0.0000001417), you win the jackpot. The jackpot on July 23, 2004, was $2,600,000.

a. Construct the probability distribution of your winnings. Make sure to include the probability of not winning anything (in effect, losing $1), which equals 1 minus the four probabilities specified above.

b. Find the expected winnings. Compare this with the price to play.

SECTION 6.2

5. Gestational Diabetes. Gestational diabetes occurs in 8% of pregnancies, according to the American Diabetes Association. A random sample of 20 pregnancies is taken.

a. Find the probability that none of the pregnancies results in gestational diabetes.

b. Find the probability that at least 1 of the pregnancies results in gestational diabetes.

c. Find the probability that at most 2 of the pregnancies result in gestational diabetes.

6. Female Students at DuPage. According to the National Center for Education Statistics, 57% of the students at the College of DuPage in Glen Ellyn, Illinois, are female. A random sample of 10 students from the College of DuPage is taken.

a. Find the probability that all 10 of the students are female.

b. Find the probability that at most 9 of the students are female.

c. Find the probability that at least 8 of the students are female.

7. Watching the Price of Gas. The Pew Research Center reports that, for the week of May 28, 2008, 35% of Americans said that the price of gasoline was the news story that they followed more closely than any other news item. A random sample of 15 Americans is taken.

a. Find the probability that 5 Americans said that the price of gas was the news story they followed most closely.

b. Find the probability that 4 Americans said that the price of gas was the news story they followed most closely.

c. Find the probability that between 3 and 5 Americans said that the price of gas was the news story they followed most closely.

For Exercises 8–10, find the mean, variance, and standard deviation. Interpret the mean for each.

8. Gestational Diabetes. Gestational diabetes occurs in 8% of pregnancies, according to the American Diabetes Association. A random sample of 20 pregnancies is taken and the number of those with gestational diabetes is recorded.

9. Female Students at DuPage. According to the National Center for Education Statistics, 57% of the students at the College of DuPage in Glen Ellyn, Illinois, are female. A random sample of 10 students from the College of DuPage is taken and the number of females is recorded.

10. Watching the Price of Gas. The Pew Research Center reports that, for the week of May 28, 2008, 35% of Americans said that the price of gasoline was the news story that they followed more closely than any other news item. A random sample of 15 Americans is taken and the number who follow the price of gasoline most closely is recorded.

SECTION 6.3

For each of the following situations, assume that the requirements for the Poisson probability distribution are met. Use the mean to find the indicated probability.

11. $\mu = 5$; find $P(X = 5)$.

12. $\mu = 5$; find $P(3 \le X \le 5)$.

13. $\mu = 5$; find $P(X < 3)$.

14. $\mu = 5$; find $P(0 \le X \le 5)$.

15. Aircraft fatalities. The mean number of fatalities per crash of small aircraft in California is 1.65.[28] Let X refer to the number of fatalities per crash. Find the following probabilities.
- **a.** Probability that $X = 1$
- **b.** $P(X = 0)$
- **c.** $P(X \le 2)$
- **d.** $P(X > 2)$

SECTION 6.4

Systolic Blood Pressure. Use the following information for Exercises 16–23. A study found that the mean systolic blood pressure was 106 mm Hg.[29] Assume that systolic blood pressure follows a normal distribution with mean $\mu = 106$ and standard deviation $\sigma = 8$.

16. What is the probability that a randomly chosen systolic blood pressure is equal to 106 mm Hg?

17. What is the probability that a randomly selected systolic blood pressure is more than 106 mm Hg?

18. What is the probability that a randomly chosen systolic blood pressure is at least 106 mm Hg?

19. Is the area to the right of $X = 110$ mm Hg greater than or less than 0.5? How do you know this?

20. Is the area to the left of $X = 110$ mm Hg greater than or less than 0.5? How do you know this?

21. What is the probability that a randomly selected systolic blood pressure is between 98 and 114 mm Hg?

22. What is the probability that a randomly chosen systolic blood pressure is between 90 and 122 mm Hg?

23. What is the probability that a randomly selected systolic blood pressure is between 82 and 130 mm Hg?

SECTION 6.5

For Exercises 24–29, **(a)** draw the graph, and **(b)** find the indicated area using the Z table or technology.

Find the area under the standard normal curve that lies to the left of the following.
24. $Z = 2.1$
25. $Z = 2.9$

Find the area under the standard normal curve that lies to the right of the following.
26. $Z = -2.2$
27. $Z = -2.9$

Find the area under the standard normal curve that lies between the following.
28. $Z = -1.28$ and $Z = 1.28$
29. $Z = -1.04$ and $Z = 1.51$

30. South Dakota Speeds. The National Motorists Association reports that, in South Dakota, the mean speed on interstate highways is 68.3 mph. Denote the mean to be $\mu = 68.3$ mph, and assume that the distribution is normal and $\sigma = 4$ mph.

- **a.** Find the probability that a randomly chosen vehicle is traveling faster than the 65 mph speed limit.
- **b.** What percentage of vehicles travel slower than 60 mph?
- **c.** What proportion of vehicles travel at speeds between 65 and 68.3 mph?
- **d.** The National Motorists Association asserts that speeding tickets should be issued only for drivers whose speeds exceed the 85th percentile. If the police in South Dakota followed this rule, then at what speed would they start handing out speeding tickets?
- **e.** Suppose that someone from South Dakota never drives faster than 55 mph on the interstate. Is this unusual? On what do you base your answer?

SECTION 6.6

31. Drunk-Driving Deaths. In the United States, a mean of 48 people *per day* are killed in vehicle accidents involving a drunk driver. Assume that the distribution of drunk-driving accident deaths per day is normal, $\mu = 48$, and $\sigma = 12$.
- **a.** Find the probability that at most 12 people will be killed in drunk-driving accidents today.
- **b.** Find the probability that between 50 and 80 people will be killed in drunk-driving accidents today.
- **c.** Find the 99.5th percentile of the number of drunk-driving accident deaths.
- **d.** Suppose on one particular day in the United States, 60 people are killed in drunk-driving accidents. Is this unusual? On what do you base your answer?

32. Latino Favorite: *Copa America*. According to Nielsen Media Research, the highest-rated television program among Latino Americans is *Copa America,* with a rating of 23.4 among Latino viewers for the week ending July 18, 2004. Assume that the ratings for this program for any given week are normally distributed with mean $\mu = 23.4$ and standard deviation $\sigma = 5$.
- **a.** Find the probability that the ratings for a randomly selected week for *Copa America* will be lower than 18.4.
- **b.** Find the probability that the ratings for a randomly selected week for *Copa America* will be between 15 and 20.
- **c.** Suppose that the show's producer must report to the UNI network executives any time the ratings fall below the 10th percentile. What is the ratings value that will trigger this report?
- **d.** Suppose that the ratings for *Copa America* in one particular week were 8.4. Is this unusual? On what do you base your answer? Will the producer have to file a report?

SECTION 6.7

33. Generation Worse Off? A *New York Times*/CBS News Poll conducted in 2007 found that 48% of young

Americans (aged 17–29) think that their generation will be worse off than the previous generation. Suppose we take a random sample of 100 young Americans. Use the normal approximation to approximate the following probabilities.

    a. Exactly 50 think that their generation will be worse off.

    b. At least 50 think that their generation will be worse off.

    c. More than 50 think that their generation will be worse off.

    d. At most 50 think that their generation will be worse off.

    e. Fewer than 50 think that their generation will be worse off.

    f. Between 48 and 52 (inclusive) think that their generation will be worse off.

34. Reinstate the Draft? A *New York Times*/CBS News Poll found that 97% of young Americans (aged 17–29) oppose reinstating the military draft. Suppose we take a random sample of 400 young Americans. Use the normal approximation to approximate the following probabilities.

    a. Exactly 388 oppose reinstating the military draft.

    b. All 400 oppose reinstating the military draft.

    c. More than 388 oppose reinstating the military draft.

    d. At most 388 oppose reinstating the military draft.

    e. Fewer than 388 oppose reinstating the military draft.

    f. Between 385 and 390 (inclusive) oppose reinstating the military draft.

Chapter 6 QUIZ

TRUE OR FALSE

1. True or false: The following is a continuous and not a discrete random variable: How much coffee there is in your next cup of coffee.

2. True or false: The following is an example of a binomial experiment: Rolling a pair of dice 3 times and observing the sum of the two dice.

3. True or false: Our distributions for continuous random variables are for samples and not for populations.

FILL IN THE BLANK

4. The probability that a randomly chosen value of a normally distributed random variable will be greater than the mean is _____.

5. The probability that a randomly chosen value of a normally distributed random variable will be equal to the mean is _____.

6. The standard deviation of a normal random variable can never take a value that is less than _____.

SHORT ANSWER

7. Is the following a discrete or continuous random variable: The number of goals your college soccer team will score in its next game.

8. Recording the gender of the next 20 babies born at City Hospital is an example of what kind of experiment?

9. What are the values for the mean and standard deviation of the standard normal distribution?

CALCULATIONS AND INTERPRETATIONS

10. Church Bazaar. Lenny has gone down to the church bazaar with his family. There is a game there where if you roll two dice and get a sum of at least 9, you will win $5; otherwise, you don't win anything.

    a. Construct the probability distribution for the amount you win playing this game.

    b. What are the expected winnings?

    c. What would be a fair (break-even) price for the church to ask you to pay to play this game?

11. CEOs Driving Luxury Cars. According to CareerBuilder.com, 19% of company CEOs drive luxury cars. Suppose a random sample is taken of 100 company CEOs.

    a. Find the probability that the sample contains 20 CEOs who drive luxury cars.

    b. What is the most likely number of CEOs who drive luxury cars?

    c. Find the mean, variance, and standard deviation. Interpret the mean.

    d. Suppose the sample contains 40 CEOs who drive luxury cars. Is this unusual? Explain how you determine this.

12. Gambling Losses. Treatment providers for problem gamblers report that men who approached them for intervention had lost a mean of $2849 in the preceding four weeks, according to a 2002 report.[30] Assume that the distribution of gambling losses is normally distributed with mean $\mu = \$2849$ and standard deviation $\sigma = \$900$.

    a. Find the probability that a randomly selected male had lost more than $4000.

    b. What percentage of males lost between $3000 and $4000?

    c. Suppose that a gambling support group is trying to identify those who lose the most, as measured by the 95th percentile. How much money in gambling losses does this represent?

    d. Suppose you know of a male problem gambler who lost $1000 in four weeks and then approached a treatment provider. Is this amount unusual? On what do you base your answer?

13. Cats and Dogs. The American Veterinary Medical Association reported that there were 61.1 million cats in America and 53.6 million dogs. It also reported that 31.4% of American households had a cat while 34.3% of American households had a dog. A random sample of 1000 households is taken. Use the normal approximation.

a. Find the probability that the sample contains 320 households with a cat.

b. Find the probability that the sample contains 320 households with a dog.

c. Find the mean, variance, and standard deviation of the number of cats. Interpret the mean. Now do the same for dogs.

d. Suppose that the sample contains 290 households with a cat. Is this unusual? Explain how you determine this.

14. Attendance at the Magic Kingdom. The Magic Kingdom at Walt Disney World in Orlando, Florida, has a mean of 38,000 customers per day. Assume that the distribution of attendance is normal, $\mu = 38{,}000$, and $\sigma = 10{,}000$.

a. Find the probability that more than 40,000 people visit the Magic Kingdom in one day.

b. Find the probability that between 35,000 and 41,000 people visit the Magic Kingdom in one day.

c. Suppose that special overflow parking lots are opened for the days with the highest 10% attendance levels. What is the cutoff attendance number that triggers the opening of the overflow parking areas?

d. Suppose that on one rainy day, only 15,000 people visit the Magic Kingdom. Is this unusual? On what do you base your answer?

7

Sampling Distributions

Introduction

In Chapter 7, students are introduced to point estimation, sampling distributions, and one of the most important results in statistical inference, the Central Limit Theorem. Section 7.1 introduces sampling distributions. In Section 7.2, the Central Limit Theorem for means is introduced, followed by the Central Limit Theorem for proportions in Section 7.3.

From the Author

- **Section 7.1 Introduction to Sampling Distributions**
  - We streamlined much of the material in this chapter, in order to make Sampling Distributions more teachable.
  - The *point estimate* topic has been moved to Section 8.1, where it appears more naturally just before confidence intervals.
  - The *sampling error* topic has been omitted, to streamline the coverage.
  - The topic *Using normal probability plots to assess normality* has been moved to Section 7.2, "just in time" for it to be applied for the Central Limit Theorem.
- **Section 7.2 Central Limit Theorem for Means**
  - We increased the pace in this section in order to get to the Central Limit Theorem more quickly.
  - The inference for the population mean in subsequent chapters depends either on Section 7.1 (if the population is normal), or on Section 7.2 (if the sample size is large). Instructors may wish to point out that sometimes neither condition is fulfilled, and that sometimes there is insufficient information to solve the problem (Example 7.9 on page 352).
- **Section 7.3 Central Limit Theorem for Proportions**
  - We have greatly streamlined this section, omitting over a page of derivation. Most instructors do not have time to derive the sampling distribution of the sample proportion.

Teaching Tips

Chapter 7 is a pivotal chapter. The preceding two chapters showed us the rules of probability and the characteristics of the normal distribution. The reason we learned these things is so that we can perform statistical inference in Chapters 8–11. That statistical inference depends on the sampling distributions that we learn about here in Chapter 7.

It is important for students to understand that sample statistics, such as the sample mean, have patterns of behavior when the sample size is large. If we repeatedly take samples from a population, then the mean of all the sample means will equal the mean of the population. We can also find what the standard deviation of all these sample means will be. Armed with this knowledge of the mean and standard deviation of the sample mean, we can determine what is an *unusual* or *extreme* value of the sample mean. This is the basis for statistical inference.

In-Class Activities

1. Use class test scores or homework scores as a population. Then determine all the samples of size 2 and their corresponding sample means. Show that the population mean of the samples of test scores is equal to the population mean of all the individual test scores but that the standard deviation of the sample means is less than the standard deviation of the individual test scores.

2. Simulate the rolling of a six-sided die, in Minitab, for instance, using the integer distribution. Simulate several columns of data. Row means for different sample sizes can then be computed and histograms for these means can be displayed. The shapes of these histograms should generate discussion. Also, the descriptive statistics for these sample means can be computed. In-class discussions about the means and standard deviations for the sample means can be related to the required formulas for the Central Limit Theorem for sample means.

Sampling Distributions

3. Perform the following activity as a class. Use the *Random Sample* applet to generate the random samples requested.

    a. Each student in the class should write down an estimate of the length of the following line segment. Use your eyes only! No rulers.

_____

    b. Consider your class to be a population. Find the mean μ and the standard deviation σ of all student estimates.

    c. Choose one student at random from the class. Ask for this student's estimate.

    d. Take a random sample of two students from the class, and find the mean $\bar{x}$ of their estimates. What is the mean $\mu_{\bar{x}}$ and standard deviation $\sigma_{\bar{x}}$ of the sampling distribution of $\bar{x}$? Given these values for $\mu_{\bar{x}}$ and $\sigma_{\bar{x}}$, which values for the length of the line segment would be considered unusual? (*Hint:* Which would be outliers?)

    e. Take a random sample of 10 students from the class, and find the mean $\bar{x}$ of their estimates. What are $\mu_{\bar{x}}$ and $\sigma_{\bar{x}}$ for $n = 10$? Now, which values for the length of the line segment would be considered unusual?

    f. Take a random sample of 20 students and find their estimates. What are $\mu_{\bar{x}}$ and $\sigma_{\bar{x}}$? Now, which values for the length of the line segment would be considered unusual?

    g. As the sample size increases, what is happening to $\sigma_{\bar{x}}$, and what is happening to the estimates that are considered unusual? How can you state this phenomenon in terms of sample size and precision of the estimate?

Supplements

- StatTutor 11.1–11.5(a) and (b), 20.1, 20.2(a) and (b)

Applets

The *Law of Large Numbers for Means*, *Law of Large Numbers for Proportions*, *Central Limit Theorem*, and *Random Sample* applets are referenced in Chapter 7.

    The *Central Limit Theorem* is used for Exercises 49 and 50 in Section 7.2.

    This Web site has an applet for the Central Limit Theorem: **http://wise.cgu.edu/**.

Videos

- *Against All Odds* **www.learner.org/resources/series65.html**
  - Program 18: The Sample Mean and Control Charts

Web Sites

- This Web site has a collection of 20 class projects, one of which deals with sampling distribution: **www.amstat.org/publications/jse/v6n3/smith.html**.

- The site Online Statistics: An Interactive Multimedia Course of Study has a *Sampling Distribution* applet that demonstrates several simulations, and it has a link to the Rice Virtual Lab in Statistics with numerous simulation demonstrations along with other topics related to statistics: **http://onlinestatbook.com/index.html**.

- This site lists other sites that do statistical calculations: **http://statpages.org/**.

- This site lists numerous activities on all topics: **http://mathforum.org/mathtools/sitemap2/ps/**.

- This site has several activities using Excel and Minitab: **www.mathspace.com/NSF_ProbStat/Teaching_Materials/Primarily_Statistics.htm**.

© IMAGEMORE CO., LTD/Imagemore Co., Ltd./Corbis

OVERVIEW

7

Sampling Distributions

CASE STUDY

Trial of the Pyx: How Much Gold Is in Your Gold Coins?

The kings of bygone England had a problem: How much gold should they put into their gold coins? After all, the very commerce of the kingdom depended on the purity of the currency. How did the lords of the realm ensure that the coins floating around the kingdom contained reliable amounts of gold?

From the year 1282, the Trial of the Pyx has been held annually in London to ensure that newly minted coins adhere to the standards of the realm. It is the responsibility of the presiding judge to ensure that the trial proceeds lawfully and to inform Her Majesty's Treasury of the verdict. Six members of the Company of Goldsmiths compose the jury, who are given two months to test the coins. It works like this: A ceremonial boxwood chest, called the Pyx, is brought forth, and a sample of 100 of the coins cast that year at the mint is put into it. The Pyx is then weighed. In times past, each gold coin, called a guinea, had an expected weight of 128 grams, so the total weight of the guineas in the Pyx was expected to be 12,800 grams.

If the weight of the coins in the Pyx was much less than 12,800 grams, the jury concluded that the Master of the Mint was cheating the crown by pocketing the excess gold, and he was severely punished. On the other hand, if the coins in the Pyx weighed much more than 12,800 grams, that wasn't good either, since it cut down on the profits produced by the kings' coin-minting monopoly.

By how much could the Master of the Mint debase the coinage before getting caught? We shall see in this chapter's Case Study, Trial of the Pyx, which unfolds in Section 7.2.

The Big Picture

Where we are coming from, and where we are headed . . .

- In Chapters 1–4 we learned ways to describe data sets using numbers, tables, and graphs. Then in Chapters 5 and 6 we learned the tools of probability and probability distributions that allow us to quantify uncertainty.

- Here, in Chapter 7, "Sampling Distributions," we will discover that seemingly random statistics, such as the sample mean $\bar{x}$, have *predictable behaviors*. The special type of distribution we use to describe these behaviors is called the *sampling distribution of the sample mean*. This leads us to perhaps the most important result in statistical inference: the Central Limit Theorem.

- The sampling distributions we learn in this chapter form the basis for most of the statistical inference we perform in the remainder of the book. For example, in Chapter 8, "Confidence Intervals," we will learn how to estimate an unknown parameter with a certain level of confidence.

7.1 Introduction to Sampling Distributions

OBJECTIVES By the end of this section, I will be able to . . .

1 Explain the sampling distribution of the sample mean $\bar{x}$.

2 Describe the sampling distribution of the sample mean $\bar{x}$ when the population is normal.

3 Find probabilities and percentiles for the sample mean when the population is normal.

In Chapter 6 we dealt with probability distributions, which describe populations. Here, in Chapter 7, we return to the use of sample data, in order to show how populations and their samples are connected.

1 Sampling Distribution of the Sample Mean $\bar{x}$

In this chapter we will develop methods that will allow us to quantify the *behavior* of statistics like $\bar{x}$. For the sample mean $\bar{x}$, this behavior is expressed in the **sampling distribution of the sample mean.**

> The **sampling distribution of the sample mean** $\bar{x}$ for a given sample size n consists of the collection of the means of all possible samples of size n from the population.

First, we illustrate the collection of the sample means into the sampling distribution of the sample mean $\bar{x}$.

Example 7.1 Constructing the sampling distribution of the sample mean $\bar{x}$

Suppose we are interested in how long it takes the five members of the student government to commute to school. The times (in minutes) are given in Table 7.1 Since these five people are *all* the members of the student government, they represent a *population*.

Table 7.1 Commuting times for the five members of the student government

Amber	Brandon	Chantal	Dave	Emma
10	20	5	30	15

a. Calculate the population mean commuting time μ.
b. Take all possible samples of size $n = 3$ and calculate the mean $\bar{x}$ of each sample.

Solution

a. The mean commuting time of this population is

$$\mu = \frac{\sum x}{n} = \frac{10 + 20 + 5 + 30 + 15}{5} = 16 \text{ minutes}$$

b. Table 7.2 shows all possible samples of size $n = 3$ from the five students, along with the respective sample means.

Table 7.2 All possible samples of size 3 from population of student government members

Sample	Amber Brandon Chantal	Amber Brandon Dave	Amber Brandon Emma	Amber Chantal Dave	Amber Chantal Emma	Amber Dave Emma	Brandon Chantal Dave	Brandon Chantal Emma	Brandon Dave Emma	Chantal Dave Emma
	10	10	10	10	10	10	20	20	20	5
Data	20	20	20	5	5	30	5	5	30	30
	5	30	15	30	15	15	30	15	15	15
$\bar{x}$	11.67	20	15	15	10	18.33	18.33	13.33	21.67	16.67

The bottom row in Table 7.2 contains the sample means for all possible samples of size $n = 3$. That is, this row represents the sampling distribution of the sample mean $\bar{x}$ for $n = 3$. ∎

Note from Table 7.2 that the value for the sample mean $\bar{x}$ varies from sample to sample. Thus, $\bar{x}$ is a *random variable*. This random variable exhibits *sampling variability* because its value changes from sample to sample. Fortunately, there are patterns (predictable behaviors) in how the sample mean $\bar{x}$ varies. Like any distribution, the sampling distribution of the sample mean has a balance point, and therefore a mean.

Figure 7.1 provides a dotplot of the sample means in Table 7.2, along with the mean of these sample means, indicated at the balance point $\mu = 16$. Figure 7.1 represents the sampling distribution of the sample mean for this example.

FIGURE 7.1
Sampling distribution of the sample mean for Example 7.1.

The mean value of the ten sample means is

$$\frac{11.67 + 20 + 15 + 15 + 10 + 18.33 + 18.33 + 13.33 + 21.67 + 16.67}{10} = 16$$

Note that this value is exactly equal to the population mean $\mu = 16$. That is, the sampling distribution of $\bar{x}$ is centered at μ. We generalize this result as follows.

Fact 1: Mean of the Sampling Distribution of the Sample Mean $\bar{x}$

The mean of the sampling distribution of the sample mean $\bar{x}$ is the value of the population mean μ. It can be denoted as $\mu_{\bar{x}} = \mu$ and read as "the mean of the sampling distribution of $\bar{x}$ is μ."

Next we would like to uncover information regarding the spread of the sampling distribution of $\bar{x}$. The population standard deviation of the original commute times in Table 7.1 is

$$\sigma = \sqrt{\frac{\sum(x - \mu)^2}{N}}$$

$$= \sqrt{\frac{[(10 - 16)^2 + (20 - 16)^2 + (5 - 16)^2 + (30 - 16)^2 + (15 - 16)^2]}{5}}$$

$$\approx 8.6023$$

And the population standard deviation of the sampling distribution of $\bar{x}$ is

$$\sigma_{\bar{x}} = \sqrt{\frac{\sum(\bar{x} - \mu)^2}{10}} = \sqrt{\frac{[(11.67 - 16)^2 + (20 - 16)^2 + \cdots + (16.67 - 16)^2]}{10}}$$

$$\approx 3.5119$$

Note: It is convenient to number a set of important *facts*, as we build toward the Central Limit Theorem for Means and the Central Limit Theorem for Proportions.

Note: In this example, the precise relationship between the two standard deviations is

$$\sigma_{\bar{x}} = \sqrt{\frac{N - n}{N - 1}} \cdot \frac{\sigma}{\sqrt{n}}$$

where N is the population size and n is the sample size. This gives

$$\sigma_{\bar{x}} = \sqrt{\frac{5 - 3}{5 - 1}} \cdot \frac{8.6023}{\sqrt{3}} \approx 3.5119$$

However, the coefficient

$$\sqrt{\frac{N - n}{N - 1}}$$

called the *finite population correction factor*, is required only for special cases (like this textbook example) where the population is not much larger than the sample.

(Continued)

This finite population correction factor does not apply when sampling with replacement, and its value tends to zero as the sample size approaches the population size. However, for most real-world problems, and for the remainder of this book, we dispense with this coefficient and assume that the population size is very large compared to the sample size.

Note that the standard deviation of the sample means is smaller than the original standard deviation.

> **Fact 2: Standard Deviation of the Sampling Distribution of the Sample Mean $\bar{x}$**
>
> The standard deviation of the sampling distribution of the sample mean $\bar{x}$ is $\sigma_{\bar{x}} = \sigma/\sqrt{n}$, where σ is the population standard deviation and n is the sample size. $\sigma_{\bar{x}}$ is called the **standard error of the mean.**

Note the $\sqrt{n}$ in the denominator of the formula. Because of this factor, the larger the sample size, the tighter the resulting sampling distribution. Larger sample sizes lead to smaller variability, which results in more precise estimation.

Example 7.2 Finding the mean and standard deviation of the sampling distribution of $\bar{x}$

According to CanEquity Mortgage Company, the mean age of mortgage applicants in the city of Toronto is 37 years old. Assume that the population standard deviation is $\sigma = 6$ years. Find the mean and standard deviation for the sampling distribution of $\bar{x}$ for the following sample sizes: (a) 4, (b) 100, (c) 225.

Solution

We have $\mu_{\bar{x}} = \mu = 37$. Note that this value for $\mu_{\bar{x}}$ does not depend on the sample size, so the value is true for any sample size. We also have $\sigma = 6$.

a. $n = 4$. Then $\sigma_{\bar{x}} = \dfrac{\sigma}{\sqrt{n}} = \dfrac{6}{\sqrt{4}} = 3$. The standard error of the mean for $n = 4$ is $\sigma_{\bar{x}} = 3$.

b. $n = 100$. Then standard error $\sigma_{\bar{x}} = \dfrac{\sigma}{\sqrt{n}} = \dfrac{6}{\sqrt{100}} = 0.6$.

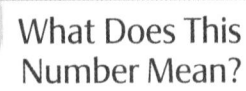
Now You Can Do
Exercises 5–10.

c. $n = 225$. Then standard error $\sigma_{\bar{x}} = \dfrac{\sigma}{\sqrt{n}} = \dfrac{6}{\sqrt{225}} = 0.4$. ∎

What Does This Number Mean?

Consider $\sigma_{\bar{x}} = 0.6$ for $n = 100$. This is a measure of the variability of the sampling distribution of $\bar{x}$ for this sample size. That is, if we take samples of size 100, our estimation of the population mean age μ of all mortgage applicants in Toronto will be within 0.6 year of the true population mean most of the time. ◢

2 Sampling Distribution of $\bar{x}$ for a Normal Population

To find out what form the sampling distribution of $\bar{x}$ takes when the population is normal, we consider the following example, in which we examine a small, normally distributed population and find the sample means for all possible samples of a certain size.

Example 7.3 Sampling distribution of $\bar{x}$ for a normal population

In Example 6.38 (page 313), the average statewide temperature in Georgia in the month of April was normally distributed with a mean of $\mu = 61.5°F$ and a standard deviation of $\sigma = 8°F$. Using Minitab, 1000 samples of size $n = 2$ were generated from this normal distribution, and the sample means $\bar{x}$ were calculated for each sample. Construct a histogram and observe the shape of the distribution.

Solution

Figure 7.2 shows the histogram of the means from the 1000 samples of size $n = 2$. As you may have expected, the histogram looks quite normal, even with this tiny sample size of $n = 2$. ∎

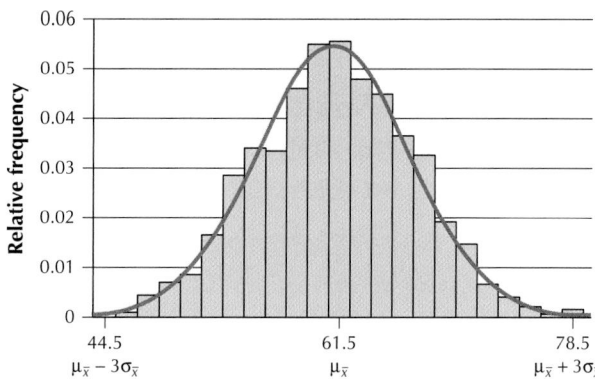

FIGURE 7.2 Sampling distribution of the sample means of size $n = 2$ from a normal population.

Example 7.3 considered a very small sample size, $n = 2$. In fact, this outcome is true for all normal populations. Using Facts 1 and 2, we can summarize this sampling distribution as follows.

Note: Let the notation

$$\text{normal } (\mu, \sigma/\sqrt{n})$$

denote a normal distribution with mean of μ and standard deviation of $\sigma/\sqrt{n}$.

> **Fact 3: Sampling Distribution of the Sample Mean for a Normal Population**
>
> For a normal population, the sampling distribution of the sample mean $\bar{x}$ is distributed as normal $(\mu, \sigma/\sqrt{n})$, where μ is the population mean and σ is the population standard deviation.

Once we know that the sample mean is normally distributed, we can use the method we learned in Section 6.6 (page 313) to standardize and produce Z, just as we would for any normal random variable.

> **Fact 4: Standardizing a Normal Sampling Distribution for Means**
>
> When the sampling distribution of $\bar{x}$ is normal, we may standardize to produce the standard normal random variable Z as follows:
>
> $$Z = \frac{\bar{x} - \mu_{\bar{x}}}{\sigma_{\bar{x}}} = \frac{\bar{x} - \mu}{\sigma/\sqrt{n}}$$
>
> where μ is the population mean, σ is the population standard deviation, and n is the sample size.

3 Finding Probabilities and Percentiles Using a Sampling Distribution

Since we know that the sampling distribution of the sample mean $\bar{x}$ is normal when the population is normally distributed, we can use the techniques of Section 6.6 to answer questions about the means of samples taken from normal populations.

Example 7.4 Finding probabilities using the sample mean: comparing $P(x > 80)$ with $P(\bar{x} > 80)$

Suppose that statistics quiz scores for a certain instructor are normally distributed with mean 70 and standard deviation 10.
a. Find the probability that a randomly chosen student's score will be above 80.
b. Suppose that, over the years, the instructor has had many sections of size $n = 25$. Describe the sampling distribution of the sample mean.

c. Find the probability that a sample of 25 quiz scores will have a mean score greater than 80.

Solution

a. This is a normal probability problem, which we learned how to do in Section 6.6.

$$P(X > 80) = P\left(\frac{X - 70}{10} > \frac{80 - 70}{10}\right)$$

$$= P(Z > 1) = 1 - 0.8413 = 0.1587$$

using Case 2 from Table 6.6 (page 303). Therefore, there is a 15.87% probability that a randomly chosen student will have a quiz score above 80 (Figure 7.3a).

Case 2 shows how to find area to the right of a Z-value.

b. We are given $\mu = 70$ and $\sigma = 10$. So by Fact 1, $\mu_{\bar{x}} = \mu = 70$. And by Fact 2,

$$\sigma_{\bar{x}} = \frac{\sigma}{\sqrt{n}} = \frac{10}{\sqrt{25}} = 2.$$

Next, we are given that the population of quiz scores is normal. Therefore, by Fact 3, the sampling distribution of $\bar{x}$ is distributed as normal (70, 2) (see Figure 7.3b).

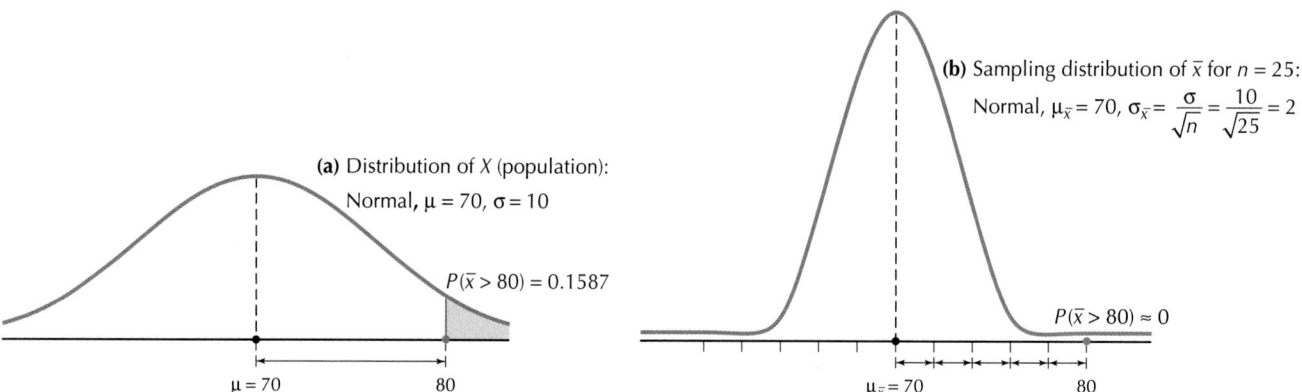

(a) Distribution of X (population):
Normal, $\mu = 70$, $\sigma = 10$

$P(\bar{x} > 80) = 0.1587$

$\mu = 70$ 80

(b) Sampling distribution of $\bar{x}$ for $n = 25$:
Normal, $\mu_{\bar{x}} = 70$, $\sigma_{\bar{x}} = \frac{\sigma}{\sqrt{n}} = \frac{10}{\sqrt{25}} = 2$

$P(\bar{x} > 80) \approx 0$

$\mu_{\bar{x}} = 70$ 80

FIGURE 7.3 Distribution of X and sampling distribution of $\bar{x}$ for Example 7.4.

c. Once we know that the sample mean is normally distributed, we can standardize the quiz score, as we have for other normal random variables. Just be sure to use $\sigma_{\bar{x}} = 2$, the standard error of the mean, and not $\sigma = 10$, the standard deviation for the population. $\sigma_{\bar{x}}$ is always smaller.

Applying Fact 4,

$$Z = \frac{\bar{x} - \mu_{\bar{x}}}{\sigma_{\bar{x}}} = \frac{\bar{x} - \mu}{\sigma/\sqrt{n}} = \frac{\bar{x} - 70}{10/\sqrt{25}} = \frac{\bar{x} - 70}{2}$$

We need to standardize the score of 80 as well.

$$Z = \frac{80 - \mu_{\bar{x}}}{\sigma_{\bar{x}}} = \frac{80 - \mu}{\sigma/\sqrt{n}} = \frac{80 - 70}{10/\sqrt{25}} = \frac{80 - 70}{2} = 5$$

Hence,

$$P(\bar{x} > 80) = P\left(\frac{\bar{x} - 70}{10/\sqrt{25}} > \frac{80 - 70}{10/\sqrt{25}}\right) = P\left(\frac{\bar{x} - 70}{2} > \frac{80 - 70}{2}\right) = P(Z > 5) \approx 0$$

as shown in Figure 7.3b. Since Z is standard normal, nearly all observations lie between -3 and 3. Thus, the Z table does not go up to 5 since the probabilities are so close to zero. The TI-83 provides the more precise probability of $P(Z > 5) = 0.000000287$, or about 3 in 10 million. This instructor just does not give easy quizzes! ∎

*Now You Can Do
Exercises 11–16.*

> **What Does This Probability Mean?**
>
> There is essentially no chance that the sample mean $\bar{x}$ on one of the quizzes will be greater than 80. Compare this to the nearly 16% chance that a *particular* student's score would be above 80. Figure 7.3 shows the graphs of the distributions of quiz scores and class means. Both distributions are centered at $\mu_{\bar{x}} = \mu = 70$, but the standard deviations differ. The arrow in Figure 7.3a represents the standard deviation of X, $\sigma = 10$, and it shows that $x = 80$ is only 1 standard deviation above the mean $\mu = 70$. The arrows in Figure 7.3b represent the standard error of the mean, $\sigma_{\bar{x}} = 2$, and they illustrate that $\bar{x} = 80$ lies 5 standard errors above the mean $\mu_{\bar{x}} = 70$. Thus, class means are less variable than individual student scores. ◢

In Chapter 6, we found the percentiles of normally distributed random variables. Since the sampling distribution of $\bar{x}$ is normal, we are able to find the percentiles of the $\bar{x}$'s as well. Once the appropriate Z-value is found, we use the following equation to transform the Z-value into an $\bar{x}$-value.

$$\bar{x} = Z \cdot \sigma_{\bar{x}} + \mu = Z \cdot \frac{\sigma}{\sqrt{n}} + \mu$$

Example 7.5 Finding a value of $\bar{x}$, given a probability or area

Using the information in Example 7.4, find the 95th percentile of the class mean quiz scores.

Solution

The 95th percentile of the class means is the value of $\bar{x}$ with area 0.95 to the left of it.

Since we want the 95th percentile, we seek 0.95 on the *inside* of the Z table. Since 0.95 is not in the Z table, we take the closest value. Since the two closest values, 0.9495 and 0.9505, are equally close, we split the difference. Working backward from 0.9495, we find $Z = 1.64$, and for 0.9505 we find $Z = 1.65$. Splitting the difference, we get $Z = 1.645$. This value of $Z = 1.645$ is the 95th percentile of the standard normal distribution.

Since we are looking for a sample mean quiz score, 1.645 cannot be the answer. We need to "unstandardize" by transforming this value of Z to an $\bar{x}$-value:

$$\bar{x} = Z \cdot \sigma_{\bar{x}} + \mu = 1.645(2) + 70 = 73.29$$

Now You Can Do
Exercises 17–20.

Thus, the 95th percentile of the sample means for the statistics quizzes is 73.29. ∎

Example 7.6 Finding probabilities and percentiles using sample means

Use the information from Examples 7.4 and 7.5.
a. Find the 5th percentile of the class mean quiz scores.
b. What two symmetric values for the sample mean quiz score contain the middle 90% of all sample means between them?
c. Verify that $P(66.71 \leq \bar{x} \leq 73.29) = 0.90$.

Solution

a. Since the sampling distribution is normal, it is also symmetric. Thus, the 95th percentile and the 5th percentile are the same distance away from the mean. Since the 95th percentile is $(73.29 - 70) = 3.29$ above the mean, the 5th percentile must be 3.29 below the mean, or $(70 - 3.29) = 66.71$.
b. This is just another way of asking for the 5th and 95th percentiles, which we found in Example 7.5 and here in part (a). (See Figure 7.4) The answer is 66.71 and 73.29.

Middle 90% of
sample means
between 66.71 and 73.29

$P(66.71 < \bar{x} < 73.29) = 0.90$

FIGURE 7.4
Middle 90% of the
sample means.

Area = 0.90

65   66.71   73.29   75

$\mu_{\bar{x}} = 70$

Now You Can Do
Exercises 21–28.

c. We seek $P(66.71 < \bar{x} < 73.29)$, as shown in Figure 7.4. Proceeding with the calculations, we have, as expected,

$$P(66.71 < \bar{x} < 73.29) = P\left(\frac{66.71 - 70}{2} < \frac{\bar{x} - 70}{2} < \frac{73.29 - 70}{2}\right)$$

$$= P(-1.645 < Z < 1.645) = 0.95 - 0.05 = 0.90 \quad \blacksquare$$

In Section 7.2, we tackle the more challenging problem of finding the sampling distribution of the sample mean for non-normal populations.

Section 7.1 Summary

1 The sampling distribution of the sample mean $\bar{x}$ for a given sample size n consists of the collection of the means of all possible samples of size n from the population. The mean of the sampling distribution of $\bar{x}$ is the value of the population mean μ (Fact 1). The standard error is $\sigma_{\bar{x}} = \sigma/\sqrt{n}$, where σ is the population standard deviation (Fact 2).

2 For a normal population, the sampling distribution of $\bar{x}$ is distributed as normal $(\mu, \sigma/\sqrt{n})$, where μ is the population mean and σ is the population standard deviation (Fact 3).

3 We can use Fact 3 and Fact 4 to find probabilities and percentiles using sample means.

Section 7.1 Exercises

CLARIFYING THE CONCEPTS

1. Explain in your own words what statistical inference means.

2. Explain what a sampling distribution is. Why are sampling distributions so important?

3. For a normal population, what can we say about the sampling distribution of the sample mean?

4. True or false: $\mu_{\bar{x}} = \mu$ and $\sigma_{\bar{x}} = \sigma/\sqrt{n}$ regardless of whether or not the sampling distribution of $\bar{x}$ is normal.

PRACTICING THE TECHNIQUES

For Exercises 5–10, find $\mu_{\bar{x}}$ and $\sigma_{\bar{x}}$, the mean and standard deviation of the sampling distribution of $\bar{x}$.

5. $\mu = 100, \sigma = 20, n = 25$
6. $\mu = 100, \sigma = 20, n = 100$
7. $\mu = 0, \sigma = 10, n = 9$
8. $\mu = 0, \sigma = 10, n = 25$
9. $\mu = -10, \sigma = 5, n = 100$
10. $\mu = -10, \sigma = 5, n = 400$

For Exercises 11–16, let the random variable X be normally distributed, with mean $\mu = 5$ and standard deviation $\sigma = 3$. Let $n = 9$. Find the following probabilities.

11. $P(\bar{x} > 6)$ **14.** $P(\bar{x} < 7)$
12. $P(\bar{x} < 4)$ **15.** $P(\bar{x} > 3)$
13. $P(4 < \bar{x} < 6)$ **16.** $P(3 < \bar{x} < 7)$

For Exercises 17–22, let the random variable X be normally distributed, with mean $\mu = 100$ and standard deviation $\sigma = 15$. Let $n = 4$. Find the following values of $\bar{x}$.

17. The value of $\bar{x}$ greater than 95% of values of $\bar{x}$
18. The value of $\bar{x}$ smaller than 95% of values of $\bar{x}$
19. The 97.5th percentile of the sample means
20. The 2.5th percentile of the sample means
21. The two symmetric values for the sample mean that contain the middle 90% of sample means. (*Hint:* Use your answers to Exercises 17 and 18.)
22. The two symmetric values for $\bar{x}$ that contain the middle 95% of $\bar{x}$ values

For Exercises 23–30, assume that the random variable X follows a normal distribution, with mean $\mu = 50$ and standard deviation $\sigma = 10$. That is, X is normal (50, 10). Let $n = 25$.

23. Describe the sampling distribution of $\bar{x}$ for $n = 25$.
24. Calculate the probability that $\bar{x}$ is less than 48.
25. Without using your calculator, use the symmetry of the normal distribution to calculate the probability that $\bar{x}$ is greater than 52.
26. Without using your calculator, use your answers from Exercises 24 and 25 to compute the probability that $\bar{x}$ lies between 48 and 52.
27. Find the value of $\bar{x}$ that is greater than 95% of all values of $\bar{x}$.
28. Without using your calculator, use the symmetry of the normal distribution to calculate the value of $\bar{x}$ that is smaller than 95% of all values of $\bar{x}$.
29. What are the two symmetric values for the sample mean that contain the middle 90% of sample means?
30. What proportion of $\bar{x}$ values lies outside the values you found in the previous exercise?

For Exercises 31–38, assume that the random variable X is normally distributed, with mean $\mu = 10$ and standard deviation $\sigma = 4$. Let $n = 16$.

31. Describe the sampling distribution of $\bar{x}$ for $n = 16$.
32. Calculate the probability that $\bar{x}$ exceeds 11.
33. Without using your calculator, use the symmetry of the normal distribution to calculate the probability that $\bar{x}$ is less than 9.
34. Without using your calculator, use your answers from Exercises 32 and 33 to compute the probability that $\bar{x}$ lies between 9 and 11.
35. Find the value of $\bar{x}$ that is greater than 97.5% of all values of $\bar{x}$.
36. Without using your calculator, use the symmetry of the normal distribution to calculate the value of $\bar{x}$ that is smaller than 97.5% of all values of $\bar{x}$.
37. What are the two symmetric values for the sample mean that contain the middle 95% of sample means?
38. What proportion of $\bar{x}$ values lies outside the values you found in the previous exercise?

APPLYING THE CONCEPTS
39. **Lab Rat Reaction Time.** A laboratory rat's mean reaction time to a stimulus is $\mu = 1.7$ seconds, with a standard deviation of $\sigma = 0.3$ second. Let the sample size be $n = 9$.
   a. Find the mean of the sampling distribution $\mu_{\bar{x}}$ and the standard error $\sigma_{\bar{x}}$.
   b. Calculate the probability that the sample mean reaction time will be less than 1.6 seconds.
   c. Compute $P(\bar{x} > 1.8)$.
40. **Student Heights.** The heights of a population of students have a mean of 68 inches (5 feet 8 inches) and a standard deviation of 4 inches. Suppose we take a sample of $n = 16$ students.
   a. Find the mean of the sampling distribution $\mu_{\bar{x}}$ and the standard error $\sigma_{\bar{x}}$.

   b. Calculate the probability that the sample mean student height will be greater than 70 inches.
   c. Compute $P(\bar{x} < 65)$.
41. **Initial Public Offerings.** A monitor of initial public offerings (IPOs) reports that the mean amount of stock offered was $100 million with a standard deviation of $40 million. Suppose that IPO amounts are normally distributed and that we take a sample of 4 IPOs. Find the probability that the sample mean IPO amount will have the following values.
   a. Greater than $125 million
   b. Between $120 million and $140 million
   c. Less than $95 million
42. **Teacher Salaries.** Suppose the salaries of teachers in your city are normally distributed with a mean of $50,000 and a standard deviation of $5000. Suppose we take samples of size 25 teachers. Find the probability that the sample mean salary will have the following values.
   a. More than $52,000
   b. Less than $47,000
   c. Between $52,000 and $53,000
43. **Lab Rat Reaction Time.** Refer to Exercise 39.
   a. Find the sample mean reaction time greater than 95% of all sample mean reaction times.
   b. Find the value of $\bar{x}$ smaller than 95% of all sample mean reaction times.
   c. What are the two symmetric values of $\bar{x}$ that contain the middle 90% of sample means?
   d. Draw a graph of the sampling distribution of $\bar{x}$, with Figure 7.4 as a guide. On the number line, show $\mu_{\bar{x}} = \mu$, along with the two symmetric values of $\bar{x}$ from part (c). Shade the area under the curve between these two values of $\bar{x}$, and indicate the amount of area this represents.
44. **Student Heights.** Refer to Exercise 40.
   a. Find the sample mean student height greater than 97.5% of all sample mean student heights.
   b. Find the value of $\bar{x}$ smaller than 97.5% of all sample mean student heights.
   c. What are the two symmetric values of $\bar{x}$ that contain the middle 95% of sample means?
   d. Draw a graph of the sampling distribution of $\bar{x}$, with Figure 7.4 as a guide. On the number line, show $\mu_{\bar{x}} = \mu$, along with the two symmetric values of $\bar{x}$ from part (c). Shade the area under the curve between these two values of $\bar{x}$, and indicate the amount of area this represents.
45. **Initial Public Offerings.** Refer to Exercise 41.
   a. Calculate the 99.5th percentile of sample mean IPO amounts.
   b. Compute the 0.5th percentile of sample mean IPO amounts.
   c. What are the two symmetric values of $\bar{x}$ that contain the middle 99% of sample means?
   d. Draw a graph of the sampling distribution of $\bar{x}$, showing $\mu_{\bar{x}}$, along with the two symmetric values of $\bar{x}$ from part (c). Shade the area under the curve

between these two values of $\bar{x}$, and indicate the amount of area this represents.

46. Teacher Salaries. Refer to Exercise 42.
   a. Calculate the 90th percentile of sample mean salaries.
   b. Compute the 10th percentile of sample mean salaries.
   c. What are the two symmetric values of $\bar{x}$ that contain the middle 80% of sample means?
   d. Draw a graph of the sampling distribution of $\bar{x}$, showing $\mu_{\bar{x}}$, along with the two symmetric values of $\bar{x}$ from part **(c)**. Shade the area under the curve between these two values of $\bar{x}$, and indicate the amount of area this represents.

47. Carbon Dioxide Concentration. The Environmental Protection Agency reports that the mean concentration of the greenhouse gas carbon dioxide is 365 parts per million (ppm). Suppose the population is normally distributed, assume that the standard deviation is 100 ppm, and suppose we take atmospheric samples from 25 cities.
   a. Find the probability that the sample mean carbon dioxide concentration will be above 385 ppm.
   b. Find the probability that the sample mean carbon dioxide concentration will be between 305 and 425 ppm.
   c. Find the probability that the sample mean carbon dioxide concentration will be below 345.
   d. Find the sample mean carbon dioxide concentration higher than 97.5% of all such sample means.
   e. Find the sample mean carbon dioxide concentration lower than 97.5% of all such sample means.
   f. Describe the area that lies between the values you found in **(a)** and **(b)**.

48. Short-Term Memory. In a famous research paper in the psychology literature, George Miller found that the amount of information humans could process in short-term memory was 7 bits (pieces of information), plus or minus 2 bits.[1] Assume that the mean number of bits is 7 and the standard deviation is 2, and that the distribution is normal. Suppose we take a sample of 100 people and test their short-term memory skills.
   a. Find the probability that the sample mean number of bits retained in short-term memory is greater than 7.5.
   b. Find the probability that the sample mean number of bits retained in short-term memory is between 6.8 and 7.2.
   c. Find the probability that the sample mean number of bits retained in short-term memory is less than 6.75.
   d. Find the 97.5th percentile of the sample mean number of bits retained in short-term memory.
   e. Find the 2.5th percentile of the sample mean number of bits retained in short-term memory.
   f. Between which two values do the middle 95% of sample mean number of bits retained in short-term memory lie?

Japan Earthquakes. Use the following information for Exercises 49–51. On March 11, 2011, a magnitude 9.0 earthquake struck off the shore of Honshu, Japan. The quake

and the resulting tsunami led to massive destruction and the deaths of thousands of people. Shown here are the magnitudes of a set of 5 aftershocks that occurred later that same day.[2] *Consider these magnitudes to be a population.*

Aftershock magnitudes: 7.9   7.7   6.5   6.3   6.1

49. Answer the following.
   a. How many samples of size $n = 2$ can we generate from this tiny population of size 5?
   b. Compute the population mean μ.
   c. Calculate the population standard deviation σ.

50. Take every possible sample of size $n = 2$ from this population.
   a. Find the mean magnitude $\bar{x}$ of each sample.
   b. Construct a dotplot of the sample mean magnitudes, using Figure 7.1 as a guide.
   c. Where would the balance point be located in the dotplot from **(b)**? Indicate it on the plot.
   d. Recall that the balance point represents the mean. What is your estimate of the mean $\mu_{\bar{x}}$ using this balance point?

51. Refer to your work in Exercises 49 and 50.
   a. Find the mean of all the sample mean magnitudes in Exercise 50(a).
   b. Does the value for the mean from Exercise 51(a) agree with the value of the population mean from Exercise 49(b)? Which fact from this section does this reflect?

Avian Flu Deaths. Use the following information for Exercises 52–53. The World Health Organization reported the following numbers of deaths due to avian flu (H5N1) in 2010, by country. *These data represent a population.* 🦢 **avianflu**

Country	Avian flu deaths
Cambodia	1
China	1
Egypt	13
Indonesia	7
Vietnam	2

52. Answer the following.
   a. How many samples of size $n = 3$ can we generate from this tiny population of size 5?
   b. Compute the population mean μ.
   c. Calculate the population standard deviation σ.

53. Take every possible sample of size $n = 3$ from this population.
   a. Find the mean number of deaths $\bar{x}$ of each sample.
   b. Construct a dotplot of the sample mean number of deaths, using Figure 7.1 as a guide.
   c. Find the mean of all the sample mean numbers of deaths in part **(a)**.
   d. Compare your answer from part **(c)** with your answer from Exercise 52(b).

54. A Fair Die. Consider a fair six-sided die. Suppose we take samples of size 16 and are interested in the population mean of the die rolls.

a. Find $\mu_{\bar{x}}$.
b. Find $\sigma_{\bar{x}}$. (*Hint:* First find the standard deviation of a fair die roll using a frequency distribution.)

Stock Portfolios. Use this information for Exercises 55–59. A stockbroker is examining her track record. Over the last 12 quarters, the mean net gain in stock price for all her clients' portfolios was $4, with a standard deviation of $6. She investigates and finds that the distribution is normal.

55. What is the probability that a randomly selected client will have a net loss in stock price (a gain less than 0)?

56. Suppose the stockbroker takes random samples of size $n = 9$ from all her clients.
  a. Find $\mu_{\bar{x}}$.
  b. Find $\sigma_{\bar{x}}$.
  c. What can you say about the sampling distribution of the sample mean? How do you know this?

57. Refer to Exercise 56.
  a. What is the probability that a sample of 9 clients have a sample mean net loss in stock price?
  b. Why is the probability so much lower for the sample mean than for a particular client?
  c. Which figure would look better on the broker's résumé?

? 58. *What if* the population standard deviation was less than $6. Explain how this would affect the following, if at all.
  a. μ
  b. n
  c. Probability that a randomly selected client will have a net loss in stock price
  d. $\mu_{\bar{x}}$
  e. $\sigma_{\bar{x}}$

? 59. *What if* the population standard deviation was less than $6. Explain how this would affect the following, if at all.

  a. Sampling distribution of the sample mean
  b. Probability that a sample of nine clients have a sample mean net loss in stock price

BRINGING IT ALL TOGETHER
SAT Math Scores. Use this information for Exercises 60–64. The College Board (www.collegeboard.com) reports that the nationwide mean math SAT score was 515 in 2007. Assume that the standard deviation is 116 and that the scores are normally distributed.

60. What is the probability that a randomly selected SAT math score will be less than 500?

61. As a researcher, you are looking at samples of SAT math scores of size 16.
  a. Find $\mu_{\bar{x}}$.
  b. Find $\sigma_{\bar{x}}$.
  c. What can you say about the sampling distribution of the sample mean? How do you know this?

62. Refer to Exercise 61.
  a. What is the probability that a sample of 16 students will have a sample mean math SAT score below 500?
  b. Why is the probability so much lower for the sample mean than for a particular student?

63. Refer to Exercise 62. Suppose the population standard deviation was greater than 116. Explain how this would affect the following, if at all.
  a. Probability that a randomly selected SAT math score will be less than 500
  b. $\mu_{\bar{x}}$
  c. $\sigma_{\bar{x}}$
  d. Sampling distribution of the sample mean

? 64. *What if* the population standard deviation was greater than $116. Explain how this would affect the following, if at all.
  a. Probability that a sample of 16 SAT math scores will have a mean less than 500
  b. 99.5th percentile of the sample mean SAT math scores
  c. 0.5th percentile of the sample mean SAT math scores

7.2 Central Limit Theorem for Means

OBJECTIVES By the end of this section, I will be able to . . .

1   Use normal probability plots to assess normality.

2   Describe the sampling distribution of $\bar{x}$ for skewed and symmetric populations as the sample size increases.

3   Apply the Central Limit Theorem for Means to solve probability questions about the sample mean.

1 Assessing Normality Using Normal Probability Plots

Much of the analysis we carry out in this text requires that the sample data come from a population that is normally distributed. But how do we assess whether a data set is normally distributed? Histograms, dotplots, and stem-and-leaf displays may be used.

But a more precise graphical tool for assessing normality is the **normal probability plot.** A normal probability plot is a scatterplot of the estimated cumulative normal probabilities (expressed as percents) against the corresponding data values in the data set.

Figure 7.5 shows the normal probability plot for a sample of normally distributed data. The points are arrayed nicely along the straight line, and all the points lie within the curved bounds. Figure 7.6 shows the normal probability plot for a sample of right-skewed data. The points do not line up in a straight line, and many points lie outside the curved bounds, indicating that the data set is not normal.

> **Analyzing Normal Probability Plots**
>
> If the points in the normal probability plot either cluster around a straight line or nearly all fall within the curved bounds, then it is likely that the data set is normal. Systematic deviations off the straight line are evidence against the claim that the data set is normal.

Now You Can Do
Exercises 7–10.

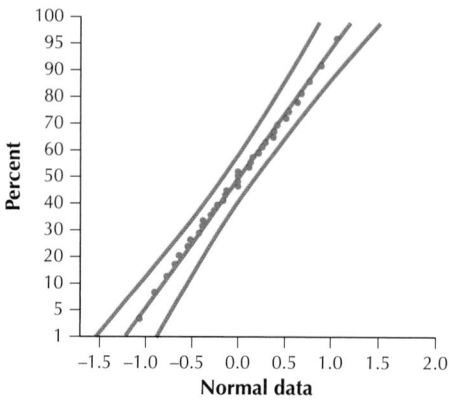

FIGURE 7.5 Normal probability plot of normal data.

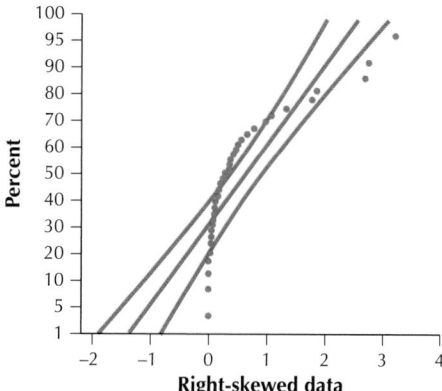

FIGURE 7.6 Normal probability plot of right-skewed data.

2 Sampling Distribution of $\bar{x}$ for Skewed Populations

In Section 7.1, we discovered that the sampling distribution for the sample mean for a normal population is also normal. What if the population is not normal? In this section, we use a simulation study to learn how the sampling distribution of the sample mean $\bar{x}$ for non-normal populations becomes approximately normal as the sample size increases.

Example 7.7 Simulation study: sample means from strongly skewed population

Nutrition

The data set **Nutrition** on your CD and the companion Web site contains nutrition information on a population of 961 foods.
a. Construct a histogram of the potassium content of these 961 foods, and describe the shape of the population distribution.
b. Using Minitab, take 500 random samples of sizes $n = 10$, 20, and 30 from the population. Assess the normality of the resulting sampling distributions of $\bar{x}$ using histograms and normal probability plots.

Solution

a. A histogram of the potassium content of these foods is shown in Figure 7.7, revealing a strongly right-skewed, non-normal data set.

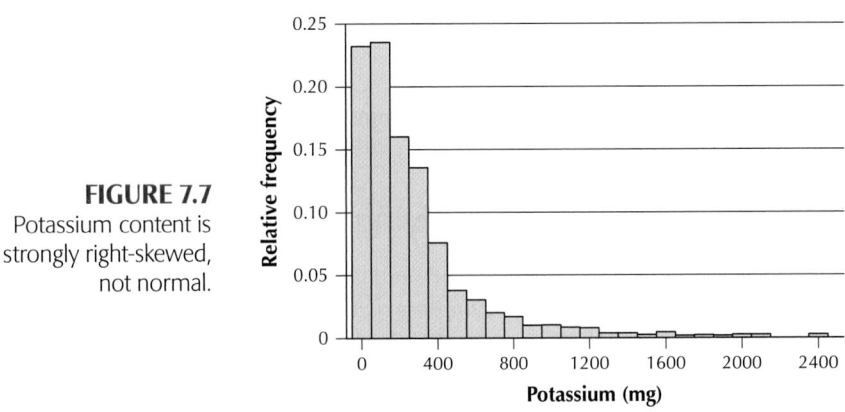

FIGURE 7.7
Potassium content is strongly right-skewed, not normal.

b. Using Minitab, we take 500 random samples of size $n = 10$ from the population. We find the means of the 500 samples shown in the graphs in Figure 7.8.

	Sampling distribution	Normal probability plot
(a) Sample means for samples of size $n = 10$ Still very skewed		
(b) Sample means for samples of size $n = 20$ Still somewhat skewed		
(c) Sample means for samples of size $n = 30$ Approximately normal		

FIGURE 7.8 Sampling distribution of $\bar{x}$ and normal probability plots for $n = 10$, 20, and 30.

- $n = 10$: The sampling distribution of $\bar{x}$ is skewed (Figure 7.8a).
- $n = 20$: The sampling distribution of $\bar{x}$ is still somewhat skewed (Figure 7.8b).
- $n = 30$: Despite a few outliers, the sampling distribution of $\bar{x}$ is approximately normal (Figure 7.8c). ■

For a skewed population, we have seen that the sampling distribution of the sample mean becomes approximately normal as the sample size reaches 30. For a less skewed population, we can expect that the sampling distribution of $\bar{x}$ approximates a normal distribution for smaller sample sizes.

3 Applying the Central Limit Theorem for Means

Based on our simulation study, we may conclude that *regardless of the population, the sampling distribution of the sample mean becomes approximately normal as the sample size gets larger*. We can then combine this statement with Fact 3 (page 341) to form the **Central Limit Theorem for Means.**

> **Central Limit Theorem for Means**
>
> Given a population with mean μ and standard deviation σ, the sampling distribution of the sample mean $\bar{x}$ becomes approximately normal $(\mu, \sigma/\sqrt{n})$ as the sample size gets larger, regardless of the shape of the population.

How large does the sample size have to be before the Central Limit Theorem for Means takes effect? In general, it depends on the degree of symmetry, or skewness, of the population. In the simulation study (Figure 7.8), we saw that the sampling distribution of $\bar{x}$ was approximately normal even for a skewed population when $n = 30$. Thus, we shall abide by the following rule of thumb.

> **Rule of Thumb for When to Use the Central Limit Theorem for Means**
>
> We consider $n \geq 30$ as large enough to apply the Central Limit Theorem for Means for any population.

Developing Your Statistical Sense

The Central Limit Theorem

The Central Limit Theorem (CLT) is one of the most important results in statistics. Worldwide, much statistical inference is based on the CLT. It actually makes fairly intuitive sense, doesn't it? If we find the mean of a sample of data values, in many cases the extreme values will tend to be blended away. However, remember that the mean is very sensitive to outliers. In a small sample, there may not be enough nonextreme values to balance the influence of the outliers. This is what was happening early in the potassium simulation (for example, Figure 7.8a). However, as the sample sizes increase, the influence of extreme values diminishes and the resulting sample means start to migrate toward the center. ◢

Combining Fact 3 and the Central Limit Theorem for Means, we can identify three possible situations for the sampling distribution of $\bar{x}$.

> **Three Possible Situations for the Sampling Distribution of the Sample Mean $\bar{x}$**
>
> 1. **The population is normal.** Therefore the sampling distribution of $\bar{x}$ is *normal* (Fact 3, page 341).
> 2. **The population is either non-normal or of unknown distribution *and* the sample size is at least 30.** Therefore the sampling distribution of $\bar{x}$ is *approximately normal* (Central Limit Theorem for Means).
> 3. **The population is either non-normal or of unknown distribution *and* the sample size is less than 30.** Therefore we have *insufficient information* to conclude that the sampling distribution of the sample mean $\bar{x}$ is either normal or approximately normal.

Of course, in the real world, no one will tell you which of the three situations applies. You need to investigate the assumptions of each of the situations to determine for yourself which one applies.

Example 7.8   Application of the Central Limit Theorem for the Mean

The U.S. Small Business Administration (SBA) provides information on the number of small businesses for each metropolitan area in the United States.[3] Figure 7.9 shows a histogram of our population for this example, the number of small businesses in each of the 328 cities nationwide. (For example, Austin, Texas, has 22,305 small businesses, while Pensacola, Florida, has 6020.) The mean is $\mu = 12{,}485$ and the standard deviation is $\sigma = 21{,}973$.

a.   Find the probability that a random sample of size $n = 36$ cities will have a mean number of small businesses greater than 17,000.
b.   Find the 90th percentile of sample means.

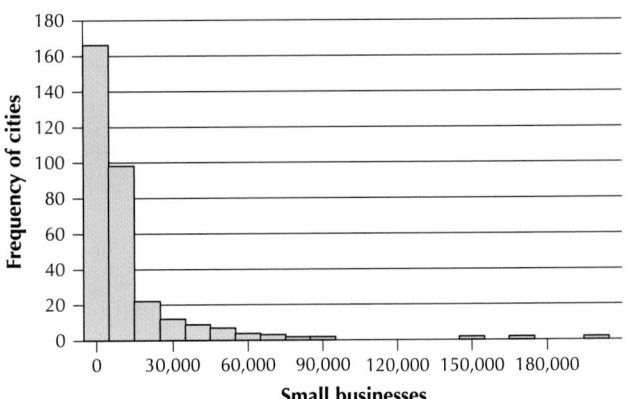

FIGURE 7.9 Population is skewed, so a large sample is needed to apply the Central Limit Theorem.

Solution

a.   Clearly, the population is not normal, but the sample size $n = 36$ is large enough, so the Central Limit Theorem applies. The sampling distribution of the sample mean $\bar{x}$ is approximately normal. Next we need to find $\mu_{\bar{x}}$ and $\sigma_{\bar{x}}$. Facts 1 and 2 tell us that

$$\mu_{\bar{x}} = \mu = 12{,}485 \qquad \text{and} \qquad \sigma_{\bar{x}} = \frac{\sigma}{\sqrt{n}} = \frac{21{,}973}{\sqrt{36}} \approx 3662.1667$$

Therefore, as the CLT indicates, the sampling distribution of $\bar{x}$ is approximately normal ($\mu_{\bar{x}} = 12{,}485$, $\sigma_{\bar{x}} = 3662.1667$). We are then left to solve a normal probability problem using the methods of Sections 6.5 and 6.6. Figure 7.10 shows the sampling distribution of $\bar{x}$ and the probability we are interested in, $P(\bar{x} > 17{,}000)$. Using Fact 4, we standardize:

> Since the CLT has shown the distribution is approximately normal, we can use normal distribution methods to solve the problem.

$$Z = \frac{17{,}000 - \mu_{\bar{x}}}{\sigma_{\bar{x}}} = \frac{17{,}000 - 12{,}485}{3662.1667} \approx 1.2329 \approx 1.23$$

> We round Z to 2 decimal places to allow use of the Z table in finding $P(Z > 1.23)$.

Thus, $P(\bar{x} > 17{,}000) \approx P(Z > 1.23)$, as shown in Figure 7.11. We therefore look up $Z = 1.23$ in the Z table and subtract this table area (0.8907) from 1 to get the desired tail area:

$$P(Z > 1.23) = 1 - 0.8907 = 0.1093$$

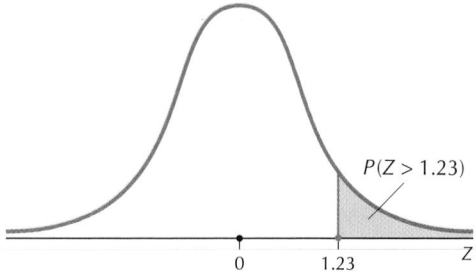

FIGURE 7.10 Area to the right of $\bar{x} = 17,000$ equals. . . . **FIGURE 7.11** Area to the right of $Z = 1.23$.

Now You Can Do
Exercises 17–22.

The probability is 0.1093 that a random sample of 36 cities will have a mean number of small businesses greater than 17,000.

b. We proceed just as we did for Example 7.5 in Section 7.1 (page 343). We seek the area 0.90 on the inside of the Z table. We find the closest area $= 0.8997$, which gives us $Z = 1.28$. Transforming Z to a sample mean value, we calculate:

$$\bar{x} = Z \cdot \sigma_{\bar{x}} + \mu = 1.28(3662.1667) + 12,485 \approx 17,173$$

Now You Can Do
Exercises 23–28.

The value of $\bar{x} \approx 17,173$ is the 90th percentile of sample means. That is, of all possible sample means for $n = 36$, $\bar{x} \approx 17,173$ lies at or above 90% of them. ■

Example 7.9 | Sometimes there is insufficient information to solve the problem

Using the same data set as in Example 7.8, suppose the sample size is only $n = 10$. Now try again to find the probability that a random sample of size $n = 10$ will have a mean number of small businesses greater than 17,000.

Solution

The population is skewed (not normal) and the sample size $n = 10$ is less than the minimum $n = 30$ required to apply the Central Limit Theorem. Therefore, we have insufficient information to conclude that the sampling distribution of the sample mean $\bar{x}$ is either normal or approximately normal. Unfortunately, we cannot find the probability that a random sample of $n = 10$ cities will have a mean number of small businesses greater than 17,000. ■

CASE STUDY Trial of the Pyx: How Much Gold Is in Your Gold Coins?
Medieval English kings devised a procedure to ensure that the coins of the realm contained the proper amount of gold. A sample of 100 of the gold coins that were cast each year was placed in a ceremonial box called the Pyx. At the chosen time, the Company of Goldsmiths jury weighed the gold coins. The weight of the entire sample of coins was supposed to be 12,800 grams. If the weight was much less than 12,800 grams, the jury concluded that the Master of the Mint was cheating the crown by pocketing the excess gold, and he was severely punished.

Problem 1. How did the jury determine what was "much less than 12,800 grams"?

Solution

If the weight of the coins was within 32 grams of the expected 12,800 grams, the jury accepted the year's gold coins as pure. Thus, the *sum* of the weights of the gold coins had to lie between 12,768 grams and 12,832 grams. However, the methods we have learned in this chapter have dealt with the sampling distribution of the sample *mean*, not the sum. Since the sample mean $\bar{x} = \frac{\sum X}{n}$, we divide the total weight of the coins by $n = 100$. So the probability that the Master of the Mint passed the Trial of the Pyx is

$$P(12{,}768 < \sum X < 12{,}832)$$

which, divided through by $n = 100$, becomes

$$P\left(127.68 < \frac{\sum X}{n} < 128.32\right) \qquad \text{or} \qquad P(127.68 < \bar{x} < 128.32)$$

That is, the throne would have accepted the coins as pure if the mean weight of the guineas lay between 127.68 and 128.32 grams, as shown in Figure 7.12.

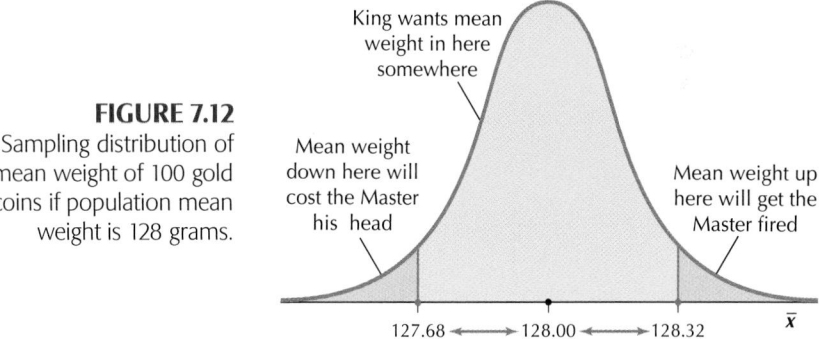

FIGURE 7.12
Sampling distribution of mean weight of 100 gold coins if population mean weight is 128 grams.

Problem 2. Can we estimate what the jury used for a standard deviation?

Solution
Let's assume that "much less than" indicated a measurement that is 2 or more standard deviations below average. For the sampling distribution of $\bar{x}$, then, this would indicate a range of $0.32 = 2\,\sigma_{\bar{x}}$ between 127.68 and the mean 128, as indicated by the arrows in Figure 7.12. Therefore, $\sigma_{\bar{x}} = 0.16$. And therefore, by the Empirical Rule, for instance, approximately 95% of the sample mean observations for the Trial of the Pyx would have been between 127.68 and 128.32. Since $\sigma_{\bar{x}} = \sigma/\sqrt{n}$, it follows that $\sigma = \sqrt{100} \cdot 0.16 = 1.6$ grams.

Problem 3. What were the chances that the Master of the Mint would have been caught and punished if he were in fact cheating the throne?

Solution
What if the Master of the Mint set the mean amount of gold in the population of all coins to be $\mu = 127.9$ grams instead of the required 128, shortchanging the crown by a tenth of a gram of gold per coin? The jury would never have noticed this, would they?

Let's calculate the probability that the Master of the Mint would have passed the Trial of the Pyx if the mean amount of gold in the coins had been only 127.9 grams. We've seen that the Master of the Mint would have passed the Trial of the Pyx if $127.68 < \bar{x} < 128.32$. Now, because 100 is a large sample size, the Central Limit

Theorem tells us that the sampling distribution of $\bar{x}$ is approximately normal, with $\mu_{\bar{x}} = \mu = 127.9$ and $\sigma_{\bar{x}} = \dfrac{\sigma}{\sqrt{n}} = \dfrac{1.6}{\sqrt{100}} = 0.16$.

Standardizing using Fact 5:

$$Z = \frac{127.68 - \mu_{\bar{x}}}{\sigma_{\bar{x}}} = \frac{127.68 - 127.9}{0.16} \approx -1.38 \qquad \text{and}$$

$$Z = \frac{128.32 - \mu_{\bar{x}}}{\sigma_{\bar{x}}} = \frac{128.32 - 127.9}{0.16} \approx 2.63$$

Solving using Table 6.6 in Section 6.5 (page 303):

$$P(-1.38 < Z < 2.63) = 0.9957 - 0.0838 = 0.9119$$

That is, the chances of the crown accepting the coins as pure, even if the Master of the Mint had been shortchanging by a tenth of a gram per coin, were over 91% (Figure 7.13).

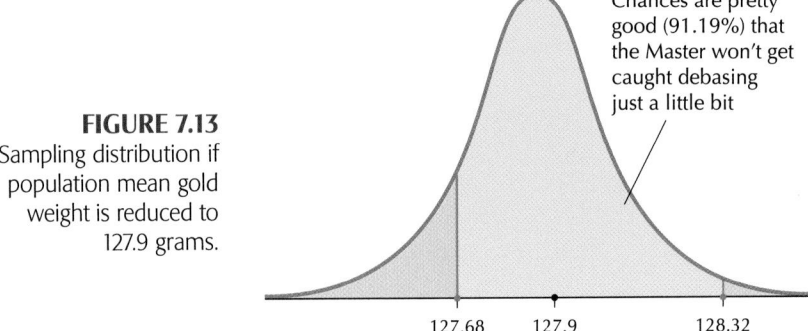

Chances are pretty good (91.19%) that the Master won't get caught debasing just a little bit

FIGURE 7.13
Sampling distribution if population mean gold weight is reduced to 127.9 grams.

127.68   127.9   128.32

Clipart.com

Note: Sir William Sharington, 1493–1553, Master of the Mint during the turbulent Tudor era in England. He debased the currency, issued worthless coinage, and diverted the real gold to fund Thomas Seymour's conspiracy to topple the government and seize young King Edward VI. Sharington was arrested in 1548 or 1549, but he later received pardon and became Sheriff of Wiltshire for a short time before he died.

Problem 4. Would the Master of the Mint have been satisfied with this small amount of debasement? Would he have quit while he was ahead?

Solution

No way! The following year the Master of the Mint decided to debase the currency even further, setting the mean amount of gold in the coins to be $\mu = 127.3$ grams per coin.

We need to find the probability of the Master passing the Trial of the Pyx if the mean amount of gold in a coin was 127.3 grams instead of the required 128 grams per coin. We use the same calculations, with $\mu_{\bar{x}} = 127.3$ grams. Standardizing:

$$Z = \frac{127.68 - \mu_{\bar{x}}}{\sigma_{\bar{x}}} = \frac{127.68 - 127.3}{0.16} \approx 2.38 \qquad \text{and}$$

$$Z = \frac{128.32 - \mu_{\bar{x}}}{\sigma_{\bar{x}}} = \frac{128.32 - 127.3}{0.16} \approx 6.38$$

Then $P(2.38 < Z < 6.38) \approx 1 - 0.9913 = 0.0087$.

In other words, the Master of the Mint actually would have stood very little chance—less than 1% probability—of passing the Trial of the Pyx if he cheated by this much (Figure 7.14).

England is a great country for retaining fine old traditions. Today England's Company of Goldsmiths still operates the London Assay Office where the purity of the kingdom's coin is tested at the annual Trial of the Pyx. ∎

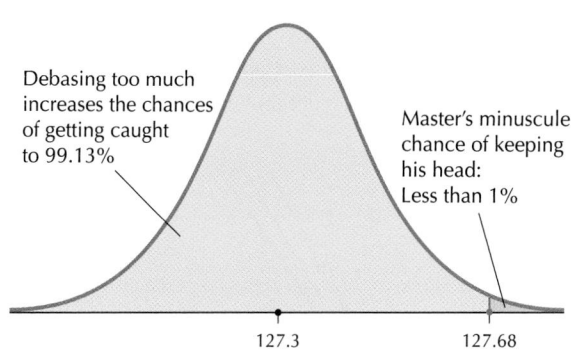

FIGURE 7.14
Sampling distribution if population mean gold weight is reduced to 127.3 grams.

Debasing too much increases the chances of getting caught to 99.13%

Master's minuscule chance of keeping his head: Less than 1%

127.3   127.68

Now You Can Do
Exercises 44–48.

The *Central Limit Theorem* applet allows you to experiment with various sample sizes and see how the Central Limit Theorem for Means behaves in action.

STEP-BY-STEP TECHNOLOGY GUIDE: Constructing Normal Probability Plots

TI-83/84
Assume that the data set is in list L1.
Step 1   Access STAT PLOTS by pressing **2nd Y**.
Step 2   Select **1:Plot1**. Press **ENTER**.
Step 3   Move the cursor over **On** and press **ENTER**.
Step 4   Select the normal probability plot type by moving the cursor to the lower-right plot among the choices for Type. Press **ENTER**.

Step 5   For **Data List**, enter **L1**.
Step 6   For **Data Axis**, choose **X**.
Step 7   Press **ZOOM**, then **9: ZoomStat**.

MINITAB
Assume that the data set is in column **C1**.
Step 1   From the menu, select **Graph**, then click **Probability Plot**.
Step 2   Select **Single** and click **OK**.

Step 3   In the Probability Plot dialog box, select **C1**, and click **OK**. The normal probability plot for the data set in **C1** is then generated.

CRUNCHIT!
We will use the data from Example 7.8, Small Businesses.
Step 1   Click **File . . .** then highlight **Load from Larose2e . . . Chapter 7 . . .** and click on **Example 7.8**.

Step 2   Click **Graphics** and select **QQ Plot**. For **Sample** select **Businesses**. Then click **Calculate**.

Section 7.2 Summary

1 Normal probability plots are used to assess the normality of a data set.

2 A simulation study showed that the sampling distribution of $\bar{x}$ for a skewed population achieved approximate normality when n reached 30.

3 The Central Limit Theorem is one of the most important results in statistics and is stated as follows: given a population with mean μ and standard deviation σ, the sampling distribution of the sample mean $\bar{x}$ becomes approximately normal $(\mu, \sigma/\sqrt{n})$ as the sample size gets larger, regardless of the shape of the population.

Section 7.2 Exercises

CLARIFYING THE CONCEPTS
1. Explain what we use a normal probability plot for. What should we look for in a normal probability plot?
2. Use the Central Limit Theorem to explain what happens to the sampling distribution of $\bar{x}$ as the sample size gets larger.
3. According to our rule of thumb, what is the minimum sample size for approximate normality of the sampling distribution of $\bar{x}$?

4. State the three possible situations for the sampling distribution of $\bar{x}$.
5. Suppose we would like to decrease the size of the standard error to half its original size. How much do we have to increase the sample size?
6. State the conditions when the sampling distribution of $\bar{x}$ is neither normal nor approximately normal.

PRACTICING THE TECHNIQUES

For Exercises 7–10, determine whether the normal probability plots indicate acceptable normality of the data set.

7.

8.

9.

10.
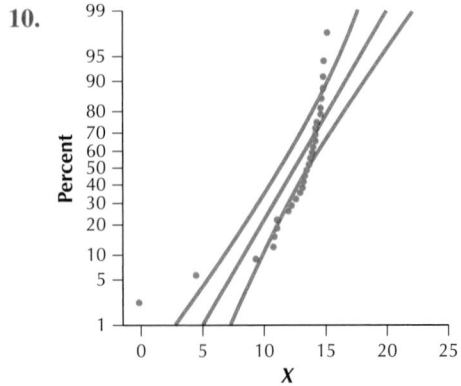

For Exercises 11–16, provide (a) $\mu_{\bar{x}}$ and (b) $\sigma_{\bar{x}}$, and determine whether the sampling distribution of $\bar{x}$ is normal, approximately normal, or unknown. (*Hint:* See the three possible situations on page 350.)

11. SAT scores are normally distributed, with $\mu = 516$ and $\sigma = 116$. A sample of size $n = 9$ is taken.

12. SAT scores are not normally distributed, with $\mu = 516$ and $\sigma = 116$. A sample of size $n = 36$ is taken.

13. Systolic blood pressure readings are not normally distributed, with $\mu = 80$ and $\sigma = 8$. A sample of size $n = 64$ is taken.

14. Systolic blood pressure readings are not normally distributed, with $\mu = 80$ and $\sigma = 8$. A sample of size $n = 25$ is taken.

15. The gas mileage for 2010 Toyota Prius hybrid vehicles is not normally distributed, with $\mu = 50$ miles per gallon and $\sigma = 6$. A sample of size $n = 16$ is taken.

16. The gas mileage for 2010 Toyota Prius hybrid vehicles is not normally distributed, with $\mu = 50$ miles per gallon and $\sigma = 6$. A sample of size $n = 64$ is taken.

For the situations in Exercises 17–22, if possible find the indicated probability. If not possible, explain why not.

17. The situation in Exercise 11—find $P(\bar{x} > 540)$.

18. The situation in Exercise 12—find $P(\bar{x} < 500)$.

19. The situation in Exercise 13—find $P(\bar{x} < 82)$.

20. The situation in Exercise 14—find $P(\bar{x} < 78)$.

21. The situation in Exercise 15—find $P(\bar{x} < 48)$.

22. The situation in Exercise 16—find $P(\bar{x} < 52)$.

For the situations in Exercises 23–28, if possible find the indicated value of $\bar{x}$. If not possible, explain why not.

23. The pollen count distribution for Los Angeles in September is not normally distributed, with $\mu = 8$ and $\sigma = 1$. A sample of size 64 is taken. Find the sample mean pollen count larger than 75% of all sample means.

24. The pollen count distribution for Los Angeles in September is not normally distributed, with $\mu = 8$ and $\sigma = 1$. A sample of size 16 is taken. Find the sample mean pollen count larger than 75% of all sample means.

25. Prices for boned trout are normally distributed, with $\mu = \$3.10$ per pound and $\sigma = \$0.30$. A sample of size 16 is taken. Find the sample mean price that is smaller than 90% of sample means.

26. Prices for boned trout are not normally distributed, with $\mu = \$3.10$ per pound and $\sigma = \$0.30$. A sample of size 16 is taken. Find the sample mean price that is smaller than 90% of sample means.

27. Accountant incomes are not normally distributed, with $\mu = \$60,000$ per year and $\sigma = \$10,000$. A sample of 100 is taken. Find the 5th percentile of sample mean incomes.

28. Accountant incomes are normally distributed, with $\mu = \$60,000$ per year and $\sigma = \$10,000$. A sample of 100 is taken. Find the 95th percentile of sample mean incomes.

APPLYING THE CONCEPTS

29. Cholesterol Levels. The Centers for Disease Control and Prevention reports that the mean serum cholesterol level

in Americans is 202. Assume that the standard deviation is 45. There is no information about the distribution. We take a sample of 36 Americans.
- **a.** Find $P(\bar{x} > 212)$.
- **b.** Calculate $P(192 < \bar{x} < 212)$.

30. Tennessee Temperatures. According to the National Oceanic and Atmospheric Administration, the mean temperature for Nashville, Tennessee, in the month of January between 1872 and 2011 was 38.6°F. Assume that the standard deviation is 10°F, but the distribution is unknown. If we take a sample of $n = 36$, find the following probabilities.
- **a.** $P(\bar{x} < 40)$
- **b.** $P(40 < \bar{x} < 41)$

31. Computers per School. The National Center for Educational Statistics (http://nces.ed.gov) reported that the mean number of instructional computers per public school nationwide was 124. Assume that the standard deviation is 50 computers and that there is no information about the shape of the distribution. Suppose we take a sample of size 100 public schools. Compute the following probabilities.
- **a.** $P(\bar{x} < 110)$
- **b.** $P(110 < \bar{x} < 124)$
- **c.** How do we know the distribution of the sample mean?

32. Stock Prices. A stockbroker was examining her track record. The mean net gain in stock price for all her clients' portfolios was $4, with a standard deviation of $6. She has no information about the distribution.
- **a.** She takes a sample of 16 stocks. If possible, find the probability that the sample will have a mean net loss in stock price (i.e., $P(\bar{x} < 0)$). If not possible, explain why not.
- **b.** Now she takes a sample of 36 stocks. Calculate $P(\bar{x} < 0)$.

33. Cholesterol Levels. Refer to Exercise 29.
- **a.** Find the sample mean serum cholesterol level that is larger than 95% of all such sample means.
- **b.** Calculate the sample mean serum cholesterol level that is smaller than 95% of all such sample means.
- **c.** Draw a graph of the sampling distribution of $\bar{x}$. On the number line, show $\mu_{\bar{x}} = \mu$, along with the two symmetric values of $\bar{x}$ from (a) and (b). Shade the area under the curve between these two values of $\bar{x}$, and indicate the amount of area this represents.

34. Tennessee Temperatures. Refer to Exercise 30.
- **a.** Find the sample mean temperature that is larger than 97.5% of all such sample means.
- **b.** Calculate the sample mean temperature that is smaller than 97.5% of all such sample means.
- **c.** Draw a graph of the sampling distribution of $\bar{x}$. Indicate $\mu_{\bar{x}}$, the two $\bar{x}$ values from (a) and (b), and the area between them.

35. Computers per School. Refer to Exercise 31.
- **a.** Find the 0.5th percentile of sample mean numbers of computers.
- **b.** Compute the 99.5th percentile of sample mean numbers of computers.

- **c.** Draw a graph of the sampling distribution of $\bar{x}$. Indicate $\mu_{\bar{x}}$, the two $\bar{x}$ values from (a) and (b), and the area between them.

36. Stock Prices. Refer to Exercise 32 for $n = 36$.
- **a.** Find the 90th percentile of sample mean net gains.
- **b.** Compute the 10th percentile of sample mean net gains.
- **c.** Draw a graph of the sampling distribution of $\bar{x}$. Indicate $\mu_{\bar{x}}$, the two $\bar{x}$ values from (a) and (b), and the area between them.

Blood Glucose Levels. Use the following information for Exercises 37–39. The population mean blood glucose levels is $\mu = 80$ with standard deviation $\sigma = 10$. Here is the normal probability plot for the population of patients.

Normal probability plot of blood glucose levels.

37. Does the normal probability plot show evidence in favor of normality or against normality? What characteristics of the plot illustrate this evidence?

38. If possible, find the probability that a random sample of $n = 9$ patients will have a mean blood glucose level greater than 86. If not possible, explain why not.

39. If possible, find the probability that a random sample of $n = 36$ patients will have a mean blood glucose level greater than 86. If not possible, explain why not.

Adjusted Gross Income. Use the following information for Exercises 40–43. The population mean adjusted gross income for instructors at a certain college is $\mu = \$50,000$ with standard deviation $\sigma = \$30,000$. Here is the normal probability plot for the population of instructors.

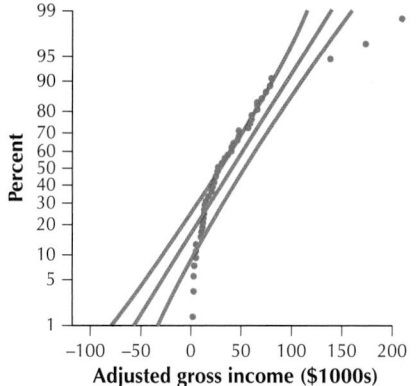

Normal probability plot of adjusted gross income.

40. Does the normal probability plot show evidence in favor of normality or against normality? What characteristics of the plot illustrate this evidence?

41. If possible, find the probability that a random sample of $n = 16$ instructors will have a mean adjusted gross income between $40,000 and $60,000. If not possible, explain why not.

42. If possible, find the probability that a random sample of $n = 36$ instructors will have a mean adjusted gross income between $40,000 and $60,000. If not possible, explain why not.

43. Refer to Exercise 42. *What if* the sample size used was some unspecified value greater than 36? Describe how and why this change would have affected the following, if at all. Would the quantities increase, decrease, remain unchanged? Or is there insufficient information to tell what would happen? Explain your answers.

    a. $\mu_{\bar{x}}$
    b. $\sigma_{\bar{x}}$
    c. $Z = \dfrac{\bar{x} - \mu_{\bar{x}}}{\sigma_{\bar{x}}}$
    d. $P(\$40{,}000 < \bar{x} < \$60{,}000)$

CHAPTER 7 CASE STUDY
Refer to the Case Study on pages 352–355 for Exercises 44–48.

44. What were the chances that the Master of the Mint would have been accused of cheating if he had in fact been completely honest?

In the Case Study, we interpreted the phrase "much less than" to mean a measurement that is 2 or more standard deviations below the mean. For Exercises 45–48, suppose we interpret the phrase "much less than" to mean a measurement that is 3 or more standard deviations below the mean.

45. Use the methods shown in the Case Study to answer the following questions.
    a. What would be the new value of $\sigma_{\bar{x}}$?
    b. What would be the standard deviation σ for each gold piece?
    c. By the Empirical Rule, about what proportion of the mean weights would you now expect to lie between 127.68 and 128.32?

46. Assume "just a little debasement" from 128 grams per coin to 127.9 grams per coin.
    a. Find $P(127.68 < \bar{x} < 128.32)$.
    b. What was the probability that the Master of the Mint would get away with just this little debasement? That he would get caught?
    c. Compare the probabilities in (**b**) with those in the Case Study in the text. Which values favor the Master of the Mint?

47. Assume that greed attacked the Master of the Mint and he went for the big debasement from 128 grams per coin to 127.3 grams per coin.
    a. Find $P(127.68 < \bar{x} < 128.32)$.
    b. What was the probability that the Master of the Mint would get away with this big debasement? That he would get caught?
    c. Compare the probabilities in (**b**) with those in the Case Study in the text. Which values favor the Master of the Mint?

48. The Master of the Mint wanted to choose a mean value so that his chances of failing the Trial of the Pyx were 25%. Which mean value is this?

Use the *Central Limit Theorem* applet for Exercises 49 and 50.

49. Describe the shape of the sampling distribution of $\bar{x}$ for the following sample sizes.
    a. 2   **b.** 5   **c.** 30

50. At what sample size would you say the sampling distribution of $\bar{x}$ becomes approximately normal?

7.3   Central Limit Theorem for Proportions

OBJECTIVES By the end of this section, I will be able to . . .

1   Explain the sampling distribution of the sample proportion $\hat{p}$.

2   Apply the Central Limit Theorem for Proportions to solve probability questions about the sample proportion.

1 Sampling Distribution of the Sample Proportion $\hat{p}$

The sample mean is not the only statistic that can have a sampling distribution. Every sample statistic has a sampling distribution. One of the most important is the sampling distribution of the sample proportion $\hat{p}$.

Suppose each individual in a population either has or does not have a particular characteristic. If we take a sample of size n from this population, the **sample proportion** $\hat{p}$ (read "p-hat") is

$$\hat{p} = \frac{X}{n}$$

where X represents the number of individuals in the sample that have the particular characteristic. We use $\hat{p}$ to estimate the unknown value of the population proportion p. In Section 6.2, we were introduced to $\hat{p}$ as the sample proportion of successes in a binomial experiment.

Example 7.10 Calculating the sample proportion $\hat{p}$

Hemera/Thinkstock

In 2010, the Pew Internet and American Life Project surveyed 3000 Americans, and found 1410 who owned an MP3 player (such as an iPod). Calculate the sample proportion of Americans who own an MP3 player.

Solution

The survey sample size is $n = 30$, and the number of successes is $X = 1410$. We calculate

$$\hat{p} = \frac{X}{n} = \frac{1410}{3000} = 0.47$$

Thus, the sample proportion of Americans who own an MP3 player is 0.47. That is, $\hat{p} = 0.47$, or 47%, of Americans in the sample own an MP3 player. ∎

Like $\bar{x}$, the sample proportion $\hat{p}$ varies from sample to sample. And since we do not know its value prior to taking the sample, $\hat{p}$ is a random variable. Just as we learned the Central Limit Theorem for Means in Section 7.2, here in Section 7.3, we develop a Central Limit Theorem for Proportions, where the **sampling distribution of the sample proportion** becomes approximately normal if the right conditions are satisfied.

The **sampling distribution of the sample proportion $\hat{p}$** for a given sample size n consists of the collection of the sample proportions of all possible samples of size n from the population.

In general, the **sampling distribution of any particular statistic** for a given sample size n consists of the collection of the values of that sample statistic across all possible samples of size n.

Recall that in Section 7.1 we found that the mean of the sampling distribution of the sample mean $\bar{x}$ is $\mu_{\bar{x}} = \mu$ and the standard error of the mean is $\sigma_{\bar{x}} = \sigma/\sqrt{n}$. We now learn the mean and standard error of the sampling distribution of the sample proportion $\hat{p}$.

Fact 5: Mean of the Sampling Distribution of the Sample Proportion $\hat{p}$

The mean of the sampling distribution of the sample proportion $\hat{p}$ is the value of the population proportion p. This may be denoted as $\mu_{\hat{p}} = p$ and read as "the mean of the sampling distribution of $\hat{p}$ is p."

Fact 5 provides a measure of center for the sampling distribution of the sample proportion $\hat{p}$, and Fact 6 provides a measure of spread.

Note: Just as for $\sigma_{\bar{x}}$ (see page 339), the *finite population correction factor*

$$\sqrt{\frac{N - n}{N - 1}}$$

should be used when the population is not much larger than the sample.

> **Fact 6: Standard Deviation of the Sampling Distribution of the Sample Proportion p**
>
> The standard deviation of the sampling distribution of the sample proportion $\hat{p}$ is
>
> $\sigma_{\hat{p}} = \sqrt{\dfrac{p \cdot (1 - p)}{n}}$, where p is the population proportion and n is the sample size. $\sigma_{\hat{p}}$ is called the **standard error of the proportion.**

Example 7.11 | Mean and standard error of $\hat{p}$

The National Institutes of Health reported that color blindness linked to the X chromosome afflicts 8% of men. Suppose we take a random sample of 100 men and let p denote the proportion of men in the population who have color blindness linked to the X chromosome. Find $\mu_{\hat{p}}$ and $\sigma_{\hat{p}}$.

Solution

First, we note that this is a binomial experiment with $p = 0.08$ and $n = 100$. Fact 5 tells us that $\mu_{\hat{p}} = p$, that is, the sampling distribution of the sample proportion $\hat{p}$ has a mean of $p = 0.08$. Fact 6 states that the standard error is

$$\sigma_{\hat{p}} = \sqrt{\frac{p \cdot (1 - p)}{n}} = \sqrt{\frac{0.08 \cdot (1 - 0.08)}{100}} = \sqrt{0.000736} \approx 0.02713 \qquad \blacksquare$$

What Do These Numbers Mean?

Imagine that we repeatedly draw random samples of 100 men and observe the proportion of men $\hat{p}$ in each sample who have color blindness linked to the X chromosome. Each sample provides us with a value for $\hat{p}$. Eventually, the values of $\hat{p}$, when graphed, form the sampling distribution shown in Figure 7.15.

FIGURE 7.15 Sampling distribution of sample proportion $\hat{p}$.

Note that $\mu_{\hat{p}} = p = 0.08$ is located at the balance point of this distribution, which we should expect since the mean proportion of these samples is $\mu_{\hat{p}} = p = 0.08$. Each arrow represents 1 standard error $\sigma_{\hat{p}} = 0.02713$. Note that nearly all the sample proportions lie within 3 standard errors of the mean. ◢

Unfortunately, the sampling distribution of $\hat{p}$ is not always normal. Recall from Section 7.2 that the approximate normality provided by the Central Limit Theorem for Means was a useful tool for solving probability problems for the sample mean $\bar{x}$. Similarly, in order to solve probability problems for the sample proportion $\hat{p}$, we need a way to achieve approximate normality for the sampling distribution of $\hat{p}$. Conditions for the approximate normality of the sampling distribution of $\hat{p}$ are as follows.

Fact 7: Conditions for Approximate Normality of the Sampling Distribution of the Sample Proportion $\hat{p}$

The sampling distribution of the sample proportion $\hat{p}$ may be considered approximately normal only if both the following conditions hold:

$$np \geq 5 \quad \text{and} \quad n(1 - p) \geq 5$$

The **minimum sample size** required to produce approximate normality in the sampling distribution of $\hat{p}$ is the *larger* of either

$$n_1 = \frac{5}{p} \quad \text{or} \quad n_2 = \frac{5}{(1 - p)}$$

(rounded up to the next integer).

---

2 Applying the Central Limit Theorem for Proportions

Using information from Facts 5, 6, and 7, we express the Central Limit Theorem for Proportions.

Central Limit Theorem for Proportions

The sampling distribution of the sample proportion $\hat{p}$ follows an approximately normal distribution with mean $\mu_{\hat{p}} = p$ and standard deviation $\sigma_{\hat{p}} = \sqrt{\dfrac{p \cdot (1 - p)}{n}}$ when both the following conditions are satisfied: $np \geq 5$ and $n(1 - p) \geq 5$.

Example 7.12 Applying the Central Limit Theorem for Proportions

In Example 7.11, we learned that color blindness linked to the X chromosome afflicts 8% of men. Determine the approximate normality of the sampling distribution of $\hat{p}$, the proportion of men who have color blindness linked to the X chromosome, for samples of size (a) 50 and (b) 100.

Solution

We need to check both conditions to find whether the sampling distribution of $\hat{p}$ is approximately normal.

a. We are given that $p = 0.08$ and $n = 50$.

$$np = 50 \cdot 0.08 = 4 \quad \text{and} \quad n(1 - p) = 50 \cdot (0.92) = 46$$

Since 4 is not ≥ 5, the first condition is not satisfied. The Central Limit Theorem for Proportions cannot be used. We cannot conclude that the sampling distribution of $\hat{p}$ is approximately normal.

b. Here $p = 0.08$ and $n = 100$.

$$np = 100 \cdot 0.08 = 8 \quad \text{and} \quad n(1 - p) = 100 \cdot (0.92) = 92$$

Since both 8 and 92 are ≥ 5, both conditions are satisfied. The Central Limit Theorem for Proportions applies, and we can conclude that the sampling distribution of $\hat{p}$ is approximately normal. From Example 7.11 we have $\mu_{\hat{p}} = 0.08$ and $\sigma_{\hat{p}} = 0.02713$. Thus, the sampling distribution of $\hat{p}$ is approximately normal with $\mu_{\hat{p}} = 0.08$ and $\sigma_{\hat{p}} = 0.02713$. ∎

Now You Can Do
Exercises 7–18.

Example 7.13 Minimum sample size for approximate normality

The Texas Workforce Commission reported that the state unemployment rate in March 2007 was 4.3%. Let $p = 0.043$ represent the population proportion of unemployed workers in Texas.
a. Find the minimum size of the samples that produces a sampling distribution of $\hat{p}$ that is approximately normal.
b. Describe the sampling distribution of $\hat{p}$ if we use this minimum sample size.

Solution
a. Using Fact 7, the minimum sample size required is the *larger* of either

$$n_1 = \frac{5}{p} \quad \text{or} \quad n_2 = \frac{5}{1-p}$$

Here

$$n_1 = \frac{5}{p} = \frac{5}{0.043} \approx 116.3 \quad \text{and} \quad n_2 = \frac{5}{1-p} = \frac{5}{0.957} \approx 5.2$$

The larger of n_1 and n_2 is $n_1 = 116.3$. However, it is unclear what "0.3" of a worker means. So we round up to the next integer: $n = 117$. Therefore, the minimum sample size required to produce a sampling distribution of $\hat{p}$ that is approximately normal is $n = 117$ Texas workers. We confirm that this satisfies our conditions:

$$np = (117)(0.043) = 5.031 \geq 5 \quad \text{and} \quad n(1-p) = (117)(0.957) = 111.969 \geq 5$$

b. We have $\mu_{\hat{p}} = 0.043$ and

$$\sigma_{\hat{p}} = \sqrt{\frac{p(1-p)}{n}} = \sqrt{\frac{0.043(0.957)}{117}} \approx \sqrt{0.00035172} \approx 0.01875$$

Since the conditions are met, the Central Limit Theorem for Proportions applies. The sampling distribution of $\hat{p}$ is approximately normal ($\mu_{\hat{p}} = 0.043$, $\sigma_{\hat{p}} = 0.01875$). ∎

Now You Can Do
Exercises 19–24.

In those cases where we determine that the sampling distribution of $\hat{p}$ is approximately normal, we can then proceed to determine probabilities or find percentiles using the normal distribution methods we learned in Chapter 6. Fact 8 is similar to Fact 4.

Fact 8: Standardizing a Normal Sampling Distribution for Proportions

When the sampling distribution of $\hat{p}$ is approximately normal, we can standardize to produce the standard normal Z:

$$Z = \frac{\hat{p} - \mu_{\hat{p}}}{\sigma_{\hat{p}}} = \frac{\hat{p} - p}{\sqrt{\frac{p(1-p)}{n}}}$$

where p is the population proportion of successes and n is the sample size.

Example 7.14 Applying the Central Limit Theorem for proportions

Using the information in Example 7.13, find the probability that a sample of Texas workers will have a proportion unemployed greater than 9% for samples of size (a) 30 respondents and (b) 117 respondents.

Solution
a. We found in Example 7.13(a) that this sample size of $n = 30$ does not meet the minimum sample size required for the sampling distribution of $\hat{p}$ to be

approximately normal, so we cannot conclude that the sampling distribution of $\hat{p}$ is approximately normal. Thus, we cannot solve this problem.

b. From Example 7.13(b), the sampling distribution of $\hat{p}$ is approximately normal with mean $\mu_{\hat{p}} = 0.043$ and standard deviation $\sigma_{\hat{p}} = 0.01875$. We are then faced with a normal probability problem similar to those in Section 6.6. Figure 7.16 shows the sampling distribution of $\hat{p}$ and the probability we are interested in, $P(\hat{p} > 0.09)$. Using Fact 8, we standardize as follows:

Again we can use our normal distribution methods since the CLT for proportions gives us approximate normality.

$$Z = \frac{0.09 - \mu_{\hat{p}}}{\sigma_{\hat{p}}} = \frac{0.09 - 0.043}{0.01875} \approx 2.51$$

Thus, $P(\hat{p} > 0.09) = P(Z > 2.51)$, as shown in Figure 7.17.

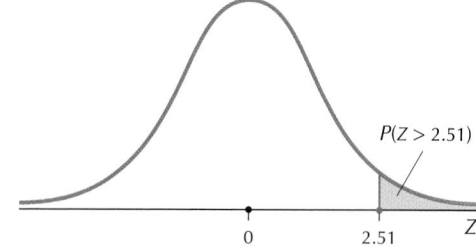

FIGURE 7.16 Area to the right of $\hat{p} = 0.09$ equals. . . .

FIGURE 7.17 Area to the right of $Z = 2.51$.

Following Table 6.6 (page 303), we look up $Z = 2.51$ in the Z table and subtract this table area (0.9940) from 1 to get the desired tail area. That is,

$$P(Z > 2.51) = 1 - 0.9940 = 0.0060$$

Now You Can Do
Exercises 25–32.

So the probability that the sample proportion of unemployed Texas workers will exceed 0.09 is 0.0060. ■

Example 7.15 Applying the CLT for proportions to find a percentile

Using the information from Example 7.13, find the 99th percentile of sample proportions for $n = 117$.

Solution

The 99th percentile shown in Figure 7.18 separates the top 1% of sample proportions from the lower 99%. Thus, the area to the left of the 99th percentile is 0.99. We look up $Z = 0.99$ on the inside of the Z table, and the closest value we can find is 0.9901. The Z-value associated with 0.9901 is 2.33. We need to transform this Z-value back to the scale of sample proportions. Use

$$\hat{p} = Z \cdot \sigma_{\hat{p}} + \mu_{\hat{p}} = (2.33)(0.01875) + 0.043 \approx 0.0867$$

The 99th percentile of the sampling distribution of $\hat{p}$ is 0.0867. ■

Now You Can Do
Exercises 33–38.

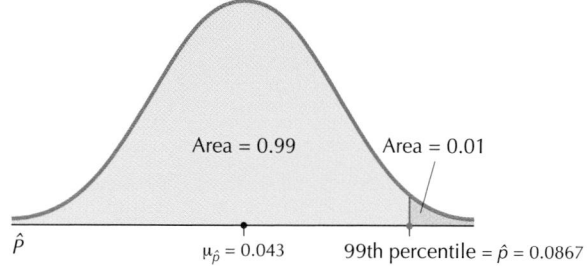

FIGURE 7.18 The 99th percentile of sample proportions.

Example 7.16 Pitfalls of using an approximation

Use symmetry and the results from Example 7.15 to find the 1st percentile of the sampling distribution of $\hat{p}$ for $n = 117$.

Note: What can we do to estimate the 1st percentile? One way is to use simulation. Generate samples of size $n = 117$ from the population of the original survey respondents, record the sample proportion from each, and simply choose the 1st percentile. Proceeding in this manner, we estimate the 1st percentile as 0.0128.

Solution

By symmetry, the 1st percentile will be the same distance below the mean that the 99th percentile is above the mean. The 99th percentile, 0.0867, lies $(0.0867 - 0.043) = 0.0437$ above the mean. Therefore, the 1st percentile lies 0.0437 below the mean:

$$\hat{p} = (0.043 - 0.0437) = -0.0007$$

However, this value of -0.0007 is negative and cannot represent a sample proportion. This negative result is obtained because the normality of the sampling distribution of $\hat{p}$ is only approximate and not exact. ∎

Section 7.3 Summary

1 The sampling distribution of the sample proportion $\hat{p}$ for a given sample size n consists of the collection of the sample proportions of all possible samples of size n from the population.

2 According to the Central Limit Theorem for Proportions, the sampling distribution of the sample proportion $\hat{p}$ follows

an approximately normal distribution with mean $\mu_{\hat{p}} = p$ and standard deviation $\sigma_{\hat{p}} = \sqrt{p \cdot (1 - p)/n}$ when both the following conditions are satisfied: (1) $np \geq 5$ and (2) $n(1 - p) \geq 5$.

Section 7.3 Exercises

CLARIFYING THE CONCEPTS

1. Explain what a sample proportion is, using as an example the courses for which you got an A last semester.
2. What is the mean of the sampling distribution of $\hat{p}$?
3. Give the formula for the standard error of the proportion.
4. What are the requirements for the sampling distribution of $\hat{p}$ to be approximately normal?
5. Suppose you double the sample size. What happens to the standard error of the proportion?
6. For the following values of X and n, calculate the sample proportion $\hat{p}$.
   a. $X = 10, n = 40$
   b. $X = 25, n = 75$
   c. Number of successes = 27, number of trials = 54
   d. Number of successes = 1000, number of trials = 1 million

PRACTICING THE TECHNIQUES

In Exercises 7–18, samples are taken. Find (a) $\mu_{\hat{p}}$ and (b) $\sigma_{\hat{p}}$, and (c) determine whether the sampling distribution of $\hat{p}$ is approximately normal or unknown.
7. $p = 0.5, n = 100$
8. $p = 0.5, n = 5$
9. $p = 0.01, n = 100$
10. $p = 0.01, n = 500$
11. $p = 0.9, n = 40$

12. $p = 0.9, n = 50$
13. $p = 0.02, n = 200$
14. $p = 0.02, n = 250$
15. $p = 0.98, n = 250$
16. $p = 0.98, n = 200$
17. $p = 0.99, n = 500$
18. $p = 0.99, n = 100$

In Exercises 19–24, find the minimum sample size that produces a sampling distribution of $\hat{p}$ that is approximately normal.
19. $p = 0.5$
20. $p = 0.25$
21. $p = 0.1$
22. $p = 0.05$
23. $p = 0.01$
24. $p = 0.001$

For Exercises 25–32, if possible find the indicated probability. If it is not possible, explain why not.
25. $p = 0.5, n = 100, P(\hat{p} > 0.55)$
26. $p = 0.5, n = 5, P(\hat{p} > 0.55)$
27. $p = 0.01, n = 100, P(\hat{p} > 0.011)$
28. $p = 0.01, n = 500, P(\hat{p} > 0.011)$
29. $p = 0.9, n = 40, P(0.88 < \hat{p} < 0.91)$
30. $p = 0.9, n = 50, P(0.88 < \hat{p} < 0.91)$
31. $p = 0.02, n = 200, P(\hat{p} < 0.021)$
32. $p = 0.02, n = 250, P(\hat{p} < 0.021)$

For Exercises 33–38, find the indicated value of $\hat{p}$. If it is not possible, explain why not.

33. $p = 0.5$, $n = 100$, value of $\hat{p}$ larger than 90% of all values of $\hat{p}$
34. $p = 0.5$, $n = 400$, value of $\hat{p}$ larger than 90% of all values of $\hat{p}$
35. $p = 0.9$, $n = 64$, 95th percentile of values of $\hat{p}$
36. $p = 0.9$, $n = 144$, 95th percentile of values of $\hat{p}$
37. $p = 0.1$, $n = 64$, 10th percentile of values of $\hat{p}$
38. $p = 0.1$, $n = 144$, 10th percentile of values of $\hat{p}$

APPLYING THE CONCEPTS

39. **Abandoning Landlines.** The National Health Interview Survey reports that 25% of telephone users no longer use landlines, and have switched completely to cell phone use. Suppose we take samples of size 36.
    a. Find the mean and standard error of the sampling distribution of $\hat{p}$, the sample proportion of telephone users who no longer use landlines.
    b. Describe the sampling distribution of $\hat{p}$.
    c. Compute the probability that $\hat{p}$ exceeds 0.26.
40. **LeBron James.** In the 2009–2010 National Basketball Association season, 50.3% of LeBron James's shots from the floor were successful. Suppose we take a sample of 50 of LeBron's shots.
    a. Find $\mu_{\hat{p}}$ and $\sigma_{\hat{p}}$ for the sample proportion of LeBron's shots that were good.
    b. Describe the sampling distribution of $\hat{p}$.
    c. Calculate $P(\hat{p} > 0.60)$.
41. **Small Business Jobs.** According to the U.S. Small Business Administration, small businesses provide 75% of the new jobs added to the economy. Suppose we take samples of 20 new jobs.
    a. Find $\mu_{\hat{p}}$ and $\sigma_{\hat{p}}$ for the sample proportion of new jobs added to the economy that are provided by small businesses.
    b. Calculate $P(\hat{p} > 0.69)$.
    c. Compute $P(0.775 < \hat{p} < 0.8)$.
42. **AIDS and Drug Use.** The Centers for Disease Control and Prevention reported that, in 2008, 13% of males living with AIDS contracted it through intravenous drug use. Suppose we take samples of 49 males living with AIDS.
    a. Find $\mu_{\hat{p}}$ and $\sigma_{\hat{p}}$ for the sample proportion of males living with AIDS who contracted it through intravenous drug use.
    b. Calculate $P(\hat{p} < 0.04)$.
    c. Compute $P(0.10 < \hat{p} < 0.15)$.
43. **Abandoning Landlines.** Refer to Exercise 39.
    a. Find the 5th and 95th percentiles of the sample proportions.
    b. Draw a graph showing the sampling distribution of $\hat{p}$, centered at p, with the 5th and 95th percentiles, and the area of 0.90 under the curve between them shaded.
    c. Suppose only 2 of 36 phone users abandoned their landlines. Would this be considered an outlier? Explain your reasoning. (*Hint*: Use the Z-score method.)

    d. Determine which sample proportions would be considered outliers.
44. **LeBron James.** Refer to Exercise 40.
    a. Find the 2.5th and 97.5th percentiles of the sample proportions.
    b. Draw a graph showing the sampling distribution of $\hat{p}$, centered at p, with the 2.5th and 97.5th percentiles, and the area of 0.95 under the curve between them shaded.
    c. Suppose LeBron James was shooting at 65% accuracy in a particular game. Would that be considered "hot shooting" by his standards? Explain your reasoning. (*Hint*: Use the Z-score method.)
    d. Suppose LeBron James was shooting at 35% accuracy in a particular game. Would that be considered "poor shooting" by his standards? Explain your reasoning.
45. **Small Business Jobs.** Refer to Exercise 41.
    a. Find the 0.5th and 99.5th percentiles of the sample proportions.
    b. Draw a graph showing the sampling distribution of $\hat{p}$, with the area between the 0.5th and 99.5th percentiles shaded.
    c. Suppose 14 of 20 new jobs added to the economy were provided by small business. Would this be considered unusual? Explain your reasoning.
46. **AIDS and Drug Use.** Refer to Exercise 42.
    a. Find the 2.5th and 97.5th percentiles of the sample proportions.
    b. Draw a graph showing the sampling distribution of $\hat{p}$, with the area between the 2.5th and 97.5th percentiles shaded.
    c. Calculate $P(\hat{p} < 0.12)$.
    d. Suppose someone claimed that the proportion of all males living with AIDS who contracted it through intravenous drug use was less than 0.12. Based on the probability you calculated in (c), do you think there is strong evidence against this claim?
47. **AIDS and Drug Use.** Refer to Exercises 42 and 46. *What if* we increased the sample size to some unspecified larger number. Describe how and why the following quantities would change, if at all.
    a. $\mu_{\hat{p}}$
    b. $\sigma_{\hat{p}}$
    c. $P(\hat{p} < 0.04)$
    d. $P(0.10 < \hat{p} < 0.15)$
    e. $P(0.45 < \hat{p} < 0.49)$
    f. 2.5th percentile of the sample proportions
    g. 97.5th percentile of the sample proportions

BRINGING IT ALL TOGETHER
Partners Checking Up On Each Other. Use the following information for Exercises 48–51. According to a study in the journal *Computers in Human Behavior*,[4] 65% of the college women surveyed checked the call histories on the cell phones of their partners, while 41% of the males did so.

48. Suppose we take a sample of 100 college females and 100 college males.
   a. Find $\mu_{\hat{p}}$ and $\sigma_{\hat{p}}$ for the sample proportion of females checking the call histories of their partners.
   b. Find $\mu_{\hat{p}}$ and $\sigma_{\hat{p}}$ for the sample proportion of males checking the call histories of their partners.

49. Refer to Exercise 48. Calculate the following probabilities.
   a. That more than 65% of the females checked the call histories of their partners
   b. That more than 65% of the males checked the call histories of their partners
   c. That less than 41% of the females checked the call histories of their partners

d. That less than 41% of the males checked the call histories of their partners

50. Refer to Exercise 48.
   a. Find the 2.5th and 97.5th percentiles of the sample proportions of females checking the call histories of their partners.
   b. Find the 2.5th and 97.5th percentiles of the sample proportions of males checking the call histories of their partners.

51. Suppose someone claimed that there really was no difference in the proportions of females and males who check the call histories on their partners' cell phones. How would you use the results from Exercises 49 and 50 to address this claim?

Chapter 7 Formulas and Vocabulary

SECTION 7.1
- **Mean of the sampling distribution of the sample mean $\bar{x}$, Fact 1** (p. 339). Denoted as $\mu_{\bar{x}} = \mu$.
- **Sampling distribution of the sample mean $\bar{x}$** (p. 338)
- **Sampling distribution of $\bar{x}$ for a normal population, Fact 3** (p. 341)
- **Standard error of the mean, Fact 2** (p. 340). $\sigma_{\bar{x}} = \sigma/\sqrt{n}$.
- **Standardizing a normal sampling distribution for means, Fact 4** (p. 341).

$$Z = \frac{\bar{x} - \mu_{\bar{x}}}{\sigma_{\bar{x}}} = \frac{\bar{x} - \mu}{\sigma/\sqrt{n}}$$

SECTION 7.2
- **Central Limit Theorem for Means** (p. 350)
- **Normal probability plot** (p. 348)

SECTION 7.3
- **Central Limit Theorem for Proportions** (p. 361)

- **Conditions for approximate normality, Fact 7** (p. 361)
- **Mean of the sampling distribution of the sample proportion $\hat{p}$, Fact 5** (p. 359). Denoted as $\mu_{\hat{p}} = p$.
- **Minimum sample size required** (p. 361)
- **Sample proportion $\hat{p}$** (p. 359). $\hat{p} = x/n$.
- **Sampling distribution for any statistic** (p. 359)
- **Sampling distribution of the sample proportion $\hat{p}$** (p. 359)
- **Standard error of the proportion, Fact 6** (p. 360).

$$\sigma_{\hat{p}} = \sqrt{p \cdot (1 - p)/n}$$
- **Standardizing a normal sampling distribution for proportions, Fact 8** (p. 362).

$$Z = \frac{\hat{p} - \mu_{\hat{p}}}{\sigma_{\hat{p}}} = \frac{\hat{p} - p}{\sqrt{\frac{p(1 - p)}{n}}}$$

Chapter 7 Review Exercises

SECTION 7.1
For Exercises 1–5, find $\mu_{\bar{x}}$ and $\sigma_{\bar{x}}$, the mean and standard deviation of the sampling distribution of $\bar{x}$.
1. $\mu = 10, \sigma = 5, n = 25$
2. $\mu = 10, \sigma = 5, n = 36$
3. $\mu = 10, \sigma = 5, n = 49$
4. $\mu = 50, \sigma = 40, n = 4$
5. $\mu = 50, \sigma = 40, n = 16$

For Exercises 6–9, assume that X is normal ($\mu = 10, \sigma = 4$) and $n = 25$.
6. Find the sampling distribution of $\bar{x}$ for $n = 25$.
7. Find the probability that $\bar{x}$ exceeds 11.
8. Without using your calculator, find the probability that $\bar{x}$ is less than 9.
9. Without using your calculator, find the probability that $\bar{x}$ lies between 9 and 11.

SECTION 7.2
For Exercises 10 and 11, if possible find the indicated probability. If it is not possible, explain why not.

10. Scores on a psychological test are not normally distributed, with $\mu = 100$ and $\sigma = 15$. A sample of size 25 is taken. Find $P(94 < \bar{x} < 103)$.
11. Scores on a psychological test are normally distributed, with $\mu = 100$ and $\sigma = 15$. A sample of size 25 is taken. Find $P(94 < \bar{x} < 103)$.

For Exercises 12 and 13, find the indicated value of $\bar{x}$. If it is not possible, explain why not.
12. Scores on a psychological test are not normally distributed, with $\mu = 100$ and $\sigma = 15$. A sample of size 25 is taken. Find the 50th percentile of sample means.
13. Scores on a psychological test are normally distributed, with $\mu = 100$ and $\sigma = 15$. A sample of size 25 is taken. Find the 50th percentile of sample means.
14. **Cocaine and Heart Attacks.** The American Medical Association reported: "During the first hour after using cocaine, the user's risk of heart attack increases nearly 24 times. The average age of people in the study who suffered heart attacks soon after using cocaine was only 44. That's about 17 years

younger than the average heart attack patient. Of the 38 cocaine users who had heart attacks, 29 had no prior symptoms of heart disease."[5] Assume that the standard deviation of the age of people who suffered heart attacks soon after using cocaine was 10 years and we take a sample of size 38.

  a. Find the 97.5th percentile of the mean age at heart attack after using cocaine.
  b. Find the 2.5th percentile of the mean age at heart attack after using cocaine.
  c. Between which two sample mean ages that are symmetric about the population mean lie 95% of mean ages of all people who suffered heart attacks soon after using cocaine?
  d. By hand, sketch a plot of how this would look.

SECTION 7.3
For Exercises 15 and 16, if possible find the indicated probability. If it is not possible, explain why not.
15. $p = 0.1$, $n = 40$, $P(\hat{p} < 0.12)$
16. $p = 0.1$, $n = 50$, $P(\hat{p} < 0.12)$

For Exercises 17 and 18, find the indicated value of $\hat{p}$. If it is not possible, explain why not.
17. $p = 0.02$, $n = 400$, the value of $\hat{p}$ smaller than 75% of all p values
18. $p = 0.02$, $n = 625$, the value of $\hat{p}$ smaller than 75% of all p values
19. **Women and Men and Depression.** According to the National Institute for Mental Health, 12% of women are affected by a depressive disorder each year. Suppose we take samples of 49 women. Answer the following.

  a. Find $P(\hat{p} > 0.15)$, where $\hat{p}$ represents the sample proportion of women who are affected by a depressive disorder each year.
  b. Calculate $P(0.12 < \hat{p} < 0.15)$.
  c. Use your answer to (a) to calculate $P(\hat{p} < 0.15)$.
  d. Find the 5th and 95th percentiles of the sample proportion.

Chapter 7 QUIZ

TRUE OR FALSE
1. True or false: For a normal population, the sampling distribution of the sample mean is always normal.
2. True or false: Since the Central Limit Theorem takes effect at $n = 30$, it doesn't make sense to get larger samples.

FILL IN THE BLANK
3. The distance between the point estimate and its target parameter is called the _____ _____ [two words].
4. If the population is either non-normal or of unknown distribution and the sample size is large, then the sampling distribution of $\bar{x}$ is _____ _____ (two words).

SHORT ANSWER
5. If the population is either non-normal or of unknown distribution and the sample size is small, then do we know the sampling distribution of $\bar{x}$?
6. The sampling distribution of the sample proportion $\hat{p}$ may be considered approximately normal only if *both* the following conditions hold: (1) _____ and (2) _____.

CALCULATIONS AND INTERPRETATIONS
Soybean Crop. Protein content in a particular farmer's soybean crop is normally distributed, with a mean of 40 grams and a standard deviation of 20 grams. Suppose we take samples of size 100 soy plants. Use this information for Exercises 7 and 8.
7. **a.** Find the probability that the sample mean protein content will be less than 38 grams.
  b. Find the probability that the sample mean protein content will be between 36.08 and 43.92 grams.

  c. Find the probability that the sample mean protein content will be greater than 42.5 grams.
8. Refer to Exercise 7.
  a. Find the sample mean protein content higher than 99.5% of all such sample means.
  b. Find the sample mean protein content lower than 99.5% of all such sample means.
  c. Between which two values does the middle 99% of sample mean protein content lie?

Student Heights. Use this information for Exercises 9 and 10. The heights of the population of students at a college are normally distributed with a mean of 68 inches (5 feet 8 inches) and a standard deviation of 3 inches. Suppose we take samples of 100 students.
9. **a.** Find the probability that the sample mean height will exceed 68.6 inches.
  b. Find the probability that the sample mean height will be less than 67.4 inches.
  c. Find the probability that the sample mean height will be between 67.4 and 68.6 inches.
10. **a.** Find the 99.5th percentile of sample mean heights.
  b. Find the 0.5th percentile of sample mean heights.
  c. Between which two values do the middle 99% of sample mean heights lie?
11. **Men and Depression.** According to the National Institute for Mental Health, 6.6% of men are affected by a depressive disorder each year.
  a. If we take samples of 100 men, find $P(\hat{p} < 0.066)$.
  b. If we take samples of 100 men, find $P(0.05 < \hat{p} < 0.066)$.
  c. If we take samples of 100 men, find the 2.5th and 97.5th percentiles of the sample proportion.

8

Confidence Intervals

Introduction

In Chapter 7, students learned that point estimation cannot determine how close a point estimate is to its target parameter. In Chapter 8, they discover confidence interval estimations, using their knowledge of sampling distributions from Chapter 7. By studying the patterns implicit in the sampling distribution of a statistic (such as the sample mean or sample proportion), students can infer with a certain degree of confidence that the associated population parameters lie within a certain interval.

This chapter builds confidence intervals for a population mean, a population proportion, and the population variance and standard deviation. The relationship between sample size and the precision of the interval estimate is also discussed.

From the Author

- **Section 8.1 Z Interval for the Population Mean**

  - The *point estimate* topic has been moved here from Section 7.1.

  - The material on the Z interval for the population mean has been completely rewritten, making it simpler and more straightforward.

  - Instructors may wish to stress that the $\pm$ notation refers to two different quantities, and that $\bar{x} + E$ refers to an interval on the number line.

  - Instructors may wish to refer to previous examples where intervals on the number line were discussed in earlier chapters, such as Example 6.36 (page 309), Example 6.42 (page 317), and Example 7.6 (page 343).

- **Section 8.2 t Interval for the Population Mean**

  - Instructors may point out that, if the population standard deviation σ is unknown, it is wrong to use the Z interval. Use the *t* interval instead.

  - Note that the *t* table used in *Discovering Statistics* provides the confidence levels for finding the values of $t_{\alpha/2}$, so students need not calculate $\alpha/2$.

  - Newer models of the TI-84 can calculate $t_{\alpha/2}$.

- **Section 8.3 Z Interval for the Population Proportion**

  - Instructors may wish to highlight Example 8.19, since many students may have heard of the phrase "plus or minus 3 percentage points."

  - Note the new Chapter 8 Case Study: Health Effects of the *Deepwater Horizon* Oil Spill.

- **Section 8.4 Confidence Intervals for the Population Variance and Standard Deviation**
  - This is where the chi-square distribution is introduced. Instructors who plan on covering Chapter 11, "Categorical Data Analysis," but are not covering confidence intervals for the population standard deviation, may wish to return to this section for a quick review of the chi-square distribution before starting Chapter 11.

Teaching Tips

Discuss the polls that are in the news. For instance, discuss the president's approval rating plus or minus 3 percentage points.

You may want to make sure that students understand the $\pm$ notation. That is, $a \pm b$ refers to two quantities: $a + b$, and $a - b$.

For t intervals, note that the t table has the confidence levels provided at the top of the table, so that it is not necessary to find $1 - \alpha$ or $1 - \frac{\alpha}{2}$.

In-Class Activities

1. Estimate the proportion of females at your university.
   a. Guess the population proportion of females at your school.
   b. Find the sample proportion of females in your class.
   c. What would you say is the probability that the value for the sample proportion from (b) is exactly equal to the actual population proportion of females at your school?
   d. If appropriate, construct a 90% confidence interval for the population proportion of females at your school, using the sample size and sample proportion from your class.
   e. Does your guess from (a) fall within the confidence interval from (d)?

2. To illustrate what "confidence" means as it relates to a confidence interval, you can simulate 100 confidence intervals (or more) by sampling from a normal distribution with known mean and standard deviation. If the appropriate technology (e.g., Minitab) is available, students also can simulate these confidence intervals for different means and standard deviations. The percentages of the number of intervals that contain the population mean can then be computed and related to the level of confidence. If students participate, the class can pool the percentages to find the average percent, a better estimate for the level of confidence.

3. **Estimating the Mean Shoe Size for All Female and Male Students at Your School**

   a. Make a guess at what the population mean shoe size might be for all female students at your school. Do the same for the males.

   b. Collect data on the shoe sizes of the female students in your class. Find the mean of this sample.

   c. What would you say is the probability that the value for the sample mean from (b) is exactly equal to the mean foot size of all female students at your school?

   d. Use technology to determine if the female shoe sizes are normally distributed. If not, and if the number of females is not at least 30, discuss whether it is appropriate to construct a *t* confidence interval for the population mean shoe size of all females at your school, and go to (g).

   e. Construct a 95% confidence interval for the population mean shoe size for all female students at your school.

   f. Does your guess for the population mean shoe size from (a) fall within the confidence interval from (e)?

   g. Repeat (b)–(f) for the males in your class.

Supplements

- StatTutor 14.1–14.4, 18.1–18.3, 20.3–20.5
- Stats@Work Simulations
  - What Does It Really Mean? Confidence Level; Mike Mobile
  - What Does It Really Mean? Confidence Level; Vicki Vitamin
  - What Does It Really Mean? Confidence Level; Ruby Sweet
  - What Does It Really Mean? Confidence Level; Justine Red
- EESEE case studies
  - Columbus' 1993 Election Poll (Questions 1, 2, 3, 4, and 5 on estimation and confidence interval for a population proportion)
  - Radar Detectors and Speeding (Questions 1, 2, and 3 on confidence interval for a population proportion)

Applets

The *Normal Density Curve* and *Confidence Interval* applets are referenced in Chapter 8 for demonstrations.

The *Confidence Interval* applet is used for Exercises 72 and 73 in Section 8.1 and the *Normal Density Curve* applet for Exercises 74 and 75 in Section 8.1.

This Web site has an applet for confidence interval: **http://wise.cgu.edu/**.

Videos

- *Against All Odds* **www.learner.org/resources/series65.html**
  - Program 19: Confidence Intervals

Web Sites

- The site Online Statistics: An Interactive Multimedia Course of Study has information on confidence intervals and a link to the Rice Virtual Lab in Statistics with numerous simulation demonstrations along with other topics related to statistics: **http://onlinestatbook.com/index .html**.
- This Web site lists other sites that do statistical calculations: **http://statpages.org/**.
- This Web site lists activities on all topics: **http://mathforum.org/mathtools/sitemap2/ps/**.
- This site has several activities using Excel and Minitab: **www.mathspace.com/NSF_ProbStat/ Teaching_Materials/Primarily_Statistics.htm**.

AP Photo/Tertius Pickard

OVERVIEW

8

Confidence Intervals

CASE STUDY Health Effects of the *Deepwater Horizon* Oil Spill

On April 20, 2010, an explosion occurred on the *Deepwater Horizon* oil drilling rig 48 miles off the coast of Louisiana, causing a fireball visible 35 miles away. The *Deepwater Horizon* sank, leaving oil gushing from the seafloor into the Gulf of Mexico and creating the largest oil spill in United States history.

An army of cleanup workers fanned out across the states bordering the Gulf of Mexico in an effort to rescue wildlife, protect beaches, and save wetlands. Many of these workers were exposed to oil, chemical dispersants, cleaners, and other chemicals. The National Institute for Occupational Safety and Health was concerned about the health effects on the workers of exposure to the oil and chemicals. A survey was taken of the exposed workers to determine the extent of their injuries or symptoms. We shall use the new statistical tools that we learn in Chapter 8 to examine the results of this survey in Section 8.3 in the Case Study, Health Effects of the *Deepwater Horizon* Oil Spill.

The Big Picture

Where we are coming from, and where we are headed . . .

- We stand on the threshold of the two most important statistical inference methods: confidence intervals and hypothesis testing. From descriptive statistics in Chapters 1–4 through probability and probability distributions in Chapters 5–6 and sampling distributions in Chapter 7, everything that we have studied thus far has been in preparation for this moment.

- Here in Chapter 8, we learn about *confidence interval estimation*, where we can infer with a certain level of confidence that our target parameter lies within a particular interval.

- Every chapter from here to the end of the book will uncover a new and different topic in statistical inference. In Chapter 9, "Hypothesis Testing," we will learn about the most prevalent method of statistical inference.

8.1   Z Interval for the Population Mean

OBJECTIVES By the end of this section, I will be able to . . .

1   Calculate a point estimate of the population mean.

2   Calculate and interpret a Z interval for the population mean when the population is normal and when the sample size is large.

3   Find ways to reduce the margin of error.

4   Calculate the sample size needed to estimate the population mean.

1 Calculate a Point Estimate of the Population Mean

Recall from Section 1.2 that characteristics of a sample, such as the sample mean $\bar{x}$, are called **statistics**, while characteristics of a population, like the population mean μ, are called **parameters. Statistical inference** consists of methods for estimating and drawing conclusions about parameters, based on the corresponding statistic. For example, we use the known value of $\bar{x}$ to estimate the unknown value of μ.

Suppose a random sample of 30 male students at your school produced a sample mean height of $\bar{x} = 70$ inches. We could then use this statistic $\bar{x} = 70$ to *infer* that the population mean height μ of all male students at your school was close to 70 inches. This value of $\bar{x} = 70$ is called a **point estimate** of the population mean μ.

> **Point estimation** is the process of estimating unknown population parameters by known sample statistics. The value of each sample statistic used as an estimate is called a **point estimate.**

Example 8.1 Calculating a point estimate

istockphoto.com

Suppose we are interested in estimating the population mean price for pumpkins across all 50 states. Shown here is the mean 2008 price per state for pumpkins for a sample of 5 states, in cents per pound, as published by the United States Department of Agriculture.
a. Find the sample mean price $\bar{x}$.
b. Express $\bar{x}$ as the point estimate of μ, the unknown population mean price for pumpkins.

State	Price per pound (in cents)
California	15
Michigan	16
New York	36
Ohio	24
Pennsylvania	16

Solution

a. The sample mean price per pound is calculated as

$$\bar{x} = \frac{\sum x}{n} = \frac{15 + 16 + 36 + 24 + 16}{5} = 21.4$$

b. The point estimate of μ, the unknown nationwide mean price per pound of pumpkins, is the sample mean $\bar{x} = 21.4$ cents per pound. ■

Now You Can Do
Exercises 11–14.

However, since a sample is only a small subset of the population, generalizing from a sample to the population carries the risk that the point estimate may not be very accurate. For example, do you think that the population mean price of pumpkins μ exactly equals our point estimate of 21.4 cents per pound? It's not likely, since we learned in Example 7.1 (page 338) that different samples will produce different sample means, and thus different point estimates of μ. Our point estimate $\bar{x} = 21.4$ may be close to μ or it may be far from μ. In other words, *we have no measure of confidence* that our point estimate is close to μ. There has to be a better way, and there is: *confidence intervals*, the subject of this chapter.

2 The *Z* Interval for the Population Mean

Although we cannot measure how confident we are of $\bar{x}$ as a point estimate for μ, we can use the point estimate $\bar{x}$ to find an interval that is likely to contain μ. Suppose we are interested in estimating the mean height of the students at your school. Since the students in your class are a sample of the population of students at your school, suppose we calculate the sample mean height of the students in your class to be $\bar{x} = 67.5$ inches (5 feet 7½ inches tall).

We may then use $\bar{x} = 67.5$ inches as a point estimate of the unknown population mean height of all students at your school. However, this estimate is not likely to be exactly correct. To address this uncertainty in our estimate, we can use a range of heights instead, such as 67.5 inches, give or take an inch, which we write

$$67.5 \text{ inches} \pm 1 \text{ inch}$$

and would equal the interval

$$(66.5 \text{ inches}, 68.5 \text{ inches})$$

The "1 inch" is called the *margin of error*. We might then say that

> we are 90% confident that the mean height of all students at our school lies in the interval 67.5 inches ± 1 inch (see the figure in the margin).

We are 90% confident that μ lies between 66.5 inches and 68.5 inches.

To increase the confidence in our estimate, we increase the margin of error, so that we might say

> we are 95% confident that the mean height of all students at our school lies in the interval 67.5 inches ± 2 inches

or the interval (65.5 inches, 69.5 inches). These two intervals are examples of what are called **confidence intervals.**

> A **confidence interval** is an estimate of a parameter consisting of an interval of numbers based on a point estimate, together with a **confidence level** specifying the probability that the interval contains the parameter.

For example, our estimate that the mean height of all students at our school would lie in the interval (66.5 inches, 68.5 inches) was reported with confidence level

$$90\% = (1 - 0.10) \cdot 100\%$$

Confidence intervals are often reported in the format:

$$(\text{lower bound, upper bound})$$

In the 90% confidence interval above, we have lower bound = 66.5 and upper bound = 68.5.

A confidence level of 90% for a confidence interval means that the probability is 0.9 that the population parameter lies between the lower bound and the upper bound. Recall that in previous chapters we calculated probabilities for normal distributions using the standard normal Z. We can use Z to develop the formula for the Z confidence intervals for the population mean.

But before we do so, we need to define some notation.

- Let α (alpha) be some small constant, usually $(0 < \alpha \le 0.10)$.

- Define $Z_{\alpha/2}$ to be the value of (standard normal) Z that has area $\alpha/2$ to the right of it. (Figure 8.1).

    For example, for $\alpha = 0.05$, $\alpha/2 = 0.25$ and $Z_{\alpha/2} = Z_{0.025} = 1.96$, as we know from Example 6.36 in Section 6.5.

- Since the Z distribution is symmetric, the area to the left of $-Z_{\alpha/2}$ is also $\alpha/2$.

- Thus, area $1 - \alpha$ lies in the interval of values of Z between $-Z_{\alpha/2}$ and $Z_{\alpha/2}$. That is, the area $1 - \alpha$ lies in the interval $-Z_{\alpha/2} < Z < Z_{\alpha/2}$ (see Figure 8.1).

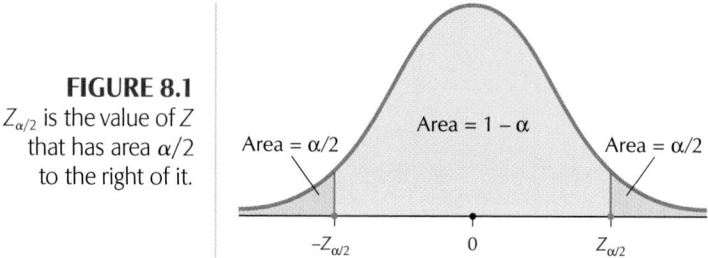

FIGURE 8.1
$Z_{\alpha/2}$ is the value of Z that has area $\alpha/2$ to the right of it.

Area $= \alpha/2$ Area $= 1 - \alpha$ Area $= \alpha/2$

$-Z_{\alpha/2}$ 0 $Z_{\alpha/2}$

Next, we use the facts we learned in Chapter 7 about the sampling distribution of the sample mean to develop the formula for the confidence interval for the mean.

- Fact 1: $\mu_{\bar{x}} = \mu$.

- Fact 2: $\sigma_{\bar{x}} = \sigma/\sqrt{n}$ (standard error of the mean).

- Fact 3: Sampling distribution is normal when the population is normal.

- Fact 4: Standardize $\bar{x}$ to get

$$Z = \frac{\bar{x} - \mu}{\sigma/\sqrt{n}}$$

Plugging this formula for Z back into the earlier inequality, $-Z_{\alpha/2} < Z < Z_{\alpha/2}$, gives

$$-Z_{\alpha/2} < \frac{\bar{x} - \mu}{\sigma/\sqrt{n}} < Z_{\alpha/2}$$

We then use algebra to isolate μ as the middle term:

$$\bar{x} - Z_{\alpha/2}(\sigma/\sqrt{n}) < \mu < \bar{x} + Z_{\alpha/2}(\sigma/\sqrt{n})$$

Therefore, since areas represent probabilities, we can write

$$P(\bar{x} - Z_{\alpha/2}(\sigma/\sqrt{n}) < \mu < \bar{x} + Z_{\alpha/2}(\sigma/\sqrt{n})) = 1 - \alpha$$

The quantities on either side of μ in this inequality represent the lower bound and the upper bound for a $100(1 - \alpha)\%$ confidence interval for μ. Since this confidence interval for μ is based on the standard normal Z distribution, it is called the **Z interval for the population mean μ.**

> **Z Interval for the Population Mean μ**
>
> The *Z* interval for μ may be constructed only when either of the following two conditions are met:
>
> - The population is normally distributed, and the value of σ is known.
> - The sample size is large (≥ 30), and the value of σ is known.
>
> When a random sample of size n is taken from a population, a $100(1 - \alpha)\%$ confidence interval for μ is given by
>
> $$\text{lower bound} = \bar{x} - Z_{\alpha/2}(\sigma/\sqrt{n})$$
> $$\text{upper bound} = \bar{x} + Z_{\alpha/2}(\sigma/\sqrt{n})$$
>
> where $1 - \alpha$ is the confidence level. The *Z* interval can also be written as
>
> $$\bar{x} \pm Z_{\alpha/2}(\sigma/\sqrt{n})$$
>
> and is denoted
>
> $$(\text{lower bound, upper bound})$$

To use the *Z* interval for μ, the value of σ must be known.

Now You Can Do
Exercises 15–20.

Two important results from Chapter 7 form the conditions that allow us to construct the *Z* interval for μ:

- The first condition comes from Fact 3 in Section 7.1: if the population is normal, then the sampling distribution of $\bar{x}$ is also normal.

- The second condition is a result of the Central Limit Theorem for Means (from Section 7.2): if the sample size is large, then the sampling distribution of $\bar{x}$ is approximately normal.

Table 8.1 provides a listing of $Z_{\alpha/2}$ values for the most common confidence levels.

Now You Can Do
Exercises 21–26.

Table 8.1 $Z_{\alpha/2}$ values for common confidence levels

Confidence level $(1 - \alpha)100\%$	α	$\alpha/2$	$Z_{\alpha/2}$
$100(1 - 0.10)\% = 90\%$	0.10	0.05	1.645
$100(1 - 0.05)\% = 95\%$	0.05	0.025	1.96
$100(1 - 0.01)\% = 99\%$	0.01	0.005	2.576

Example 8.2 Constructing a confidence interval for the mean of a normal population

The College Board reports that the scores on the 2010 SAT Math test were normally distributed. A sample of 25 SAT scores had a mean of $\bar{x} = 510$. Assume that the population standard deviation of such scores is $\sigma = 100$. Construct a 90% confidence interval for the population mean SAT score on the 2010 SAT Math test.

Solution

Because the population is normal and the population standard deviation σ is known, the requirements for the *Z* interval are met:

$$\text{lower bound} = \bar{x} - Z_{\alpha/2}(\sigma/\sqrt{n}) \qquad \text{upper bound} = \bar{x} + Z_{\alpha/2}(\sigma/\sqrt{n})$$

We are given $\bar{x} = 510$, $\sigma = 100$, and $n = 25$. From Table 8.1 we have $Z_{\alpha/2} = 1.645$. Thus

$$\text{lower bound} = 510 - 1.645(100/\sqrt{25}) = 477.1$$
$$\text{upper bound} = 510 + 1.645(100/\sqrt{25}) = 542.9$$

Now You Can Do
Exercises 27–29.

We are 90% confident that the population mean SAT score on the 2010 Mathematics SAT test lies between 477.1 and 542.9. ■

What Does This Confidence Interval Mean?

What does the 90% mean in the phrase *90% confidence interval*? If we take sample after sample for a very long time, then in the long run, the proportion of intervals that will contain the population mean μ will equal 90%.

Interpreting Confidence Intervals

You may use the following generic interpretation for the confidence intervals that you construct: "We are 90% (or 95% or 99% and so on) confident that the population mean _____ (for example, SAT Math score) lies between _____ (lower bound) and _____ (upper bound)." ◢

The Z interval for the population mean μ takes the form

$$\text{point estimate} \pm \text{margin of error } E$$

where the point estimate $\bar{x}$ and the margin of error E equals $Z_{\alpha/2}(\sigma/\sqrt{n})$.

> The **margin of error E** is a measure of the precision of the confidence interval estimate. For the Z interval, the margin of error takes the form $E = Z_{\alpha/2}(\sigma/\sqrt{n})$.

For example, the confidence interval from Example 8.2 has the form

$$\text{point estimate} \pm \text{margin of error } E$$
$$= \bar{x} \pm E$$
$$= \bar{x} \pm Z_{\alpha/2}(\sigma/\sqrt{n})$$
$$= 510 \pm 32.9$$

Later in this section we learn ways to reduce the margin of error.

Developing Your Statistical Sense

What Is Random Here?

It is important to understand that *it is the interval that is random, not the population mean μ*. The interval is formed by sample statistics like $\bar{x}$, and for each different sample we get different values for the statistics. So the interval is random because it is constructed using $\bar{x}$, which is also random. The population mean μ, though unknown, is nevertheless *constant*.

Examine Figure 8.2, which shows a set of 10 90% confidence intervals in the form $\bar{x} \pm E$, along with the population mean μ. Note that the intervals are random while μ is constant. It turns out that 9 out of 10 of the samples (90%) produced confidence intervals that contained μ. But it did not have to turn out this way. The

90% refers to the proportion of intervals that will contain μ after a great many samples are taken. ◢

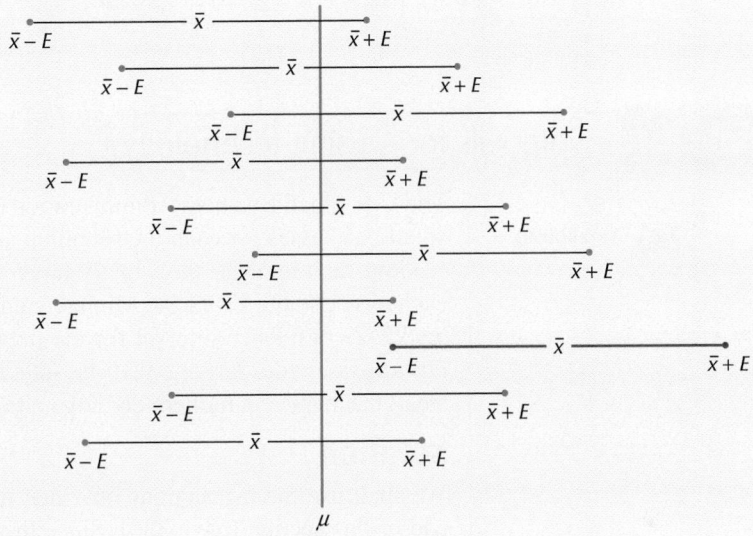

FIGURE 8.2 The intervals are random; μ is constant.

Example 8.3   Constructing a *Z* interval for the population mean for a large sample size

The Washington State Department of Ecology reported that the mean lead contamination in trout in the Spokane River is 1 part per million (ppm), with a standard deviation of 0.5 ppm.[1] Suppose a sample of $n = 100$ trout has a mean lead contamination of $\bar{x} = 1$ ppm. Assume that $\sigma = 0.5$ ppm.

a. Determine whether the requirements are met for constructing the *Z* interval for μ.

b. Construct a 95% confidence interval for μ, the population mean lead contamination in all trout in the Spokane River.

c. Interpret the confidence interval.

Solution

a. We are not given any information about the distribution of the population, so we don't know if the population is normally distributed. However, the sample size $n = 100$ is greater than 30 and the value of $\sigma = 0.5$ is known; therefore we can proceed to construct the confidence interval.

b. The formula for the confidence interval is given by

$$\text{lower bound} = \bar{x} - Z_{\alpha/2}(\sigma/\sqrt{n})$$
$$\text{upper bound} = \bar{x} + Z_{\alpha/2}(\sigma/\sqrt{n})$$

We are given $n = 100$, $\bar{x} = 1$, and $\sigma = 0.5$. For a confidence level of 95%, Table 8.1 provides the value of $Z_{\alpha/2} = Z_{0.025} = 1.96$. Plugging in the formula:

$$\text{lower bound} = 1 - 1.96(0.5/\sqrt{100}) = 1 - 1.96(0.05) = 1 - 0.098 = 0.902$$
$$\text{upper bound} = 1 + 1.96(0.5/\sqrt{100}) = 1 + 1.96(0.05) = 1 + 0.098 = 1.098$$

c. We are 95% confident that μ, the population mean lead contamination for all trout on the Spokane River, lies between 0.902 ppm and 1.098 ppm. (See Figure 8.3.) ∎

Now You Can Do
Exercises 30–32.

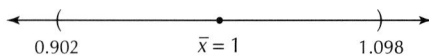

FIGURE 8.3 95% confidence interval for the population mean lead contamination.

Example 8.4 | Z intervals for μ using technology

smallbiz30

The U.S. Small Business Administration (SBA) provides information on the number of small businesses for each metropolitan area in the United States. Table 8.2 contains a random sample of 30 moderately large cities and the number of small businesses in each city. Use the TI-83/84, Minitab, and the WHFStat Add-ins for Excel to construct a 95% Z confidence interval for the population mean number of small businesses in cities nationwide. Assume that the standard deviation is $\sigma = 4300$ for the number of small businesses in moderately large cities.

Solution

We shall use the instructions provided in the Step-by-Step Technology Guide at the end of this section (page 380). Since the sample size $n = 30$ is large (≥ 30), it is not necessary to check for normality.

Table 8.2 Small businesses in a sample of 30 cities

City	Small businesses	City	Small businesses	City	Small businesses
Orlando, FL	32,751	Cincinnati, OH	25,618	Nashville, TN	21,736
Kansas City, MO	32,750	Salt Lake City, UT	25,107	New Orleans, LA	21,565
San Jose, CA	30,921	Las Vegas, NV	24,867	Oklahoma City, OK	21,102
West Palm Beach, FL	30,226	Monmouth, NJ	24,255	Hartford, CT	20,677
Charlotte, NC	28,739	Columbus, OH	23,786	Jacksonville, FL	20,168
Indianapolis, IN	27,397	Raleigh, NC	23,566	Grand Rapids, MI	18,636
Sacramento, CA	27,189	Providence, RI	23,205	Buffalo, NY	18,285
Milwaukee, WI	26,456	Norfolk, VA	22,844	Richmond, VA	18,015
Fort Worth, TX	25,735	Greensboro, NC	22,359	Louisville, KY	17,754
Middlesex, NJ	25,726	Austin, TX	22,305	Greenville, SC	16,791

FIGURE 8.4 TI-83/84 results.

The results for the TI-83/84 in Figure 8.4 show that the 95% Z confidence interval for the population mean number of small businesses per city is

lower bound = 22,479, upper bound = 25,556

Figure 8.4 also shows the sample mean $\bar{x} = 24{,}017.7$, the sample standard deviation $s = 4322.473886$, and the sample size $n = 30$.

The Minitab results are provided in Figure 8.5. The "assumed standard deviation" is indicated to be $\sigma = 4300$. Then the sample size $n = 30$, the sample mean $\bar{x} = 24{,}018$ (rounded), and the sample standard deviation $s = 4322$ (rounded) are displayed. "SE Mean" refers to the standard error of the mean, but we don't need it here. Finally, the 95% confidence interval is given as (lower bound = 22,479, upper bound = 25,556).

```
One-Sample Z: Small Businesses

The assumed standard deviation = 4300

Variable              N    Mean   StDev  SE Mean      95% CI
Small Businesses     30   24018    4322      785  (22479, 25556)
```

FIGURE 8.5 Minitab results.

The results from the WHFStat Add-ins for Excel are shown in Figure 8.6.

SUMMARY STATISTICS		
Sample Mean	Sample Size	Standard Deviation
24017.7	30	4300

ONE SAMPLE Z CONFIDENCE INTERVAL	
Confidence Level	Critical Z Value
95 %	1.96

Confidence Interval		
24017.7	+/-	1538.735
22478.96	to	25556.43

FIGURE 8.6 WHFStats Add-ins results.

The confidence level 95% is shown, along with the critical *Z* value, $Z_{\alpha/2} = 1.96$. The confidence interval is then shown:

$$\text{lower bound} = 22{,}478.96, \text{ upper bound} = 25{,}556.43$$

This 99% confidence interval can also be expressed as (22,478.96, 25,556.43). ■

3 Ways to Reduce the Margin of Error

Recall that the *Z* interval for μ takes the form

$$\text{point estimate} \pm \text{margin of error} = \bar{x} \pm E$$

where $E = Z_{\alpha/2}(\sigma/\sqrt{n})$.

We interpret the margin of error *E* for a $(1 - \alpha)100\%$ confidence interval for μ as follows:

We can estimate μ to within *E* units with $(1 - \alpha)100\%$ confidence.

Example 8.5 Finding and interpreting the margin of error

In Example 8.3, the *Z* interval for the population mean lead contamination (in ppm) for all trout on the Spokane River is

$$\text{lower bound} = 1 - 1.96\,(0.5/\sqrt{100}) = 1 - 1.96\,(0.05) = 1 - 0.098 = 0.902$$

$$\text{upper bound} = 1 + 1.96\,(0.5/\sqrt{100}) = 1 + 1.96\,(0.05) = 1 + 0.098 = 1.098$$

a. Find the margin of error *E*.
b. Express the confidence interval in the form "point estimate ± margin of error."
c. Interpret the margin of error *E*.

Solution

a. We find the margin of error as follows:

$$E = Z_{\alpha/2}(\sigma/\sqrt{n}) = 1.96(0.5/\sqrt{100}) = 1.96(0.05) = 0.098$$

b. The point estimate is $\bar{x} = 1$. Thus, the 95% confidence interval for the population mean lead contamination (in ppm) for all trout on the Spokane River takes the following form:

$$\text{point estimate} \pm \text{margin of error}$$
$$= \bar{x} \pm Z_{\alpha/2}(\sigma/\sqrt{n})$$
$$= 1 \pm 0.098$$

c. We interpret the margin of error E by saying that we can estimate the population mean lead contamination for all trout in the Spokane River to *within 0.098 ppm with 95% confidence.* ■

Now You Can Do
Exercises 33–38.

Of course, we would like our confidence interval estimates to be as precise as possible. Therefore, we would like the margin of error to be as small as possible, which would in turn result in a tighter confidence interval. Tighter confidence intervals are better, since the likely maximum difference between the sample mean and the population mean is reduced. So how do we reduce the size of the margin of error? Let's look at the margin of error for the Z interval:

Note: When it comes to the margin of error E, smaller is better!

$$E = Z_{\alpha/2}(\sigma/\sqrt{n})$$

Since the population standard deviation σ is fixed, only $Z_{\alpha/2}$ and n can vary. There are therefore two strategies for decreasing the margin of error:

- *Decrease the confidence level*, which would decrease the value of $Z_{\alpha/2}$ (see Table 8.1), and

- *Increase the sample size n*, since dividing by a larger $\sqrt{n}$ will reduce E.

Example 8.6 Decreasing the margin of error by decreasing the confidence level

For the confidence interval for the population mean lead contamination in Example 8.3, suppose we reduce the confidence level from 95% to 90% and leave everything else unchanged. Find the new margin of error. Describe how the margin of error has changed.

Solution

For confidence level 90%, $Z_{\alpha/2} = 1.645$, giving the following margin of error:

$$E = Z_{\alpha/2}(\sigma/\sqrt{n}) = 1.645\,(0.5/\sqrt{100}) \approx 0.082$$

Decreasing the confidence level from 95% to 90% decreases the margin of error from 0.098 to 0.082 ppm. ■

Developing Your Statistical Sense

There's No Free Lunch

The margin of error in Example 8.6 is smaller than the one in Example 8.3, which is good because it gives a more precise estimate of μ. However, this smaller margin of error is due entirely to the decrease in the confidence level, which is not good. In statistical data analysis, there is rarely a free lunch. The trade-off here is that, while the margin of error went down, so did the confidence level, from 95% to 90%. On the other hand, confidence intervals that are too wide can be useless. For example, we can be 99.9999% confident that the population mean age of college students in Florida lies between 15 and 75 years old. But, so what? The interval is too wide to be of practical use. More useful would be a 95% confidence interval that the population mean age of college students in Florida lies between 20 and 27. ◢

This leads us to Strategy 2 for reducing the margin of error: increase the sample size. *The only way to have both high confidence and a tight interval is to boost the sample size.*

Example 8.7   Decreasing the margin of error by increasing the sample size

For the confidence interval for the population mean lead contamination in Example 8.3, suppose the results were based on a sample of size $n = 400$ rather than $n = 100$. Leaving everything else unchanged, find the new margin of error, and describe how the margin of error has changed.

Solution

For $n = 400$, the margin of error is

$$E = Z_{\alpha/2}(\sigma/\sqrt{n}) = 1.96(0.5/\sqrt{400}) = 0.049$$

Increasing the sample size from $n = 100$ to $n = 400$ has decreased the margin of error from 0.098 to 0.049 ppm. ∎

"More data" is a familiar refrain in statistical analysis circles. Of course, increasing the sample size often raises pocketbook issues, since large samples can get very expensive ("We would like a large-sample estimate of the amount of damage sustained by Corvettes hitting a wall at 90 mph"). Sometimes obtaining large samples is simply impossible. Suppose an astronomer has developed a new technique for predicting corona effects during solar eclipses; she will have to wait a while (say, a few hundred years) to build up a large sample. So, take samples as large as realistically possible to keep the width of the confidence interval as narrow as possible.

4 Sample Size for Estimating the Population Mean

When samples are plentiful and cheap, *arbitrarily precise confidence intervals with arbitrarily high confidence are possible simply by taking sufficiently large samples.*
Therefore, the question arises: *How large a sample size do I need* to get a tight confidence interval with a high confidence level?

Example 8.8   Sample size for estimating the population mean

Suppose we want to estimate to within $1000 the mean salary μ of all college graduates who were business majors. How many business majors would we sample to estimate the mean salary to within $1000 with 95% confidence?

Solution

Note: We solve for *n* as follows:

$$1000 = 1.96\,(\sigma/\sqrt{n})$$

Multiply both sides by $\sqrt{n}$:

$$1000\sqrt{n} = 1.96\sigma$$

Divide both sides by 1000:

$$\sqrt{n} = \left(\frac{1.96\sigma}{1000}\right)$$

Square both sides to get the formula for *n*:

$$n = \left(\frac{1.96\sigma}{1000}\right)^2$$

"Within $1000" means that the margin of error E is $1000. Recall that the margin of error for 95% confidence is given by

$$E = 1.96\,(\sigma/\sqrt{n})$$

where 1.96 is the $Z_{\alpha/2}$ value associated with 95% confidence. Since the desired margin of error is 1000,

$$E = 1000 = 1.96\,(\sigma/\sqrt{n})$$

Solving for *n* gives us

$$n = \left(\frac{1.96\sigma}{1000}\right)^2$$

Suppose we know that $\sigma = \$5000$. Then:

$$n = \left(\frac{1.96 \cdot 5000}{1000} \right)^2 = 96.04$$

Now You Can Do
Exercises 41–48.

When finding the required sample size, if the formula results in a decimal, we always round up to the next whole number. Thus, we need a sample size of $n = 97$ for a confidence level of 95%. ∎

We generalize the result from Example 8.8 as follows.

Sample Size for Estimating the Population Mean

The sample size for a Z interval that estimates the population mean μ to within a margin of error E with confidence $100(1 - \alpha)\%$ is given by

$$n = \left(\frac{(Z_{\alpha/2}) \sigma}{E} \right)^2$$

We round up because (a) the sample size n must be a whole number and (b) rounding down will lead to a value of n with less than the desired confidence level.

where $Z_{\alpha/2}$ is the value associated with the desired confidence level (Table 8.1), E is the desired margin of error, and σ is the population standard deviation. By convention, whenever this formula yields a sample size with a decimal, *always round up to the next whole number*.

 The *Normal Density Curve* applet may be used to find $Z_{\alpha/2}$ critical values for confidence levels not listed in Table 8.1.

 The *Confidence Interval* applet allows you to see for yourself how individual samples generate intervals that either do or do not contain the population mean.

STEP-BY-STEP TECHNOLOGY GUIDE: Z Confidence Intervals

We illustrate how to construct the confidence interval for Example 8.4 (page 376).

TI-83/84

If you have the data values:
Step 1 Enter the data into list **L1** (Figure 8.7).
Step 2 Press **STAT**, highlight **TESTS**.
Step 3 Press **7** (for **ZInterval**).
Step 4 For input (**Inpt**), highlight **Data** and press **ENTER** (Figure 8.8).
a. For σ, enter the assumed value of **4300**.
b. For **List**, press **2nd** then **L1**.
c. For **Freq**, enter **1**.
d. For **C-Level** (confidence level), enter the appropriate confidence level (e.g., **0.95**), and press **ENTER**.
e. Highlight **Calculate** and press **ENTER**. The results are shown in Figure 8.4 in Example 8.4.

If you have the summary statistics:
Step 1 Press **STAT**, highlight **TESTS**.
Step 2 Press **7** (for **ZInterval**).
Step 3 For input (**Inpt**), highlight **Stats** and press **ENTER** (Figure 8.9).
a. For σ, enter the assumed value of **4300**.
b. For $\bar{x}$, enter the sample mean **24017.7**.
c. For n, enter the sample size **30**.
d. For **C-Level** (confidence level), enter the appropriate confidence level (e.g., **0.95**), and press **ENTER**.
e. Highlight **Calculate** and press **ENTER**. The results are shown in Figure 8.4 in Example 8.4.

FIGURE 8.7

FIGURE 8.8

FIGURE 8.9

EXCEL

If you have the data values:
Step 1 Enter the data into column A.
Step 2 Load the **WHFStat Add-ins**.
Step 3 Select **Add-ins > Macros > Estimating a Mean > Z Confidence Interval**.
Step 4 Click **Select Dataset Range**, highlight A1–A30, and click **OK**.
Step 5 Input **4300** for the **Population Standard Deviation**, select the **95%** confidence level, and click **OK**.
The results are displayed in Figure 8.6 in Example 8.4.

If you have the summary statistics:
Step 1 Load the **WHFStat Add-ins**.
Step 2 Select **Add-ins > Macros > Estimating a Mean > Z Confidence Interval**.
Step 3 Click **Input Summary Statistics**, enter 24017.7 for the **Sample Mean**, enter **30** for the **Sample Size**, and click **OK**.
Step 4 Input **4300** for the **Population Standard Deviation**, select the **95%** confidence level, and click **OK**.
The results are displayed in Figure 8.6 in Example 8.4.

MINITAB

If you have the data values:
Step 1 Enter the data into column C1.
Step 2 Click **Stat > Basic Statistics > 1-Sample Z**.
Step 3 Click **Samples in Columns** and select **C1**.
Step 4 Click **Options**, enter **95** as the **Confidence Level**, and click **OK**.
Step 5 Enter **4300** for **Sigma** and click **OK**.
The results are displayed in Figure 8.5 in Example 8.4.

If you have the summary statistics:
Step 1 Click **Stat > Basic Statistics > 1-Sample Z**.
Step 2 Click **Summarized Data**.
Step 3 Enter the **Sample Size 30** and the **Sample Mean 24017.7**.
Step 4 Enter **4300** for the **Standard Deviation**.
Step 5 Click **Options**, enter **95** as the **Confidence Level**, click **OK**, and click **OK** again.
The results are displayed in Figure 8.5 in Example 8.4.

CRUNCHIT!

If you have the data values:
Step 1 Click **File ...** then highlight **Load from Larose2e ... Chapter 8 ...** and click on **Example 8.4**.
Step 2 Click **Statistics ... Z** and select **1-sample**.
Step 3 With the **Columns** tab chosen, for **Sample** select **Businesses**. For **Standard Deviation**, enter **4300**.
Step 4 Select the **Confidence Interval** tab, and enter **95** for the **Confidence Interval Level**.
Then click **Calculate**.

If you have the summary statistics:
Step 1 Click **Statistics ... Z** and select **1-sample**.
Step 2 Choose the **Summarized** tab. For **n** enter the sample size **30**; for **Sample Mean** enter 24017.7. For **Standard Deviation**, enter **4300**.
Step 3 Select the **Confidence Interval** tab, and enter **95** for the **Confidence Interval Level**.
Then click **Calculate**.

Section 8.1 Summary

1 Using a single statistic only, such as $\bar{x}$, to estimate a population parameter is called point estimation. The value of the statistic is called the point estimate.

2 A confidence interval estimate of a parameter consists of an interval of numbers generated by a point estimate, together with an associated confidence level specifying the probability that the interval contains the parameter. The $100(1 - \alpha)\%$ Z confidence interval for μ is given by the interval

$$\text{lower bound} = \bar{x} - Z_{\alpha/2}(\sigma/\sqrt{n})$$
$$\text{upper bound} = \bar{x} + Z_{\alpha/2}(\sigma/\sqrt{n})$$

where $1 - \alpha$ is the confidence level. If σ is not known, then the Z interval cannot be used.

3 The margin of error E is a measure of the precision of the confidence interval estimate. For the Z interval, the margin of error takes the form

$$E = Z_{\alpha/2}(\sigma/\sqrt{n})$$

Usually, our confidence intervals take the form

$$\text{point estimate} \pm \text{margin of error}$$

4 To use a Z interval to estimate the population mean μ to within a margin of error E with confidence $100(1 - \alpha)\%$, the required sample size is given by

$$n = \left[\frac{(Z_{\alpha/2})\sigma}{E}\right]^2$$

where $Z_{\alpha/2}$ is associated with the desired confidence level (Table 8.1), E is the desired margin of error, and σ is the population standard deviation. Round up to the next integer if there is a decimal.

Section 8.1 Exercises

CLARIFYING THE CONCEPTS

1. Explain why a point estimate, together with a margin of error, is more likely to capture the value of a population parameter than a point estimate alone.

2. What are two ways of presenting a confidence interval?

3. Suppose that a 95% confidence interval for the population mean football score is (15, 25). Interpret this confidence interval.

4. True or false: It is the confidence interval that is random, not the population mean μ.

5. Let E represent the margin of error. Explain what the "$\pm$" notation means in $\bar{x} \pm E$.

6. What is the difference between *confidence interval* and *confidence level*?

7. Assume that the confidence level increases.
  a. What happens to the value of $Z_{\alpha/2}$?
  b. Explain why this happens. Draw a sketch to help you.

8. Suppose your supervisor wants to (a) increase the confidence level from 95% to 99% and (b) keep the width of the confidence interval small. What is the only way to accomplish this?

9. What happens to the required sample size for estimating the population mean as the confidence level is increased? Decreased?

10. What happens to the required sample size for estimating the population mean as the margin of error is increased? Decreased?

PRACTICING THE TECHNIQUES

For the data sets shown in Exercises 11–14, calculate the point estimate of the population mean μ.

11.

2	3	1	3	1

12.

8	4	6	4	8

13.

11	17	14	17	11

14.

96	104	100	96	104

For Exercises 15–20, random samples are drawn. Indicate whether or not we can use the Z confidence interval for μ.

15. The sample size is large ($n \geq 30$) and σ is unknown.

16. The original population is normal and σ is known.

17. The sample size is large ($n \geq 30$) and σ is known.

18. The sample size is small ($n < 30$), the original population is normal, and σ is known.

19. The sample size is large ($n \geq 30$), the original population is not normal, and σ is known.

20. The original population is not normal, and σ is not known.

For Exercises 21–26, find the value of $Z_{\alpha/2}$.

21. Confidence level = 99%

22. $\alpha = 0.05$

23. Confidence level = 95%

24. $\alpha/2 = 0.025$

25. Confidence level = 90%

26. $\alpha = 0.01$

For Exercises 27–32, answer the following questions.
  a. Calculate $\sigma/\sqrt{n}$.
  b. Find $Z_{\alpha/2}$ for a confidence interval for μ with 95% confidence.
  c. Construct and interpret a 95% confidence interval for μ.

27. A random sample of $n = 16$ with sample mean $\bar{x} = 35$ is drawn from a normal population in which $\sigma = 2$.

28. A random sample of $n = 25$ with sample mean $\bar{x} = 50$ is drawn from a normal population in which $\sigma = 5$.

29. A random sample of $n = 9$ with sample mean $\bar{x} = 15$ is drawn from a normal population in which $\sigma = 6$.

30. A random sample of $n = 64$ with sample mean $\bar{x} = 10$ is drawn from a population in which $\sigma = 4$.

31. A random sample of $n = 49$ with sample mean $\bar{x} = 20$ is drawn from a population in which $\sigma = 7$.

32. A random sample of $n = 81$ with sample mean $\bar{x} = 100$ is drawn from a population in which $\sigma = 18$.

For Exercises 33–38, do the following.
  a. Compute the margin of error for the confidence interval constructed in the indicated exercise.
  b. Interpret this value for the margin of error.

33. Confidence interval from Exercise 27

34. Confidence interval from Exercise 28

35. Confidence interval from Exercise 29

36. Confidence interval from Exercise 30

37. Confidence interval from Exercise 31

38. Confidence interval from Exercise 32

39. A random sample of $n = 25$ is drawn from a normal population in which $\sigma = 2$. The sample mean is $\bar{x} = 10$. For (a)–(c), construct and interpret confidence intervals for μ with the indicated confidence levels. Then answer the question in (d).
  a. 90%
  b. 95%
  c. 99%
  d. What can you conclude about the width of the interval as the confidence level increases?

40. A random sample of $n = 100$ is drawn from a population in which $\sigma = 5$. The sample mean is $\bar{x} = 50$. For parts (a)–(c), construct and interpret confidence intervals for μ with the indicated confidence levels. Then answer the question in (d).
  a. 99%
  b. 95%
  c. 90%
  d. What can you conclude about the width of the interval as the confidence level decreases?

Suppose we are estimating μ. For Exercises 41–43, find the required sample size.

41. $\sigma = 10$, confidence level 90%, margin of error 32

42. $\sigma = 10$, confidence level 90%, margin of error 16

43. $\sigma = 10$, confidence level 90%, margin of error 8

44. What happens to the required sample size when the margin of error is halved and σ and the confidence level stay the same?

Suppose we are estimating μ. For Exercises 45–47, find the required sample size.
45. $\sigma = 10$, confidence level 90%, margin of error 8
46. $\sigma = 10$, confidence level 95%, margin of error 8
47. $\sigma = 10$, confidence level 99%, margin of error 8
48. What happens to the required sample size when the confidence level increases and the margin of error and σ stay the same?

APPLYING THE CONCEPTS

For each of Exercises 49–52, do the following.
   a. Find the point estimate of the population mean.
   b. Calculate $\sigma/\sqrt{n}$.
   c. Find $Z_{\alpha/2}$ for a confidence interval for the indicated confidence level.
   d. Construct and interpret a confidence interval with the indicated confidence level for the population mean.

49. Consumption of Carbonated Beverages. The U.S. Department of Agriculture reports that the mean American consumption of carbonated beverages per year is greater than 52 gallons. A random sample of 30 Americans yielded a sample mean of 69 gallons. Assume that the population standard deviation is 20 gallons. Let the confidence level be 95%.

50. Stock Shares Traded. The *Statistical Abstract of the United States* reports that the mean daily number of shares traded on the New York Stock Exchange (NYSE) in March 2010 was 2129 million. Assume that the population standard deviation equals 500 million shares. Suppose that, in a random sample of 36 days from the present year, the mean daily number of shares traded equals 2 billion. Let the confidence level be 95%.

51. Engaging with Science. A psychological study found that the mean length of time that boys remained engaged with a science exhibit at a museum was 107 seconds with a standard deviation of 117 seconds.[2] Assume that the 117 seconds represents the population standard deviation. The sample size is 36 and let the confidence level be 95%.

52. Latino Tobacco Consumption. The Bureau of Labor Statistics reported that the mean amount spent by all American citizens on tobacco products and smoking supplies was $308; the mean for American Latinos was $177. Assume that σ, the standard deviation for American Latinos, equals $150. Assume that the data on American Latinos represents a sample of size 36. Let the confidence level be 90%.

53. Consumption of Carbonated Beverages. Refer to Exercise 49.
   a. Compute and interpret the margin of error.
   b. How large a sample size is needed to estimate μ to within 25 gallons with 95% confidence?
   c. How large a sample size is needed to estimate μ to within 5 gallons with 95% confidence?

54. Stock Shares Traded. Refer to Exercise 50.
   a. Calculate and interpret the margin of error.
   b. How large a sample size (trading days) is needed to estimate the population mean number of shares traded per day to within 100 million with 95% confidence?
   c. How large a sample size (trading days) is needed to estimate the population mean number of shares traded per day to within 10 million with 95% confidence? How many years does this number of days translate into?

55. Engaging with Science. Refer to Exercise 51.
   a. Find and interpret the margin of error.
   b. How large a sample size is needed to estimate μ to within 30 seconds with 95% confidence?
   c. How large a sample size is needed to estimate μ to within 3 seconds with 95% confidence?

56. Latino Tobacco Consumption. Refer to Exercise 52.
   a. Compute and interpret the margin of error.
   b. How large a sample size would have been required if the BLS had wanted to estimate the population mean amount spent by American Latinos to within $50 with 95% confidence?
   c. How large a sample size would have been required if the BLS had wanted to estimate the population mean amount spent by American Latinos to within $10 with 95% confidence?

57. Carbon Emissions. The following table represents the carbon emissions (in millions of tons) from consumption of fossil fuels, for a random sample of 5 nations.[3] Assume $\sigma = 200$ million tons. 🔵 **carbon**

Nation	Emissions
Brazil	361
Germany	844
Mexico	398
Great Britain	577
Canada	631

   a. Assess the normality of the data, using a normal probability plot. (*Hint:* See page 348.)
   b. Assuming that carbon emissions are normally distributed, construct and interpret a 90% confidence interval for the population mean carbon emissions.
   c. Calculate and interpret the margin of error for the confidence interval in part (**b**).
   d. How large a sample size do we need to estimate μ to within 50 million tons with 90% confidence?

58. *Deepwater Horizon* Cleanup Costs. The following table represents the amount of money distributed by BP to a random sample of 6 Florida counties, for cleanup of the *Deepwater Horizon* oil spill, in millions of dollars.[4] Assume $\sigma = \$350,000$. 🔵 **deepwaterclean**

County	Cleanup costs ($ millions)
Broward	0.85
Escambia	0.70
Franklin	0.50
Pinellas	1.15
Santa Rosa	0.50
Walton	1.35

a. Assess the normality of the data, using a normal probability plot.
b. Assuming that the cleanup costs are normally distributed, construct and interpret a 95% confidence interval for the population mean cleanup cost.
c. Calculate and interpret the margin of error for the confidence interval in part (b).
d. How large a sample size do we need to estimate μ to within $50,000 with 95% confidence?

59. Wii Game Sales. The following table represents the number of units sold in the United states for the week ending March 26, 2011, for a random sample of 8 Wii games.[5] Assume $\sigma = 30,000$. 🎮 **wiisales**

Game	Units (1000s)	Game	Units (1000s)
Wii Sports Resort	65	Zumba Fitness	56
Super Mario All Stars	40	Wii Fit Plus	36
Just Dance 2	74	Michael Jackson	42
New Super Mario Bros.	16	Lego Star Wars	110

a. Assess the normality of the data, using a normal probability plot.
b. Assuming that the game sales are normally distributed, construct and interpret a 99% confidence interval for the population mean number of units sold.
c. Calculate and interpret the margin of error for the confidence interval in part (b).
d. How large a sample size do we need to estimate μ to within 5000 units with 99% confidence?

60. A Rainy Month in Georgia? The following table represents the total rainfall (in inches) for the month of February 2011 for a random sample of ten locations in Georgia.[6] Assume $\sigma = 0.64$ inches. 🌧 **georgiarain**

Location	Rainfall (inches)	Location	Rainfall (inches)
Athens	4.72	Atlanta	4.25
Augusta	4.31	Cartersville	3.03
Dekalb	2.96	Fulton	4.36
Gainesville	4.06	Lafayette	3.75
Marietta	3.20	Rome	3.26

a. Assess the normality of the data, using a normal probability plot.
b. Assuming that the rainfall amounts are normally distributed, construct and interpret a 95% confidence interval for the population mean rainfall in inches.
c. Calculate and interpret the margin of error for the confidence interval in part (b).
d. How large a sample size do we need to estimate μ to within 0.1 inch with 95% confidence?

61. Short-Term Memory. In a famous research paper in the psychology literature, George Miller found that the amount of information humans could process in short-term memory was 7 bits (pieces of information), plus or minus 2 bits.[7] Let us assume that the title of Miller's paper ("The Magical Number Seven, Plus or Minus Two") refers to a confidence interval.

a. What is the point estimate for the amount of information all humans can process in short-term memory?
b. What is the margin of error? Interpret this number.
c. The most common confidence level in the psychological literature is 95%. Which value for $Z_{\alpha/2}$ is associated with 95% confidence?
d. What is the value of $\sigma/\sqrt{n}$?
e. Describe the confidence interval given by Miller in his title.

62. Catholic Church Membership. A random sample of 50 Roman Catholic Church parishes had a mean size of 2600 members. Assume that the population standard deviation is 1000 members.

a. Find the point estimate of the number of members in a Roman Catholic Church parish.
b. Calculate $\sigma/\sqrt{n}$.
c. Find $Z_{\alpha/2}$ for a confidence interval with 99% confidence.
d. Compute and interpret the margin of error for a confidence interval with 99% confidence.
e. Construct and interpret a 99% confidence interval for μ, the population mean number of members in a Roman Catholic Church parish.

63. Short-Term Memory. Refer to Exercise 61. Assume that $\sigma = 10$ bits.

a. How large a sample size did Miller use to find the confidence interval in the title, assuming that he used 95% confidence?
b. Suppose he had wanted the title to read "The Magical Number Seven, Plus or Minus One"? How large a sample size would he have needed?

64. Catholic Church Membership. Refer to Exercise 62. How large a sample size is required to estimate the population mean number of church members to within 200 with the following levels of confidence.

a. 95% confidence

b. 99% confidence

c. If we asked for 99.9% confidence, would the required sample size be larger or smaller than **(b)**? Explain.

65. Commuting Distances. A university is trying to attract more commuting students from the local community. As part of the research into the modes of transportation students use to commute to the university, a survey was conducted asking how far commuting students commuted from home to school each day. A random sample of 30 students provided the distances (in miles) shown in the table below. Assume that the standard deviation is $\sigma - 3$ miles. 🌀 **commutedist**

14	10	14	12	12	11	5	6	9	14	9	9	4	7	15
9	7	7	12	10	15	10	6	11	9	11	10	11	7	12

a. Compute and interpret the margin of error for a confidence interval with 95% confidence.

b. Construct and interpret a 95% confidence interval for the population mean commuting distance.

66. Herbicide Concentration. Human exposure to herbicides is a potential hazard in America's grain-producing areas. One study found that, in a random sample of 112 homes in Iowa, the median concentration of the herbicide dicamba was 179.5 ng/g (nanograms per gram).[8] Suppose that the sample mean was 180 ng/g, and assume that the population standard deviation is 20 ng/g.

a. Compute and interpret the margin of error for a confidence interval with 95% confidence.

b. Construct and interpret a 95% confidence interval for the population mean concentration of the herbicide dicamba in Iowa homes.

c. How large a sample size is needed to estimate μ to within 3.7 ng/g with 95% confidence? Comment.

d. How large a sample size is needed to estimate μ to within 3.7 ng/g with 99% confidence?

67. Asthma and Quality of Life. A study examined the relationship between perceived neighborhood problems, quality of life, and mental health among adults with asthma.[9] Among those reporting the most serious neighborhood problems, the 95% confidence interval for the population mean quality of life score was (2.7152, 9.1048).

a. What is $Z_{\alpha/2}$?

b. Find $\bar{x}$.

c. Compute and interpret the margin of error.

d. Suppose $n = 36$. Find the value for σ.

68. TV Viewing and Physical Activity. A study examined the relationship between television viewing and physical activity.[10] The study found that, for each additional hour of television viewing, subjects walked between 12 and 276 fewer steps that day, as measured by a pedometer. This interval was reported with a 95% confidence level; suppose $n = 100$.

a. What is $Z_{\alpha/2}$?

b. Find $\bar{x}$.

c. Compute and interpret the margin of error.

d. Find the value for σ.

Lead Contamination in Trout. Use this information for Exercises 69 and 70. In Example 8.3, a 95% confidence interval was constructed for the population mean lead contamination in Spokane River trout, based on a sample of 100 trout.

69. *What if* the sample size is increased to some unspecified higher number. Describe what effect, if any, the increase has on the following:

a. σ

b. $\sigma/\sqrt{n}$

c. Width of the confidence interval

d. Margin of error

e. Confidence level

70. *What if* the confidence level is decreased from 95% to some unspecified lower value. Explain whether and how this decrease would affect the following:

a. σ

b. $\sigma/\sqrt{n}$

c. Width of the confidence interval

d. $\bar{x}$

e. Margin of error

Small Businesses. Use this information for Exercise 71. The United States Small Business Administration publishes data on the number of small businesses in each of 327 metropolitan areas. This data is in the data file **Small Businesses.** 🌀 **smallbusinesses**

71. Follow steps **(a)–(e)**.

a. Find the sample mean number of small firms per metropolitan area.

b. Generate a histogram of the number of small firms per metropolitan area.

c. Generate a normal probability plot of the number of small firms in each metropolitan area. What is your conclusion regarding the normality of the distribution of the number of firms?

d. Construct and interpret a 95% confidence interval for the population number of small firms per metropolitan area. Assume that the standard deviation is 25,000 firms.

e. On the histogram, indicate the location of the confidence interval.

Use the *Confidence Interval* applet for Exercises 72 and 73.

72. Set the confidence level to 90%. Click "Sample 50" to produce 50 simple random samples (SRSs) and display the resulting 90% confidence intervals for μ.

a. What is the percent hit, that is, the proportion of the confidence intervals that actually contain the true value of μ?

b. Keep clicking "Sample 50" until 1000 confidence intervals are generated. What is the percent hit?

c. It is not likely (though it is possible) that the percent hit in **(b)** exactly equals 90%. Explain why the percent hit is not equal to 90% when we asked for a confidence level of 90%.

73. Set the confidence level to 99%. Click "Sample 50" to produce 50 99% confidence intervals for μ.

a. Compare the widths of these intervals with the width of the 90% confidence intervals computed in Exercise 72. Which set of intervals is wider?

b. Explain why the intervals you identified in **(a)** are wider, using the concept of *margin of error*.

Use the *Normal Density Curve* applet for Exercises 74 and 75.

74. Use the applet to find $Z_{\alpha/2}$ critical values for unusual confidence levels. Select **2-Tail,** and click and drag the flags so that the central area and not the tail area is highlighted. Verify that the $Z_{\alpha/2}$ critical value for 95% confidence is 1.96.

75. Use the applet to find $Z_{\alpha/2}$ critical values for the following confidence levels.

   a. 80%
   b. 85%
   c. 98%

8.2 *t* Interval for the Population Mean

OBJECTIVES By the end of this section, I will be able to . . .

1 Describe the characteristics of the *t* distribution.

2 Calculate and interpret a *t* interval for the population mean.

1 Introducing the *t* Distribution

In Section 8.1 we constructed confidence intervals for the population mean μ assuming that the population standard deviation σ was known. This assumption may be valid for certain fields such as quality control. However, in many real-world problems, we do not know the value of σ, and thus cannot use a Z interval to estimate the mean. When σ is unknown, we use the sample standard deviation s to construct a confidence interval that is likely to contain the population mean.

Fact 4 from Chapter 7 showed us that we could standardize $\bar{x}$ to derive the standard normal random variable:

$$Z = \frac{\bar{x} - \mu}{\sigma/\sqrt{n}}$$

Unfortunately, however, replacing the unknown σ in this equation with the known s, we can no longer obtain the standard normal Z because s, being a statistic, is itself a random variable. Instead, $\dfrac{\bar{x} - \mu}{s/\sqrt{n}}$ follows an entirely new and different distribution, called the *t* **distribution.**

---

t Distribution

For a normal population, the distribution of

$$t = \frac{\bar{x} - \mu}{s/\sqrt{n}}$$

follows a *t* distribution, with $n - 1$ degrees of freedom, where $\bar{x}$ is the sample mean, μ is the unknown population mean, s is the sample standard deviation, and n is the sample size.

Developing Your Statistical Sense

Degrees of Freedom

Notice that the definition of the *t* distribution includes a new concept called *degrees of freedom*. Degrees of freedom is a measure that determines how the *t* distribution changes as the sample size changes. The idea of degrees of freedom is that, in a sum of *n* numbers, you need to know only the first $n - 1$ of these numbers to find the *n*th number because you already know the sum. For example, suppose you know that the sum of $n = 3$ numbers is 10 and are told that the first two numbers are 5 and 1. Then you can deduce that the last number is $10 - (5 + 1) = 4$. The first two numbers have the *freedom* to take on any values, but the third number must take a particular value. Thus, there are only $n - 1$ independent pieces of information. The concept is similar for the *t* distribution. Since we use the sample standard deviation *s* to estimate the unknown σ and since *s* is known, only $n - 1$ independent pieces of information are needed to find the value of *t*. Thus, we say that $t = \dfrac{\bar{x} - \mu}{s/\sqrt{n}}$ follows a *t* distribution with $n - 1$ degrees of freedom. ◢

Figure 8.10 displays a comparison of some *t* curves with the *Z* curve. Note that there is only one *Z* distribution (or curve), but there is a different *t* curve for every different degrees of freedom (df), that is, for every different sample size. The degrees of freedom, $\text{df} = n - 1$, determines the shape of the *t* distribution, just as the mean and variance uniquely determine the shape of the normal distribution. All *t* curves have several characteristics in common.

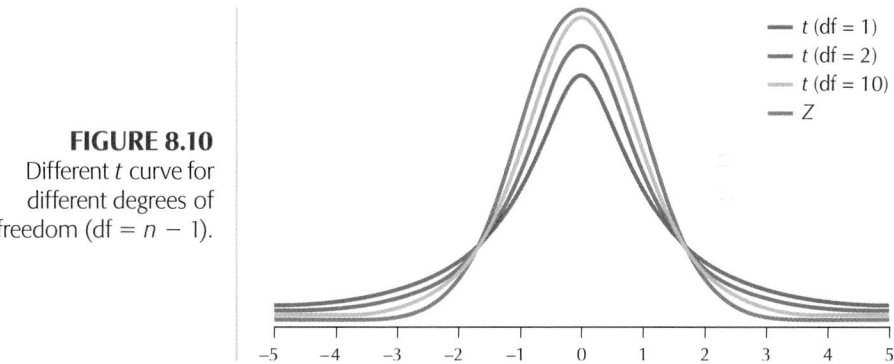

FIGURE 8.10
Different *t* curve for different degrees of freedom (df = $n - 1$).

Characteristics of the *t* Distribution

- Centered at zero. The mean of *t* is zero, just as with *Z*.
- Symmetric about its mean zero, just as with *Z*.
- As df decreases, the *t* curve gets flatter, and the area under the *t* curve decreases in the center and increases in the tails. That is, the *t* curve has heavier tails than the *Z* curve.
- As df increases toward infinity, the *t* curve approaches the *Z* curve, and the area under the *t* curve increases in the center and decreases in the tails.

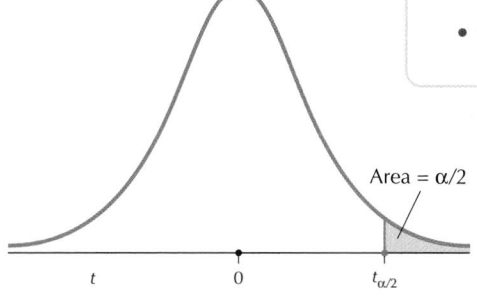

FIGURE 8.11 $t_{\alpha/2}$ has area to the right of it.

Similar to the definition of $Z_{\alpha/2}$ in Section 8.1, we can define $t_{\alpha/2}$ to be the value of the *t* distribution with area $\alpha/2$ to the right of it, as seen in Figure 8.11. Table 8.1 in Section 8.1 provides the $Z_{\alpha/2}$ values for certain common confidence levels. Unfortunately, because there is a different *t* curve for each sample size, there are many possible $t_{\alpha/2}$ values. You will need to use the *t* table (Table D in the Appendix) to find the value of $t_{\alpha/2}$, as follows.

> **Procedure for Finding $t_{\alpha/2}$**
>
> **Step 1**   Go across the row marked "Confidence level" in the t table (Table D in the Appendix) until you find the column with the desired confidence level at the top. The $t_{\alpha/2}$ value is in this column somewhere.
>
> **Step 2**   Go down the column until you see the correct number of degrees of freedom on the left. The number in that row and column is the desired value of $t_{\alpha/2}$.

Example 8.9   Finding $t_{\alpha/2}$

Note: For the newer TI-84s

1. Press **2nd DISTR** and select **4:invT**.

2. Enter the area to the *left* of the t value, then **comma**, then df $= n - 1$.

3. Press **ENTER**.

For example, **invT(0.975,19)** gives 2.093024022. The TI-83 does not have this function.

Find the value of $t_{\alpha/2}$ that will produce a 95% confidence interval for μ if the sample size is $n = 20$.

Solution

Step 1   We go across the row labeled "Confidence level" in the t table (Figure 8.12) until we see the 95% confidence level. Our $t_{\alpha/2}$ is somewhere in this column.

Step 2   The degrees of freedom are df $= n - 1 = 20 - 1 = 19$. We go down the column until we see 19 on the left. The number in that row is our $t_{\alpha/2}$, 2.093. ■

t-Distribution

		80%	90%	95%	98%	99%
		\multicolumn{5}{c}{**Confidence level**}
		\multicolumn{5}{c}{**Area in one tail**}
		0.10	0.05	0.025	0.01	0.005
		\multicolumn{5}{c}{**Area in two tails**}
		0.20	0.10	0.05	0.02	0.01
df	1	3.078	6.314	12.706	31.821	63.657
	2	1.886	2.920	4.303	6.965	9.925
	3	1.638	2.353	3.182	4.541	5.841
	14	1.345	1.761	2.145	2.624	2.977
	15	1.341	1.753	2.131	2.602	2.947
	16	1.337	1.746	2.120	2.583	2.921
	17	1.333	1.740	2.110	2.567	2.898
	18	1.330	1.734	2.101	2.552	2.878
	19	1.328	1.729	2.093	2.539	2.861
	20	1.325	1.725	2.086	2.528	2.845
	21	1.323	1.721	2.080	2.518	2.831

Now You Can Do
Exercises 5–8.

FIGURE 8.12 t table excerpt.

Use the confidence level and the degrees of freedom to find $t_{\alpha/2}$.

2 t Interval for the Population Mean

The t distribution provides the following confidence interval for the unknown population mean μ, called the **t interval**.

> **t Interval for μ**
>
> The *t* interval for μ may be constructed whenever *either* of the following conditions is met:
>
> - The population is normal.
> - The sample size is large ($n \geq 30$).
>
> A random sample of size *n* is taken from a population with unknown mean μ. A $100(1 - \alpha)\%$ confidence interval for μ is given by the interval
>
> $$\text{lower bound} = \bar{x} - t_{\alpha/2}(s/\sqrt{n}), \text{ upper bound} = \bar{x} + t_{\alpha/2}(s/\sqrt{n})$$
>
> where $\bar{x}$ is the sample mean, $t_{\alpha/2}$ is associated with the confidence level and $n - 1$ degrees of freedom, and *s* is the sample standard deviation. The *t* interval may also be written as
>
> $$\bar{x} \pm t_{\alpha/2}(s/\sqrt{n})$$
>
> and is denoted
>
> $$(\text{lower bound, upper bound})$$

Note: Suppose that σ is unknown, *and* the population is either non-normal or of unknown distribution, *and* the sample size is not large. Then we should not use the *t* interval. Rather, we need to turn to nonparametric methods, for example, the *sign interval* or the *Wilcoxon interval*. (See Chapter 14, "Nonparametric Statistics," available on the companion CD.)

Example 8.10 — Interval for μ

 fourthfeet

Suppose a children's shoe manufacturer is interested in estimating the population mean length of fourth-graders' feet. A random sample of 20 fourth-graders' feet yielded the following foot lengths, in centimeters.[11]

22.4	23.4	22.5	23.2	23.1	23.7	24.1	21.0	21.6	20.9
25.5	22.8	24.1	25.0	24.0	21.7	22.0	22.7	24.7	23.5

Construct a 95% confidence interval for μ, the population mean length of all fourth-graders' feet.

Solution

We do not know the population standard deviation σ, so we cannot use the *Z* interval. We can construct a *t* interval whenever either the population is normal or the sample size is large. The sample size here is 20, which is not large ($n \geq 30$), so we must check for normality. Figure 8.13 shows the normal probability plot of the foot lengths. The points generally line up along the line, so the assumption of normality is validated for this data set. We can then proceed to construct the *t* interval for μ.

FIGURE 8.13 Fourth-grade foot lengths are normally distributed.

The TI-83/84 provides the summary statistics shown here, giving $n = 20$, $\bar{x} = 23.095$, and $s \approx 1.280$. All that is left is to find $t_{\alpha/2}$. In Example 8.9, we found the value of $t_{\alpha/2}$ for confidence level = 95% and $n = 20$ to be $t_{\alpha/2} = 2.093$. The 95% confidence interval then becomes

lower bound $= \bar{x} - t_{\alpha/2}(s/\sqrt{n})$
$= 23.095 - 2.093(1.280/\sqrt{20}) \approx 23.095 - 0.599 = 22.496$

upper bound $= \bar{x} + t_{\alpha/2}(s/\sqrt{n})$
$= 23.095 + 2.093(1.280/\sqrt{20}) \approx 23.095 + 0.599 = 23.694$

This interval is denoted

$$(22.496, 23.694)$$

We are 95% confident that the population mean length of fourth-graders' feet lies between 22.496 and 23.694 cm. (See Figure 8.14.) ■

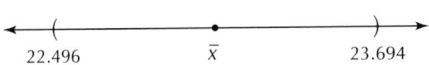

FIGURE 8.14 95% t confidence interval for population mean foot length.

Now You Can Do
Exercises 9–24.

> ◤ Developing Your
> Statistical Sense
>
> ### t Intervals May Offer More Peace of Mind than Z Intervals
>
> In Example 8.10, if we had assumed that the population standard deviation σ was known ($\sigma = 1.280$), then the 95% Z interval for the population mean length of fourth-grade feet would have been
>
> lower bound $= \bar{x} - Z_{\alpha/2}(\sigma/\sqrt{n})$
> $= 23.095 - 1.96(1.280/\sqrt{20}) \approx 23.095 - 0.561 = 22.534$
>
> upper bound $= \bar{x} + Z_{\alpha/2}(\sigma/\sqrt{n})$
> $= 23.095 + 1.96(1.280/\sqrt{20}) \approx 23.095 + 0.561 = 23.656$
>
> Note that this Z interval (22.534, 23.656) is only slightly more precise than the t interval (22.496, 23.694). However, the Z interval depends on prior knowledge of the value of σ. If the value of σ is inaccurate, then the Z interval will be misleading and overly optimistic. With even moderate sample sizes, reporting the t interval rather than the Z interval may offer peace of mind to the data analyst. ◢

If the degrees of freedom needed to find $t_{\alpha/2}$ do not appear in the df column of the t table, a conservative solution is to take the next row with smaller df. Alternatively, we can use interpolation. Both methods are illustrated in Example 8.11.

Example 8.11 | Degrees of freedom not in the t table

Water scarcity is a serious problem for the countries in the Middle East, including Israel. The Jordan River (shown here) feeds the Sea of Galilee and provides Israel with 40% of its potable water and 80% of the water used for agricultural purposes. The mean daily water consumption in Israel is reported to be 72 cubic meters per person.[12] Suppose a random sample of 49 Israelis showed a sample mean daily water consumption of 72 cubic meters, with a sample standard deviation of 28 cubic meters. Construct a 99% confidence interval for the population mean daily water consumption for all Israelis. When finding $t_{\alpha/2}$, use (a) the conservative method and (b) interpolation.

Solution

Since σ is unknown and the sample size is large, we proceed to construct the *t* interval for μ. We have $n = 49$, $\bar{x} = 72$, and $s = 28$. Now we must find $t_{\alpha/2}$. The confidence level is 99% and the degrees of freedom are $n - 1 = 49 - 1 = 48$. *Unfortunately, the value of 48 for the df does not appear in the df column.*

a. The next row with df smaller than 48 would be df = 40. Thus, the "conservative" $t_{\alpha/2}$ is 2.704. We then proceed to construct the 99% confidence interval:

$$\bar{x} \pm t_{\alpha/2}(s/\sqrt{n}) = 72 \pm 2.704(28/\sqrt{49}) = 72 \pm 10.816 = (61.184, 82.816)$$

b. Alternatively, you could interpolate as follows. Since df = 48 is 8/10 of the distance between 40 and 50, we can estimate $t_{\alpha/2}$ by taking 8/10 of the distance between the associated *t*-values for df = 40 and df = 50 and subtracting that result from the *t*-value for df = 40:

$$\frac{8}{10}\left[(t_{\alpha/2} \text{ for df} = 40) - (t_{\alpha/2} \text{ for df} = 50)\right] = \frac{8}{10}(2.704 - 2.678) = 0.0208$$

Thus, $t_{\alpha/2}$ for df = 48 would be $2.704 - 0.0208 = 2.6832$, using interpolation. The 99% confidence interval using interpolation is thus

$$\bar{x} \pm t_{\alpha/2}(s/\sqrt{n}) = 72 \pm 2.6832(28/\sqrt{49}) = 72 \pm 10.7328 = (61.2672, 82.7328)$$

Note that the confidence interval using the conservative method is somewhat wider, reflecting the conservative choice of $t_{\alpha/2}$. ∎

Using a smaller degrees of freedom is *conservative*, that is, cautious. The resulting confidence interval will not be more precise than is warranted by the data.

Now You Can Do
Exercises 25–32.

Example 8.12   We cannot use the *t* interval if the conditions are not met

cerealsodium

Research has shown that the amount of sodium consumed in food has been associated with hypertension (high blood pressure). Table 8.3 provides a list of 28 breakfast cereals, along with their sodium content, in milligrams per serving. Determine whether the conditions are met for constructing a *t* interval for the population mean sodium content per serving for all breakfast cereals.

Table 8.3 Sodium content of 28 breakfast cereals

Cereal	Sodium (mg)	Cereal	Sodium (mg)
Apple Jacks	125	Life	150
Cap'n Crunch	220	Lucky Charms	180
Cheerios	290	Maypo	0
Cinnamon Toast Crunch	210	Mueslix Crispy	150
Cocoa Puffs	180	Puffed Rice	0
Corn Flakes	290	Quaker Oatmeal	0
Count Chocula	180	Raisin Bran	210
Cream of Wheat	80	Rice Chex	240
Froot Loops	125	Rice Krispies	290
Frosted Flakes	200	Shredded Wheat	0
Frosted Mini-Wheats	0	Special K	230
Fruity Pebbles	135	Total Whole Grain	200
Grape Nuts Flakes	140	Trix	140
Kix	260	Wheaties	200

Solution

Since $n = 28 < 30$, we need to evaluate the normality of the data set. On the right-hand side of the normal probability plot in Figure 8.15 (sodium content greater than 100 mg), the points all lie within the bounds. However, on the left side a couple of points lie outside the bounds, for sodium content of 0 mg. We should probably look further into this. A histogram is called for, and it is presented in Figure 8.16. This histogram has a "spike" on the left, representing the five breakfast cereals that have zero sodium content. While very healthy for your diet, these five cereals seem to be undermining our assumption of normality. Clearly, the distribution of sodium in breakfast cereals is *not* normally distributed. It would not be appropriate to construct the t interval in this case. ■

Now You Can Do
Exercises 33–40.

FIGURE 8.15 Normal probability plot of sodium content.

FIGURE 8.16 Histogram of sodium content.

> **Developing Your Statistical Sense**
>
> ### Checking the Required Conditions
>
> There has been explosive growth in statistical software and scientific calculators. The availability of statistical inference at the touch of a button has led to neglect of the conditions required to perform the analysis. If these conditions are not met, then the statistical inference is not valid, and any conclusions drawn are questionable. ◢

Example 8.13 **Omitting a set of observations to achieve normality**

We continue with the breakfast cereals data set in Example 8.12.
a. Identify the five cereals in Table 8.3 that contained zero sodium, and omit them from the calculations.
b. Assess the normality of the reduced data set.
c. If appropriate, construct a 99% confidence interval for the population mean sodium content. We have $\bar{x} = 192.4$, $n = 23$, and $s = 57.6$.
d. Discuss the meaning of this confidence interval.

Solution

a. From Table 8.3, the five cereals containing zero sodium are Frosted Mini-Wheats, Maypo, Puffed Rice, Quaker Oatmeal, and Shredded Wheat.
b. Figure 8.17 contains the normal probability plot for the data set after omitting the sodium-free cereals. Though not perfect, all points lie within the bounds, indicating acceptable normality. Thus, we proceed to construct the 99% confidence interval.

FIGURE 8.17 Normal probability plot of sodium content with five cereals omitted.

c. For a 99% confidence level and df $= n - 1 = 22$, we find $t_{\alpha/2} = 2.819$ from Table D in the Appendix. Thus, we have

$$\bar{x} \pm t_{\alpha/2}(s/\sqrt{n})$$

$$= 192.4 \pm 2.819(57.6/\sqrt{23})$$

$$\approx 192.4 \pm 33.86$$

$$= (158.54, 226.26)$$

d. Note, however, that we can no longer claim to be constructing a confidence interval for the mean sodium content of *all* breakfast cereals, since we are ignoring an entire important class of breakfast cereals: those with no sodium at all. Therefore, our confidence interval will be for the population mean sodium content of *all breakfast cereals that contain sodium.* We are 99% confident that μ, the population mean sodium content per serving of all breakfast cereals that contain sodium, lies between 158.54 grams and 226.26 grams. ■

Analysts who do not wish to omit the five cereals may instead use nonparametric methods such as the sign interval or the Wilcoxon interval (see Chapter 14).

Recall that the margin of error for the *Z* interval equals $Z_{\alpha/2} \cdot (\sigma/\sqrt{n})$. For the *t* interval, since σ is unknown, the margin of error is given as follows.

> **Margin of Error for the *t* Interval**
>
> $$E = t_{\alpha/2} \cdot \left(\frac{s}{\sqrt{n}}\right)$$
>
> The margin of error E for a $(1 - \alpha)100\%$ *t* interval for μ can be interpreted as follows: "We can estimate μ to within E units with $(1 - \alpha)100\%$ confidence."

Example 8.14 Finding and interpreting the margin of error for the fourth-grader foot lengths

Use the statistics observed in Example 8.10.
a. Find the margin of error for the 95% confidence interval for mean foot lengths.
b. Interpret the margin of error.

Solution

a. From Example 8.10, $n = 20$ and $s = 1.280$. Also, for a confidence level of 95%, $t_{\alpha/2} = 2.093$. Therefore, the margin of error of fourth-grade foot length is

$$E = t_{\alpha/2} \cdot \left(\frac{s}{\sqrt{n}}\right) = (2.093) \cdot \frac{1.280}{\sqrt{20}} \approx 0.599$$

Now You Can Do
Exercises 44–48.

b. We can estimate the population mean of fourth-grade foot lengths to within 0.599 centimeter with 95% confidence. ■

What Does the Margin of Error Mean?	The margin of error $E = 0.599$ provides an indication of the accuracy of the confidence interval estimate for confidence level = 95%. That is, if we repeatedly take many samples of size 20 fourth-graders, our sample mean $\bar{x}$ will be within $E = 0.599$ centimeter of the unknown population mean μ in 95% of those samples. ◢

Example 8.15 t Intervals for μ using technology

 smallbiz30

In Example 8.4, we considered a sample of 30 randomly selected moderately large cities and counted the number of small businesses in each city (see Table 8.2, page 376). We found that the sample mean $\bar{x} = 24{,}017.7$ and the sample standard deviation $s = 4322.473886$. However, this time we are not assuming that we know the value of the population standard deviation, σ. Use the TI-83/84, Minitab, and the WHFStat Add-ins for Excel to construct a 95% t confidence interval for the population mean number of small businesses in moderately sized cities nationwide.

Solution

We use the instructions provided in the Step-by-Step Technology Guide on page 395. Since the sample size $n = 30$ is large (≥ 30), it is not necessary to check for normality.

The results for the TI-83/84 in Figure 8.18 display the 95% t confidence interval for the population mean number of small businesses per city to be

(lower bound = 22,404, upper bound = 25,632)

They also show the sample mean $\bar{x} = 24{,}017.7$, the sample standard deviation $s = 4322.473886$, and the sample size $n = 30$.

The Minitab results are shown in Figure 8.19, providing the sample size $n = 30$, the sample mean $\bar{x} = 24{,}017.7$, the sample standard deviation $s = 4322.5$, the standard error (SE mean) $s_{\bar{x}} = \dfrac{s}{\sqrt{n}} = \dfrac{4322.5}{\sqrt{30}} = 789.2$, and the 95% t confidence interval (22,403.7, 25,631.7).

```
TInterval
(22404,25632)
x̄=24017.7
Sx=4322.473886
n=30
```

FIGURE 8.18 TI-83/84 results.

One-Sample T: Small Business

Variable	N	Mean	StDev	SE Mean	95% CI
Small Business	30	24017.7	4322.5	789.2	(22403.7, 25631.7)

FIGURE 8.19 Minitab results.

The results from the WHFStat Add-ins for Excel are shown in Figure 8.20. Displayed are the sample mean $x = 24{,}017.7$, the sample size $n = 30$, the degrees of freedom $df = n - 1 = 29$, the sample standard deviation $s = 4322.474$, and the standard error

$$s_{\bar{x}} = \frac{s}{\sqrt{n}} = \frac{4322.474}{\sqrt{30}} \approx 789.1722.$$

SUMMARY STATISTICS		
Sample Mean	**Sample Size**	**Sample Standard Deviation**
24017.7	30	4322.474
	Deg of Freedom	**Standard Error (SE)**
	29	789.1722
ONE SAMPLE T CONFIDENCE INTERVAL		
Confidence Level		**Critical T Value**
95 %		2.045231
Confidence Interval		
24017.7 +/-	1614.039	
22403.66 to	25631.74	

FIGURE 8.20 Results from WHFStat Add-ins for Excel.

The confidence level 95% is shown, along with the critical *t* value, $t_{\alpha/2} = 2.045231$. The confidence interval is then shown in the form

$$\text{point estimate} \pm \text{margin of error}$$
$$= 24{,}017.7 \pm 1614.039$$

so the margin of error is

$$E = t_{\alpha/2}\,(s/\sqrt{n}) = 1614.039$$

The confidence interval is also shown as "22,403.66 to 25,631.74." ∎

STEP-BY-STEP TECHNOLOGY GUIDE: *t* Confidence Intervals

We illustrate how to construct the *t* confidence interval for Example 8.15 (page 394).

TI-83/84

If you have the data values:
Step 1   Enter the data into list **L1**.
Step 2   Press **STAT**, highlight **TESTS**.
Step 3   Press **8** (for **TInterval**, see Figure 8.21).
Step 4   For input (**Inpt**), highlight **Data** and press **ENTER** (Figure 8.22).
a. For **List**, press **2nd** then **L1**.
b. For **Freq**, enter **1**.
c. For **C-Level** (confidence level), enter the appropriate confidence level (for example, **0.95**), and press **ENTER**.
d. Highlight **Calculate** and press **ENTER**. The results are shown in Figure 8.18 in Example 8.15.

If you have the summary statistics:
Step 1   Press **STAT**, highlight **TESTS**.
Step 2   Press **8** (for **TInterval**, see Figure 8.21).
Step 3   For input (**Inpt**), highlight **Stats** and press **ENTER** (Figure 8.23).
a. For $\bar{x}$, enter the sample mean 24017.7.
b. For **Sx**, enter the sample standard deviation 4322.473886.
c. For *n*, enter the sample size **30**.
d. For **C-Level** (confidence level), enter the appropriate confidence level (for example, **0.95**), and press **ENTER**.
e. Highlight **Calculate** and press **ENTER**. The results are shown in Figure 8.18 in Example 8.15.

FIGURE 8.21

FIGURE 8.22

FIGURE 8.23

EXCEL

If you have the data values:
Step 1   Enter the data into column A.
Step 2   Load the **WHFStat Add-ins**.
Step 3   Select **Add-ins > Macros > Estimating a Mean > t Confidence Interval**.
Step 4   Click **Select Dataset Range**, highlight A1–A30, and click **OK**.
Step 5   Select the **95%** confidence level, and click **OK**.
The results are shown in Figure 8.20 in Example 8.15.

If you have the summary statistics:
Step 1   Load the **WHFStat Add-ins**.
Step 2   Select **Add-ins > Macros > Estimating a Mean > Z Confidence Interval**.
Step 3   Click **Input Summary Statistics**, enter 24017.7 for the **Sample Mean**, enter **30** for the **Sample Size**, enter **4322.473886** for the **Sample Standard Deviation**, and click **OK**.
Step 4   Select the **95%** confidence level and click **OK**.
The results are shown in Figure 8.20 in Example 8.15.

MINITAB

If you have the data values:
Step 1   Enter the data into column C1.
Step 2   Click **Stat > Basic Statistics > 1-Sample t**.
Step 3   Click **Samples in Columns** and select **C1**.
Step 4   Click **Options**, enter **95** as the **Confidence Level**, click **OK**, and click **OK** again.
The results are shown in Figure 8.19 in Example 8.15.

If you have the summary statistics:
Step 1   Click **Stat > Basic Statistics > 1-Sample t**.
Step 2   Click **Summarized Data**.
Step 3   Enter the **Sample Size 30**, the **Sample Mean 24017.7**, and **4322.473886** for the **Standard Deviation**.
Step 4   Click **Options**, enter **95** as the **Confidence Level**, click **OK**, and click **OK** again.
The results are shown in Figure 8.19 in Example 8.15.

CRUNCHIT!

If you have the data values:
Step 1 Click **File**... then highlight **Load from Larose2e**... **Chapter 8**... and click on **Example 8.15**.
Step 2 Click **Statistics ... t** and select **1-sample**.
Step 3 With the **Columns** tab chosen, for **Sample** select **Businesses**.
Step 4 Select the **Confidence Interval** tab, and enter **95** for the **Confidence Interval Level**. Then click **Calculate**.

If you have the summary statistics:
Step 1 Click **Statistics ... t** and select **1-sample**.
Step 2 Choose the **Summarized** tab. For **n** enter the sample size **30**; for **Sample Mean** enter **24017.7**. For **Standard Deviation**, enter **4322.473886**.
Step 3 Select the **Confidence Interval** tab, and enter **95** for the **Confidence Interval Level**. Then click **Calculate**.

Section 8.2 Summary

1 For a normal population, the distribution of

$$t = \frac{\bar{x} - \mu}{s/\sqrt{n}}$$

follows a t distribution, with $n - 1$ degrees of freedom, where $\bar{x}$ is the sample mean, μ is the unknown population mean, s is the sample standard deviation, and n is the sample size. The t distribution is symmetric about its mean 0, just like the Z distribution. However, the t distribution is flatter.

2 A $100(1 - \alpha)\%$ confidence interval for μ is given by the interval

$$\bar{x} \pm t_{\alpha/2} (s/\sqrt{n})$$

where $\bar{x}$ is the sample mean, $t_{\alpha/2}$ is associated with the confidence level and $n - 1$ degrees of freedom, s is the sample standard deviation, and n is the sample size. We can construct a t interval whenever *either* of the following conditions is met: the population is normal, or the sample size is large ($n \geq 30$).

Section 8.2 Exercises

CLARIFYING THE CONCEPTS

1. Why do we need the t interval? Why can't we always use Z intervals?
2. Suppose that σ is known. Can we still use a t interval?
3. As the sample size gets larger and larger, what happens to the t curve?
4. State the formula for the margin of error for the t interval.

PRACTICING THE TECHNIQUES

5. For the following scenarios, we are taking a random sample from a normal population with σ unknown. Find $t_{\alpha/2}$.
   a. Confidence level 90%, sample size 10
   b. Confidence level 95%, sample size 10
   c. Confidence level 99%, sample size 10
6. For the following scenarios we are taking a random sample from a normal population with σ unknown. Find $t_{\alpha/2}$.
   a. Confidence level 95%, sample size 10
   b. Confidence level 95%, sample size 15
   c. Confidence level 95%, sample size 20
7. Refer to Exercise 5.
   a. Describe what happens to the value of $t_{\alpha/2}$, as the confidence level increases, for a given sample size.
   b. Draw a sketch of the t curve for sample size $n = 10$, and explain why the value of $t_{\alpha/2}$ changes as it does.

8. Refer to Exercise 6.
   a. Describe what happens to the value of $t_{\alpha/2}$, as the sample size increases, for a given confidence level.
   b. Draw a sketch of the t curve for a confidence level of 95%, and explain why the value of $t_{\alpha/2}$ changes as it does.

For the data sets shown in Exercises 9–12, do the following.
   a. Calculate $\bar{x}$ and s.
   b. Find $t_{\alpha/2}$.
   c. Construct and interpret a 95% confidence interval for μ.

9.

| 2 | 3 | 1 | 3 | 1 |

10.

| 8 | 4 | 6 | 4 | 8 |

11.

| 11 | 17 | 14 | 17 | 11 |

12.

| 96 | 104 | 100 | 96 | 104 |

For Exercises 13–18, we are taking a random sample from a normal population with σ unknown.
   a. Find $t_{\alpha/2}$.
   b. Construct the confidence interval for μ with the indicated confidence level.
   c. Sketch the confidence interval on a number line.

13. Confidence level 95%, sample size 25, sample mean 10, sample standard deviation 5

14. Confidence level 90%, sample size 9, sample mean 22, sample standard deviation 3
15. Confidence level 95%, $n = 4, \bar{x} = 50, s = 6$
16. Confidence level 99%, $n = 16, \bar{x} = 0, s = 8$
17. Confidence level 90%, $n = 9, \bar{x} = -20, s = 6$
18. Confidence level 95%, $n = 25, \bar{x} = 0, s = 15$

For Exercises 19–24, we are taking a random sample from a population with σ unknown. However, do not assume that the population is normally distributed.
   a. Find $t_{\alpha/2}$.
   b. Construct the confidence interval for μ with the indicated confidence level.
   c. Sketch the confidence interval on a number line.
19. Confidence level 95%, sample size 100, sample mean 100, sample standard deviation 10.
20. Confidence level 90%, sample size 64, sample mean 250, sample standard deviation 20.
21. Confidence level 99%, $n = 64, \bar{x} = 35, s = 8$
22. Confidence level 95%, $n = 400, \bar{x} = 42, s = 10$
23. Confidence level 90%, $n = 81, \bar{x} = -20, s = 6$
24. Confidence level 95%, $n = 225, \bar{x} = 0, s = 15$

For Exercises 25–28, find the value of $t_{\alpha/2}$ using the following methods.
   a. The conservative approach
   b. Interpolation
25. Confidence level 95%, $n = 55, \bar{x} = 100, s = 15$
26. Confidence level 99%, $n = 117, \bar{x} = 100, s = 15$
27. Confidence level 90%, $n = 46, \bar{x} = 10, s = 2$
28. Confidence level 95%, $n = 46, \bar{x} = 10, s = 2$

For Exercises 29–32, assume the data come from a normal distribution. Calculate and interpret the confidence interval for μ using the value of $t_{\alpha/2}$ you found in the indicated exercises.
29. Exercise 25
   a. Part **(a)**   **b.** Part **(b)**
30. Exercise 26
   a. Part **(a)**   **b.** Part **(b)**
31. Exercise 27
   a. Part **(a)**   **b.** Part **(b)**
32. Exercise 28
   a. Part **(a)**   **b.** Part **(b)**

For each of Exercises 33–40, we are taking a random sample from a population with σ unknown. If the conditions are met, construct the indicated t interval for μ. If not, explain why not.
33. Confidence level 95%, $n = 25, \bar{x} = 100, s = 10$
34. Confidence level 90%, $n = 16, \bar{x} = 250, s = 20$
35. Confidence level 95%, $n = 225, \bar{x} = 10, s = 5$, normal population
36. Confidence level 90%, $n = 81, \bar{x} = 22, s = 3$
37. Confidence level 99%, $n = 16, \bar{x} = 35, s = 8$
38. Confidence level 95%, $n = 25, \bar{x} = 42, s = 10$, normal population
39. Confidence level 95%, $n = 36, \bar{x} = 50, s = 6$
40. Confidence level 99%, $n = 64, \bar{x} = 0, s = 8$

For Exercises 41–48, calculate and interpret the margin of error for the confidence interval from the indicated exercise.

41. Exercise 9	**45.** Exercise 13
42. Exercise 10	**46.** Exercise 14
43. Exercise 11	**47.** Exercise 15
44. Exercise 12	**48.** Exercise 16

APPLYING THE CONCEPTS
49. Sickle-Cell Anemia. The U.S. Department of Health and Human Services reports that the mean length of stay in hospital for sickle-cell anemia patients in 2008 was $\bar{x} = 5.3$ days with a standard deviation of $s = 7.6$ days. For a sample of 100 patients, do the following.
   a. Find $t_{\alpha/2}$ for a confidence interval with 95% confidence.
   b. Construct and interpret a 95% confidence interval for the population mean length of stay for all sickle-cell anemia patients.
50. Student Loans. The Pew Research Center (**pewresearch.org**) reports that the mean student loan amount in 2008 was $15,425 for students obtaining a bachelor's degree. Suppose a sample of 400 students had a sample mean loan amount of $15,425 and a sample standard deviation student loan amount of $20,000. Do the following.
   a. Find $t_{\alpha/2}$ for a confidence interval with 90% confidence.
   b. Construct and interpret a 90% confidence interval for the population mean student loan amount for all students obtaining a bachelor's degree.
51. Parking Meters. A tried-and-true revenue stream for large cities has been the funds collected from parking meters. A random sample of 75 parking meters yielded a mean of $120 per meter with a standard deviation of $30.
   a. Find $t_{\alpha/2}$ for a confidence interval with 95% confidence.
   b. Construct and interpret a 95% confidence interval for the population mean revenue collected from all parking meters.
52. Teachers Graded. A 2007 study reported in *Science* magazine stated that fifth-grade teachers scored a mean of 3.4 (out of 7) points for "providing evaluative feedback to students on their work."[13] Assume that the sample size was 36 and the sample standard deviation was 1.5.
   a. Find $t_{\alpha/2}$ for a confidence interval with 90% confidence.
   b. Construct and interpret a 90% confidence interval for the population mean points scored by fifth-grade teachers for providing evaluative feedback.
53. Sickle-Cell Anemia. Refer to Exercise 49.
   a. Calculate and interpret the margin of error.
   b. If the sample size is increased to 400, describe what will happen to the margin of error.
54. Student Loans. Refer to Exercise 50.
   a. Calculate and interpret the margin of error.
   b. If the sample size is decreased to 100, describe what will happen to the margin of error.

55. **Parking Meters.** Refer to Exercise 51.
    a. Compute the margin of error and interpret it.
    b. Describe two ways of reducing this margin of error. Which method is more desirable, and why?
56. **Teachers Graded.** Refer to Exercise 52.
    a. Compute the margin of error and interpret it.
    b. Describe two ways of reducing this margin of error. Which method is more desirable, and why?

For Exercises 57–60, the normality of the data was confirmed in the Section 8.1 exercises.

57. **Carbon Emissions.** The following table represents the carbon emissions (in millions of tons) from consumption of fossil fuels, for a random sample of 5 nations.[14] 🐾 **carbon**

Nation	Emissions
Brazil	361
Germany	844
Mexico	398
Great Britain	577
Canada	631

   a. Construct and interpret a 90% t confidence interval for the population mean carbon emissions.
   b. Calculate and interpret the margin of error for the confidence interval in part (a).
   c. Explain two ways we could decrease the margin of error. Which method is preferable, and why?

58. *Deepwater Horizon* **Cleanup Costs.** The following table represents the amount of money disbursed by BP to a random sample of 6 Florida counties, for cleanup of the *Deepwater Horizon* oil spill, in millions of dollars.[15] 🐾 **deepwaterclean**

County	Cleanup costs ($ millions)
Broward	0.85
Escambia	0.70
Franklin	0.50
Pinellas	1.15
Santa Rosa	0.50
Walton	1.35

   a. Construct and interpret a 95% t confidence interval for the population mean cleanup cost.
   b. Calculate and interpret the margin of error for the confidence interval in part (a).
   c. Explain two ways we could decrease the margin of error. Which method is preferable, and why?

59. **Wii Game Sales.** The following table represents the number of units sold in the United States for the week ending March 26, 2011, for a random sample of 8 Wii games.[16] 🐾 **wiisales**

Game	Units (1000s)	Game	Units (1000s)
Wii Sports Resort	65	Zumba Fitness	56
Super Mario All Stars	40	Wii Fit Plus	36
Just Dance 2	74	Michael Jackson	42
New Super Mario Bros.	16	Lego Star Wars	110

   a. Construct and interpret a 99% confidence interval for the population mean number of units sold.
   b. Calculate and interpret the margin of error for the confidence interval in part (b).
   c. How could we increase the precision of our confidence interval without decreasing the confidence level?

60. **A Rainy Month in Georgia?** The following table represents the total rainfall (in inches) for the month of February 2011 for a random sample of 10 locations in Georgia.[17] 🐾 **georgiarain**

Location	Rainfall (inches)	Location	Rainfall (inches)
Athens	4.72	Atlanta	4.25
Augusta	4.31	Cartersville	3.03
Dekalb	2.96	Fulton	4.36
Gainesville	4.06	Lafayette	3.75
Marietta	3.20	Rome	3.26

   a. Construct and interpret a 95% confidence interval for the population mean rainfall in inches.
   b. Calculate and interpret the margin of error for the confidence interval in part (b).
   c. How could we increase the precision of our confidence interval without decreasing the confidence level?

61. **Hybrid Car Gas Mileage.** The accompanying table shows the city gas mileage for 6 hybrid cars, as reported by the Environmental Protection Agency and www.hybridcars.com in 2007. 🐾 **hybridmiles**

Vehicle	Mileage (mpg)
Honda Accord	30
Ford Escape (2wd)	36
Toyota Highlander	33
Saturn VUE Green Line	27
Lexus RX 400h	31
Lexus GS 450h	25

   a. Use technology to construct a normal probability plot of the gas mileages. Confirm that the distribution appears to be normal.
   b. Find $t_{\alpha/2}$ for a confidence interval with 90% confidence.
   c. Compute and interpret the margin of error E for a confidence interval with 90% confidence.
   d. Construct and interpret a 90% confidence interval (t interval) for the population mean mileage.

62. **Hybrid Car Gas Mileage II.** The table contains the complete listing of 12 hybrid vehicle gas mileages shown on www.hybridcars.com in 2007. 🐾 **hybridmiles2**

Vehicle	Mileage (mpg)
Honda Insight	61
Toyota Prius	60
Honda Civic	50
Toyota Camry	43
Honda Accord	30
Ford Escape (2wd)	36
Ford Escape	33
Mercury Mariner	33
Toyota Highlander	33
Saturn VUE Green Line	27
Lexus RX 400h	31
Lexus GS 450h	25

a. Use technology to construct a normal probability plot of the gas mileages.

b. Is there evidence that the distribution is not normal?

c. Can you proceed to construct a *t* interval? Why or why not?

63. Calories in Breakfast Cereals. What is the mean number of calories in a bowl of breakfast cereal? A random sample of 6 well-known breakfast cereals yielded the following calorie data. **cerealcalories**

Cereal	Calories
Apple Jacks	110
Cocoa Puffs	110
Mueslix	160
Cheerios	110
Corn Flakes	100
Shredded Wheat	80

a. Use technology to construct a normal probability plot of the number of calories.

b. Is there evidence that the distribution is not normal?

c. Can we proceed to construct a *t* interval? Why or why not?

64. Commuting Distances. A university is trying to attract more commuting students from the local community. As part of the research into the modes of transportation students use to commute to the university, a survey was conducted asking how far commuting students commuted from home to school each day. A random sample of 30 students provided the distances (in miles) shown. **commutedist**

14	10	14	12	12	11	5	6	9	14	9	9	4	7	15
9	7	7	12	10	15	10	6	11	9	11	10	11	7	12

a. Find $t_{\alpha/2}$ for a confidence interval with 95% confidence.

b. Compute and interpret the margin of error for a confidence interval with 95% confidence.

c. Construct and interpret a 95% *t* confidence interval for the population mean commuting distance.

65. Van Gogh's Palette. A random sample of 30 paintings by Vincent van Gogh yielded a sample mean number of colors in his palette of 15 with a sample standard deviation of 3. Assume that the number of palette colors is normally distributed.

a. Calculate and interpret a 90% confidence interval for the mean number of colors in van Gogh's palette for all his paintings.

b. Calculate and interpret a 95% confidence interval for the mean number of colors in van Gogh's palette for all his paintings

c. Calculate and interpret a 99% confidence interval for the mean number of colors in van Gogh's palette for all his paintings.

d. Write a sentence explaining what happens to the width of the confidence interval as the confidence level increases.

e. Is it possible to find a 100% confidence interval for the mean number of colors in van Gogh's palette for all his paintings? Why or why not?

66. HIV-Related Deaths. A random sample of ten large American cities found a sample mean number of HIV-related deaths per week of 42 and a sample standard deviation of 12. Assume that the numbers of HIV-related deaths are normally distributed with a population standard deviation of 12.

a. Construct and interpret a 99% confidence interval for the mean weekly number of HIV-related deaths in all large American cities.

b. Suppose your research supervisor now tells you that the interval you reported in part **(a)** is too wide. What are two possible solutions to the problem? Discuss the benefits and drawbacks of each.

67. Baby Weights. A random sample of 20 babies born in Brisbane (Australia) Hospital had the histogram of the babies' weights shown here. The sample mean is 3227 grams, and the sample standard deviation is 560 grams.

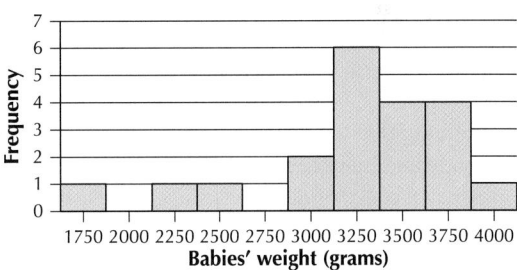

a. Discuss the normality of the data. Do the data appear acceptably normal?

b. Is it appropriate to apply the *t* interval or not? Explain why or why not.

c. Is there something you could do to make the data set more normal?

d. How would the changes described in **(c)** affect the meaning and interpretation of the confidence interval?

e. Would it be possible to find a valid value for the population standard deviation? Discuss how you might go about finding this value or something close to it.

68. Most Active Stocks. The 10 most traded stocks on the New York Stock Exchange on October 3, 2007, are shown in the table (see the next page), together with their closing prices and net change, in dollars. Use only the net change data for this analysis. **activestock**

Stock	Closing price	Net change
Micron Technology	$10.74	−1.05
Ford Motor Company	$ 8.43	−0.14
Citigroup	$47.89	0.03
Advanced Micro Devices	$13.23	0.03
EMC Corporation	$21.13	−0.24
Commerce Bancorp	$38.84	−0.63
General Electric	$41.55	−0.57
Avaya	$16.95	−0.07
Sprint Nextel Corporation	$18.76	−0.24
iShares:Taiwan	$17.18	−0.18

Source: USA Today. **http://markets.usatoday.com.**

    a. Check the normality assumption using a normal probability plot or histogram.
    b. What are the sample size, sample mean, and sample standard deviation?
    c. What is $t_{\alpha/2}$?
    d. Estimate the mean net change for the population of high-volume NYSE stocks using a 95% confidence interval.
    e. What is the margin of error? Explain what this number means.

69. Assistant Professor Salaries. As a background to a wage discrimination lawsuit, officials compiled the salaries of 12 randomly selected assistant professors nationwide. Their salaries were as follows, in thousands of dollars:

46.10	44.50	43.80	41.50	59.40	49.40
44.86	45.50	43.80	43.90	43.00	46.70

profsalary
    a. Check the normality assumption using a normal probability plot or histogram.
    b. Do you find an outlier? If you do, how should you deal with it?
    c. Assuming that the distribution of salaries is normal, provide and interpret a 90% confidence interval for the mean salary of all American assistant professors. Omit the outlier from the sample on the assumption that it is a typo.

BRINGING IT ALL TOGETHER
70. Cigarette Consumption. Health officials are interested in estimating the population mean number of cigarettes smoked annually per capita in order to evaluate the efficacy

of their antismoking campaign. A random sample of 8 U.S. counties yielded the following numbers of cigarettes smoked per capita: 2206, 2391, 2540, 2116, 2010, 2791, 2392, 2692.

    a. Evaluate the normality assumption using the accompanying histogram. Is it appropriate to construct a *t* interval using this data set? Why or why not? What is it about the histogram that tells you one way or the other?
    b. Find the point estimate of μ, the population mean number of cigarettes smoked per capita.
    c. Compute the sample standard deviation *s*.
    d. Find $t_{\alpha/2}$ for a confidence interval with 90% confidence.
    e. Compute and interpret the margin of error *E* for a confidence interval with 90% confidence. What is the meaning of this number?
    f. Construct and interpret a 90% confidence interval for the population mean number of cigarettes smoked per capita.

71. Consider the confidence interval we found for the fourth-graders' foot lengths in Example 8.10. *What if* we increased the sample size to some unspecified value but everything else stayed the same. Describe what, if anything, would happen to each of the following measures and why.
    a. $t_{\alpha/2}$
    b. Margin of error *E*
    c. Width of the confidence interval

72. Consider the 95% confidence interval we found in Example 8.10 for the mean length of fourth-graders' feet. *What if* we increased the confidence level to some unspecified value but everything else stayed the same. Describe what, if anything, would happen to each of the following, and why.
    a. $t_{\alpha/2}$
    b. Margin of error *E*
    c. Width of the confidence interval

8.3   Z Interval for the Population Proportion

OBJECTIVES By the end of this section, I will be able to . . .

1   Calculate the point estimate $\hat{p}$ of the population proportion *p*.

2   Construct and interpret a Z interval for the population proportion *p*.

3   Compute and interpret the margin of error for the Z interval for *p*.

4   Determine the sample size needed to estimate the population proportion.

1 Point Estimate $\hat{p}$ of the Population Proportion p

So far we have dealt with interval estimates of the population mean μ only. However, we may also be interested in an interval estimate for the population proportion of successes, p. Recall from Section 7.3 that the sample proportion of successes

$$\hat{p} = \frac{x}{n} = \frac{\text{number of successes}}{\text{sample size}}$$

is a point estimate of the population proportion p.

Example 8.16   Community College Survey of Student Engagement

Collaborative learning in college helps students prepare for life in the business world, where employees are required to work together in teams. The Community College Survey of Student Engagement reports on the proportion of students who have worked with classmates outside class to prepare a group assignment during the current academic year.[18] Suppose that a random sample of 300 students is polled, and 174 students respond that they did indeed work on a group project this year. Calculate the point estimate $\hat{p}$ of the population proportion p.

Solution

We have $n = 300$ students and $x = 174$. Thus

$$\hat{p} = \frac{x}{n} = \frac{174}{300} = 0.58$$

Now You Can Do
Exercises 3–6.

The point estimate of the population proportion p of community college students who have worked with classmates outside class to prepare a group assignment during the current academic year is $\hat{p} = 0.58$. ∎

Of course, different samples of community college students may turn up different sample proportions $\hat{p}$. These are point estimates, and thus they carry no measure of confidence in their accuracy. The point estimates are probably close to the true values, but it's possible that they are not. They may be far from the true values. Only by using confidence intervals can we make probability statements about the accuracy of the estimates.

2 Z Interval for the Population Proportion p

Recall the Central Limit Theorem for Proportions in Section 7.3.

> **Central Limit Theorem for Proportions**
>
> The sampling distribution of the sample proportion $\hat{p}$ follows an approximately normal distribution with mean $\mu_{\hat{p}} = p$ and standard deviation $\sigma_{\hat{p}} = \sqrt{\dfrac{p \cdot (1-p)}{n}}$ when *both* the following conditions are satisfied: (1) $np \geq 5$ and (2) $n(1-p) \geq 5$.

We can use the Central Limit Theorem for Proportions to construct confidence intervals for the population proportion p. Because the confidence interval for p is based on the standard normal Z distribution, it is called the **Z interval for the population proportion p.** Because p is unknown, the conditions and the formula for $\sigma_{\hat{p}}$ substitute $\hat{p}$ for p.

> ### Z Interval for p
>
> The Z interval for p may be performed only if *both* the following conditions are met: $n\hat{p} \geq 5$ and $n(1 - \hat{p}) \geq 5$. When a random sample of size n is taken from a binomial population with unknown population proportion p, the $100(1 - \alpha)\%$ confidence interval for p is given by
>
> $$\text{lower bound} = \hat{p} - Z_{\alpha/2}\sqrt{\frac{\hat{p}(1 - \hat{p})}{n}}$$
>
> $$\text{upper bound} = \hat{p} + Z_{\alpha/2}\sqrt{\frac{\hat{p}(1 - \hat{p})}{n}}$$
>
> Alternatively,
>
> $$\hat{p} \pm Z_{\alpha/2}\sqrt{\frac{\hat{p}(1 - \hat{p})}{n}}$$
>
> where $\hat{p}$ is the sample proportion of successes, n is the sample size, and $Z_{\alpha/2}$ depends on the confidence level.

For convenience, we repeat Table 8.1 here, showing the $Z_{\alpha/2}$ values for the most common confidence levels.

Table 8.1 $Z_{\alpha/2}$ values for common confidence levels

Confidence level	α	$\alpha/2$	$Z_{\alpha/2}$
90%	0.10	0.05	1.645
95%	0.05	0.025	1.96
99%	0.01	0.005	2.576

Example 8.17 Z interval for the population proportion p

Note that the population is binomial because each student either (a) has worked with classmates in this way or (b) has not.

Using the survey data from Example 8.16, (a) verify that the conditions for constructing the Z interval for p have been met, and (b) construct a 95% confidence interval for the population proportion of community college students who have worked with classmates outside class to prepare a group assignment during the current academic year.

Solution

a. We have $n = 300$ students and $x = 174$. We check the conditions for the confidence interval:

$$n\hat{p} = (300) \cdot (0.58) = 174 \geq 5 \quad \text{and} \quad n(1 - \hat{p}) = (300) \cdot (0.42) = 126 \geq 5.$$

The conditions for constructing the Z interval for p have been met.

b. From Table 8.1, the confidence level of 95% gives $Z_{\alpha/2} = 1.96$. Thus, the confidence interval is

$$\text{lower bound} = \hat{p} - Z_{\alpha/2}\sqrt{\frac{\hat{p}(1 - \hat{p})}{n}} = 0.58 - 1.96\sqrt{\frac{0.58(0.42)}{300}}$$

$$= 0.58 - 1.96(0.0284956137) \approx 0.58 - 0.05585 = 0.52415$$

$$\text{upper bound} = \hat{p} + Z_{\alpha/2}\sqrt{\frac{\hat{p}(1 - \hat{p})}{n}} = 0.58 + 1.96\sqrt{\frac{0.58(0.42)}{300}}$$

$$= 0.58 + 1.96(0.0284956137) \approx 0.58 + 0.05585 = 0.63585$$

We are 95% confident that the population proportion of community college students who have worked with classmates outside class to prepare a group assignment during the current academic year lies between 0.52415 and 0.63585. (See Figure 8.24.) ■

FIGURE 8.24 95% confidence interval for the population proportion of community college students who have worked with classmates outside class to prepare a group assignment.

Now You Can Do
Exercises 7–22.

Example 8.18 | *Z* intervals for *p* using technology

A 2005 poll by the Center for Social Research at Stony Brook University asked, "Should high school athletes who test positive for steroids or other performance-enhancing drugs be banned from high school athletic teams, or not?" Of the 830 randomly selected respondents, 631 responded, "Yes, they should be banned." Use technology to find a 95% confidence interval for the population proportion of all Americans who think such athletes should be banned.

Solution

We use the instructions provided in the Step-by-Step Technology Guide at the end of this section (page 407). The results for the TI-83/84 in Figure 8.25 display the 95% confidence interval for the population proportion of Americans who think such athletes should be banned to be

(lower bound = 0.7312, upper bound = 0.78929)

They also show the sample proportion $\hat{p} = 0.7602409639$ and the sample size $n = 830$.

The results for Minitab are shown in Figure 8.26. At this point, we consider only the statistics in blue. The remaining material will be explained in Chapter 9. Minitab provides the sample number of successes $X = 631$, the sample size $n = 830$, the sample proportion $\hat{p} = 0.7602409639$ (rounded to 0.760241), and the 95% confidence interval for p (0.731196, 0.789286). ■

FIGURE 8.25 TI-83/84 results.

FIGURE 8.26 Minitab results.

3 Margin of Error for the *Z* Interval for *p*

For the *Z* interval for the population proportion *p*, the margin of error is given as follows.

> **Margin of Error for the *Z* Interval for *p***
> $$E = Z_{\alpha/2} \cdot \sqrt{\frac{\hat{p}(1 - \hat{p})}{n}}$$
> The margin of error *E* for a $(1 - \alpha)100\%$ *Z* interval for *p* can be interpreted as follows:
> We can estimate *p* to within *E* with $(1 - \alpha)100\%$ confidence.

Note that, just like the confidence interval for μ, the Z interval for p takes the form

point estimate $\pm$ margin of error

$$= \hat{p} \pm Z_{\alpha/2} \sqrt{\frac{\hat{p}(1-\hat{p})}{n}}$$

$$= \hat{p} \pm E$$

Example 8.19 Polls and the famous "plus or minus 3 percentage points"

There is hardly a day that goes by without some new poll coming out. Especially during election campaigns, polls influence the choice of candidates and the direction of their policies. For example, the Gallup Organization polled 1012 American adults, asking them, "Do you think there should or should not be a law that would ban the possession of handguns, except by the police and other authorized persons?" Of the 1012 randomly chosen respondents, 638 said that there should NOT be such a law.
a. Check that the conditions for the Z interval for p have been met.
b. Find and interpret the margin of error E.
c. Construct and interpret a 95% confidence interval for the population proportion of all American adults who think there should not be such a law.

Solution

The sample size is $n = 1012$. The observed proportion is $\hat{p} = \frac{638}{1012} \approx 0.63$, so $(1 - \hat{p}) = 0.37$.

a. We next check the conditions for the confidence interval:

$n\hat{p} = (1012) \cdot (0.63) = 637.56 \geq 5$ and $n(1 - \hat{p}) = (1012) \cdot (0.37) = 374.44 \geq 5$

b. The confidence level of 95% implies that our $Z_{\alpha/2}$ equals 1.96 (from Table 8.1). Thus, the margin of error equals

$$E = Z_{\alpha/2} \cdot \sqrt{\frac{\hat{p}(1-\hat{p})}{n}} = 1.96 \cdot \sqrt{\frac{0.63(0.37)}{1012}} \approx 0.02975 \approx 0.03$$

c. The 95% confidence interval is

point estimate $\pm$ margin of error

$$= \hat{p} \pm Z_{\alpha/2} \sqrt{\frac{\hat{p}(1-\hat{p})}{n}}$$

$$= \hat{p} \pm E$$

$$\approx 0.63 \pm 0.03$$

$$= (\text{lower bound} = 0.60, \text{ upper bound} = 0.66)$$

Now You Can Do
Exercises 23–34.

Thus, we are 95% confident that the population proportion of all American adults who think that there should not be such a law lies between 60% and 66%. ∎

Developing Your Statistical Sense

Famous "Plus or Minus 3 Points"

Note that this confidence interval was obtained by adding and subtracting 3% from the 63% point estimate. That is, the poll has a margin of error of $E = 3$ percentage points $= 0.03$. This is the famous "plus or minus 3 percentage points" used in many news reports. However, newscasters rarely announce the confidence level of the poll. National pollsters almost always use 95% as their confidence level and usually try to select the sample size necessary to create a margin of error of about 3%. We learn how they do this next. ◢

4 Sample Size for Estimating the Population Proportion

Next we consider the question: How large a sample size do I need to estimate the population proportion p to within margin of error E with $100(1 - \alpha)\%$ confidence? The margin of error of the confidence interval for proportions equals

$$E = Z_{\alpha/2} \cdot \sqrt{\frac{\hat{p}\,(1 - \hat{p})}{n}}$$

Solving for n gives us

$$n = \hat{p}(1 - \hat{p})\left(\frac{Z_{\alpha/2}}{E}\right)^2 \qquad \text{(Equation 8.1)}$$

Unfortunately, Equation 8.1 depends on prior knowledge of $\hat{p}$. So, if we have such information about $\hat{p}$ available from some earlier sample, then we use Equation 8.1 to determine the required sample. However, what if we do not know the value of $\hat{p}$?

Figure 8.27 plots the sample size requirements for a 95% confidence interval for p, with a desired margin of error of 0.03, for values of $\hat{p}$ ranging from 0.01 to 0.99, representing all sample proportions from 1% to 99%. Note that the plot is symmetric, and therefore the largest required sample size occurs at the midpoint $\hat{p} = 0.5$. Thus, $\hat{p} = 0.5$ is the most conservative value for $\hat{p}$. When the actual value of $\hat{p}$ is not known, we use the following formula:

$$n = \left(\frac{0.5 \cdot Z_{\alpha/2}}{E}\right)^2$$

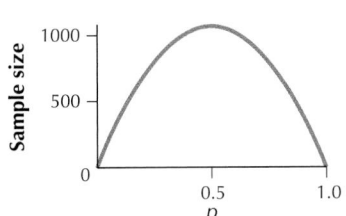

FIGURE 8.27 Sample size required for the range of values p.

Sample Size for Estimating a Population Proportion

When $\hat{p}$ is known, the sample size needed to estimate the population proportion p to within a margin of error E with confidence $100(1 - \alpha)\%$ is given by

$$n = \hat{p}(1 - \hat{p})\left(\frac{Z_{\alpha/2}}{E}\right)^2$$

where $Z_{\alpha/2}$ is the value associated with the desired confidence level, E is the desired margin of error, and $\hat{p}$ is the sample proportion of successes available from some earlier sample. Round up to the next integer.

When $\hat{p}$ is unknown, we use

$$n = \left(\frac{0.5 \cdot Z_{\alpha/2}}{E}\right)^2$$

These formulas are illustrated using the following two examples.

Example 8.20 Sample size for estimating a sample proportion when $\hat{p}$ is known

Refer to Example 8.19. Suppose that the Gallup Organization now wanted to estimate the population proportion of those who think there should not be a law that would ban the possession of handguns to within a margin of error of $E = 0.01$ with 95% confidence. How large a sample size is needed?

Solution

From Example 8.19, we have the sample proportion $\hat{p} = 0.63$. The confidence level of 95% implies that our $Z_{\alpha/2} = 1.96$, and the desired margin of error is $E = 0.01$. Thus, the required sample size is

$$n = \hat{p}(1 - \hat{p})\left(\frac{Z_{\alpha/2}}{E}\right)^2 = 0.63(1 - 0.63)\left(\frac{1.96}{0.01}\right)^2 \approx 8954.77$$

Now You Can Do
Exercises 35–40.

Rounding up, this gives us a required sample size of 8955. The smaller margin of error requires a larger sample size. ∎

Example 8.21 Required sample size for polls

Suppose the Dimes-Newspeak organization would like to take a poll on the proportion of Americans who will vote Republican in the next presidential election. How large a sample size does the Dimes-Newspeak organization need to estimate the proportion to within plus or minus 3 percentage points ($E = 0.03$) with 95% confidence?

Solution

The 95% confidence implies that the value for $Z_{\alpha/2}$ is 1.96. Since there is no information available about the value of the population proportion of all Americans who will vote Republican in the next election, we use 0.5 as our most conservative value of p:

$$n = \left[\frac{0.5 \cdot Z_{\alpha/2}}{E}\right]^2 = \left[\frac{(0.5)(1.96)}{0.03}\right]^2 \approx 1067.11$$

Now You Can Do
Exercises 41–48.

So if the pollsters would like to estimate the population proportion of all American voters who will vote Republican in the upcoming election to within 3% with 95% confidence, they will need a sample of 1068 voters (don't forget to round up!). ∎

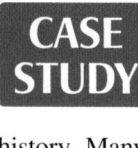

CASE STUDY Health Effects of the *Deepwater Horizon* Oil Spill

The *Deepwater Horizon* oil drilling platform exploded on April 20, 2010, killing 11 workers and causing the largest oil spill in American history. Many Americans participated in the cleanup of coastal property and wildlife habitat, including the cleaning of the wildlife. The National Institute for Occupational Safety and Health (NIOSH) conducted a randomly sampled survey of 54 of these workers who were exposed to oil, dispersant, cleaners, and other chemicals. Of these 54 workers, 25 reported skin problems, such as itchy skin or rash, as a result of exposure to these chemicals. Suppose we are interested in constructing a 95% confidence interval for the population proportion of all wildlife workers who reported such skin problems.

a. What is the point estimate of p, the population proportion of workers reporting skin problems?

b. Are the conditions met for constructing the desired confidence interval?

c. What is the critical value $Z_{\alpha/2}$?

d. Calculate the margin of error $E = Z_{\alpha/2} \cdot \sqrt{\frac{\hat{p}(1 - \hat{p})}{n}}$. Interpret the margin of error.

e. Express the confidence interval for p in terms of the values for the point estimate ± the margin of error.

f. Calculate the lower and upper bounds for the confidence interval. Interpret the confidence interval.

g. How large a sample size would be needed to estimate the population proportion of all wildlife workers who reported such skin problems to within 0.1330 with 95% confidence? Comment on your answer.

h. Suppose we now want the estimate to be within 0.1330 with 99% confidence rather than 95%. Will the required sample size be larger or smaller and why? Verify your statement by finding the required sample size.

Solution

a. Of the 54 workers, 25 reported skin problems, so the point estimate of p, the population proportion of workers reporting skin problems, is $\hat{p} = 25/54 \approx 0.4630$.

b. The conditions for constructing the confidence interval for p have been met, since

$$n\hat{p} = (54)(0.4630) \approx 25 \geq 5 \qquad \text{and} \qquad n(1 - \hat{p}) = (54)(0.5370) \approx 29 \geq 5.$$

c. For confidence level 95%, we have from Table 8.1 (page 402), $Z_{\alpha/2} = 1.96$.

d. The margin of error is:

$$E = Z_{\alpha/2} \cdot \sqrt{\frac{\hat{p}(1-\hat{p})}{n}} \approx (1.96) \cdot \sqrt{\frac{0.4630(0.5370)}{54}} \approx 0.1330.$$

We interpret this as follows: "We can estimate the population proportion of workers reporting skin problems to within 0.1330 with 95% confidence."

e. We may express our confidence interval in terms of point estimate $\pm$ the margin of error, as follows: 0.4630 ± 0.1330.

f. Lower bound $= 0.4630 - 0.1330 = 0.3300$ Upper bound $= 0.4630 + 0.1330 = 0.5960$

We are 95% confident that the population proportion of all wildlife cleanup workers who suffered from skin problems lies between 0.3300 and 0.5960.

g. We have

$$n = \hat{p}(1-\hat{p})\left(\frac{Z_{\alpha/2}}{E}\right)^2 = 0.4630(0.5370)\left(\frac{1.96}{0.1330}\right)^2 \approx 53.9963$$

which rounds up to $n = 54$. This is precisely the sample size that we originally had, which did in fact give us precisely this margin of error of $E = 0.1330$.

h. Because the confidence level has increased while all other quantities have stayed the same, the required sample size will also increase. We now have

$$n = \hat{p}(1-\hat{p})\left(\frac{Z_{\alpha/2}}{E}\right)^2 = 0.4630(0.5370)\left(\frac{2.576}{0.1330}\right)^2 \approx 93.2704$$

which rounds up to $n = 94$, a larger required sample size for a larger desired confidence level. ∎

STEP-BY-STEP TECHNOLOGY GUIDE: *Z* Confidence Intervals for *p*

We illustrate how to construct the *Z* confidence interval for *p* from Example 8.18 (page 403).

TI-83/84

Step 1 Press **STAT** and highlight **TESTS**.
Step 2 Scroll down to **A** (for **1-PropZInt**, see Figure 8.28), and press **ENTER**.
Step 3 For **x**, enter the number of success, **631**.
Step 4 For **n**, enter the sample size **830**.
Step 5 For **C-Level** (confidence level), enter the appropriate confidence level (e.g., **0.95**), and press **ENTER** (Figure 8.29).
Step 6 Highlight **Calculate** and press **ENTER**. The results are shown in Figure 8.25 in Example 8.18.

FIGURE 8.28

FIGURE 8.29

MINITAB

Step 1 Click **Stat > Basic Statistics > 1-Proportion**.
Step 2 Click **Summarized Data**.
Step 3 Enter the **Number of Trials** (n) **830** and the **Number of Events** (X) **631**.

Step 4 Click on **Options**, enter **95** as the **Confidence Level**, select **Use test and interval based on normal distribution**, and click **OK**. Then click **OK** again.
The results are shown in Figure 8.26 in Example 8.18.

CRUNCHIT!

Step 1 Click **Statistics . . . Proportion** and select **1-sample**.
Step 2 Choose the **Summarized** tab. For **n** enter the number of trials **830**; for **Successes** enter 631.

Step 3 Select the **Confidence Interval** tab, and enter **95** for the **Confidence Interval Level**. Then click **Calculate**.

Section 8.3 Summary

1 The sample proportion of successes

$$\hat{p} = \frac{x}{n} = \frac{\text{number of successes}}{\text{sample size}}$$

is a point estimate of the population proportion p.

2 The $100(1 - \alpha)\%$ confidence interval for the population proportion p is given by

$$\hat{p} \pm Z_{\alpha/2} \sqrt{\frac{\hat{p}(1 - \hat{p})}{n}}$$

where $\hat{p}$ is the sample proportion of successes, n is the sample size, and $Z_{\alpha/2}$ depends on the confidence level. The Z interval for p may be constructed only if *both* the following conditions apply: $n\hat{p} \geq 5$ and $n(1 - \hat{p}) \geq 5$.

3 Note that the confidence interval for p takes on the form

point estimate $\pm$ margin of error

where $\hat{p}$ is the point estimate of p and $E = Z_{\alpha/2}\sqrt{\hat{p}(1 - \hat{p})/n}$ is the margin of error.

4 Suppose we would like to estimate the population proportion p to within a margin of error E with confidence $100(1 - \alpha)\%$. If $\hat{p}$ is known, then the required sample size needed is given by

$$n = \hat{p}(1 - \hat{p}) \left(\frac{Z_{\alpha/2}}{E} \right)^2$$

If $\hat{p}$ is not known, then the required sample size needed is given by

$$n = \left(\frac{0.5 \cdot Z_{\alpha/2}}{E} \right)^2$$

Section 8.3 Exercises

CLARIFYING THE CONCEPTS

1. Suppose the population proportion of successes p is known. Is it useful to construct a confidence interval for p?

2. A news broadcast mentions that the sample size of a poll is about 1000 and that the margin of error is plus or minus 3 percentage points. How do we know that the pollsters are using a 95% confidence level?

PRACTICING THE TECHNIQUES

For Exercises 3–6, calculate the point estimate $\hat{p}$ of the population proportion p.

3. Sample size = 100, number of successes = 40

4. Sample size = 500, number of successes = 100

5. $n = 1000$, $x = 560$

6. $n = 10{,}000$, $x = 2057$

For Exercises 7–22, do the following:
  a. Find $Z_{\alpha/2}$.
  b. Determine whether the conditions for constructing a confidence interval for p are met.
  c. If the conditions are met, construct a confidence interval for p with the indicated confidence level.
  d. If the conditions are met, sketch the confidence interval using a graph similar to Figure 8.24.

7. Confidence level 95%, sample size 100, sample proportion 0.2

8. Confidence level 95%, sample size 100, sample proportion 0.1

9. Confidence level 95%, sample size 100, sample proportion 0.05

10. Confidence level 95%, sample size 100, sample proportion 0.04

11. Confidence level 90%, $n = 25$, $\hat{p} = 0.2$

12. Confidence level 95%, $n = 25$, $\hat{p} = 0.2$

13. Confidence level 99%, $n = 25$, $\hat{p} = 0.2$

14. Confidence level 95%, $n = 25$, $\hat{p} = 0.16$

15. Confidence level 95%, sample size 25, number of successes 12

16. Confidence level 90%, sample size 81, number of successes 8

17. Confidence level 99%, sample size 100, number of successes 50

18. Confidence level 99%, sample size 20, number of successes 1

19. Confidence level 95%, $n = 64$, $x = 26$

20. Confidence level 99%, $n = 144$, $x = 80$

21. Confidence level 90%, $n = 49$, $x = 18$

22. Confidence level 95%, $n = 15$, $x = 26$

For Exercises 23–34, calculate the margin of error for the confidence interval from the indicated exercise.

23. Exercise 7

24. Exercise 8

25. Exercise 9

26. Refer to Exercises 23–25.
  a. Write a sentence describing what happens to the margin of error as the sample proportion decreases, while the sample size and confidence level stay the same.
  b. What effect does the behavior you observed in **(a)** have on the width of the confidence interval?

27. Exercise 11

28. Exercise 12

29. Exercise 13

30. Refer to Exercises 27–29.
  a. Write a sentence describing what happens to the margin of error as the confidence level increases, while the sample size and the sample proportion stay the same.

b. What effect does the behavior you observed in **(a)** have on the width of the confidence interval?

31. For the following samples, find the margin of error E for a 95% confidence interval for p.
  a. 5 successes in 10 trials
  b. 50 successes in 100 trials
  c. 500 successes in 1000 trials
  d. 5000 successes in 10,000 trials

32. For the following samples, find the margin of error E for a 95% confidence interval for p.
  a. 10 successes in 100 trials
  b. 20 successes in 100 trials
  c. 30 successes in 100 trials
  d. 40 successes in 100 trials
  e. 50 successes in 100 trials

33. Refer to Exercise 31.
  a. Write a sentence describing what happens to the margin of error as the sample size increases while $\hat{p}$ remains constant.
  b. What effect will the behavior you observed in **(a)** have on the width of the confidence interval?

34. Refer to Exercise 32.
  a. Write a sentence describing what happens to the margin of error as the sample proportion approaches 0.5 while the sample size remains constant.
  b. What effect will the behavior you observed in **(a)** have on the width of the confidence interval?

For Exercises 35–39, we are estimating p and we know the value of $\hat{p}$. Find the required sample size.

35. Confidence level 95%, margin of error 0.03, $\hat{p} = 0.3$
36. Confidence level 95%, margin of error 0.03, $\hat{p} = 0.7$
37. Confidence level 95%, margin of error 0.03, $\hat{p} = 0.1$
38. Confidence level 95%, margin of error 0.03, $\hat{p} = 0.01$
39. Confidence level 95%, margin of error 0.03, $\hat{p} = 0.001$
40. Using Exercises 37–39, describe what happens to the required sample size when $\hat{p}$ gets very small.

For Exercises 41–46, we are estimating p and we do not know the value of $\hat{p}$. Find the required sample size.

41. Confidence level 90%, margin of error 0.03
42. Confidence level 95%, margin of error 0.03
43. Confidence level 99%, margin of error 0.03
44. Confidence level 95%, margin of error 0.015
45. Confidence level 95%, margin of error 0.0075
46. Confidence level 95%, margin of error 0.00375
47. Using Exercises 41–43, describe what happens to the required sample size as the confidence level increases.
48. Using Exercises 44–46, describe what happens to the required sample size when the margin of error is halved and the confidence level stays constant.

APPLYING THE CONCEPTS
For Exercises 49–52, do the following.
  a. Find $Z_{\alpha/2}$.
  b. Determine whether the conditions are met for constructing a confidence interval for p.
  c. If the conditions are met, construct and interpret a confidence interval for p with the indicated confidence level, and sketch the confidence interval on the number line. If the conditions are not met, state why not.

49. Married Millennials. *Millennials* refers to the generation of young people aged 18–29 in 2010, because they are the first generation to come of age in the new millennium. A 2010 Pew Research Center study found that 183 of a sample of 830 American millennials were married. Use a 99% confidence level.

50. Rather Be Fishing? A study found that Minnesota, at 38%, leads the nation in the proportion of people who go fishing.[19] Assume that the study sample size was 100 and use a 95% confidence level.

51. Spring Break and Drinking. A study released by the American Medical Association found that 83% of college female respondents agreed that heavier drinking occurs on spring break trips than is typically found on campus. Assume that the sample size was 25 and use a 90% confidence level.

52. NASCAR Fans and Pickup Trucks. *American Demographics* magazine reported that 40% of a sample of NASCAR racing attendees said they owned a pickup truck. Suppose the sample size was 1000. Construct a 95% confidence interval for the population proportion of NASCAR racing attendees who own a pickup truck.

For Exercises 53–56, do the following for the confidence interval from the indicated exercises.
  a. Calculate the margin of error.
  b. Explain what this value for the margin of error means.

53. Married Millennials. Exercise 49
54. Rather Be Fishing? Exercise 50
55. Spring Break and Drinking. Exercise 51
56. NASCAR Fans and Pickup Trucks. Exercise 52

57. Hawaii Residents Thriving. The Gallup Organization collects data on the well-being of residents in the 50 states. In 2011, the highest proportion of residents that are reported to be "thriving" is in Hawaii, with 65.5% thriving. (Gallup categorizes respondents as thriving who report fewer health problems, fewer sick days, lower levels of stress, sadness and anger, and higher levels of happiness and respect.) Suppose the poll is based on 1000 Hawaii residents.[20]
  a. Find the margin of error using a 95% confidence level. What does this number mean?
  b. Construct and interpret a 95% confidence interval for the population proportion of all Hawaiians who are thriving.

58. Ecstasy Use in Twelfth Grade. According to the National Institute on Drug Abuse (www.drugabuse.gov), in 2005 there was a decline in the proportion of 12-graders who were using MDMA (Ecstasy).[21] Among whites, 3.9% reported use of the drug. Assume that the sample size is 200.
  a. Is it appropriate to use the Z interval to estimate the population proportion?

b. Find the margin of error. What does this number mean?

c. Construct and interpret a 99% confidence interval for the population proportion of all white 12th-graders who were using Ecstasy.

59. Does Heavy Debt Lead to Ulcers? An AP–AOL Poll reported on June 9, 2008, that 27% of respondents carrying heavy mortgage or credit card debt also said that they had stomach ulcers.[22] How large a sample size is needed to estimate the population proportion of respondents carrying heavy debt who also have stomach ulcers to within 1% with 99% confidence?

60. Male Binge Drinking. The American Medical Association is interested in commissioning a study on the population proportion of males who binge drink during spring break.

a. How large a sample size is required to estimate p to within 0.05 with 90% confidence?

b. How large a sample size is required to estimate p to within 0.01 with 90% confidence?

61. Most Churchgoers Are Not Drinkers. According to Gallup.com, 60% of Americans who attend church weekly do not drink alcohol. How large a sample size do we need to estimate the population proportion to within 3% with 99% confidence?

62. Most Churchgoers Are Not Drinkers. According to Gallup.com, 60% of Americans who attend church weekly do not drink alcohol. The poll reported that the sample size was 1006 respondents. Assuming 95% confidence, what is the margin of error of this poll?

63. Objective News Source? A random sample of 1113 American adults found 240 who cited CNN as the media outlet that provides the most objective news.

a. If appropriate, find the margin of error for confidence level 99%. What does this number mean?

b. If appropriate, construct a 99% confidence interval for the population proportion of all American adults who cite CNN as the media outlet that provides the most objective news.

64. Most Churchgoers Are Not Drinkers. Refer to Exercise 62. Try to think about the relationship between the various statistics rather than calculating the statistics. *What if* the sample size is increased from 1006 and everything else stays the same.

a. What will be the effect on the margin of error?

b. What will be the effect on the reported sample proportion?

c. What will be the effect on the confidence level?

65. Mozart Effect. Harvard University's Project Zero (**pzweb.harvard.edu**) found that listening to certain kinds of music, including Mozart, improved spatial-temporal reasoning abilities in children. Suppose that, in a sample of 100 randomly chosen fifth-graders, 65 performed better on a spatial-temporal achievement test after listening to a Mozart sonata. If appropriate, find a 95% confidence interval for the population proportion of all fifth-graders who performed better after listening to a Mozart sonata.

66. Taxes Too High? In a Gallup Poll of 1005 randomly selected Americans, 482 responded "Yes" to the question "Do you consider the amount of federal income tax you have to pay as too high?"

a. If appropriate, find a 90% confidence interval for the population proportion of all Americans who consider that the amount of federal income tax they pay is too high.

b. If appropriate, find a 99% confidence interval for the population proportion of all Americans who consider that the amount of federal income tax they pay is too high.

67. Mozart Effect. Refer to Exercise 65. *What if* we increase the confidence level to 99% while changing nothing else. Explain what would happen to the following statistics and why.

a. $Z_{\alpha/2}$

b. Margin of error

c. Width of the confidence interval

The Famous ± 3 Percentage Points. Use the information from Example 8.19 for Exercises 68 and 69.

68. *What if* the sample size is higher than 1012, but otherwise everything else is the same as in the example. How would this affect the following?

a. Margin of error

b. $Z_{\alpha/2}$

c. Width of the confidence interval

69. *What if* the confidence level is lower than 95%, but otherwise everything else is the same as in the example. How would this affect the following?

a. Margin of error

b. $Z_{\alpha/2}$

c. Width of the confidence interval

BRINGING IT ALL TOGETHER

Drug Companies and Research Studies. Use this information for Exercises 70–72. The *Annals of Internal Medicine* reported that 39 of the 40 research studies with acknowledged sponsorship by a drug company had outcomes favoring the drug under investigation.[23]

70. If appropriate, construct and interpret a 90% confidence interval for the population proportion of all studies sponsored by drug companies that have outcomes favoring the drug. If not appropriate, clearly state why not.

71. The article in the *Annals of Internal Medicine* found that 89 of the 112 studies *without* acknowledged drug company support had outcomes favoring the drug. If appropriate, construct a 95% confidence interval for the population proportion of all studies without acknowledged drug company support which have outcomes favoring the drug. If not appropriate, clearly state why not.

72. Refer to Exercise 71. *What if* we decrease the confidence level to 90%, while changing nothing else. Explain precisely what would happen to the following statistics and why.

a. $Z_{\alpha/2}$

b. Margin of error

c. Width of the confidence interval

8.4   Confidence Intervals for the Population Variance and Standard Deviation

OBJECTIVES By the end of this section, I will be able to . . .

1   Describe the properties of the χ^2 (chi-square) distribution, and find critical values for the χ^2 distribution.

2   Construct and interpret confidence intervals for the population variance and standard deviation.

We have seen how confidence intervals can be used to estimate the unknown value of a population mean or a population proportion. However, the variability of a population is also important. As we have learned, less variability is usually better. For example, a tool manufacturer relies on a quality control technician (who has a strong background in statistics) to make sure that the tools the company is making do not vary appreciably from the required specifications. Otherwise, the tools may be too large or too small. Data analysts therefore construct confidence intervals to estimate the unknown value of the population parameters that measure variability: the population variance σ^2 and the population standard deviation σ.

We first need to become acquainted with the χ^2 **(chi-square) distribution,** which is used to construct these confidence intervals.

1 Properties of the χ^2 (Chi-Square) Distribution

The χ^2 (pronounced *ky-square*, to rhyme with "my square") distribution was discovered in 1875 by the German physicist Friedrich Helmert and further developed in 1900 by the English statistician Karl Pearson.

The χ^2 random variable is continuous. Just as we did with the normal and t distributions, we can find probabilities associated with values of χ^2, and vice versa. Like any continuous distribution, probability is represented by area below the curve above an interval. We examine the properties of the χ^2 distribution and then learn how to use the χ^2 table to find the critical values of the χ^2 distribution.

Properties of the χ^2 Distribution

- Just as for any continuous random variable, the total area under the χ^2 curve equals 1.
- The value of the χ^2 random variable is never negative, so the χ^2 curve starts at 0. However, it extends indefinitely to the right, with no upper bound.
- Because of the characteristics just described, the χ^2 curve is right-skewed.
- There is a different curve for every different degrees of freedom, $n - 1$. As the number of degrees of freedom increases, the χ^2 curve begins to look more symmetric (Figure 8.30).

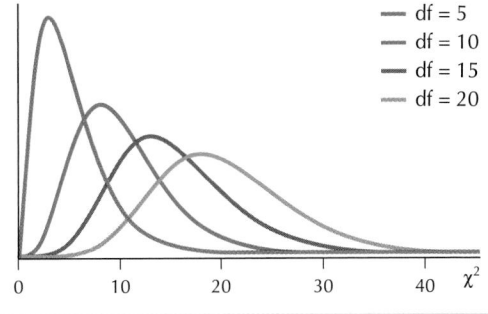

FIGURE 8.30
Shape of the χ^2 distribution for different degrees of freedom.

Now You Can Do
Exercises 5–8.

To construct the confidence intervals in this section, we shall need to find the critical values of a χ^2 distribution for the given confidence level $100(1 - \alpha)\%$, using either the χ^2 table (Table E in the Appendix) or technology. The χ^2 table is somewhat similar to the t table (Table D in the Appendix); both tables show the degrees of freedom in the left column. The area to the right of the χ^2 critical value is given across the top of the table.

Since the χ^2 distribution is not symmetric, we cannot construct the confidence interval for σ^2 using the "point estimate $\pm$ margin of error" method. Rather, the lower bound and upper bound for the confidence interval are determined using two χ^2 critical values:

$\chi^2_{1-\alpha/2}$ = the value of the χ^2 distribution with area $1 - \alpha/2$ to its right (Figure 8.31)

$\chi^2_{\alpha/2}$ = the value of the χ^2 distribution with area $\alpha/2$ to its right (Figure 8.31).

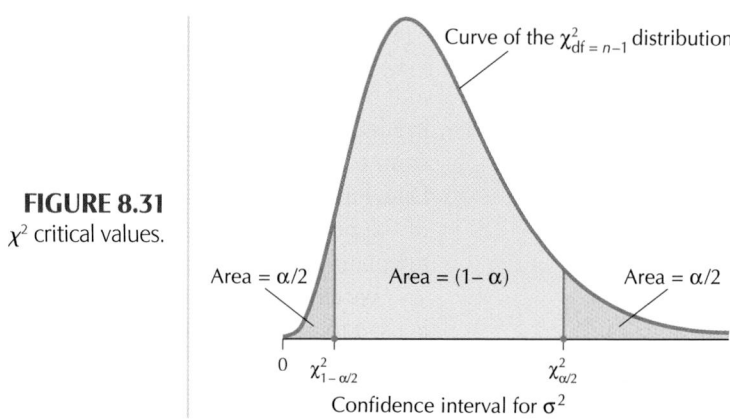

FIGURE 8.31
χ^2 critical values.

For instance, for a 95% confidence interval $(1 - \alpha) = 0.95$, $\alpha/2 = 0.025$ and $1 - \alpha/2 = 0.975$. Thus, $\chi^2_{0.975}$ represents the value of the χ^2 distribution with area $1 - \alpha/2 = 0.975$ to the right of the χ^2 critical value. The second critical value $\chi^2_{0.025}$ represents the value of the χ^2 distribution with area $\alpha/2 = 0.025$ to the right of the χ^2 critical value.

Example 8.22 Finding the χ^2 critical values

Find χ^2 critical values for a 90% confidence interval, where we have a sample size of size $n = 10$.

Solution
For a 90% confidence interval

$$(1 - \alpha) = 0.90 \qquad \frac{\alpha}{2} = \frac{0.10}{2} = 0.05 \qquad 1 - \frac{\alpha}{2} = 1 - 0.05 = 0.95$$

Note: If the appropriate degrees of freedom are not given in the χ^2 table, the conservative solution is to take the next row with the smaller df.

So we are seeking (1) $\chi^2_{0.95}$, the critical value with area $1 - \alpha/2 = 0.95$ to the right of it, and (2) $\chi^2_{0.05}$, the critical value with area $\alpha/2 = 0.05$ to the right of it.

Since $n = 10$, the degrees of freedom is df $= n - 1 = 10 - 1 = 9$. To find $\chi^2_{0.95}$ for df $= 9$, go across the top of the χ^2 table (Table E in the Appendix) until you see 0.95 (Figure 8.32). $\chi^2_{0.95}$ is somewhere in that column. Now go down that column until you see your number of degrees of freedom df $= 9$. Thus, for df $= 9$, $\chi^2_{0.95} = 3.325$. For a χ^2 distribution with 9 degrees of freedom, there is area $= 0.95$ to the right of 3.325. Similarly, $\chi^2_{0.05}$ is found in the column labeled "0.05" and the row corresponding to df $= 9$. We find that $\chi^2_{0.05} = 16.919$, as shown in Figure 8.33. ■

Now You Can Do
Exercises 9–16.

Degrees of Freedom	Chi-Square (χ^2) Distribution Area to the Right of Critical Value									
	0.995	0.99	0.975	0.95	0.90	0.10	0.05	0.025	0.01	0.005
1	—	—	0.001	0.004	0.016	2.706	3.841	5.024	6.635	7.879
2	0.010	0.020	0.051	0.103	0.211	4.605	5.991	7.378	9.210	10.597
3	0.072	0.115	0.216	0.352	0.584	6.251	7.815	9.348	11.345	12.838
4	0.207	0.297	0.484	0.711	1.064	7.779	9.488	11.143	13.277	14.860
5	0.412	0.554	0.831	1.145	1.610	9.236	11.071	12.833	15.086	16.750
6	0.676	0.872	1.237	1.635	2.204	10.645	12.592	14.449	16.812	18.548
7	0.989	1.239	1.690	2.167	2.833	12.017	14.067	16.013	18.475	20.278
8	1.344	1.646	2.180	2.733	3.490	13.362	15.507	17.535	20.090	21.955
9	1.735	2.088	2.700	3.325	4.168	14.684	16.919	19.023	21.666	23.589
10	2.156	2.558	3.247	3.940	4.865	15.987	18.307	20.483	23.209	25.188

FIGURE 8.32 Finding $\chi^2_{0.95}$ and $\chi^2_{0.05}$ using the χ^2 table.

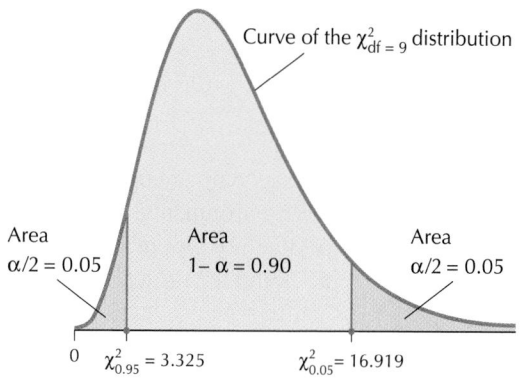

FIGURE 8.33 χ^2 critical values for the χ^2 distribution with df = 9.

2 Constructing Confidence Intervals for the Population Variance and Standard Deviation

We derive the formula for a $100(1 - \alpha)\%$ confidence interval for the population variance σ^2. Suppose we take a random sample of size n from a normal population with mean μ and standard deviation σ. Then the statistic

$$\chi^2 = \frac{(n - 1)s^2}{\sigma^2}$$

follows a χ^2 distribution with $n - 1$ degrees of freedom, where s^2 represents the sample variance. From Figure 8.31, we see that $100(1 - \alpha)\%$ of the values of χ^2 lie between $\chi^2_{1-\alpha/2}$ and $\chi^2_{\alpha/2}$. These values are described as

$$\chi^2_{1-\alpha/2} < \frac{(n - 1)s^2}{\sigma^2} < \chi^2_{\alpha/2}$$

Rearranging this inequality so that σ^2 is in the numerator gives us the formula for the $100(1 - \alpha)\%$ confidence interval for σ^2:

$$\frac{(n - 1)s^2}{\chi^2_{\alpha/2}} < \sigma^2 < \frac{(n - 1)s^2}{\chi^2_{1-\alpha/2}}$$

Thus the lower bound of the confidence interval for σ^2 is $\dfrac{(n - 1)s^2}{\chi^2_{\alpha/2}}$, and the upper bound is $\dfrac{(n - 1)s^2}{\chi^2_{1-\alpha/2}}$. Taking the square root of each gives us the lower and upper bounds for the confidence interval for σ.

Confidence Interval for the Population Variance σ^2

Suppose we take a sample of size n from a normal population with mean μ and standard deviation σ. Then a $100(1 - \alpha)\%$ confidence interval for the population variance σ^2 is given by

$$\text{lower bound} = \frac{(n - 1)s^2}{\chi^2_{\alpha/2}}, \text{ upper bound} = \frac{(n - 1)s^2}{\chi^2_{1-\alpha/2}}$$

where s^2 represents the sample variance and $\chi^2_{1-\alpha/2}$ and $\chi^2_{\alpha/2}$ are the critical values for a χ^2 distribution with $n - 1$ degrees of freedom.

Confidence Interval for the Population Standard Deviation σ

A $100(1 - \alpha)\%$ confidence interval for the population standard deviation σ is then given by

$$\text{lower bound} = \sqrt{\frac{(n - 1)s^2}{\chi^2_{\alpha/2}}}, \text{ upper bound} = \sqrt{\frac{(n - 1)s^2}{\chi^2_{1-\alpha/2}}}$$

Example 8.23 Constructing confidence intervals for the population variance σ^2 and population standard deviation σ

hybridmiles

The accompanying table shows the city gas mileage for 6 hybrid cars, as reported by the Environmental Protection Agency and **www.hybridcars.com** in 2007. The normal probability plot in Figure 8.34 indicates that the data are normally distributed.

a. Find the critical values $\chi^2_{1-\alpha/2}$ and $\chi^2_{\alpha/2}$ for a confidence interval with a 95% confidence level.

b. Construct and interpret a 95% confidence interval for the population variance of hybrid gas mileage.

c. Construct and interpret a 95% confidence interval for the population standard deviation of hybrid gas mileage.

FIGURE 8.34 Normal probability plot of mileage.

Vehicle	Mileage (mpg)
Honda Accord	30
Ford Escape (2wd)	36
Toyota Highlander	33
Saturn VUE Green Line	27
Lexus RX 400h	31
Lexus GS 450h	25

Solution

a. There are $n = 6$ hybrid cars in our sample, so the degrees of freedom equal $n - 1 = 5$. For a 95% confidence interval,

$$(1 - \alpha) = 0.95 \qquad \alpha/2 = 0.025 \qquad 1 - \alpha/2 = 0.975$$

From the χ^2 table (Table E in the Appendix), therefore,

$$\chi^2_{1-\alpha/2} = \chi^2_{0.975} = 0.831 \qquad \chi^2_{\alpha/2} = \chi^2_{0.025} = 12.833$$

Figures 8.35 and 8.36 show these results using Excel and Minitab.

A1	▼		fx	=CHIINV(0.975,5)

	A	B	C	D	E
1	0.831212				
2	12.8325				

(a)

A2	▼		fx	=CHIINV(0.025, 5)

	A	B	C	D	E
1	0.831212				
2	12.8325				

(b)

FIGURE 8.35 Excel results.

```
Inverse Cumulative Distribution Function
Chi-Square with 5 DF

P( X <= x )         x
     0.025   0.831212
```

(a)

```
Inverse Cumulative Distribution Function
Chi-Square with 5 DF

P( X <= x )         x
     0.975   12.8325
```

(b)

FIGURE 8.36 Minitab results.

```
1-Var Stats
x̄=30.33333333
Σx=182
Σx²=5600
Sx=3.983298466
σx=3.636237372
↓n=6
```

FIGURE 8.37 TI-83/84 results.

b. Figure 8.37 shows the descriptive statistics for the hybrid car gas mileages, as obtained by the TI-83/84. The sample standard deviation is $s = 3.983298466$. Thus, our 95% confidence interval for σ^2 is given by

$$\text{lower bound} = \frac{(n-1)s^2}{\chi^2_{\alpha/2}} = \frac{(5)3.983298466^2}{12.833} \approx 6.181978754 \approx 6.18$$

$$\text{upper bound} = \frac{(n-1)s^2}{\chi^2_{1-\alpha/2}} = \frac{(5)3.983298466^2}{0.831} \approx 95.46730848 \approx 95.47$$

We are 95% confident that the population variance σ^2 lies between 6.18 and 95.47 miles per gallon squared, that is, (mpg)². (Recall that the variance is measured in *units squared*.) Since it is unclear what miles per gallon squared means, we prefer to construct a confidence interval for the population standard deviation σ.

c. Using the results from part (b),

$$\text{lower bound} = \sqrt{\frac{(n-1)s^2}{\chi^2_{\alpha/2}}} = \sqrt{6.181978754} \approx 2.486358533 \approx 2.49$$

$$\text{upper bound} = \sqrt{\frac{(n-1)s^2}{\chi^2_{1-\alpha/2}}} = \sqrt{95.46730848} \approx 9.770737356 \approx 9.77$$

We are 95% confident that the population standard deviation σ lies between 2.49 and 9.77 miles per gallon. Figure 8.38 shows the two confidence intervals obtained using Minitab. ■

```
                             CI for        CI for
Variable  Method      StDev          Variance
Mileage   Standard   (2.49, 9.77)   (6.2, 95.4)
```

Now You Can Do
Exercises 17–24 and 33.

FIGURE 8.38 Minitab results showing the confidence intervals.

STEP-BY-STEP TECHNOLOGY GUIDE: χ^2 Distribution

EXCEL

Finding the Critical Values $\chi^2_{1-\alpha/2}$ and $\chi^2_{\alpha/2}$
Step 1 Select cell **A1**. Click the **Insert Function** icon f_x.
Step 2 For **Search for a Function**, type **chiinv**, click **GO**, then click **OK**.
Step 3 To find $\chi^2_{1-\alpha/2}$: For **Probability**, enter $1 - \alpha/2$ (such as **0.975** for a 95% confidence interval), and for **Deg_freedom**

enter the degrees of freedom. Excel displays the value of $\chi^2_{1-\alpha/2}$ in the cell.
Step 4 To find $\chi^2_{\alpha/2}$: Repeat Steps 1 – 2. For **Probability**, enter $\alpha/2$ (such as **0.025** for a 95% confidence interval), and for **Deg_freedom** enter the degrees of freedom. Excel displays the value of $\chi^2_{\alpha/2}$ in the cell.

MINITAB

Finding the Critical Values $\chi^2_{1-\alpha/2}$ and $\chi^2_{\alpha/2}$
Step 1 Click **Calc > Probability Distributions > Chi-Square**.
Step 2 Select **Inverse cumulative probability**, and enter the **Degrees of freedom**.
Step 3 To find $\chi^2_{1-\alpha/2}$: For **Input constant**, enter the area to the *left* of the desired critical value. For $\chi^2_{1-\alpha/2}$, this will be $\alpha/2$ (such as **0.025**). Click **OK**.
Step 4 To find $\chi^2_{\alpha/2}$: Repeat Steps 1 and 2. For **Input constant**, enter the area to the *left* of the desired critical value. For $\chi^2_{\alpha/2}$, this will be $1 - \alpha/2$ (such as **0.975**). Click **OK**.

CRUNCHIT!

Finding the Critical Values $\chi^2_{1-\alpha/2}$ and $\chi^2_{\alpha/2}$
Step 1 Click **Distribution Calculator** and select **Chi-square**.
Step 2 For **df** enter the degrees of freedom.
Step 3 Select the **Quantile** tab. Enter the area $\alpha/2$ (such as **0.025** for a 95% confidence interval). Click **Calculate**. CrunchIt! displays the value of $\chi^2_{1-\alpha/2}$.

Step 5 Minitab displays the values of $\chi^2_{1-\alpha/2}$ and $\chi^2_{\alpha/2}$ in the session window.

Finding a $100(1 - \alpha)$% Confidence Interval for σ
Step 1 Enter the data into column C1.
Step 2 Select **Stat > Basic Statistics > 1 Variance . . .**
Step 3 For **Samples in columns**, select C1.
Step 4 Click **Options**, choose the confidence level, and click **OK**. The confidence interval for σ is reported in the output, as shown in Figure 8.38.

Step 4 Enter the area $1 - \alpha/2$ (such as **0.975** for a 95% confidence interval). Click **Calculate**. CrunchIt! displays the value of $\chi^2_{\alpha/2}$.

Section 8.4 Summary

1 The χ^2 continuous random variable takes values that are never negative, so the χ^2 distribution curve starts at 0 and extends indefinitely to the right. Thus, the χ^2 curve is right-skewed and not symmetric. There is a different curve for every different degrees of freedom, $n - 1$. To find χ^2 critical values, we can use either the χ^2 table or technology.

2 If the population is normally distributed, we use the χ^2 distribution to construct a $100(1 - \alpha)$% confidence

interval for the population variance σ^2, which is given by

$$\text{lower bound} = \frac{(n-1)s^2}{\chi^2_{\alpha/2}}, \text{ upper bound} = \frac{(n-1)s^2}{\chi^2_{1-\alpha/2}}$$

where s^2 represents the sample variance and $\chi^2_{1-\alpha/2}$ and $\chi^2_{\alpha/2}$ are the critical values for a χ^2 distribution with $n - 1$ degrees of freedom. The confidence interval for σ is found by taking the square root of these lower and upper bounds.

Section 8.4 Exercises

CLARIFYING THE CONCEPTS

1. To construct a confidence interval for σ^2 or σ, what must be true about the population?
2. Explain the difference between σ^2 and s^2.
3. Explain why we need to find two different critical values to construct the confidence intervals in this section. Why can't we just use the "point estimate $\pm$ margin of error" method we used earlier in this chapter?
4. Provide an example from the real world where it would be important to estimate the variability of a data set.

Determine whether each proposition in Exercises 5–8 is true or false. If it is false, restate the proposition correctly.
5. The χ^2 curve is symmetric.
6. The value of the χ^2 random variable is never negative.

7. The χ^2 curve is right-skewed.
8. The total area under the χ^2 curve equals 1.

PRACTICING THE TECHNIQUES

For Exercises 9–14, find the critical values $\chi^2_{1-\alpha/2}$ and $\chi^2_{\alpha/2}$ for the given confidence level and sample size.
9. Confidence level 90%, $n = 25$
10. Confidence level 95%, $n = 25$
11. Confidence level 99%, $n = 25$
12. Confidence level 95%, $n = 10$
13. Confidence level 95%, $n = 15$
14. Confidence level 95%, $n = 20$
15. Consider the critical values you calculated in Exercises 9–11. Describe what happens to the critical values for a given sample size as the confidence level increases.

16. Consider the critical values you calculated in Exercises 12–14. Describe what happens to the critical values for a given confidence level as the sample size increases.

In Exercises 17–22, a random sample is drawn from a normal population. The sample of size $n = 25$ has a sample variance of $s^2 = 10$. Construct the specified confidence interval.

17. 90% confidence interval for the population variance σ^2

18. 95% confidence interval for the population variance σ^2

19. 99% confidence interval for the population variance σ^2

20. 90% confidence interval for the population standard deviation σ

21. 95% confidence interval for the population standard deviation σ

22. 99% confidence interval for the population standard deviation σ

23. Consider the confidence intervals you constructed in Exercises 17–19. Describe what happens to the lower bound and upper bound of a confidence interval for σ^2 as the confidence level increases but the sample size stays the same.

24. Consider the confidence intervals you constructed in Exercises 20–22. Describe what happens to the lower bound and upper bound of a confidence interval for σ as the confidence level increases but the sample size stays the same.

In Exercises 25–30, a random sample is drawn from a normal population. The sample variance is $s^2 = 10$. Construct the specified confidence interval.

25. 95% confidence interval for the population variance σ^2 for a sample of size $n = 10$

26. 95% confidence interval for the population variance σ^2 for a sample of size $n = 15$

27. 95% confidence interval for the population variance σ^2 for a sample of size $n = 20$

28. 95% confidence interval for the population standard deviation σ for a sample of size $n = 10$

29. 95% confidence interval for the population standard deviation σ for a sample of size $n = 15$

30. 95% confidence interval for the population standard deviation σ for a sample of size $n = 20$

31. Consider the confidence intervals you constructed in Exercises 25–27. Describe what happens to the lower bound and upper bound of a confidence interval for σ^2 as the sample size increases but the confidence level stays the same.

32. Consider the confidence intervals you constructed in Exercises 28–30. Describe what happens to the lower bound and upper bound of a confidence interval for σ as the sample size increases but the confidence level stays the same.

APPLYING THE CONCEPTS

33. Prisoner Deaths. The table contains the numbers of prisoners who died in state custody in 2005 for a random sample of 5 states. The normal probability plot in the figure indicates acceptable normality. 🖐 **prisonerdeath**

State	Prisoner deaths
New York	171
Pennsylvania	149
Michigan	140
Ohio	121
Georgia	122

Source: U.S. Bureau of Justice Statistics.

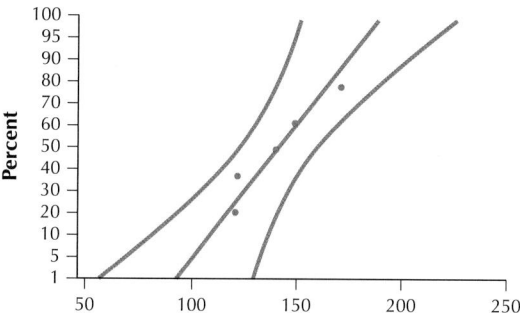

Normal probability plot of prisoner deaths.

   a. Find the critical values $\chi^2_{1-\alpha/2}$ and $\chi^2_{\alpha/2}$ for a 95% confidence interval for σ^2.

   b. Construct and interpret a 95% confidence interval for the population variance σ^2 of the number of prisoners who died in state custody.

   c. Construct and interpret a 95% confidence interval for the population standard deviation σ of the number of prisoners who died in state custody.

34. Most Active Stocks. The table shows the ten most traded stocks on the New York Stock Exchange on October 3, 2007, together with their closing prices and net change in price, in dollars. Use only the net change data for this analysis. Assume that the net change data are normally distributed. 🖐 **activestock**

Stock	Closing price	Net change
Micron Technology	$10.74	−1.05
Ford Motor Company	$ 8.43	−0.14
Citigroup	$47.89	0.03
Advanced Micro Devices	$13.23	0.03
EMC Corporation	$21.13	−0.24
Commerce Bancorp	$38.84	−0.63
General Electric Company	$41.55	−0.57
Avaya	$16.95	−0.07
Sprint Nextel Corporation	$18.76	−0.24
iShares:Taiwan	$17.18	−0.18

Source: USA Today. http://markets.usatoday.com.

a. Find the critical values $\chi^2_{1-\alpha/2}$ and $\chi^2_{\alpha/2}$ for a 95% confidence interval for σ^2.

b. Construct and interpret a 95% confidence interval for the population variance σ^2 of net price changes.

35. Prisoner Deaths. Refer to Exercise 33.

    a. What are the units you used to interpret your confidence interval in **(b)**?

    b. What are the units you used to interpret your confidence interval in **(c)**?

    c. Which units are more easily understood by most people?

36. Most Active Stocks. Refer to Exercise 34.

    a. What are the units you used to interpret your confidence interval in **(b)**?

    b. Do you think that those units would be easily understood by most people?

    c. What would the units be for a confidence interval for the population standard deviation σ?

    d. Construct and interpret a 95% confidence interval for σ.

37. Fourth-Grade Feet. Suppose a children's shoe manufacturer is interested in estimating the variability of fourth-graders' feet. A random sample of 20 fourth-graders' feet[24] yielded the following foot lengths, in centimeters. The normality of the data was verified in Example 8.10 in Section 8.2. 🐦 **fourthfeet**

| 22.4 | 23.4 | 22.5 | 23.2 | 23.1 | 23.7 | 24.1 | 21.0 | 21.6 | 20.9 |
| 25.5 | 22.8 | 24.1 | 25.0 | 24.0 | 21.7 | 22.0 | 22.7 | 24.7 | 23.5 |

    a. Find the critical values $\chi^2_{1-\alpha/2}$ and $\chi^2_{\alpha/2}$ for a 95% confidence interval for σ^2.

    b. Construct and interpret a 95% confidence interval for σ^2.

    c. Construct and interpret a 95% confidence interval for σ.

    d. Is the interpretation in **(b)** or **(c)** easier to understand?

38. Sodium in Breakfast Cereal. Refer to the sodium data in Example 8.12 (page 391). Use only the 23 non-zero values. The normality of the data was confirmed in Example 8.13.

    a. Find the critical values $\chi^2_{1-\alpha/2}$ and $\chi^2_{\alpha/2}$ for a 95% confidence interval for σ^2.

    b. Construct and interpret a 95% confidence interval for σ^2.

    c. Construct and interpret a 95% confidence interval for σ.

    d. Is the interpretation in **(b)** or **(c)** easier to understand? Explain.

39. Biomass Power Plants. Power plants around the country are retooling in order to consume biomass instead of or in addition to coal. The table contains a random sample of 10 such power plants and the amount of biomass they consumed in 2006 in trillions of Btu (British thermal units). The normal probability plot indicates acceptable normality. 🐦 **biomass**

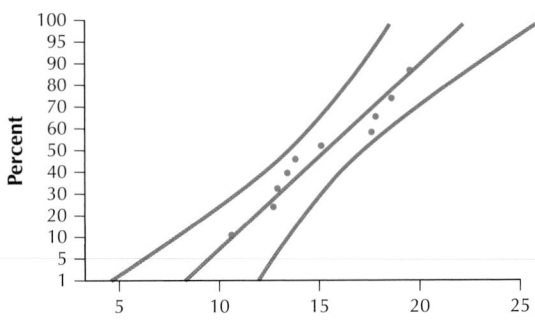

Normal probability plot of biomass consumed (trillions of Btu).

    a. Find the critical values for a 99% confidence interval for σ.

    b. Construct and interpret a 99% confidence interval for σ.

Power plant	Location	Biomass consumed (trillions of Btu)
Georgia Pacific	Choctaw, AL	13.4
Jefferson Smurfit	Nassau, FL	12.9
International Paper	Richmond, GA	17.8
Gaylord Container	Washington, LA	15.1
Escanaba Paper	Delta, MI	19.5
Weyerhaeuser	Martin, NC	18.6
International Paper	Georgetown, SC	13.8
Bowater Newsprint	McMinn, TN	10.6
Covington Facility	Covington, VA	12.7
Mosinee Paper	Marathon, WI	17.6

Sources: Energy Information Administration, Form EIA-860, "Annual Electric Generator Report," and Form EIA-906, "Power Plant Report."

40. *Deepwater Horizon* Cleanup Costs. The following table represents the amount of money disbursed by BP to a random sample of 6 Florida counties, for cleanup of the *Deepwater Horizon* oil spill, in millions of dollars.[25] The normality of the data was confirmed in the Section 8.1 exercises. Construct and interpret a 95% confidence interval for σ. 🐦 **deepwaterclean**

County	Cleanup costs ($ millions)
Broward	0.85
Escambia	0.70
Franklin	0.50
Pinellas	1.15
Santa Rosa	0.50
Walton	1.35

41. Wii Game Sales. The following table represents the number of units sold in the United States for the week ending March 26, 2011, for a random sample of 8 Wii games.[26] The normality of the data was confirmed in the Section 8.1 exercises. Construct and interpret a 95% confidence interval for σ. 🐦 **wiisales**

Game	Units (1000s)	Game	Units (1000s)
Wii Sports Resort	65	Zumba Fitness	56
Super Mario All Stars	40	Wii Fit Plus	36
Just Dance 2	74	Michael Jackson	42
New Super Mario Bros.	16	Lego Star Wars	110

Chapter 8 Formulas and Vocabulary

SECTION 8.1
- Confidence interval (p. 371)
- Confidence level (p. 371)
- Margin of error E for the Z interval for μ (p. 374).

$$E = Z_{\alpha/2}(\sigma/\sqrt{n})$$

- Point estimate (p. 370)
- Point estimation (p. 370)
- Sample size for estimating the population mean (p. 380).

$$n = \left[\frac{(Z_{\alpha/2})\sigma}{E}\right]^2$$

- Z interval for μ (p. 373).

$$\text{lower bound} = \bar{x} - Z_{\alpha/2}(\sigma/\sqrt{n})$$
$$\text{upper bound} = \bar{x} + Z_{\alpha/2}(\sigma/\sqrt{n})$$

SECTION 8.2
- Degrees of freedom (p. 387)
- Margin of error E for the t interval for μ (p. 393).

$$E = t_{\alpha/2}(s/\sqrt{n})$$

- t Distribution (p. 386)
- t Distribution characteristics (p. 387)
- t Interval for μ (p. 389).

$$\text{lower bound} = \bar{x} - t_{\alpha/2}(s/\sqrt{n})$$
$$\text{upper bound} = \bar{x} + t_{\alpha/2}(s/\sqrt{n})$$

SECTION 8.3
- Central limit theorem for proportions (p. 401)

- Margin of error E for the Z interval for p (p. 403).

$$E = Z_{\alpha/2}\sqrt{\frac{\hat{p}(1-\hat{p})}{n}}$$

- Sample size for estimating a population proportion when $\hat{p}$ is known (p. 405).

$$n = \hat{p}(1-\hat{p})\left(\frac{Z_{\alpha/2}}{E}\right)^2$$

- Sample size for estimating a population proportion when $\hat{p}$ is not known (p. 405).

$$n = \left[\frac{(0.5)(Z_{\alpha/2})}{E}\right]^2$$

- Z Interval for p (p. 402).

$$\text{lower bound} = \hat{p} - Z_{\alpha/2}\sqrt{\frac{\hat{p}(1-\hat{p})}{n}}$$
$$\text{upper bound} = \hat{p} + Z_{\alpha/2}\sqrt{\frac{\hat{p}(1-\hat{p})}{n}}$$

SECTION 8.4
- χ^2 (chi square) distribution properties (p. 411)
- Confidence interval for the population standard deviation σ (p. 414).

$$\text{lower bound} = \sqrt{\frac{(n-1)s^2}{\chi^2_{\alpha/2}}} \quad \text{upper bound} = \sqrt{\frac{(n-1)s^2}{\chi^2_{1-\alpha/2}}}$$

- Confidence interval for the population variance σ^2 (p. 414).

$$\text{lower bound} = \frac{(n-1)s^2}{\chi^2_{\alpha/2}} \quad \text{upper bound} = \frac{(n-1)s^2}{\chi^2_{1-\alpha/2}}$$

Chapter 8 Review Exercises

SECTION 8.1
For Exercises 1 and 2, answer the following questions.
- **a.** Calculate $\sigma/\sqrt{n}$.
- **b.** Find $Z_{\alpha/2}$ for a confidence interval for μ with 95% confidence.
- **c.** Compute and interpret E, the margin of error for a confidence interval μ with 95% confidence.
- **d.** Construct and interpret a 95% confidence interval for μ.

1. A sample of $n = 25$ with sample mean $\bar{x} = 50$ is drawn from a normal population in which $\sigma = 10$.

2. A sample of $n = 100$ with sample mean $\bar{x} = 50$ is drawn from a population in which $\sigma = 10$.

3. The Mozart Effect. A random sample of 45 children showed a mean increase of 7 IQ points after listening to a Mozart piano sonata for about 10 minutes. The distribution of such increases is unknown, but the standard deviation is assumed to be 2 IQ points.
- **a.** Find the point estimate of the increase in IQ points for all children after listening to Mozart.
- **b.** Calculate $\sigma/\sqrt{n}$.
- **c.** Find $Z_{\alpha/2}$ for a confidence interval with 90% confidence.
- **d.** Compute and interpret the margin of error for a confidence interval with 90% confidence.

- **e.** Construct and interpret a 90% confidence interval for the mean increase in IQ points for all children after listening to a Mozart piano sonata for about 10 minutes.

4. Working Women's Salaries. A random sample of 25 working women in California yielded a sample mean income of $45,000. Assume that the population standard deviation is $6000 and that the distribution of such incomes is normal.
- **a.** Find the point estimate of the income of all working women.
- **b.** Find $\sigma/\sqrt{n}$.
- **c.** Find $Z_{\alpha/2}$ for a confidence interval with 99% confidence.
- **d.** Compute and interpret the margin of error for a confidence interval with 99% confidence.
- **e.** Construct and interpret a 99% confidence interval for the mean income of the population of all working women in California.

Suppose we are estimating μ. For Exercises 5–7, find the required sample size.

5. $\sigma = 50$, confidence level 95%, margin of error 10
6. $\sigma = 30$, confidence level 95%, margin of error 10
7. $\sigma = 10$, confidence level 95%, margin of error 10

8. Clinical Psychology. A clinical psychologist would like to estimate the population mean number of episodes her patients have suffered in the past year. Assume that the standard deviation is 10 episodes. How many patients will she have to examine if she wants her estimate to be within 2 episodes with 90% confidence?

SECTION 8.2

For Exercises 9–11, construct the indicated confidence interval if appropriate. If it is not appropriate, explain why not.

9. Confidence level 90%, $n = 25$, $\bar{x} = 22$, $s = 5$, non-normal population

10. Confidence level 90%, $n = 25$, $\bar{x} = 22$, $s = 5$, normal population

11. Confidence level 90%, $n = 100$, $\bar{x} = 22$, $s = 5$, non-normal population

12. Cigarette Consumption. Health officials are interested in estimating the population mean number of cigarettes smoked per capita in order to evaluate the efficacy of the antismoking campaign. A random sample of 8 U.S. counties yielded the following numbers of cigarettes smoked annually per capita: 2206, 2391, 2540, 2116, 2010, 2791, 2392, 2692. Assume the data are normally distributed.

a. Construct a 95% confidence interval for the population mean per capita number of cigarettes smoked in all U.S. counties.

b. Construct a 99% confidence interval for the population mean per capita number of cigarettes smoked in all U.S. counties.

c. Compare the intervals from (a) and (b). Name one strength and one weakness of each interval.

13. Parking Meters. A random sample of 75 parking meters yielded a mean of $120 per meter with a standard deviation of $30.

a. Find $t_{\alpha/2}$ for a confidence interval with 90% confidence.

b. Compute and interpret the margin of error E for a confidence interval with 90% confidence.

c. Construct and interpret a 90% t confidence interval for the population mean amount of money collected by all parking meters.

SECTION 8.3

For Exercises 14 and 15, follow steps (a)–(d).

a. Find $Z_{\alpha/2}$.

b. Determine whether the conditions are met.

c. Calculate and interpret the margin of error,
$E = Z_{\alpha/2} \sqrt{\hat{p}(1 - \hat{p})/n}$

d. Construct a confidence interval for p with the indicated confidence level, and sketch the confidence interval on the number line.

14. Confidence level 95%, $n = 100$, $\hat{p} = 0.1$

15. Confidence level 95%, $n = 500$, $\hat{p} = 0.99$

16. Ecstasy and Emergency Room Visits. According to the National Institute on Drug Abuse (www.drugabuse.gov), 77% of the emergency room patients who mentioned MDMA (Ecstasy) as a factor in their admission were age 25 and under. Assume that the sample size is 200.

a. Calculate and interpret the margin of error for confidence level 95%.

b. Construct and interpret a 95% confidence interval for the population proportion of all emergency room patients mentioning MDMA (Ecstasy) as a factor in their admission who are age 25 and under.

17. Too Many Erasures? The Iowa Test of Basic Skills is a comprehensive national test given annually to many third-graders and fifth-graders. At one school, investigators found that 3 to 5 times as many erasures were made to the tests, compared to other schools. They also found that 89% of the erasures resulted in a correct answer, compared to less than 70% for other schools.[27] Assume that the sample size is 1000. Let's investigate whether there is evidence of tampering.

a. Calculate and interpret the margin of error for confidence level 99% for the school under investigation.

b. Construct a 99% confidence interval for p.

c. Compare this confidence interval to the proportion for other such schools. Do you think there is evidence of tampering?

For Exercises 18–20, we are estimating p and we know the value of $\hat{p}$. Find the required sample size.

18. Confidence level 99%, margin of error 0.03, $\hat{p} = 0.9$

19. Confidence level 95%, margin of error 0.03, $\hat{p} = 0.99$

20. Confidence level 95%, margin of error 0.03, $\hat{p} = 0.999$

For Exercises 21–23, we are estimating p and we do not know the value of $\hat{p}$. Find the required sample size.

21. Confidence level 90%, margin of error 0.05

22. Confidence level 90%, margin of error 0.03

23. Confidence level 90%, margin of error 0.01

SECTION 8.4

For Exercises 24–27, a random sample is drawn from a normal population. The sample of size $n = 36$ has a sample variance of $s^2 = 100$. Construct the specified confidence interval.

24. 90% confidence interval for the population variance σ^2

25. 95% confidence interval for the population variance σ^2

26. 90% confidence interval for the population standard deviation σ

27. 95% confidence interval for the population standard deviation σ

28. Union Membership. The table contains the total union membership for seven randomly selected states. Construct and interpret a 95% confidence interval for σ. Assume the data are normally distributed. ⬤ **unionmember**

State	Union membership (1000s)
Florida	397
Indiana	334
Maryland	342
Massachusetts	414
Minnesota	395
Texas	476
Wisconsin	386

Source: U.S. Bureau of Labor Statistics.

Chapter 8 QUIZ

TRUE OR FALSE

1. True or false: In Figure 8.2 (page 375), since the confidence level is 90%, then 90% of the intervals must contain μ. Explain your answer.

2. True or false: The t curve is symmetric about 0, just like the Z curve is. Therefore we can use all our symmetry techniques with the t curve as well.

FILL IN THE BLANK

3. Suppose we cut a margin of error in half. The sample size requirement then becomes _____ times larger.

4. Our estimate of μ is _____ precise using the t curve rather than the Z curve.

SHORT ANSWER

5. α is used to find the value of $Z_{\alpha/2}$. Is α a probability or a value of x or a value of Z?

6. What are the conditions for constructing a t interval?

CALCULATIONS AND INTERPRETATIONS

7. College Education Costs. A random sample of 49 colleges yielded a mean cost of college education of $30,500 per year. Assume that the population standard deviation is $3000.

  a. Compute and interpret the margin of error for a confidence interval with 90% confidence.

  b. Construct and interpret a 90% confidence interval for the population mean cost of college education.

8. Crash Test Data. The National Highway Traffic Safety Administration collects data on crash tests for new motor vehicles. They reported that the mean femur load (force applied to the femur) in a frontal crash for the passenger in a 2005 Ford Equinox SUV was 1003 pounds. Assume that the population standard deviation was 210 pounds and the sample size was 49.

  a. Compute and interpret the margin of error for a confidence interval with 90% confidence.

  b. Construct and interpret a 90% confidence interval for the population mean femur load in a frontal crash for the passenger in a 2005 Ford Equinox SUV.

9. Wolves Returning to Isle Royale? A random sample of 81 day-counts of wolves from Isle Royale in the middle of Lake Superior resulted in a mean of 57 wolves and a standard deviation of 10 wolves. Assume that the data are normally distributed. Calculate and interpret a 90% confidence interval for the population mean day-count of wolves in Isle Royale.

10. The Fog Index. The Fog Index is a scale that measures the readability of a particular English passage. For example, a Fog Index of 11.5 indicates that the material is about 11th-grade level. A random sample of 64 passages by a well-known horror author yielded a mean Fog Index of 9.5 with a standard deviation of 0.8. Construct and interpret a 95% confidence interval for the mean Fog Index for all the books by this horror author.

11. 9/11 and Religious Attendance. The Pew Research Center reported that, in a survey of 3733 randomly selected respondents, 991 had attended a religious service in response to the attacks on the World Trade Center and the Pentagon.

  a. If appropriate, find the margin of error for confidence level 95%. What does this number mean?

  b. Construct, if appropriate, a 95% confidence interval for the population proportion of Americans who attended a religious service in response to the attacks on the World Trade Center and the Pentagon.

12. Independence for Quebec? A poll conducted by the newspaper *La Presse* reported that 340 of 1000 randomly chosen Quebec adults surveyed would vote "Yes" in a referendum for independence from Canada.

  a. If appropriate, find the margin of error for confidence level 99%. What does this number mean?

  b. If appropriate, find a 99% confidence interval for the population proportion of all Quebec residents who favor independence for the province of Quebec.

13. Delivery Times. Recall from Section 3.2 that Amanda and Bethany have contracted with a local document dispatch service to deliver documents in midtown Manhattan. One particularly important client kept careful track of the delivery times (in minutes) for documents delivered by Amanda and Bethany, shown in the accompanying table. Assume both data sets are normally distributed. **deliverytime**

Amanda	15	17	12	15	10	16	14	20	16	15
Bethany	5	22	15	25	4	18	10	29	17	5

  a. Construct and interpret a 95% confidence interval for the population standard deviation of Amanda's delivery times.

  b. Construct and interpret a 95% confidence interval for the population standard deviation of Bethany's delivery times.

14. Rather Be Fishing? A study found that Minnesota, at 38%, leads the nation in the proportion of people who go fishing. How large a sample size is required to estimate p to within 0.05 with 95% confidence?

15. Genetic Analysis. A biotechnician would like to estimate the mean number of genes that she will have to analyze in her research. Assume that the standard deviation is 120 genes. How many genes does she have to sample if she would like the estimate to be accurate to within 10 genes with 95% confidence?

16. Quality of Education in America. The National Assessment of Educational Progress (NAEP) administers exams to a nationwide sampling of students to assess the quality of education in America. Suppose NAEP would like to estimate the population proportion of American schoolchildren who would answer a given question correctly. Find a sample size which would give a margin of error of 0.03 with 90% confidence.

9

Hypothesis Testing

Introduction

Chapter 9 introduces *statistical hypothesis testing*. In Section 9.1, students learn how to make decisions about the value of a population parameter, and they examine different types of errors that can be made. The Z test for the population mean is covered in Section 9.2 (*p*-value method) and Section 9.3 (critical-value method). The t test for the population mean is covered in Section 9.4, followed by the Z test for the population proportion in Section 9.5 and the chi-square test for the population standard deviation in Section 9.6. Finally, Section 9.7 covers the probability of Type II error and the power of a hypothesis test.

From the Author

Some instructors like to cover the critical-value method but not the *p*-value method. Some like to cover the *p*-value method but not the critical-value method. Others like to cover both. We offer the following suggestions:

- For those who like to cover the critical-value method but not the *p*-value method:
  - Simply cover Section 9.2, "Critical-Value Method," but not Section 9.3, "*p*-Value Method." However, you may wish to cover Objective 4 of Section 9.3, Using Confidence Intervals to Perform Two-Tailed Tests.
- For those who like to cover the *p*-value method but not the critical-value method:
  - Cover only Objective 1 in Section 9.2.
  - Then cover Section 9.3, "*p*-Value Method."
- For those who like to cover both methods: Simply cover both Sections 9.2 and 9.3.
- Note that we have moved coverage of the critical-value method ahead of the *p*-value method. This aligns our coverage with that of most other textbooks, making it easier for instructors who have previously taught using a different book to use *Discovering Statistics*.
- Similarly, we have brought our hypothesis testing into line with most other textbooks in the following two aspects.
  - The null hypothesis for tests about the mean, proportion, and standard deviation now contain an equal sign "=" rather than the inequalities "≥" or "≤." For example, $H_0 : \mu = 110$ versus $H_a : \mu < 110$ rather than $H_0 : \mu \geq 110$ versus $H_a : \mu < 110$.
  - We changed the rejection rules as follows, to be applied throughout the book:
    - Critical-value method (right-tailed test example): Changed from "Reject H_0 if test statistic > critical value" to "Reject H_0 if test statistic ≥ critical value."
    - *p*-Value method: Changed from "Reject H_0 if *p*-value < α" to "Reject H_0 if *p*-value ≤ α."
- **Section 9.1 Introduction to Hypothesis Testing**
  - Students usually relate well to the analogy of the criminal trial for learning about hypothesis testing. It is a good way to learn the difference between the null and alternative hypotheses, the two types of error, and the two ways of making a right decision.

- I have found that the "key words" strategy for constructing hypotheses works well for students who need to construct hypotheses from a word problem.

- Students are sometimes overwhelmed by all the notation in the hypotheses. You may wish to stress that these are the only possible three forms for the hypotheses, that equal signs always appear in H_0, and that the three types of inequalities appear once each in H_0.

- **Section 9.2 Z Test for the Population Mean: Critical-Value Method**

  - We use Z_{data} to denote the test statistic primarily to distinguish it from the critical value Z_{crit}. We call it Z_{data} because its value depends on the data, whereas Z_{crit} does not depend on the sample data.

  - We provide a template for interpreting the conclusion. Note that the interpretation for not rejecting H_0 differs from that for rejecting H_0 by the inclusion of the single word "insufficient" before the word "evidence."

  - The value of the test statistic for each example in this section is a whole number. This lets the students concentrate on learning hypothesis testing rather than dealing with decimals.

- **Section 9.3 Z Test for the Population Mean: p-Value Method**

  - Instructors wishing to omit the critical-value method should cover Objective 1 in Section 9.2 before moving on to Section 9.3.

  - Instructors covering both methods may wish to mention that the critical-value method works by comparing one Z-value with another Z-value, while the p-value method works by comparing one probability with another probability.

  - Instructors may wish to have a copy of Table 6.6 (page 303) handy when teaching the new Example 9.8 on finding the p-value for each form of the hypothesis test.

  - Students may question why they have to learn the p-value method if it gives the same conclusions as the critical-value method. Instructors may wish to respond by teaching Objective 2 in this section, Assessing the Strength of Evidence Against the Null Hypothesis. Here, we may dispense with the level of significance α and assess the strength of evidence against the null hypothesis using the p-value alone.

  - Instructors teaching both methods may find Objective 3 of this section useful. Figures 9.13 and 9.14 illustrate the intimate relationships among Z_{data}, Z_{crit}, the p-value, and α.

  - My doctoral adviser used to say that a single confidence interval was worth 1000 hypothesis tests. Instructors may wish to show students how this may be true by teaching Objective 4 of this section, Using Confidence Intervals to Perform Two-Tailed Hypothesis Tests.

- **Section 9.4 t Test for the Population Mean**

  - Students may wish to review the characteristics of the t distribution, from Section 8.2.

  - Instructors should stress that, if the population standard deviation σ is unknown, it is wrong to use the Z test.

  - The value of the test statistic t_{data} represents the number of standard errors the sample mean lies above or below the hypothesized mean.

- From this point on, you will find that the method to be used to solve Applying the Concepts exercises will no longer be specified. However, I still specify either the critical-value method or p-value method for the Practicing the Techniques exercises.
- **Section 9.5 Z test for the Population Proportion**
  - Instructors may wish to point out that, though the test statistic for Section 9.5 has the same name, Z_{data}, as the test statistic in Sections 9.2 and 9.3, the formula is different. On the other hand, once Z_{data} is calculated, we may compare it with Z_{crit} just as we did for those earlier sections.
- **Section 9.6 Chi-Square Test for the Population Standard Deviation**
  - Instructors may wish to review the chi-square distribution in Section 8.4.
- **Section 9.7 Probability of a Type II Error and the Power of a Hypothesis Test**
  - We formed this material into its own section.

Teaching Tips

Discuss how hypothesis testing is similar to a court case. Just as a person is innocent until proven guilty, the null hypothesis is assumed true unless the sample evidence indicates that the alternate hypothesis is true instead. Sometimes an innocent person is found guilty, which is analogous to making a Type I error. Sometimes the court fails to convict a guilty person, which is analogous to making a Type II error.

Hypothesis testing can be a bit scary for some students. You may want to stress the essential idea: If the observed value of $\bar{x}$ is extreme under the hypothesis that H_0 is correct, then the null hypothesis is rejected. All the rest is just mechanics. Emphasize that a hypothesis is just an idea or a claim; and when there is a conflict between a hypothesis and the data, the data win.

Unlike what is taught in some textbooks, it is not correct to use the Z test for μ unless the population standard deviation σ is known. If σ is not known, then one may use the t test if the sample size is large or the population is normal.

If you are pressed for time, then the material on calculating a Type II error and the power of a test may be omitted without loss of continuity.

In-Class Activities

1. Ask students to consider this scenario: Your friend has made a claim that the average price for sneakers for men is no more than $75. You feel the average price is higher. To illustrate how your friend's claim can be tested, direct students to collect data from males for the price they paid for their most recent sneakers. A large enough sample ($n > 30$) should be taken. Use this example to help motivate the idea of hypotheses and hypothesis testing. Students can find the average for their collected data and compare this value to $75.

Center the discussion on the question of whether any difference is "significant." The idea of large sample tests for a population mean can be addressed and the Z test can be introduced. Also, the t test can be introduced for the case when the population standard deviation is unknown. If each student participates, then the class can pool their data to help find an estimate for the population standard deviation to be used in the Z test. The data should be collected before the topic is presented in class.

Testing for the Population Mean of the Sum of Two Fair Dice

2. Is the population mean μ of the sum of two fair dice equal to 7? The population standard deviation is $\sigma = 2.4152$. Each student will generate sample data to perform the following hypothesis test with level of significance $\alpha = 0.10$: $H_0 : \mu = 7$ versus $H_a : \mu \neq 7$, where μ represents the population mean sum of two fair dice. Assume that the distribution is normal. The instructor should prepare a number line on the board to display the collection of test statistic Z_{data} values. For $\alpha = 0.10$ and a two-tailed test, the value of Z_{crit} is 1.645. Thus, the instructor should draw lines separating the critical regions $Z_{data} < -1.645$ and $Z_{data} > 1.645$ from the noncritical region $-1.645 < Z_{data} < 1.645$.

    a. Each student should toss two dice 10 times, recording the sum each time, and then calculate the mean sum $\bar{x}$ of this sample of size 10.

b. Using $n = 10$, $\sigma = 2.4152$, and $\mu_0 = 7$, each student should calculate his or her own value for the test statistic Z_{data} using his or her own value of $\bar{x}$ generated above.

c. Give each student a Post-It Note®. Each student should record the following on the note: his or her name and the sample mean $\bar{x}$ and test statistic Z_{data} for his or her sample.

d. Each student should place the Post-It Note® on the number line that the instructor prepared earlier.

e. Identify any Post-It Note® that indicates evidence against the null hypothesis that the population mean is 7. What is the value of Z_{data}? Of the sample mean $\bar{x}$? Do you agree that these sample means are unusual?

f. Approximately what percentage of sample means indicate evidence against $H_0 : \mu_0 = 7$? Approximately what percentage of sample means indicate evidence consistent with $H_0 : \mu_0 = 7$?

g. Overall, what is your personal conclusion about whether or not the population mean of the dice equals 7? What evidence can you point to in support of your conclusion?

Supplements

- StatTutor 15.1–15.6(a) and (b), 16.1–16.7(c), 18.4, 18.5, 20.6
- Stats@Work Simulations
  - Picture This, *p*-Value; Gary Pop
  - Picture This, *p*-Value; Ruby Sweet
  - Picture This, *p*-Value; Bodhi Behav
  - Picture This, *p*-Value; Mike Mobile

Note: Not all parts of the following simulations deal with a single population parameter.
  - Which Method to Use? Hypothesis Testing: Means and Proportions; Gary Pop
  - Which Method to Use? Hypothesis Testing: Means and Proportions; Sam Sport
  - Which Method to Use? Hypothesis Testing: Means and Proportions; Justine Red
  - Which Method to Use? Hypothesis Testing: Means and Proportions; Mindy Admin

- EESEE case studies
  - Psychic Probability (Questions 1 and 2 on estimation and hypothesis tests for a population proportion)

Applets

The *p*-Value applet is referenced in Chapter 9 for demonstrations and for Exercises 57–60 in Section 9.3.

Videos

- *Against All Odds* **www.learner.org/resources/series65.html**
  - Program 20: Significance Tests
  - Program 21: Inference for One Mean
  - Program 23: Inference for Proportions

Web Sites

- The site Online Statistics: An Interactive Multimedia Course of Study addresses hypothesis testing and has a link to the Rice Virtual Lab in Statistics with numerous simulation demonstrations along with other topics related to statistics: **http://onlinestatbook.com/index.html**.
- This Web site lists other sites that do statistical calculations: **http://statpages.org/**.
- This Web site lists activities on topics relating to hypothesis testing: **http://mathforum.org/mathtools/sitemap2/ps/**.
- This site has several activities using Excel and Minitab: **www.mathspace.com/NSF_ProbStat/Teaching_Materials/Primarily_Statistics.htm**.

Getty Images

OVERVIEW

9

Hypothesis Testing

CASE STUDY

The Golden Ratio

What do Euclid's *Elements,* the Parthenon of ancient Greece, the *Mona Lisa,* and the beadwork of the Shoshone tribe of Native Americans have in common? An appreciation for the *golden ratio.* Suppose we have two quantities A and B, with $A > B > 0$. Then, A/B is called the golden ratio if

$$\frac{A + B}{A} = \frac{A}{B}$$

that is, if the ratio of the sum of the quantities to the larger quantity equals the ratio of the larger to the smaller.

The golden ratio permeates ancient, medieval, Renaissance, and modern art and architecture. For example, the Egyptians constructed their great pyramids using the golden ratio. (Specifically, in Figure 9.1, if $A = \overline{XY}$ is the height from the top vertex to the base, and $B = \overline{YZ}$ is the distance from the center of the base to the edge, then $(A + B)/A = A/B$.) Some mathematicians have said that the golden ratio may be intrinsically pleasing to the human species. Support for this conjecture would be especially strong if evidence was found for the use of the golden ratio in non-Western artistic traditions. In the Case Study on page 462, we use hypothesis testing to determine whether the decorative beaded rectangles sewn by the Shoshone tribe of Native Americans follow the golden ratio.

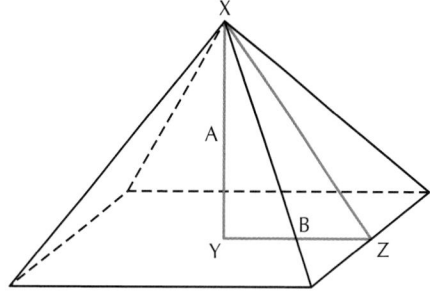

FIGURE 9.1

The Big Picture

Where we are coming from, and where we are headed . . .

- Chapter 8's topic, confidence intervals, represents only the first of a large family of topics in statistical inference.

- Hypothesis testing is the most widely used method for statistical inference, forming the bedrock of the scientific method, and touching nearly every field of scientific endeavor, from biology to chemistry to psychology. It is also the basis for business-oriented decision-making methods. Here, in Chapter 9, we learn how to perform hypothesis tests for the population mean, the population proportion, and the population standard deviation.

- In Chapter 10, "Two-Sample Inference," we will learn confidence intervals and hypothesis tests for comparing parameters from two populations.

9.1 Introduction to Hypothesis Testing

OBJECTIVES By the end of this section, I will be able to . . .

1   Construct the null hypothesis and the alternative hypothesis from the statement of the problem.

2   State the two types of errors made in hypothesis tests: the Type I error, made with probability α, and the Type II error, made with probability β.

Researchers are interested in investigating many different types of questions, such as the following:

- An accountant may wish to examine whether evidence exists for corporate tax fraud.

- A Department of Homeland Security executive may want to test whether a new surveillance method will uncover terrorist activity.

- A sociologist may want to examine whether the mayor's economic policy is increasing poverty in the city.

Questions such as these can be tackled using statistical **hypothesis testing,** which is a statistical inference process for using sample data to render a decision about claims regarding the unknown value of a population parameter. In this section we will learn how to make decisions about the values of a population mean.

1 Constructing the Hypotheses

The basic idea of hypothesis testing is the following:

1.   We need to make a *decision* about the value of a population parameter, such as the population mean μ or the population proportion p.

2.   Unfortunately, the true value of that parameter is *unknown*.

3.   Therefore, there may be different *hypotheses* about the true value of this parameter.

Statistical hypothesis testing is a way of formalizing the decision-making process so that a decision can be rendered about the value of the parameter. We craft *two competing statements (hypotheses)* about the value of the population parameter (either μ, p, or σ) and gather evidence to conclude that one of the hypotheses is likely to be true.

The Hypotheses
- The status quo hypothesis represents what has been tentatively assumed about the value of the parameter and is called the **null hypothesis,** denoted as H_0.
- The **alternative hypothesis,** or **research hypothesis,** denoted as H_a, represents an alternative claim about the value of the parameter.

Hypothesis testing is like conducting a criminal trial. In a trial in the United States, the defendant is innocent until proven guilty, and the jury must evaluate the truth of two competing hypotheses:

$$H_0: \text{defendant is not guilty} \quad \text{versus} \quad H_a: \text{defendant is guilty}$$

The not-guilty hypothesis is considered the **null hypothesis H_0** because the jurors must assume it is true until proven otherwise. The **alternative hypothesis H_a,** that the defendant is guilty, *must be demonstrated* to be true, beyond a reasonable doubt. How does a court of law determine whether the defendant is convicted or acquitted? This judgment is based upon the *evidence,* the hard facts heard in court. Similarly, in hypothesis testing, the researcher draws a conclusion based on the evidence provided by the sample data.

In Sections 9.1–9.4, we will examine hypotheses for the unknown mean μ. The null hypothesis will be a claim about a certain specified value for μ denoted μ_0, and the alternative hypothesis will be a claim about other values for μ. The hypotheses have one of the three possible forms shown in Table 9.1. The right-tailed test and the left-tailed test are called one-tailed tests. In Section 9.2 we will find out why we use this terminology.

Table 9.1 The three possible forms for the hypotheses for a test for μ

Form	Null and alternative hypotheses
Right-tailed test	$H_0: \mu = \mu_0$ versus $H_a: \mu > \mu_0$
Left-tailed test	$H_0: \mu = \mu_0$ versus $H_a: \mu < \mu_0$
Two-tailed test	$H_0: \mu = \mu_0$ versus $H_a: \mu \neq \mu_0$

Example 9.1 Invasive species in the Great Lakes

Edward Kinsman/Photo Researchers

Invasive species discharged from the ballast tanks of transoceanic ships are a growing problem in the Great Lakes. The round goby is an invasive species that carries the parasite *Neochasmus umbellus*. A 2007 study reported that the mean intensity (mean number of parasites per infected host) was 7.2 parasites.[1] Scientists worry that the population mean number of parasites in the round goby has *increased* since 2007 and want to test that hypothesis.

Solution

We can write this situation as two hypotheses about the mean population number of parasites. Note that the term *increased* means *greater than*. Thus, we write a null hypothesis and an alternative hypothesis for a right-tailed test:

$$H_0: \mu = 7.2 \quad \text{versus} \quad H_a: \mu > 7.2$$

The null hypothesis H_0 states that the population mean μ equals 7.2 parasites per fish. The alternative hypothesis H_a states that the population mean number of parasites is *more than* 7.2. Here, $\mu_0 = 7.2$, which is the possible value of μ specified in the example. ■

The first task in hypothesis testing is to form hypotheses. To convert a word problem into two hypotheses, look for certain key words that can be expressed mathematically. Table 9.2 shows how to convert words typically found in word problems into symbols.

Table 9.2 Key English words, with mathematical symbols and synonyms

English words	Symbol	Synonyms
Equal	$=$	Is; has stayed the same
Not equal	$\neq$	Is different from; has changed from; differs from
Greater than	$>$	Is more than; exceeds; has increased
Less than	$<$	Is below; is smaller than; has decreased

Once you have identified the key words, use the associated mathematical symbol to write the two hypotheses. The following strategy can be used to write the hypotheses.

Strategy for Constructing the Hypotheses About μ

Step 1 Search the word problem for certain key English words and select the associated symbol from Table 9.2.

Step 2 Determine the form of the hypotheses listed in Table 9.1 that uses this symbol.

Step 3 Find the value of μ_0 (the number that answers the question: "greater than what?" or "less than what?") and write your hypotheses in the appropriate forms.

Example 9.2 Has Arizona's mean rainfall been decreasing?

The mean annual rainfall in Arizona has been 8 inches per year, according to the *World Almanac*. But weather researchers are interested in whether this already small amount of rain will decrease, leading to drought conditions in the state. Write a null hypothesis and an alternative hypothesis that describe this situation.

Solution

Let's use our strategy to construct the hypotheses needed to test this claim.

[Step 1] **Search the word problem for certain key English words and select the appropriate symbol.** The problem uses the word "decrease," which means, "less than." Thus we will write a hypothesis that contains the $<$ symbol.

[Step 2] **Determine the form of the hypotheses.** From Table 9.1, we see that the symbol $<$ means that we use a left-tailed test:

$$H_0 : \mu = \mu_0 \quad \text{versus} \quad H_a : \mu < \mu_0$$

[Step 3] **Find the value for μ_0 and write your hypotheses.** The alternative hypothesis H_a states that the mean annual rainfall μ is less than some value μ_0. Less than what? Eight inches per year. Write the two hypotheses with $\mu_0 = 8$.

$$H_0 : \mu = 8 \quad \text{versus} \quad H_a : \mu < 8$$

Now You Can Do
Exercises 9–14.

Do not blindly apply this strategy without thinking about what you are doing. Rather, use the strategy to help formulate your own hypotheses. *There is no substitute for thinking through the problem!*

Now that we know how to construct hypotheses, we next consider when sufficient evidence exists to reject the null hypothesis.

Statistical Significance

A result is said to be **statistically significant** if it is unlikely to have occurred due to chance.

Suppose that you are a researcher for a pharmaceutical research company. You are investigating the side effects of a new cholesterol-lowering medication and would like to determine whether the medication will decrease the population mean systolic blood pressure level from the current mean of 110. If so, then a warning will have to be given not to prescribe the new medication to patients whose blood pressure is already low. The appropriate hypotheses are

$$H_0 : \ \mu = 110 \quad \text{versus} \quad H_a : \ \mu < 110$$

where μ represents the population mean systolic blood pressure and $\mu_0 = 110$. To determine which of these hypotheses is correct, we take a sample of randomly selected patients who are taking the medication. We record their systolic blood pressure levels and calculate the sample mean $\bar{x}$ and sample standard deviation s. Most likely, the mean of this sample of patients' systolic blood pressure levels will not be exactly equal to 110, even if the null hypothesis is true.

Now, suppose that the sample mean blood pressure $\bar{x}$ is less than the hypothesized population mean of 110. *Is the difference due simply to chance variation, or is it evidence of a real side effect of the cholesterol medication?* Let's consider some possible values for $\bar{x}$:

- $\bar{x} = 109$: The difference between $\bar{x}$ and $\mu = 110$ is only 1. Depending on the variability present in the sample, the researcher would likely not reject the null hypothesis because this small difference is probably due to chance variation. The result is not statistically significant.

- $\bar{x} = 90$: The difference between $\bar{x}$ and $\mu = 110$ is 20. Depending on the variability present in the sample, the researcher would probably conclude that this difference is so large that it is unlikely that it is due to chance variation. Thus, the researcher would reject the null hypothesis H_0 in favor of the alternative hypothesis H_a. The result is statistically significant.

To summarize: *in a hypothesis test, we compare the sample mean with the value μ_0 of the population mean used in the H_0 hypothesis. If the difference is large, then H_0 is rejected. If the difference is not large, then H_0 is not rejected.* The question is, "Where do you draw the line?" Just how large a difference is large enough? The hypothesis-testing procedure will show us.

2 Type I and Type II Errors

Next, we take a closer look at some of the thorny issues involved in performing a hypothesis test. Let's return to the example of a criminal trial. The jury will convict the defendant if they find evidence compelling enough to reject the null hypothesis of "not guilty" *beyond a reasonable doubt.* However, jurors are only human; sometimes their decisions are correct and sometimes they are not. Thus, the jury's verdict will be one of the following outcomes:

1. An innocent defendant is wrongfully convicted.
2. A guilty defendant is convicted.
3. A guilty defendant is wrongfully acquitted.
4. An innocent defendant is acquitted.

Recall that we can write the two hypotheses for a criminal trial as

$$H_0 : \ \text{defendant is not guilty} \quad \text{versus} \quad H_a : \ \text{defendant is guilty}$$

Table 9.3 shows the possible verdicts on the left and the two hypotheses across the top.

Tetra/Getty Images

Table 9.3 Four possible outcomes of a criminal trial

		Reality	
		H_0 true: Defendant did not commit the crime	H_0 false: Defendant did commit the crime
Jury's decision	Reject H_0: Find defendant guilty	Type I error	Correct decision
	Do not reject H_0: Find defendant not guilty	Correct decision	Type II error

Let's look at the two possible decisions the jury can make. It can find the defendant guilty: the jury *rejects the claim* in the null hypothesis H_0. Alternatively, the jury can find the defendant not guilty: the jury *does not reject* the null hypothesis H_0. There are two ways for the jury to render the *correct decision.*

> **Two Ways of Making the Correct Decision**
> - To not reject H_0 when H_0 is true. Example: To find the defendant not guilty when in reality he did not commit the crime.
> - To reject H_0 when H_0 is false. Example: To find the defendant guilty when in reality he did commit the crime.

Unfortunately, there are also two ways for the jury to render an incorrect decision. In statistics, the two incorrect decisions are called **Type I** and **Type II** errors.

> **Two Types of Errors**
> - **Type I error:** To reject H_0 when H_0 is true. Example: To find the defendant guilty when in reality he did not commit the crime.
> - **Type II error:** To not reject H_0 when H_0 is false. Example: To find the defendant not guilty when in reality he did commit the crime.

Now You Can Do
Exercises 15–24.

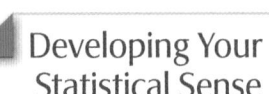 Developing Your
Statistical Sense

A Decision Is Not Proof

It is important to understand that the decision to reject or not reject H_0 does not prove anything. The decision represents whether or not there is sufficient evidence against the null hypothesis. This is our best judgment given the data available. You cannot claim to have *proven* anything about the value of a population parameter unless you elicit information from the entire population, which is usually not possible. ◢

We can make decisions about population parameters using the limited information available in a sample because we base our decisions on *probability.* When the difference between the sample mean $\bar{x}$ and the hypothesized population mean μ_0 is large, then the null hypothesis is *probably* not correct. When the difference is small, then the data are *probably* consistent with the null hypothesis. But we don't know for sure.

> The probability of a Type I error is denoted as α **(alpha).** We set the value of α to be some small constant, such as 0.01, 0.05, or 0.10, so that there is only a small probability of rejecting a true null hypothesis.

To say that $\alpha = 0.05$ means that, if this hypothesis test were repeated over and over again, the long-term probability of rejecting a true null hypothesis would be 5%. The **level of significance** of a hypothesis test is another name for α, the probability of rejecting H_0 when H_0 is true. A smaller α makes it harder to wrongfully reject H_0 just by chance. If the consequences of making a Type I error are serious, then the level of significance should be small, such as $\alpha = 0.01$. If the consequences of making a Type I error are not so serious, then one may choose a larger value for the level of significance, such as $\alpha = 0.05$ or $\alpha = 0.10$.

The probability of a Type II error is denoted as **β (beta).** This is the probability of not rejecting H_0 when H_0 is false, such as acquitting someone who is really guilty. Making α smaller inevitably makes β larger (for a fixed sample size). Of course, our goal is to simultaneously minimize both α and β. Unfortunately, the only way to do this is to increase the sample size.

There are only two possible hypothesis-testing conclusions:

Note: When we reject H_0, we say that the results are statistically significant. If we do not reject H_0, the results are not statistically significant.

- Reject H_0, or
- Do not reject H_0.

Section 9.1 Summary

1 Statistical hypothesis testing is a way of formalizing the decision-making process so that a decision can be rendered about the unknown value of the parameter. The status quo hypothesis that represents what has been tentatively assumed about the value of the parameter is called the null hypothesis and is denoted as H_0. The alternative hypothesis, or research hypothesis, denoted as H_a, represents an alternative conjecture about the value of the parameter.

2 When performing a hypothesis test, there are two ways of making a correct decision: to not reject H_0 when H_0 is true and to reject H_0 when H_0 is false. Also, there are two types of error: a Type I error is to reject H_0 when H_0 is true, and a Type II error is to not reject H_0 when H_0 is false. The probability of a Type I error is denoted as α (alpha). The probability of a Type II error is denoted as β (beta).

Section 9.1 Exercises

CLARIFYING THE CONCEPTS

1. What are some characteristics of the null hypothesis? The alternative hypothesis?

2. Explain what is meant by μ_0.

3. In the hypothesis test for the population mean, how many forms of the hypotheses are there? Write out these forms.

4. In a criminal trial, what are the two possible decision errors? What do statisticians call these errors?

5. When does a Type I error occur? A Type II error?

6. What are the two correct decisions that can be made?

7. Say we want to test whether the population mean is less than 100, and the sample we take yields a sample mean of 90. Is this sufficient evidence that the population mean is less than 10? Explain why or why not.

8. True or false: If the consequences of making a Type I error are serious, then the data analyst should choose a larger level of significance.

PRACTICING THE TECHNIQUES

For Exercises 9–14, provide the null and alternative hypotheses.

9. Test whether μ is greater than 10.

10. Test whether μ is less than 100.

11. Test whether μ is different from 0.

12. Test whether or not μ equals 4.0.

13. Test whether μ has changed from 36.

14. Test whether μ exceeds -4.

For Exercises 15–18, do the following.

    a. Provide the null and alternative hypotheses.

    b. Determine if a correct decision has been made. If an error has been made, indicate which type of error.

15. Child Abuse. The U.S. Administration for Children and Families reported that the national rate for child abuse referrals was 43.9 per 1000 children in 2005. A hypothesis test was carried out that tested whether the population mean referral rate had increased this year from the 2005 level. The null hypothesis was not rejected. Suppose that, in actuality, the population mean child abuse referral rate for this year is 45 per 1000 children.

16. Travel Costs. A motorists' guide reported that travel costs were greater than 15 cents per mile. Suppose that this report was based on a hypothesis test and that in actuality the population mean travel costs were lower than 15 cents per mile.

17. Eating Trends. According to the NPD Group, higher gasoline prices are causing consumers to go out to eat less and eat at home more.[2] Suppose that this report found that the mean number of meals prepared and eaten at home is less than 700 per year, and that in actuality the population mean number of such meals is 600.

18. Hybrid Vehicles. A study by Edmunds.com showed that owners of hybrid vehicles can recoup their initial increased cost through reduced fuel consumption in less than three years. Suppose that the report was based on a hypothesis test and that in actuality the population mean number of years it takes to recoup their initial cost is two years.

APPLYING THE CONCEPTS

For Exercises 19–24, do the following.
    a. Provide the null and alternative hypotheses.
    b. Describe the two ways a correct decision could be made in the context of the problem.
    c. Describe what a Type I error would mean in the context of the problem.
    d. Describe what a Type II error would mean in the context of the problem.

19. Shares Traded on the Stock Market. The *Statistical Abstract of the United States* reports that the mean daily number of shares traded on the New York Stock Exchange in 2005 was 1.602 billion. Based on a sample of this year's trading results, a financial analyst would like to test whether the mean number of shares traded will be larger than the 2005 level.

20. Traffic Light Cameras. The Ministry of Transportation in the province of Ontario reported that the installation of cameras that take pictures at traffic lights has decreased the mean number of fatal and injury collisions to 339.1 per year. A hypothesis test was performed to determine whether the population mean number of such collisions has changed.

21. Price of Milk. The Bureau of Labor Statistics reports that the mean price for a gallon of milk in January 2011 was $3.34. Suppose that we conduct a hypothesis test to investigate if the population mean price of milk this year has increased.

22. Americans' Height. Americans used to be on average the tallest people in the world. That is no longer the case, according to a study by Dr. Richard Steckel, professor of economics and anthropology at The Ohio State University. The Norwegians and Dutch are now the tallest, at 178 centimeters, followed by the Swedes at 177, and then the Americans, with a mean height of 175 centimeters (approximately 5 feet 9 inches). According to Dr. Steckel, "The average height of Americans has been pretty much stagnant for 25 years."[3] Suppose that we conduct a hypothesis test to investigate whether the population mean height of Americans this year has changed from 175 centimeters.

23. Credit Score in Florida. According to CreditReport .com, the mean credit score in Florida in 2006 was 673. Suppose that a hypothesis test was conducted to determine if the mean credit score in Florida has decreased since that time.

24. Salary of College Grads. According to the U.S. Census Bureau, the mean salary of college graduates in 2002 was $52,200. Suppose that a hypothesis test was carried out to determine whether the population mean salary of college graduates has increased.

9.2   Z Test for the Population Mean: Critical-Value Method

OBJECTIVES By the end of this section, I will be able to . . .

1   Explain the essential idea about hypothesis testing for the population mean.

2   Perform the Z test for the mean, using the critical-value method.

1 The Essential Idea About Hypothesis Testing for the Mean

Recall that in Section 9.1 we wanted to determine whether the population mean systolic blood pressure μ was less than 110 and we considered the hypotheses

$$H_0 : \mu = 110 \quad \text{versus} \quad H_a : \mu < 110$$

We stated that a large difference between the observed sample mean $\bar{x}$ and the hypothesized mean $\mu_0 = 110$ would result in the rejection of the null hypothesis H_0. The question is, "How large is large?"

    The Z test for the mean tells us when our results are statistically significant. To learn how this test works, consider the following. A sample of $n = 25$ patients who are taking the medication shows a sample mean systolic blood pressure level of $\bar{x} = 104$; further assume that the population standard deviation systolic blood pressure reading is $\sigma = 10$, and that the population of such readings is normal. Would this value $\bar{x} = 104$ represent sufficient evidence to reject H_0 and conclude that $\mu < 110$?

Recall from Chapter 7 that the sampling distribution of the sample mean $\bar{x}$ is the collection of sample means of all possible samples of size n. When the population is normal, or the sample size is large, the sampling distribution of $\bar{x}$ is approximately normal, with mean $\mu_{\bar{x}} = \mu$ and standard error $\sigma_{\bar{x}} = \sigma/\sqrt{n}$. The idea behind the Z test is to determine where our sample mean $\bar{x} = 104$ falls within the sampling distribution. Is $\bar{x} = 104$ somewhere near the middle of the sampling distribution, or is it an outlier? Now, if H_0 is true, then $\mu = \mu_0 = 110$ and we may standardize $\bar{x}$ to get

Note: Here we are using Facts 1–4 and the Central Limit Theorem from Chapter 7.

$$Z = \frac{\bar{x} - \mu_0}{\sigma/\sqrt{n}}$$

Substituting, we get

$$Z = \frac{\bar{x} - \mu_0}{\sigma/\sqrt{n}} = \frac{104 - 110}{10/\sqrt{25}} = -3$$

In other words, $\bar{x} = 104$ lies 3 standard errors below the hypothesized mean $\mu_0 = 110$. Thus, if we accept that the null hypothesis is true, then $\bar{x} = 104$ is an outlier, an extreme value (see Figure 9.2). That is, if H_0 is true, then the probability of observing $\bar{x} \leq 104$ is very small ($P(Z < -3) = 0.0013$), since the corresponding Z-value lies in the tail of the distribution, and nearly all the values of $\bar{x}$ are greater than 104.

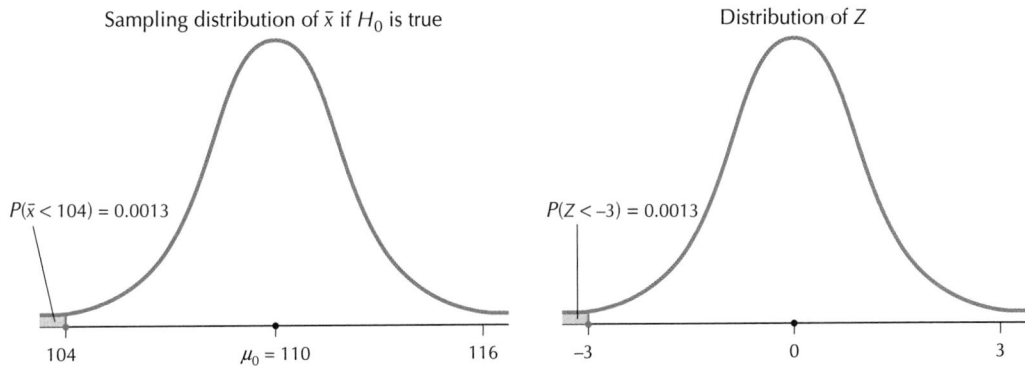

FIGURE 9.2   An extreme value of $\bar{x}$ calls for rejection of H_0.

Thus we must choose one of the following two scenarios:

1. H_0 is true, the value of μ_0 is accurate, and our observation of this extreme value of $\bar{x}$ is an amazingly unlikely event.

2. H_0 is not correct, and the true value of μ is closer to $\bar{x}$.

> ### Developing Your Statistical Sense
>
> ### The Data Prevail!
> When faced with the above situation, since we don't want to base our decisions on "amazingly unlikely events," we therefore would conclude that H_0 is not correct. Remember that the null hypothesis is just a conjecture, but the sample mean $\bar{x}$ represents directly observable "hard data." The scientific method states that, when there is a conflict between a conjecture and the observed data, the data prevail, and we need to rethink our null hypothesis. ◢

This conclusion illustrates the **essential idea about hypothesis testing for the mean.**

> **The Essential Idea About Hypothesis Testing for the Mean**
> When the observed value of $\bar{x}$ is unusual or extreme in the sampling distribution of $\bar{x}$ that assumes H_0 is true, we should reject H_0. Otherwise, we should not reject H_0.

We are developing the Z test using a left-tailed test, but the essential idea applies to right-tailed tests and two-tailed tests as well.

All the remaining parts of Sections 9.2–9.4, all the steps and all the calculations, are really just ways to implement this essential idea.

Note that our Z statistic

$$Z = \frac{\bar{x} - \mu_0}{\sigma/\sqrt{n}}$$

contains four quantities, three of which are taken from data. The sample mean $\bar{x}$ and the sample size n are characteristics of the sample data, and the population standard deviation σ represents the population data. Thus, we call this statistic $\mathbf{Z_{data}}$.

> **The Test Statistic Z_{data}**
>
> The test statistic used for the Z test for the mean is
>
> $$Z_{data} = \frac{\bar{x} - \mu_0}{\sigma/\sqrt{n}}$$

For the blood pressure data, we have

$$Z_{data} = \frac{\bar{x} - \mu_0}{\sigma/\sqrt{n}} = \frac{104 - 110}{10/\sqrt{25}} = -3$$

Z_{data} is an example of a **test statistic,** a statistic generated from a data set for the purposes of testing a statistical hypothesis. We will meet several other test statistics throughout the remainder of the text. The hypothesis test in this section and Section 9.3 is called the Z *test* because the test statistic Z_{data} comes from the standard normal Z distribution.

Example 9.3   Calculating Z_{data}

Do you have a debit card? How often do you use it? ATM network operator Star System of San Diego reported that active users of debit cards used them an average of 11 times per month.[4] Suppose a random sample of 36 people used debit cards last month an average of $\bar{x} = 11.5$ times. Assume the population standard deviation $\sigma = 3$. We would like to test whether people use debit cards on average more than 11 times per month.

Solution

Using our strategy for constructing the hypotheses from Section 9.1, the key words "more than" mean ">," and the ">" symbol occurs only in the right-tailed test. Answering the question "More than what?" is $\mu_0 = 11$. Thus our hypotheses are

$$H_0 : \mu = 11 \quad \text{versus} \quad H_a : \mu > 11$$

so that $\mu_0 = 11$. The sample size is $n = 36$, with a sample mean of $\bar{x} = 11.5$, and $\sigma = 3$. Thus

Now You Can Do
Exercises 9–16.

$$Z_{data} = \frac{\bar{x} - \mu_0}{\sigma/\sqrt{n}} = \frac{11.5 - 11}{3/\sqrt{36}} = 1$$ ■

2 Performing the Z Test for the Mean, Using the Critical-Value Method

In the critical-value method for the Z test, we compare Z_{data} with a *threshold value,* or **critical value** of Z, called $\mathbf{Z_{crit}}$. The value of Z_{crit} separates Z into two regions (see Figure 9.3):

- **Critical region:** the values of Z_{data} for which we reject H_0
- **Noncritical region:** the values of Z_{data} for which we do not reject H_0

- The **critical region** consists of the range of values of the test statistic Z_{data} for which we reject the null hypothesis.
- The **noncritical region** consists of the range of values of the test statistic Z_{data} for which we do not reject the null hypothesis.
- The value of Z that separates the critical region from the noncritical region is called the **critical value Z_{crit}**.

Z_{crit} represents the *boundary* between values of Z_{data} which are statistically significant and those which are not statistically significant. The value of Z_{crit} depends on the value of α, the probability of wrongly rejecting H_0. A smaller value of α will make it harder to reject H_0, that is, harder to find statistical significance. Thus, α is called the **level of significance** of the hypothesis test.

The value of Z_{crit} depends on (a) the form of the hypothesis test, and (b) the level of significance α. Table 9.4 shows values of Z_{crit} for the most commonly used levels of significance α. It also shows the location of the critical region.

Table 9.4 Table of critical values Z_{crit} for common values of the level of significance α

	Form of Hypothesis Test		
Level of significance α	**Right-tailed** $H_0 : \mu = \mu_0$ $H_a : \mu > \mu_0$	**Left-tailed** $H_0 : \mu = \mu_0$ $H_a : \mu < \mu_0$	**Two-tailed** $H_0 : \mu = \mu_0$ $H_a : \mu \neq \mu_0$
0.10	$Z_{crit} = 1.28$	$Z_{crit} = -1.28$	$Z_{crit} = 1.645$
0.05	$Z_{crit} = 1.645$	$Z_{crit} = -1.645$	$Z_{crit} = 1.96$
0.01	$Z_{crit} = 2.33$	$Z_{crit} = -2.33$	$Z_{crit} = 2.58$
Critical region	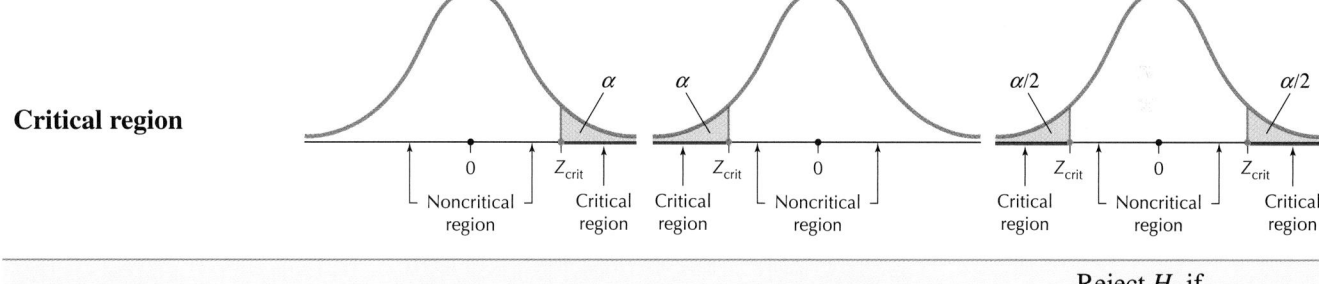		
Rejection rule:	Reject H_0 if $Z_{data} \geq Z_{crit}$	Reject H_0 if $Z_{data} \leq Z_{crit}$	Reject H_0 if $Z_{data} \leq -Z_{crit}$ or $Z_{data} \geq Z_{crit}$

Example 9.4   Finding Z_{crit} and the critical region

For the hypotheses

$$H_0 : \mu = 110 \quad \text{versus} \quad H_a : \mu < 110$$

where μ represents the population mean systolic blood pressure, let the level of significance $\alpha = 0.05$.
a. Find the critical value Z_{crit}.
b. Graph the distribution of Z, showing the critical region.

Solution

We have a left-tailed test and level of significance $\alpha = 0.05$, so Table 9.4 tells us that the critical value is $Z_{crit} = -1.645$. The graph showing the critical region is provided in Figure 9.3. We would reject H_0 for values of Z_{data} that are $\leq Z_{crit} = -1.645$. ∎

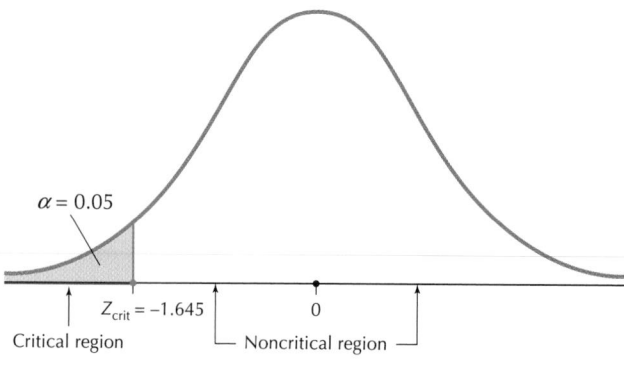

FIGURE 9.3
Critical region for a left-tailed test lies in the left (lower) tail.

$\alpha = 0.05$

$Z_{crit} = -1.645$

0

Critical region

Noncritical region

Now You Can Do
Exercises 17–24.

What Does the Left-Tailed Test Mean?

A hypothesis test of the form

$$H_0 : \mu = \mu_0 \quad \text{versus} \quad H_a : \mu < \mu_0$$

is called a *left-tailed* test because the critical region lies in the left (lower) tail. Similarly, the critical region for a right-tailed test lies in the right (upper) tail. The critical region for a two-tailed test lies in both the lower and upper tails. ◢

We are now ready to learn the steps for performing the Z test for the population mean using the critical-value method.

Z Test for the Population Mean μ: Critical-Value Method

When a random sample of size n is taken from a population where the population standard deviation σ is known, you can use the Z test if (a) the population is normal, or (b) the sample size is large ($n \geq 30$).

Step 1 State the hypotheses.
Use one of the forms from Table 9.4. State the meaning of μ.

Step 2 Find Z_{crit} and state the rejection rule.
Use Table 9.4 and the given level of significance α.

Step 3 Calculate Z_{data}.

$$Z_{data} = \frac{\bar{x} - \mu_0}{\sigma/\sqrt{n}}$$

Step 4 State the conclusion and the interpretation.
If Z_{data} falls in the critical region, then reject H_0; otherwise, do not reject H_0. Interpret your conclusion so that a nonspecialist (that is, someone who has not had a course in statistics) can understand.

What Does This Conclusion Mean?

Interpreting Your Conclusion for Nonspecialists

Recall that a data analyst needs to interpret the results so that nonspecialists can understand them. You can use the following generic interpretation for the two possible conclusions. Just remember that generic interpretations are no substitute for thinking clearly about the problem and the implications of the conclusion.

Interpreting the Conclusion

- If you reject H_0, the interpretation is: *There is evidence at level of significance α that [whatever H_a says].*

- If you do not reject H_0, the interpretation is: *There is insufficient evidence at level of significance α that [whatever H_a says].* ◢

Next, we illustrate the critical-value method of performing a right-tailed *Z* test, a left-tailed *Z* test, and a two-tailed *Z* test for μ.

Example 9.5   *Z* Test for μ, critical-value method, right-tailed test

Using the debit card sample described in Example 9.3, test at level of significance $\alpha = 0.01$ whether people use debit cards on average more than 11 times per month.

Solution

We may apply the *Z* test because the sample is large ($n \geq 30$), and the population standard deviation σ is known.

Step 1 **State the hypotheses.** From Example 9.3, our hypotheses are

$$H_0 : \mu = 11 \quad \text{versus} \quad H_a : \mu > 11$$

where μ represents the population mean number of times people use their debit cards per month.

Step 2 **Find Z_{crit} and state the rejection rule.** We have a right-tailed test and level of significance $\alpha = 0.01$, which, from Table 9.4, tell us that $Z_{\text{crit}} = 2.33$. Because we have a right-tailed test, the rejection rule will be "Reject H_0 if $Z_{\text{data}} \geq Z_{\text{crit}}$," that is, "Reject H_0 if $Z_{\text{data}} \geq 2.33$" (see Figure 9.4).

Step 3 **Find Z_{data}.** From Example 9.3, we have $Z_{\text{data}} = 1$.

Step 4 **State the conclusion and interpretation.** Our rejection rule states that we will reject H_0 if $Z_{\text{data}} \geq 2.33$. Since $Z_{\text{data}} = 1$, which is *not* ≥ 2.33, the conclusion is to *not* reject H_0 (Figure 9.4). Even though the sample mean of 11.5 exceeds 11, it does not do so by a wide enough margin to overcome the reasonable doubt that the difference between this sample mean $\bar{x} = 11.5$ and the hypothesized value $\mu_0 = 11$ may have been due to chance. We interpret our conclusion as follows: "There is insufficient evidence at the 0.01 level of significance that the population mean monthly debit card use is greater than 11 times per month." ∎

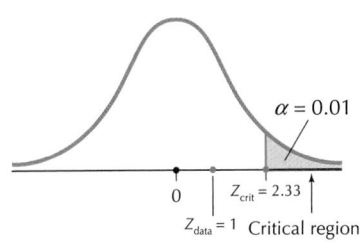

FIGURE 9.4 Critical region for a right-tailed test.

Now You Can Do
Exercises 27–29.

Example 9.6   *Z* Test for μ, critical-value method, left-tailed test

For the hypotheses in Example 9.4, perform the *Z* test for the population mean, using level of significance $\alpha = 0.05$.

Solution

Step 1 **State the hypotheses.** From Example 9.4, we have

$$H_0 : \mu = 110 \quad \text{versus} \quad H_a : \mu < 110$$

where μ represents the population mean systolic blood pressure reading.

Step 2 **Find Z_{crit} and state the rejection rule.** Example 9.4 gives us the critical value $Z_{\text{crit}} = -1.645$, and Table 9.4 tells us that, for level of significance $\alpha = 0.05$, we will reject H_0 if $Z_{\text{data}} \leq Z_{\text{crit}}$, that is, if $Z_{\text{data}} \leq -1.645$ (Figure 9.5).

Step 3 **Calculate Z_{data}.** From page 432, we know that

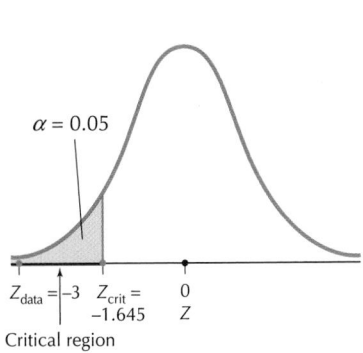

FIGURE 9.5 Critical region for a left-tailed test.

$$Z_{\text{data}} = \frac{\bar{x} - \mu_0}{\sigma/\sqrt{n}} = \frac{104 - 110}{10/\sqrt{25}} = -3$$

Now You Can Do
Exercises 30–32.

Step 4 **State the conclusion and the interpretation.** In Step 2 we stated that we would reject H_0 if $Z_{data} \leq -1.645$. Since our $Z_{data} = -3 \leq -1.645$, we therefore reject H_0. Our interpretation is: "There is evidence at level of significance $\alpha = 0.05$ that the population mean systolic blood pressure reading is less than 110." ∎

Example 9.7 | Z Test for μ, critical-value method, two-tailed test

When the level of hemoglobin in the blood is too low, a person is anemic. Unusually high levels of hemoglobin are undesirable as well and can be associated with dehydration. The optimal hemoglobin level is 13.8 grams per deciliter (g/dl). Suppose a random sample of $n = 25$ women at a certain college showed a sample mean hemoglobin of $\bar{x} = 11.8$ g/dl, the population standard deviation of hemoglobin level is $\sigma = 5$ g/dl, and hemoglobin level is normally distributed. We are interested in testing whether the population mean hemoglobin level differs from 13.8 g/dl. Perform the appropriate hypothesis test, using level of significance $\alpha = 0.10$.

Solution

We may use the Z test, since the population of hemoglobin levels is normally distributed, and the population standard deviation σ is known.

Step 1 **State the hypotheses.** The key words "differs from" indicate a two-tailed test, with $\mu_0 = 13.8$. Thus, our hypotheses are

$$H_0 : \mu = 13.8 \quad \text{versus} \quad H_a : \mu \neq 13.8$$

where μ represents the population mean hemoglobin level.

Step 2 **Find Z_{crit} and state the rejection rule.** We have a two-tailed test and level of significance $\alpha = 0.10$. Using this information, Table 9.4 tells us that the critical value $Z_{crit} = 1.645$ and that we will reject H_0 if $Z_{data} \leq -1.645$ or if $Z_{data} \geq 1.645$ (Figure 9.6).

Step 3 **Calculate Z_{data}.** We have $\bar{x} = 11.8$, $n = 25$, $\sigma = 5$, and $\mu_0 = 13.8$. Substituting:

$$Z_{data} = \frac{\bar{x} - \mu_0}{\sigma/\sqrt{n}} = \frac{11.8 - 13.8}{5/\sqrt{25}} = -2$$

Step 4 **State the conclusion and the interpretation.** $Z_{data} = -2$, which is ≤ -1.645. Therefore we reject H_0. There is evidence at level of significance $\alpha = 0.10$ that the population mean hemoglobin level differs from 13.8. ∎

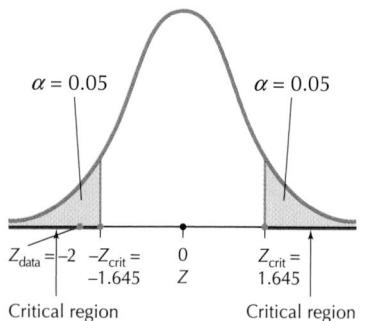

$\alpha = 0.05$ $\alpha = 0.05$

$Z_{data} = -2$ $-Z_{crit} = -1.645$ 0 Z $Z_{crit} = 1.645$

Critical region   Critical region

FIGURE 9.6 Critical region for a two-tailed test.

Now You Can Do
Exercises 33 and 34.

STEP-BY-STEP TECHNOLOGY GUIDE: Z Test for μ

To learn how to use technology to perform the Z test for the mean, see the Step-by-Step Technology Guide on page 448.

Section 9.2 Summary

1 The essential idea about hypothesis testing for the mean is as follows: When the observed value of $\bar{x}$ is unusual or extreme in the sampling distribution of $\bar{x}$ that assumes H_0 is true, we should reject H_0. Otherwise, we should not reject H_0.

2 The critical region consists of the range of values of the test statistic Z_{data} for which we reject the null hypothesis. The value of Z that separates the critical region from the noncritical region is called the critical value Z_{crit}. In the critical-value method for the Z test for the mean, we compare Z_{data} with Z_{crit}.

Section 9.2 Exercises

CLARIFYING THE CONCEPTS

1. What is the essential idea about hypothesis testing for the mean?
2. What does Z_{data} represent?
3. Explain what a test statistic is.
4. Describe the difference between the critical region and the noncritical region.
5. Clearly describe what Z_{crit} is.
6. Suppose we reject H_0 for the hypothesis test $H_0 : \mu = 5$ versus $H_a : \mu < 5$. Provide the generic interpretation.
7. How did the right-tailed test get its name?
8. True or false: The value of Z_{crit} does not depend at all on the sample data.

PRACTICING THE TECHNIQUES

For Exercises 9–34, assume that the conditions for performing the Z test are met.

For Exercises 9–16, calculate Z_{data}.

9. $H_0 : \mu = 10$ vs. $H_a : \mu > 10, \bar{x} = 11, \sigma = 5, n = 25$
10. $H_0 : \mu = 10$ vs. $H_a : \mu > 10, \bar{x} = 12, \sigma = 5, n = 25$
11. $H_0 : \mu = 10$ vs. $H_a : \mu > 10, \bar{x} = 12.5, \sigma = 5, n = 25$
12. $H_0 : \mu = 7$ vs. $H_a : \mu < 7, \bar{x} = 6, \sigma = 4, n = 16$
13. $H_0 : \mu = 7$ vs. $H_a : \mu < 7, \bar{x} = 5.5, \sigma = 4, n = 16$
14. $H_0 : \mu = 7$ vs. $H_a : \mu < 7, \bar{x} = 4, \sigma = 4, n = 16$
15. $H_0 : \mu = 100$ vs. $H_a : \mu \neq 100, \bar{x} = 90, \sigma = 10, n = 25$
16. $H_0 : \mu = -50$ vs. $H_a : \mu \neq -50, \bar{x} = -55, \sigma = 5, n = 9$

For Exercises 17–24, do the following:
   a. Find the critical value Z_{crit}.
   b. Sketch the critical region, using the figures in Table 9.4 as a guide.
   c. State the rejection rule.

17. $H_0 : \mu = 10$ vs. $H_a : \mu > 10$, level of significance $\alpha = 0.10$
18. $H_0 : \mu = 10$ vs. $H_a : \mu > 10$, level of significance $\alpha = 0.05$
19. $H_0 : \mu = 10$ vs. $H_a : \mu > 10$, level of significance $\alpha = 0.01$
20. $H_0 : \mu = 7$ vs. $H_a : \mu < 7$, level of significance $\alpha = 0.10$
21. $H_0 : \mu = 7$ vs. $H_a : \mu < 7$, level of significance $\alpha = 0.05$
22. $H_0 : \mu = 7$ vs. $H_a : \mu < 7$, level of significance $\alpha = 0.01$
23. $H_0 : \mu = 100$ vs. $H_a : \mu \neq 100$, level of significance $\alpha = 0.05$
24. $H_0 : \mu = -50$ vs. $H_a : \mu \neq -50$, level of significance $\alpha = 0.01$
25. Consider your results from Exercises 17–19. Describe what happens to (a) Z_{crit} and (b) the critical region, for a right-tailed test when the only change is the decrease in the level of significance α.

26. Consider your results from Exercises 20–22. Explain what happens to (a) Z_{crit} and (b) the critical region, for a left-tailed test as the level of significance α decreases but everything else stays the same.

For Exercises 27–34, use the hypotheses and data from the indicated exercises to perform the Z test for μ by doing the following steps.
   a. State the hypotheses.
   b. Find Z_{crit} and state the rejection rule.
   c. State the value of Z_{data} from the indicated exercise.
   d. State the conclusion and the interpretation.

27. Use Z_{data} from Exercise 9 and Z_{crit} from Exercise 17.
28. Use Z_{data} from Exercise 10 and Z_{crit} from Exercise 18.
29. Use Z_{data} from Exercise 11 and Z_{crit} from Exercise 19.
30. Use Z_{data} from Exercise 12 and Z_{crit} from Exercise 20.
31. Use Z_{data} from Exercise 13 and Z_{crit} from Exercise 21.
32. Use Z_{data} from Exercise 14 and Z_{crit} from Exercise 22.
33. Use Z_{data} from Exercise 15 and Z_{crit} from Exercise 23.
34. Use Z_{data} from Exercise 16 and Z_{crit} from Exercise 24.

APPLYING THE CONCEPTS

For Exercises 35–42, do the following.
   a. State the hypotheses.
   b. Find Z_{crit} and the critical region.
   c. Find Z_{data}. Also, draw a standard normal Z curve showing Z_{crit}, the critical region, and Z_{data}.
   d. State the conclusion and the interpretation.

35. **Facebook Connections.** According to Facebook.com, the mean number of community pages, groups, and events that users are connected to is 80. A random sample of 64 Facebook users showed a mean of 86 connections to community pages, groups, and events. Assume $\sigma = 48$. Test using level of significance $\alpha = 0.05$ whether the population mean number of connections to community pages, groups, and events is greater than 80.

36. **Marketing Manager Salaries.** The Web site salary.com reports that the mean salary for marketing managers is $80,000. A random sample of 25 marketing managers taken during the recession showed a mean salary of $75,000. Assume normality and $\sigma = \$10,000$. Test using level of significance $\alpha = 0.01$ whether the population mean salary for marketing managers fell during the recession.

37. **Text Messages.** The Pew Internet and American Life Project reports that American adults send a mean of 10 text messages per day. A random sample of 100 American adults showed a mean of 12 text messages per day. Assume $\sigma = 20$. Test using level of significance $\alpha = 0.01$ whether the population mean number of text messages per day differs from 10.

38. **Video Gamers.** Can't pry the PlayStation away from your dad? The Entertainment Software Association reports that the mean age of video gamers is 37 years old. A random sample of 36 video gamers had a mean age of 36. Assume

$\sigma = 6$. Test using level of significance $\alpha = 0.05$ whether the population mean age of video gamers is less than 37.

39. Gas Prices. The American Automobile Association reported in June 2011 that the mean price for a gallon of regular gasoline was $3.70. A random sample of 25 gas stations had a mean price of $3.90. Assume normality and $\sigma = \$0.50$. Test using level of significance $\alpha = 0.05$ whether the population mean price for a gallon of regular gasoline has risen since June 2011.

40. Household Size. The U.S. Census Bureau reports that the mean household size equals 2.58 persons. A random sample of 900 households provides a mean size of 2.56 persons. Assume $\sigma = 0.6$. Conduct a hypothesis test using level of significance $\alpha = 0.10$ to determine whether the population mean household size this year is less than 2.58.

41. Americans' Height. A random sample of 400 Americans yields a mean height of 176 centimeters. Assume $\sigma = 2.5$. Conduct a hypothesis test to investigate whether the population mean height of Americans has changed from 175 centimeters, using level of significance $\alpha = 0.10$.

42. Price of Milk. The U.S. Bureau of Labor Statistics reported that the mean price for a gallon of milk in 2011 was $3.34. A random sample of 100 retail establishments this year provides a mean price of $3.39. Assume $\sigma = \$0.25$. Perform a hypothesis test using level of significance $\alpha = 0.05$ to investigate whether the population mean price of milk this year has increased from the 2011 value.

43. Accountants' Salaries. According to the *Wall Street Journal*, the mean salary for accountants in Texas in 2007 was $50,529. A random sample of 16 Texas accountants this year showed a mean salary of $52,000. We assume that the population standard deviation equals $4000. The histogram of the salary (in $1000s) is shown here. If it is appropriate to apply the Z test, then do so, using the critical-value method and level of significance $\alpha = 0.05$. If not, then explain clearly why not.

Salaries of 16 accountants.

44. Honda Civic Gas Mileage. Cars.com reported in 2007 that the mean city gas mileage for the Honda Civic was 30 mpg. This year, a random sample of 20 Honda

Civics had a mean gas mileage of 36 mpg. Assume $\sigma = 5$ mpg. A Minitab histogram of the data is shown here.

Miles per gallon of 20 imported Hondas.

a. Is it appropriate to apply the Z test? Explain clearly why or why not.
b. Test at level of significance $\alpha = 0.10$ whether the population mean city gas mileage has increased since 2007.
c. What if we now performed the same test on the same data but used $\alpha = 0.05$ instead? Without carrying out the hypothesis test, state whether this would affect our conclusion. Why or why not?

45. Honda Civic Gas Mileage. Refer to Exercise 44. Try to answer the following questions by thinking about the relationship between the statistics rather than by redoing all the calculations. *What if* the 36 mpg is a typo. We are not sure what the actual sample mean is, but it is less than 36 mpg.

a. How does this affect Z_{data}?
b. How does this affect Z_{crit}?
c. How does this affect the conclusion?

46. Automobile Operation Cost. The Bureau of Transportation Statistics reports that the mean cost of operating an automobile in the United States, including gas and oil, maintenance and tires, is 5.9 cents per mile. Suppose that a sample taken this year of 100 automobiles shows a mean operating cost of 6.2 cents per mile, and assume that the population standard deviation is 1.5 cents per mile. Test whether the population mean cost is greater than 5.9 cents per mile, using level of significance $\alpha = 0.05$.

a. Is it appropriate to apply the Z test? Why or why not?
b. We have a sample mean that is greater than the mean in the null hypothesis of 5.9 cents. Isn't this enough by itself to reject the null hypothesis? Explain why or why not.
c. How many standard deviations above the mean is the 6.2 cents per mile? Do you think this is extreme?

47. Automobile Operation Cost. Refer to Exercise 46.
a. Construct the hypotheses.
b. Find the Z critical value and state the rejection rule.
c. Calculate the value of the test statistic Z_{data}.
d. State the conclusion and the interpretation.

48. Calories. Work with the **Nutrition** data set. 🐾 **Nutrition**
  a. How many observations are in the data set? How many variables?
  b. Use technology to explore the variable *calories*, which lists the calories in the sample of foods. Generate numerical summary statistics and graphs for the number of calories. What is the sample mean number of calories? The sample standard deviation?
  c. Use technology to test at level of significance $\alpha = 0.05$ whether the population mean number of calories per food item differs from 300. Let $\sigma = 540$ calories.
  d. Use technology to test at level of significance $\alpha = 0.05$ whether the population mean number of calories per food item differs from 320. Let $\sigma = 540$ calories.

49. Sodium. Work with the **Nutrition** data set. 🐾 **Nutrition**
  a. Use technology to explore the variable *sodium*.
  b. Use technology to test at level of significance $\alpha = 0.05$ whether the population mean amount of sodium is greater than 280 mg. Let $\sigma = 625$ mg.
  c. Use technology to test at level of significance $\alpha = 0.05$ whether the population mean amount of sodium is greater than 290 mg. Let $\sigma = 625$ mg.

9.3   *Z* Test for the Population Mean: *p*-Value Method

OBJECTIVES By the end of this section, I will be able to . . .

1   Perform the *Z* test for the mean, using the *p*-value method.

2   Assess the strength of evidence against the null hypothesis.

3   Describe the relationship between the *p*-value method and the critical-value method.

4   Use the *Z* confidence interval for the mean to perform the two-tailed *Z* test for the mean.

1 The *p*-Value Method of Performing the *Z* Test for the Mean

In Section 9.2 we considered the critical-value method for performing the *Z* test, which works by comparing one *Z*-value (Z_{data}) with another *Z*-value (Z_{crit}). In this section we introduce the *p*-value method, which works by comparing one probability (the *p*-value) to another probability (α). The two methods are equivalent for the same level of significance α, giving you the same conclusion.

The ***p*-value** is a measure of how well (or how poorly) the data fit the null hypothesis.

_p_-Value

The ***p*-value** is the probability of observing a sample statistic (such as $\bar{x}$ or Z_{data}) at least as extreme as the statistic actually observed if we assume that the null hypothesis is true.

Roughly speaking, the *p*-value represents the probability of observing the sample statistic if the null hypothesis is true. Since the term *p-value* mean "probability value," its value must always lie between 0 and 1.

A *p*-value is a probability associated with Z_{data} and tells us whether or not Z_{data} is an extreme value. The method for calculating *p*-values depends on the form of the hypothesis test (Table 9.5).

- For a right-tailed test, the *p*-value is in the right (or upper) tail area.

- For a left-tailed test, the *p*-value is in the left (or lower) tail area.

- For a two-tailed test, the *p*-value lies in both tails.

Table 9.5 Finding the p-value depends on the form of the hypothesis test

	Right-tailed test	Left-tailed test	Two-tailed test
Type of hypothesis test	$H_0: \mu = \mu_0$ $H_a: \mu > \mu_0$	$H_0: \mu = \mu_0$ $H_a: \mu < \mu_0$	$H_0: \mu = \mu_0$ $H_a: \mu \neq \mu_0$
p-Value is tail area associated with Z_{data}	$p\text{-value} = P(Z > Z_{\text{data}})$ Area to right of Z_{data}	$p\text{-value} = P(Z < Z_{\text{data}})$ Area to left of Z_{data}	$p\text{-value} = P(Z > |Z_{\text{data}}|)$ $+ P(Z < -|Z_{\text{data}}|)$ $= 2 \cdot P(Z > |Z_{\text{data}}|)$ Sum of the two tail areas.

Example 9.8 | Finding the p-value

For each of the following hypothesis tests, calculate and graph the p-value.

a. $H_0: \mu = 3.0$ versus $H_a: \mu > 3.0, Z_{\text{data}} = 1$

b. $H_0: \mu = 10$ versus $H_a: \mu < 10, Z_{\text{data}} = -1.5$

c. $H_0: \mu = 100$ versus $H_a: \mu \neq 100, Z_{\text{data}} = -2$

Solution

a. We have a right-tailed test, so that the p-value equals the area in the right tail:

$$p\text{-value} = P(Z > Z_{\text{data}}) = P(Z > 1)$$

To review how to calculate these probabilities, see Table 6.6 on page 303.

The Z table gives the probability for $P(Z < 1)$, and thus

$$p\text{-value} = P(Z > 1) = 1 - P(Z < 1) = 1 - 0.8413 = 0.1587 \text{ (Figure 9.7a)}.$$

b. We have a left-tailed test, so that the p-value equals the area in the left tail:

$$p\text{-value} = P(Z < Z_{\text{data}}) = P(Z < -1.5) = 0.0668 \text{ (Figure 9.7b)}.$$

Remember that probability is represented by area under the curve.

c. Here we have a left-tailed test, so that the p-value equals the sum of the areas in the two tails:

$$p\text{-value} = P(Z > |Z_{\text{data}}|) + (Z < -|Z_{\text{data}}|)$$
$$= P(Z > |-2|) + (Z < -|-2|)$$
$$= P(Z > 2) + (Z < -2)$$
$$= 0.0228 + 0.0228 = 0.0456 \text{ (Figure 9.7c)}$$

Now You Can Do Exercises 7–14.

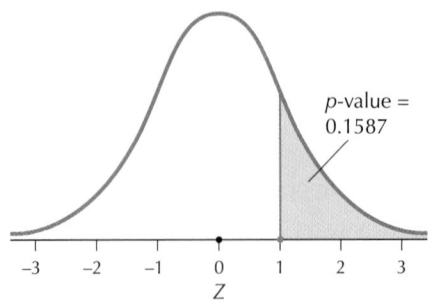

FIGURE 9.7a p-Value for a right-tailed test.

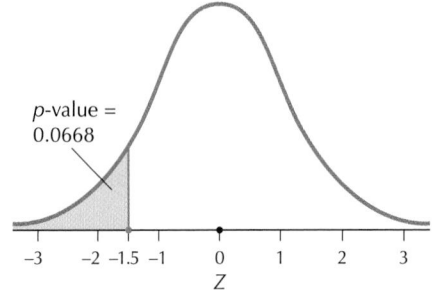

FIGURE 9.7b p-Value for a left-tailed test.

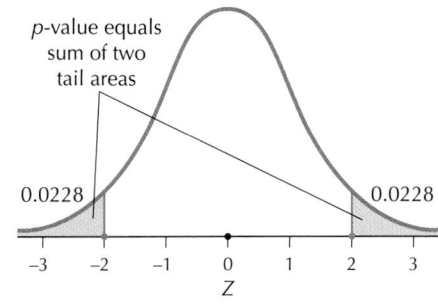

FIGURE 9.7c p-Value for a two-tailed test.

Since a *p*-value is based on the value of Z_{data}, the *p*-value tells us whether or not Z_{data} is an extreme value. Unusual and extreme values of $\bar{x}$, and therefore of Z_{data}, will have a small *p*-value, while values of $\bar{x}$ and Z_{data} nearer to the center of the distribution will have a large *p*-value.

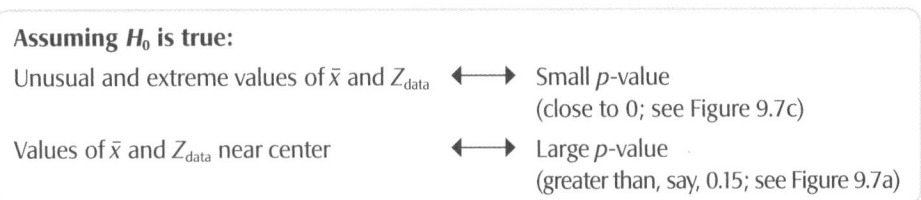

Assuming *H*₀ is true:

Unusual and extreme values of $\bar{x}$ and Z_{data} ⟷ Small *p*-value
(close to 0; see Figure 9.7c)

Values of $\bar{x}$ and Z_{data} near center ⟷ Large *p*-value
(greater than, say, 0.15; see Figure 9.7a)

A small *p*-value indicates a conflict between your sample data and the null hypothesis, and will thus *lead us to reject H₀*. However, how small is small? We learned in Section 9.1 that the probability of Type I error α is chosen by the researcher to be small, usually 0.01, 0.05, or 0.10. Thus, a *p*-value is small if it is $\leq \alpha$. This leads us to the **rejection rule** that tells us when we may reject the null hypothesis.

> This rejection rule can be applied to any type of hypothesis test we perform in Chapters 9–13 using the *p*-value method.

The rejection rule for performing a hypothesis test using the *p*-value method is:
Reject *H*₀ when the *p*-value ≤ α. Otherwise, do not reject *H*₀.

The value of α represents the boundary between results that are statistically significant (where we reject H_0) and results that are not statistically significant (where we do not reject H_0). Thus, α is called the *level of significance* of the hypothesis test.

Here are the steps for performing the *Z* test for μ using the *p*-value method.

Z Test for the Population Mean μ: *p*-Value Method

When a random sample of size *n* is taken from a population where the standard deviation σ is known, you can use the *Z* test if either (a) the population is normal, or (b) the sample size is large ($n \geq 30$).

Step 1 **State the hypotheses and the rejection rule.**

Use one of the forms from Table 9.5 to write the hypotheses. State the meaning of μ. The rejection rule is "Reject H_0 if the *p*-value $\leq \alpha$."

Step 2 **Calculate Z_{data}.**

$$Z_{\text{data}} = \frac{\bar{x} - \mu_0}{\sigma/\sqrt{n}}$$

where the sample mean $\bar{x}$ and the sample size *n* represent the sample data, and the population standard deviation σ represents the population data.

Step 3 **Find the *p*-value.**

Either use technology to find the *p*-value, or calculate it using the form in Table 9.5 that corresponds to your hypotheses.

Step 4 **State the conclusion and interpretation.**

If the *p*-value $\leq \alpha$, then reject H_0. Otherwise do not reject H_0. Interpret your conclusion so that a nonspecialist (someone who has not had a course in statistics) can understand, as follows:

- Interpretation when you reject H_0 : *There is evidence at level of significance α that [whatever H_a says].*
- Interpretation when you do not reject H_0 : *There is insufficient evidence at level of significance α that [whatever H_a says].*

Example 9.9 | The Z test for the mean using the p-value method: left-tailed test

The technology Web site www.cnet.com publishes user reviews of computers, software, and other electronic gadgetry. The mean user rating, on a scale of 1–10, for the Dell XPS 410 desktop computer as of September 10, 2007, was 7.2. Assume that the population standard deviation of user ratings is known to be $\sigma = 0.9$. A random sample taken this year of $n = 81$ user ratings for the Dell XPS 410 showed a mean of $\bar{x} = 7.05$. Using level of significance $\alpha = 0.05$, test whether the population mean user rating for this computer has fallen since 2007.

Solution

The sample size $n = 81$ is large, and the population standard deviation σ is known. We may therefore perform the Z test for the mean.

Step 1 **State the hypotheses and the rejection rule.** The key words here are "has fallen," which means "is less than." The answer to the question "Less than what?" gives us $\mu_0 = 7.2$. Thus, our hypotheses are

$$H_0: \mu = 7.2 \quad \text{versus} \quad H_a: \mu < 7.2$$

where μ refers to the population mean user rating for the Dell XPS 410 computer. We will reject H_0 if the p-value $\leq \alpha = 0.05$.

Step 2 **Calculate Z_{data}.** We have $\bar{x} = 7.05$, $\mu_0 = 7.2$, $n = 81$, and $\sigma = 0.9$. Thus, our test statistic is

$$Z_{data} = \frac{\bar{x} - \mu_0}{\sigma/\sqrt{n}} = \frac{7.05 - 7.2}{0.9/\sqrt{81}} = -1.5$$

Step 3 **Find the p-value.** Our hypotheses represent a left-tailed test from Table 9.5. Thus

$$p\text{-value} = P(Z < Z_{data}) = P(Z < -1.5)$$

This is a Case 1 problem from Table 6.6 (page 303). The Z table (Appendix Table C) provides us with the area to the left of $Z = -1.5$ (Figure 9.8):

$$P(Z < -1.5) = 0.0668$$

Thus, the p-value is 0.0668.

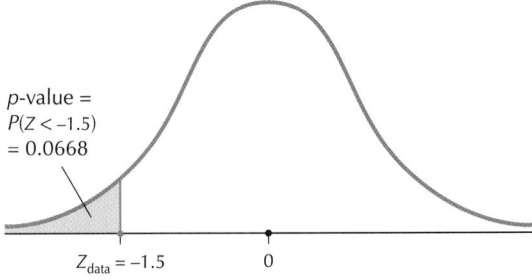

p-value =
$P(Z < -1.5)$
$= 0.0668$

$Z_{data} = -1.5$ 0

FIGURE 9.8 The p-value 0.0668 is not ≤ 0.05, so do not reject H_0.

Step 4 **State the conclusion and interpretation.** Our level of significance is $\alpha = 0.05$ (from Step 1). Since the p-value $= 0.0668$ is *not* < 0.05, we therefore do *not* reject H_0. There is insufficient evidence at level of significance $\alpha = 0.05$ that the population mean user rating for a Dell XPS 410 computer is less than 7.2. ∎

Now You Can Do
Exercises 17–19.

Example 9.10   The *p*-value method using technology: two-tailed test

Brisbane

The birth weights, in grams (1000 grams = 1 kilogram ≈ 2.2 pounds), of a random sample of 44 babies from Brisbane, Australia, have a sample mean weight $\bar{x}$ = 3276 grams. Formerly, the mean birth weight of babies in Brisbane was 3200 grams. Assume that the population standard deviation σ = 528 grams. Is there evidence that the population mean birth weight of Brisbane babies now differs from 3200 grams? Use technology to perform the appropriate hypothesis test, with level of significance α = 0.10.

What Results Might We Expect?

Note from Figure 9.9 that the sample mean birth weight $\bar{x}$ = 3276 grams is close to the hypothesized mean birth weight of μ_0 = 3200 grams. This value of $\bar{x}$ is not extreme and thus does not seem to offer strong evidence that the hypothesized mean birth weight is wrong. Therefore, we might expect to *not reject* the hypothesis that μ_0 = 3200 grams. ◢

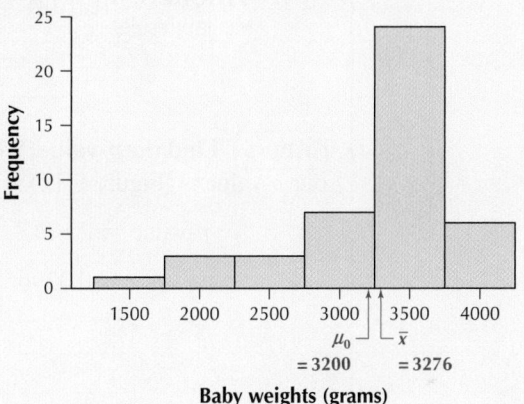

FIGURE 9.9 Sample mean, $\bar{x}$ = 3276, is close to hypothesized mean, μ_0 = 3200.

Solution

Since the sample size n = 44 is large and σ = 528 is known, we may proceed with the *Z* test for μ.

Step 1 **State the hypotheses and the rejection rule.** The key words "differs from" mean that we have a two-tailed test:

$$H_0: \mu = 3200 \quad \text{versus} \quad H_a: \mu \neq 3200$$

where μ refers to the population mean birth weight of Brisbane babies. We will reject H_0 if the *p*-value ≤ α = 0.10.

Step 2 **Calculate Z_{data}.** We will use the instructions provided in the Step-by-Step Technology Guide at the end of this section (page 448). Figure 9.10 shows the TI-83/84 results from the *Z* test for μ:

$$Z_{\text{data}} = \frac{\bar{x} - \mu_0}{\sigma/\sqrt{n}} = \frac{3276 - 3200}{528/\sqrt{44}} = 0.9547859245 \approx 0.9548$$

FIGURE 9.10
TI-83/84 results.

Form of H_a:
Z_{data}
p-value
Sample mean $\bar{x}$
Sample size n

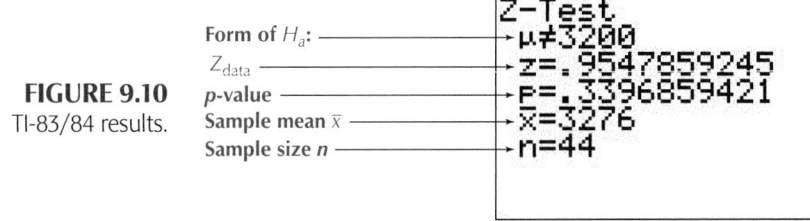

```
Z-Test
 μ≠3200
 z=.9547859245
 P=.3396859421
 x̄=3276
 n=44
```

Figure 9.11 shows the Minitab results, where

- "Test of $\mu = 3200$ versus not 3200" refers to the hypotheses being tested, $H_0 : \mu = 3200$ versus $H_a : \mu \neq 3200$.

- "The assumed standard deviation = 528" refers to our assumption that $\sigma = 528$.

- SE Mean refers to the standard error of the mean, that is, $\sigma/\sqrt{n}$. You can see that $528/\sqrt{44} \approx 79.60$.

- 90% CI represents a 90% Z confidence interval for μ.

- Z refers to our test statistic:

Different software rounds the results to different numbers of decimal places.

$$Z_{data} = \frac{\bar{x} - \mu_0}{\sigma/\sqrt{n}} = (3276 - 3200)/(528/\sqrt{44}) = 0.9547859245 \approx 0.9548$$

- P represents our p-value of 0.340.

FIGURE 9.11
Minitab results.

```
One-Sample Z

Test of mu = 3200 vs not = 3200
The assumed standard deviation = 528

  N    Mean   SE Mean       90% CI         Z      P
 44   3276.0     79.6   (3145.1, 3406.9)  0.95  0.340
```

Step 3 **Find the p-value.** We have a two-tailed test from Step 1, so that from Table 9.5 our p-value is (Figure 9.12)

$$p\text{-value} = 2 \cdot P(Z > |Z_{data}|) = 2 \cdot P(Z > 0.9548) \approx 2 \cdot (0.1698)$$

$$= 0.3396$$

FIGURE 9.12
p-Value is sum of two tail areas.

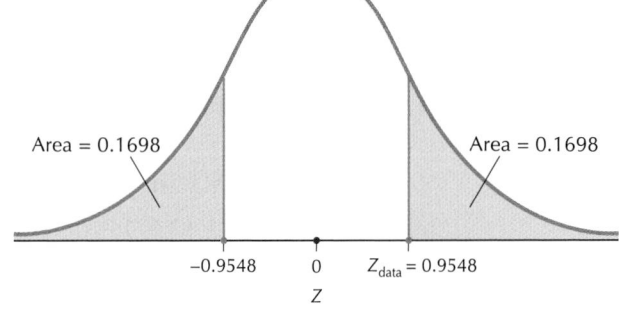

Area = 0.1698   Area = 0.1698

−0.9548   0 $Z_{data} = 0.9548$

Z

Step 4 **State the conclusion and interpretation.** Since 0.3396 is not ≤ 0.10, we do not reject H_0. There is insufficient evidence that the population mean birth weight differs from 3200 grams. ■

Now You Can Do
Exercises 20–22.

The *p-Value* applet allows you to experiment with various hypotheses, means, standard deviations, and sample sizes in order to see how changes in these values affect the p-value.

2 Assessing the Strength of Evidence Against the Null Hypothesis

The hypothesis-testing methods we have shown so far deliver a simple "yes-or-no" conclusion: either "Reject H_0" or "Do not reject H_0." There is no indication of how strong the evidence is for rejecting the null hypothesis. Was the decision close? Was it a no-brainer? On the other hand, the p-value itself represents the *strength of evidence against the null hypothesis*. There is extra information here, which we should not ignore.

For instance, we can directly compare the results of hypothesis tests. Suppose that we have two hypothesis tests that both result in not rejecting the null hypothesis, with level of significance $\alpha = 0.05$. However, Test A has a *p*-value of 0.06, while Test B has a *p*-value of 0.57. Clearly, Test A came very close to rejecting the null hypothesis and shows a fair amount of evidence against the null hypothesis, while Test B shows no evidence at all against the null hypothesis. A simple statement of the "yes-or-no" conclusion misses the clear distinction between these two situations.

The *p*-value provides us with the smallest level of significance at which the null hypothesis would be rejected, that is, the smallest value of α at which the results would be considered significant.

Of course, we are free to determine whether the results are significant using whatever α level we wish. For example. Test A would have rejected H_0 for any α value 0.06 or higher. Some data analysts in fact do not think in terms of rejecting or not rejecting the null hypothesis. Rather, they think completely in terms of *assessing the strength of evidence against the null hypothesis*.

For many (though not all) data domains, Table 9.6 provides a thumbnail impression of the strength of evidence against the null hypothesis for various *p*-values. For certain domains (such as the physical sciences), however, alternative interpretations are appropriate.

Table 9.6 Strength of evidence against the null hypothesis for various levels of *p*-value

p-Value	Strength of evidence against H_0
p-value ≤ 0.001	Extremely strong evidence
$0.001 < p$-value ≤ 0.01	Very strong evidence
$0.01 < p$-value ≤ 0.05	Solid evidence
$0.05 < p$-value ≤ 0.10	Moderate evidence
$0.10 < p$-value ≤ 0.15	Slight evidence
$0.15 < p$-value	No evidence

Note: Use Table 9.6 for all exercises that ask for an assessment of the strength of evidence against the null hypothesis.

Example 9.11 Assessing the strength of evidence against H_0

Assess the strength of evidence against H_0 shown by the *p*-values in (a) Example 9.9 and (b) Example 9.10.

Solution

a. In Example 9.9, we tested $H_0: \mu = 7.2$ versus $H_a: \mu < 7.2$, where μ refers to the population mean user rating for the Dell XPS 410 computer. Our *p*-value of 0.0668 implies that there is *moderate* evidence against the null hypothesis that the population mean user rating for the Dell XPS 410 computer is 7.2 or higher.

b. In Example 9.10, we tested $H_0: \mu = 3200$ versus $H_a: \mu \neq 3200$, where μ refers to the population mean birth weight of Brisbane babies (in grams). Our *p*-value of 0.3397 implies that there is *no* evidence against the null hypothesis that the population mean birth weight of Brisbane babies equals 3200 grams. ∎

Now You Can Do
Exercises 23–28.

Developing Your
Statistical Sense

The Role of the Level of Significance α

Suppose that in Example 9.9, our level of significance α was 0.10 rather than 0.05. Would this have changed anything? Certainly. Since our *p*-value of 0.0668 is less than the new $\alpha = 0.10$, we would reject H_0. Think about that for a moment. *The data* *haven't changed at all, but our conclusion is reversed simply by changing α. What is a data analyst to make of a situation like this? There are two alternatives.*

1. Since we don't want the choice of α to dictate our conclusion, then perhaps we should turn to a direct assessment of the strength of evidence against the null hypothesis, as provided in Table 9.6. In this case, the p-value of about 0.0668 would offer moderate evidence against the null hypothesis, *regardless of the value of α.*

2. Obtain more data, perhaps through a call for further research. ◢

3 The Relationship Between the p-Value Method and the Critical-Value Method

Figure 9.13 shows the relationships between the p-value method and the critical-value method. The top half represents values of Z and the critical-value method that we studied in Section 9.2. The bottom half represents probabilities and the p-value method that we studied in this section. The left half represents statistics associated with the observed sample data. The right half represents critical-value thresholds for significance that these statistics are compared against.

FIGURE 9.13
Critical-value method
and p-value method
are equivalent.

Since Z_{data} helps us to determine the p-value, these two values are related. Similarly, since the level of significance α helps to determine the value of Z_{crit}, these two values are related. Moreover, just as we compare Z_{data} with the threshold Z_{crit}, we compare the p-value statistic with the α threshold to determine significance. Thus, the two methods for carrying out hypothesis tests are equivalent and, in fact, are quite thoroughly interwoven.

Figures 9.14a and 9.14b illustrate this equivalence for a right-tailed test. The rejection rule for the p-value method is to reject H_0 when the p-value $\leq \alpha$. The rejection rule for the critical-value method is to reject H_0 when $Z_{\text{data}} \geq Z_{\text{crit}}$. Note in Figures 9.14a and 9.14b how the p-value is determined by Z_{data}, and α is determined by Z_{crit}. In Figure 9.14a, when $Z_{\text{data}} \leq Z_{\text{crit}}$, it must also happen that the p-value $\geq \alpha$. In both cases we do not reject H_0. However, in Figure 9.14b, when $Z_{\text{data}} \geq Z_{\text{crit}}$, it also follows that the p-value is $\leq \alpha$. In both cases we reject H_0. Thus, the p-value method and the critical-value method are equivalent.

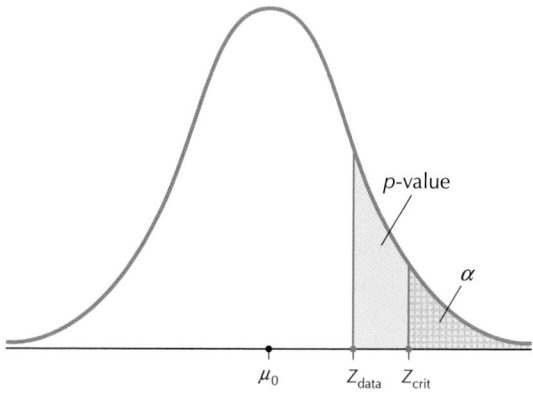

FIGURE 9.14a For a right-tailed test, $Z_{data} \leq Z_{crit}$ only when *p*-value $\geq \alpha$.

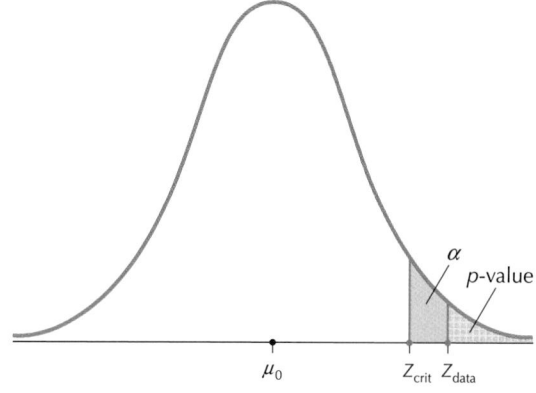

FIGURE 9.14b For a right-tailed test, $Z_{data} \geq Z_{crit}$ only when *p*-value $\leq \alpha$.

4 Using Confidence Intervals for μ to Perform Two-Tailed Hypothesis Tests About μ

Consider a two-tailed hypothesis test for μ:

$$H_0: \mu = \mu_0 \quad \text{versus} \quad H_a: \mu \neq \mu_0$$

and recall the $100(1 - \alpha)\%$ *Z* confidence interval for μ from Section 8.1:

$$\bar{x} \pm Z_{\alpha/2}(\sigma/\sqrt{n})$$

Both inference methods are based on the *Z* statistic:

$$Z = \frac{\bar{x} - \mu}{\sigma/\sqrt{n}}$$

so it makes sense that the two-tailed hypothesis test and the confidence interval are equivalent.

> **Equivalence of a Two-Tailed Hypothesis Test and a Confidence Interval**
> - If a certain value for μ_0 lies *outside* the corresponding $100(1 - \alpha)\%$ *Z* confidence interval for μ, then the null hypothesis specifying this value for μ_0 would be *rejected* for level of significance α (see Figure 9.15).
> - Alternatively, if a certain value for μ_0 lies *inside* the $100(1 - \alpha)\%$ *Z* confidence interval for μ, then the null hypothesis specifying this value for μ_0 would *not be rejected* for level of significance α.

FIGURE 9.15
Reject H_0 for values of μ_0 that lie outside confidence interval (a, b).

Lower Bound = a   Upper Bound = b

Reject H_0 Do not reject H_0 Reject H_0

Table 9.7 shows the confidence levels and associated α levels of significance that will produce the equivalent inference.

Table 9.7 Confidence levels for equivalent α levels of significance

Confidence level	Level of significance α
90%	0.10
95%	0.05
99%	0.01

We may thus use a single confidence interval to test as many values of μ_0 as we like.

AP Photo/Jeff T. Green

| Example 9.12 | Lead contamination in trout, revisited |

Recall Example 8.3 from Section 8.1 (page 375), where we were 95% confident using a Z interval that the population mean lead contamination for all trout in the Spokane River lies between 0.902 and 1.098 ppm. Once we have constructed the 95% confidence interval, we may test as many possible values for μ_0 as we like. If any values of μ_0 lie inside the confidence interval, that is, between 0.902 and 1.098, we will not reject H_0 for this value of μ_0. If any values of μ_0 lie outside the confidence interval, that is, either to the left of 0.902 or to the right of 1.098, we will reject H_0, as shown in Figure 9.16.

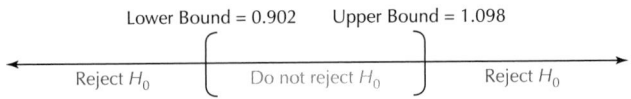

FIGURE 9.16 Reject H_0 for values of μ_0 that lie outside (0.902, 1.098).

Test using level of significance $\alpha = 0.05$ whether the population mean lead contamination differs from these values: **(a)** 0.900, **(b)** 0.910, **(c)** 1.100.

Solution

We set up the three two-tailed hypothesis tests as follows:
a. $H_0: \mu = 0.900$ versus $H_a: \mu \neq 0.900$
b. $H_0: \mu = 0.910$ versus $H_a: \mu \neq 0.910$
c. $H_0: \mu = 1.100$ versus $H_a: \mu \neq 1.100$

To perform each hypothesis test, simply observe where each value of μ_0 falls on the number line shown in Figure 9.16. For example, in the first hypothesis test, the hypothesized value $\mu_0 = 0.900$ lies outside the interval (0.902, 1.098). Thus, we reject H_0. The three hypothesis tests are summarized here. ∎

Now You Can Do
Exercises 29–34.

Value of μ_0	Form of hypothesis test, with $\alpha = 0.01$	Where μ_0 lies in relation to 95% confidence interval	Conclusion of hypothesis test
a. 0.900	$H_0: \mu = 0.900$ vs. $H_a: \mu \neq 0.900$	Outside	Reject H_0
b. 0.910	$H_0: \mu = 0.910$ vs. $H_a: \mu \neq 0.910$	Inside	Do not reject H_0
c. 1.100	$H_0: \mu = 1.100$ vs. $H_a: \mu \neq 1.100$	Outside	Reject H_0

STEP-BY-STEP GUIDE TO TECHNOLOGY: Z test for μ

We will use the birth weight data from Example 9.10 (page 443).

TI-83/84

If you have the data values:
Step 1 Enter the data into list **L1**.
Step 2 Press **STAT**, highlight **TESTS**, and press **ENTER**.
Step 3 Press **1** (for **Z-Test**; see Figure 9.17).
Step 4 For input (**Inpt**), highlight **Data** and press **ENTER** (Figure 9.18).
a. For μ_0, enter the value of μ_0, **3200**.
b. For σ, enter the value of σ, **528**.

c. For **List**, press **2ⁿᵈ**, then **L1**.
d. For **Freq**, enter **1**.
e. For μ, select the form of H_a. Here we have a right-tailed test, so highlight $> \mu_0$ and press **ENTER**.
f. Highlight **Calculate** and press **ENTER**. The results are shown in Figure 9.10 in Example 9.10.

If you have the summary statistics:
Step 1 Press **STAT**, highlight **TESTS**, and press **ENTER**.
Step 2 Press **1** (for **Z-Test**; see Figure 9.18).
Step 3 For input (**Inpt**), highlight **Stats** and press **ENTER** (Figure 9.19).
a. For μ_0, enter the value of μ_0, **3200**.
b. For σ, enter the value of σ, **528**.

c. For $\bar{x}$, enter the sample mean **3276**.
d. For **n**, enter the sample size **44**.
e. For μ, select the form of H_a. Here we have a right-tailed test, so highlight $> \mu_0$ and press **ENTER**.
f. Highlight **Calculate** and press **ENTER**. The results are shown in Figure 9.10 in Example 9.10.

FIGURE 9.17

FIGURE 9.18

FIGURE 9.19

EXCEL

WHFStat Macros
Step 1 Enter the data into column A. (If you have only the summary statistics, go to Step 2.)
Step 2 Load the **WHFStat Macros**.
Step 3 Select **Add-Ins > Macros > Testing a Mean > Z Test − Confidence Interval − One Sample**.

Step 4 Select cells A1 to A44 as the **Dataset Range**. (Alternatively, you may enter the summary statistics.)
Step 5 Select your **Confidence level**, which should be $1 - \alpha$. Here, because $\alpha = 0.10$, we select **90%**.
Step 6 Enter the **Population Standard Deviation**, $\sigma = 528$.
Step 7 Enter the **Null Hypothesis Value**, $\mu_0 = 3200$, and click **OK**.

MINITAB

If you have the data values:
Step 1 Enter the data into column C1.
Step 2 Click **Stat > Basic Statistics > 1-Sample Z**.
Step 3 Click **Samples in Columns** and select **C1**.
Step 4 Enter **528** as **Standard Deviation**.
Step 5 For **Test Mean**, enter **3200**.
Step 6 Click **Options**.
a. Choose your **Confidence Level** as $100(1 - \alpha)$. Our level of significance α here is 0.10, so the confidence level is 90.0.
b. Select **Greater Than** to symbolize the right-tailed test.
Step 7 Click **OK** and click **OK** again. The results are shown in Figure 9.11 in Example 9.10.

If you have the summary statistics:
Step 1 Click **Stat > Basic Statistics > 1-Sample Z**.
Step 2 Click **Summarized Data**.
Step 3 Enter the **Sample Size 44** and the **Sample Mean 3276**.
Step 4 Click **Options**.
a. Choose your **Confidence Level** as $100(1 - \alpha)$. Our level of significance α here is 0.10, so the confidence level is 90.0.
b. Select **Greater Than** to symbolize the right-tailed test.
Step 5 Click **OK** and click **OK** again. The results are shown in Figure 9.11 in Example 9.10.

CRUNCHIT!

If you have the data values:
Step 1 Click **File . . .** then highlight **Load from Larose2e . . . Chapter 9 . . .** and click on **Example 9.10**.
Step 2 Click **Statistics . . . Z** and select **1-sample**.
Step 3 With the **Columns** tab chosen, for **Sample** select **Weight**. For **Standard Deviation**, enter **528**.
Step 4 Select the **Hypothesis Test** tab. For **Mean under null hypothesis**, enter **3200**. For **Alternative** select **Greater than**. Then click **Calculate**.

If you have the summary statistics:
Step 1 Click **File . . .** then highlight **Load from Larose2e . . . Chapter 9 . . .** and click on **Example 9.10**.
Step 2 Click **Statistics . . . Z** and select **1-sample**.
Step 3 Choose the **Summarized** tab. For **n** enter the sample size 44; for **Sample Mean** enter 3276. For **Standard Deviation**, enter **528**.
Step 4 Select the **Hypothesis Test** tab. For **Mean under null hypothesis**, enter **3200**. For **Alternative** select **Greater than**. Then click **Calculate**.

Section 9.3 Summary

1 The *p*-value can be thought of as the probability of observing a sample statistic at least as extreme as the statistic in your sample if we assume that the null hypothesis is true. The rejection rule for the *p*-value method is to reject H_0 when the *p*-value $\leq \alpha$, the level of significance.

2 The p-value can be used to assess the strength of evidence against the null hypothesis.

3 The critical-value method and the p-value method are equivalent, and related in several ways.

4 We can use a single confidence interval for μ to help us perform any number of corresponding two-tailed hypothesis tests about μ.

Section 9.3 Exercises

CLARIFYING THE CONCEPTS

1. True or false: It is possible to get a p-value equal to 1.5.
2. State the rejection rule for the p-value method for performing the Z test for μ.
3. Explain why we might want to assess the strength of evidence against the null hypothesis, rather than delivering a simple "reject H_0 or do not reject H_0" conclusion.
4. What is the criterion for rejecting H_0 when using a confidence interval to perform a two-tailed hypothesis test for μ?
5. True or false: For a right-tailed test, when $Z_{data} \leq Z_{crit}$, the p-value is always $\leq \alpha$.
6. For **(a)–(c)**, indicate whether or not the quantity represents a probability.
   a. Z_{data}
   b. p-value
   c. α

PRACTICING THE TECHNIQUES

For Exercises 7–34, assume that the conditions for performing the Z test are met.

For Exercises 7–14, find the p-value.

7. $H_0: \mu = 5$ vs. $H_a: \mu > 5, Z_{data} = 1$
8. $H_0: \mu = 5$ vs. $H_a: \mu > 5, Z_{data} = 2$
9. $H_0: \mu = 5$ vs. $H_a: \mu > 5, Z_{data} = 3$
10. $H_0: \mu = 20$ vs. $H_a: \mu < 20, Z_{data} = -2.5$
11. $H_0: \mu = 42$ vs. $H_a: \mu < 42, Z_{data} = -2.5$
12. $H_0: \mu = 50$ vs. $H_a: \mu \neq 50, Z_{data} = 2.9$
13. $H_0: \mu = 50$ vs. $H_a: \mu \neq 50, Z_{data} = -2.9$
14. $H_0: \mu = 100$ vs. $H_a: \mu \neq 100, Z_{data} = -1.27$
15. Refer to Exercises 7–9. Explain what happens to the p-value for a right-tailed test as Z_{data} increases.
16. Refer to Exercises 12 and 13. What can we say about the p-values of two two-tailed tests whose values of Z_{data} have the same absolute value?

For Exercises 17–22, perform the Z test for μ using level of significance $\alpha = 0.05$ by doing the following steps.
   a. State the hypotheses and the rejection rule.
   b. Calculate Z_{data}.
   c. Find the p-value.
   d. State the conclusion and the interpretation.
17. $H_0: \mu = 98.6$ vs. $H_a: \mu > 98.6, \bar{x} = 99.1, \sigma = 10, n = 100$
18. $H_0: \mu = 32$ vs. $H_a: \mu < 32, \bar{x} = 27, \sigma = 20, n = 25$
19. $H_0: \mu = -0.1$ vs. $H_a: \mu > -0.1, \bar{x} = 0, \sigma = 1, n = 400$
20. $H_0: \mu = 100$ vs. $H_a: \mu \neq 100, \bar{x} = 102.3, \sigma = 15, n = 100$

21. $H_0: \mu = -50$ vs. $H_a: \mu \neq -50, \bar{x} = -46, \sigma = 15, n = 100$
22. $H_0: \mu = 0$ vs. $H_a: \mu \neq 0, \bar{x} = -1.7, \sigma = 4.5, n = 81$

For Exercises 23–28, use the indicated p-value to assess the strength of evidence against the null hypothesis, using Table 9.6.
23. p-value from Exercise 17
24. p-value from Exercise 18
25. p-value from Exercise 19
26. p-value from Exercise 20
27. p-value from Exercise 21
28. p-value from Exercise 22

For Exercises 29–34, a $100(1 - \alpha)\%$ confidence interval is given. Use the confidence interval to test using level of significance α whether μ differs from each of the indicated hypothesized values.
29. A 95% Z confidence interval for μ is $(-2.7, 6.9)$. Hypothesized values μ_0 are
   a. -3 **b.** -2 **c.** 0
   d. 5 **e.** 7
30. A 99% Z confidence interval for μ is $(45, 55)$. Hypothesized values μ_0 are
   a. 0 **b.** 44 **c.** 50
   d. 54 **e.** 56
31. A 90% Z confidence interval for μ is $(-10, -5)$. Hypothesized values μ_0 are
   a. -3 **b.** -8 **c.** -11
   d. 0 **e.** 7
32. A 95% Z confidence interval for μ is $(1024, 2056)$. Hypothesized values μ_0 are
   a. 1000 **b.** 2000 **c.** 3000
   d. 0 **e.** 1025
33. A 95% Z confidence interval for μ is $(0, 1)$. Hypothesized values μ_0 are
   a. 1.5 **b.** -1 **c.** 0.5
   d. 0.9 **e.** 1.2
34. A 95% Z confidence interval for μ is $(1.3275, 1.4339)$. Hypothesized values μ_0 are
   a. 1.3 **b.** 1.35 **c.** 1.4
   d. 1.45 **e.** 1.3275

APPLYING THE CONCEPTS

For Exercises 35–42, do the following.
   a. State the hypotheses and the rejection rule.
   b. Calculate Z_{data}.
   c. Find the p-value.
   d. State the conclusion and the interpretation.

35. Child Abuse. The U.S. Administration for Children and Families reports that the national rate for child abuse referrals is 43.9 per 1000 children. Suppose that a random sample of 1000 children shows 47 child abuse referrals. Assume $\sigma = 5$. Test whether the population mean referral rate has increased, using level of significance $\alpha = 0.10$.

36. California Warming. A 2007 report found that the mean temperature in California increased from 1950 to 2000 by 2 degrees Fahrenheit (°F). Suppose that a random sample of 36 California locations showed a mean increase of 4°F over 1950 levels. Assume $\sigma = 0.5$. Test whether the population mean temperature increase in California is greater than 2°F, at level of significance $\alpha = 0.05$.

37. Eating Trends. According to an NPD Group report, the mean number of meals prepared and eaten at home is less than 700 per year. Suppose that a random sample of 100 households showed a sample mean number of meals prepared and eaten at home of 650. Assume $\sigma = 25$. Test whether the population mean number of such meals is less than 700, using level of significance $\alpha = 0.10$.

38. DDT in Breast Milk. Researchers compared the amount of DDT in the breast milk of 12 Latina women in the Yakima Valley of Washington State with the amount of DDT in breast milk in the general U.S. population.[5] They measured the mean DDT level in the general population to be 47.2 parts per billion (ppb) and the mean DDT level in the 12 Latina women to be 219.7 ppb. Assume $\sigma = 36$ and a normally distributed population. Test whether the population mean DDT level in the breast milk of Latina women in the Yakima Valley is greater than that of the general population, using level of significance $\alpha = 0.01$.

39. Stock Market. The *Statistical Abstract of the United States* reports that the mean daily number of shares traded on the New York Stock Exchange in 2010 was 2 billion. Let this value represent the hypothesized population mean, and assume that the population standard deviation equals 0.5 billion shares. Suppose that, in a random sample of 36 days from the present year, the mean daily number of shares traded equals 2.1 billion. We are interested in testing whether the population mean daily number of shares traded differs from 2 billion using level of significance $\alpha = 0.05$.

40. Tree Rings. Do trees grow more quickly when they are young? The International Tree Ring Data Base collected data on a particular 440-year-old Douglas fir tree.[6] The mean annual ring growth in the tree's first 80 years of life was 1.4261 millimeters (mm). A random sample of size 100 taken from the tree's later years showed a sample mean growth of 0.56 mm per year. Assume $\sigma = 0.5$ mm and a normally distributed population. Test whether the population mean annual ring growth in the tree's later years is less than 1.4261 mm, using level of significance $\alpha = 0.05$.

41. Hybrid Vehicles. A study by Edmunds.com examined the time it takes for owners of hybrid vehicles to recoup their additional initial cost through reduced fuel consumption. Suppose that a random sample of 9 hybrid cars showed a sample mean time of 2.1 years. Assume that the population is normal with $\sigma = 0.2$. Test using level of significance $\alpha = 0.01$ whether the population mean time it takes owners of hybrid cars to recoup their initial cost is less than three years.

42. Americans' Height. Americans used to be on average the tallest people in the world. That is no longer the case, according to a study by Dr. Richard Steckel, professor of economics and anthropology at The Ohio State University. The Norwegians and Dutch are now the tallest, at 178 centimeters, followed by the Swedes at 177, and then the Americans, with a mean height of 175 centimeters (approximately 5 feet 9 inches). According to Dr. Steckel, "The average height of Americans has been pretty much stagnant for 25 years."[7] Suppose a random sample of 100 Americans taken this year shows a mean height of 174 centimeters, and we assume $\sigma = 10$ centimeters. Test using level of significance $\alpha = 0.01$ whether the population mean height of Americans this year has changed from 175 centimeters.

43. Cost of Education. The College Board reports that the mean annual cost of education at a private four-year college was $22,218 for the 2006–2007 school year. Suppose that a random sample of 49 private four-year colleges this year gives a mean cost of $24,000 per year. Assume the population standard deviation is $3000.
  a. Construct a 95% confidence interval for the population mean annual cost.
  b. Use the confidence interval to test at level of significance $\alpha = 0.05$ whether the population mean annual cost differs from the following amounts.
     i. $24,000
     ii. $23,000
     iii. $23,200
     iv. $25,000

Health Care Premiums. Use the following information for Exercises 44–46. According to the National Coalition on Health Care, the mean annual premium for an employer health plan covering a family of four cost $13,100 in 2010. A random sample of 100 families of four showed a mean annual premium of $13,700. Assume $\sigma = $3000.

44. Test whether the population mean annual premium is >$13,100, using level of significance $\alpha = 0.05$.

45. *What if* the sample mean premium equaled some value larger than $13,700, while everything else stayed the same. Explain how this change would affect the following, if at all.
  a. The hypotheses
  b. Z_{crit}
  c. The critical region
  d. Z_{data}
  e. The conclusion

46. Test whether the population mean annual premium is >$13,100 using level of significance $\alpha = 0.01$. Compare your conclusion with the conclusion in Exercise 44. Comment.

Mean Family Size. Use the following information for Exercises 47–50. According to the *Statistical Abstract of the United States,* the mean family size in 2010 was 3.14 persons, reflecting a slow decrease since 1980, when the mean family size was 3.29 persons. Has this trend continued to the present day? Suppose a random sample of 225 families taken this year yields a sample mean size of 3.05 persons, and suppose we assume that the population standard deviation of family sizes is 1 person.

47. We are interested in testing whether the population mean family size in America has decreased since 2010, using the *p*-value method and level of significance $\alpha = 0.05$. (Try using the *P-Value* applet to help you solve this problem.)

    a. State the hypotheses and the rejection rule.
    b. Calculate Z_{data}.
    c. Find the *p*-value.
    d. State the conclusion and interpretation.

48. Refer to the previous exercise. Suppose that we used level of significance $\alpha = 0.10$ rather than $\alpha = 0.05$. Redo **(a)–(d)**. Comment on any apparent contradictions. Suggest two ways to resolve this dilemma.

49. Refer to Exercise 47, with our original hypothesis test (with $\alpha = 0.05$).

    a. What is the smallest *p*-value for which you will reject H_0?
    b. What do you think of the assumption of 1 person for the value of σ? How would this have been obtained, if at all possible?
    c. Which type of error is it possible that we are making, a Type I error or a Type II error? Which type of error are we certain we are not making?
    d. Suppose a newspaper headline referring to the study was "Mean Family Size Decreasing." Is the headline supported or not supported by the data and the hypothesis test?

50. Refer to Exercise 49 and our original hypothesis test (with level of significance $\alpha = 0.05$) in Exercise 47. Try to answer the following questions by thinking about the relationship between the statistics rather than by redoing all the calculations. *What if* the 3.05 persons had been a typo, and the actual sample mean was 3.00 persons. How would this have affected the following?

    a. The standard deviation of the sampling distribution
    b. Z_{data}
    c. The *p*-value
    d. The conclusion
    e. Write a sentence describing what happens to the elements in **(a)–(d)** when the sample mean becomes more extreme.

51. Women's Heart Rates. A random sample of 15 women produced the normal probability plot for their heart rates shown here. The sample mean was 75.6 beats per minute. Suppose the population standard deviation is known to be 9.

    a. Discuss the evidence for or against the normality assumption. Should we use the *Z* test? Why or why not?
    b. Assume that the plot does not contradict the normality assumption; test whether the population mean heart rate for all women *is less than* 78, using level of significance $\alpha = 0.05$.
    c. Test whether the population mean heart rate for all women *differs from* 78, using $\alpha = 0.05$.

52. Challenge Exercise. Refer to the previous exercise.

    a. Compare your conclusions from Exercises 51**(b)** and 51**(c)**. Note that the conclusions differ but the meanings of the hypotheses tested also differ. Combine the two conclusions into a single sentence. Do you find this sentence difficult to explain?
    b. Explain in your own words the difference between the hypotheses in Exercises 51**(b)** and 51**(c)**. Also, explain how there could be evidence that the population mean heart rate is *less than 78 but not different from 78.*
    c. Assess the strength of the evidence against the null hypothesis for the hypothesis tests in Exercises 51**(b)** and 51**(c)**.

BRINGING IT ALL TOGETHER

Sodium in Breakfast Cereal. Use the following information for Exercises 53–56. A random sample of 23 breakfast cereals containing sodium had a mean sodium content per serving of 192.39 grams. Assume that the population standard deviation equals 50 grams. We are interested in whether the population mean sodium content per serving is less than 210 grams.

53. a. The normal probability plot of the sodium content is shown here. Should we proceed to apply the *Z* test? Why or why not?
    b. Test whether the population mean sodium content per serving is less than 210 grams, using level of significance $\alpha = 0.01$.

54. *What if* the population standard deviation of 50 grams had been a typo, and the actual population standard deviation was smaller. How would this have affected the following?
  a. The standard deviation of the sampling distribution
  b. Z_{data}
  c. *p*-value
  d. The conclusion

55. *What if* our level of significance α equaled 0.05 instead of 0.01.
  a. Perform the appropriate hypothesis test using the manual *p*-value method, but this time using level of significance $\alpha = 0.05$.
  b. Note that your conclusion differs from that obtained using level of significance $\alpha = 0.01$. Have the data changed? Why did your conclusion change?
  c. Suggest two alternatives for addressing the contradiction between Exercise 53(**b**) and Exercise 55(**a**).

56. Assess the strength of the evidence against the null hypothesis.

Online Shopping Privacy Protection. Use the *P-Value* applet and the following information for Exercises 57–60. A 2007 Carnegie Mellon University study reports that online shoppers were willing to pay an average of an extra 60 cents on a $15 purchase in order to have better online privacy protection.[8] Assume that the population standard deviation

is 20 cents. Suppose that a study conducted this year found that the mean amount online shoppers were willing to pay for privacy was $\bar{x} = 65$ cents. Does this represent evidence that the mean amount online shoppers are willing to pay for privacy has increased from 60 cents? As it turns out, the answer depends on the sample size. If this $\bar{x} = 65$ cents comes from a large sample, then the evidence against H_0 will be stronger than if it comes from a small sample. Use the *P-Value* applet to see this, using level of significance $\alpha = 0.05$.

57. Enter $H_0 : \mu \leq 60$, $H_a : \mu > 60$, $\sigma = 20$, and $\bar{x} = 65$.
  a. Enter $n = 30$. Click **Show P** to get the *p*-value. What is the *p*-value? Sketch the normal curve, showing the *p*-value.
  b. Would we reject the null hypothesis based on these values of $\bar{x}$ and n?

58. Repeat Exercise 57 for $n = 40$. Compare the *p*-value with that from Exercise 57.

59. Repeat Exercise 57 for $n = 50$. Compare the *p*-value with those from Exercises 57 and 58.

60. Note that $\bar{x}$ has not changed in Exercises 57–59; only the sample size has changed. Write a sentence to describe the pattern you see in the *p*-values as the sample size increases.

61. Texas Towns. Work with the **Texas** data set for the following. **Texas**
  a. How many observations are in the data set? How many variables?
  b. Use technology to explore the variable *tot_occ*, which lists the total occupied housing units for each county in Texas. Generate numerical summary statistics and graphs for the total occupied housing units. What is the sample mean? The sample standard deviation? Comment on the symmetry or skewness of the data set.
  c. Suppose we are using the data in this data set as a sample of the total occupied housing units of all the counties in the southwestern United States and let $\sigma = 88,400$. Use technology to test at level of significance $\alpha = 0.05$ whether the population mean total occupied housing units for these counties differs from 40,000.

9.4   *t* Test for the Population Mean

OBJECTIVES By the end of this section, I will be able to . . .

1   Perform the *t* test for the mean using the critical-value method.

2   Carry out the *t* test for the mean using the *p*-value method.

3   Use confidence intervals to perform two-tailed hypothesis tests.

1 t Test for μ Using the Critical-Value Method

Note: Students may wish to review the characteristics of the t distribution on pages 386–387.

In many real-world scenarios, the value of the population standard deviation σ is unknown. When this occurs, we should use neither the Z interval nor the Z test. Recall that in Section 8.2 we used the t distribution to find a confidence interval for the mean when σ was not known. The situation is similar for hypothesis testing.

Let $\bar{x}$ be the sample mean, μ be the unknown population mean, s be the sample standard deviation, and n be the sample size. The t statistic

$$t = \frac{\bar{x} - \mu}{s/\sqrt{n}}$$

with $n - 1$ degrees of freedom may be used when either the population is normal or the sample size is large. We call this t statistic t_{data} because its value depends largely on the sample data and the population data.

> The test statistic used for the t test for the mean is
>
> $$t_{\text{data}} = \frac{\bar{x} - \mu_0}{s/\sqrt{n}}$$

t_{data} represents the number of standard errors $\bar{x}$ lies above or below μ_0.

Extreme values of $\bar{x}$, that is, values of $\bar{x}$ that are significantly far from the hypothesized μ, will translate into extreme values of t_{data}. In other words, just as with Z_{data}, when $\bar{x}$ is far from μ_0, t_{data} will be far from 0. We answer the question "How extreme is extreme?" using the critical-value method by finding a *critical value* of t, called t_{crit}. This threshold value t_{crit} separates the values of t_{data} for which we reject H_0 (the *critical region*) from the values of t_{data} for which we will not reject H_0 (the *noncritical region*). Because there is a different t curve for every different sample size, you need to know the following to find the value of t_{crit}:

- the form of the hypothesis test (one-tailed or two-tailed)

The degrees of freedom is a measure of how the t distribution changes as the sample size changes.

- the degrees of freedom (df $= n - 1$)
- the level of significance α

> **t Test for the Population Mean μ: Critical-Value Method**
>
> When a random sample of size n is taken from a population, you can use the t test if either the population is normal or the sample size is large ($n \geq 30$).
>
> **Step 1 State the hypotheses.**
> Use one of the forms from Table 9.8. State the meaning of μ.
>
> **Step 2 Find t_{crit} and state the rejection rule.**
> Use Table D in the Appendix and Table 9.8.
>
> **Step 3 Calculate t_{data}.**
>
> $$t_{\text{data}} = \frac{\bar{x} - \mu_0}{s/\sqrt{n}}$$
>
> **Step 4 State the conclusion and the interpretation.**
> If t_{data} falls within the critical region, then reject H_0. Otherwise, do not reject H_0. Interpret your conclusion so that a nonspecialist can understand.

Table 9.8 contains the critical regions and rejection rules for the t test.

Table 9.8 Critical regions and rejection rules for various forms of the *t* test for μ

	Right-tailed test	Left-tailed test	Two-tailed test
Form of test	$H_0 : \mu = \mu_0$ $H_a : \mu > \mu_0$ level of significance α	$H_0 : \mu = \mu_0$ $H_a : \mu < \mu_0$ level of significance α	$H_0 : \mu = \mu_0$ $H_a : \mu \neq \mu_0$ level of significance α
Critical region	[normal curve with area α in right tail; 0 and t_{crit} marked; Noncritical region, Critical region]	[normal curve with area α in left tail; $-t_{crit}$ and 0 marked; Critical region, Noncritical region]	[normal curve with areas $\alpha/2$ in each tail; $-t_{crit}$, 0, t_{crit} marked; Critical region, Noncritical region, Critical region]
Rejection rule	Reject H_0 if $t_{data} \geq t_{crit}$	Reject H_0 if $t_{data} \leq -t_{crit}$	Reject H_0 if $t_{data} \geq t_{crit}$ or $t_{data} \leq -t_{crit}$

Example 9.13   *t* Test for μ using critical-value method: left-tailed test

```
Variable        N   Mean    StDev
Patient Age    20  14.251   1.512
```

Minitab description statistics.

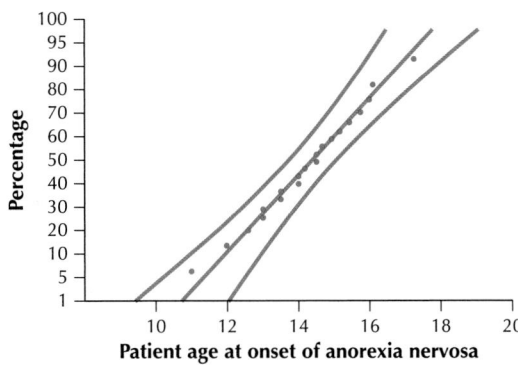

FIGURE 9.20 Normal probability plot for age at onset of anorexia nervosa.

We are interested in testing, using level of significance $\alpha = 0.05$, whether the mean age at onset of anorexia nervosa in young women has been decreasing. Assume that the previous mean age at onset was 15 years old. Data were gathered for a study of the onset age for this disorder.[9] From these data, a random sample was taken of $n = 20$ young women who were admitted under this diagnosis to the Toronto Hospital for Sick Children. The Minitab descriptive statistics shown here indicate a sample mean age of $\bar{x} = 14.251$ years and a sample standard deviation of $s = 1.512$ years. If appropriate, perform the *t* test.

Solution

Since the sample size $n = 20$ is not large, we need to verify normality. The normal probability plot of the ages at onset in Figure 9.20 indicates that the ages in the sample are normally distributed. We may proceed to perform the *t* test for the mean.

Step 1 **State the hypotheses.** The key word "decreasing" guides us to state our hypotheses as follows:

$$H_0 : \mu = 15 \quad \text{versus} \quad H_a : \mu < 15$$

where μ refers to the population mean age at onset.

Step 2 **Find t_{crit} and state the rejection rule.** Our hypotheses from Step 1 indicate that we have a left-tailed test, meaning that the critical region represents an area in the left tail (see Figure 9.22). To find t_{crit}, we turn to the *t* table, an excerpt of which is shown in Figure 9.21. Since we have a one-tailed test, under "Area in one tail," select the column with our α value 0.05. Then choose the row with our df $= n - 1 = 20 - 1 = 19$, so that we get $t_{crit} = 1.729$. Because we have a left-tailed test, the rejection rule from Table 9.8 is "Reject H_0 if $t_{data} \leq -t_{crit}$"; that is, we will reject H_0 if $t_{data} \leq -1.729$.

		0.10	0.05	Area in one tail 0.025
				Area in two tails
		0.20	0.10	0.05
df	1	3.078	6.314	12.706
	2	1.886	2.920	4.303
	3	1.638	2.353	3.182
	4	1.533	2.132	2.776
	5	1.476	2.015	2.571
	6	1.440	1.943	2.447
	7	1.415	1.895	2.365
	8	1.397	1.860	2.306
	9	1.383	1.833	2.262
	10	1.372	1.812	2.228
	11	1.363	1.796	2.201
	12	1.356	1.782	2.179
	13	1.350	1.771	2.160
	14	1.345	1.761	2.145
	15	1.341	1.753	2.131
	16	1.337	1.746	2.120
	17	1.333	1.740	2.110
	18	1.330	1.734	2.101
	19	1.328	1.729	2.093
	20	1.325	1.725	2.086

FIGURE 9.21 Finding t_{crit} for a one-tailed test. For a two-tailed test, use "Area in two tails."

Step 3 **Calculate t_{data}.** We have $n = 20$, $\bar{x} = 14.251$, and $s = 1.512$ years. Also, $\mu_0 = 15$, since this is the hypothesized value of μ stated in H_0. Therefore, our test statistic is

$$t_{data} = \frac{\bar{x} - \mu_0}{s/\sqrt{n}} = \frac{14.251 - 15}{1.512/\sqrt{20}} \approx -2.2154$$

Step 4 **State the conclusion and interpretation.** The rejection rule from Step 2 says to reject H_0 if $t_{data} \leq -1.729$. From Step 3, we have $t_{data} = -2.2154$. Since -2.2154 is less than -1.729, our conclusion is to reject H_0. If you prefer the graphical approach, consider Figure 9.22, which shows where t_{data} falls in relation to the critical region. Since $t_{data} = -2.2154$ falls within the critical region, our conclusion is to reject H_0. There is evidence at level of significance $\alpha = 0.05$ that the population mean age of onset has decreased from its previous level of 15 years. ■

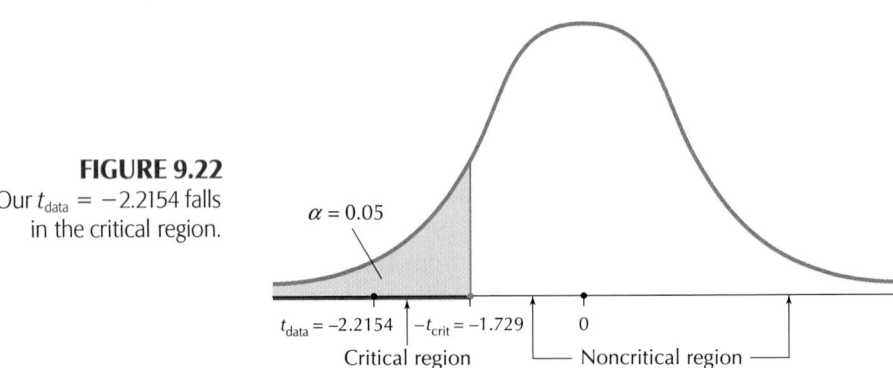

FIGURE 9.22
Our $t_{data} = -2.2154$ falls in the critical region.

Now You Can Do
Exercises 3–8.

Example 9.14   *t* Test for μ using critical value method: two-tailed test

The Pew Internet and American Life Project reported in 2010 that the mean number of text messages sent and received daily by teenagers is 50. Suppose another researcher disputes this finding and is interested in testing whether the population mean number of text messages differs from 50. A random sample of $n = 100$ teenagers yields a sample mean of $\bar{x} = 47.75$ text messages, with a sample standard deviation of $s = 15$ messages. If the conditions are met, perform the appropriate hypothesis test using level of significance $\alpha = 0.10$.

Solution

Since $n = 36 > 30$, we may proceed with the *t* test.

See Example 8.11 (page 390) for why we are taking the next higher df.

Step 1 **State the hypotheses.** The key words "differs from" indicate a two-tailed test, with $\mu_0 = 50$, because we are testing whether μ differs from 50. So our hypotheses are

$$H_0 : \mu = 50 \quad \text{versus} \quad H_a : \mu \neq 50$$

where μ represents the population mean number of text messages sent and received by teenagers daily.

Step 2 **Find t_{crit} and state the rejection rule.** To find t_{crit} for a two-tailed test with level of significance $\alpha = 0.10$, we look in the 0.10 column in the "Area in two tails" section of Table D in the Appendix. The degrees of freedom df $= n - 1 = 99$ are not listed, so we take the next higher degrees of freedom, df $= 90$, giving us $t_{\text{crit}} = 1.662$. From Table 9.8, the rejection rule is: "Reject H_0 if $t_{\text{data}} \geq 1.662$ or $t_{\text{data}} \leq -1.662$.

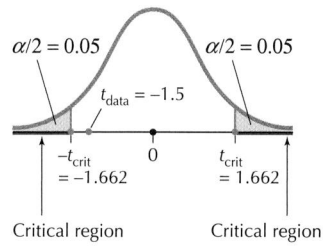

FIGURE 9.23 Critical region for two-tailed test.

Step 3 **Calculate t_{data}:**

$$t_{\text{data}} = \frac{\bar{x} - \mu_0}{s/\sqrt{n}} = \frac{47.75 - 50}{15/\sqrt{100}} = -1.5$$

Step 4 **State the conclusion and the interpretation.** See Figure 9.23. $t_{\text{data}} = -1.5$ is not ≥ 1.662 and it is not ≤ -1.662; therefore, we do not reject H_0. There is insufficient evidence at level of significance $\alpha = 0.10$ that the population mean number of text messages differs from 50. ∎

Now You Can Do
Exercises 9–14.

2 *t* Test for μ Using the *p*-Value Method

We may also use the *p*-value method for performing the *t* test for μ. The critical-value method and the *p*-value are equivalent, so they will provide identical conclusions.

---

t Test for the Population Mean μ: p-Value Method

When a random sample of size n is taken from a population, you can use the *t* test if either the population is normal or the sample size is large ($n \geq 30$).

Step 1 **State the hypotheses and the rejection rule.**
Use one of the forms from Table 9.9. State the meaning of μ. The rejection rule is "Reject H_0 if the *p*-value $\leq \alpha$."

Step 2 **Calculate t_{data}.**

$$t_{\text{data}} = \frac{\bar{x} - \mu_0}{s/\sqrt{n}}$$

Step 3 **Find the *p*-value.**
Either use technology to find the *p*-value or estimate the *p*-value using Table D, *t* Distribution, in the Appendix.

Step 4 **State the conclusion and the interpretation.**
If the *p*-value $\leq \alpha$, then reject H_0. Otherwise, do not reject H_0. Interpret your conclusion so that a nonspecialist can understand.

The definition of a p-value for a t test is similar to the p-value for a Z test. Unusual and extreme values of $\bar{x}$, and therefore of t_{data}, will have a small p-value, while values of $\bar{x}$ and t_{data} nearer to the center of the distribution will have a large p-value. Table 9.9 summarizes the definition of the p-value for t tests. Note that we will not be finding these p-values manually but will either (a) use a computer or calculator or (b) estimate them using the t table.

Table 9.9 p-Values for t tests

	Right-tailed test	**Left-tailed test**	**Two-tailed test**
Form of test	$H_0: \mu = \mu_0$ $H_a: \mu > \mu_0$ level of significance α	$H_0: \mu = \mu_0$ $H_a: \mu < \mu_0$ level of significance α	$H_0: \mu = \mu_0$ $H_a: \mu \neq \mu_0$ level of significance α
p-Value is tail area associated with t_{data}	$p\text{-value} = P(t > t_{data})$ Area to the right of t_{data}	$p\text{-value} = P(t < t_{data})$ Area to the left of t_{data}	$p\text{-value} = P(t > \lvert t_{data}\rvert) + P(t < -\lvert t_{data}\rvert)$ $= 2 \cdot P(t > \lvert t_{data}\rvert)$ Sum of the two tail areas

---

Example 9.15 t Test using the p-value method: right-tailed test

City	Price
Baltimore	$3.75
Chicago	$3.00
Detroit	$2.70
Hartford	$3.66
Houston	$3.36
Los Angeles	$3.32
Miami	$3.80
New York	$3.92
Philadelphia	$3.91
St. Louis	$3.58

 milkprice

The U.S. Bureau of Labor Statistics reports that the mean price for a gallon of milk in January 2011 was $3.34. Gallons of milk were bought in a sample of $n = 10$ different cities, with the prices shown in the accompanying table. Test using level of significance $\alpha = 0.10$ whether the population mean price for a gallon of milk is greater than $3.34.

Solution

We first check whether the conditions for performing the t test are met. Because our sample size is small, we must check for normality. The normal probability plot in Figure 9.24 shows acceptable normality, allowing us to proceed with the t test.

FIGURE 9.24
Normal probability plot of milk prices.

Step 1 **State the hypotheses and the rejection rule.** The key words "is greater than" means that we have a right-tailed test. Answering the question "Greater than what?" gives us $\mu_0 = 3.34$.

$$H_0: \mu = 3.34 \quad \text{versus} \quad H_a: \mu > 3.34$$

where μ represents the population mean price of milk. We will reject H_0 if the *p*-value $\leq$ $\alpha = 0.10$.

$\boxed{\text{Step 2}}$ **Calculate t_{data}.** We use the instructions from the Step-by-Step Technology Guide on page 464. Figure 9.25 shows the TI-83/84 results from the *t* test for μ.

Form of H_a: ────────────
t_{data} ────────────
p-value ────────────
Sample mean $\bar{x}$ ────────────
Sample standard deviation *s* ────────────
Sample size *n* ────────────

```
T-Test
μ>3.34
t=1.251511662
P=.1211489193
x̄=3.5
Sx=.4042826294
n=10
```

FIGURE 9.25
TI-83/84 results for
right-tailed *t* test.

Using the statistics from Figure 9.25 we have the test statistic

$$t_{\text{data}} = \frac{\bar{x} - \mu_0}{s/\sqrt{n}} = \frac{3.5 - 3.34}{0.4042826294/\sqrt{10}} = 1.251511662 \approx 1.2515$$

For a more accurate calculation of the *p*-value, we retain 9 decimal places for the value of t_{data}.

$\boxed{\text{Step 3}}$ **Find the *p*-value.** From Figures 9.25 and 9.26, we have

$$\text{*p*-value} = P(t \geq 1.251511662) = 0.1211489193 \approx 0.1211$$

$\boxed{\text{Step 4}}$ **State the conclusion and the interpretation.** The *p*-value ≈ 0.1211 is not less than the level of significance $\alpha = 0.10$, so therefore do not reject H_0. There is insufficient evidence at level of significance $\alpha = 0.10$ that the population mean price of milk is greater than \$3.34. ∎

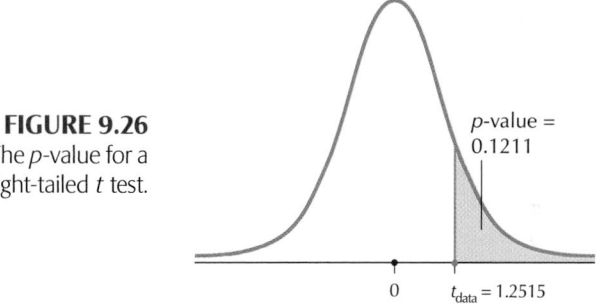

FIGURE 9.26
The *p*-value for a
right-tailed *t* test.

p-value = 0.1211

$0 \quad t_{\text{data}} = 1.2515$

Now You Can Do
Exercises 15–20.

Example 9.16 | *t* Test using the *p*-value method: two-tailed test

cancercare

The table below contains a random sample of 10 highly rated cancer care facilities, along with their nursing index (nurse-to-patient ratio), in 2007.[10] Suppose that the population mean nursing index in 2005 was 1.6 nurses per cancer patient. Test whether the population mean index has changed using level of significance $\alpha = 0.05$.

Hospital	Index
Memorial Sloan Kettering Cancer Center	1.5
M. D. Anderson Cancer Center	2.0
Johns Hopkins Hospital	2.3
Mayo Clinic	2.8
Dana Farber Cancer Institute	0.8
Univ. of Washington Medical Center	2.2
Duke University Medical Center	1.8
Univ. of Chicago Hospitals	2.3
UCLA Medical Center	2.2
UC San Francisco Medical Center	2.3

Solution

Since the sample size is small, we check normality. The normal probability plot (Figure 9.27) is not perfectly linear, but there are no points outside the bounds, and it is difficult to determine normality for such small sample sizes. We proceed to perform the *t* test, with the caveat that the normality assumption could be better supported and that more data would be helpful.

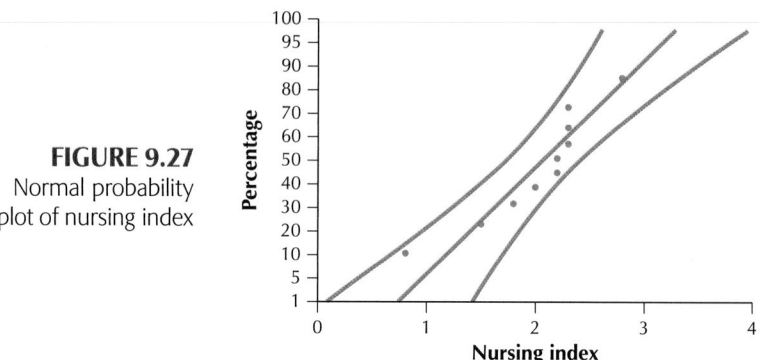

FIGURE 9.27
Normal probability plot of nursing index

Step 1 **State the hypotheses and the rejection rule.** The key words "has changed" means that we have a two-tailed test:

$$H_0: \mu = 1.6 \quad \text{versus} \quad H_a: \mu \neq 1.6$$

where μ represents the population mean nursing index. We will reject H_0 if the *p*-value $\leq \alpha = 0.05$.

Step 2 **Calculate t_{data}.** We use the instructions supplied in the Step-by-Step Technology Guide at the end of this section. Figure 9.28 shows the TI-83/84 results from the *t* test for μ.

FIGURE 9.28
TI-83/84 results.

Form of H_a:
t_{data}
p-value
Sample mean $\bar{x}$
Sample standard deviation s
Sample size n

We are retaining decimal places for more accurate calculation of the *p*-value.

Using the statistics from Figure 9.28, we have the test statistic

$$t_{\text{data}} = \frac{\bar{x} - \mu_0}{s/\sqrt{n}} = \frac{2.02 - 1.6}{0.549343042/\sqrt{10}} \approx 2.417718103 \approx 2.4177$$

Step 3 **Find the *p*-value.** From Figures 9.28 and 9.29, we have

$$p\text{-value} = P(t \geq |2.417718103|) + P(t \leq -|2.417718103|) \approx 0.03876$$

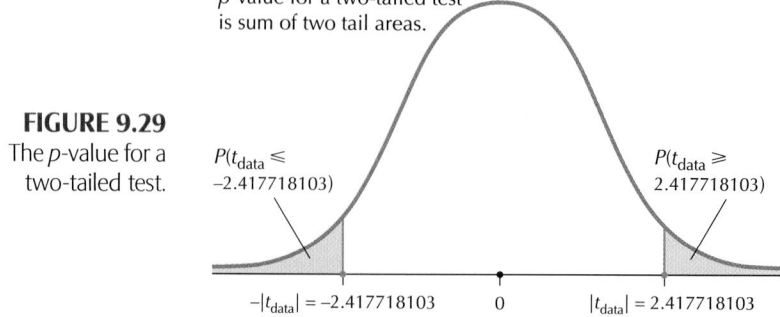

FIGURE 9.29
The *p*-value for a two-tailed test.

p-value for a two-tailed test is sum of two tail areas.

$P(t_{\text{data}} \leq -2.417718103)$

$P(t_{\text{data}} \geq 2.417718103)$

$-|t_{\text{data}}| = -2.417718103$ 0 $|t_{\text{data}}| = 2.417718103$

Now You Can Do
Exercises 21–26.

Step 4 **State the conclusion and interpretation.** The *p*-value of 0.03876 is less than $\alpha = 0.05$. We therefore reject H_0. There is evidence at level of significance $\alpha = 0.05$ that the population mean nurse-to-patient ratio differs from 1.6. ∎

Example 9.17   Estimating the *p*-value using the *t* table

Suppose we did not have access to technology. Estimate the *p*-value from Example 9.16 using the *t* table (Appendix Table D).

Solution

Now You Can Do
Exercises 27–30.

For a two-tailed test, choose the row of the *t* table with the heading "Area in two tails." Then select the row in the table with the appropriate degrees of freedom df $= n - 1 = 9$. Of the *t*-values in this row, find the two *t*-values between which the value of $t_{data} = 2.4177$ would lie, shown as 2.262 and 2.821 in Figure 9.30. The *p*-value must, therefore, lie between the corresponding *p*-values, 0.05 and 0.02. Thus we estimate the *p*-value for Example 9.16 to lie between 0.02 and 0.05, which of course it does: *p*-value ≈ 0.03876. ∎

		Area in two tails				
		0.20	0.10	0.05	0.02	0.01
df	9	1.383	1.833	2.262	2.821	3.250

t_{data} lies between 2.262 and 2.821, so the *p*-value lies between 0.05 and 0.02

FIGURE 9.30 Estimating the *p*-value using the *t* table.

3 Using Confidence Intervals to Perform Two-Tailed *t* Tests

Just as we did for two-tailed *Z* tests in Section 9.3, we may use a $100(1 - \alpha)\%$ *t* confidence interval to perform a two-tailed *t* test with level of significance α for various hypothesized values of μ_0. The strategy is the same: if a certain value for μ_0 lies outside the $100(1 - \alpha)\%$ *t* confidence interval for μ, then the null hypothesis specifying this value for μ_0 would be rejected. Otherwise it would not be rejected.

Example 9.18   Using a confidence interval to perform two-tailed *t* tests

Example 8.10 (page 389) provided a 95% confidence interval for the population mean length (in centimeters) of fourth-graders' feet as (22.496, 23.694). Test using level of significance $\alpha = 0.05$ whether the population mean length of fourth-graders' feet differs from these values: (a) 22 cm, (b) 23 cm, (c) 24 cm.

Solution

The key words "differs from" mean that we are using two-tailed tests. Then, for each hypothesized value of μ_0, we determine whether it falls inside or outside the given confidence interval.

    a. $H_0: \mu = 22$ versus $H_a: \mu \neq 22$

      The confidence interval is (22.496, 23.694), and since $\mu_0 = 22$ lies outside the interval (see Figure 9.31), we reject H_0.

b. $H_0: \mu = 23$ versus $H_a: \mu \neq 23$
$\mu_0 = 23$ lies inside the interval, so we do not reject H_0.

c. $H_0: \mu = 24$ versus $H_a: \mu \neq 24$
$\mu_0 = 24$ lies outside the interval, so we reject H_0. ∎

Lower Bound = 22.496   Upper Bound = 23.694

$\mu_0 = 22$ $\mu_0 = 23$ $\mu_0 = 24$

Reject H_0 Do not reject H_0 Reject H_0

FIGURE 9.31 Reject H_0 for values of μ_0 that lie outside (22.496, 23.694).

Now You Can Do
Exercises 31–36.

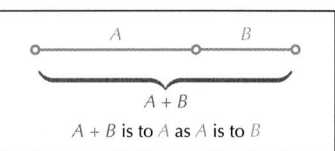

A B

$A + B$
$A + B$ is to A as A is to B

FIGURE 9.32 The golden ratio.

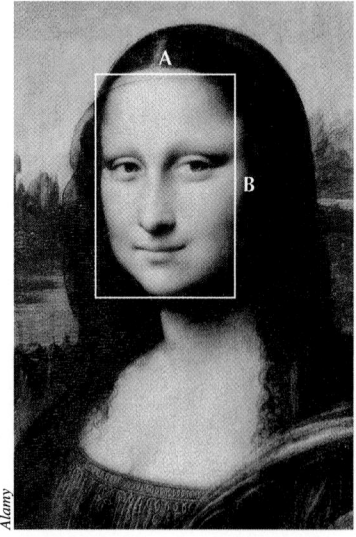

FIGURE 9.33 Mona Lisa's face follows the golden ratio.

CASE STUDY

The Golden Ratio

Euclid's *Elements*, the Parthenon, the *Mona Lisa*, and the beadwork of the Shoshone tribe all have in common an appreciation for the *golden ratio*.

Suppose we have two quantities A and B, with $A > B > 0$. Then A/B is called the *golden ratio* if

$$\frac{A + B}{A} = \frac{A}{B}$$

that is, if the ratio of the sum of the quantities to the larger quantity equals the ratio of the larger to the smaller (see Figure 9.32).

Euclid wrote about the golden ratio in his *Elements*, calling it the "extreme and mean ratio." The ratio of the width A and height B of the Parthenon, one of the most famous temples in ancient Greece, equals the golden ratio (Figure 9.32). If you enclose the face of Leonardo da Vinci's *Mona Lisa* in a rectangle, the resulting ratio of the long side to the short side follows the golden ratio (Figure 9.33). The golden ratio has a value of approximately 1.618.

Now we will test whether there is evidence for the use of the golden ratio in the artistic traditions of the Shoshone, a Native American tribe from the American West. Figure 9.34 shows a detail of a nineteenth-century Shoshone beaded dress that belonged to Nahtoma, the daughter of Chief Washakie of the Eastern Shoshone.[11] It is intriguing to consider whether Shoshone beaded rectangles such as those on this dress follow the golden ratio.

William R. McIver Collection, American Heritage Center, University of Wyoming.

FIGURE 9.34 Beaded dress of Nahtoma, daughter of Chief Washakie, showing rectangles that may follow the golden ratio.

Table 9.10 contains the ratios of lengths to widths of 18 beaded rectangles made by Shoshone artisans.[12] We will perform a hypothesis test to determine whether the population mean ratio of Shoshone beaded rectangles equals the golden ratio of 1.618.

Shoshone

Table 9.10 Ratio of length to width of a sample of Shoshone beaded rectangles

1.44300	1.75439	1.64204	1.66389	1.63666
1.51057	1.33511	1.52905	1.73611	1.80832
1.44928	1.48810	1.62602	1.49254	
1.65017	1.59236	1.49701	1.65017	

Since the population standard deviation for such rectangles is unknown, we must use a *t* test rather than a *Z* test. Our sample size $n = 18$ is not large, so we must assess whether the data are normally distributed. Figure 9.35 shows the normal probability plot indicating acceptable support for the normality assumption. We proceed with the *t* test, using level of significance $\alpha = 0.05$.

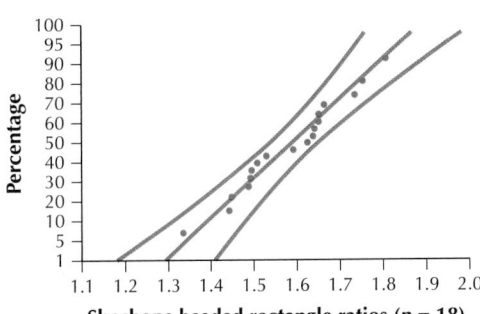

FIGURE 9.35
Normal probability plot.

Solution

We use the TI-83/84 to perform this hypothesis test, using the Step-by-Step Technology Guide at the end of this section.

FIGURE 9.36 TI-83/84 results.

Step 1 **State the hypotheses and the rejection rule.** Since we are interested in whether the population mean length-to-width ratio of Shoshone beaded rectangles *equals* the golden ratio of 1.618, we perform a two-tailed test:

$$H_0 : \mu = 1.618 \quad \text{versus} \quad H_a : \mu \neq 1.618$$

where μ represents the population mean length-to-width ratio of Shoshone beaded rectangles. We will reject H_0 if the *p*-value ≤ 0.05.

Step 2 **Find t_{data}.** From Figure 9.36, we have $t_{\text{data}} \approx -1.1822$

Step 3 **Find the *p*-value.** From Figure 9.36, we have *p*-value $\approx 0.1267 + 0.1267 = 0.2534$ (Figure 9.37).

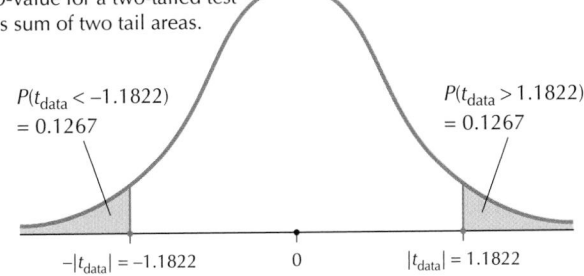

FIGURE 9.37
p-Value for *t* test.

Step 4 **State the conclusion and interpretation.** Since *p*-value ≈ 0.2534 is *not* $\leq \alpha = 0.05$, we do *not* reject H_0. Thus, there is insufficient evidence at level of significance $\alpha = 0.05$ that the population mean ratio differs from 1.618. In other words, the data do not reject the claim that Shoshone beaded rectangles follow the same golden ratio exhibited by the Parthenon and the *Mona Lisa*. ∎

STEP-BY-STEP TECHNOLOGY GUIDE: *t* test for μ

We will use the nurse-to-patient ratio data from Example 9.16 (page 459).

TI-83/84

If you have the data values:
Step 1 Enter the data into list **L1**.
Step 2 Press **STAT**, highlight **TESTS**, and press **ENTER**.
Step 3 Press **2** (for **T-Test**; see Figure 9.38).
Step 4 For input (**Inpt**), highlight **Data** and press **ENTER** (Figure 9.39).
a. For μ_0, enter the value of μ_0, **1.6**.
b. For **List**, press **2nd**, then **L1**.
c. For **Freq**, enter **1**.
d. For μ, select the form of H_a. Here we have a two-tailed test, so highlight $\neq \mu_0$ and press **ENTER** (Figure 9.39).
e. Highlight **Calculate** and press **ENTER**. The results are shown in Figure 9.28 in Example 9.16.

If you have the summary statistics:
Step 1 Press **STAT**, highlight **TESTS**, and press **ENTER**.
Step 2 Press **2** (for **T-Test**; see Figure 9.38).
Step 3 For input (**Inpt**), highlight **Stats** and press **ENTER** (Figure 9.40).
a. For μ_0, enter the value of μ_0, **1.6**.
b. For **Sx**, enter the value of s, **0.549343042**.
c. For $\bar{x}$, enter the sample mean **2.02**.
d. For **n**, enter the sample size **10**.
e. For μ, select the form of H_a. Here we have a two-tailed test, so highlight $\neq \mu_0$ and press **ENTER** (Figure 9.40).
f. Highlight **Calculate** and press **ENTER**. The results are shown in Figure 9.28 in Example 9.16.

FIGURE 9.38

FIGURE 9.39

FIGURE 9.40

EXCEL

WHFStat Add-ins
Step 1 Enter the data into column A. (If you have only the summary statistics, go to Step 2.)
Step 2 Load the **WHFStat Add-ins**.
Step 3 Select **Add-Ins > Macros > Testing a Mean > t Test − Confidence Interval − One Sample**.

Step 4 Select cells A1 to A10 as the **Dataset Range**. (Alternatively, you may enter the summary statistics.)
Step 5 Select your **Confidence level**, which should be $1 - \alpha$. Here, because $\alpha = 0.05$, we select **95%**.
Step 6 Enter the **Null Hypothesis Value**, $\mu_0 = $ **1.6**, and click **OK**.

MINITAB

If you have the data values:
Step 1 Enter the data into column C1.
Step 2 Click **Stat > Basic Statistics > 1-Sample t**.
Step 3 Click **Samples in Columns** and select **C1**.
Step 4 For **Test Mean**, enter **1.6**.
Step 5 Click **Options**.
a. Choose your **Confidence Level** as $100(1 - \alpha)$. Our level of significance α here is 0.05, so the confidence level is 95.0.
b. Select **not Equal** for the **Alternative**.
Step 6 Click **OK** and click **OK** again.

If you have the summary statistics:
Step 1 Click **Stat > Basic Statistics > 1-Sample t**.
Step 2 Click **Summarized Data**.
Step 3 Enter the **Sample Size 10**, the **Sample Mean 2.02**, and the **Sample Standard Deviation 0.549343042**.
Step 4 Click **Options**.
a. Choose your **Confidence Level** as $100(1 - \alpha)$. Our level of significance α here is 0.05, so the confidence level is 95.0.
b. Select **not Equal** for the two-tailed test.
Step 5 Click **OK** and click **OK** again.

CRUNCHIT!

If you have the data values:
Step 1 Click **File . . .** then highlight **Load from Larose2e . . . Chapter 9 . . .** and click on **Example 9.16**.
Step 2 Click **Statistics . . . t** and select **1-sample**. With the **Columns** tab chosen, for **Sample** select **Index**.
Step 3 Select the **Hypothesis Test** tab. For **Mean under null hypothesis**, enter **1.6**. For **Alternative** select **Two-sided**. Then click **Calculate**.

If you have the summary statistics:
Step 1 Click **File . . .** then highlight **Load from Larose2e . . . Chapter 9 . . .** and click on **Example 9.16**.
Step 2 Click **Statistics . . . t** and select **1-sample**.
Step 3 Choose the **Summarized** tab. For **n** enter the sample size **10**; for **Sample Mean** enter **2.02**. For **Standard Deviation**, enter **0.549343042**.
Step 4 Select the **Hypothesis Test** tab. For **Mean under null hypothesis**, enter **1.6**. For **Alternative** select **Two-sided**. Then click **Calculate**.

Section 9.4 Summary

1 The test statistic used for the *t* test for the mean is

$$t_{\text{data}} = \frac{\bar{x} - \mu_0}{s/\sqrt{n}}$$

with $n - 1$ degrees of freedom. The *t* test may be used under either of the following conditions: (a) the population is normal, or (b) the sample size is large ($n \geq 30$). For the

critical-value method, we compare the values of t_{data} and t_{crit}. If t_{data} falls in the critical region, we reject H_0.

2 For the *p*-value method, we reject H_0 if the *p*-value $\leq \alpha$.

3 We may use $100(1 - \alpha)\%$ *t* confidence interval to perform two-tailed *t* tests at level of significance α for various values of μ_0.

Section 9.4 Exercises

CLARIFYING THE CONCEPTS
1. What assumption is required for performing the Z test that is not required for the *t* test?
2. What do we use to estimate the unknown population standard deviation σ?

PRACTICING THE TECHNIQUES
For Exercises 3–14, do the following.
  a. State the hypotheses.
  b. Calculate the *t* critical value t_{crit} and state the rejection rule. Also, sketch the critical region.
  c. Find the test statistic t_{data}.
  d. State the conclusion and the interpretation.
3. $H_0: \mu = 22$ vs. $H_a: \mu < 22, \bar{x} = 20, s = 4, n = 31, \alpha = 0.05$
4. $H_0: \mu = 3$ vs. $H_a: \mu < 3, \bar{x} = 2, s = 1, n = 41, \alpha = 0.10$
5. $H_0: \mu = 11$ vs. $H_a: \mu > 11, \bar{x} = 12, s = 3, n = 16, \alpha = 0.01$, population is normal
6. $H_0: \mu = 80$ vs. $H_a: \mu > 80, \bar{x} = 82, s = 5, n = 9, \alpha = 0.05$, population is normal
7. A random sample of size 25 from a normal population yields $\bar{x} = 104$ and $s = 10$. Researchers are interested in finding whether the population mean exceeds 100, using level of significance $\alpha = 0.01$.
8. A random sample of size 100 from a population with an unknown distribution yields a sample mean of -5 and a sample standard deviation of 5. Researchers are interested in finding whether the population mean is less than -4, using level of significance $\alpha = 0.05$.
9. $H_0: \mu = 102$ vs. $H_a: \mu \neq 102, \bar{x} = 106, s = 10, n = 81, \alpha = 0.05$
10. $H_0: \mu = 95$ vs. $H_a: \mu \neq 95, \bar{x} = 99, s = 10, n = 31, \alpha = 0.01$
11. $H_0: \mu = 1000$ vs. $H_a: \mu \neq 1000, \bar{x} = 975, s = 100, n = 25, \alpha = 0.10$, population is normal
12. $H_0: \mu = -10$ vs. $H_a: \mu \neq -10, \bar{x} = -8, s = 5, n = 25, \alpha = 0.05$, population is normal
13. A random sample of size 36 from a population with an unknown distribution yields $\bar{x} = 10$ and $s = 3$. Researchers are interested in finding whether the population mean differs from 9, using level of significance $\alpha = 0.10$.

14. A random sample of size 16 from a normal population yields $\bar{x} = 995$ and $s = 15$. Researchers are interested in finding whether the population mean differs from 1000, using level of significance $\alpha = 0.01$.

For Exercises 15–26, do the following.
  a. State the hypotheses and the rejection rule using the *p*-value method.
  b. Calculate the test statistic t_{data}.
  c. Find the *p*-value. (Use technology or estimate the *p*-value.)
  d. State the conclusion and the interpretation.
15. $H_0: \mu = 10$ vs. $H_a: \mu < 10, \bar{x} = 7, s = 5, n = 81, \alpha = 0.01$
16. $H_0: \mu = 50$ vs. $H_a: \mu < 50, \bar{x} = 42, s = 8, n = 41, \alpha = 0.05$
17. $H_0: \mu = 100$ vs. $H_a: \mu > 100, \bar{x} = 120, s = 50, n = 25, \alpha = 0.10$, population is normal
18. $H_0: \mu = 3.0$ vs. $H_a: \mu > 3.0, \bar{x} = 3.2, s = 0.5, n = 25, \alpha = 0.05$, population is normal
19. A random sample of size 400 from a population with an unknown distribution yields a sample mean of 230 and a sample standard deviation of 5. Researchers are interested in finding whether the population mean is greater than 200, using level of significance $\alpha = 0.05$.
20. A random sample of size 100 from a population with an unknown distribution yields $\bar{x} = 27$ and $s = 10$. Researchers are interested in finding whether the population mean is less than 28, using level of significance $\alpha = 0.05$.
21. $H_0: \mu = 25$ vs. $H_a: \mu \neq 25, \bar{x} = 25, s = 1, n = 31, \alpha = 0.01$
22. $H_0: \mu = 98.6$ vs. $H_a: \mu \neq 98.6, \bar{x} = 99, s = 10, n = 81, \alpha = 0.05$
23. $H_0: \mu = 3.14$ vs. $H_a: \mu \neq 3.14, \bar{x} = 3.17, s = 0.5, n = 9, \alpha = 0.10$, population is normal
24. $H_0: \mu = 2.72$ vs. $H_a: \mu \neq 2.72, \bar{x} = 2.57, s = 0.1, n = 25, \alpha = 0.05$, population is normal
25. A random sample of size 9 from a normal population yields $\bar{x} = 1$ and $s = 0.5$. Researchers are interested in finding whether the population mean differs from 0, using level of significance $\alpha = 0.05$.

26. A random sample of size 16 from a normal population yields $\bar{x} = 2.2$ and $s = 0.3$. Researchers are interested in finding whether the population mean differs from 2.0, using level of significance $\alpha = 0.01$.

For Exercises 27–30, use the t table to estimate the p-value for the hypothesis tests in the indicated exercises.
27. Exercise 3
28. Exercise 4
29. Exercise 9
30. Exercise 10

For Exercises 31–36, a $100(1 - \alpha)\%$ t confidence interval is given. Use the confidence interval to test using level of significance α whether μ differs from each of the indicated hypothesized values.
31. A 95% t confidence interval for μ is $(1, 4)$. Hypothesized values μ_0 are
    a. 0   **b.** 2   **c.** 5
32. A 99% t confidence interval for μ is $(57, 58)$. Hypothesized values μ_0 are
    a. 55.5   **b.** 59.5   **c.** 57.5
33. A 90% t confidence interval for μ is $(-20, -10)$. Hypothesized values μ_0 are
    a. -21 **b.** -5 **c.** -12
34. A 95% t confidence interval for μ is $(2010, 2015)$. Hypothesized values μ_0 are
    a. 2012   **b.** 2007   **c.** 2014
35. A 95% t confidence interval for μ is $(-1, 1)$. Hypothesized values μ_0 are
    a. 1.5   **b.** -1.5 **c.** 0
36. A 95% t confidence interval for μ is $(19,570, 20,105)$. Hypothesized values μ_0 are
    a. 20,000   **b.** 21,000   **c.** 19,571

APPLYING THE CONCEPTS
37. Health Care Costs. The U.S. Agency for Healthcare Research and Quality (www.ahrq.gov) reports that, in 2010, the mean cost of a stay in the hospital for American women aged 18–44 was $15,200. A random sample of 400 hospital stays of women aged 18–44 showed a mean cost of $16,000, with a standard deviation of $5000. Test whether the population mean cost has increased since 2010, using level of significance $\alpha = 0.05$.
38. iPhone Apps. According to a 2010 Nielsen survey,[13] the mean number of apps downloaded by iPhone users is 40. Suppose a sample of 36 iPhone users downloaded an average of 45 apps, with a standard deviation of 24. Test whether the population mean number of apps is greater than 40, using level of significance $\alpha = 0.10$.
39. Facebook Friends. According to Facebook.com, the mean number of Facebook friends is 130. Suppose a sample of 100 Facebook users has a mean number of 110 Facebook friends, with a standard deviation of 50. Test whether the population mean number of Facebook friends is less than 130, using level of significance $\alpha = 0.05$.

40. Small Business Employees. The U.S. Census Bureau reports that the average number of employees in a small business is 16.1. Suppose a sample of 49 small businesses showed a mean of 15 employees, with a standard deviation of 25. Test whether the population mean number of employees in a small business is different from 16.1, using level of significance $\alpha = 0.01$.

Internet Response Times. Use the following information for Exercises 41–42. The Web site www.Internettrafficreport.com monitors Internet traffic worldwide and reports on the response times of randomly selected servers.
41. On June 6, 2011, the Web site reported the following response times to Asia, in milliseconds:

165 175 2221 872 311 127 195 1801 769 225 261 249 421

We would like to test whether the population mean response time is slower than 180 milliseconds, using a t test and level of significance $\alpha = 0.05$. A boxplot of the data is provided.

(*Hint:* The boxplot is right-skewed and the normal distribution is symmetric.) Can we proceed with the t test? Explain.
42. On June 6, 2011, the Web site reported the following response times to Asia, in milliseconds:

61 32 50 73 51 42 55 65 59 57 76 77 67 71

The normal probability plot of the data is also shown. We would like to perform a t test.
    a. Are the conditions for performing the t test satisfied? Explain how.
    b. Test using level of significance $\alpha = 0.05$ whether the population mean response time is less than 60 milliseconds.
    c. Explain why we can't use a Z test for this problem.

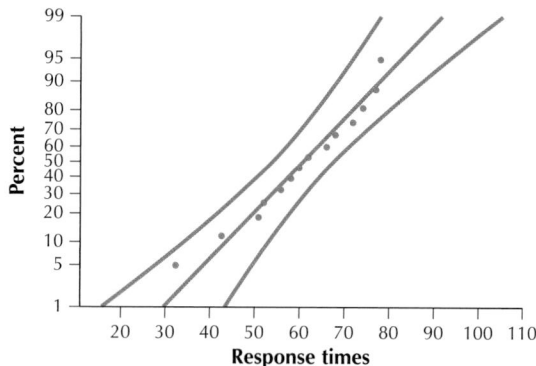

Obsession. Use the following information for Exercises 43–45. Perfume.com listed Obsession by Calvin Klein as its fifth best-selling fragrance for the 2006 holiday season. The mean price per bottle in 2006 was $46.42, according to the NPD Group. Suppose a random sample of 15 retail establishments yielded a mean retail price for Obsession this year of $48.92, with a standard deviation of $2.50. Assume these prices are normally distributed.

43. We are interested in whether the population mean price for Obsession perfume has increased.
  a. Is it appropriate to apply the *t* test for the mean? Why or why not?
  b. We have a sample mean of $48.92, which is greater than the mean of $46.42 in the null hypothesis. Isn't this enough by itself to reject the null hypothesis? Explain why or why not.
  c. Perform the appropriate hypothesis test at level of significance $\alpha = 0.01$.

44. Answer the following.
  a. Assess the strength of the evidence against the null hypothesis.
  b. What value of α, if any, would be necessary to alter the conclusion in your hypothesis test?
  c. What value of α, if any, would alter the strength of the evidence against H_0?

45. Try to answer the following questions by thinking about the relationship between the statistics rather than by redoing all the calculations. *What if* the sample size was not 15 but rather some number greater than 15. Otherwise, everything else remains unchanged. How does this affect the following?
  a. $s/\sqrt{n}$
  b. t_{data}
  c. t_{crit}
  d. The *p*-value
  e. The conclusion
  f. The strength of the evidence against the null hypothesis
  g. Write a sentence summarizing what happens to the elements in **(a)–(f)** when the sample size increases.

Top Gas Mileage. Use the following information for Exercises 46–48. The top ten vehicles for city gas mileage in 2007, as reported by the Environmental Protection Agency, are shown in the following table, along with the normal probability plot. **topmileage**

Car	Mileage	Car	Mileage
Toyota Yaris	39	Honda Fit	38
Chevrolet Aveo	37	Nissan Versa	34
Pontiac G5	34	Dodge Caliber	32
VW Eos	32	Ford Escape	31
Saturn Sky	30	BMW 525	30

Normal probability plot.

46. We are interested in testing whether the population mean city mileage of such cars is greater than 30 mpg.
  a. Is it appropriate to apply the *t* test for the mean? Why or why not?
  b. Test, using the estimated *p*-value method at level of significance $\alpha = 0.01$, whether the population mean city mileage exceeds 30 mpg.

47. Answer the following.
  a. Repeat your test from Exercise 46(**b**), this time using level of significance $\alpha = 0.001$.
  b. How do you think we should resolve the apparent contradiction in 46(**b**) and part (**a**) of this exercise?
  c. Assess the strength of the evidence against the null hypothesis. Does this change depend on which level of α you use?

48. *What if* we changed μ_0 to some larger value (though still smaller than $\bar{x}$). Otherwise, everything else remains unchanged. Describe how this change would affect the following, if at all.
  a. t_{data}
  b. t_{crit}
  c. The *p*-value
  d. The conclusion from Exercise 46(**b**)
  e. The conclusion from Exercise 47(**a**)
  f. The strength of the evidence against the null hypothesis

BRINGING IT ALL TOGETHER
Community College Tuition. Use the following information for Exercises 49–51. The College Board reported that the mean tuition and fees at community colleges nationwide in 2006 was $2272. Data were gathered on the total tuition and fees for a random sample of ten community colleges this year. The normal probability plot and Minitab *t* test output are shown here.

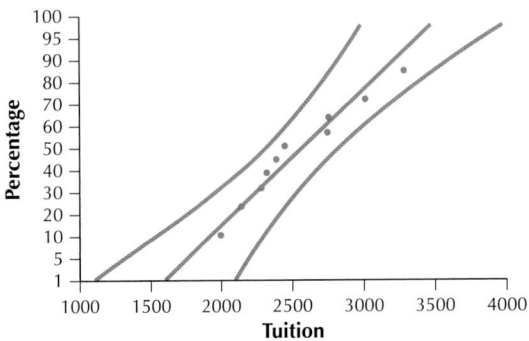

Normal probability plot.

```
Test of mu = 2272 vs not = 2272

Variable   N    Mean    StDev   SE Mean      95% CI            T      P
tuition    10  2538.92  404.75  127.99   (2249.38, 2828.46)  2.09  0.067
```

Minitab *t* test output.

49. Analysts are interested in whether the population mean tuition and fees this year have increased.
  a. Is it appropriate to apply the *t* test for the mean? Why or why not?
  b. What are the sample size, sample mean cost, and sample standard deviation of the cost?
  c. Verify the value for the standard error of the mean.
  d. Find t_{data} in the Minitab output. Interpret t_{data} using the standard error.
  e. It appears that the data analyst who produced the Minitab printout asked for the wrong hypothesis test. How can we tell?

50. Refer to your work in the previous exercise.
  a. Test whether the population mean tuition and fees have increased using level of significance $\alpha = 0.05$. How can we use the *p*-value on the Minitab printout to find the *p*-value needed for this right-tailed hypothesis test?
  b. Compare the conclusion from **(a)** with the conclusion we would have gotten had we not noticed that the data analyst performed the wrong hypothesis test. What are some of the possible consequences of making an error of this sort?
  c. Based on your experiences in these exercises, write a sentence about the importance of understanding the statistical modeling behind the "point and click" power of statistical software.

51. Challenge Exercise. Refer to your work in the previous exercise.
  a. Note that we have concluded that there is insufficient evidence that the population mean cost has changed, but that there is evidence that the population mean cost has increased. How can the mean cost have increased without changing? Explain what is going on here, in terms of either critical regions or *p*-values.
  b. Assess the strength of the evidence against the null hypothesis for the test in Exercise 50(a).
  c. Suppose a newspaper story referred to the study under the headline "College Costs Rising." How would you respond? Is the headline supported or not supported by the data and the hypothesis test?

Marriage Age. Use the following information for Exercises 52–55. The U.S. Census Bureau reported that the median age at first marriage for females in 2003 was 25.3.

Let's assume that the mean age at first marriage among females in 2003 was 25.3 years old. A random sample of 157 females this year yielded a mean age at first marriage of 26.5 with a standard deviation of 4 years. A histogram of the ages was decidedly not normal.

52. Answer the following.
  a. Is it appropriate to apply the *t* test for the mean? Why or why not?
  b. Is there evidence that the population mean age at first marriage for females differs from 25.3? Test using the critical-value method at level of significance $\alpha = 0.10$.

53. Test using level of significance $\alpha = 0.10$ whether the population mean age at first marriage for females >25.3.

54. Challenge Exercise.
  a. Compare your conclusions in the previous two exercises. Note that we have concluded that there is insufficient evidence that the population mean marriage age has changed, but that there is evidence that the population mean marriage age has increased. How can the mean marriage age have increased without changing? Explain what is going on here, in terms of either critical regions or *p*-values.
  b. For which of the two hypothesis tests is the test statistic closer to the critical value?

55. Answer the following.
  a. Find or estimate the *p*-value for the test in Exercise 52(**b**).
  b. Assess the strength of the evidence against the null hypothesis for the test in Exercise 52(**b**).
  c. Is the *p*-value closer to 0.05 or 0.10? Why?
  d. Suppose a newspaper story referred to the study under the headline "Mean Female Marriage Age Increasing." How would you respond? Is the headline supported or not supported by the data and the hypothesis test?

56. New York Towns. Work with the **New York** data set for the following. **New York**
  a. Use technology to find the summary statistics for the variable *tot_pop*, which lists the population for each of the towns and cities in New York with at least 1000 people.
  b. Suppose we are using the data in this data set as a sample of the population of all the towns and cities in the northeastern United States with at least 1000 people. Use technology to test at level of significance $\alpha = 0.05$ whether the population mean population of these towns differs from 50,000.

9.5 Z Test for the Population Proportion

OBJECTIVES By the end of this section, I will be able to . . .

1   Perform the Z test for *p* using the critical-value method.

2   Carry out the Z test for *p* using the *p*-value method.

3   Use confidence intervals for *p* to perform two-tailed hypothesis tests about *p*.

1 The *Z* Test for *p* Using the Critical-Value Method

For example, if a baseball player has $x = 30$ hits in $n = 100$ at-bats, his batting average is $\hat{p} = x/n = 30/100 = 0.3$ (or .300).

Thus far, we have dealt with testing hypotheses about the population mean μ only. In this section, we will learn how to perform the *Z* test for the population proportion *p*.

For our point estimate of the unknown population proportion *p*, we use the sample proportion $\hat{p} = x/n$, where *x* equals the number of successes.

Just as with the *Z* test for the mean, in the *Z* test for the proportion the null hypothesis will include a certain hypothesized value for the unknown parameter, which we call p_0. For example, the hypotheses for the two-tailed test have the following form:

$$H_0 : p = p_0 \quad \text{versus} \quad H_a : p \neq p_0$$

where p_0 represents a particular hypothesized value of the unknown population proportion *p*. For instance, if a researcher is interested in determining whether the population proportion of Americans who support increased funding for higher education differs from 50%, then $p_0 = 0.50$.

If we assume H_0 is correct, then the population proportion of successes is p_0. Then Facts 5 and 6 from Section 7.3 tell us that the sampling distribution of *p* has a mean of p_0 and the standard deviation

$$\sigma_{\hat{p}} = \sqrt{\frac{p(1-p)}{n}} = \sqrt{\frac{p_0(1-p_0)}{n}}$$

since we claim in H_0 that $p = p_0$. $\sigma_{\hat{p}}$ is called the **standard error of the proportion.** Fact 7 from Section 7.3 tells us that the sampling distribution of $\hat{p}$ is approximately normal whenever both of the following conditions are met: $np \geq 5$ and $n(1-p) \geq 5$. This leads us to the following statement of the **essential idea about hypothesis testing for the proportion.**

The Essential Idea About Hypothesis Testing for the Proportion

When the sample proportion $\hat{p}$ is unusual or extreme in the sampling distribution of $\hat{p}$ that is based on the assumption that H_0 is correct, we reject H_0. Otherwise, there is insufficient evidence against H_0, and we should not reject H_0.

The remainder of this section explains the details of implementing hypothesis testing for the proportion. The critical-value method for the *Z* test for *p* is similar to that of the *Z* test for μ, in that we compare one *Z*-value (Z_{data}) with another *Z*-value (Z_{crit}). In this section, Z_{data} represents the number of standard errors ($\sigma_{\hat{p}}$) the sample proportion $\hat{p}$ lies above or below the hypothesized proportion p_0.

The test statistic used for the *Z* test for the proportion is

$$Z_{\text{data}} = \frac{\hat{p} - p_0}{\sqrt{\dfrac{p_0(1-p_0)}{n}}}$$

where $\hat{p}$ is the observed sample proportion of successes, p_0 is the value of *p* hypothesized in H_0, and *n* is the sample size.

Now You Can Do
Exercises 7–14.

To find the t_{crit} critical values, the critical regions, or the rejection rules, you can use Table 9.11.

Table 9.11 Table of critical values Z_{crit} for common values of the level of significance α

Level of significance α	Form of Hypothesis Test		
	Right-tailed $H_0: p = p_0$ $H_a: p > p_0$	**Left-tailed** $H_0: p = p_0$ $H_a: p < p_0$	**Two-tailed** $H_0: p = p_0$ $H_a: p \neq p_0$
0.10	$Z_{crit} = 1.28$	$Z_{crit} = -1.28$	$Z_{crit} = 1.645$
0.05	$Z_{crit} = 1.645$	$Z_{crit} = -1.645$	$Z_{crit} = 1.96$
0.01	$Z_{crit} = 2.33$	$Z_{crit} = -2.33$	$Z_{crit} = 2.58$
Rejection rule	Reject H_0 if $Z_{data} \geq Z_{crit}$	Reject H_0 if $Z_{data} \leq Z_{crit}$	Reject H_0 if $Z_{data} \leq -Z_{crit}$ or $Z_{data} \geq Z_{crit}$

Example 9.19 Calculating Z_{data} for the Z test for the proportion

The Centers for Disease Control and Prevention reported in 2010 that 20% of Americans smoked tobacco.[14] A random sample of $n = 400$ Americans found 76 who smoked. We are interested in testing whether the population proportion of Americans who smoke has changed from 20%. Calculate the test statistic Z_{data}.

Solution

The key words "has changed" indicate a two-tailed test. "Changed from what?" The hypothesized proportion $p_0 = 0.20$. The hypotheses are

$$H_0: p = 0.20 \quad \text{versus} \quad H_a: p \neq 0.20$$

The sample proportion of those who smoke is

$$\hat{p} = \frac{x}{n} = \frac{\text{number in sample who smoke}}{\text{sample size}} = \frac{76}{400} = 0.19$$

We then calculate the value of the test statistic Z_{data}:

$$Z_{data} = \frac{\hat{p} - p_0}{\sqrt{\frac{p_0(1 - p_0)}{n}}} = \frac{0.19 - 0.20}{\sqrt{\frac{0.20(1 - 0.20)}{400}}} = \frac{-0.01}{0.02} = -0.5$$

Now You Can Do
Exercises 7–14.

Z Test for the Population Proportion p: Critical-Value Method

When a random sample of size n is taken from a population, you can use the Z test for the proportion if both of the normality conditions are satisfied:

$$np_0 \geq 5 \quad \text{and} \quad n(1 - p_0) \geq 5$$

Step 1 State the hypotheses.
Use one of the forms from Table 9.11. State the meaning of p.

Step 2 Find Z_{crit} and state the rejection rule.
Use Table 9.11.

Step 3   **Calculate Z_{data}.**

$$Z_{\text{data}} = \frac{\hat{p} - p_0}{\sigma_{\hat{p}}} = \frac{\hat{p} - p_0}{\sqrt{\dfrac{p_0(1 - p_0)}{n}}}$$

Step 4   **State the conclusion and the interpretation.**
If Z_{data} falls in the critical region, then reject H_0. Otherwise, do not reject H_0. Interpret the conclusion so that a nonspecialist can understand.

Example 9.20   *Z* Test for *p* using the critical-value method

Refer to Example 9.19. Test whether the population proportion of Americans who smoke has changed from 20%, using the critical-value method and level of significance $\alpha = 0.10$.

Solution

First we check that both of our normality conditions are met. From Example 9.19, we have $p_0 = 0.20$ and $n = 400$.

$$np_0 = (400)(0.20) = 80 \geq 5 \quad \text{and} \quad n(1 - p_0) = (400)(0.80) = 320 \geq 5$$

The normality conditions are met and we may proceed with the hypothesis test.

As a check on your arithmetic, the two quantities you obtain when checking the normality conditions should add up to *n*. Here 80 + 320 = 400.

Step 1   **State the hypotheses.** From Example 9.19 our hypotheses are

$$H_0 : p = 0.20 \quad \text{versus} \quad H_a : p \neq 0.20$$

where p represents the population proportion of Americans who smoke tobacco.

Step 2   **Find Z_{crit} and state the rejection rule.** We have a two-tailed test, with $\alpha = 0.10$. This gives us our critical value $Z_{\text{crit}} = 1.645$ and the rejection rule from Table 9.11: Reject H_0 if $Z_{\text{data}} \geq 1.645$ or $Z_{\text{data}} \leq -1.645$ (Figure 9.41).

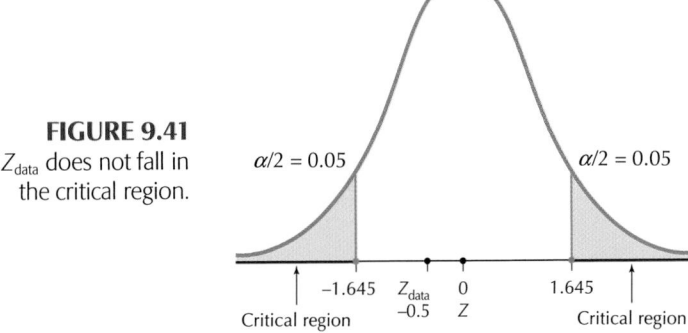

FIGURE 9.41
Z_{data} does not fall in the critical region.

Step 3   **Calculate Z_{data}.** From Example 9.19, we have

$$Z_{\text{data}} = -0.5$$

Step 4   **State the conclusion and the interpretation.** The test statistic $Z_{\text{data}} = -0.5$ is not ≥ 1.645 and not ≤ -1.645. Thus, we do not reject H_0. There is insufficient evidence at level of significance $\alpha = 0.10$ that the population proportion of Americans who smoke tobacco differs from 20%. ∎

Now You Can Do
Exercises 15–18.

2 *Z* Test for *p*: The *p*-Value Method

The *p*-value method for the *Z* test for *p* is equivalent to the critical-value method. The *p*-values are defined similarly to those for the *Z* test for μ, as shown in Table 9.12.

Table 9.12 Finding the p-value depends on the form of the hypothesis test

	Right-tailed test	Left-tailed test	Two-tailed test
Type of hypothesis test	$H_0: p = p_0$ $H_a: p > p_0$	$H_0: p = p_0$ $H_a: p < p_0$	$H_0: p = p_0$ $H_a: p \neq p_0$
p-Value is tail area associated with Z_{data}	p-value $= P(Z > Z_{data})$ Area to right of Z_{data}	p-value $= P(Z < Z_{data})$ Area to left of Z_{data}	p-value $= P(Z > \lvert Z_{data}\rvert)$ $+ P(Z < -\lvert Z_{data}\rvert)$ $= 2 \cdot P(Z > \lvert Z_{data}\rvert)$ Sum of the two tail areas.

Note that the p-value has precisely the same definition and behavior as in the Z test for the mean. That is, the p-value is roughly a measure of how extreme your value of Z_{data} is and takes values between 0 and 1, with small values indicating extreme values of Z_{data}.

Developing Your Statistical Sense

The Difference Between the p-Value and the Population Proportion p

Be careful to distinguish between the p-value and the population proportion p. The latter represents the population proportion of successes for a binomial experiment and is a population parameter. The p-value is the probability of observing a value of Z_{data} at least as extreme as the Z_{data} actually observed. The p-value depends on the sample data, but the population proportion p does not depend on the sample data. ◢

Z Test for the Population Proportion p: p-Value Method

When a random sample of size n is taken from a population, you can use the Z test for the proportion if both of the normality conditions are satisfied:

$$np_0 \geq 5 \quad \text{and} \quad n(1 - p_0) \geq 5$$

Step 1 State the hypotheses and the rejection rule.
Use one of the forms from Table 9.12. State the meaning of p. State the rejection rule as "Reject H_0 when the p-value $\leq \alpha$."

Step 2 Calculate Z_{data}.

$$Z_{data} = \frac{\hat{p} - p_0}{\sqrt{\dfrac{p_0(1 - p_0)}{n}}}$$

Step 3 Find the p-value.
Either use technology to find the p-value, or calculate it using the form in Table 9.12 that corresponds to your hypotheses.

Step 4 State the conclusion and the interpretation.
If the p-value $\leq \alpha$, then reject H_0. Otherwise do not reject H_0. Interpret your conclusion so that a nonspecialist can understand.

Example 9.21   Z test for p using the p-value method

The National Transportation Safety Board publishes statistics on the number of automobile crashes that people in various age groups have. Young people aged 18–24 have an accident rate of 12%, meaning that on average 12 out of every 100 young drivers per year had an accident. A researcher claims that the population proportion of young drivers having accidents is greater than 12%. Her study examined 1000 young drivers aged 18–24 and found that 134 had an accident this year. Perform the appropriate hypothesis test using the p-value method with level of significance $\alpha = 0.05$.

Solution

First we check that both of our normality conditions are met. Since we are interested in whether the proportion has increased from 12%, we have $p_0 = 0.12$.

$$np_0 = (1000)(0.12) = 120 \geq 5 \quad \text{and} \quad n(1 - p_0) = (1000)(0.88) = 880 \geq 5$$

The normality conditions are met and we may proceed with the hypothesis test.

Step 1   **State the hypotheses and the rejection rule.** Our hypotheses are

$$H_0 : p = 0.12 \quad \text{versus} \quad H_a : p > 0.12$$

where p represents the population proportion of young people aged 18–24 who had an accident. We reject the null hypothesis if the p-value $\leq \alpha = 0.05$.

Step 2   **Calculate Z_{data}.** Our sample proportion is $\hat{p} = 134/1000 = 0.134$. Since $p_0 = 0.12$, the standard error of $\hat{p}$ is

We report Z_{data} to 2 decimal places to allow the use of the Z table to calculate the p-value.

$$\sigma_{\hat{p}} = \sqrt{\frac{p_0(1 - p_0)}{n}} = \sqrt{\frac{(0.12)(0.88)}{1000}} \approx 0.0103$$

Thus, our test statistic is

$$Z_{\text{data}} = \frac{\hat{p} - p_0}{\sqrt{\frac{p_0(1 - p_0)}{n}}} = \frac{0.134 - 12}{\sqrt{\frac{(0.12)(0.88)}{1000}}} \approx 1.36$$

That is, the sample proportion $\hat{p} = 0.134$ lies approximately 1.36 standard errors above the hypothesized proportion $p_0 = 0.12$.

Step 3   **Find the p-value.** Since we have a right-tailed test, our p-value from Table 9.12 is $P(Z > Z_{\text{data}})$. This is a Case 2 problem from Table 6.6 (page 303), where we find the tail area by subtracting the Z table area from 1 (Figure 9.42):

$$P(Z > Z_{\text{data}}) = P(Z > 1.36) = 1 - 0.9131 = 0.0869$$

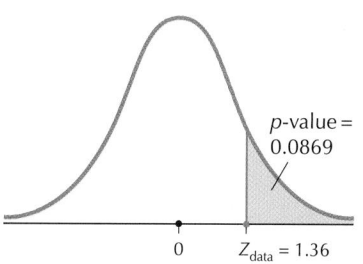

FIGURE 9.42 p-Value for a right-tailed test equals area to right of Z_{data}.

Step 4   **State the conclusion and the interpretation.** Since the p-value is not $\leq \alpha = 0.05$, we do not reject H_0. There is insufficient evidence that the population proportion of young people aged 18–24 who had an accident has increased. ■

Now You Can Do
Exercises 19–22.

Example 9.22   Performing the Z test for p using technology

A study reported that 1% of American Internet users who are married or in a long-term relationship met on a blind date or through a dating service.[15] A survey of 500 American Internet users who are married or in a long-term relationship found 8 who met on a blind date or through a dating service. If appropriate, test whether the population proportion has increased. Use the p-value method with level of significance $\alpha = 0.05$.

Solution

We have $p_0 = 0.01$ and $n = 500$. Checking the normality conditions, we have

$$np_0 = (500)(0.01) = 5 \geq 5 \quad \text{and} \quad n(1 - p_0) = (500)(0.99) = 495 \geq 5$$

The normality conditions are met and we may proceed with the hypothesis test.

Step 1 **State the hypotheses and the rejection rule.** Our hypotheses are

$$H_0: p = 0.01 \quad \text{versus} \quad H_a: p > 0.01$$

where p represents the population proportion of American Internet users who are married or in a long-term relationship and who met on a blind date or through a dating service. We will reject H_0 if the p-value ≤ 0.05.

Step 2 **Calculate Z_{data}.** We use the instructions supplied in the Step-by-Step Technology Guide on page 476. Figure 9.43 shows the TI-83/84 results from the Z test for p, and Figure 9.44 shows the results from Minitab.

Form of H_a: ⎯⎯⎯⎯⎯⎯⎯⎯⎯⎯⎯
Z_{data} ⎯⎯⎯⎯⎯⎯⎯⎯⎯⎯⎯⎯
p-value ⎯⎯⎯⎯⎯⎯⎯⎯⎯⎯⎯
Sample proportion $\hat{p}$ ⎯⎯⎯⎯
Sample size n ⎯⎯⎯⎯⎯⎯⎯

```
1-PropZTest
 prop>.01
 z=1.348399725
 p=.0887649866
 p̂=.016
 n=500
```

FIGURE 9.43 TI-83/84 results.

```
Test of p = 0.01 vs p > 0.01
                          95%
                         Lower
Sample  X    N  Sample p  Bound    Z-Value  P-Value
1       8  500  0.016000  0.006770    1.35    0.089
        X    n     p̂    (not used)  Z_data  p-value
```

FIGURE 9.44 Minitab results.

We have

$$Z_{\text{data}} = \frac{\hat{p} - p_0}{\sqrt{\dfrac{p_0(1 - p_0)}{n}}} = \frac{0.016 - 0.01}{\sqrt{\dfrac{(0.01)(0.99)}{500}}} \approx 1.348399725$$

which concurs with the TI-83/84 results in Figure 9.43.

Step 3 **Find the p-value.** From Figures 9.43, 9.44, and 9.45, we have

$$p\text{-value} = P(Z > 1.348399725) = 0.0887649866 \approx 0.08876$$

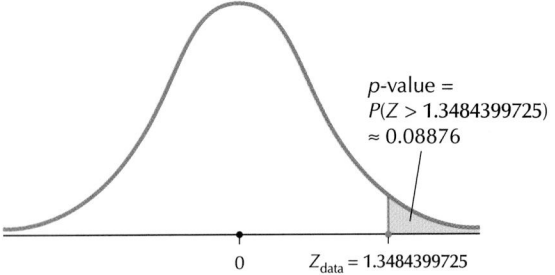

p-value =
$P(Z > 1.3484399725)$
≈ 0.08876

0    $Z_{\text{data}} = 1.3484399725$

FIGURE 9.45 p-Value for a right-tailed test.

Step 4   **State the conclusion and interpretation.** Since *p*-value ≈ 0.08876 is *not* ≤ $\alpha = 0.05$, we do *not* reject H_0. There is insufficient evidence that the population proportion of American Internet users who are married or in a long-term relationship and who met on a blind date or through a dating service has increased. ∎

3 Using Confidence Intervals for *p* to Perform Two-Tailed Hypothesis Tests About *p*

Just as for μ, we can use a $100(1 - \alpha)\%$ confidence interval for the population proportion *p* in order to perform a set of two-tailed hypothesis tests for *p*.

Example 9.23   Using a confidence interval for *p* to perform two-tailed hypothesis tests about *p*

In 2007, the Pew Internet and American Life Project reported that 91% of Americans who have completed a bachelor's degree currently use the Internet. Pew also reports that the margin of error for this survey (confidence level = 95%) was ±3%. The 95% confidence interval for the population proportion of Americans with a bachelor's degree who currently use the Internet is therefore

$$0.91 \pm 0.03 = (0.88, 0.94)$$

Use the confidence interval to test, using level of significance $\alpha = 0.05$, whether the population proportion differs from
a. 0.85   **b.** 0.90   **c.** 0.95

Solution

There is equivalence between a $100(1 - \alpha)\%$ confidence interval for *p* and a two-tailed test for *p* with level of significance α. Values of p_0 that lie outside the confidence interval lead to rejection of the null hypothesis, while values of p_0 within the confidence interval lead to not rejecting the null hypothesis. Figure 9.46 illustrates the 95% confidence interval for *p*.

FIGURE 9.46 H_0 for values p_0 that lie outside the interval (0.88, 0.94).

We would like to perform the following two-tailed hypothesis tests:

a. $H_0 : p = 0.85$ versus $H_a : p \neq 0.85$
b. $H_0 : p = 0.90$ versus $H_a : p \neq 0.90$
c. $H_0 : p = 0.95$ versus $H_a : p \neq 0.95$

To perform each hypothesis test, simply observe where each value of p_0 falls on the number line. For example, in the first hypothesis test, the hypothesized value $p_0 = 0.85$ lies outside the interval (0.88, 0.94). Thus, we reject H_0. The three hypothesis tests are summarized here. ∎

Now You Can Do
Exercises 23–26.

Value of p_0	Form of hypothesis test, with $\alpha = 0.05$		Where p_0 lies in relation to 95% confidence interval	Conclusion of hypothesis test
a. 0.85	$H_0 : p = 0.85$	$H_a : p \neq 0.85$	Outside	Reject H_0
b. 0.90	$H_0 : p = 0.90$	$H_a : p \neq 0.90$	Inside	Do not reject H_0
c. 0.95	$H_0 : p = 0.95$	$H_a : p \neq 0.95$	Outside	Reject H_0

STEP-BY-STEP TECHNOLOGY GUIDE: *Z* test for *p*

We will use the information from Example 9.22 (page 473).

TI-83/84
Step 1 Press **STAT**, highlight **TESTS**, and press **ENTER**.
Step 2 Press 5 (for **1-PropZTest**; see Figure 9.47).
Step 3 For p_0, enter the value of p_0, **0.01**.
Step 4 For **x**, enter the number of successes, **8**.
Step 5 For **n**, enter the number of trials **500**.
Step 6 For **prop**, enter the form of H_a. Here we have a right-tailed test, so highlight **>p_0** and press **ENTER** (see Figure 9.48).
Step 7 Highlight **Calculate** and press **ENTER**. The results are shown in Figure 9.43 in Example 9.22.

FIGURE 9.47   **FIGURE 9.48**

EXCEL
WHFStat Add-ins
Step 1 Enter the data into column A. (If you have only the summary statistics, go to Step 2.)
Step 2 Load the **WHFStat Add-ins**.
Step 3 Select **Add-Ins > Macros > Testing a Proportion > One Sample**.

Step 4 Enter the **Number of successes 8**.
Step 5 Enter the **Sample size 500**.
Step 6 Enter the **Testing Proportion, p_0 = 0.01**.
Step 7 Select your **Confidence level**, which should be $1 - \alpha$. Here, because $\alpha = 0.05$, we select **95%**.
Step 8 Click **OK**.

MINITAB
If you have the summary statistics:
Step 1 Click **Stat > Basic Statistics > 1 Proportion**.
Step 2 Click **Summarized Data**.
Step 3 Enter the **Number of trials 500** and the **Number of Events 8**.
Step 4 Click **Options**.
a. Choose your **Confidence Level** as $100(1 - \alpha)$. Our level of significance α here is 0.05, so the confidence level is 95.0.

b. Enter **0.01** for the **Test Proportion**.
c. Select **Greater than** for the **Alternative**.
d. Check **Use test and interval based on normal distribution**.
Step 5 Click **OK** and click **OK** again. The results are shown in Figure 9.44 in Example 9.22.

CRUNCHIT!
Step 1 Click **File . . .** then highlight **Load from Larose2e . . . Chapter 9 . . .** and click on **Example 9.22**.
Step 2 Click **Statistics . . . Proportion** and select **1-sample**.
Step 3 Choose the **Summarized** tab. For **n** enter the number of trials **500**; for **Successes** enter **8**.

Step 4 Select the **Hypothesis Test** tab. For **Proportion under null hypothesis**, enter **0.01**.
For **Alternative** select **Greater than**. Then click **Calculate**.

Section 9.5 Summary

1 The test statistic used for the *Z* test for the proportion is

$$Z_{\text{data}} = \frac{\hat{p} - p_0}{\sqrt{\dfrac{p_0(1 - p_0)}{n}}}$$

where $\hat{p}$ is the observed sample proportion of successes, p_0 is the value of p hypothesized in H_0, and n is the sample size. Z_{data} represents the number of standard deviations ($\sigma_{\hat{p}}$) the sample proportion $\hat{p}$ lies above or below the hypothesized proportion p_0. Extreme values of $\hat{p}$ will be associated with

extreme values of Z_{data}. The *Z* test for the proportion may be performed using either the *p*-value method or the critical-value method. For the critical-value method, we compare the values of Z_{data} and Z_{crit}. If Z_{data} falls in the critical region, we reject H_0.

2 For the *p*-value method, we reject H_0 if the *p*-value $\leq \alpha$.

3 We can use a single $100(1 - \alpha)\%$ confidence interval for p to help us perform any number of two-tailed hypothesis tests about p with level of significance α.

Section 9.5 Exercises

CLARIFYING THE CONCEPTS

1. What is the difference between $\hat{p}$ and p?
2. What are the conditions for the Z test for p?
3. Explain the essential idea about hypothesis testing for the proportion.
4. Explain what p_0 refers to.
5. What possible values can p_0 take?
6. What is the difference between p and a p-value?

PRACTICING THE TECHNIQUES

For Exercises 7–9, find the value of the test statistic Z_{data} for a right-tailed test with $p_0 = 0.4$.

7. A sample of size 50 yields 30 successes.
8. A sample of size 50 yields 40 successes.
9. A sample of size 50 yields 45 successes.
10. What kind of pattern do we observe in the value of Z_{data} for a right-tailed test as the number of successes becomes more extreme?

For Exercises 11–13, find the value of the test statistic Z_{data} for a two-tailed test with $p_0 = 0.5$.

11. A sample of size 80 yields 20 successes.
12. A sample of size 80 yields 30 successes.
13. A sample of size 80 yields 40 successes.
14. What kind of pattern do we observe in the value of Z_{data} as the sample proportion approaches p_0?

For Exercises 15–18, do the following.
   a. Check the normality conditions.
   b. State the hypotheses.
   c. Find Z_{crit} and the rejection rule.
   d. Calculate Z_{data}.
   e. Compare Z_{crit} with Z_{data}. State the conclusion and the interpretation.

15. Test whether the population proportion is less than 0.5. A random sample of size 225 yields 100 successes. Let level of significance $\alpha = 0.05$.
16. Test whether the population proportion differs from 0.3. A random sample of size 100 yields 25 successes. Let level of significance $\alpha = 0.01$.
17. Test whether the population proportion exceeds 0.6. A random sample of size 400 yields 260 successes. Let level of significance $\alpha = 0.05$.
18. Test whether p differs from 0.4. A random sample of size 900 yields 400 successes. Let level of significance $\alpha = 0.10$.

For Exercises 19–22, do the following.
   a. Check the normality conditions.
   b. State the hypotheses and the rejection rule for the p-value method, using level of significance $\alpha = 0.05$.
   c. Find Z_{data}.
   d. Find the p-value.
   e. Compare the p-value with level of significance $\alpha = 0.05$. State the conclusion and the interpretation.

19. Test whether the population proportion exceeds 0.4. A random sample of size 100 yields 44 successes.
20. Test whether the population proportion is less than 0.2. A random sample of size 400 yields 75 successes.
21. Test whether the population proportion differs from 0.5. A random sample of size 900 yields 475 successes.
22. Test whether the population proportion exceeds 0.9. A random sample of size 1000 yields 925 successes.

For Exercises 23–26, a $100(1 - \alpha)\%$ Z confidence interval for p is given. Use the confidence interval to test using level of significance α whether p differs from each of the indicated hypothesized values.

23. A 95% Z confidence interval for p is $(0.1, 0.9)$. Hypothesized values p_0 are
   a. 0
   b. 1
   c. 0.5
24. A 99% Z confidence interval for p is $(0.51, 0.52)$. Hypothesized values p_0 are
   a. 0.511
   b. 0.521
   c. 0.519
25. A 90% Z confidence interval for p is $(0.1, 0.2)$. Hypothesized values p_0 are
   a. 0.09
   b. 0.9
   c. 0.19
26. A 95% Z confidence interval for p is $(0.05, 0.95)$. Hypothesized values p_0 are
   a. 0.01
   b. 0.5
   c. 0.06

APPLYING THE CONCEPTS

27. **Baptists in America.** A study reported that 17.2% of Americans identified themselves as Baptists.[16] A survey of 500 randomly selected Americans showed that 85 of them were Baptists. If appropriate, test using level of significance $\alpha = 0.10$ whether the population proportion of Americans who are Baptists has changed.

28. **Births to Unmarried Women.** The National Center for Health Statistics reported: "Childbearing by unmarried women increased to record levels for the Nation in 2005."[17] In that year, 36.8% of all births were to unmarried women. Suppose that a random sample taken this year of 1000 births showed 380 to unmarried women. If appropriate, test whether the population proportion has increased since 2005, using level of significance $\alpha = 0.05$.

29. **Twenty-Somethings.** According to the U.S. Census Bureau, 7.1% of Americans living in 2004 were between the ages of 20 and 24. Suppose that a random sample of 400 Americans taken this year yields 35 between the ages of 20 and 24. If appropriate, test whether the population proportion of Americans aged 20–24 is different from the 2004 proportion. Use level of significance $\alpha = 0.01$.

30. Nonmedical Pain Reliever Use. The National Survey on Drug Use and Health reported that 4.8% of persons aged 12 or older used a prescription pain reliever nonmedically.[18] Suppose that a random sample of 900 persons aged 12 or older found 54 that had used a prescription pain reliever nonmedically. If appropriate, test whether the population proportion has increased, using level of significance $\alpha = 0.01$.

31. Ethnic Asians in California. A research report states that 12.3% of California residents were of Asian ethnicity.[19] Suppose that a random sample of 400 California residents yields 52 of Asian ethnicity. We are interested in whether the population proportion of California residents of Asian ethnicity has risen.
   a. Is it appropriate to perform the Z test for the proportion? Why or why not?
   b. How many standard errors does $\hat{p}$ lie above p_0? Is this extreme? Why or why not?
   c. Is there evidence that the population proportion of California residents of Asian ethnicity has risen since 2005? Test using the p-value method at level of significance $\alpha = 0.05$.

32. Affective Disorders Among Women. What do you think is the most common nonobstetric (not related to pregnancy) reason for hospitalization among 18- to 44-year-old American women? According to the U.S. Agency for Healthcare Research and Quality (www.ahrq.gov), this is the category of *affective* disorders, such as depression. Of hospitalizations among 18- to 44-year-old American women, 7% were for affective disorders. Suppose that a random sample taken this year of 1000 hospitalizations of 18- to 44-year-old women showed 80 admitted for affective disorders. We are interested in whether the population proportion of hospitalizations for affective disorders has changed since 2002. Test using the p-value method and level of significance $\alpha = 0.10$.

33. Latino Household Income. The U.S. Census Bureau reported that 15.3% of Latino families had household incomes of at least \$75,000. We are interested in whether the population proportion has changed, using the critical-value method and level of significance $\alpha = 0.01$. Suppose that a random sample of 100 Latino families reported 23 with household incomes of at least \$75,000.
   a. Is it appropriate to perform the Z test for the proportion? Why or why not?
   b. How many standard errors does $\hat{p}$ lie above p_0? Is this extreme? Why or why not?
   c. Perform the appropriate hypothesis test.

34. Eighth-Grade Alcohol Use. The National Institute on Alcohol Abuse and Alcoholism reported that 45.6% of eighth-graders had used alcohol.[20] A random sample of 100 eighth-graders this year showed that 41 of them had used alcohol.
   a. Is it appropriate to perform the Z test for the proportion? Why or why not?
   b. How many standard errors does $\hat{p}$ lie below p_0? Is this extreme? Why or why not?

   c. Is there evidence that the population proportion of eighth-graders who used alcohol has changed? Test using the p-value method at level of significance $\alpha = 0.05$.

35. Eighth-Grade Alcohol Use. Refer to Exercise 34.
   a. Evaluate the strength of evidence against the null hypothesis.
   b. Suppose that we decide to carry out the same Z test as Exercise 34(c), however, this time using the critical-value method. Without actually performing the test, what would the conclusion be and why?
   c. Would a 95% Z interval for p contain $p = 0.456$? Explain.
   d. Suppose that a newspaper headline reported "Alcohol Use Down Among Eighth-Graders." How would you respond? Does your hypothesis test support this headline?

36. Eighth-Grade Alcohol Use. Refer to Exercise 34. *What if* we cut the sample size down to between 50 and 60 eighth-graders, and we cut the sample number of successes as well, so that the sample proportion p stayed the same. Suppose that everything else stayed the same. Describe what would happen to the following, and why.
   a. $\sigma_{\hat{p}}$
   b. Z_{data}
   c. The p-value
   d. α
   e. The conclusion

BRINGING IT ALL TOGETHER
Children and Environmental Tobacco Smoke at Home. Use the following information for Exercises 37–40. The Environmental Protection Agency reported that 11% of children aged 6 and under were exposed to environmental tobacco smoke (ETS) at home on a regular basis (at least four times per week).[21] A random sample of 100 children aged 6 and under showed that 6% of these children had been exposed to ETS at home on a regular basis.

37. Answer the following.
   a. Is it appropriate to perform the Z test for the proportion? Why or why not?
   b. Test at level of significance $\alpha = 0.05$ whether the population proportion of children aged 6 and under exposed to ETS at home on a regular basis has decreased.

38. Refer to Exercise 37.
   a. Which is the only possible error you can be making here, a Type I or a Type II error? What are some consequences of this error?
   b. Suppose that a newspaper headline reported "Second-hand Smoke Prevalence Down." How would you respond? Does your inference support this headline?

39. Refer to your work in Exercise 37.
  a. Test at level of significance $\alpha = 0.10$ whether the population proportion of children aged 6 and under exposed to ETS at home on a regular basis has decreased.
  b. How do you explain the different conclusions you got in the two hypothesis tests above?
  c. Evaluate the strength of evidence against the null hypothesis.

40. Refer to Exercise 37. *What if* the sample proportion $\hat{p}$ decreased, but everything else stayed the same. Describe what would happen to the following, and why.
  a. $\sigma_{\hat{p}}$
  b. Z_{data}
  c. The p-value
  d. α
  e. The conclusion

41. Chapter 8 Case Study, Continued. On page 407 we calculated the 95% confidence interval for p, the population proportion of all wildlife cleanup workers who experienced skin problems, to be (0.330, 0.596). Test using level of significance $\alpha = 0.05$ whether p differs from: **(a)** 0.3, **(b)** 0.4, **(c)** 0.5, **(d)** 0.6.

Car Accidents Among Young Drivers. For Exercises 42 and 43, refer to Example 9.21.

42. Suppose that our sample size and the number of successes are doubled, so that $\hat{p}$ remains the same. Otherwise, everything else is the same as in the original example. Describe how this change would affect the following.
  a. $\sigma_{\hat{p}}$
  b. Z_{data}
  c. The p-value
  d. α
  e. The conclusion

43. Suppose that the hypothesized proportion p_0 was no longer 0.12. Instead, p_0 takes some value between 0.12 and 0.134. Otherwise, everything else is the same as in the original example. Describe how this change would affect the following.
  a. $\sigma_{\hat{p}}$
  b. Z_{data}
  c. The p-value
  d. α
  e. The conclusion

9.6 Chi-Square Test for the Population Standard Deviation

OBJECTIVES By the end of this section, I will be able to . . .

1 Perform the χ^2 test for σ using the critical-value method.

2 Carry out the χ^2 test for σ using the p-value method.

3 Use confidence intervals for σ to perform two-tailed hypothesis tests about σ.

1 χ^2 (Chi-Square) Test for σ Using the Critical-Value Method

In Section 8.4 (pages 411–418) we used the χ^2 distribution to help us construct confidence intervals for the population variance and standard deviation. Here, in Section 9.6, we will use the χ^2 distribution to perform hypothesis tests about the population standard deviation σ. Why might we be interested in doing so? A pharmaceutical company that wishes to ensure the safety of a particular new drug would perform statistical tests to make sure that the drug's effect was consistent and did not vary widely from patient to patient. The biostatisticians employed by the company would therefore perform a hypothesis test to make sure that the population standard deviation σ was not too large.

Under the assumption that $H_0 : \sigma = \sigma_0$ is true, the χ^2 statistic takes the following form:

$$\chi^2_{\text{data}} = \frac{(n-1)s^2}{\sigma_0^2}$$

For the hypothesis test about σ, our test statistic is called χ^2_{data} because the values of $n - 1$ and s^2 come from the observed data. The test statistic χ^2_{data} takes a moderate value when the value of s^2 is moderate assuming H_0 is true, and χ^2_{data} takes an extreme value when the value of s^2 is extreme assuming H_0 is true. This leads us to the following.

> **The Essential Idea About Hypothesis Testing for the Standard Deviation**
> When the observed value of χ^2_{data} is unusual or extreme on the assumption that H_0 is true, we should reject H_0. Otherwise, there is insufficient evidence against H_0, and we should not reject H_0.

The remainder of Section 9.6 explains the details of implementing hypothesis testing for the standard deviation. The χ^2 test for σ may be performed using the p-value method or the critical-value method. We begin with the critical-value method.

> **χ^2 Test for σ: Critical-Value Method**
> This hypothesis test is valid only if we have a random sample from a normal population.
>
> **Step 1 State the hypotheses.**
> Use one of the forms in Table 9.13. State the meaning of σ.
>
> **Step 2 Find the χ^2 critical value or values and state the rejection rule.**
> Use Table 9.13.
>
> **Step 3 Calculate χ^2_{data}.**
> Either use technology to find the value of the test statistic χ^2_{data} or calculate the value of χ^2_{data} as follows:
>
> $$\chi^2_{data} = \frac{(n-1)s^2}{\sigma_0^2}$$
>
> which follows a χ^2 distribution with $n-1$ degrees of freedom, and where s^2 represents the sample variance.
>
> **Step 4 State the conclusion and the interpretation.**
> If χ^2_{data} falls in the critical region, then reject H_0. Otherwise do not reject H_0. Interpret your conclusion so that a nonspecialist can understand.

The χ^2 critical values in the right-tailed, left-tailed, or two-tailed tests use the following notations: χ^2_α, $\chi^2_{1-\alpha}$, $\chi^2_{\alpha/2}$, and $\chi^2_{1-\alpha/2}$ (see Table 9.13). In each case, *the subscript indicates the area to the right* of the χ^2 critical value. Find these values just as you did in Section 8.4, using either technology or Table E, Chi-Square (χ^2) Distribution, in the Appendix.

Table 9.13 Critical values and rejection rules for the χ^2 test for σ

Right-tailed test	Left-tailed test	Two-tailed test
$H_0 : \sigma = \sigma_0$ $H_a : \sigma > \sigma_0$	$H_0 : \sigma = \sigma_0$ $H_a : \sigma < \sigma_0$	$H_0 : \sigma = \sigma_0$ $H_a : \sigma \neq \sigma_0$
Critical value: χ^2_α Reject H_0 if $\chi^2_{data} \geq \chi^2_\alpha$ level of significance α	Critical value: $\chi^2_{1-\alpha}$ Reject H_0 if $\chi^2_{data} \leq \chi^2_{1-\alpha}$ level of significance α	Critical values: $\chi^2_{\alpha/2}$ and $\chi^2_{1-\alpha/2}$ Reject H_0 if $\chi^2_{data} \geq \chi^2_{\alpha/2}$ or if $\chi^2_{data} \leq \chi^2_{1-\alpha/2}$ level of significance α

Example 9.24 χ^2 Test for σ using the critical-value method

Alabama	48
Arkansas	37
Iowa	33
Massachusetts	50
Minnesota	45
Oregon	63
South Carolina	66
Utah	52

 lowincome

The table contains the numbers of children (in 1000s) living in low-income households without health insurance for a random sample of 8 states.[22] Test whether the population standard deviation σ of children living in low-income households without health insurance differs from 10,000, using level of significance $\alpha = 0.05$.

Solution

The normal probability plot indicates acceptable normality.

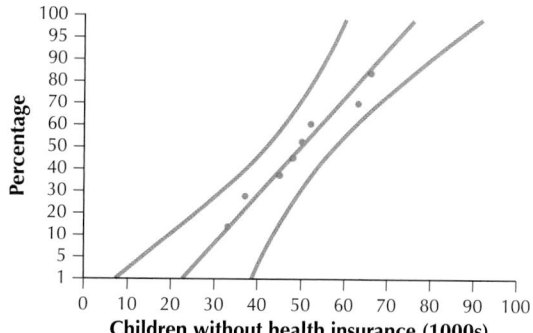

Normal probability plot for children without health insurance.

Step 1 **State the hypotheses.** The phrase "differs from" indicates that we have a two-tailed test. The value $\sigma_0 = 10$ answers the question "Differs from what?" (Note that σ_0 is 10, and not 10,000, since the data are expressed in thousands.) Thus, we have our hypotheses:

$$H_0 : \sigma = 10 \quad \text{versus} \quad H_a : \sigma \neq 10$$

where σ represents the population standard deviation of number of children living in low-income households without health insurance.

Step 2 **Find the χ^2 critical values and state the rejection rule.** We have $n = 8$, so degrees of freedom $= n - 1 = 7$. Since α is given as 0.05, $\alpha/2 = 0.025$ and $1 - \alpha/2 = 0.975$. Then, from the χ^2 table (Appendix Table E), we have $\chi^2_{\alpha/2} = \chi^2_{0.025} = 16.013$, and $\chi^2_{1-\alpha/2} = \chi^2_{0.975} = 1.690$. We will reject H_0 if χ^2_{data} is either $\geq \chi^2_{\alpha/2} = 16.013$ or $\leq \chi^2_{1-\alpha/2} = 1.690$.

Step 3 **Find χ^2_{data}.** The TI-83/84 descriptive statistics in Figure 9.49 tell us that the sample variance is

$$s^2 = 11.41114743^2$$

Thus

$$\chi^2_{data} = \frac{(n-1)s^2}{\sigma_0^2} = \frac{(8-1)11.41114743^2}{10^2} \approx 9.115$$

FIGURE 9.49 TI-83/84 results.

Step 4 **State the conclusion and the interpretation.** In Step 2 we said that we would reject H_0 if χ^2_{data} was either ≥ 16.013 or ≤ 1.690. Since $\chi^2_{data} = 9.115$ is neither ≥ 16.013 nor ≤ 1.690 (see Figure 9.50), we do not reject H_0. There is insufficient evidence at level of significance $\alpha = 0.05$ that the population standard deviation of the numbers of children living in low-income households without health insurance differs from 10,000. ■

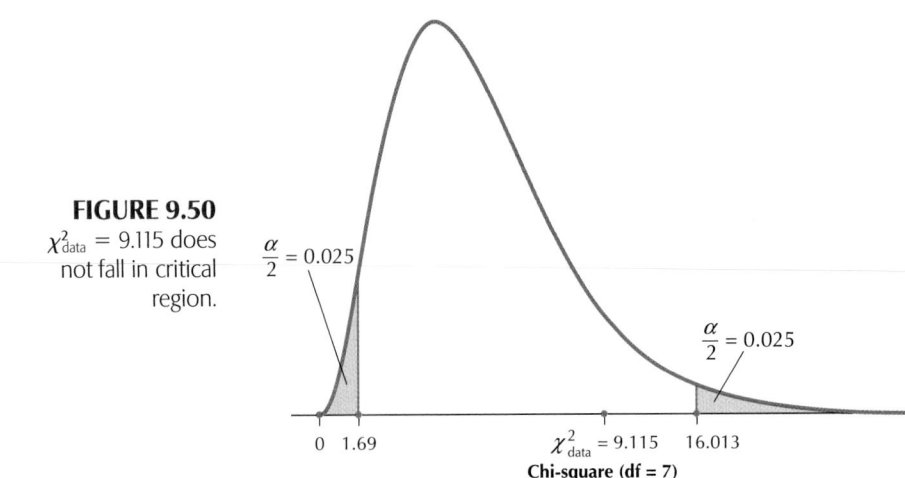

FIGURE 9.50
$\chi^2_{data} = 9.115$ does not fall in critical region.

$\frac{\alpha}{2} = 0.025$

$\frac{\alpha}{2} = 0.025$

0   1.69 $\chi^2_{data} = 9.115$ 16.013
Chi-square (df = 7)

Now You Can Do
Exercises 17–28.

2 χ^2 Test for σ Using the *p*-Value Method

We may also use the *p*-value method to perform the χ^2 test for σ.

χ^2 Test for σ: *p*-Value Method

This hypothesis test is valid only if we have a random sample from a normal population.

Step 1 **State the hypotheses and the rejection rule.**
Use one of the forms in Table 9.14. State the rejection rule as "Reject H_0 when the *p*-value $\leq \alpha$."
State the meaning of σ.

Step 2 **Calculate χ^2_{data}.**
Either use technology to find the value of the test statistic χ^2_{data} or calculate the value of χ^2_{data} as follows:

$$\chi^2_{data} = \frac{(n-1)s^2}{\sigma^2_0}$$

which follows a χ^2 distribution with $n - 1$ degrees of freedom, and where s^2 represents the sample variance.

Step 3 **Find the *p*-value.**
Use Table 9.14.

Step 4 **State the conclusion and the interpretation.**
If the *p*-value $\leq \alpha$, then reject H_0. Otherwise, do not reject H_0. Interpret your conclusion so that a nonspecialist can understand.

Table 9.14 *p*-Value method for the χ^2 test for σ

Right-tailed test	**Left-tailed test**	**Two-tailed test**
$H_0 : \sigma = \sigma_0$	$H_0 : \sigma = \sigma_0$	$H_0 : \sigma = \sigma_0$
$H_a : \sigma > \sigma_0$	$H_a : \sigma < \sigma_0$	$H_a : \sigma \neq \sigma_0$
p-value $= P(\chi^2 > \chi^2_{data})$	*p*-value $= P(\chi^2 < \chi^2_{data})$	If $P(\chi^2 > \chi^2_{data}) \leq 0.5$, then
Area to right of χ^2_{data}	Area to left of χ^2_{data}	**a.** χ^2_{data} is on the right side of the distribution
		b. *p*-value $= 2 \cdot P(\chi^2 > \chi^2_{data})$
		If $P(\chi^2 > \chi^2_{data}) > 0.5$, then
		a. χ^2_{data} is on the left side of the distribution
		b. *p*-value $= 2 \cdot P(\chi^2 < \chi^2_{data})$

p-value =
$P(\chi^2 > \chi^2_{data})$

p-value =
$P(\chi^2 < \chi^2_{data})$

0   χ^2_{data} 0 χ^2_{data}

Example 9.25 χ^2 Test for σ using the *p*-value method and technology

powerplants

Power plants around the country are retooling in order to consume biomass instead of or in addition to coal. The following table contains a random sample of 10 such power plants and the amount of biomass they consumed in 2006, in trillions of Btu (British thermal units).[23] Test whether the population standard deviation is greater than 2 trillion Btu using level of significance $\alpha = 0.05$.

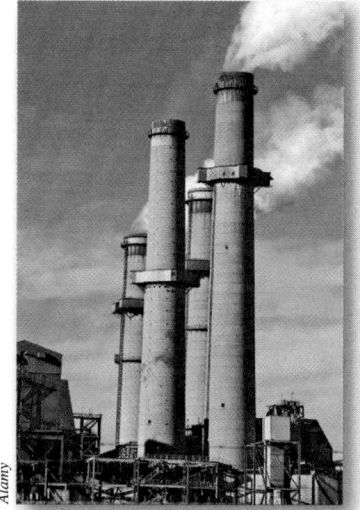

Power plant	Location	Biomass consumed (trillions of Btu)
Georgia Pacific Naheola Mill	Choctaw, AL	13.4
Jefferson Smurfit Fernandina Beach	Nassau, FL	12.9
International Paper Augusta Mill	Richmond, GA	17.8
Gaylord Container Bogalusa	Washington, LA	15.1
Escanaba Paper Company	Delta, MI	19.5
Weyerhaeuser Plymouth NC	Martin, NC	18.6
International Paper	Georgetown, SC	13.8
Bowater Newsprint	McMinn, TN	10.6
Covington Facility	Covington, VA	12.7
Mosinee Paper	Marathon, WI	17.6

Solution

The normal probability plot in Figure 9.51 indicates acceptable normality, allowing us to proceed with the hypothesis test.

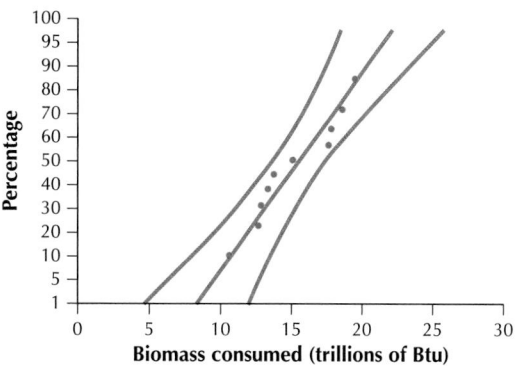

FIGURE 9.51 Normal probability of biomass.

Step 1 **State the hypotheses and the rejection rule.** The phrase "greater than" indicates that we have a right-tailed test. The question "Greater than what?" tells us that $\sigma_0 = 2$, giving us

$$H_0 : \sigma = 2 \quad \text{versus} \quad H_a : \sigma > 2$$

We reject H_0 if the *p*-value $\leq \alpha = 0.05$.

Step 2 **Find χ^2_{data}.** We use the Step-by-Step Technology Guide on page 485. The TI-83/84 descriptive statistics in Figure 9.52 tell us that the sample variance is

$$s^2 = 2.990354866^2$$

Thus

$$\chi^2_{\text{data}} = \frac{(n-1)s^2}{\sigma_0^2} = \frac{(10-1)2.990354866^2}{2^2} \approx 20.12$$

```
1-Var Stats
 x̄=15.2
 Σx=152
 Σx²=2390.88
 Sx=2.990354866
 σx=2.836899716
↓n=10
```

FIGURE 9.52 TI-83/84 results.

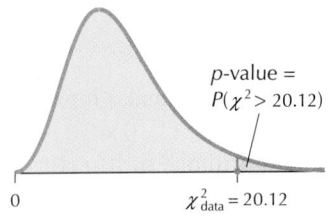

FIGURE 9.53 *p*-Value for χ^2 test.

Step 3 **Find the *p*-value.** For our right-tailed test, Table 9.14 tells us that

$$p\text{-value} = P(\chi^2 > \chi^2_{data}) = P(\chi^2 > 20.12)$$

That is, the *p*-value is the area to the right of $\chi^2_{data} = 20.12$, as shown in Figure 9.53. To find the *p*-value, we use the instructions provided in the Step-by-Step Technology Guide provided at the end of this section. The TI-83/84 results shown in Figure 9.54a tell us that *p*-value $= P(\chi^2 > 20.12) = 0.0171861114$.

The Excel and Minitab results in Figures 9.54b and 9.54c agree with this *p*-value. (Excel and Minitab do not exactly match the TI-83/84 *p*-value because they round the *p*-values to fewer decimal places.) Instead of providing the *p*-value directly, Minitab gives the area to the left of χ^2_{data}: $P(X \leq 20.12) = 0.982814$. We therefore need to subtract the given value from 1 to get the *p*-value:

$$p\text{-value} = 1 - 0.982814 = 0.017186$$

FIGURE 9.54a TI-83/84 results.

A1		f_x	=CHIDIST(20.12,9)	
	A	B	C	D	E
1	0.017186				

FIGURE 9.54b Excel results.

FIGURE 9.54c Minitab results.

Now You Can Do
Exercises 29–34.

Step 4 **State the conclusion and the interpretation.** Since *p*-value $= 0.0171861114 \leq \alpha = 0.05$, we reject H_0. There is evidence that the population standard deviation is greater than 2 trillion Btu. ∎

3 Using Confidence Intervals for σ to Perform Two-Tailed Hypothesis Tests for σ

Suppose we have a $100(1 - \alpha)\%$ confidence interval for σ, of the form (lower bound, upper bound), and are interested in two-tailed hypothesis tests using level of significance α of the form:

$$H_0: \sigma = \sigma_0 \quad \text{versus} \quad H_a: \sigma \neq \sigma_0$$

We will not reject H_0 for values of σ_0 that lie between the lower bound and upper bound of the confidence interval, and we will reject H_0 for values of σ_0 that lie outside this interval.

Example 9.26 Using confidence intervals for σ to conduct two-tailed χ^2 tests for σ

A 95% confidence interval for the population mean sodium content of breakfast cereals, in milligrams (mg) per serving, is given by

$$(44.53 \text{ mg}, 81.50 \text{ mg})$$

Assume that the data are normally distributed. Test using level of significance $\alpha = 0.05$ whether σ differs from the following.
a. 80 mg
b. 40 mg

Solution

a. For the hypothesis test $H_0: \sigma = 80$ versus $H_a: \sigma \neq 80$, $\sigma_0 = 80$ lies between the lower bound 44.53 and the upper bound 81.50 of the confidence interval, and we therefore do not reject H_0. There is insufficient evidence that the population standard deviation of sodium content differs from 80 mg.

b. For the hypothesis test $H_0 : \sigma = 40$ versus $H_a : \sigma \neq 40$, $\sigma_0 = 40$ lies outside the confidence interval, and we therefore reject H_0. There is evidence that the population standard deviation of sodium content differs from 40 mg. ■

Now You Can Do
Exercises 35–38.

STEP-BY-STEP TECHNOLOGY GUIDE: Finding χ^2 *p*-value

We will use the information from Example 9.25 (page 483). The steps for finding the χ^2 critical values are given in the Step-by-Step Technology Guide at the end of Section 8.4 (pages 415–416).

TI-83/84
Step 1   Enter the data into List **L1**.
Step 2   Press **2nd > DISTR**, then χ^2 **cdf(**, and press **ENTER**.
Step 3   On the home screen, enter the value of χ^2_{data}, comma, 1E99, comma, degrees of freedom, close parenthesis, as shown

in Figure 9.54a. (Remember that this "ε" is inserted by pressing **2nd**, followed by the comma key.)
Step 4   Press **ENTER**. The results for Example 9.25 are shown in Figure 9.54a.

EXCEL
Step 1   Select cell **A1**. Click the **Insert Function** icon f_x.
Step 2   For **Search for a Function**, type **chidist** and click **OK**.

Step 3   For **x**, enter the value of χ^2_{data}, and for **Deg_freedom**, enter the degrees of freedom. Excel displays the *p*-value in the cell in the dialog box, as shown in Figure 9.54b.

MINITAB
Step 1   Click on **Calc > Probability Distributions > Chi-Square**.
Step 2   Select **Cumulative probability**, and enter the **Degrees of freedom**.
Step 3   For **Input constant**, enter the value of χ^2_{data} and click **OK**.

Step 4   Minitab displays the area to the left of χ^2_{data} in the session window, as shown in Figure 9.54c. To find the *p*-value, subtract this area from 1.

CRUNCHIT!
Step 1   Click **Distribution Calculator** and select **Chi-square**.
Step 2   For **df** enter the degrees of freedom.
Step 3   Select the **Probability** tab. Enter the value of χ^2_{data} and click **Calculate**. CrunchIt! displays the cumulative probability,

that is, the area to the left of χ^2_{data}. To find the *p*-value, subtract this value from 1.

Section 9.6 Summary

1 Under the assumption that H_0 is true, the χ^2 statistic takes the following form:

$$\chi^2_{data} = \frac{(n-1)s^2}{\sigma_0^2}$$

The hypothesis test about σ may be performed using the *p*-value method or the critical-value method. Either way, the test is valid only if we have a random sample from a normal population. The critical-value method compares χ^2_{data} with one or two critical values.

2 The *p*-value method compares the *p*-value to level of significance α.

3 If we have a $100(1 - \alpha)\%$ confidence interval for σ, of the form (lower bound, upper bound), and are interested in a two-tailed hypothesis test, using α, of the form

$$H_0 : \sigma = \sigma_0 \quad \text{versus} \quad H_a : \sigma \neq \sigma_0$$

we will not reject H_0 for values of σ_0 that lie between the lower bound and upper bound of the confidence interval. We will reject H_0 for values of σ_0 that lie outside this interval.

Section 9.6 Exercises

CLARIFYING THE CONCEPTS

1. Think of one instance where an analyst would be interested in performing a hypothesis test about the population standard deviation σ.

2. What is the difference between σ and σ_0?

3. Does it make sense to test whether $\sigma < 0$? Explain.

4. What condition must be fulfilled for us to perform a hypothesis test about σ?

5. Explain how we can use a confidence interval to determine significance.

6. In the previous exercise, what must be the relationship between α and the confidence level?

PRACTICING THE TECHNIQUES

For Exercises 7–10, construct the hypotheses.

7. Test whether the population standard deviation is greater than 10.

8. Test whether the population standard deviation is less than 5.

9. Test whether the population standard deviation differs from 3.

10. Test whether the population standard deviation is greater than 100.

For Exercises 11–16, a random sample is drawn from a normal population. Calculate χ^2_{data}.

11. We are testing whether $\sigma > 1$ and have a sample of size $n = 21$ with a sample variance of $s^2 = 3$.

12. We are testing whether $\sigma < 5$ and have a sample of size $n = 11$ with a sample variance of $s^2 = 25$.

13. We are testing whether $\sigma \neq 3$ and have a sample of size $n = 16$ with a standard deviation of $s = 2.5$.

14. We are testing whether $\sigma > 10$ and have a sample of size $n = 14$ with a standard deviation of $s = 12$.

15. We are testing whether $\sigma < 20$, and have a sample of size $n = 8$ and a sample variance of $s^2 = 350$.

16. We are testing whether $\sigma \neq 5$ and have a sample of size $n = 26$ with a standard deviation of $s = 5$.

For Exercises 17–22, a random sample is drawn from a normal population. The values of χ^2_{data} for these exercises are found in Exercises 11–16. Find the critical value or values.

17. We are testing whether $\sigma > 1$, using $\alpha = 0.05$, and have a sample of size $n = 21$ and a sample variance of $s^2 = 3$. Find χ^2_{α}.

18. We are testing whether $\sigma < 5$, using $\alpha = 0.05$, and have a sample of size $n = 11$ and a sample variance of $s^2 = 25$. Find $\chi^2_{1-\alpha}$.

19. We are testing whether $\sigma \neq 3$, using $\alpha = 0.05$, and have a sample of size $n = 16$ and a standard deviation of $s = 2.5$. Find $\chi^2_{\alpha/2}$ and $\chi^2_{1-\alpha/2}$.

20. We are testing whether $\sigma > 10$, using $\alpha = 0.01$, and have a sample of size $n = 14$ and a standard deviation of $s = 12$. Find χ^2_{α}.

21. We are testing whether $\sigma < 20$, using $\alpha = 0.10$, and have a sample of size $n = 8$ and a sample variance of $s^2 = 350$. Find $\chi^2_{1-\alpha}$.

22. We are testing whether $\sigma \neq 5$, using $\alpha = 0.05$, and have a sample of size $n = 26$ with a standard deviation of $s = 5$. Find $\chi^2_{\alpha/2}$ and $\chi^2_{1-\alpha/2}$.

For Exercises 23–28, a random sample is drawn from a normal population. The values of χ^2_{data} for these exercises were found in Exercises 11–16. The critical values were found in Exercises 17–22. Do the following.

    a. State the rejection rule.

    b. Compare χ^2_{data} with the critical value or values. State the conclusion and interpretation.

23. The data in Exercise 17

24. The data in Exercise 18

25. The data in Exercise 19

26. The data in Exercise 20

27. The data in Exercise 21

28. The data in Exercise 22

For Exercises 29–34, a random sample is drawn from a normal population. Do the following.

    a. Draw a χ^2 distribution and indicate the location of χ^2_{data}.

    b. Find the p-value and indicate the p-value in your distribution in **(a)**.

    c. Compare the p-value with level of significance $\alpha = 0.05$. State the conclusion and interpretation.

29. The data in Exercise 11

30. The data in Exercise 12

31. The data in Exercise 13

32. The data in Exercise 14

33. The data in Exercise 15

34. The data in Exercise 16

For Exercises 35–38 a $100(1 - \alpha)\%$ χ^2 confidence interval for σ is given. Use the confidence interval to test using level of significance α whether σ differs from each of the indicated hypothesized values.

35. A 95% χ^2 confidence interval for σ is (1, 4). Hypothesized values σ_0 are

    a. 0

    b. 2

    c. 5

36. A 99% χ^2 confidence interval for σ is (10, 25). Hypothesized values σ_0 are

    a. 15

    b. 26

    c. 5

37. A 90% χ^2 confidence interval for σ is (100, 200). Hypothesized values σ_0 are

    a. 150

    b. 250

    c. 0

38. A 95% χ^2 confidence interval for σ is (127, 698). Hypothesized values σ_0 are

    a. 125

    b. 128

    c. 700

APPLYING THE CONCEPTS

39. DDT in Breast Milk. Researchers compared the amount of DDT in the breast milk of a random sample of 12 Latina women in Yakima Valley in Washington State with the amount of DDT in breast milk in the general U.S. population.[24] They measured the standard deviation of the amount of DDT in the general population to be 36.5 parts per billion (ppb). Assume that the population is normally distributed. We are interested in testing whether the population standard deviation of DDT level in the breast milk of Latina women in Yakima Valley is greater than that of the general population, using level of significance $\alpha = 0.01$.

    a. The sample variance is $s^2 = 119{,}025$. Calculate χ^2_{data}.

    b. Perform the appropriate hypothesis test.

40. Tree Rings. Does the growth of trees vary more when the trees are young? The International Tree Ring Data Base collected data on a particular 440-year-old Douglas fir tree.[25] The standard deviation of the annual ring growth in the tree's first 80 years of life was 0.8 millimeter (mm) per year. Assume that the population is normal. We are interested in testing whether the population standard deviation of annual ring growth in the tree's later years is less than 0.8 mm per year.

    a. The sample variance for a random sample of size 100 taken from the tree's later years is $s^2 = 0.3136$. Calculate χ^2_{data}.

    b. Perform the appropriate hypothesis test.

41. Union Membership. The following table contains the total union membership (in 1000s) for 7 randomly selected states.[26] Assume that the distribution is normal. We are interested in whether the population standard deviation of union membership σ differs from 30,000, using level of significance $\alpha = 0.05$. **unionmember**

Florida	397
Indiana	334
Maryland	342
Massachusetts	414
Minnesota	395
Texas	476
Wisconsin	386

    a. The sample variance is $s^2 = 2245.67$. Calculate χ^2_{data}.

    b. Perform the appropriate hypothesis test.

    c. Would $\sigma = 30{,}000$ lie inside or outside a 95% Z interval for σ? Explain.

42. Fourth-Grade Feet. Suppose a children's shoe manufacturer is interested in estimating the variability of fourth-graders' feet. A random sample of 20 fourth-graders' feet yielded the following foot lengths, in centimeters.[27] The normality of the data was verified in Example 8.10 (page 389). Test whether the population standard deviation of foot lengths σ is less than 1 centimeter using level of significance $\alpha = 0.05$. **fourthfeet**

22.4	23.4	22.5	23.2	23.1	23.7	24.1	21.0	21.6	20.9
25.5	22.8	24.1	25.0	24.0	21.7	22.0	22.7	24.7	23.5

43. Does Score Variability Differ by Gender? Recently, researchers have been examining the evidence for whether there is greater variability in boys' scores than girls' scores on cognitive abilities tests. For example, one study found that boys were overrepresented at both the top and the bottom of nonverbal reasoning tests and quantitative reasoning tests.[28] Suppose that the standard deviation for girls' scores is known to be 50 points for a particular test and that the population of all scores is normal. A random sample of 101 boys has a sample variance of 2600. Test whether the population standard deviation for boys exceeds 50 points, using level of significance $\alpha = 0.05$.

44. Heart Rate Variability. A reduction in heart rate variability is associated with elevated levels of stress, since the body continues to pump adrenaline after high-stress situations, even when at rest.[29] Suppose the standard deviation of heartbeats in the general population is 20 beats per minute, and that the population of heart rates is normal. A random sample of 50 individuals leading high-stress lives has a sample variance of 200 beats per minute. Test using level of significance $\alpha = 0.05$ whether the population standard deviation for those leading high-stress lives is lower than that in the general population.

9.7 Probability of Type II Error and the Power of a Hypothesis Test

OBJECTIVES By the end of this section, I will be able to . . .

1   Calculate the probability of Type II error for a Z test for μ.

2   Compute the power of a Z test for μ and construct a power curve.

1 Probability of a Type II Error

In Section 9.1 we defined a Type II error as follows:

Type II error: not rejecting H_0 when H_0 is false

For example, the criminal trial scenario on page 427 had the following hypotheses:

H_0 : defendant is not guilty   versus H_a : defendant is guilty

In this case, a Type II error was to find the defendant not guilty (not reject H_0) when in reality he did commit the crime (H_0 is false). In this section we learn how to calculate the probability of making a Type II error for a Z test for μ, called β (beta), and to use the value of β to compute the power of a Z test for μ.

Calculating β, the Probability of a Type II Error

Use the following steps to calculate β, the probability of a Type II error.

Step 1
Recall that Z_{crit} divides the critical region from the noncritical region. Let $\bar{x}_{crit}$ be the value of the sample mean $\bar{x}$ associated with Z_{crit}. The following table shows how to calculate $\bar{x}_{crit}$ for the three forms of the hypothesis test.

Form of test		Value of $\bar{x}_{crit}$
Right-tailed	$H_0 : \mu = \mu_0$ vs. $H_a : \mu > \mu_0$	$\bar{x}_{crit} = \mu_0 + Z_{crit} \cdot \frac{\sigma}{\sqrt{n}}$
Left-tailed	$H_0 : \mu = \mu_0$ vs. $H_a : \mu < \mu_0$	$\bar{x}_{crit} = \mu_0 - Z_{crit} \cdot \frac{\sigma}{\sqrt{n}}$
Two-tailed	$H_0 : \mu = \mu_0$ vs. $H_a : \mu \neq \mu_0$	$\bar{x}_{crit, lower} = \mu_0 - Z_{crit} \cdot \frac{\sigma}{\sqrt{n}}$ $\bar{x}_{crit, upper} = \mu_0 + Z_{crit} \cdot \frac{\sigma}{\sqrt{n}}$

Here, μ_0 is the hypothesized value of the population mean, σ is the population standard deviation, and n is the sample size.

Step 2
Let μ_a represent a particular value for the population mean μ chosen from the values indicated in the alternative hypothesis H_a. Draw a normal curve centered at μ_a, with the value or values of $\bar{x}_{crit}$ from Step 1 indicated (see Example 9.27).

Step 3
Calculate β for the particular μ_a chosen using the following table.

Form of test		β = probability of Type II error
Right-tailed	$H_0 : \mu = \mu_0$ vs. $H_a : \mu > \mu_0$	The area under the normal curve drawn in Step 2 to the left of $\bar{x}_{crit}$.
Left-tailed	$H_0 : \mu = \mu_0$ vs. $H_a : \mu < \mu_0$	The area under the normal curve drawn in Step 2 to the right of $\bar{x}_{crit}$.
Two-tailed	$H_0 : \mu = \mu_0$ vs. $H_a : \mu \neq \mu_0$	The area under the normal curve drawn in Step 2 between $\bar{x}_{crit, lower}$ and $\bar{x}_{crit, upper}$.

Let us illustrate the steps for calculating β, the probability of a Type II error, using an example.

Example 9.27   Calculating β, the probability of a Type II error

In Example 9.3, we tested whether people use debit cards on average more than 11 times per month. The hypotheses are

$$H_0: \mu = 11 \quad \text{versus} \quad H_a: \mu > 11$$

where μ represents the population mean debit card usage per month. From Example 9.3 we have $n = 36$, $\bar{x} = 11.5$, and $\sigma = 3$, and from Example 9.5 we have $Z_{\text{crit}} = 2.33$.

a.   State what a Type II error would be in this case.
b.   Let $\mu_a = 13$. That is, suppose the population mean debit card usage is actually 13 times per month. Calculate β, the probability of making a Type II error when $\mu_a = 13$.

Solution

a.   We make a Type II error when we do not reject H_0 when H_0 is false. In this case, a Type II error would be to conclude that the population mean debit card usage was 11 times per month when in actuality it was more than 11 times per month.
b.   We follow the steps for calculating β.

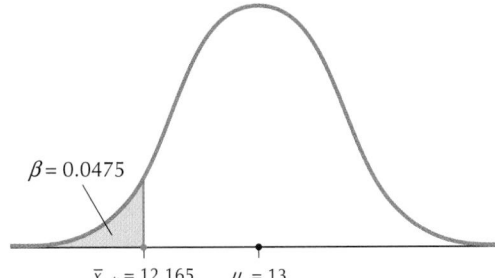

FIGURE 9.55 β probability of Type II error.

This is a Case 1 problem from Table 6.6 on page 303.

Step 1   We have a right-tailed test, so that

$$\bar{x}_{\text{crit}} = \mu_0 + Z_{\text{crit}} \cdot \frac{\sigma}{\sqrt{n}} = 11 + 2.33 \cdot \frac{3}{\sqrt{36}} = 12.165$$

Step 2   Figure 9.55 shows the normal curve centered at $\mu_a = 13$, with $\bar{x}_{\text{crit}} = 12.165$ labeled.

Step 3   The right-tailed test tells us that β equals the area under the normal curve drawn in Step 2 to the left of $\bar{x}_{\text{crit}} = 12.165$. This is the shaded area in Figure 9.55. Since area represents probability, we have

$$\beta = P(\bar{x} < 12.165) \text{ when } \mu_a = 13$$

Standardizing with $\mu_a = 13$, $\sigma = 3$, and $n = 36$:

$$\beta = P(\bar{x} < 12.165)$$
$$= P\left(Z < \frac{12.165 - 13}{3/\sqrt{36}}\right)$$
$$= P(Z < -1.67) = 0.0475$$

Thus, $\beta = 0.0475$. This represents the probability of making a Type II error, that is, of not rejecting the hypothesis that the population mean debit card usage is 11 times per month when in actuality it is 13 times per month. ∎

Now You Can Do
Exercises 5a, b, c–16a, b, c.

2 Power of a Hypothesis Test

It is a correct decision to reject the null hypothesis when the null hypothesis is false. The probability of making this type of correct decision is called the **power of the test.**

> **Power of a Hypothesis Test**
>
> The **power of a hypothesis test** is the probability of rejecting the null hypothesis when the null hypothesis is false. Power is calculated as
>
> $$\text{power} = 1 - \beta$$

Example 9.28 Power of a hypothesis test

Calculate the power, for the particular alternative value of the mean, of the hypothesis test in Example 9.27.

Solution

The probability of a Type II error was found in Example 9.27 to be $\beta = 0.0475$. Thus, the power of the hypothesis test is

$$\text{power} = 1 - \beta = 1 - 0.0475 = 0.9525$$

The probability of correctly rejecting the null hypothesis is 0.9525. ■

Now You Can Do
Exercises 5d–16d.

 Type II Error and Power of the Test

Suppose that we have the same hypothesis test from Example 9.27 and the same value $\bar{x}_{\text{crit}} = 12.165$. Now, *what if* we decrease μ_a such that it is less than 13 but still larger than 12.165. Describe what will happen to the following, and why.

a. The probability of a Type II error, β

b. The power of the test, $1 - \beta$

Solution

a. Consider Figure 9.56. The distribution of sample means remains centered at μ_a, so that a smaller μ_a will "slide" the normal curve toward the value of $\bar{x}_{\text{crit}} = 12.165$. This results in a larger area to the left of 12.165, as you can see by comparing Figure 9.56 with Figure 9.55. Therefore, a smaller μ_a leads to an *increase* in the probability of a Type II error, β.

b. As β increases, $1 - \beta$ decreases. Therefore, a smaller μ_a leads to a decrease in the power of the test. ■

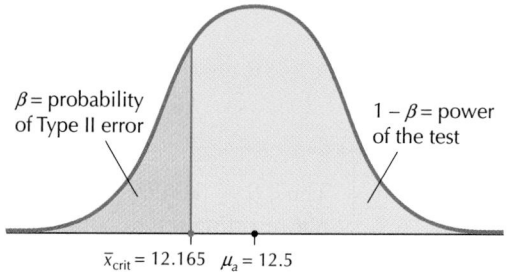

FIGURE 9.56 Smaller μ_a leads to an increase in β.

A **power curve** plots the values for the power of the test versus the values of μ_a.

Example 9.29 Power curve

a. Calculate the power of the hypothesis test from Example 9.27 for the following values of μ_a: 11.0, 11.5, 12.0, 12.165, 12.5, 13.5.
b. Construct the power curve by graphing the values for the power of the test on the vertical axis against the values of μ_a on the horizontal axis.

Solution

a. We have $\bar{x}_{\text{crit}} = 12.165$, $\sigma = 3$, and $n = 36$. The calculations are provided in the following table.

μ_a	Probability of Type II error: β	Power of the test: $1 - \beta$
11.0	$P\left(Z < \dfrac{12.165 - 11}{3/\sqrt{36}}\right) = P(Z < 2.33) = 0.9901$	$1 - 0.9901 = 0.0099$
11.5	$P\left(Z < \dfrac{12.165 - 11.5}{3/\sqrt{36}}\right) = P(Z < 1.33) = 0.9082$	$1 - 0.9082 = 0.0918$
12.0	$P\left(Z < \dfrac{12.165 - 12}{3/\sqrt{36}}\right) = P(Z < 0.33) = 0.6293$	$1 - 0.6293 = 0.3707$
12.165	$P\left(Z < \dfrac{12.165 - 12.165}{3/\sqrt{36}}\right) = P(Z < 0.00) = 0.5$	$1 - 0.5 = 0.5$
12.5	$P\left(Z < \dfrac{12.165 - 12.5}{3/\sqrt{36}}\right) = P(Z < -0.67) = 0.2514$	$1 - 0.2514 = 0.7486$
13.5	$P\left(Z < \dfrac{12.165 - 13.5}{3/\sqrt{36}}\right) = P(Z < -2.67) = 0.0038$	$1 - 0.0038 = 0.9962$

b. Figure 9.57 represents a power curve, since it plots the values for the power of the test on the vertical axis against the values of μ_a on the horizontal axis. Note that, as μ_a moves farther away from the hypothesized mean $\mu_0 = 11$, the power of the test increases. This is because it is more likely that the null hypothesis will be correctly rejected as the actual value of the mean μ_a gets farther away from the hypothesized value μ_0. ■

For completeness, we include the power for $\mu_a = 13$ from Example 9.28 in this power curve.

FIGURE 9.57 Power curve.

Now You Can Do
Exercises 17 and 18.

Section 9.7 Summary

1 We may calculate β, the probability of making a Type II error for a Z test for μ, given a particular alternative value for the population mean, μ_a.

2 The power of a hypothesis test is the probability of rejecting a false null hypothesis, and is calculated as *power* = $1 - \beta$. We may then build the power curve by plotting the power against values of μ_a.

Section 9.7 Exercises

CLARIFYING THE CONCEPTS
1. Explain what a Type II error is.
2. Describe what $\bar{x}_{crit}$ is.
3. In words, what do we mean by the power of a hypothesis test?
4. How do we calculate the power of a test?

PRACTICING THE TECHNIQUES
For Exercises 5–18, assume that the conditions for performing the Z test are met. Do the following.
    a. Calculate the value or values of $\bar{x}_{crit}$.
    b. Draw a normal curve, centered at μ_a, with the value or values of $\bar{x}_{crit}$ indicated.
    c. Calculate β, the probability of a Type II error for that value of μ_a. Shade the corresponding area under the normal curve.
    d. Calculate the power of the hypothesis test.

5. $H_0: \mu = 50$ vs. $H_a: \mu > 50$, $\alpha = 0.10$, $\sigma = 4$, $n = 25$, $\mu_a = 51$
6. $H_0: \mu = 50$ vs. $H_a: \mu > 50$, $\alpha = 0.10$, $\sigma = 4$, $n = 25$, $\mu_a = 52$
7. $H_0: \mu = 50$ vs. $H_a: \mu > 50$, $\alpha = 0.10$, $\sigma = 4$, $n = 25$, $\mu_a = 53$
8. $H_0: \mu = 50$ vs. $H_a: \mu > 50$, $\alpha = 0.10$, $\sigma = 4$, $n = 25$, $\mu_a = 54$
9. $H_0: \mu = 50$ vs. $H_a: \mu > 50$, $\alpha = 0.10$, $\sigma = 4$, $n = 25$, $\mu_a = 55$
10. $H_0: \mu = 50$ vs. $H_a: \mu > 50$, $\alpha = 0.10$, $\sigma = 4$, $n = 25$, $\mu_a = 56$
11. $H_0: \mu = 100$ vs. $H_a: \mu < 100$, $\alpha = 0.05$, $\sigma = 12$, $n = 36$, $\mu_a = 96$
12. $H_0: \mu = 100$ vs. $H_a: \mu < 100$, $\alpha = 0.05$, $\sigma = 12$, $n = 36$, $\mu_a = 94$
13. $H_0: \mu = 100$ vs. $H_a: \mu < 100$, $\alpha = 0.05$, $\sigma = 12$, $n = 36$, $\mu_a = 92$
14. $H_0: \mu = 100$ vs. $H_a: \mu < 100$, $\alpha = 0.05$, $\sigma = 12$, $n = 36$, $\mu_a = 90$
15. $H_0: \mu = 100$ vs. $H_a: \mu < 100$, $\alpha = 0.05$, $\sigma = 12$, $n = 36$, $\mu_a = 88$
16. $H_0: \mu = 100$ vs. $H_a: \mu < 100$, $\alpha = 0.05$, $\sigma = 12$, $n = 36$, $\mu_a = 86$
17. Refer to Exercises 5–10. Construct the power curve for the given values of μ_a.
18. Refer to Exercises 11–16. Construct the power curve for the given values of μ_a.

APPLYING THE CONCEPTS
19. **Stock Market.** The *Statistical Abstract of the United States* reports that the mean daily number of shares traded on the New York Stock Exchange in 2005 was 1.6 billion. Let this value represent the hypothesized population mean, and assume that the population standard deviation equals 0.5 billion shares. Suppose that we have a random sample of 36 days from the present year, and we are interested in testing whether the population mean daily number of shares traded has increased since 2005, using level of significance $\alpha = 0.05$.
    a. Describe what a Type II error would mean in the context of this problem.
    b. What is the probability of making a Type II error when the actual mean number of shares traded is 1.65 billion?
    c. What is the probability of making a Type II error when the actual mean number of shares traded is 1.70 billion?
    d. What is the probability of making a Type II error when the actual mean number of shares traded is 1.75 billion?
    e. What is the probability of making a Type II error when the actual mean number of shares traded is 1.80 billion?
    f. Calculate the power of the hypothesis test for the values of μ_a given in (b)–(e).
    g. Construct the power curve for the values of μ_a given in (b)–(e).

20. **Credit Score in Florida.** According to **CreditReport**.com, the mean credit score in Florida in 2006 was 673. Suppose we have a random sample of 900 credit scores in Florida, and assume that the population standard deviation is 150. We are interested in testing using level of significance $\alpha = 0.05$ whether the population mean credit score in Florida has decreased since that time.
    a. Describe what a Type II error would mean in the context of this problem.
    b. What is the probability of making a Type II error when the actual mean credit score is 670?
    c. What is the probability of making a Type II error when the actual mean credit score is 665?
    d. What is the probability of making a Type II error when the actual mean credit score is 660?
    e. What is the probability of making a Type II error when the actual mean credit score is 655?
    f. Calculate the power of the hypothesis test for the values of μ_a given in (b)–(e).
    g. Construct the power curve for the values of μ_a given in (b)–(e).

21. **Accountants' Salary.** According to **Salary.com**, the mean salary for entry-level accountants in 2010 was \$41,560. Let this value represent the hypothesized population mean, and assume that the population standard deviation equals \$5000. Suppose we have a random sample of 100 entry-level accountants and wish to test using level of significance $\alpha = 0.05$ whether the population mean salary has changed since 2010.
    a. Describe what a Type II error would mean in the context of this problem.
    b. What is the probability of making a Type II error when the actual mean salary is \$42,000?

c. What is the probability of making a Type II error when the actual mean salary is $43,000?

d. What is the probability of making a Type II error when the actual mean salary is $44,000?

e. What is the probability of making a Type II error when the actual mean salary is $45,000?

f. Calculate the power of the hypothesis test for the values of μ_a given in **(b)–(e)**.

g. Construct the power curve for the values of μ_a given in **(b)–(e)**.

22. Mean Deduction. According to the U.S. Internal Revenue Service, the mean tax deduction for itemizers who claimed mortgage interest in 2003 was $11,350. Suppose we have a random sample of 625 such deductions and assume that the population standard deviation is $5000. We would like to test using level of significance $\alpha = 0.05$ whether the population mean tax deduction for itemizers who claim mortgage interest on this year's tax return has decreased since 2003.

a. Describe what a Type II error would mean in the context of this problem.

b. What is the probability of making a Type II error when the actual mean deduction is $11,000?

c. What is the probability of making a Type II error when the actual mean deduction is $10,000?

d. What is the probability of making a Type II error when the actual mean deduction is $9000?

e. What is the probability of making a Type II error when the actual mean deduction is $8000?

f. Calculate the power of the hypothesis test for the values of μ_a given in **(b)–(e)**.

g. Construct the power curve for the values of μ_a given in **(b)–(e)**.

23. Price of Milk. The U.S. Bureau of Labor Statistics reports that the mean price for a gallon of milk in 2005 was $3.24. Suppose that we have a random sample taken this year of 400 gallons of milk, and assume that the population standard deviation equals $1.00. We would like to conduct a hypothesis test using level of significance $\alpha = 0.01$ to investigate if the population mean price of milk this year has increased.

a. Describe what a Type II error would mean in the context of this problem.

b. What is the probability of making a Type II error when the actual mean price is $3.30?

c. What is the probability of making a Type II error when the actual mean price is $3.50?

d. What is the probability of making a Type II error when the actual mean price is $3.70?

e. What is the probability of making a Type II error when the actual mean price is $3.90?

f. Calculate the power of the hypothesis test for the values of μ_a given in **(b)–(e)**.

g. Construct the power curve for the values of μ_a given in **(b)–(e)**.

24. Hybrid Vehicles. A 2006 study by **Edmunds.com** examined the time it takes for owners of hybrid vehicles to recoup their additional initial cost through reduced fuel consumption. Suppose we have a random sample of 9 hybrid cars. Assume that the population is normal with $\sigma = 0.2$. We would like to test using level of significance $\alpha = 0.01$ whether the population mean time it takes owners of hybrid cars to recoup their initial cost is less than three years.

a. Describe what a Type II error would mean in the context of this problem.

b. What is the probability of making a Type II error when the actual mean time is 2.5 years?

c. What is the probability of making a Type II error when the actual mean time is 2 years?

d. What is the probability of making a Type II error when the actual mean time is 1.5 years?

e. What is the probability of making a Type II error when the actual mean time is 1 year?

f. Calculate the power of the hypothesis test for the values of μ_a given in **(b)–(e)**.

g. Construct the power curve for the values of μ_a given in **(b)–(e)**.

Chapter 9 Formulas and Vocabulary

SECTION 9.1
- α **(alpha)** (p. 428)
- **Alternative hypothesis** (p. 424)
- β **(beta)** (p. 429)
- **Hypothesis testing** (p. 424)
- **Level of significance** (p. 429)
- **Null hypothesis** (p. 424)
- **Statistical significance** (p. 426)
- **Type I error** (p. 428)
- **Type II error** (p. 428)

SECTION 9.2
- **Critical region** (p. 433)
- **Critical value, Z_{crit}** (p. 433)

- **Essential idea about hypothesis testing for the mean** (p. 431)
- **Level of significance α** (p. 433)
- **Noncritical region** (p. 433)
- **Test statistic** (p. 432)
- Z_{data} (p. 432).

$$Z_{data} = \frac{\bar{x} - \mu_0}{\sigma/\sqrt{n}}$$

SECTION 9.3
- **p-Value** (p. 439)
- **Rejection rule for performing a hypothesis test using the p-value method** (p. 441)

SECTION 9.4
- **Critical value, t_{crit}** (p. 454)
- t_{data} (p. 454).

$$t_{data} = \frac{\bar{x} - \mu_0}{s/\sqrt{n}}$$

SECTION 9.5
- **Essential idea about hypothesis testing for the proportion** (p. 469)
- **Standard error of the proportion** (p. 469)
- Z_{data} **for the hypothesis test for the population proportion** (p. 469).

$$Z_{data} = \frac{\hat{p} - p_0}{\sqrt{\dfrac{p_0(1 - p_0)}{n}}}$$

SECTION 9.6
- χ^2_{data} (p. 479).

$$\chi^2_{data} = \frac{(n - 1)s^2}{\sigma^2_0}$$

- **Essential idea about hypothesis testing for the standard deviation** (p. 480)

SECTION 9.7
- **Power curve** (p. 490)
- **Power of a hypothesis test** (p. 489)

Chapter 9 Review Exercises

SECTION 9.1
For Exercises 1–3, provide the null and alternative hypotheses.
1. Test whether $\mu < 12$.
2. Test whether $\mu > 10$.
3. Test whether μ is below zero.

For Exercises 4–6, do the following.
- **a.** Provide the null and alternative hypotheses.
- **b.** Describe the two ways a correct decision could be made.
- **c.** Describe what a Type I error would mean in the context of the problem.
- **d.** Describe what a Type II error would mean in the context of the problem.

4. **Household Size.** The U.S. Census Bureau reported that the mean household size is 2.58 persons. We conduct a hypothesis test to determine whether the population mean household size has changed.
5. **Speeding-Related Traffic Fatalities.** The National Highway Traffic Safety Administration reports that the mean number of speeding-related traffic fatalities over the Thanksgiving holiday period is 202.7. We conduct a hypothesis test to examine whether the population mean number of such fatalities has decreased.
6. **Salaries of Assistant Professors. Salaries.com** reports that the median salary for assistant professors in science was $49,934. We use this median salary to estimate that the mean salary in 2005 was $50,000. A hypothesis test was conducted to determine if the population mean salary of assistant professors in science has increased.

SECTION 9.2
For Exercises 7–9, find the value of Z_{data}.
7. $\bar{x} = 59, \sigma = 10, n = 100, \mu_0 = 60$

8. $\bar{x} = 59, \sigma = 5, n = 100, \mu_0 = 60$
9. $\bar{x} = 59, \sigma = 1, n = 100, \mu_0 = 60$

For each of the following hypothesis tests in Exercises 10–12, do the following.
- **a.** Find the value of Z_{crit}.
- **b.** Find the critical-value rejection rule.
- **c.** Draw a standard normal curve and indicate the critical region.
- **d.** State the conclusion and interpretation.

10. $H_0 : \mu = \mu_0$ versus $H_a : \mu \neq \mu_0$, $\alpha = 0.01$, $Z_{data} = -2.5$
11. $H_0 : \mu = \mu_0$ versus $H_a : \mu > \mu_0$, $\alpha = 0.10$, $Z_{data} = 1.5$
12. $H_0 : \mu = \mu_0$ versus $H_a : \mu > \mu_0$, $\alpha = 0.05$, $Z_{data} = -2.5$

For Exercises 13 and 14, do the following.
- **a.** State the hypotheses.
- **b.** Find the value of Z_{crit} and the rejection rule. Also, draw a standard normal curve, indicating the critical region.
- **c.** Calculate Z_{data}. Draw a standard normal curve showing Z_{crit}, the critical region, and Z_{data}.
- **d.** State the conclusion and the interpretation.

13. **Credit Scores in Florida.** According to **CreditReport** .com, the mean credit score in Florida in 2006 was 673. A random sample of 144 Florida residents this year shows a mean credit score of 650. Assume $\sigma = 50$. Perform a hypothesis test using level of significance $\alpha = 0.05$ to determine if the population mean credit score in Florida has decreased.
14. **Salary of College Grads.** It pays to stay in school. According to the U.S. Census Bureau, the mean salary of college graduates is $52,200, whereas the mean salary of those with "some college" is $36,800. A random sample of

100 college graduates provides a sample mean salary of $55,000. Assume $\sigma = \$3000$. Perform a hypothesis test to determine whether the population mean salary of college graduates has increased, using level of significance $\alpha = 0.10$.

SECTION 9.3

For Exercises 15 and 16, perform the following steps.

a. State the hypotheses and the rejection rule for the p-value method.

b. Calculate Z_{data}.

c. Find the p-value. Draw the standard normal curve, with Z_{data} and the p-value indicated on it.

d. State the conclusion and the interpretation.

15. We are interested in testing at level of significance $\alpha = 0.05$ whether the population mean differs from 500. A random sample of size 100 is taken, with a mean of 520. Assume $\sigma = 50$.

16. We would like to test at level of significance $\alpha = 0.01$ whether the population mean is less than -10. A random sample of size 25 is taken from a normal population. The sample mean is -12. Assume $\sigma = 2$.

17. Health Care Expenditures. We are interested in whether the population mean per capita annual expenditures on health care have increased since 2007, when the mean was $6096 per person.[30] A random sample taken this year of 100 Americans shows mean annual health care expenditures of $8000. Suppose that prior research has indicated that the population standard deviation of such expenditures is $1600. Perform the appropriate hypothesis test, using the p-value method and level of significance $\alpha = 0.01$.

18. The Old Coffee Machine. A random sample of 36 cups of coffee dispensed from the old coffee machine in the lobby had a mean amount of coffee of 7 ounces per cup. Assume that the population standard deviation is 1 ounce.

a. Construct a 95% confidence interval for the population mean amount of coffee dispensed by the old coffee machine in the lobby.

b. Use the confidence interval to test at level of significance $\alpha = 0.05$ whether the population mean amount of coffee dispensed by the old coffee machine in the lobby differs from the following amounts, in ounces.

   i. 6.9

   ii. 7.5

   iii. 6.7

   iv. 7

SECTION 9.4

For Exercises 19–21, find the critical value t_{crit} and sketch the critical region. Assume normality.

19. $H_0: \mu = 100, H_a: \mu > 100, n = 8, \alpha = 0.10$

20. $H_0: \mu = 100, H_a: \mu > 100, n = 8, \alpha = 0.05$

21. $H_0: \mu = 100, H_a: \mu > 100, n = 8, \alpha = 0.01$

22. Describe what happens to the t critical value t_{crit} for right-tailed tests as α decreases.

23. A random sample of size 16 from a normal population yields a sample mean of 10 and a sample standard deviation of 3. Test whether the population mean differs from 9, using level of significance $\alpha = 0.10$.

24. A random sample of size 144 from an unknown population yields a sample mean of 45 and a sample standard deviation of 10. Test whether the population mean differs from 45, using level of significance $\alpha = 0.10$.

SECTION 9.5

For Exercises 25–27, do the following.

a. Check the normality conditions.

b. State the hypotheses.

c. Find Z_{crit} and the rejection rule.

d. Calculate Z_{data}.

e. State the conclusion and the interpretation.

25. Test whether the population proportion exceeds 0.8. A random sample of size 1000 yields 830 successes. Let $\alpha = 0.10$.

26. Test whether the population proportion is below 0.2. A random sample of size 900 yields 160 successes. Let $\alpha = 0.05$.

27. Test whether the population proportion is not equal to 0.4. A random sample of size 100 yields 55 successes. Let $\alpha = 0.01$.

For Exercises 28 and 29, do the following.

a. Check the normality conditions.

b. State the hypotheses and the rejection rule for the p-value method, using level of significance $\alpha = 0.05$.

c. Calculate Z_{data}.

d. Calculate the p-value.

e. State the conclusion and the interpretation.

28. Test whether the population proportion differs from 0.7. A random sample of size 144 yields 110 successes.

29. Test whether the population proportion is less than 0.25. A random sample of size 100 yields 25 successes.

30. DSL Internet Service. The U.S. Department of Commerce reports that 41.6% of Internet users preferred DSL as their method of service delivery.[31] A random sample of 1000 Internet users shows 350 who preferred DSL. If appropriate, test whether the population proportion who prefer DSL has decreased, using level of significance $\alpha = 0.05$.

SECTION 9.6

For Exercises 31 and 32, do the following.

a. State the hypotheses.

b. Find the χ^2 critical value or values, and state the rejection rule.

c. Find χ^2_{data}. Also, draw a χ^2 distribution and indicate χ^2_{data} and the χ^2 critical value or values.

d. State the conclusion and the interpretation.

31. We are testing whether $\sigma > 6$ and have a random sample of size 20 with a standard deviation of $s = 9$. Let $\alpha = 0.05$.

32. We are testing whether $\sigma \neq 10$ and have a random sample of size 26 with a sample variance of 90. Let $\alpha = 0.05$.

For Exercises 33 and 34, do the following.
  a. State the hypotheses and the p-value rejection rule for $\alpha = 0.05$.
  b. Find χ^2_{data}.
  c. Find the p-value. Also, draw a χ^2 distribution and indicate χ^2_{data} and the p-value.
  d. State the conclusion and the interpretation.
33. We are testing whether $\sigma < 35$ and have a random sample of size 8 with a sample variance of 1200.
34. We are testing whether $\sigma \neq 50$ and have a random sample of size 26 with a standard deviation of $s = 45$.
35. Prisoner Deaths in State Custody. The following table contains the numbers of prisoners who died in state custody for a random sample of 5 states.[32] Assume normality. Using $\alpha = 0.01$ and the p-value method, test whether the population standard deviation of prisoners who died in state custody differs from 50. 🌐 **prisonerdeath**

New York	171
Pennsylvania	149
Michigan	140
Ohio	121
Georgia	122

SECTION 9.7
For Exercises 36–40, assume that the conditions for performing the Z test are met. Do the following.
  a. Calculate the value or values of $\bar{x}_{crit}$.
  b. Draw a normal curve, centered at μ_a, with the value or values of $\bar{x}_{crit}$ indicated.
  c. Calculate β, the probability of a Type II error for that value of μ_a. Shade the corresponding area under the normal curve.
  d. Calculate the power of the hypothesis test.
36. $H_0 : \mu = 100$ vs. $H_a : \mu \neq 100$, $\alpha = 0.01$, $\sigma = 15$, $n = 64$, $\mu_a = 103$
37. $H_0 : \mu = 100$ vs. $H_a : \mu \neq 100$, $\alpha = 0.01$, $\sigma = 15$, $n = 64$, $\mu_a = 106$
38. $H_0 : \mu = 100$ vs. $H_a : \mu \neq 100$, $\alpha = 0.01$, $\sigma = 15$, $n = 64$, $\mu_a = 109$
39. $H_0 : \mu = 100$ vs. $H_a : \mu \neq 100$, $\alpha = 0.01$, $\sigma = 15$, $n = 64$, $\mu_a = 112$
40. $H_0 : \mu = 100$ vs. $H_a : \mu \neq 100$, $\alpha = 0.01$, $\sigma = 15$, $n = 64$, $\mu_a = 115$
41. Refer to Exercises 36–40. Construct the power curve for the given values of μ_a.

Chapter 9 QUIZ

TRUE OR FALSE
1. True or false: It is possible that both the null and alternative hypotheses are correct at the same time.
2. True or false: The conclusion you draw from performing the critical-value method for the Z test is the same as the conclusion you draw from performing the p-value method for the Z test.
3. True or false: We do not need the estimated p-value method if we have access to a computer or calculator.

FILL IN THE BLANK
4. To reject H_0 when H_0 is true is a Type _____ error.
5. An extreme value of $\bar{x}$ is associated with a _____ p-value.
6. The rejection rule for performing a hypothesis test using the p-value method is to reject H_0 when the p-value is less than _____.

SHORT ANSWER
7. Under what conditions may we apply the Z test for the population proportion?
8. What does a small p-value indicate with respect to the null hypothesis? A large p-value?
9. Does the value of Z_{data} change when the form of the hypothesis test changes (for example, left-tailed instead of right-tailed)?

CALCULATIONS AND INTERPRETATIONS
10. ATM Fees. Do you hate paying the extra fees imposed by banks when withdrawing funds from an automated teller machine (ATM) not owned by your bank? The Federal Reserve System reports that the mean such fee is $1.14. A random sample of 36 such transactions yielded a mean of $1.07 in extra fees. Suppose the population standard deviation of such extra fees is $0.25.
  a. Test using level of significance $\alpha = 0.05$ whether there has been a reduction in the population mean fee charged on such transactions.
  b. Which type of error is it possible that we are making, a Type I error or a Type II error? Which type of error are we certain we are not making?
11. Alcohol-Related Fatal Car Accidents. The National Traffic Highway Safety Commission keeps statistics on the "mean years of potential life lost" in alcohol-related fatal automobile accidents. For males the mean years of life lost is 32. That is, on average, males involved in fatal drinking-and-driving accidents had their lives cut short by 32 years. A random sample of 36 alcohol-related fatal accidents had a mean years of life lost of 33.8, with a standard deviation of 6 years.
  a. Test whether the population mean years of life lost has changed, using a t test and level of significance $\alpha = 0.10$.
  b. Assess the strength of the evidence against the null hypothesis.

12. Preterm Births. The U.S. National Center for Health Statistics reports that, in 2005, the percentage of infants delivered at less than 37 weeks of gestation was 12.7%, up from 10.6% in 1990.[33] Has this upward trend continued? A random sample taken this year of 400 births contained 57 preterm births. Test whether the population proportion of preterm births has increased from 12.7%, using the p-value method and level of significance $\alpha = 0.05$.

13. Active Stocks. On October 3, 2007, the 10 most traded stocks on the New York Stock Exchange were those shown in the following table, which gives their closing prices and net change in price, in dollars. Use only the net change data for this analysis. Assume normality. Using for level of significance $\alpha = 0.10$ and the critical-value method, test whether the population standard deviation of net price change is less than 25 cents. **activestock**

Stock	Closing price	Net change
Micron Technology, Inc.	$10.74	−1.05
Ford Motor Company	$ 8.43	−0.14
Citigroup, Inc.	$47.89	0.03
Advanced Micro Devices	$13.23	0.03
EMC Corporation	$21.13	−0.24
Commerce Bancorp, Inc.	$38.84	−0.63
General Electric	$41.55	−0.57
Avaya, Inc.	$16.95	−0.07
Sprint Nextel Corporation	$18.76	−0.24
iShares:Taiwan	$17.18	−0.18

10

Two-Sample Inference

Introduction

This chapter examines differences in the characteristics of two populations. In Section 10.1, students construct confidence intervals and perform hypothesis tests to compare two dependent samples. Section 10.2 introduces inference techniques for comparing independent samples. Section 10.3 introduces the sampling distribution of the difference in sample proportions $\hat{p}_1 - \hat{p}_2$ and shows how to construct confidence intervals and hypothesis tests for $p_1 - p_2$.

Finally, Section 10.4 covers inference for two independent standard deviations.

From the Author

- **Section 10.1 Inference for Mean Difference–Dependent Samples**
  - Starting in Section 10.1 we have moved coverage of hypothesis testing ahead of confidence intervals for the remainder of the book, in line with common practice.
  - Instructors may wish to point out the similarity of the inference for μ_d to that of the t interval in Section 8.2 and the t test in Section 9.3.
- **Section 10.2 Inference for Two Independent Means**
  - Students often confuse μ_d with $\mu_1 - \mu_2$. Instructors may wish to point out that μ_d represents the population mean of the paired differences, while $\mu_1 - \mu_2$ refers to the difference in population means.
  - We use the terms "Welch's Hypothesis Test" and "Welch's Confidence Interval" for methods not using the pooled variance.
  - We have added two new topics to this section:
    - Objective 4: t Inference for $\mu_1 - \mu_2$ Using Pooled Variance, and
    - Objective 5: Z Inference for $\mu_1 - \mu_2$ When σ_1 and σ_2 Are Known
- **Section 10.3 Inference for Two Independent Proportions**
  - Instructors may wish to inform students, as a check on their calculations, that $\hat{p}_{\text{pooled}}$ must lie between $\hat{p}_1$ and $\hat{p}_2$.
- **Section 10.4 Inference for Two Independent Standard Deviations**
  - New section.
  - This is where the F distribution is introduced. Instructors who plan on covering Chapter 12, "Analysis of Variance," but are not covering inference for two independent standard deviations, may wish to return to this section for a quick review of the F distribution before starting Chapter 12.

Teaching Tips

The following are motivating examples for the three sections. For Section 10.1, compare the running times of students on the track team at the beginning and at the end of the season. For

Section 10.2, compare the amount of time per week spent studying of males and females. For Section 10.3, compare the difference between the proportion of males and the proportion of females who have a certain characteristic, such as blue eyes or an education major.

For Section 10.1, dependent samples, emphasize that, after taking the differences, what we are left with is essentially a *single sample* of the differences. Therefore, the formulas are similar to the t inference from Chapters 8 and 9, except that we are estimating the population mean of the differences.

For Section 10.2, independent samples, mention that $\bar{x}_1 - \bar{x}_2$ plays the same role that $\bar{x}$ played in the t inference from Chapters 8 and 9. For Section 10.3, mention that $\hat{p}_1 - \hat{p}_2$ plays the same role that $\hat{p}$ played in the Z interval for the proportion and the Z test for the proportion from Chapters 8 and 9.

In-Class Activities

1. **EESEE** case study: Is Friday the 13th Unhealthy? Let students conduct the projects listed at the end of this case study.

Confidence Interval for the Difference in True Mean Height Between Men and Women

2. **a.** What do you think is the difference in true mean height between men and women?

   b. Have each student generate a random sample of 10 male students from your class, using the random generator from the Chapter 1 activities.

   c. Have each student generate a random sample of 10 female students from your class, using the random generator from the Chapter 1 activities.

   d. Calculate the mean of each of your samples in (a) and (b). Then calculate the difference in sample means.

   e. Give each student a Post-It Note® to record his or her name and the difference in sample means calculated in (d).

   f. Have each student place his or her Post-It Note® on the number line that the instructor prepared on the blackboard. We thus have a collection of the differences in sample means.

   g. Using the evidence collected in (f), what would be a point estimate of the difference in true mean height for men and women?

   h. Is it plausible that the differences in sample means are normally distributed?

   i. Using his or her own sample, have each student calculate a 90% confidence interval for the difference in true mean heights between men and women.

   j. Are there any confidence intervals that contain the zero value? What would this indicate?

Hypothesis Test for the Difference in Population Mean Heights of Men and Women

3. **a.** Suppose we believe that there is no difference between the population mean heights of men and women, and we want to test this hypothesis. State the appropriate hypotheses.

b. Suppose we found the difference between sample mean heights of men and women to be 0.1 inch. Do you think this would be sufficient evidence to reject the null hypothesis that both sexes have the same mean height?

c. Suppose we found the difference between sample mean heights of men and women to be 1 inch. Do you think this would be sufficient evidence to reject the null hypothesis that both sexes have the same mean height?

d. Suppose we found the difference between sample mean heights of men and women to be 5 inches. Do you think this would be sufficient evidence to reject the null hypothesis that both sexes have the same mean height?

e. Generate a random sample of 10 male students from your class, using either (a) technology or (b) the *Random Sample* applet. Measure the heights of these students.

f. Generate a random sample of size 10 female students from your class, using either (a) technology or (b) the *Random Sample* applet. Measure the heights of these students.

g. Calculate the mean of each of your samples in (e) and (f). Then calculate the difference in sample means.

h. Do you think your difference in sample means is evidence against or in favor of the null hypothesis?

i. Each student, using his or her own sample, should perform a hypothesis test to determine whether or not there is no difference between mean heights of men and women. Use level of significance $\alpha = 0.10$. Will everyone in the class necessarily report the same conclusion? Why or why not?

j. Use the data from the entire class to perform a hypothesis test to determine whether or not there is no difference between mean heights of men and women. Use level of significance $\alpha = 0.10$. Are you guaranteed to come up with the same conclusion as in (i)? Why or why not?

Supplements

- StatTutor 18.6, 18.7(a), (b), and (c), 19.1–19.8, 21.1–21.6

Note: Not all parts of the following simulations deal with two population parameters.

- Stats@Work Simulations
  - Which Method to Use? Hypothesis Testing: Means and Proportions; Gary Pop
  - Which Method to Use? Hypothesis Testing: Means and Proportions; Sam Sport
  - Which Method to Use? Hypothesis Testing: Means and Proportions; Justine Red
  - Which Method to Use? Hypothesis Testing: Means and Proportions; Mindy Admin
- EESEE case studies
  - Sleeping Patterns in Ducks (Questions 1 and 2 on estimation and hypothesis tests for population means)
  - Surgery in a Blanket (Questions 1, 2, 4, 5, 6, and 7)
  - Keeping Balance as You Age (Questions 1 and 4. Students can be asked to compare the two groups through confidence intervals and hypothesis testing)
  - Is Caffeine Dependence Real? (Questions 1, 2, 3, 4, and 5)
  - Checkmating and Reading Skills (Questions 1, 2, 3, and 5)
  - Leave Survey After the Beep (Question 3)

Videos

- *Against All Odds* **www.learner.org/resources/series65.html**
  - Program 22: Comparing Two Means
  - Program 23: Inference for Proportions

Web Sites

- The site Online Statistics: An Interactive Multimedia Course of Study has information on hypothesis testing and confidence intervals, and it has a link to the Rice Virtual Lab in Statistics with numerous simulation demonstrations and other topics related to statistics: **http://onlinestatbook.com/index.html**.

- This Web site lists other sites that do statistical calculations: **http://statpages.org/**.

- This Web site lists activities on topics relating to hypothesis testing: **http://mathforum.org/mathtools/sitemap2/ps/**.

- This site has several activities using Excel and Minitab: **www.mathspace.com/NSF_ProbStat/Teaching_Materials/Primarily_Statistics.htm**.

Design Pics/Superstock

OVERVIEW

10

Two-Sample Inference

CASE STUDY Do Prior Student Evaluations Influence Students' Ratings of Professors?

A study in 1950 reported that instructor reputation affected students' ratings of their instructors.[1] Towler and Dipboye uncovered experimental evidence in support of this phenomenon.[2] They randomly assigned to students one of two summaries of prior student evaluations, one for a "charismatic instructor" and the other for a "punitive instructor." The "charismatic" summary included such phrases as "always lively and stimulating in class" and "always approachable and treated students as individuals." The "punitive" summary included such phrases as "did not show an interest in students' progress" and "consistently seemed to grade students harder." All subjects were then shown the same 20-minute lecture video given by the same instructor. They were asked to rate the instructor using three questions, and a summary rating score was calculated.

Were students' ratings influenced by the prior student evaluations? We examine this question further in the Case Study on page 520.

The Big Picture

Where we are coming from, and where we are headed . . .

- Thus far, our statistical inference has been limited to one population and one sample. In Chapter 8 we learned to construct confidence intervals, and in Chapter 9 we learned how to perform hypothesis tests, but all for a single population parameter.

- Here, in Chapter 10, "Two-Sample Inference," we perform inference on the differences in the parameters of two populations. For example, we may be interested in whether there is a difference in the population proportions of women and men who post personal information on the Internet.

- In Chapter 11, we will turn to inference methods for categorical data, such as contingency tables.

10.1 Inference for Mean Difference—Dependent Samples

OBJECTIVES By the end of this section, I will be able to . . .

1 Distinguish between independent samples and dependent samples.

2 Perform hypothesis tests for the population mean difference for dependent samples.

3 Construct and interpret confidence intervals for the population mean difference for dependent samples.

4 Use a t interval for μ_d to perform t tests about μ_d.

1 Independent Samples and Dependent Samples

Chapter 10 is about two-sample inference. The type of inference we apply depends on whether the data come from **independent samples** or **dependent samples.**

Independent Samples and Dependent Samples

Two samples are **independent** when the subjects selected for the first sample do not determine the subjects in the second sample. Two samples are **dependent** when the subjects in the first sample determine the subjects in the second sample. The data from dependent samples are called **matched-pair** or **paired** samples.

For example, suppose we are interested in comparing the heights of girl-boy fraternal twins. Selecting the girl twin for the first sample automatically results in the boy twin's being selected for the second sample. This is an example of dependent sampling, and the boy-girl pairs are called **matched-pair** samples or **paired** samples. However, suppose we are interested in comparing the heights of females and males in general. Then, if we took a random sample of 20 females at your school and another random sample of 20 males at your school, these samples would be **independent,** because the females selected in the first sample do not determine the males selected in the second sample.

Example 10.1 Dependent or independent sampling?

Indicate whether each of the following experiments uses an independent or dependent sampling method.

a. A study wished to compare the differences in price between name-brand merchandise and store-brand merchandise. Name-brand and store-brand items of the same size were purchased from each of the following six categories: paper towels, shampoo, cereal, ice cream, peanut butter, and milk.

b. A study wished to compare traditional acupuncture with usual clinical care for a certain type of lower-back pain.[3] The 241 subjects suffering from persistent nonspecific lower-back pain were randomly assigned to receive either traditional acupuncture or the usual clinical care. The results were measured at 12 and 24 months.

Solution

a. For a given store, each name-brand item in the first sample is associated with exactly one store-brand item of that size in the second sample. Therefore, the items in the first sample determine the items in the second sample. This is an example of dependent sampling.

Now You Can Do
Exercises 5–8.

b. The subjects were randomly assigned to receive either of the two treatments. Thus, the subjects that received acupuncture did not determine those who received clinical care, and vice versa. This is an example of independent sampling. ■

2 Dependent Sample *t* Test for the Population Mean of the Differences

Table 10.1 shows students' scores on two statistics quizzes. The "After" row (sample 1) contains scores after the students sought help in the Math Center, and the "Before" row (sample 2) shows scores before they had help. The observations are taken from the same students before and after they had help. Thus, sample 1 and sample 2 are dependent, matched-pair data.

Table 10.1 Statistics quiz scores of seven students before and after visiting the Math Center

Student	Ashley	Brittany	Chris	Dave	Emily	Fran	Greg
After (sample 1)	66	68	74	88	89	91	100
Before (sample 2)	50	55	60	70	75	80	88

Notice that each student's score improved on the second quiz:

Ashley: $66 - 50 = 16$ Emily: $89 - 75 = 14$
Brittany: $68 - 55 = 13$ Fran: $91 - 80 = 11$
Chris: $74 - 60 = 14$ Greg: $100 - 88 = 12$
Dave: $88 - 70 = 18$

The key idea behind dependent sampling is that we consider the set of these seven differences {16, 13, 14, 18, 14, 11, 12} as a sample so that we can perform inference on these differences. In other words, we no longer have two samples. By matching the samples element by element and taking the difference, we have transformed two samples into one that is the sample of differences (Figure 10.1). We have already learned how to perform inference using a single sample, so the remainder of this section uses techniques you have used before.

FIGURE 10.1
Taking the differences reduces a two-sample problem to a single sample of differences.

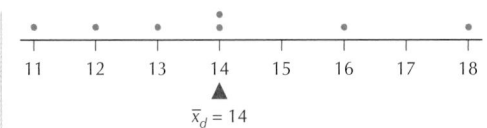

Difference in quiz scores (after – before)

Now You Can Do
Exercises 9–14.

The sample mean of the set of differences is

$$\bar{x}_d = \frac{16 + 13 + 14 + 18 + 14 + 11 + 12}{7} = 14$$

as illustrated in Figure 10.1. The sample of differences can be considered representative of the *population* of these differences, where the population represents all students who took statistics quizzes before and after visiting the Math Center. The sample mean difference $\bar{x}_d = 14$ is a point estimate of the *population mean difference* μ_d, the unknown mean difference in the (after – before) quiz scores for all students who visited the Math Center. Since μ_d is unknown, we need to perform hypothesis tests and construct confidence intervals to learn about its value.

Note that μ_d always refers to sample 1 minus sample 2, never sample 2 minus sample 1. For example, μ_d represents the mean difference between the students' "after" scores and the "before" scores on the statistics quizzes in Table 10.1.

Notice that since we have only one sample of differences this procedure is very similar to the one-sample *t* test from Section 9.4.

Paired Sample *t* Test for the Population Mean of the Differences μ_d: Critical-Value Method

For matched-pair data taken from dependent samples of two populations, find the differences to produce a random sample of the differences between the populations. You can use the *t* test whenever *either* of the following conditions is met:

- The population of differences is normal, or
- The sample size of differences is large ($n \geq 30$).

Step 1 State the hypotheses. Use one of the hypothesis test forms in Table 10.2. State the meaning of μ_d.

Step 2 Find t_{crit}, and state the rejection rule. To find t_{crit}, use the *t* table and degrees of freedom $n - 1$. To find the rejection rule, use Table 10.2.

Step 3 Calculate t_{data}.

$$t_{data} = \frac{\bar{x}_d}{s_d/\sqrt{n}}$$

which follows an approximate *t* distribution with degrees of freedom $n - 1$.

Step 4 State the conclusion and the interpretation. Compare t_{data} with t_{crit}.

Table 10.2 Critical regions and rejection rules for dependent sample *t* test

	Right-tailed test	**Left-tailed test**	**Two-tailed test**
Form of test	$H_0 : \mu_d = \mu_0$ $H_a : \mu_d > \mu_0$ level of significance α	$H_0 : \mu_d = \mu_0$ $H_a : \mu_d < \mu_0$ level of significance α	$H_0 : \mu_d = \mu_0$ $H_a : \mu_d \neq \mu_0$ level of significance α
Critical region			
Rejection rule	Reject H_0 if $t_{data} \geq t_{crit}$	Reject H_0 if $t_{data} \leq -t_{crit}$	Reject H_0 if $t_{data} \geq t_{crit}$ or $t_{data} \leq -t_{crit}$

Example 10.2 Paired *t* test using the critical-value method

groceries

Are name-brand groceries more expensive than store-brand groceries? A sample of 6 randomly selected grocery items yielded the price data shown in Table 10.3. Test at level of significance $\alpha = 0.05$ whether the population mean μ_d of the differences in price (name brand minus store brand) is greater than zero. Or, more informally, test whether the name-brand items at the grocery store cost more on average than the store-brand items.

Table 10.3 Prices of name-brand and store-brand grocery items

Item	Paper towels	Shampoo	Cereal	Ice cream	Peanut butter	Milk
Name brand	$1.29	$4.69	$3.59	$3.49	$2.79	$2.99
Store brand	$1.29	$3.99	$3.39	$2.69	$2.39	$3.49
Differences	$0.00	$0.70	$0.20	$0.80	$0.40	−$0.50

Solution

The normal probability plot of the differences shows acceptable normality, allowing us to proceed with the hypothesis test.

Difference in price (name brand – store brand)

Step 1 **State the hypotheses.** "Greater than" implies that $\mu_d > 0$, leading to the hypotheses

$$H_0 : \mu_d = 0 \qquad H_a : \mu_d > 0$$

where μ_d represents the population mean difference in price between name-brand and store-brand merchandise.

Step 2 **Find the critical value t_{crit} and state the rejection rule.** Use $n - 1$ degrees of freedom. Here $n = 6$, so df $= n - 1 = 5$. Since we have a right-tailed test with $\alpha = 0.05$, we find our t-critical value by choosing the column in the t table with area 0.05 in one tail: $t_{\text{crit}} = 2.015$. The right-tailed test tells us that our rejection rule is to reject H_0 when t_{data} is greater than 2.015.

Step 3 **Find t_{data}.** We need to calculate $\bar{x}_d$ and s_d.

$$\bar{x}_d = \frac{\sum x}{n} = \frac{0.00 + 0.70 + 0.20 + 0.80 + 0.40 - 0.50}{6} \approx \$0.267$$

$$s_d = \sqrt{\frac{\sum(x - \bar{x})^2}{n - 1}}$$

$$= \sqrt{\frac{(0.00 - 0.267)^2 + (0.70 - 0.267)^2 + (0.20 - 0.267)^2 + (0.80 - 0.267)^2 + (0.40 - 0.267)^2 + (-0.50 - 0.267)^2}{5}}$$

$$\approx \$0.48$$

This gives

$$t_{\text{data}} = \frac{\bar{x}_d}{s_d/\sqrt{n}} = \frac{0.267}{0.48/\sqrt{6}} \approx 1.36$$

Step 4 **State the conclusion and the interpretation.** Since $t_{\text{data}} = 1.36$ is not greater than $t_{\text{crit}} = 2.015$ (Figure 10.2), do not reject H_0. There is insufficient evidence that brand-name grocery items cost more, on average, than store-brand items at the $\alpha = 0.05$ level of significance. It appears that the brand-name milk was on sale; otherwise the conclusion may very well have been different. ∎

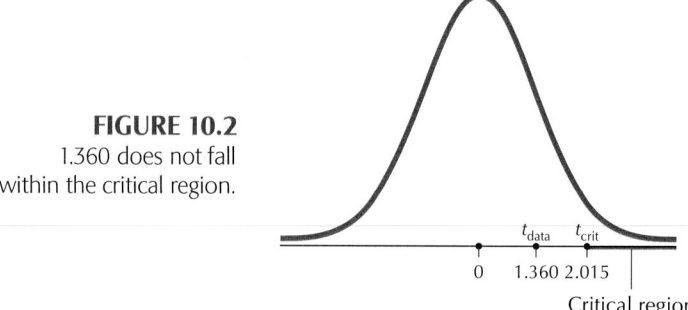

FIGURE 10.2
1.360 does not fall
within the critical region.

Now You Can Do
Exercises 15–17.

The paired sample t test may also be performed using the p-value method.

Paired Sample t Test for the Population Mean of the Differences μ_d: p-Value Method

For matched-pair data taken from dependent samples of two populations, find the differences to produce a random sample of the differences between the populations. You can use the t test whenever *either* of the following conditions is met:

- The population of differences is normal, or
- The sample size of differences is large ($n \geq 30$).

Step 1 State the hypotheses and the rejection rule. Use one of the hypothesis test forms from Table 10.4 for a test at level of significance α. State the meaning of μ_d. The rejection rule is reject H_0 if the p-value is less than α.
Step 2 Calculate t_{data}.

$$t_{data} = \frac{\bar{x}_d}{s_d/\sqrt{n}}$$

which follows an approximate t distribution with degrees of freedom $n - 1$.
Step 3 Find the p-value. If you have access to technology, use it to find the p-value. Otherwise, calculate the p-value using one of the test forms in Table 10.4.
Step 4 State the conclusion and the interpretation. Compare the p-value with α.

Table 10.4 p-Values for dependent sample t tests

	Right-tailed test	**Left-tailed test**	**Two-tailed test**
Form of test	$H_0 : \mu_d = \mu_0$ $H_a : \mu_d > \mu_0$	$H_0 : \mu_d = \mu_0$ $H_a : \mu_d < \mu_0$	$H_0 : \mu_d = \mu_0$ $H_a : \mu_d \neq \mu_0$
p-Value	p-value $= P(t > t_{data})$ Area to the right of t_{data}	p-value $= P(t < t_{data})$ Area to the left of t_{data}	p-value $= P(t > \lvert t_{data}\rvert) + P(t < -\lvert t_{data}\rvert)$ $= 2 \cdot P(t > \lvert t_{data}\rvert)$ Sum of the two-tailed areas

Example 10.3   Paired sample *t* test for μ_d: The *p*-value method

www.imagesource.com/Punchstock

A study was carried out to determine whether Reiki touch therapy was useful in the reduction of mean pain level in chronic pain sufferers, including cancer patients.[4] The pain level reported by a random sample of 13 patients before and after Reiki touch therapy is shown in Table 10.5. Test whether there has been a mean reduction in pain level after the Reiki therapy, using level of significance $\alpha = 0.05$. In other words, test whether the population mean difference μ_d is less than zero, where μ_d is defined as the (after – before) difference in pain level.

Table 10.5 Pain level reported by 13 patients before and after Reiki touch therapy

Patient	1	2	3	4	5	6	7	8	9	10	11	12	13
After	3	1	0	0	2	1	2	1	0	4	1	4	8
Before	6	2	2	3	3	4	2	5	1	6	6	4	8
Difference	−3	−1	−2	−3	−1	−3	0	−4	−1	−2	−5	0	0

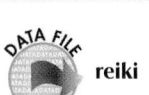
reiki

Solution

For each patient, we subtract the "before" pain level from the "after" pain level to arrive at a set of $n = 13$ differences, highlighted in Table 10.5. The normal probability plot of the differences indicates acceptable normality, given the small sample size. The Minitab results from the *t* test are provided here.

```
Test of mu = 0 vs < 0

                                          95%
                                        Upper
Variable    N      Mean     StDev  SE Mean    Bound       T       P
[Diff]     13  -1.92308   1.60528  0.44522 -1.12956   -4.32   0.000
```

Step 1 **State the hypotheses and the rejection rule.** We are interested in testing whether there was a mean reduction in pain level, which would mean that the mean pain level would be lower after the Reiki therapy than before. This implies that the population mean difference in pain level, μ_d = (after – before), is *less than* 0. Thus, from Table 10.4, the hypotheses are

$$H_0 : \mu_d = 0 \qquad H_a : \mu_d < 0$$

where μ_d represents the population mean difference in pain level. We will reject H_0 if the *p*-value < 0.05.

Step 2 **Find t_{data}.** As provided in the Minitab results,

$$t_{data} = \frac{\bar{x}_d}{s_d/\sqrt{n}} = \frac{-1.92308}{1.60528/\sqrt{13}} \approx -4.32$$

which follows an approximate *t* distribution with degrees of freedom $n - 1 = 13 - 1 = 12$.

$\boxed{\text{Step 3}}$ **Find the p-value.** For a left-tailed test, the p-value is the area to the left of t_{data}. This area is essentially 0, as shown in Figure 10.3 and provided by Minitab,

$$P(t < t_{\text{data}}) = P(t < -4.32) \approx 0.000$$

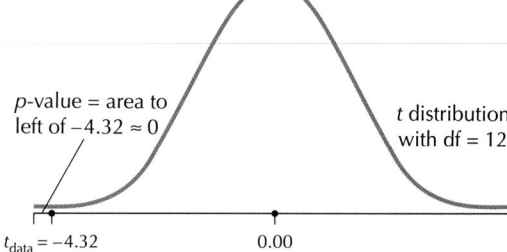

FIGURE 10.3
The p-value $=$
$P(t < -4.32) \approx 0.000.$

p-value = area to
left of $-4.32 \approx 0$

t distribution
with df = 12

$t_{\text{data}} = -4.32$ 0.00

$\boxed{\text{Step 4}}$ **State the conclusion and the interpretation.** Since p-value $\approx 0.000 \le \alpha = 0.05$, we reject H_0. There is evidence that $\mu_d < 0$ and hence that the population mean difference in pain level (after $-$ before) has decreased. That is, there is evidence at level of significance $\alpha = 0.05$ that the Reiki touch therapy has worked to reduce the mean pain level for chronic pain sufferers. ■

Now You Can Do
Exercises 18–20.

3 t Intervals for the Population Mean Difference for Dependent Samples

Recall that in Section 8.2 we used the formula $\bar{x} \pm t_{\alpha/2} (s/\sqrt{n})$ to calculate the t interval for the population mean μ. Here, to estimate the population mean of the differences μ_d, we use essentially the same formula, substituting $\bar{x}_d$ for $\bar{x}$ and s_d for s.

To construct this confidence interval, we need

$\bar{x}_d$ = mean of the differences of the two samples

s_d = standard deviation of the differences of the two samples

n = sample size of differences

$t_{\alpha/2}$ = critical value associated with confidence level $1 - \alpha$ and degrees of freedom $n - 1$.

Confidence Interval for Population Mean Difference μ_d (Dependent Samples)

For matched-pair data taken from dependent samples of two populations, find the differences to produce a random sample of the differences between the populations. A $100(1 - \alpha)\%$ confidence interval for μ_d, the population mean of the differences, is given by

$$\text{lower bound} = \bar{x}_d - t_{\alpha/2}\left(\frac{s_d}{\sqrt{n}}\right) \qquad \text{upper bound} = \bar{x}_d + t_{\alpha/2}\left(\frac{s_d}{\sqrt{n}}\right)$$

where $\bar{x}_d$ and s_d represent the sample mean and sample standard deviation of the differences, respectively, of the set of n paired differences, $d_1, d_2, d_3, \ldots, d_n$, and where $t_{\alpha/2}$ is based on $n - 1$ degrees of freedom. This t interval applies whenever *either* of the following conditions is met:

- The population of differences is normal, or
- The sample size of differences is large ($n \ge 30$).

The $100(1 - \alpha)\%$ confidence interval for μ_d may also be expressed in the form

$$\bar{x}_d \pm t_{\alpha/2}\left(\frac{s_d}{\sqrt{n}}\right)$$

$\boxed{\textbf{Example 10.4}}$ **t confidence interval for μ_d**

Use the "before" and "after" quiz scores from Table 10.1 to construct a 95% t confidence interval for the population mean of the differences in the statistics quiz scores. Is there evidence that the Math Center tutoring leads to a mean improvement in the quiz scores?

Solution

The normal probability plot of the differences shows acceptable normality, allowing us to construct the confidence interval.

We ignore the original raw data (see Table 10.1) and concentrate only on the set of sample differences: {16, 13, 14, 18, 14, 11, 12}. For the data set of $n = 7$ differences, we find the mean and standard deviation. We found earlier that $\bar{x}_d = 14$. Now we calculate

$$s_d = \sqrt{\frac{\sum(x - \bar{x})^2}{n - 1}}$$

$$= \sqrt{\frac{(16 - 14)^2 + (13 - 14)^2 + (14 - 14)^2 + (18 - 14)^2 + (14 - 14)^2 + (11 - 14)^2 + (12 - 14)^2}{7 - 1}}$$

$$\approx 2.3805$$

For 95% confidence with $n - 1 = 6$ degrees of freedom, $t_{\alpha/2}$ equals 2.447 (see Appendix Table D). Using these values,

$$\text{lower bound} = \bar{x}_d - t_{\alpha/2}(s_d/\sqrt{n}) \qquad \text{upper bound} = \bar{x}_d + t_{\alpha/2}(s_d/\sqrt{n})$$

$$= 14 - (2.447)(2.3805/\sqrt{7}) \qquad\qquad = 14 + (2.447)(2.3805/\sqrt{7})$$

$$\approx 14 - 2.2017 = 11.7983 \qquad\qquad \approx 14 + 2.2017 = 16.2017$$

We are 95% confident that the population mean of the differences between quiz scores before and after visiting the Math Center lies between 11.7983 points and 16.2017 points. If there were no mean change in the quiz scores, the difference would be 0, which is not in this confidence interval. Thus, we have evidence that the Math Center tutoring leads to a significant mean improvement in the quiz scores with 95% confidence. ∎

Now You Can Do
Exercises 21–26.

4 Use a t Interval for μ_d to Perform t Tests About μ_d

Given a $100(1 - \alpha)\%$ t confidence interval for μ_d, we may perform two-tailed t tests for various values of μ_d, just as we did for the single sample case in Section 9.4. The methodology is the same: if a certain value for μ_d lies outside the $100(1 - \alpha)\%$ t confidence interval for μ_d, then the null hypothesis specifying this value for μ_d would be rejected. Otherwise it would not be rejected.

Example 10.5 Using a t interval for μ_d to perform t tests about μ_d

Example 10.4 provided a 95% t confidence interval for the population mean of the differences between quiz scores before and after visiting the Math Center as (11.7983, 16.2017). Test using level of significance $\alpha = 0.05$ whether the population mean of the differences between quiz scores before and after visiting the Math Center differs from these values: (a) 15 points, (b) 16 points, (c) 17 points.

Solution

We state the hypotheses and determine if each proposed value μ_0 lies inside or outside of the t confidence interval (11.7983, 16.2017).

a. $H_0 : \mu_d = 15$ versus $H_a : \mu_d \neq 15$
   $\mu_0 = 15$ lies inside the interval (11.7983, 16.2017), so we do not reject H_0 (Figure 10.4).

b. $H_0 : \mu_d = 16$ versus $H_a : \mu_d \neq 16$
   $\mu_0 = 16$ lies inside the interval, so we do not reject H_0.

c. $H_0 : \mu_d = 17$ versus $H_a : \mu_d \neq 17$
   $\mu_0 = 17$ lies outside the interval, so we reject H_0. ∎

Now You Can Do
Exercises 27–30.

FIGURE 10.4   Reject H_0 for values of μ_d that lie outside the t confidence interval.

STEP-BY-STEP TECHNOLOGY GUIDE: Confidence Intervals and Hypothesis Tests for μ_d

TI-83/84

Hypothesis Test
(Example 10.2 is used to illustrate the procedure.)
Step 1   Enter samples 1 and 2 in lists L1 and L2.
Step 2   Type **(L1 − L2) STO→ L3** and press **ENTER**.
Step 3   Press **STAT** and highlight **TESTS**.
Step 4   For the hypothesis test, press **2** (for the **T-Test**). The T-Test menu appears.
Step 5   For input (**Inpt**), highlight **Data** and press **ENTER**. (If given the summary statistics for the differences, choose **STATS**.)
Step 6   For μ_0, enter the hypothesized value. For **List**, press **2nd** then **L3**. For **Freq**, enter **1**. Choose the form of the hypothesis test, and press **ENTER** (Figure 10.5).

Step 7   When the cursor is over **Calculate**, make sure all your entries are correct, and press **ENTER**. The results are shown in Figure 10.6.

FIGURE 10.5

FIGURE 10.6

Confidence Interval
(Example 10.4 is used to illustrate the procedure.)
Step 1   Enter samples 1 and 2 in lists L1 and L2.
Step 2   Type **(L1 − L2) STO→ L3** and press **ENTER** (Figure 10.7).
Step 3   Press **STAT** and highlight **TESTS**.
Step 4   Press **8** (for the **TInterval**).

Step 5   For input (**Inpt**), highlight **Data** and press **ENTER**. (If given the summary statistics for the differences, choose **STATS**.)
Step 6   For **List**, press **2nd** then **L3**. For **Freq**, enter **1**. Enter the **C-Level** (confidence level, such as **0.95** for 95%), and press **ENTER** (Figure 10.8).
Step 7   Highlight **Calculate** and press **ENTER**. The results are shown in Figure 10.9.

FIGURE 10.7

FIGURE 10.8

FIGURE 10.9

EXCEL

Hypothesis Test
Step 1   Enter samples 1 and 2 in columns A and B.
Step 2   Click **Data > Data Analysis > t-Test: Paired Two Sample for Means**, and click **OK**.

MINITAB

Confidence Interval and Hypothesis Test
Step 1   Enter samples 1 and 2 in columns C1 and C2.
Step 2   Click **Stat > Basic Statistics > Paired t**.
Step 3   For **First Sample**, enter **C1**, and for **Second Sample**, enter **C2**.

CRUNCHIT!

Paired *t* test and *t* interval for μ_d.
We will use the data from Example 10.3.
Step 1   Click **File** . . . then highlight **Load from Larose2e** . . . **Chapter 10** . . . and click on **Example 10.3**.
Step 2   Click **Statistics** and select **t** . . . **Paired**. For **First Variable** select **After**. For **Second Variable** select **Before**.

Step 3   For **Variable 1 Range**, highlight the cells for sample 1 in column A, and for **Variable 2 Range**, highlight the cells for sample 2 in column B.
Step 4   Enter the **Hypothesized Mean Difference** (usually 0), and enter a value for **alpha**. Then click **OK**.

Step 4   Click **Options**.
a. For the confidence interval, specify the **Confidence Level**, then click **OK** twice.
b. For the hypothesis test, specify the form of the alternative hypothesis, then click **OK** twice.

Hypothesis Test
Step 3   Select the **Hypothesis Test** tab, choose the correct form of the **Alternative** hypothesis, and click **Calculate**.
For the confidence interval:
Step 4   Select the **Confidence Interval** tab, enter the **Confidence Interval Level**, and click **Calculate**.

Section 10.1 Summary

1 Two samples are independent when the subjects selected for the first sample do not determine the subjects in the second sample. Two samples are dependent when the subjects in the first sample determine the subjects in the second sample. The data from dependent samples are called matched-pair or paired samples. The key concept in this section is that we consider the differences of matched-pair data as a single sample, and perform inference on this sample of differences.

2 The paired sample *t* test for the population mean of the differences μ_d can be used either when the population is normal or the sample size is large ($n \geq 30$). The test may be

carried out using either the critical-value method or the *p*-value method.

3 A $100(1 - \alpha)\%$ confidence interval for μ_d, the population mean of the differences, is given by $\bar{x}_d \pm t_{\alpha/2}(s_d/\sqrt{n})$, where $\bar{x}_d$ and s_d represent the sample mean and sample standard deviation of the differences, respectively, of the set of n paired differences, $d_1, d_2, d_3, \ldots, d_n$, and where $t_{\alpha/2}$ is based on $n - 1$ degrees of freedom.

4 This confidence interval may be used to conduct two-tailed hypothesis tests for μ_d.

Section 10.1 Exercises

CLARIFYING THE CONCEPTS

1. When are two samples considered independent?
2. When are two samples considered dependent?
3. What do we call the data obtained from dependent sampling?
4. How do we interpret the meaning of μ_d?

PRACTICING THE TECHNIQUES

Determine whether the experiments in Exercises 5–8 represent an independent sampling method or a dependent sampling method. Explain your answer.

5. The Jacksonville Jaguars are interested in comparing the performance of their first-year players. For each player, a sample is taken of their games from their last year in college

and compared to a sample of games taken from their first year in the pros.

6. For her senior project, an exercise science major takes a sample of females majoring in exercise science, and a sample of females from her college not majoring in exercise science. She records the body mass index for each subject.

7. Before the first lecture, an algebra instructor gives a pretest to his students to determine the students' algebra readiness. At the end of the course, the instructor gives a post-test to the same students and compares the results with the pretest.

8. The sheriff's department takes a sample of vehicle speeds on a certain stretch of road and compares the results to a sample of vehicle speeds on a certain stretch of a different road. Both roads have the same posted speed limit.

In Exercises 9–14, assume that samples of differences are obtained through dependent sampling and follow a normal distribution. Calculate $\bar{x}_d$ and s_d.

9.

Subject	1	2	3	4	5
Sample 1	3.0	2.5	3.5	3.0	4.0
Sample 2	2.5	2.5	2.0	2.0	1.5

10.

Subject	1	2	3	4	5	6
Sample 1	10	12	9	14	15	8
Sample 2	8	11	10	12	14	9

11.

Subject	1	2	3	4	5	6	7
Sample 1	20	25	15	10	20	30	15
Sample 2	30	30	20	20	25	35	25

12.

Subject	1	2	3	4	5	6	7
Sample 1	1.5	1.8	2.0	2.5	3.0	3.2	4.0
Sample 2	1.0	1.7	2.1	2.0	2.7	2.9	3.3

13.

Subject	1	2	3	4	5	6	7	8
Sample 1	0	0.5	0.75	1.25	1.9	2.5	3.2	3.3
Sample 2	0.25	0.25	0.75	1.5	1.8	2.2	3.3	3.4

14.

Subject	1	2	3	4	5	6	7	8
Sample 1	105	88	103	97	115	125	122	92
Sample 2	110	95	108	97	116	127	125	95

15. For the data in Exercise 9, test whether $\mu_d > 0$, using the critical-value method and level of significance $\alpha = 0.05$.

16. For the data in Exercise 10, test whether $\mu_d \neq 0$, using the critical-value method and level of significance $\alpha = 0.01$.

17. For the data in Exercise 11, test whether $\mu_d < 0$, using the critical-value method and level of significance $\alpha = 0.10$.

18. For the data in Exercise 12, test whether $\mu_d > 0$, using the p-value method and level of significance $\alpha = 0.01$.

19. For the data in Exercise 13, test whether $\mu_d \neq 0$, using the p-value method and level of significance $\alpha = 0.05$.

20. For the data in Exercise 14, test whether $\mu_d < 0$, using the p-value method and level of significance $\alpha = 0.10$.

21. Using the data from Exercise 9, construct a 95% confidence interval for μ_d.

22. Using the data from Exercise 10, construct a 99% confidence interval for μ_d.

23. Using the data from Exercise 11, construct a 90% confidence interval for μ_d.

24. Using the data from Exercise 12, construct a 99% confidence interval for μ_d.

25. Using the data from Exercise 13, construct a 95% confidence interval for μ_d.

26. Using the data from Exercise 14, construct a 90% confidence interval for μ_d.

For Exercises 27–30 a $100(1 - \alpha)\%$ t confidence interval for μ_d is given. Use the confidence interval to test using level of significance α whether μ_d differs from each of the indicated hypothesized values.

27. A 95% t confidence interval for μ_d is $(-5, 5)$. Hypothesized values are
   a. 0
   b. -6
   c. 4

28. A 99% t confidence interval for μ_d is $(-10, -4)$. Hypothesized values are
   a. -12
   b. 0
   c. 4

29. A 90% t confidence interval for μ_d is $(10, 20)$. Hypothesized values are
   a. -10
   b. 25
   c. 0

30. A 95% t confidence interval for μ_d is $(0, 1)$. Hypothesized values are
   a. 0.41
   b. 0.29
   c. 1.23

APPLYING THE CONCEPTS

31. New Car Prices. Kelley's Blue Book (kbb.com) publishes data on new and used cars. The following table contains the manufacturer's suggested retail price for four vehicles, model years 2006 and 2007. We are interested in the difference in price between the 2006 models and the 2007 models. Assume that the population of price differences is normally distributed. 🚗 **carprice**
   a. Find the mean of the differences, $\bar{x}_d$, and the standard deviation of the differences, s_d.
   b. Test whether 2007 models are on average more expensive, using level of significance $\alpha = 0.05$.

	Subaru Forester	Honda CR-V	Toyota RAV-4	Nissan Sentra
2006	$22,420	$20,990	$22,980	$13,815
2007	$21,820	$22,395	$23,630	$15,375

32. Mozart Effect? A researcher claims that listening to Mozart improves scores on math quizzes. A random sample of five students took math quizzes, first before and then after listening to Mozart. 🎵 **mozart**
   a. Find the mean of the differences, $\bar{x}_d$, and the standard deviation of the differences, s_d.
   b. Perform the appropriate hypothesis test for determining whether the results support the researcher's claim, using level of significance $\alpha = 0.10$. Assume normality.

Student	1	2	3	4	5
Before	75	50	80	85	95
After	85	45	85	95	95

33. High and Low Temperatures. The University of Waterloo Weather Station tracks the daily low and high temperatures in Waterloo, Ontario, Canada. Table 10.6 contains a random sample of the daily high and low temperatures for May 1–May 10, 2006, in degrees centigrade. Assume that the temperature differences are normally distributed. 🐾 **waterlootemp**

    a. Find the mean of the differences, $\bar{x}_d$, and the standard deviation of the differences, s_d.

    b. Test using level of significance $\alpha = 0.01$ whether the population mean difference between high and low temperatures differs from zero.

TABLE 10.6 High and low temperatures

May date	1	2	3	4	5	6	7	8	9	10
High temp.	19.0	19.8	23.3	21.1	15.2	9.9	17.2	21.7	21.2	23.9
Low temp.	7.4	3.0	3.9	7.9	4.4	0.7	−1.1	2.3	6.6	5.8

34. Falling Home Sales Prices. A credit crunch gripped the nation in 2007–2008, leading to record numbers of mortgage foreclosures and declines in home sales prices. The following table provides the median home sales prices for four regions of the country in the first quarter (January–March) of 2007 and the first quarter of 2008. Assume that the differences are normally distributed. 🐾 **homesales**

    a. Find the mean of the differences, $\bar{x}_d$, and the standard deviation of the differences, s_d.

    b. Test whether the population mean difference between the first quarter 2007 median price and the first quarter 2008 median price differs from zero, using level of significance $\alpha = 0.10$.

	Northeast	Midwest	South	West
Jan.–Mar. 2007	$370,300	$212,800	$222,900	$341,500
Jan.–Mar. 2008	$326,600	$201,900	$204,800	$298,900

Source: U.S. Census Bureau.

35. New Car Prices. Use the information in Exercise 31 to construct and interpret a 95% confidence interval for μ_d, the population mean difference in price.

36. Mozart Effect? Use the data from Exercise 32 to construct and interpret a 95% confidence interval for μ_d, the population mean difference in quiz scores before and after listening to Mozart.

37. High and Low Temperatures. Use the information in Exercise 33 for the following.

    a. Construct and interpret a 99% confidence interval for μ_d, the population mean difference in temperature.

    b. Explain how your confidence interval supports your conclusion to the hypothesis test in Exercise 33.

38. Falling Home Sales Prices. Use the information in Exercise 34 for the following.

    a. Construct and interpret a 99% confidence interval for μ_d, the population mean difference in price.

    b. Explain how your confidence interval supports your conclusion to the hypothesis test in Exercise 34.

39. Spell-Checking. A software manufacturer claims that its spell-checker can reduce spelling errors in text documents. A random sample of nine documents were written and the number of spelling errors counted before and after the spell-checker was used. Assume that the differences are normally distributed. 🐾 **spellcheck**

Document	1	2	3	4	5	6	7	8	9
Before	5	3	10	2	0	1	5	0	3
After	2	1	2	0	0	1	0	0	0

Is there evidence for the manufacturer's claim? Perform the appropriate hypothesis test, using level of significance $\alpha = 0.10$.

40. Science Scores Worldwide. The National Center for Educational Statistics publishes the results from the Trends in International Math and Science Study (TIMSS). Table 10.7 contains the 1995 and 2003 mean science scores for fourth-graders from various countries. Assume that the population of score differences is normally distributed. 🐾 **sciencescore**

    a. Construct a 90% confidence interval for μ_d, the population mean difference in score.

    b. Using level of significance $\alpha = 0.10$, test whether the 2003 scores are higher than the 1995 scores, on average.

TABLE 10.7 Fourth-grade science scores

Country	1995	2003
Singapore	523	565
Japan	553	543
Hong Kong	508	542
England	528	540
United States	542	536
Hungary	508	530
Latvia	486	530
Netherlands	530	525
New Zealand	505	523
Australia	521	521
Scotland	514	502
Slovenia	464	490
Cyprus	450	480
Norway	504	466
Iran	380	414

41. Reading Levels. An advertisement for a phonetics game claims that it will improve reading scores by at least 10 points. The reading levels of eight randomly selected children were tested without the phonetics game and retested after exposure to the game. Assume that the differences are normally distributed. 🐾 **reading**

Child	1	2	3	4	5	6	7	8
Pretest	70	65	85	50	75	80	90	60
Post-test	75	70	90	70	90	80	95	70

a. Find a 95% confidence interval for the population mean of the differences, μ_d.

b. Should we use the confidence interval in (a) to test the manufacturer's claim? Why or why not?

c. Using level of significance $\alpha = 0.05$, perform the appropriate hypothesis test.

42. Collisions Before and After. The Washington Department of Transportation compared collision data on particular sections of roadway before and after a series of road improvements to determine whether road improvements lowered the number of collisions per year (Table 10.8).[5] Assume that the differences are normally distributed. 🔊 **collisions**

TABLE 10.8   Collision data

Location	Before	After
Seattle	77.5	43.8
Shoreline	63.3	33.6
Othello	7.4	2.0
Ephrata	5.7	2.9
Alderton	49.9	40.3
Ellensburg	14.9	10.7
Snoqualmie	19.4	10.4
Sunnyside	12.0	11.7
Ritzville	39.0	23.7
Milton	14.5	11.2
Skagit	8.8	17.5
Spokane	114.7	77.3
Kent	25.3	13.8
Vancouver	22.4	4.3
Poulsbo	5.0	12.8

a. Find the point estimate of the mean decrease in collisions per year.

b. Find a 95% confidence interval for the population mean of the differences, μ_d.

c. Using level of significance $\alpha = 0.01$, test whether the improvements have lowered the population mean number of collisions per year.

43. NHL Goals Scored. The entire 2004–2005 National Hockey League season was canceled due to a lockout by the owners looking to introduce a player salary cap. During this time, the league also introduced rule changes designed to increase the number of goals scored per game. Table 10.9 shows the goals scored per game for a random sample of six NHL teams in the season before (2003–2004) and the season after (2005–2006) the lockout. Assume that the differences are normally distributed. Test whether the population mean

number of goals scored per game increased, using level of significance $\alpha = 0.01$. 🔊 **nhlgoals**

44. Refer to Exercise 43. *What if* we added a certain amount to every entry in the 2005–2006 season results. How would this change affect the conclusion?

BRINGING IT ALL TOGETHER

Home Sales. Use the following information for Exercises 45–49. The number of sales of single family residences in a random sample of towns in eastern Connecticut is provided in Table 10.10 for the time periods January–September 2006 and January–September 2007. Assume that the differences are normally distributed. 🔊 **cthomesales**

TABLE 10.10   Home sales in eastern Connecticut

Town	2006	2007
Andover	31	32
Bolton	46	39
Coventry	180	137
East Hartford	469	405
Ellington	121	121
Hebron	98	74
Manchester	475	479
Somers	60	73
South Windsor	154	161
Stafford	114	89
Suffield	114	121
Tolland	146	141
Vernon	210	213
Windsor	327	288
Windsor Locks	120	128

Source: Manchester (CT) *Journal-Inquirer,* November 7, 2007.

45. Explain why these are dependent samples and not independent samples.

46. Calculate the following statistics.
   a. $\bar{x}_d$
   b. s_d
   c. t_{data}

47. Test using level of significance $\alpha = 0.05$ whether the population mean number of home sales μ_d differs from 2006 to 2007.

48. Construct a 95% confidence interval for μ_d.

49. *What if* we added a certain number of home sales to every entry in the table. How would this change affect the conclusion?

TABLE 10.9   NHL goals scored

	Detroit Red Wings	Tampa Bay Lightning	Phoenix Coyotes	Atlanta Thrashers	Colorado Avalanche	Dallas Stars
2003–2004 season	3.11	2.99	2.29	2.61	2.88	2.37
2005–2006 season	3.67	3.00	2.95	3.37	3.42	3.08

10.2   Inference for Two Independent Means

OBJECTIVES By the end of this section, I will be able to . . .

1   Perform and interpret t tests about $\mu_1 - \mu_2$ using Welch's method.[6]

2   Compute and interpret t intervals for $\mu_1 - \mu_2$ using Welch's method.

3   Use confidence intervals for $\mu_1 - \mu_2$ to perform two-tailed t tests about $\mu_1 - \mu_2$.

4   Perform and interpret t tests and t intervals about $\mu_1 - \mu_2$ using the pooled variance method.

5   Apply Z tests and Z intervals for $\mu_1 - \mu_2$ when σ_1 and σ_2 are known.

1 Independent Sample t Test for $\mu_1 - \mu_2$

On page 142 in Chapter 3 we used boxplots to find evidence of a difference between male and female body temperature for a sample of 65 women and a sample of 65 men. The summary statistics are shown in Table 10.11.

Table 10.11 Summary statistics for female versus male body temperatures in °F

Gender	Sample size	Sample mean body temperature	Sample standard deviation	Population mean body temperature
Females (sample 1)	$n_1 = 65$	$\bar{x}_1 = 98.394$	$s_1 = 0.743$	$\mu_1 = ?$
Males (sample 2)	$n_2 = 65$	$\bar{x}_2 = 98.105$	$s_2 = 0.699$	$\mu_2 = ?$

However, since the female subjects did not determine the male subjects, and vice versa, the 65 women and 65 men represent independent samples, so we cannot use the dependent sampling methods we learned in Section 10.1.

Note that for independent samples, we have two sample sizes, n_1 and n_2, two sample means, $\bar{x}_1$ and $\bar{x}_2$, two sample standard deviations, s_1 and s_2, and two unknown population means, μ_1 and μ_2. Since we are interested in the difference in the population means, we consider the quantity

$$\mu_1 - \mu_2$$

Developing Your Statistical Sense

The Difference Difference

There is a difference in interpretation between the quantity $\mu_1 - \mu_2$ and the quantity μ_d from Section 10.1. Here, $\mu_1 - \mu_2$ refers to the difference in population means, whereas μ_d represents the population mean of the paired differences. ◢

In previous chapters we used the statistic $\bar{x}$ to learn about the parameter μ. Here we shall use the statistic $\bar{x}_1 - \bar{x}_2$ to perform inference about the parameter $\mu_1 - \mu_2$, whose value is unknown. Note from Table 10.11 that the value of $\bar{x}_1 - \bar{x}_2$ for these samples is

$$\bar{x}_1 - \bar{x}_2 = 98.394 - 98.105 = 0.289$$

We use $\bar{x}_1 - \bar{x}_2 = 0.289$ as a *point estimate* of $\mu_1 - \mu_2$. If we repeat the experiment an infinite number of times, then the values of $\bar{x}_1 - \bar{x}_2$ will form a distribution called the **sampling distribution of $\bar{x}_1 - \bar{x}_2$.**

It is unlikely that the experimenter will have knowledge of both population standard deviations σ_1 and σ_2. Therefore, we use the estimates of σ_1 and σ_2 provided by the sample standard deviations s_1 and s_2. Recall from Section 8.2 that, when the population standard deviation σ is unknown, and if either the population is normal or the sample size is large, the quantity

$$t = \frac{\bar{x} - \mu}{s/\sqrt{n}}$$

has a t distribution with $n - 1$ degrees of freedom. By analogy, we have the following sampling distribution.

Sampling Distribution of $\bar{x}_1 - \bar{x}_2$

When random samples are drawn independently from two populations with population means μ_1 and μ_2, and either (a) the two populations are normally distributed, or (b) the two sample sizes are large (at least 30), then the quantity

$$t = \frac{(\bar{x}_1 - \bar{x}_2) - (\mu_1 - \mu_2)}{\sqrt{\frac{s_1^2}{n_1} + \frac{s_2^2}{n_2}}}$$

approximately follows a t distribution with degrees of freedom equal to the smaller of $n_1 - 1$ and $n_2 - 1$, where $\bar{x}_1$ and s_1 represent the mean and standard deviation of the sample taken from population 1, and $\bar{x}_2$ and s_2 represent the mean and standard deviation of the sample taken from population 2.

This t statistic is called *Welch's approximate t*, after the twentieth-century English statistician Bernard Lewis Welch. Although there are other distributions that statisticians use to estimate the difference between two population means, we use this approximation because it is conservative and easy to calculate.

Researchers are often interested in testing whether the mean of one population is greater than, less than, or different from the mean of another population. Thus, we next learn how to perform hypothesis tests for the difference in population means $\mu_1 - \mu_2$. Usually the most important hypothesized value for $\mu_1 - \mu_2$ is 0. Consider the two-tailed hypothesis test

$$H_0 : \mu_1 - \mu_2 = 0 \quad \text{versus} \quad H_a : \mu_1 - \mu_2 \neq 0$$

which is equivalent to

$$H_0 : \mu_1 = \mu_2 \quad \text{versus} \quad H_a : \mu_1 \neq \mu_2$$

In practice, the hypothesized difference between the two population means is nearly always $(\mu_1 - \mu_2)_0 = 0$. Thus, the test statistic takes the following form:

$$t_{\text{data}} = \frac{(\bar{x}_1 - \bar{x}_2) - 0}{\sqrt{\frac{s_1^2}{n_1} + \frac{s_2^2}{n_2}}} = \frac{(\bar{x}_1 - \bar{x}_2)}{\sqrt{\frac{s_1^2}{n_1} + \frac{s_2^2}{n_2}}}$$

Just as in Section 9.3, if t_{data} is extreme, then it represents evidence against the null hypothesis. The hypothesis test may be carried out using either the critical-value method or the p-value method.

> **Welch's Hypothesis Test for the Difference in Two Population Means: Critical-Value Method**
>
> The hypothesis test applies whenever *either*
>
> **a.** Both populations are normally distributed, or
>
> **b.** Both samples are large, that is $n_1 \geq 30$ and $n_2 \geq 30$.
>
> *Step 1* **State the hypotheses.** Use one of the forms from Table 10.12. State the meaning of μ_1 and μ_2.
>
> *Step 2* **Find t_{crit} and state the rejection rule.** To find t_{crit}, use the t table and degrees of freedom the *smaller* of $n_1 - 1$ and $n_2 - 1$. To find the rejection rule, use Table 10.12.
>
> *Step 3* **Calculate t_{data}.**
>
> $$t_{\text{data}} = \frac{(\bar{x}_1 - \bar{x}_2)}{\sqrt{\dfrac{s_1^2}{n_1} + \dfrac{s_2^2}{n_2}}}$$
>
> which follows an approximate t distribution with degrees of freedom the smaller of $n_1 - 1$ and $n_2 - 1$.
>
> *Step 4* **State the conclusion and the interpretation.** Compare t_{data} with t_{crit}.

Table 10.12 Critical regions and rejection rules for t test for $\mu_1 - \mu_2$

	Right-tailed test	**Left-tailed test**	**Two-tailed test**
Form of test	$H_0: \mu_1 = \mu_2$ $H_a: \mu_1 > \mu_2$ level of significance α	$H_0: \mu_1 = \mu_2$ $H_a: \mu_1 < \mu_2$ level of significance α	$H_0: \mu_1 = \mu_2$ $H_a: \mu_1 \neq \mu_2$ level of significance α
Critical region			
Rejection rule	Reject H_0 if $t_{\text{data}} \geq t_{\text{crit}}$	Reject H_0 if $t_{\text{data}} \leq -t_{\text{crit}}$	Reject H_0 if $t_{\text{data}} \geq t_{\text{crit}}$ or $t_{\text{data}} \leq -t_{\text{crit}}$

Example 10.6 t Test for $\mu_1 - \mu_2$: critical-value method

Using Table 10.11, test whether women's population mean body temperature differs from that of men, using the critical-value method and $\alpha = 0.05$.

Solution

Both sample sizes are large ($n_1 = n_2 = 65 \geq 30$), so we can perform the hypothesis test.

Step 1 **State the hypotheses.** The key words "differs from" indicate a two-tail test:

$$H_0: \mu_1 = \mu_2 \quad \text{versus} \quad H_a: \mu_1 \neq \mu_2$$

where μ_1 and μ_2 represent the population mean body temperature for women and men, respectively.

Step 2 **Find t_{crit} and state the rejection rule.** The required degrees of freedom is the smaller of $n_1 - 1$ and $n_2 - 1$, which is $65 - 1 = 64$. Again df $= 64$, but we use the conservative df $= 60$ in the t table in Appendix Table D. For $\alpha = 0.05$, this gives

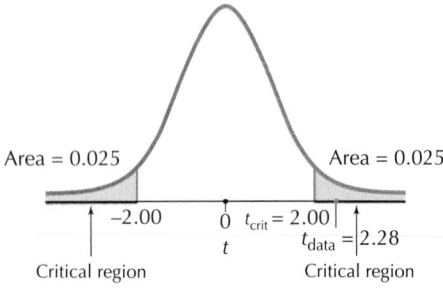

Area = 0.025   Area = 0.025

−2.00   0 t_{crit} = 2.00

t t_{data} = 2.28

Critical region   Critical region

FIGURE 10.10 $t_{data} = 2.28$ falls within the critical region.

Now You Can Do
Exercises 3–6.

$t_{crit} = 2.000$. We have a two-tailed test, so Table 10.12 gives us the following rejection rule:

$$\text{Reject } H_0 \text{ if } t_{data} > 2.000 \text{ or } t_{data} < -2.000$$

Step 3 Find t_{data}.

$$t_{data} = \frac{(\bar{x}_1 - \bar{x}_2)}{\sqrt{\dfrac{s_1^2}{n_1} + \dfrac{s_2^2}{n_2}}} = \frac{(98.394 - 98.105)}{\sqrt{\dfrac{(0.743)^2}{65} + \dfrac{(0.699)^2}{65}}} \approx 2.28$$

Step 4 **State the conclusion and the interpretation.** The test statistic $t_{data} = 2.28$ is greater than $t_{crit} = 2.000$ (see Figure 10.10).

We therefore reject H_0. There is evidence at level of significance $\alpha = 0.05$ that the difference in population mean body temperatures is not the same for women and men. ■

We may also use the p-value method to perform the independent sample t test for $\mu_1 - \mu_2$.

Welch's Hypothesis Test for the Difference in Two Population Means: p-Value Method

The hypothesis test applies whenever *either*

    a. Both populations are normally distributed, or

    b. Both samples are large, that is $n_1 \geq 30$ and $n_2 \geq 30$.

Step 1 **State the hypotheses and the rejection rule.** Use one of the forms from Table 10.13. State the meaning of μ_1 and μ_2. The rejection rule is *Reject H_0 if the p-value is $\leq \alpha$.*

Step 2 **Calculate t_{data}.**

$$t_{data} = \frac{(\bar{x}_1 - \bar{x}_2)}{\sqrt{\dfrac{s_1^2}{n_1} + \dfrac{s_2^2}{n_2}}}$$

which follows an approximate t distribution with degrees of freedom the smaller of $n_1 - 1$ and $n_2 - 1$.

Step 3 **Find the p-value.** Use technology or estimate using the t table.

Step 4 **State the conclusion and the interpretation.** Compare the p-value with α.

Table 10.13 p-Values for t test for $\mu_1 - \mu_2$

	Right-tailed test	**Left-tailed test**	**Two-tailed test**
Form of test	$H_0 : \mu_1 = \mu_2$ $H_a : \mu_1 > \mu_2$	$H_0 : \mu_1 = \mu_2$ $H_a : \mu_1 < \mu_2$	$H_0 : \mu_1 = \mu_2$ $H_a : \mu_1 \neq \mu_2$
p-Value	$p\text{-value} = P(t > t_{data})$ Area to the right of t_{data}	$p\text{-value} = P(t < t_{data})$ Area to the left of t_{data}	$p\text{-value} = P(t > \lvert t_{data}\rvert) +$ $P(t < -\lvert t_{data}\rvert) = 2 \cdot P(t > \lvert t_{data}\rvert)$ Sum of the two tail areas

Example 10.7 t Test for $\mu_1 - \mu_2$ using the p-value method and technology

amleague
natleague

Many baseball fans hold that, because of the designated hitter rule, there are more runs scored in the American League than in the National League. Perform an independent samples t test to find out whether that was indeed the case in 2006. Use the TI-83/84 or Excel, the p-value method, and level of significance $\alpha = 0.05$. Table 10.14 contains the mean runs per game (RPG) for a random sample of six teams from each league.

Table 10.14 Major League Baseball runs scored per game, 2006 regular season

American League: Sample 1		National League: Sample 2	
Team	**RPG**	**Team**	**RPG**
New York Yankees	5.74	Philadelphia Phillies	5.34
Chicago White Sox	5.36	Atlanta Braves	5.24
Texas Rangers	5.15	Colorado Rockies	5.02
Detroit Tigers	5.07	Arizona Diamondbacks	4.77
Boston Red Sox	5.06	Florida Marlins	4.68
Los Angeles Angels	4.73	Houston Astros	4.54

Solution

Because the samples are small, we must determine whether both populations are normally distributed. The normal probability plots for RPG for each league indicate acceptable normality, so we may perform the hypothesis test.

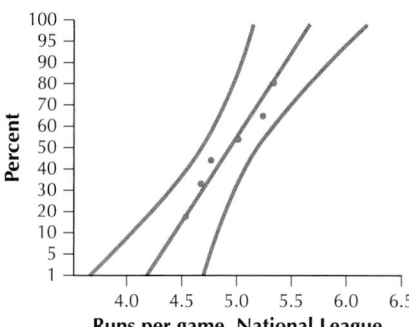

Note: Our degrees of freedom, the smaller of $n_1 - 1$ and $n_2 - 1$, is $6 - 1 = 5$. However, the TI-83/84 shows df = 9.966314697, and the Excel output rounds this to 10. Why does the technology use different degrees of freedom than we do? Recall that we are using Welch's approximation to the t distribution. The TI-83/84, Excel, Minitab, and other technology calculate the degrees of freedom as follows:[7]

$$ df = \frac{\left(\dfrac{s_1^2}{n_1} + \dfrac{s_2^2}{n_2}\right)^2}{\dfrac{\left(\dfrac{s_1^2}{n_1}\right)^2}{n_1 - 1} + \dfrac{\left(\dfrac{s_2^2}{n_2}\right)^2}{n_2 - 1}} $$

This provides a more accurate determination of the degrees of freedom than our method. However, our method is a conservative estimate that is easier to calculate, and it is recommended for hand calculations.

Step 1 **State the hypotheses and the rejection rule.** Since the American League represents sample 1 and we are interested in whether the American League has scored *more* runs than the National League, we have the following hypotheses:

$$ H_0 : \mu_1 = \mu_2 \quad \text{versus} \quad H_a : \mu_1 > \mu_2 $$

where μ_1 and μ_2 represent the population mean runs per game for the American League and National League, respectively. The rejection rule is to reject H_0 if p-value ≤ 0.05.

Step 2 **Find t_{data}.** We use the instructions provided in the Step-by-Step Technology Guide at the end of this section. From either Figure 10.11 or Figure 10.12,

$$ t_{\text{data}} = \frac{(\bar{x}_1 - \bar{x}_2)}{\sqrt{\dfrac{s_1^2}{n_1} + \dfrac{s_2^2}{n_2}}} \approx \frac{(5.185 - 4.932)}{\sqrt{\dfrac{0.339^2}{6} + \dfrac{0.320^2}{6}}} \approx 1.3301 $$

	American	National
Mean	5.185	4.9317
Variance	0.11515	0.1025
Observations	6	6
Hypothesized Mean Difference	0	
df	10	
t Stat	1.3301 t_{data}	
P(T<=t) one-tail	0.1065 p-value	
t Critical one-tail	1.8125	
P(T<=t) two-tail	0.2130	
t Critical two-tail	2.2281	

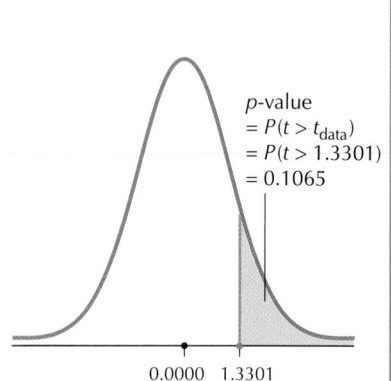

p-value
$= P(t > t_{data})$
$= P(t > 1.3301)$
$= 0.1065$

0.0000 1.3301

FIGURE 10.13 The p-value for the right-tailed t test.

```
2-SampTTest
 μ1>μ2
t=1.330123458
p=.1065564474
df=9.966314697
x̄1=5.185
↓x̄2=4.931666667
```

FIGURE 10.11
TI-83/84 output.

FIGURE 10.12 Excel output.

Step 3 **Find the p-value.** From either Figure 10.11 or Figure 10.12,

$$p\text{-value} = P(t > t_{data}) = P(t > 1.3301) = 0.1065$$

This p-value is illustrated in Figure 10.13.

Step 4 **State the conclusion and the interpretation.** Our p-value of 0.1065 is not ≤ 0.05. Therefore, we do not reject H_0. There is insufficient evidence that the population mean runs scored per game is greater in the American League than in the National League. ∎

Now You Can Do
Exercises 7–10.

2 t Confidence Intervals for $\mu_1 - \mu_2$

Recall from Section 8.2 that to estimate the unknown population mean μ, we can use a t confidence interval:

$$\bar{x} \pm E = \bar{x} \pm t_{\alpha/2} (s/\sqrt{n})$$

where E is the **margin of error.** By analogy, here the t interval for $\mu_1 - \mu_2$ takes the following form.

Welch's Confidence Interval for $\mu_1 - \mu_2$

For two independent random samples taken from two populations with population means μ_1 and μ_2, a **100$(1 - \alpha)$% confidence interval for $\mu_1 - \mu_2$** is given by

$$(\bar{x}_1 - \bar{x}_2) \pm t_{\alpha/2}\sqrt{\frac{s_1^2}{n_1} + \frac{s_2^2}{n_2}}$$

where $\bar{x}_1$, s_1, and n_1 represent the mean, standard deviation, and sample size of the sample taken from population 1 and $\bar{x}_2$, s_2, and n_2 represent the mean, standard deviation, and sample size of the sample taken from population 2, and $t_{\alpha/2}$ is associated with the confidence level and degrees of freedom of the smaller of $n_1 - 1$ and $n_2 - 1$.

The t interval applies whenever *either* of the following conditions is met:

- Both populations are normally distributed, or
- Both sample sizes are large.

Margin of Error E

The **margin of error** for a 100$(1 - \alpha)$% confidence interval for $\mu_1 - \mu_2$ is given by

$$E = t_{\alpha/2} \cdot \sqrt{\frac{s_1^2}{n_1} + \frac{s_2^2}{n_2}}$$

Thus, the confidence interval for $\mu_1 - \mu_2$ takes the form $(\bar{x}_1 - \bar{x}_2) \pm E$.

This is a confidence interval for the difference in two population means, which is not the same as in Section 10.1, which was for the population mean of the differences of matched pairs. Here, we calculate the means of the samples and then compute the difference. In Section 10.1 we calculated the differences of sample values first and then computed the mean of these differences.

Example 10.8 Confidence interval for $\mu_1 - \mu_2$

Find a 95% confidence interval for the difference in women's and men's population mean body temperatures, using the data in Table 10.11.

Solution

Both sample sizes are large ($n_1 = n_2 = 65 \geq 30$), so we may construct the interval. For $t_{\alpha/2}$, the required degrees of freedom is the smaller of $n_1 - 1$ and $n_2 - 1$, which is $65 - 1 = 64$. We again use the conservative df = 60. For 95% confidence, then, $t_{\alpha/2} = 2.00$. The margin of error is

$$E = t_{\alpha/2} \cdot \sqrt{\frac{s_1^2}{n_1} + \frac{s_2^2}{n_2}} \approx (2.00) \cdot \sqrt{\frac{(0.743)^2}{65} + \frac{(0.699)^2}{65}} = 0.253$$

The 95% confidence interval is then

$$(\bar{x}_1 - \bar{x}_2) \pm E = (98.394 - 98.105) \pm 0.253 = 0.289 \pm 0.253 = (0.036, 0.542).$$

Now You Can Do
Exercises 11–16.

We are 95% confident that the difference in population means $\mu_1 - \mu_2$ lies between 0.036°F and 0.542°F. Since 0 is not contained in this interval, we may conclude that $\mu_1 \neq \mu_2$, just as we did in Example 10.6. ■

3 Using Confidence Intervals to Perform Hypothesis Tests

As in earlier sections, we may use a $100(1 - \alpha)\%$ t confidence interval for $\mu_1 - \mu_2$ to perform two-tailed t tests about $\mu_1 - \mu_2$.

> **Equivalence of a Two-Tailed t Test About $\mu_1 - \mu_2$ and a t Confidence Interval for $\mu_1 - \mu_2$**
> - If a certain value for $\mu_1 - \mu_2$ lies *outside* the corresponding $100(1 - \alpha)\%$ t confidence interval for $\mu_1 - \mu_2$, then the null hypothesis specifying this value would be *rejected* for level of significance α.
> - Alternatively, if a certain value for $\mu_1 - \mu_2$ lies *inside* the $100(1 - \alpha)\%$ t confidence interval for $\mu_1 - \mu_2$, then the null hypothesis specifying this value would *not be rejected* for level of significance α.

Example 10.9 Using a t confidence interval to perform a two-tailed t test about $\mu_1 - \mu_2$

amleague
natleague

a. Construct a 95% confidence interval for the difference in runs scored per game in the American League and National League, using the data from Example 10.7.
b. Test using level of significance $\alpha = 0.05$ whether the population mean number of runs scored per game in the American League differs from the population mean number of runs scored in the National League.

Solution

a. Figure 10.14 shows the 95% confidence interval for $\mu_1 - \mu_2$, where μ_1 and μ_2 represent the population mean runs per game in the American and National Leagues, respectively:

$$(-0.1712, 0.6779)$$

FIGURE 10.14 TI-83/84 results.

Now You Can Do
Exercises 17–20.

b. The confidence interval in part (a) does contain 0. That is, 0 lies between –0.1712 and 0.6779. Therefore, with level of significance $\alpha = 0.05$, we do not reject the hypothesis that there is no difference between population mean runs scored per game in the American and National Leagues. ■

Design Pics/Superstock

CASE STUDY

Do Prior Student Evaluations Influence Students' Ratings of Professors?

In this case study the students in one sample were shown positive evaluations of an instructor and the students in a second sample were shown negative evaluations of the instructor. Then all subjects were shown the same 20-minute lecture video given by the same instructor. They were then asked to rate the instructor using three questions, and a summary rating score was calculated. Were students' ratings influenced by the prior student evaluations?

We investigate this question by constructing a 95% confidence interval for the difference in population mean ratings $\mu_1 - \mu_2$. Assume that both populations are normally distributed and that the samples are drawn independently.

Reputation	Subjects	Sample mean rating	Sample standard deviation
Charismatic (sample 1)	$n_1 = 25$	$\bar{x}_1 = 2.613$	$s_1 = 0.533$
Punitive (sample 2)	$n_2 = 24$	$\bar{x}_2 = 2.236$	$s_2 = 0.543$

The degrees of freedom is the smaller of $n_1 - 1 = 25 - 1 = 24$ and $n_2 - 1 = 24 - 1 = 23$. Thus, df = 23. Then, for 95% confidence, from the t table, $t_{\text{crit}} = 2.069$. Then the 95% confidence interval for $\mu_1 - \mu_2$ is

$$(\bar{x}_1 - \bar{x}_2) \pm t_{\alpha/2} \sqrt{\frac{s_1^2}{n_1} + \frac{s_2^2}{n_2}}$$

$$= (2.613 - 2.236) \pm 2.069 \sqrt{\frac{0.533^2}{25} + \frac{0.543^2}{24}}$$

$$\approx 0.377 \pm 2.069 \cdot (0.1538)$$

$$\approx (0.059, 0.695)$$

We are 95% confident that the difference in population mean instructor ratings $\mu_1 - \mu_2$ among the two groups of students lies between 0.059 and 0.695. Since this interval does not contain 0, we can conclude that the difference in population mean ratings is significant at level of significance $\alpha = 0.05$. ∎

---

4 t Inference for $\mu_1 - \mu_2$ Using Pooled Variance

An alternative method for t inference may be applied when the data analyst has reason to believe that $\sigma_1^2 = \sigma_2^2$, that is, the variances of the two populations are equal. A *pooled estimate s_{pooled}^2* of the common variance $\sigma_1^2 = \sigma_2^2 = \sigma^2$ is used.

> Recall that the variance equals the square of the standard deviation.

Pooled Estimate of the Common Variance σ^2

$$s_{\text{pooled}}^2 = \frac{(n_1 - 1)s_1^2 + (n_2 - 1)s_2^2}{n_1 + n_2 - 2}$$

> Some statisticians think that the pooled variance method should be used sparingly.[8]

The conditions for performing t inference using pooled variance are the same as for Welch's method (page 515), with the additional condition that $\sigma_1^2 = \sigma_2^2$. We illustrate the pooled variance t test and the pooled variance t confidence interval using the following two examples.

Example 10.10 | Pooled variance t test

The University of Michigan Consumer Sentiment Index measures consumer optimism, with a baseline of 100 equal to the level of consumer optimism in December 1964. Summary statistics for August 2008 are provided in the following table, for families with incomes above and below \$75,000. Use the critical-value method for the pooled variance t test to test whether the population mean consumer sentiment index of families with income above \$75,000 is greater than that of families with income below \$75,000. Assume $\sigma_1^2 = \sigma_2^2$ and use level of significance $\alpha = 0.01$.

Income	Sample size	Sample mean index	Sample standard deviation
Above \$75,000	$n_1 = 31$	$\bar{x}_1 = 67.5$	$s_1 = 11.6$
Below \$75,000	$n_2 = 31$	$\bar{x}_2 = 60.2$	$s_2 = 11.2$

Solution

Step 1 **State the hypotheses.**

$$H_0 : \mu_1 = \mu_2 \quad \text{versus} \quad H_a : \mu_1 > \mu_2$$

where μ_1 and μ_2 represent the population mean consumer sentiment index for families with incomes above and below \$75,000, respectively.

Step 2 **Find t_{crit}.** The degrees of freedom for the pooled variance t test equals $n_1 + n_2 - 2 = 31 + 31 - 2 = 60$. From the t table we obtain the critical value $t_{\text{crit}} = 2.390$. Reject H_0 if $t_{\text{data}} > 2.390$.

Step 3 **Calculate s_{pooled}^2 and t_{data}.**

$$s_{\text{pooled}}^2 = \frac{(n_1 - 1)s_1^2 + (n_2 - 1)s_2^2}{n_1 + n_2 - 2} = \frac{(31 - 1)11.6^2 + (31 - 1)11.2^2}{31 + 31 - 2} = 130$$

Plugging this value into the following formula for the test statistic, we obtain

$$t_{\text{data}} = \frac{\bar{x}_1 - \bar{x}_2}{\sqrt{s_{\text{pooled}}^2 \left(\frac{1}{n_1} + \frac{1}{n_2}\right)}} = \frac{67.5 - 60.2}{\sqrt{130 \left(\frac{1}{31} + \frac{1}{31}\right)}} \approx 2.521$$

Step 4 **Conclusion and interpretation.** The test statistic $t_{\text{data}} \approx 2.521$ is greater than the critical value $t_{\text{crit}} = 2.390$. Therefore we reject H_0. There is evidence that the population mean consumer sentiment index of families with incomes above \$75,000 is greater than that of families with incomes below \$75,000. ∎

Now You Can Do
Exercises 21 and 22.

The pooled variance method may also be used to construct a t confidence interval for $\mu_1 - \mu_2$.

Example 10.11 | Pooled variance t confidence interval for $\mu_1 - \mu_2$

Use the data from Exercise 10.10 to construct a 99% confidence interval for the difference in population mean optimism indices. Use the pooled variance method.

Solution

The $100(1 - \alpha)\%$ confidence interval for $\mu_1 - \mu_2$ using the pooled variance method is given by the following formula:

$$\bar{x}_1 - \bar{x}_2 \pm t_{\alpha/2} \sqrt{s_{\text{pooled}}^2 \left(\frac{1}{n_1} + \frac{1}{n_2}\right)}$$

where $t_{\alpha/2}$ is found using $n_1 + n_2 - 2$ degrees of freedom. For degrees of freedom $n_1 + n_2 - 2 = 60$, we have $t_{\alpha/2} = 2.660$. Thus, our 99% confidence interval is:

$$67.5 - 60.2 \pm (2.660)\sqrt{130\left(\frac{1}{31} + \frac{1}{31}\right)} = 7.3 \pm 7.703 = (-0.403, 15.003)$$

Now You Can Do
Exercises 23 and 24.

We are 95% confident that the difference in population mean optimism indices lies between -0.403 and 15.003. ∎

Developing Your Statistical Sense

Easier to Reject H_0 Using a One-Tailed Test

Note that the 99% confidence interval for $\mu_1 - \mu_2$ contains zero, so that a two-tailed test for the difference in population means would not have rejected $H_0 : \mu_1 = \mu_2$ for level of significance $\alpha = 0.01$. Contrast this with our rejection of the null hypothesis for the right-tailed (one-tailed) test with level of significance $\alpha = 0.01$ in Example 10.10. We can therefore observe that it is easier to reject the null hypothesis for a one-tailed test than for a two-tailed test with the level of significance. ◢

5 Z Inference for $\mu_1 - \mu_2$ When σ_1 and σ_2 Are Known

When the population standard deviations σ_1 and σ_2 are known, the data analyst may prefer to use Z inference for $\mu_1 - \mu_2$, since the margin of error for Z inference is smaller than for t inference. The conditions for performing Z inference for $\mu_1 - \mu_2$ are similar to Welch's method (page 515), with the additional condition that σ_1 and σ_2 are known. We illustrate the two-sample Z test and the Z confidence interval for $\mu_1 - \mu_2$ using the following two examples.

Do not use Z inference for $\mu_1 - \mu_2$ unless both σ_1 and σ_2 are known.

Example 10.12 Two-sample Z test

A Kaiser Family Foundation report found that the mean amount of time that young people aged 8–18 spend talking on their cell phones is $\bar{x}_1 = 33$ minutes per day, while the mean amount of time spent watching TV shows on their cell phones is $\bar{x}_2 = 49$ minutes per day.[9] Assume that the sample sizes are $n_1 = 50$ and $n_2 = 40$, and that the population standard deviations are known to be $\sigma_1 = 15$ minutes and $\sigma_2 = 20$ minutes. Test using the critical-value method and level of significance $\alpha = 0.05$ whether the population mean amount of time young people spending talking on their cell phones is less than the population mean amount of time they spend watching TV shows on their cell phones.

Solution

Step 1 **State the hypotheses.**

$$H_0 : \mu_1 = \mu_2 \quad \text{versus} \quad H_a : \mu_1 < \mu_2$$

where μ_1 and μ_2 represent the population mean amount of time young people spend talking and watching TV shows on their cell phones, respectively.

Step 2 **Find Z_{crit}.** From Table 9.4 (page 433), we have $Z_{crit} = -1.645$. Reject H_0 if $Z_{data} < -1.645$.

Step 3 **Calculate Z_{data}.** The test statistic for the Z test for $\mu_1 - \mu_2$ takes the form

$$Z_{data} = \frac{\bar{x}_1 - \bar{x}_2}{\sqrt{\dfrac{\sigma_1^2}{n_1} + \dfrac{\sigma_2^2}{n_2}}} = \frac{33 - 49}{\sqrt{\dfrac{15^2}{50} + \dfrac{20^2}{40}}} \approx -4.202$$

Now You Can Do
Exercises 25 and 26.

Step 4 **Conclusion and interpretation.** The test statistic $Z_{\text{data}} \approx -4.202$ is less than the critical value $Z_{\text{crit}} = -1.645$. Therefore we reject H_0. There is evidence that the population mean amount of time young people spending talking on their cell phones is less than the population mean amount of time they spend watching TV shows on their cell phones. ■

When σ_1 and σ_2 are known, we can also construct a Z confidence interval for $\mu_1 - \mu_2$.

Example 10.13 | Z confidence interval for $\mu_1 - \mu_2$

Use the data from Example 10.12 to construct a 95% Z confidence interval for the difference in population mean amount of time spent using cell phones.

Solution

The $100(1 - \alpha)\%$ Z confidence interval for $\mu_1 - \mu_2$ is as follows:

$$\bar{x}_1 - \bar{x}_2 \pm Z_{\alpha/2}\sqrt{\frac{\sigma_1^2}{n_1} + \frac{\sigma_2^2}{n_2}}$$

From Table 8.1 (page 373) we have $Z_{\alpha/2} = 1.96$. Thus, our 95% confidence interval is

$$33 - 49 \pm (1.96)\sqrt{\frac{15^2}{50} + \frac{20^2}{40}} \approx -16 \pm 7.463 = (-23.463, -8.537)$$

Now You Can Do
Exercises 27 and 28.

We are 95% confident that the difference in population mean amounts of time spent on cell phones talking and watching TV shows lies between -23.463 minutes and -8.537 minutes. ■

STEP-BY-STEP TECHNOLOGY GUIDE: Two-Sample t Test and Confidence Interval for $\mu_1 - \mu_2$

TI-83/84

Welch's t Test and Confidence Interval for $\mu_1 - \mu_2$
We use two different examples to illustrate the two different options for performing a two-sample t test or confidence interval for $\mu_1 - \mu_2$ using the TI-83/84.

Data Option. (Example 10.7 is used to illustrate this method.)
Step 1   Enter the American League data into List **L1** and the National League data into List **L2**.
Step 2   Press **STAT** and highlight **TESTS**.
Step 3   Press **4** (for the **2-Samp TTest**). The **2-Samp TTest** menu appears.
Step 4   For input (**INPT**), move the cursor over **Data** and press **ENTER**.
Step 5   For **List1** and **List2**, enter **L1** and **L2**.
Step 6   For **Freq1** and **Freq2**, enter **1**.
Step 7   For μ_1, choose the form of H_a. For Example 10.7, choose "$> \mu_2$" and press **ENTER**.
Step 8   For **Pooled**, select **No** because we are not assuming the variances are equal, and do not need an estimate of the common variance (Figure 10.15).
Step 9   Press **Calculate**. The results for Example 10.7 are shown in Figure 10.11 on page 518.

Stats Option. (Example 10.8 is used to illustrate this method.)
Here you enter the summary statistics.
Step 1   Press **STAT** and highlight **TESTS**.
Step 2   Press **4** (for the **2-Samp TTest**). The **2-Samp TTest** menu appears.
Step 3   For input (**Inpt**), move the cursor over **Stats** and press **ENTER**.
Step 4   For $\bar{x}_1$, enter **98.394**.
Step 5   For Sx_1, enter **0.743**.
Step 6   For n_1, enter **65.**
Step 7   For $\bar{x}_2$, enter **98.105**.
Step 8   For Sx_2, enter **0.699**.
Step 9   For n_2, enter **65** (Figure 10.16).
Step 10   For μ_1, choose the form of H_a. For Example 10.8, choose "$\neq \mu_2$" and press **ENTER**.
Step 11   For **Pooled**, press **No** (Figure 10.17).
Step 12   Press **Calculate**.

Welch's Two-Sample t interval for $\mu_1 - \mu_2$
Follow the same steps as for the t test, except select **0: 2-SampTInt**. Also, to select confidence level (**C-Level**), enter **0.95** for 95%, at Step 2 for example.

FIGURE 10.15

FIGURE 10.16

FIGURE 10.17

Pooled Variance *t* Test and Confidence Interval for $\mu_1 - \mu_2$
Follow the same steps as for Welch's method, except select **Yes** for **Pooled** in Step 8.

Z Test for $\mu_1 - \mu_2$
Data Option
Step 1 Enter the data into Lists **L1** and **L2**.
Step 2 Press **STAT** and highlight **TESTS**.
Step 3 Press **3** (for the **2-Samp Z Test**). The **2-Samp Z Test** menu appears.
Step 4 For input (**INPT**), move the cursor over **Data** and press **ENTER**.
Step 5 Enter the values for σ_1 and σ_2.
Step 6 For **List1** and **List2**, enter **L1** and **L2**.
Step 7 For **Freq1** and **Freq2**, enter **1**.

EXCEL

Welch's *t* Test for $\mu_1 - \mu_2$
Step 1 Enter Sample 1 and Sample 2 data into columns A and B, respectively.
Step 2 Select **Data > Data Analysis > *t*-Test: Two-Sample Assuming Unequal Variances**, and click **OK**.
Step 3 For the **Dataset Range**, select the cells in column A for the **Variable 1 range** and the cells in column B for the **Variable 2 range**.

For the hypothesized mean difference, enter **0**, enter your value for **Alpha**, and click **OK**.

Pooled Variance *t* Test for $\mu_1 - \mu_2$
Follow the same steps as for Welch's method, except select **t-test: Two-Sample Assuming Equal Variances** in Step 2.

MINITAB

Welch's *t* Test and Confidence Interval for $\mu_1 - \mu_2$
Step 1 Enter Sample 1 and Sample 2 data into columns C1 and C2, respectively.
Step 2 Click **Stat > Basic Statistics > 2-Sample t**.
Step 3 **a.** If you have the data values, select **Samples in different columns**, and select **C1** and **C2** as your two columns.
b. If you have the summary statistics, select **summarized data** and enter the **sample size, mean,**

CRUNCHIT!

Welch's *t* Test and *t* Interval for $\mu_1 - \mu_2$
We will use the data from Example 10.7.
Step 1 Click **File . . .** then highlight **Load from Larose2e . . . Chapter 10 . . .** and click on **Example 10.7**.
Step 2 Click **Statistics** and select **t . . . 2-sample**. Select the **Columns** tab. For **Sample 1** select **American**. For **Sample 2** select **National**. Do not check the **Pooled Variance** option.

For the hypothesis test:
Step 3 Select the **Hypothesis Test** tab, choose the correct form of the **Alternative** hypothesis, and click **Calculate**.

For the confidence interval:
Step 3 Select the **Confidence Interval** tab, enter the **Confidence Interval Level**, and click **Calculate**.

Step 8 For μ_1, choose the form of H_a and press **ENTER**.
Step 9 Press **Calculate**.

Stats Option
Step 1 Press **STAT** and highlight **TESTS**.
Step 2 Press **3** (for the **2-Samp Z Test**). The **2-Samp Z Test** menu appears.
Step 3 For input (**Inpt**), move the cursor over **Stats** and press **ENTER**.
Step 4 Enter the values for σ_1, σ_2, $\bar{x}_1$, n_1, $\bar{x}_2$, and n_2.
Step 5 For μ_1, choose the form of H_a and press **ENTER**.
Step 6 Press **Calculate**.

Z Confidence Interval for $\mu_1 - \mu_2$
Follow the same steps as for the *Z* test, except select **9: 2-SampleZInt** at Step 2.

Z Test for $\mu_1 - \mu_2$
Step 1 Enter Sample 1 and Sample 2 data into columns A and B, respectively.
Step 2 Select **Data > Data Analysis > Z-Test: Two-Sample for Means**, and click **OK**.
Step 3 For the **Dataset Range**, select the cells in column A for the **Variable 1 range** and the cells in column B for the **Variable 2 range**. For the hypothesized mean difference, enter **0**.
Step 4 Enter the values for σ_1^2 and σ_2^2, and the value α for **ALPHA** and click **OK**.

and **standard deviation** for each of the **first** and **second** samples.
Step 4 Click **Options** and select the form of the **Alternative** hypothesis.
Step 5 Click **OK** and click **OK** again.

Pooled Variance *t* Test and Confidence Interval for $\mu_1 - \mu_2$
Follow the same steps as for Welch's method, except select **Assume equal variances** at the end of Step 3.

Pooled Variance *t* Test and *t* Interval for $\mu_1 - \mu_2$
Use the same steps as for Welch's *t* test and *t* interval, except make sure to check the **Pooled Variance** option in Step 2.

Z test for $\mu_1 - \mu_2$
We will use the data from Example 10.12.
Step 1 Click **File . . .** then highlight **Load from Larose2e . . . Chapter 10 . . .** and click on **Example 10.12**.
Step 2 Click **Statistics** and select **Z . . . 2-sample**. Select the **Summarized** tab. For **Sample 1** enter $n_1 = 100$ and $\bar{x}_1 = 33$, and for **Sample 2** enter $n_2 = 81$ and $\bar{x}_2 = 49$.
Step 3 Enter the population standard deviations, $\sigma_1 = 15$ and $\sigma_2 = 20$. Choose the correct form of the **Alternative** hypothesis, and click **Calculate**.

Section 10.2 Summary

1 Section 10.2 examines inferential methods for $\mu_1 - \mu_2$, the difference between the means of two independent populations. Two-sample t tests may be carried out using either the p-value method or the critical-value method.

2 $100(1 - \alpha)\%$ t confidence intervals for $\mu_1 - \mu_2$ are developed and illustrated.

3 The use of t confidence intervals for $\mu_1 - \mu_2$ to perform two-tailed t tests is illustrated.

4 The pooled variance method for t inference may be applied when the data analyst has reason to believe that the variances of the two populations are equal.

5 When the population standard deviations σ_1 and σ_2 are known, the data analyst may prefer to use Z inference for $\mu_1 - \mu_2$.

Section 10.2 Exercises

CLARIFYING THE CONCEPTS

1. What are the conditions that permit us to perform the two-sample t test?
2. If a $100(1 - \alpha)\%$ confidence interval for $\mu_1 - \mu_2$ contains 0, then with level of significance α what is our conclusion regarding the hypothesis that there is no difference in the population means?

PRACTICING THE TECHNIQUES

For Exercises 3–6, perform the indicated Welch's hypothesis test using the critical-value method. The summary statistics were taken from random samples that were drawn independently. For each exercise follow these steps.
   a. State the hypotheses.
   b. Find the critical value t_{crit} and the rejection rule for this test.
   c. Calculate t_{data}.
   d. Compare t_{data} with t_{crit}. State and interpret your conclusion.

3. Test at level of significance $\alpha = 0.10$ whether $\mu_1 \neq \mu_2$.

| Sample 1 | $n_1 = 36$ | $\bar{x}_1 = 10$ | $s_1 = 2$ |
| Sample 2 | $n_2 = 36$ | $\bar{x}_2 = 8$ | $s_2 = 2$ |

4. Test at level of significance $\alpha = 0.05$ whether $\mu_1 > \mu_2$.

| Sample 1 | $n_1 = 64$ | $\bar{x}_1 = 20$ | $s_1 = 3$ |
| Sample 2 | $n_1 = 64$ | $\bar{x}_1 = 18$ | $s_1 = 2$ |

5. Test at level of significance $\alpha = 0.01$ whether $\mu_1 < \mu_2$.

| Sample 1 | $n_1 = 100$ | $\bar{x}_1 = 70$ | $s_1 = 10$ |
| Sample 2 | $n_1 = 50$ | $\bar{x}_1 = 80$ | $s_1 = 12$ |

6. Test at level of significance $\alpha = 0.05$ whether $\mu_1 > \mu_2$.

| Sample 1 | $n_1 = 60$ | $\bar{x}_1 = 100$ | $s_1 = 20$ |
| Sample 2 | $n_2 = 40$ | $\bar{x}_2 = 90$ | $s_2 = 10$ |

For Exercises 7–10, perform the indicated Welch's hypothesis test using the p-value method. The summary statistics were taken from random samples that were drawn independently. For each exercise follow these steps.
   a. State the hypotheses and the rejection rule.
   b. Calculate t_{data}.
   c. Find the p-value.
   d. Compare the p-value with level of significance α. State and interpret your conclusion.

7. Test at level of significance $\alpha = 0.10$ whether $\mu_1 \neq \mu_2$.

| Sample 1 | $n_1 = 64$ | $\bar{x}_1 = 0$ | $s_1 = 3$ |
| Sample 2 | $n_2 = 49$ | $\bar{x}_2 = 1$ | $s_2 = 1$ |

8. Test at level of significance $\alpha = 0.05$ whether $\mu_1 > \mu_2$.

| Sample 1 | $n_1 = 255$ | $\bar{x}_1 = 103$ | $s_1 = 17$ |
| Sample 2 | $n_2 = 400$ | $\bar{x}_2 = 95$ | $s_2 = 11$ |

9. Test at level of significance $\alpha = 0.05$ whether $\mu_1 < \mu_2$.

| Sample 1 | $n_1 = 100$ | $\bar{x}_1 = 50$ | $s_1 = 10$ |
| Sample 2 | $n_2 = 100$ | $\bar{x}_2 = 75$ | $s_2 = 15$ |

10. Test at level of significance $\alpha = 0.01$ whether $\mu_1 \neq \mu_2$.

| Sample 1 | $n_1 = 30$ | $\bar{x}_1 = -10$ | $s_1 = 5$ |
| Sample 2 | $n_2 = 30$ | $\bar{x}_2 = -5$ | $s_2 = 2$ |

For Exercises 11–16, do the following for the designated data:
   a. Provide the point estimate of $\mu_1 - \mu_2$.
   b. Calculate the margin of error for the confidence level indicated.
   c. Construct and interpret a t confidence interval for $\mu_1 - \mu_2$ with the confidence level indicated.
11. Data in Exercise 3, confidence level = 90%
12. Data in Exercise 4, confidence level = 95%
13. Data in Exercise 5, confidence level = 99%

14. Data in Exercise 6, confidence level = 95%
15. Data in Exercise 7, confidence level = 95%
16. Data in Exercise 8, confidence level = 90%

For Exercises 17–20 a $100(1 - \alpha)\%$ t confidence interval for $\mu_1 - \mu_2$ is given. Use the confidence interval to test using level of significance α whether $\mu_1 - \mu_2$ differs from each of the designated hypothesized values.

17. A 95% t confidence interval for $\mu_1 - \mu_2$ is (10, 15). Hypothesized values are
    a. 0   **b.** 12   **c.** 16

18. A 99% t confidence interval for $\mu_1 - \mu_2$ is (0, 100). Hypothesized values are
    a. 1   **b.** 99   **c.** 101

19. A 90% t confidence interval for $\mu_1 - \mu_2$ is (−10, 10). Hypothesized values are
    a. −10.1   **b.** −9.9   **c.** 0

20. A 95% t confidence interval for $\mu_1 - \mu_2$ is (−25, −15). Hypothesized values are
    a. −16   **b.** −26   **c.** 0

For Exercises 21–22, perform the indicated hypothesis test using the pooled variance method. The summary statistics were taken from random samples that were drawn independently. Assume $\sigma_1^2 = \sigma_2^2$.

21. Test at level of significance $\alpha = 0.10$ whether $\mu_1 > \mu_2$.

Sample 1	$n_1 = 36$	$\bar{x}_1 = 54$	$s_1 = 10$
Sample 2	$n_2 = 36$	$\bar{x}_2 = 52$	$s_2 = 11$

22. Test at level of significance $\alpha = 0.05$ whether $\mu_1 < \mu_2$.

Sample 1	$n_1 = 250$	$\bar{x}_1 = 3.0$	$s_1 = 0.25$
Sample 2	$n_2 = 150$	$\bar{x}_2 = 3.2$	$s_2 = 0.30$

For Exercises 23–24, construct a 95% confidence interval for $\mu_1 - \mu_2$ for the indicated data using the pooled variance method.

23. The data in Exercise 21
24. The data in Exercise 22

For Exercises 25 and 26, perform the indicated hypothesis test using the Z test. The summary statistics were taken from random samples that were drawn independently. Assume that σ_1 and σ_2 are known.

25. Test at level of significance $\alpha = 0.05$ whether $\mu_1 > \mu_2$.

Sample 1	$n_1 = 49$	$\bar{x}_1 = 100$	$\sigma_1 = 1$
Sample 2	$n_2 = 36$	$\bar{x}_2 = 99$	$\sigma_2 = 2$

26. Test at level of significance $\alpha = 0.10$ whether $\mu_1 < \mu_2$.

Sample 1	$n_1 = 64$	$\bar{x}_1 = 72$	$\sigma_1 = 3$
Sample 2	$n_2 = 100$	$\bar{x}_2 = 76$	$\sigma_2 = 5$

For Exercises 27 and 28, construct a 95% Z confidence interval for $\mu_1 - \mu_2$ for the indicated data.

27. The data in Exercise 25
28. The data in Exercise 26

APPLYING THE CONCEPTS

For Exercises 29–48, use Welch's t test and t interval unless otherwise indicated.

29. PC Sales. A personal computer company launched an advertising campaign in the hopes of boosting sales. A random sample (sample 1) of 16 days before the advertising blitz showed mean sales of 120 computers per day with a standard deviation of 30. A random sample of 15 days after the advertisements appeared showed mean sales of 125 computers per day with a standard deviation of 35. If it is appropriate, test whether $\mu_1 < \mu_2$. If not, explain why not.

30. Foreclosures. A random sample (sample 1) of 20 counties in 2007 had a mean number of foreclosures on single-family residences of 50 and a standard deviation of 25. A random sample (sample 2) of 25 counties in 2008 had a mean number of foreclosures of 70 and a standard deviation of 35. Assume that the number of foreclosures per county is normally distributed in both 2007 and 2008. If it is appropriate, test whether $\mu_1 < \mu_2$. If not, explain why not.

31. Income in California and Los Angeles. According to random samples taken by the Bureau of Economic Analysis, the mean income for Sacramento County and Los Angeles County, California, in 2004 was $31,987 and $33,179, respectively. Suppose the samples had the following sample statistics.

Sacramento County	$n_1 = 36$	$\bar{x}_1 = \$31{,}987$	$s_1 = \$5000$
Los Angeles County	$n_2 = 49$	$\bar{x}_2 = \$33{,}179$	$s_2 = \$6000$

    a. Provide the point estimate of the difference in population means $\mu_1 - \mu_2$.
    b. Calculate the margin of error for a confidence level of 95%.
    c. Construct and interpret a 95% confidence interval for $\mu_1 - \mu_2$.
    d. Test at level of significance $\alpha = 0.05$ whether $\mu_1 < \mu_2$.
    e. Explain whether the confidence interval in **(c)** could have been used to perform the hypothesis test in **(d)**. Why or why not?

32. Math Scores. The Institute of Educational Sciences published the results of the Trends in International Math and Science Study for 2003. The sample mean mathematics scores for students from the United States and Hong Kong were 518 and 575, respectively. Suppose independent random samples are drawn from each population, and assume that the populations are normally distributed with the following summary statistics.

USA	$n_1 = 10$	$\bar{x}_1 = 518$	$s_1 = 80$
Hong Kong	$n_2 = 12$	$\bar{x}_2 = 575$	$s_2 = 70$

    a. Provide the point estimate of the difference in population means $\mu_1 - \mu_2$.
    b. Calculate the margin of error for a confidence level of 90%.

c. Construct and interpret a 90% confidence interval for $\mu_1 - \mu_2$.

d. Test at level of significance $\alpha = 0.01$ whether $\mu_1 < \mu_2$.

e. Provide two reasons why the confidence interval in **(c)** could not have been used to perform the hypothesis test in **(d)**.

33. Children per Classroom. According to www .localschooldirectory.com, the sample mean number of children per teacher in the towns of Cupertino, California, and Santa Rosa, California, are 20.9 and 19.3, respectively. Suppose random samples of classrooms are taken from each county, with the following sample statistics.

Cupertino	$n_1 = 36$	$\bar{x}_1 = 20.9$	$s_1 = 5$
Santa Rosa	$n_2 = 64$	$\bar{x}_2 = 19.3$	$s_2 = 4$

a. Construct and interpret a 99% confidence interval for $\mu_1 - \mu_2$.

b. Use the confidence interval in **(a)** to test at level of significance $\alpha = 0.01$ whether μ_1 differs from μ_2.

34. SAT Verbal Scores. Suppose that a random sample (sample 1) of 50 males showed a mean verbal SAT score of 517 with a standard deviation of 50 and a random sample (sample 2) of 40 females yielded a mean verbal SAT score of 507 with a standard deviation of 60.

a. Explain why it is appropriate to apply t inference.

b. Construct and interpret a 95% confidence interval for the difference in population means.

c. Will a test at level of significance $\alpha = 0.05$ of whether the population mean male SAT score differs from the population mean female SAT score reject the null hypothesis? Explain your reasoning.

35. Property Taxes. Suppose you want to move to either a small town in Ohio (sample 1) or a small town in North Carolina (sample 2). You did some research on property taxes in each state and chose two random samples shown in the table. The data represent the property taxes in dollars for a residence assessed at $250,000. Test whether $\mu_1 \neq \mu_2$ using level of significance $\alpha = 0.05$. 🖱 **propertytax**

North Carolina		Ohio	
164	206	298	270
147	129	270	315
207	176	165	177
138	120	400	245
143	154	268	180
201	123	289	292
		285	291
		225	

36. Salaries for Grads. The National Association of Colleges (NAC) reported in 2003 that the mean starting salary for college graduates majoring in management

information systems was $40,915 and for psychology majors was $27,454. Suppose the NAC data are based on surveys of size 144 for each major, with a standard deviation of $10,000 for the management information systems majors and $7000 for the psychology majors.

a. Explain why it is appropriate to apply t inference.

b. Construct and interpret a 95% confidence interval for $\mu_1 - \mu_2$.

c. Will a 99% confidence interval for $\mu_1 - \mu_2$ be wider or narrower? Explain your reasoning.

37. Park Usage. Suppose that planners for the town of The Woodlands, Texas, were interested in assessing usage of their parks. Random samples were taken of the number of daily visitors to Windvale Park and Cranebrook Park, with the statistics as reported here.

Windvale Park	$n_1 = 36$	$\bar{x}_1 = 110$	$s_1 = 60$
Cranebrook Park	$n_2 = 30$	$\bar{x}_2 = 150$	$s_2 = 75$

a. Construct and interpret a 95% confidence interval for $\mu_1 - \mu_2$.

b. Test at $\alpha = 0.05$ whether μ_1 is less than μ_2.

c. Explain whether the confidence interval in **(a)** could have been used to perform the hypothesis test in **(b)**. Why or why not?

Coaching for the SAT. Use this information for Exercises 38–40. The College Board reports that a pretest and post-test study was done to investigate whether coaching had a significant effect on SAT scores. The improvement from pretest to post-test was 29 points for the coached sample of students, with a standard deviation of 59 points. For the noncoached students, the pretest to post-test improvement was 21 points with a standard deviation of 52 points.

38. Suppose we consider a sample of 100 students from each group. Perform a test at level of significance $\alpha = 0.05$ for whether the population mean coached SAT pretest–post-test improvement is greater than that for the noncoached students.

39. Refer to Exercise 38.

a. Find a point estimate of the difference in population means.

b. Find a 99% confidence interval for the difference in population means.

c. Determine whether the population means differ, at level of significance $\alpha = 0.01$.

🔍 **40.** *What if* the sample sizes for each group were some number greater than $n = 100$.

a. How would this affect the width of the confidence interval in Exercise 39(**b**)? Is this good? Explain.

b. Would this change have any effect on our conclusion in the hypothesis test in Exercise 39(**c**)? Explain why or why not.

41. Nutrition Levels. A social worker is interested in comparing the nutrition levels of children from the inner city and children from the suburbs. She obtains the following independent random samples of daily calorie intake from children in the inner city and the suburbs. Assume that both samples are taken from normal populations.

Inner city (sample 1): 1125, 1019, 1954, 1546, 1418, 980, 1227

Suburbs (sample 2): 1540, 1967, 1886, 1924, 1863, 1756

   a. Provide the point estimate of the difference in population means $\mu_1 - \mu_2$.

   b. Construct and interpret a 90% confidence interval for the difference in population mean daily caloric intake $\mu_1 - \mu_2$.

   c. Test at level of significance $\alpha = 0.10$ whether the population mean daily caloric intake of inner-city children is less than that of children from the suburbs.

   d. Assess the strength of evidence against the null hypothesis. Using Table 9.6 on page 445.

42. Teacher Salaries. The American Federation of Teachers publishes an annual teacher salary report. In 2003, California led the nation in mean teacher salary with $55,693, with Michigan in second place with $54,020. Suppose the data are from random samples of size 100 each, with a standard deviation of $10,000 in California and $9000 in Michigan.

   a. Construct and interpret a 95% confidence interval for $\mu_1 - \mu_2$.

   b. Test at level of significance $\alpha = 0.05$ whether the population mean salary in California is greater than in Michigan.

   c. Assess the strength of evidence against the null hypothesis.

43. Working Hours. Are people working fewer hours? The Bureau of Labor Statistics reported that in 2003 the mean hours worked per week was 40.4, as compared to 41.7 in 1994. Suppose that data are from random samples of size 121 each and that the standard deviation in each sample is 5.5 hours.

   a. Construct and interpret a 99% confidence interval for $\mu_1 - \mu_2$.

   b. Test at level of significance $\alpha = 0.01$ whether the population mean number of hours worked in 2003 is less than in 1994.

   c. Write a sentence summarizing the evidence regarding whether people are working fewer hours.

44. Working Hours. Refer to Exercise 43. *What if* the 2003 sample mean is increased by a certain amount so that the 2003 sample mean is still smaller than the 1994 sample mean. Explain how this would affect each of the following.

   a. $\bar{x}_1 - \bar{x}_2$

   b. t_{data}

   c. *p*-value

   d. Conclusion

45. Nursing Support Services. A statistical study found that when nurses made home visits to pregnant teenagers to provide support services, discourage smoking, and otherwise provide care, the sample mean birth weight of the babies was higher for this treatment group (3285 grams) than for the control group (2922 grams) when the visits began before mid-gestation.[10] There were 21 patients in the treatment group and 11 in the control group. Suppose the birth weights for both groups follow a normal distribution. Assume that the population standard deviation in each sample is 500 grams.

   a. Construct and interpret a 95% *Z* confidence interval for $\mu_1 - \mu_2$.

   b. Test at level of significance $\alpha = 0.05$ whether the population birth weight differs between the two groups. Use the *Z* test.

   c. Assess the strength of evidence against the null hypothesis.

46. Nursing Support Services. Refer to Exercise 45. *What if* the birth weights of the babies in each group are the same certain amount greater. Explain how this would affect the following.

   a. $\bar{x}_1 - \bar{x}_2$

   b. t_{data}

   c. *p*-value

   d. Conclusion

47. California and New York. Use computer software to solve the following problems. **Calny**

   a. Open the **Calny** data set. Explore the variable *calif,* which lists the number of residents in the towns and cities in California (minimum of 1000 residents). Generate numerical summary statistics for the number of residents. What is the sample mean number of residents? The sample standard deviation?

   b. Explore the variable *newyork,* which lists the number of residents in the towns and cities in New York (minimum of 1000 residents). Generate numerical summary statistics for the number of residents. What is the sample mean number of residents? The sample standard deviation?

   c. A researcher claims that there is no difference in the mean number of residents in the towns and cities in California and New York. Test using independent samples at level of significance $\alpha = 0.05$.

48. Phosphorus and Potassium. Use computer software to solve the following problems. **Nutrition**

   a. Open the **Nutrition** data set. Explore the variable *phosphor,* which lists the amount of phosphorus (in milligrams) for each food item. Generate numerical summary statistics and graphs for the amount of phosphorus in the food. What is the sample mean amount of phosphorus? The sample standard deviation?

b. Explore the variable *potass,* which lists the amount of potassium (in milligrams) for each food item. Generate numerical summary statistics and graphs for the amount of potassium in the food. What is the sample mean amount of potassium? The sample standard deviation?

c. Is the independent sampling method the most appropriate way to test this hypothesis? Why or why not?

d. Create a new variable in Excel or Minitab, **phos_pot,** which equals the amount of phosphorus minus the amount of potassium in each food item. Use a paired sample hypothesis test to test at level of significance $\alpha = 0.05$ whether the population mean difference differs from 0.

10.3 Inference for Two Independent Proportions

OBJECTIVES By the end of this section, I will be able to . . .

1   Perform and interpret Z tests for $p_1 - p_2$.

2   Compute and interpret Z intervals for $p_1 - p_2$.

3   Use Z intervals for $p_1 - p_2$ to perform two-tailed Z tests.

1 Independent Sample Z Tests for $p_1 - p_2$

So far in this chapter, we have learned how to perform inference about population *means.* In this section, we learn how to perform hypothesis tests and construct confidence intervals about the difference between two population *proportions.* Recall that the sample proportion of success $\hat{p} = x/n$ is the ratio of the number of successes x to the number of trials n in a binomial experiment.

Here we consider two independent samples, each of which yields a sample proportion: $\hat{p}_1 = x_1/n_1$ and $\hat{p}_2 = x_2/n_2$. For example, a recent survey found the sample proportion of teenage boys (sample 1) and girls (sample 2) who post their last names in their online profiles to be

$$\hat{p}_1 = \frac{x_1}{n_1} = \frac{200}{500} = 0.400$$

and

$$\hat{p}_2 = \frac{x_2}{n_2} = \frac{96}{500} = 0.192$$

(See Example 10.14 for further details about these data.) Here we are interested in performing inference for the difference in population proportions $p_1 - p_2$, such as the difference in the proportions of *all* teenage boys and girls who post their last names in their online profiles. We use the difference in sample proportions $\hat{p}_1 - \hat{p}_2$ as our point estimate of the difference in population proportions $p_1 - p_2$, which is unknown. And just as in earlier sections where we investigated the sampling distribution of $\bar{x}_1 - \bar{x}_2$ to perform inference on $\mu_1 - \mu_2$, here we use the sampling distribution of $\hat{p}_1 - \hat{p}_2$ to help us perform inference about $p_1 - p_2$.

Developing Your Statistical Sense

Independent Samples Only

The inferential methods of this section are reserved for *independent* samples only. An example of a problem that would not use the methods of this section is the following. In the latest poll, suppose 45% supported the Democrat and 40% supported the Republican. Because each respondent had to choose between the Democratic candidate and the Republican candidate, their respective poll numbers are *not independent.* ◢

The distribution of all possible values of $\hat{p}_1 - \hat{p}_2$ is called the **sampling distribution of $\hat{p}_1 - \hat{p}_2$,** with mean $p_1 - p_2$ and standard error $\sigma_{\hat{p}_1-\hat{p}_2} = \sqrt{\dfrac{p_1(1-p_1)}{n_1} + \dfrac{p_2(1-p_2)}{n_2}}$.

Let x_1 and x_2 denote the number of successes, and let $n_1 - x_1$ and $n_2 - x_2$ denote the number of failures in sample 1 and sample 2, respectively. The sampling distribution of $\hat{p}_1 - \hat{p}_2$ is approximately normal when the number of successes and the number of failures in each sample are each at least 5, that is, when $x_1 \geq 5$, $(n_1 - x_1) \geq 5$, $x_2 \geq 5$, and $(n_2 - x_2) \geq 5$. Let $q_1 = 1 - p_1$, $q_2 = 1 - p_2$, $\hat{q}_1 = 1 - \hat{p}_1$ and $\hat{q}_2 = 1 - \hat{p}_2$.

Sampling Distribution of $\hat{p}_1 - \hat{p}_2$

When two random samples are drawn independently from two populations, then the quantity

$$Z = \frac{(\hat{p}_1 - \hat{p}_2) - (p_1 - p_2)}{\sqrt{\dfrac{p_1 q_1}{n_1} + \dfrac{p_2 q_2}{n_2}}}$$

has an approximately standard normal distribution when the following conditions are satisfied:

$$x_1 \geq 5, \qquad (n_1 - x_1) \geq 5, \qquad x_2 \geq 5, \qquad (n_2 - x_2) \geq 5$$

and where $\hat{p}_1$ and n_1 represent the sample proportion and sample size of the sample taken from population 1 with population proportion p_1; $\hat{p}_2$ and n_2 represent the sample proportion and sample size of the sample taken from population 2 with population proportion p_2; and $q_1 = 1 - p_1$ and $q_2 = 1 - p_2$.

The three possible forms for the Z test for $p_1 - p_2$ are as follows.

$H_0 : p_1 = p_2$	$H_a : p_1 > p_2$	Right-tailed test
$H_0 : p_1 = p_2$	$H_a : p_1 < p_2$	Left-tailed test
$H_0 : p_1 = p_2$	$H_a : p_1 \neq p_2$	Two-tailed test

The null hypothesis asserts that H_0: $p_1 = p_2$. We denote this *common population proportion* as p. Since the null hypothesis is assumed true, the test statistic takes the following form:

$$Z_{\text{data}} = \frac{(\hat{p}_1 - \hat{p}_2) - (p_1 - p_2)}{\sqrt{\dfrac{p_1(1-p_1)}{n_1} + \dfrac{p_2(1-p_2)}{n_2}}} = \frac{(\hat{p}_1 - \hat{p}_2) - 0}{\sqrt{\dfrac{p_1(1-p_1)}{n_1} + \dfrac{p_2(1-p_2)}{n_2}}}$$

$$= \frac{(\hat{p}_1 - \hat{p}_2)}{\sqrt{\dfrac{p(1-p)}{n_1} + \dfrac{p(1-p)}{n_2}}} = \frac{(\hat{p}_1 - \hat{p}_2)}{\sqrt{p(1-p)\left(\dfrac{1}{n_1} + \dfrac{1}{n_2}\right)}}$$

Since the common population proportion p is unknown, we estimate it using the following **pooled estimate of p:**

$$\hat{p}_{\text{pooled}} = \frac{x_1 + x_2}{n_1 + n_2}$$

Substituting this into the formula for the test statistic gives

$$Z_{\text{data}} = \frac{(\hat{p}_1 - \hat{p}_2)}{\sqrt{\hat{p}_{\text{pooled}} \cdot (1 - \hat{p}_{\text{pooled}})\left(\dfrac{1}{n_1} + \dfrac{1}{n_2}\right)}}$$

Z_{data} measures the distance between the sample proportions. Extreme values of Z_{data} indicate evidence against the null hypothesis.

Hypothesis Test for the Difference in Two Population Proportions: Critical-Value Method

Suppose we have two independent random samples taken from two populations with population proportions p_1 and p_2, and the required conditions are met: $x_1 \geq 5$, $(n_1 - x_1) \geq 5$, $x_2 \geq 5$, and $(n_2 - x_2) \geq 5$.

Step 1 **State the hypotheses.** Use one of the forms from Table 10.15. State the meaning of p_1 and p_2.

Step 2 **Find Z_{crit} and state the rejection rule.** Use Table 10.15.

Step 3 **Calculate Z_{data}**

$$Z_{data} = \frac{\hat{p}_1 - \hat{p}_2}{\sqrt{\hat{p}_{pooled} \cdot (1 - \hat{p}_{pooled})\left(\frac{1}{n_1} + \frac{1}{n_2}\right)}}$$

where

$$\hat{p}_{pooled} = \frac{x_1 + x_2}{n_1 + n_2}$$

Z_{data} follows an approximately standard normal distribution if the required conditions are satisfied.

Step 4 **State the conclusion and the interpretation.** Compare Z_{data} with Z_{crit}.

Table 10.15 Critical regions and rejection rules for Z test for $p_1 - p_2$

	Form of Hypothesis Test		
	Right-tailed	**Left-tailed**	**Two-tailed**
Level of significance α	$H_0 : p_1 = p_2$ $H_a : p_1 > p_2$	$H_0 : p_1 = p_2$ $H_a : p_1 < p_2$	$H_0 : p_1 = p_2$ $H_a : p_1 \neq p_2$
0.10	$Z_{crit} = 1.28$	$Z_{crit} = -1.28$	$Z_{crit} = 1.645$
0.05	$Z_{crit} = 1.645$	$Z_{crit} = -1.645$	$Z_{crit} = 1.96$
0.01	$Z_{crit} = 2.33$	$Z_{crit} = -2.33$	$Z_{crit} = 2.58$
Critical region			
	Reject H_0 if $Z_{data} \geq Z_{crit}$	Reject H_0 if $Z_{data} \leq Z_{crit}$	Reject H_0 if $Z_{data} \leq -Z_{crit}$ or $Z_{data} \geq Z_{crit}$

Example 10.14 Z test for $p_1 - p_2$ using the critical-value method

The Pew Internet and American Life Project (www.pewinternet.org) tracks the behavior of Americans on the Internet. In 2007, they published a report that described some of the behaviors of American teenagers in online social networks, such as Facebook. Teenagers who had online profiles were asked: "We'd like to know if your last name is posted to your profile or not." The results are shown in Table 10.16. Assume the samples are independent.

Punchstock/Banana Stock

Table 10.16 Proportions of teenage boys and girls who post their last names in online profiles

	Boys	**Girls**
Number responding "yes"	$x_1 = 200$	$x_2 = 96$
Sample size	$n_1 = 500$	$n_2 = 500$
Sample proportion	$\hat{p}_1 = x_1/n_1$	$\hat{p}_2 = x_2/n_2$
	$= 200/500$	$= 96/500$
	$= 0.400$	$= 0.192$

a. Find the point estimate of the difference in the population proportions of boys and girls, $\hat{p}_1 - \hat{p}_2$.
b. Compute the pooled estimate of the common proportion, $\hat{p}_{\text{pooled}}$.
c. Calculate the value of the test statistic Z_{data}.
d. Test whether the population proportion of teenage boys who post their last name in their online profiles is greater than the population proportion of teenage girls who do so. Use the critical-value method at level of significance $\alpha = 0.01$.

Solution

a. The point estimate is $\hat{p}_1 - \hat{p}_2 = 0.400 - 0.192 = 0.208$

b. $\hat{p}_{\text{pooled}} = \dfrac{x_1 + x_2}{n_1 + n_2} = \dfrac{200 + 96}{500 + 500} = 0.296$

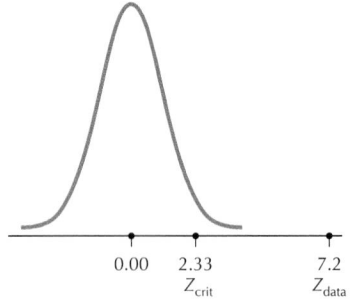

FIGURE 10.18 TI-83/84 results.

c. $Z_{\text{data}} = \dfrac{\hat{p}_1 - \hat{p}_2}{\sqrt{\hat{p}_{\text{pooled}} \cdot (1 - \hat{p}_{\text{pooled}})\left(\dfrac{1}{n_1} + \dfrac{1}{n_2}\right)}} = \dfrac{0.400 - 0.192}{\sqrt{(0.296)(0.704)\left(\dfrac{1}{500} + \dfrac{1}{500}\right)}} \approx 7.204$

d. We check the conditions for performing the Z test for $p_1 - p_2$. We have: $x_1 = 200 \geq 5$, $x_2 = 96 \geq 5$, $n_1 - x_1 = 500 - 200 = 300 \geq 5$, and $n_2 - x_2 = 500 - 96 = 404 \geq 5$. We may thus proceed with the hypothesis test.

Step 1 **State the hypotheses.** The key words "greater than," together with the fact that sample 1 represents the boys, indicate that we have a right-tailed test:

$$H_0 : p_1 = p_2 \quad \text{versus} \quad H_a : p_1 > p_2$$

where p_1 and p_2 represent the population proportion of teenage boys and girls who post their last names in their online profiles, respectively.

Step 2 **Find Z_{crit} and state the rejection rule.** For a right-tailed test with level of significance $\alpha = 0.01$, Table 10.15 gives us $Z_{\text{crit}} = 2.33$ and our rejection rule: Reject H_0 if $Z_{\text{data}} \geq 2.33$.

Step 3 **Calculate Z_{data}.** From **(c)** we have $Z_{\text{data}} \approx 7.2$ (also see Figure 10.18).

Step 4 **State the conclusion and the interpretation.** $Z_{\text{data}} \approx 7.2 \geq 2.33$, therefore reject H_0 (see Figure 10.19). There is evidence at level of significance $\alpha = 0.01$ that the population proportion of teenage boys who post their last name in their online profiles is greater than the population proportion of teenage girls who do so. ∎

FIGURE 10.19 $Z_{\text{data}} = 7.2$ is extreme.

Now You Can Do
Exercises 5–8.

We may also use the *p*-value method to perform the Z test for $p_1 - p_2$.

Hypothesis Test for the Difference in Two Population Proportions:
_p_-Value Method

Suppose we have two independent random samples taken from two populations with population proportions p_1 and p_2, and the required conditions are met: $x_1 \geq 5$, $(n_1 - x_1) \geq 5$, $x_2 \geq 5$, and $(n_2 - x_2) \geq 5$.

Step 1   State the hypotheses and the rejection rule. Use one of the forms from Table 10.16. State the meaning of p_1 and p_2. The rejection rule is _Reject H_0 if the p-value $\leq \alpha$._

Step 2   Calculate Z_{data}.

$$Z_{data} = \frac{\hat{p}_1 - \hat{p}_2}{\sqrt{\hat{p}_{pooled} \cdot (1 - \hat{p}_{pooled})\left(\frac{1}{n_1} + \frac{1}{n_2}\right)}}$$

where $\hat{p}_{pooled} = \frac{x_1 + x_2}{n_1 + n_2}$. If the required conditions are satisfied, Z_{data} follows an approximately standard normal distribution.

Step 3   Find the _p_-value. Either use technology or calculate the p-value using one of the forms in Table 10.17.

Step 4   State the conclusion and the interpretation. Compare the p-value with α.

Table 10.17 _p_-Values for Z test for $p_1 - p_2$

Right-tailed test	**Left-tailed test**	**Two-tailed test**
$H_0 : p_1 = p_2$	$H_0 : p_1 = p_2$	$H_0 : p_1 = p_2$
$H_a : p_1 > p_2$	$H_a : p_1 < p_2$	$H_a : p_1 \neq p_2$
p-value $= P(Z > Z_{data})$	p-value $= P(Z < Z_{data})$	p-value $= P(Z > \lvert Z_{data}\rvert) + P(Z < -\lvert Z_{data}\rvert)$
Area to right of Z_{data}	Area to left of Z_{data}	$= 2 \cdot P(Z > \lvert Z_{data}\rvert)$
		Sum of the two-tailed areas

Example 10.15 Z test for $p_1 - p_2$ using the _p_-value method

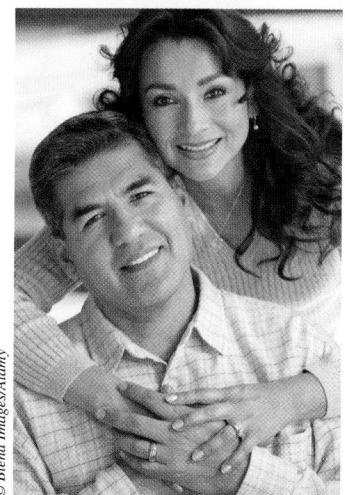
© Blend Images/Alamy

The General Social Survey tracks trends in American society through annual surveys. Married respondents were asked to characterize their feelings about being married. The results are shown here in a crosstabulation with gender. Test the hypothesis that the proportion of females who report being very happily married is smaller than the proportion of males who report being very happily married. Use the _p_-value method with level of significance $\alpha = 0.05$.

marriage

	Very happy	**Pretty happy/ Not too happy**	**Total**
Female	257	166	423
Male	242	124	366
Total	499	290	789

Solution

From the crosstabulation, we assemble the statistics in Table 10.18 for the independent random samples of men and women.

Table 10.18 Sample statistics of very happily married respondents

	Sample size	Number very happy	Sample proportion very happy
Females (sample 1)	$n_1 = 423$	$x_1 = 257$	$\hat{p}_1 = \frac{x_1}{n_1} = \frac{257}{423} \approx 0.6076$
Males (sample 2)	$n_2 = 366$	$x_2 = 242$	$\hat{p}_2 = \frac{x_2}{n_2} = \frac{242}{366} \approx 0.6612$

We first check whether the conditions for the Z test are valid: $x_1 = 257 \geq 5$, $(n_1 - x_1) = (423 - 257) = 166 \geq 5$, $x_2 = 242 \geq 5$, and $(n_2 - x_2) = (366 - 242) = 124 \geq 5$. We can therefore proceed.

Step 1 **State the hypotheses and the rejection rule.** Since we are interested in whether the proportion of females who report being very happily married *is smaller than* that of males and because the females represent sample 1, the hypotheses are

$$H_0 : p_1 = p_2 \qquad H_a : p_1 < p_2$$

where p_1 and p_2 represent the population proportions of all females and males, respectively, who report being very happily married. We will reject H_0 if the p-value $\leq \alpha = 0.05$.

Step 2 **Find Z_{data}.** First, use the data from Table 10.18 to find the values of $\hat{p}_{\text{pooled}}$.

$$\hat{p}_{\text{pooled}} = \frac{x_1 + x_2}{n_1 + n_2} = \frac{257 + 242}{423 + 366} \approx 0.63245$$

Then

$$Z_{\text{data}} = \frac{(0.6076 - 0.6612)}{\sqrt{0.63245 \cdot (1 - 0.63245)\left(\frac{1}{423} + \frac{1}{366}\right)}} \approx -1.56$$

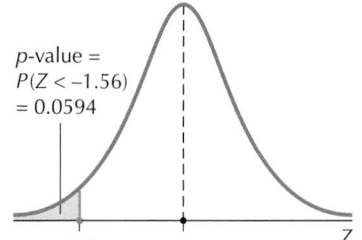

p-value = $P(Z < -1.56)$ = 0.0594

FIGURE 10.20 p-Value for left-tailed Z test.

Note: When the p-value is close to α, many data analysts prefer to simply assess the strength of evidence against the null hypothesis using criteria like those given in Table 9.6 (page 303).

Now You Can Do
Exercises 9–12.

Step 3 **Find the p-value.** Since it is a left-tailed test, the p-value is given by Table 10.17 as $P(Z < Z_{\text{data}}) = P(Z < -1.56)$, as shown in Figure 10.20. This amounts to a Case 1 problem from Table 6.6 on page 303:

$$P(Z < -1.56) = 0.0594$$

Step 4 **State the conclusion and the interpretation.** Since the p-value = 0.0594 is not less than $\alpha = 0.05$, we do not reject H_0. There is insufficient evidence that the proportion of females who report being very happily married is smaller than the proportion of males who do so. ■

2 Independent Sample Z Interval for $p_1 - p_2$

We have learned how to perform Z tests for $p_1 - p_2$. Next we learn how to use sample statistics to estimate $p_1 - p_2$ using a confidence interval.

> **Confidence Interval for $p_1 - p_2$**
>
> For two independent random samples taken from two populations with population proportions p_1 and p_2, a **$100(1 - \alpha)$% confidence interval for $p_1 - p_2$** is given by
>
> $$\hat{p}_1 - \hat{p}_2 \pm Z_{\alpha/2} \sqrt{\frac{\hat{p}_1 \cdot \hat{q}_1}{n_1} + \frac{\hat{p}_2 \cdot \hat{q}_2}{n_2}}$$
>
> where $\hat{p}_1$ and n_1 represent the sample proportion and sample size of the sample taken from population 1 with population proportion p_1; $\hat{p}_2$ and n_2 represent the sample proportion and sample size of the sample taken from population 2 with population proportion p_2; the samples are drawn independently; and the following conditions are satisfied: $x_1 \geq 5$, $(n_1 - x_1) \geq 5$, $x_2 \geq 5$, and $(n_2 - x_2) \geq 5$.
>
> **Margin of Error E**
>
> The **margin of error** for a $100(1 - \alpha)$% confidence interval for $p_1 - p_2$ is given by
>
> $$E = Z_{\alpha/2} \cdot \sqrt{\frac{\hat{p}_1 \cdot \hat{q}_1}{n_1} + \frac{\hat{p}_2 \cdot \hat{q}_2}{n_2}}$$

Example 10.16 Z confidence interval for $p_1 - p_2$

Use the sample statistics from Example 10.14 to do the following:
a. Calculate and interpret the margin of error E for confidence level 99%.
b. Construct and interpret a 99% confidence interval for $p_1 - p_2$.

Solution

The conditions for the confidence interval are the same as for the hypothesis test, and were checked in Example 10.14.

a. $\hat{q}_1 = 1 - \hat{p}_1 = 1 - 0.400 = 0.600 \qquad \hat{q}_2 = 1 - \hat{p}_2 = 1 - 0.192 = 0.808$
From Table 8.1 (page 373), the $Z_{\alpha/2}$ value for a 99% confidence level is 2.576. Therefore, the margin of error is

$$E = Z_{\alpha/2} \cdot \sqrt{\frac{\hat{p}_1 \cdot \hat{q}_1}{n_1} + \frac{\hat{p}_2 \cdot \hat{q}_2}{n_2}} = (2.576)\sqrt{\frac{(0.400)(0.600)}{500} + \frac{(0.192)(0.808)}{500}} \approx 0.072$$

Since the margin of error is 0.072, we may estimate $p_1 - p_2$ to within 0.072 with 99% confidence.

b. The point estimate $\hat{p}_1 - \hat{p}_2 = 0.400 - 0.192 = 0.208$. The 99% confidence interval is therefore

$$\hat{p}_1 - \hat{p}_2 \pm E = 0.208 \pm 0.072 = (0.136, 0.280)$$

We are 99% confident that the difference in population proportions of teenage boys and girls whose last name is posted to their profile lies between 0.136 and 0.280. ∎

Now You Can Do
Exercises 13–18.

3 Use Z Confidence Intervals to Perform Z Tests for $p_1 - p_2$

Given a $100(1 - \alpha)$% Z confidence interval for $\hat{p}_1 - \hat{p}_2$, we may perform two-tailed Z tests for various hypothesized values of $p_1 - p_2$. If a proposed value lies outside the $100(1 - \alpha)$% Z confidence interval for $p_1 - p_2$, then the null hypothesis specifying this value would be rejected. Otherwise do not reject the null hypothesis.

Example 10.17 Using a *Z* interval for $p_1 - p_2$ to perform *Z* tests about $p_1 - p_2$

Since this example asks whether $p_1 - p_2$ differs from (or is not equal to) a certain value, we can use the *Z* confidence interval to test the hypotheses. Example 10.16 provided a 99% *Z* confidence interval for $p_1 - p_2$, the difference in population proportions of teenage boys and girls whose last name is posted to their profile, as (0.136, 0.280). Test using level of significance $\alpha = 0.01$ whether the $p_1 - p_2$ differs from these values: (a) 0.1, (b) 0.2, (c) 0.3.

Solution

a. $H_0 : p_1 - p_2 = 0.1$ versus $H_a : p_1 - p_2 \neq 0.1$.
The hypothesized value 0.1 lies outside the interval (0.136, 0.280), so we reject H_0.

b. $H_0 : p_1 - p_2 = 0.2$ versus $H_a : p_1 - p_2 \neq 0.2$.
The hypothesized value 0.2 lies inside the interval, so we do not reject H_0.

Now You Can Do
Exercises 19–22.

c. $H_0 : p_1 - p_2 = 0.3$ versus $H_a : p_1 - p_2 \neq 0.3$.
The hypothesized value 0.3 lies outside the interval, so we reject H_0. ∎

STEP-BY-STEP TECHNOLOGY GUIDE: *Z* Test and *Z* Interval $p_1 - p_2$

(Example 10.14 is used to illustrate the procedure.)

TI-83/84

Z Test for $p_1 - p_2$
Step 1 Press **STAT** and highlight **TESTS**.
Step 2 Select **6** (for the **2-Prop ZTest**).
Step 3 For **x1**, enter the number of successes in the first sample, **200**.
Step 4 For **n1**, enter the size of the first sample, **500**.
Step 5 For **x2**, enter the number of successes in the second sample, **96**.
Step 6 For **n2**, enter the size of the second sample, **500**.
Step 7 For p_1, choose the form of the hypothesis test. For Example 10.14, choose $> p_2$ and press **ENTER** (Figure 10.21).
Step 8 Highlight **Calculate** and press **ENTER**. The results are shown in Figure 10.18 in Example 10.14.

FIGURE 10.21

Z Interval for $p_1 - p_2$
Follow the same steps as for the two-sample *t* test in Section 10.2, except "Select **B: 2-PropZInt.**" Also, to select confidence level (**C-Level**), enter **0.95** for 95%, for example.

EXCEL

Z Test and Z Interval for $p_1 - p_2$ Using the WHFStat Add-ins
Step 1 Load the **WHFStat Add-ins**.
Step 2 Select **Add-Ins > Macros > Testing a Proportion > Two Samples**.

Step 3 For **Proportion 1**, enter n_1 for **Sample Size** and x_1 for **Number of Successes**.
Step 4 For **Proportion 2**, enter n_2 for **Sample Size** and x_2 for **Number of Successes**. Select the **Confidence Level** and click **OK**.

MINITAB

Z Test and Z Interval for $p_1 - p_2$
Step 1 Click **Stat > Basic Statistics > 2 Proportions**.
Step 2 Select **Summarized Data**.
Step 3 For the **First** row, enter n_1 for **Trials** and x_1 for **Events**.

Step 4 For the **Second** row, enter n_2 for **Trials** and x_2 for **Events**.
Step 5 Click **Options** and select the form of the alternative hypothesis and a confidence level. Then click **OK** twice.

CRUNCHIT!

Z test and Z interval for $p_1 - p_2$
We will use the data from Example 10.14.
Step 1 Click **File** ... then highlight **Load from Larose2e** ... **Chapter 10** ... and click on **Example 10.14**.
Step 2 Click **Statistics** and select **Proportion ... 2-sample**. Select the **Summarized** tab. For **Sample 1** enter $n_1 = 500$ and $x_1 = 200$, and for **Sample 2** enter $n_2 = 500$ and $x_2 = 96$.

For the hypothesis test:
Step 3 Select the **Hypothesis Test** tab, choose the correct form of the **Alternative** hypothesis, and click **Calculate**.

For the confidence interval:
Step 3 Select the **Confidence Interval** tab, enter the **Confidence Interval Level**, and click **Calculate**.

Section 10.3 Summary

1 The section discusses inferential methods for $p_1 - p_2$, the difference between the proportions of two independent populations. Two-sample Z tests for $p_1 - p_2$ are discussed. These hypothesis tests may be carried out using either the p-value method or the critical-value method.

2 $100(1 - \alpha)\%$ Z confidence intervals for $p_1 - p_2$ are developed and illustrated.

3 We may use Z confidence intervals for $p_1 - p_2$ to conduct two-tailed Z tests.

Section 10.3 Exercises

CLARIFYING THE CONCEPTS
1. $\hat{p}_{pooled}$ must always lie between which two quantities?
2. Does it make sense to use $\hat{p}_{pooled}$ when calculating confidence intervals for $p_1 - p_2$? Why or why not?
3. What does Z_{data} measure? What do extreme values of Z_{data} indicate?
4. What might we suggest if the p-value is very close to the level of significance α?

PRACTICING THE TECHNIQUES
The summary statistics in Exercises 5–7 and 9–11 were taken from random samples that were drawn independently. Let n_1 and n_2 denote the size of samples 1 and 2, respectively. Let x_1 and x_2 denote the number of successes in samples 1 and 2, respectively.

For Exercises 5–7, perform the indicated hypothesis test using the critical-value method. Answer **(a)–(d)** for each exercise.
  a. State the hypotheses and find the critical value Z_{crit} and the rejection rule.
  b. Calculate $\hat{p}_{pooled}$.
  c. Calculate Z_{data}.
  d. Compare Z_{data} with Z_{crit}. State and interpret your conclusion.
5. Test at level of significance $\alpha = 0.10$ whether $p_1 \neq p_2$.

| Sample 1 | $n_1 = 100$ | $x_1 = 80$ |
| Sample 2 | $n_2 = 40$ | $x_2 = 30$ |

6. Test at level of significance $\alpha = 0.05$ whether $p_1 < p_2$.

| Sample 1 | $n_1 = 10$ | $x_1 = 4$ |
| Sample 2 | $n_2 = 12$ | $x_2 = 5$ |

7. Test at level of significance $\alpha = 0.01$ whether $p_1 > p_2$.

| Sample 1 | $n_1 = 200$ | $x_1 = 60$ |
| Sample 2 | $n_2 = 250$ | $x_2 = 40$ |

8. Refer to the data from Exercise 7. Test at level of significance $\alpha = 0.01$ whether $p_1 \neq p_2$.

For Exercises 9–11, perform the indicated hypothesis test using the p-value method. Answer **(a)–(e)** for each exercise.
  a. State the hypotheses and the rejection rule.
  b. Calculate $\hat{p}_{pooled}$.
  c. Calculate Z_{data}.
  d. Calculate the p-value.
  e. Compare the p-value with α. State and interpret your conclusion.
9. Test at level of significance $\alpha = 0.05$ whether $p_1 > p_2$.

| Sample 1 | $n_1 = 400$ | $x_1 = 250$ |
| Sample 2 | $n_2 = 400$ | $x_2 = 200$ |

10. Test at level of significance $\alpha = 0.05$ whether $p_1 < p_2$.

| Sample 1 | $n_1 = 1000$ | $x_1 = 490$ |
| Sample 2 | $n_2 = 1000$ | $x_2 = 620$ |

11. Test at level of significance $\alpha = 0.10$ whether $p_1 \neq p_2$.

| Sample 1 | $n_1 = 527$ | $x_1 = 412$ |
| Sample 2 | $n_2 = 613$ | $x_2 = 498$ |

12. Refer to the data from Exercise 11. Test at level of significance $\alpha = 0.10$ whether $p_1 < p_2$.

For Exercises 13–18, refer to the indicated data to answer **(a)–(d)**.

   a. We are interested in constructing a 95% confidence interval for $p_1 - p_2$. Is it appropriate to do so? Why or why not? If not appropriate, then do not perform **(b)–(e)**.

   b. Provide the point estimate of the difference in population proportions $p_1 - p_2$.

   c. Calculate the margin of error for a confidence level of 95%. What does this number mean?

   d. Construct and interpret a 95% confidence interval for $p_1 - p_2$.

13. Data from Exercise 5
14. Data from Exercise 6
15. Data from Exercise 7
16. Data from Exercise 9
17. Data from Exercise 10
18. Data from Exercise 11

For Exercises 19–22 a $100(1 - \alpha)\%$ Z confidence interval for $p_1 - p_2$ is given. Use the confidence interval to test using level of significance α whether $p_1 - p_2$ differs from each of the indicated hypothesized values.

19. A 95% Z confidence interval for $p_1 - p_2$ is (0.5, 0.6). Hypothesized values are

   a. 0   **b.** 0.1   **c.** 0.57

20. A 99% Z confidence interval for $p_1 - p_2$ is (0.01, 0.99). Hypothesized values are

   a. 0.2   **b.** 0   **c.** 0.999

21. A 90% Z confidence interval for $p_1 - p_2$ is (0.1, 0.11). Hypothesized values are

   a. 0.151   **b.** 0.115   **c.** 0.105

22. A 95% Z confidence interval for $p_1 - p_2$ is (0.43, 0.57). Hypothesized values are

   a. 0.41   **b.** 0.51   **c.** 0.61

APPLYING THE CONCEPTS

23. Online Photos. A Pew Internet and American Life Project (www.pewinternet.org) 2007 report stated that 74% of teenage boys posted their photo on their online profile, while 83% of teenage girls did so.[11] Assume that the sample sizes were each 500.

   a. Is it appropriate to perform the Z test for the difference in population proportions? Why or why not?

   b. Clearly state the meaning of p_1 and p_2.

   c. Test whether the proportion of teenage boys posting their photo in their online profile differs from the proportion of teenage girls who do so, using level of significance $\alpha = 0.05$.

24. Medicare Recipients. The Centers for Medicare and Medicaid Services reported in 2004 that 3305 of the 50,350 Medicare recipients living in Alaska were age 85 or over, and 73,289 of the 754,642 Medicare recipients living in Arizona were age 85 or over.

   a. Find a point estimate of the difference in population proportions.

   b. Clearly state the difference in meaning between p_1 and $\hat{p}_1$.

   c. Test whether the population proportions differ, using level of significance $\alpha = 0.05$.

25. Women's Ownership of Businesses. The U.S. Census Bureau tracks trends in women's ownership of businesses. A random sample of 100 Ohio businesses showed 34 that were woman-owned. A sample of 200 New Jersey businesses showed 64 that were woman-owned.

   a. Is it appropriate to perform the Z test for the difference in population proportions? Why or why not?

   b. Clearly state the meaning of p_1 and p_2.

   c. Test whether the population proportions of female-owned businesses in Ohio is greater than that of New Jersey, using level of significance $\alpha = 0.10$.

26. Fetal Cells and Breast Cancer. A number of fetal stem cells may cross the placenta from the fetus to the mother during pregnancy and remain in the mother's tissue for decades. A recent study shows that the presence of fetal cells in the mother may offer some protection against the onset of breast cancer.[12] Of the 54 women in the study with breast cancer, 14 had fetal cells. Of the 45 women without breast cancer, 25 had fetal cells.

   a. Find a point estimate of the difference in population proportions.

   b. Clearly state the difference in meaning between p_1 and $\hat{p}_1$.

   c. Test whether the population proportions of women with fetal cells is lower among women with breast cancer compared to women without breast cancer, using level of significance $\alpha = 0.01$.

27. Online Photos. Refer to Exercise 23 to answer the following questions.

   a. Calculate the margin of error for a Z interval with a confidence level of 95%. Explain what this number means.

   b. Construct and interpret a 95% confidence interval for the difference in population proportions.

   c. Use the confidence interval from **(b)** to test, using level of significance $\alpha = 0.05$, whether the population proportions differ.

   d. Does your conclusion from **(c)** agree with your conclusion from Exercise 23**(c)**?

28. Medicare Recipients. Refer to Exercise 24 to answer the following questions.

   a. Calculate the margin of error for a Z interval with a confidence level of 95%. Explain what this number means.

   b. Construct and interpret a 95% confidence interval for the difference in population proportions.

   c. Use the confidence interval from **(b)** to test using level of significance $\alpha = 0.05$ whether the population proportions differ.

   d. Does your conclusion from **(c)** agree with your conclusion from Exercise 24**(c)**?

29. Women's Ownership of Businesses. Refer to Exercise 25 to answer the following questions.
   a. Construct and interpret a 90% confidence interval for the difference in population proportions.
   b. Use the confidence interval from **(a)** to test using level of significance $\alpha = 0.10$ whether the population proportions differ.
   c. Explain whether or not we could use the confidence interval from part **(b)** to perform the hypothesis test in Exercise 25**(c)**. Why or why not?

30. Fetal Cells and Breast Cancer. Refer to Exercise 26 to answer the following questions.
   a. Construct and interpret a 99% confidence interval for the difference in population proportions.
   b. Use the confidence interval from **(a)** to test using level of significance $\alpha = 0.01$ whether the population proportions differ.
   c. Explain whether or not we could use the confidence interval from **(b)** to perform the hypothesis test in Exercise 26**(c)**. Why or why not?

31. Young People Owning Stocks. The Federal Reserve System reports that the proportion of Americans under 35 years old owning stocks is 17.4%, while the proportion of Americans aged 35–44 owning stocks is 21.6%. Assume that the sample sizes used were 1000 each. Test whether the true proportions differ, at level of significance $\alpha = 0.05$.

32. Evidence for Alternative Medical Therapies? A company called QT, Inc., sells "ionized" bracelets, called Q-Ray bracelets, that it claims help to ease pain through balancing the body's flow of "electromagnetic energy." The Mayo Clinic decided to conduct a statistical experiment to determine whether the claims for the Q-Ray bracelets were justified.[13] At the end of four weeks, of the 305 subjects who wore the "ionized" bracelet, 236 (77.4%) reported improvement in their maximum pain index (where the pain was the worst). Of the 305 subjects who wore the placebo bracelet (a bracelet identical in every respect to the "ionized" bracelet except that there was no active ingredient—presumably, here, "ionization"), 234 (76.7%) reported improvement in their maximum pain

index. Using level of significance $\alpha = 0.05$, test whether the population proportions reporting improvement differ between wearers of the ionized bracelet and wearers of the placebo bracelet.

BRINGING IT ALL TOGETHER
Males Listening to the Radio. Use the following information for Exercises 33–41. The Arbitron Corporation tracks trends in radio listening. In their publication *Radio Today*, Arbitron reported that 92% of 18- to 24-year-old males listen to the radio each week, while 87% of males 65 years and older listen to the radio each week. Suppose each sample size was 1000.

33. Is it appropriate to perform Z inference for the difference in population proportions? Why or why not?
34. Clearly describe what p_1 means and what p_2 means.
35. Explain what the difference is between p_1 and $\hat{p}_1$.
36. Calculate the margin of error for a 95% confidence interval for $p_1 - p_2$. Explain what this number means.
37. Construct and interpret a 95% confidence interval for $p_1 - p_2$.
38. Use the confidence interval from Exercise 37 to test, using level of significance $\alpha = 0.05$, whether $p_1 - p_2$ differs from the following.
   a. 0   **b.** 0.01   **c.** 0.05
39. Explain whether we could use the confidence interval from Exercise 37 to test whether the proportion of 18- of 24-year-old males who listen to the radio each week is greater than the proportion of males 65 years and older who do so. Why or why not?
40. Test using level of significance $\alpha = 0.05$ whether the proportion of 18- of 24-year-old males who listen to the radio each week is greater than the proportion of males 65 years and older who do so.
41. *What if*, instead of 1000, each sample size was 100. How would this change affect each of the following measures?
   a. Margin of error in Exercise 36.
   b. p-value in Exercise 40.
   c. Conclusion of the hypothesis test in Exercise 40.

10.4 Inference for Two Independent Standard Deviations

OBJECTIVES By the end of this section, I will be able to . . .

1 Describe the characteristics of the F distribution and the F test for two population standard deviations.

2 Perform hypothesis tests for two population standard deviations using the critical-value method.

3 Perform hypothesis tests for two population standard deviations using the p-value method.

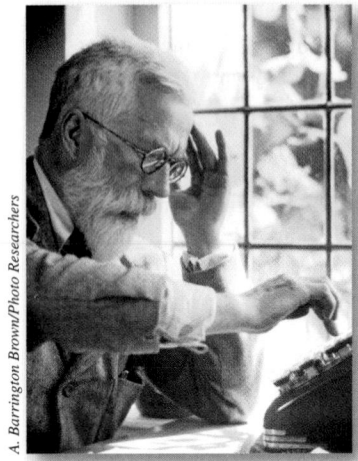

Sir Ronald A. Fisher

1 The *F* Distribution and the *F* Test

In Sections 10.1–10.3, we were introduced to inference methods for comparing two population means and two population proportions. Here we learn how to perform hypothesis tests regarding two population standard deviations. Wall Street investors are wary of excessive stock price variability. In this section, we will compare the variability of prices between two tech stocks, Google and Apple, using a new hypothesis test, called the *F* test. The *F* test will determine whether there is a significant difference in the variability of the stock prices, as measured by the respective population standard deviations. The *F* test is based on the *F* distribution, named in honor of the "grandfather of statistics," Sir Ronald A. Fisher.

Let population 1 be Google stock prices and population 2 be Apple stock prices. We can test whether Google's stock prices are more variable than those of Apple; that is, we may test whether the standard deviation of Google stock prices, σ_1, is greater than the standard deviation of Apple stock prices, σ_2. This gives us the following hypotheses for our *F* test:

$$H_0 : \sigma_1 = \sigma_2 \quad \text{versus} \quad H_a : \sigma_1 > \sigma_2$$

Table 10.19 provides the three possible forms of hypotheses available when performing the *F* test for comparing two population standard deviations for two populations with standard deviations σ_1 and σ_2, respectively.

Table 10.19 Three possible forms for the *F* test for comparing two population standard deviations

Form of test	Null hypothesis	Alternative hypothesis
Right-tailed test	$H_0 : \sigma_1 = \sigma_2$	$H_a : \sigma_1 > \sigma_2$
Left-tailed test	$H_0 : \sigma_1 = \sigma_2$	$H_a : \sigma_1 < \sigma_2$
Two-tailed test	$H_0 : \sigma_1 = \sigma_2$	$H_a : \sigma_1 \neq \sigma_2$

The requirements for performing the *F* test are the following:

1. We have two independent random samples taken from two populations.

2. The two populations are both normally distributed.

The test statistic for the *F* test is F_{data}, given as follows.

> **Test Statistic for the *F* Test for Comparing Two Population Standard Deviations**
>
> Suppose that the two population variances are equal, $\sigma_1^2 = \sigma_2^2$, and that we have independent random samples of size n_1 and n_2 from two normally distributed populations with sample variances s_1^2 and s_2^2, respectively. Then the test statistic for the *F* test.
>
> $$F_{\text{data}} = \frac{s_1^2}{s_2^2}$$
>
> follows an *F* distribution with $n_1 - 1$ degrees of freedom in the numerator and $n_2 - 1$ degrees of freedom in the denominator.

Let's become better acquainted with the *F* distribution. Like the χ^2 distribution, the *F* distribution is right-skewed, never takes negative values, and has an infinite number of different *F* curves (Figure 10.22) The shape of the curve depends on degrees of freedom.

FIGURE 10.22
Shape of the F distribution for various degrees of freedom.

Note that the F distribution resembles the χ^2 distribution. This is not surprising since the values of the F distribution represent ratios of two χ^2 distributions. Moreover, the F distribution has two different degrees of freedom, which we shall call df_1 and df_2, derived from the degrees of freedom of the two χ^2 distributions represented in the ratio. Often, df_1 is called the *numerator degrees of freedom*, and df_2 is called the *denominator degrees of freedom*.

Properties of the F Curve

1. The total area under the F curve equals 1.

2. The value of the F random variable is never negative, so the F curve starts at 0. However, it extends indefinitely to the right. The curve approaches but never quite meets the horizontal axis.

3. Because of the characteristics described in (2), the F curve is right-skewed.

4. There is a different F curve for each different pair of degrees of freedom, df_1 and df_2.

Since the F distribution is continuous, we can find probabilities associated with values of F, and vice versa, just as we did with the normal, t, and χ^2 distributions. Just as for any continuous distribution, probability is represented by the area below the F curve above and interval.

2 Perform the F Test for Comparing Two Population Standard Deviations: Critical-Value Method

To perform the hypothesis tests in this section, as well as in Chapters 12 and 13, we need to find the critical values of an F distribution for a given level of significance α. For example, we may need to find the value of an F distribution that has area $\alpha = 0.05$ to the right of it. Or we may need to find the value of an F distribution that has area $\alpha = 0.01$ to the left of it. To find these F critical values, we shall work with the F tables (see Appendix Table F). The F tables are somewhat different from the other tables that we have worked with so far.

The notation

$$F_{\text{crit}} = F_{\alpha, n_1 - 1, n_2 - 1}$$

represents the critical value of the F distribution with $df_1 = n_1 - 1$ numerator degrees of freedom and $df_2 = n_2 - 1$ denominator degrees of freedom, with area α to the right of $F_{\alpha, n_1 - 1, n_2 - 1}$. For example, $F_{0.05, 15, 10}$ represents the value of the F distribution with $df_1 = 15$ and $df_2 = 10$, with area 0.05 to the right of it. Next we learn how to find the F critical values using the F tables.

Procedure for Finding F Critical Value for a Given Area α to the Right of It

Suppose we have an F distribution with df_1 and df_2 degrees of freedom. To find the critical value F_{crit} that has area α to the right of it, do the following:

Step 1 Look across the top of the F table until you find your df_1. Then go down that column until you see your df_2 on the left.

Step 2 For each df_2 on the left, you will see a range of α values from 0.100 to 0.001. Choose the row next to df_2 that has your value of α. The F-value in that row and column is your value of F_{crit}.

Developing Your Statistical Sense

Note: When the degrees of freedom are not listed in the F table, we do not necessarily take the closest degrees of freedom we can find. This is because sometimes the closest degrees of freedom is larger than the original, which leads to misleadingly overprecise results, a level of precision not warranted by the data. For example, this could lead us to find significance where none actually exists.

Degrees of Freedom Not Listed in the Table

Just as with the t table, not all the degrees of freedom are listed in the F table. If either of the degrees of freedom df_1 or df_2 are not listed in the F table, a conservative solution is to take the next smallest value for whichever of df_1 or df_2 is not listed. For example, suppose $df_1 = n_1 - 1 = 57 - 1 = 56$ and $df_2 = n_2 - 1 = 170 - 1 = 169$. Neither $df_1 = 56$ nor $df_2 = 169$ is given in the F table. Therefore, we set df_1 to be the next smallest value given in the table, $df_1 = 50$, and we set df_2 to be the next smallest value, $df_2 = 160$. ◢

The F tables give only the F critical values for a given area α to the right. To find F critical values for a given area α to the left, we use the following property:

$$F_{1-\alpha, n_1-1, n_2-1} = \frac{1}{F_{\alpha, n_2-1, n_1-1}}$$

In other words, the value from an F distribution with degrees of freedom $df_1 = n_1 - 1$ and $df_2 = n_2 - 1$ and area α to the *left* of it equals the reciprocal of the value from an F distribution with degrees of freedom $df_1 = n_2 - 1$ and $df_2 = n_1 - 1$ and area α to the *right* of it. Note that the two degrees of freedom get switched.

Procedure for Finding F Critical Value for a Given Area α to the Left of It

1. Switch the values of df_1 and df_2.
2. Find F_{α, n_2-1, n_1-1} using the F table.
3. Calculate $F_{crit} = F_{1-\alpha, n_1-1, n_2-1} = \dfrac{1}{F_{\alpha, n_2-1, n_1-1}}$

So, for example, to find the value of an F distribution with degrees of freedom $df_1 = 10$ and $df_2 = 15$ with area $\alpha = 0.05$ to the left of it, follow steps 1 and 2 above to find the value of an F distribution with $df_1 = 15$ and $df_2 = 10$ with area $\alpha = 0.05$ to the right of it. Then compute the reciprocal.

Example 10.18 Finding critical values of the F distribution

Use the excerpt from the F distribution tables in Figure 10.23 to find the following critical values of the F distribution.

F distribution critical values

| | Area in right tail | **df₁** | | |
		1	**2**	**3**
1	0.100	39.86	49.59	53.59
	0.050	161.45	199.50	215.71
	0.025	647.79	799.50	864.16
	0.010	4052.20	4999.50	5403.40
	0.001	405284.00	500000.00	540379.00
6	0.100	3.78	3.46	3.29
	0.050	5.99	5.14	4.76
	0.025	8.81	7.26	6.60
	0.010	13.75	10.92	9.78
	0.001	35.51	27.00	23.70
7	0.100	3.59	3.26	3.07
	0.050	5.59	4.74	4.35
	0.025	8.07	6.54	5.89
	0.010	12.25	9.55	8.45
	0.001	29.25	21.69	18.77

FIGURE 10.23 *F* table (excerpt).

a. Find the critical value with area $\alpha = 0.05$ to the right of it, for an *F* distribution with $df_1 = 2$ and $df_2 = 7$.

b. Find the critical value with area $\alpha = 0.01$ to the left of it, for an *F* distribution with $df_1 = 6$ and $df_2 = 3$.

Solution

a. *Step 1.* Go across the top of the *F* table until we get to $df_1 = 2$ and go down that column until we see $df_2 = 7$ on the left.

Step 2. Next to the 7 is a range of α values from 0.100 to 0.001. We choose the row with $\alpha = 0.05$. The *F*-value in that row and column is 4.74. Thus our *F* critical value is

$$F_{\text{crit}} = F_{0.05,\,2,\,7} = 4.74$$

b. *Step 1.* Switching the two degrees of freedom, we go across the top of the *F* table until we get to $df_1 = 3$. Then we go down that column until we see $df_2 = 6$ on the left.

Step 2. Choose the row with $\alpha = 0.010 = 0.01$. The *F*-value in that row and column is 9.78. Thus our *F* critical value is

Now You Can Do
Exercises 9–20.

$$F_{\text{crit}} = F_{0.99,\,6,\,3} = \frac{1}{F_{0.01,\,6,\,3}} = \frac{1}{9.78} = 0.1023$$

Now we use the critical values of the *F* distribution to help us with the critical-value method of performing the *F* test for comparing two population standard deviations. Later we show the steps for the *p*-value method, along with an example.

F Test for Comparing Two Population Standard Deviations—Critical-Value Method

Suppose we have two independent random samples of size n_1 and n_2 taken from two normally distributed populations, with population standard deviations σ_1 and σ_2, and sample standard deviations s_1 and s_2, respectively.

Step 1 **State the hypotheses.** Use one of the forms from Table 10.20. State the meaning of σ_1 and σ_2.

Step 2 **Find the critical value(s) and state the rejection rule.** Use Table 10.20 and the F tables.

Step 3 **Find F_{data}.**

$$F_{data} = \frac{s_1^2}{s_2^2}$$

follows an F distribution with $df_1 = n_1 - 1$ and $df_2 = n_2 - 1$.

Step 4 **State the conclusion and the interpretation.** Compare F_{data} with the F critical value from Table 10.20.

Table 10.20 Critical values, rejection rules, and rejection regions

	Right-tailed test	**Left-tailed test**	**Two-tailed test**
Hypotheses	$H_0 : \sigma_1 = \sigma_2$ $H_a : \sigma_1 > \sigma_2$	$H_0 : \sigma_1 = \sigma_2$ $H_a : \sigma_1 < \sigma_2$	$H_0 : \sigma_1 = \sigma_2$ $H_a : \sigma_1 \neq \sigma_2$
Critical value(s)	F_{α, n_1-1, n_2-1} The F-value with area α to the right of it.	$F_{1-\alpha, n_1-1, n_2-1}$ The F-value with area α to the left of it.	$F_{1-\alpha/2, n_1-1, n_2-1}$ and $F_{\alpha/2, n_1-1, n_2-1}$ The F-value with area $\alpha/2$ to the left of it and the F-value with area $\alpha/2$ to the right of it.
Rejection rule	Reject H_0 if $F_{data} > F_{\alpha, n_1-1, n_2-1}$	Reject H_0 if $F_{data} < F_{1-\alpha, n_1-1, n_2-1}$	Reject H_0 if $F_{data} < F_{1-\alpha/2, n_1-1, n_2-1}$ or if $F_{data} > F_{\alpha/2, n_1-1, n_2-1}$
Critical region			

We now return to our example comparing the variability of stock prices between Google and Apple.

Example 10.19 *F* test for comparing two population standard deviations: critical-value method

Table 10.21 shows independent samples from Google and Apple stock prices taken between June 2009 and July 2010 together with the sample sizes and sample standard deviations. Test using the critical-value method whether the standard deviation of Google stock prices σ_1 is greater than the standard deviation of Apple stock prices σ_2.

Table 10.21 Independent random samples of stock prices, June 2009–July 2010

Google	Apple
426.56 418.99 452.21 457.52	139.35 142.83 165.30 166.43 180.86
487.20 537.29 585.74 623.99	188.25 196.48 196.98 214.38 195.46
531.29 564.21 571.01 482.37 439.49	218.95 238.49 255.99 260.83 248.48 257.29
$s_1 = 13$ $\sigma_1 \approx 67.0659$	$s_2 = 16$ $\sigma_2 \approx 40.0535$

Source: www.marketwatch.com/tools/quotes/historical.asp.

Solution

The normal probability plots in Figures 10.24a and 10.24b show acceptable normality for both samples. We may, therefore, proceed with the F test for comparing population standard deviations.

FIGURE 10.24a Normal probability of Google stock.

FIGURE 10.24b Normal probability plot of Apple stock.

> **Step 1** **State the hypotheses.** We are testing whether Google's stock prices are more variable than those of Apple. Thus, since Google represents population 1, we have the following hypotheses for our F test:

$$H_0 : \sigma_1 = \sigma_2 \quad \text{versus} \quad H_a : \sigma_1 > \sigma_2$$

where σ_1 represents the standard deviation of Google stock prices and σ_2 represents the standard deviation of Apple stock prices. Use level of significance $\alpha = 0.05$.

> **Step 2** **Find the critical value and state the rejection rule.** We have $df_1 = n_1 - 1 = 12$ and $df_2 = n_2 - 1 = 15$. From Table 10.20 and Appendix Table F, our critical value is the F-value with area $\alpha = 0.05$ to the right of it:

$$F_{\text{crit}} = F_{\alpha, n_1 - 1, n_2 - 1} = F_{0.05, 12, 15} = 2.48$$

Our rejection rule is, then, from Table 10.20: Reject H_0 if $F_{\text{data}} > 2.48$.

> **Step 3** **Find F_{data}.**

$$F_{\text{data}} = \frac{s_1^2}{s_2^2} = \frac{67.0659^2}{40.0535^2} \approx 2.8036$$

follows an F distribution with $df_1 = n_1 - 1$ and $df_2 = n_2 - 1$.

> **Step 4** **State the conclusion and the interpretation.** Since $F_{\text{data}} \approx 2.8036$ is greater than $F_{\text{crit}} = 2.48$, we reject H_0. There is evidence that the variability in Google stock prices is greater than the variability in Apple stock prices. ∎

Now You Can Do
Exercises 21–26.

3 Perform the *F* Test for Comparing Two Population Standard Deviations: *p*-Value Method

We may also use the *p*-value method to perform the *F* test for comparing two population standard deviations. The requirements are the same.

> ### *F* Test for Comparing Two Population Standard Deviations: *p*-Value Method
>
> Suppose we have two independent random samples of size n_1 and n_2 taken from two normally distributed populations, with population standard deviations σ_1 and σ_2, and sample standard deviations s_1 and s_2, respectively.
>
> *Step 1* **State the hypotheses and the rejection rule.** Use one of the forms from Table 10.20. Clearly state the meaning of σ_1 and σ_2. The rejection rule is: *Reject H_0 if the p-value is less than α.*
>
> *Step 2* **Find F_{data}.**
>
> $$F_{data} = \frac{s_1^2}{s_2^2}$$
>
> follows an *F* distribution with $df_1 = n_1 - 1$ and $df_2 = n_2 - 1$.
>
> *Step 3* **Find the *p*-value.** Use technology and Table 10.22 to find the *p*-value.
>
> *Step 4* **State the conclusion and the interpretation.** Compare the *p*-value with α.

Table 10.22 *p*-Value for the *F* test for comparing two standard deviations

	Right-tailed test	Left-tailed test	Two-tailed test
Hypotheses	$H_0 : \sigma_1 = \sigma_2$ $H_a : \sigma_1 > \sigma_2$	$H_0 : \sigma_1 = \sigma_2$ $H_a : \sigma_1 < \sigma_2$	$H_0 : \sigma_1 = \sigma_2$ $H_a : \sigma_1 \neq \sigma_2$
p-Value	$P(F > F_{data})$ The area to the right of F_{data}. p-value = $P(F > F_{data})$	$P(F < F_{data})$ The area to the left of F_{data}. p-value = $P(F < F_{data})$	The *smaller* of: (i) $2 \cdot P(F > F_{data})$ and (ii) $2 \cdot P(F < F_{data})$.

We illustrate the *p*-value method with an example.

Example 10.20 *F* test for comparing two population standard deviations: *p*-value method

The Web site **Medicare.gov** publishes survey information on patient attitudes about their level of care. Table 10.23 shows the percentages of respondents taken from independent random samples of hospitals in Florida and Georgia, which reported that their nurses always communicated well.

Table 10.23 Independent random samples of hospital percentages

Florida	Georgia
67 66 70 70 72 73	72 75 78 73 68 71
63 69 65 68 65	82 72 77 75 73
$n_1 = 11$ $s_1 \approx 3.1305$	$n_2 = 11$ $s_2 \approx 3.8162$

Source: Medicare.gov.

Test whether there is a difference in variability between the two states, using $\alpha = 0.10$.

Solution

Because the normal probability plots in Figures 10.25a and 10.25b show acceptable normality, we may therefore proceed with the F test for comparing population standard deviations.

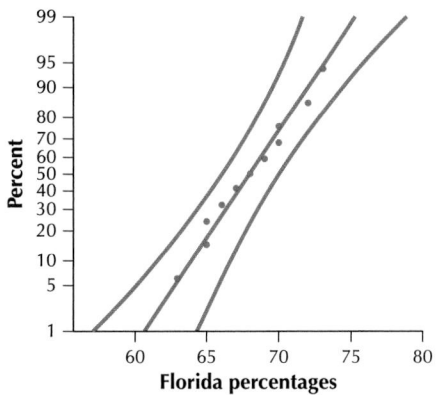

FIGURE 10.25a Normal probability plot of Florida percentages.

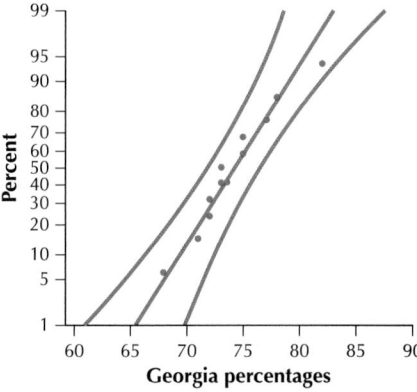

FIGURE 10.25b Normal probability plot of Georgia percentages.

Step 1 **State the hypotheses.** We are testing whether there is a difference in the standard deviation of the percentages for Florida (σ_1) and Georgia (σ_2). We therefore have a two-tailed test:

$$H_0 : \sigma_1 = \sigma_2 \quad \text{versus} \quad H_a : \sigma_1 \neq \sigma_2$$

where σ_1 and σ_2 represent the standard deviations of the percent of respondents who reported that their nurses always communicated well in Florida and Georgia, respectively. Use level of significance $\alpha = 0.10$.

Step 2 **Find F_{data}.**

$$F_{data} = \frac{s_1^2}{s_2^2} = \frac{3.1305^2}{3.8162^2} \approx 0.6729$$

follows an F distribution with $df_1 = n_1 - 1 = 10$ and $df_2 = n_2 - 1 = 10$.

Step 3 **Find the p-value.** Since we have a two-tailed test, Table 10.22 states that the p-value is

The smaller of **(i)** $2 \cdot P(F > F_{data})$ and **(ii)** $2 \cdot P(F < F_{data})$

Figure 10.26a shows the output from the TI-83/84, giving $P(F > F_{data})$ as the area under the F distribution curve between 0.6729 and infinity. This gives

$$2 \cdot P(F > F_{data}) = 2 \cdot 0.7287420993 = 1.457484199$$

This *cannot* represent a valid p-value, since it is larger than 1. Figure 10.26b shows the output from the TI-83/84, giving $P(F < F_{data})$ as the area under the F distribution curve between 0 and 0.6729. Thus, our p-value is:

$$p\text{-value} = 2 \cdot P(F < F_{data}) = 2 \cdot P(F < 0.6729) = 2 \cdot 0.2712579007 \approx 0.5425$$

since this is smaller than 1.457484199.

Step 4 **State the conclusion and the interpretation.** Since the p-value 0.5425 is not less than $\alpha = 0.10$, we do not reject H_0. There is insufficient evidence for a difference in population standard deviations between percentages of patients in Florida and Georgia hospitals who reported that their nurses always communicated well. ■

FIGURE 10.26a

```
Fcdf(0,0.6729,10
,10)
        .2712579007
```

FIGURE 10.26b

Now You Can Do
Exercises 27–32.

STEP-BY-STEP TECHNOLOGY GUIDE: *F* Test for Comparing Two Population Standard Deviations

TI-83/84

Step 1 Press **2ⁿᵈ VARS** to bring up the list of distributions.
Step 2 Press the down arrow key until you reach **Fcdf(**. Press **ENTER**.

Step 3 Enter the left endpoint, comma, the right endpoint, comma, df_1, comma, df_2, close parenthesis. Then press **ENTER**.

EXCEL

Step 1 Enter the samples from populations 1 and 2 into columns **A** and **B**.
Step 2 Select the **Data** menu, click **Data Analysis**, and select **F Test Two-Sample for Variances**.

Step 3 Put the cursor in the **Variable 1 Range** and highlight the data in column **A**. Put the cursor in the **Variable 2 Range** and highlight the data in column **B**. Enter the value for alpha (α). Then click **OK**.

MINITAB

Step 1 If you have the raw data, enter the samples from populations 1 and 2 into columns **C1** and **C2**.
Step 2 Select the **Stat** menu, highlight **Basic Statistics**, and select **2 Variances**.
Step 3 If you have the raw data, select **Samples in different columns**, enter **C1** for **First** and **C2** for **Second**. If you have the

summarized data, select **Summarized data**, and enter the sample sizes and sample variances (not the sample standard deviations) in the appropriate cells.
Step 4 Click **Options** and select a **Confidence level**, which should equal $1 - \alpha$. Then click **OK**. There is both graphical output as well as output to the session screen.

Section 10.4 Summary

1 In this section we learn how to perform hypothesis tests regarding two population standard deviations, using a new distribution, called the *F* distribution. The *F* tables can be used to find critical values of the *F* distribution.

2 The *F* test for comparing two population standard deviations may be carried out using the critical-value

method, where the test statistic F_{data} is compared to the critical value(s) of the *F* distribution.

3 The *F* test may also be performed using the *p*-value method, where the *p*-value is compared to the level of significance α.

Section 10.4 Exercises

CLARIFYING THE CONCEPTS

1. In the section, what is the *F* test used to compare?
2. True or false: To perform the *F* test, the random samples from the two populations may be either dependent samples or independent samples.
3. True of false: To perform the *F* test, the two populations must be normally distributed.
4. What is the formula for the test statistic for the *F* test?
5. For the *F* test, what distribution does the test statistic follow? What are the degrees of freedom?
6. True or false: The value of the *F* random variable can be positive or negative.

7. What does the notation F_{α, n_1-1, n_2-1} represent?
8. Briefly explain how to find the *F* critical value for a given area α to the left of it.

PRACTICING THE TECHNIQUES

For Exercises 9–12, find the *F* critical value for a right-tailed test with the given characteristics.

9. $\alpha = 0.05$, $df_1 = 10$, $df_2 = 9$
10. $\alpha = 0.10$, $df_1 = 10$, $df_2 = 9$
11. $\alpha = 0.01$, $df_1 = 5$, $df_2 = 4$
12. $\alpha = 0.01$, $df_1 = 5$, $df_2 = 20$

For Exercises 13–16, find the F critical value for a left-tailed test with the given characteristics.

13. $\alpha = 0.05$, $df_1 = 20$, $df_2 = 3$
14. $\alpha = 0.01$, $df_1 = 20$, $df_2 = 3$
15. $\alpha = 0.05$, $df_1 = 3$, $df_2 = 20$
16. $\alpha = 0.01$, $df_1 = 3$, $df_2 = 20$

For Exercises 17–20, find the F critical value for a two-tailed test with the given characteristics.

17. $\alpha = 0.05$, $df_1 = 15$, $df_2 = 6$
18. $\alpha = 0.10$, $df_1 = 30$, $df_2 = 100$
19. $\alpha = 0.05$, $df_1 = 6$, $df_2 = 15$
20. $\alpha = 0.10$, $df_1 = 60$, $df_2 = 100$

For Exercises 21–26, assume that the populations are independent and normally distributed. Perform the indicated hypothesis tests using the critical-value method. For each exercise

    a. State the hypotheses.
    b. Find the critical value(s) and state the rejection rule.
    c. Find F_{data}.
    d. State the conclusion and interpretation.

21. $H_0 : \sigma_1 = \sigma_2$ versus $H_a : \sigma_1 > \sigma_2$, $\alpha = 0.05$, $n_1 = 11$, $n_2 = 7$, $s_1 = 2$, $s_2 = 1$
22. $H_0 : \sigma_1 = \sigma_2$ versus $H_a : \sigma_1 < \sigma_2$, $\alpha = 0.05$, $n_1 = 16$, $n_2 = 8$, $s_1 = 2$, $s_2 = 3$
23. $H_0 : \sigma_1 = \sigma_2$ versus $H_a : \sigma_1 < \sigma_2$, $\alpha = 0.10$, $n_1 = 10$, $n_2 = 21$, $s_1 = 2.5$, $s_2 = 3.5$
24. $H_0 : \sigma_1 = \sigma_2$ versus $H_a : \sigma_1 > \sigma_2$, $\alpha = 0.10$, $n_1 = 31$, $n_2 = 7$, $s_1 = 10.2$, $s_2 = 5.1$
25. $H_0 : \sigma_1 = \sigma_2$ versus $H_a : \sigma_1 \neq \sigma_2$, $\alpha = 0.05$, $n_1 = 6$, $n_2 = 13$, $s_1 = 3.1$, $s_2 = 1.3$
26. $H_0 : \sigma_1 = \sigma_2$ versus $H_a : \sigma_1 \neq \sigma_2$, $\alpha = 0.05$, $n_1 = 21$, $n_2 = 7$, $s_1 = 10.7$, $s_2 = 9.9$

For Exercises 27–32, assume that the populations are normally distributed. Perform the indicated hypothesis tests using the p-value method. For each exercise

    a. State the hypotheses and the rejection rule.
    b. Find F_{data}.
    c. Find the p-value.
    d. State the conclusion and interpretation.

27. $H_0 : \sigma_1 = \sigma_2$ versus $H_a : \sigma_1 > \sigma_2$, $\alpha = 0.01$, $n_1 = 9$, $n_2 = 16$, $s_1 = 5$, $s_2 = 3$
28. $H_0 : \sigma_1 = \sigma_2$ versus $H_a : \sigma_1 < \sigma_2$, $\alpha = 0.01$, $n_1 = 21$, $n_2 = 7$, $s_1 = 4$, $s_2 = 7$
29. $H_0 : \sigma_1 = \sigma_2$ versus $H_a : \sigma_1 < \sigma_2$, $\alpha = 0.05$, $n_1 = 16$, $n_2 = 21$, $s_1 = 2.8$, $s_2 = 5.2$
30. $H_0 : \sigma_1 = \sigma_2$ versus $H_a : \sigma_1 > \sigma_2$, $\alpha = 0.05$, $n_1 = 51$, $n_2 = 101$, $s_1 = 25.1$, $s_2 = 12.7$
31. $H_0 : \sigma_1 = \sigma_2$ versus $H_a : \sigma_1 \neq \sigma_2$, $\alpha = 0.10$, $n_1 = 8$, $n_2 = 8$, $s_1 = 150$, $s_2 = 150$
32. $H_0 : \sigma_1 = \sigma_2$ versus $H_a : \sigma_1 \neq \sigma_2$, $\alpha = 0.10$, $n_1 = 11$, $n_2 = 26$, $s_1 = 15.1$, $s_2 = 20.6$

APPLYING THE CONCEPTS

33. Body Mass Index. The body mass index (BMI) is a statistical measure of an individual's body weight, based on his or her weight and height. In the Framingham Heart Study,[14] a sample of 1160 males had a mean BMI of 25.5 with a sample standard deviation of 3.3, and a sample of 1571 women had a mean BMI of 24.8 with a sample standard deviation of 4.3. Test whether the population standard deviation of the males' BMI is less than that of the females, using $\alpha = 0.05$. Assume that the samples are independent and that the two populations are normally distributed.

34. Smoking. A research paper[15] described two common types of smokers: **(a)** Morning Highs: those who tend to smoke more in the morning than the rest of the day, and **(b)** Flatlines: those who tend to smoke at the same rate all day. A sample of 43 smokers from the Morning High group had a mean of 30.7 cigarettes smoked per day, with a sample standard deviation of 10.5 cigarettes. A sample of 247 smokers from the Flatline group had a mean of 22.0 cigarettes smoked per day, with a sample standard deviation of 7.7 cigarettes. Test whether the population standard deviation of the Morning High group is greater than that of the Flatline group, using $\alpha = 0.10$. Assume that the samples are independent and that the two populations are normally distributed.

35. Autism and Asperger's Syndrome. A study[16] compared the IQ scores of children with autism and children with Asperger's syndrome. A sample of 85 children with autism had a mean IQ of 72.71 with a sample standard deviation of 15.08. A sample of 341 children with Asperger's syndrome had a mean IQ of 95.76 with a sample standard deviation of 16.56. Test whether the population standard deviations of the two groups differ, using $\alpha = 0.10$. Assume that the samples are independent and that the two populations are normally distributed.

36. Blood Pressure. A recent study[17] compared the systolic blood pressure readings of two groups of adults, those aged 30–44 and those aged 70–79. A random sample of 100 individuals in the younger group had a sample mean systolic blood pressure reading of 111 with a sample standard deviation of 5. A random sample of 100 individuals in the older group had a sample mean systolic blood pressure reading of 134 with a sample standard deviation of 13. Test whether the population standard deviation of the younger group is less than that of the older group, using $\alpha = 0.05$. Assume that the samples are independent and that the two populations are normally distributed.

37. Gold and Silver Prices. We are interested in testing whether the variability in gold prices exceeds that of silver prices. Refer to the following data, which represent random samples of the prices taken between June 2009 and July 2010, and the following normal probability plots. 🏆 **gold, silver**

a. Do the probability plots indicate violation of the normality assumption?

b. Test whether the population standard deviation of gold prices is greater than that of silver prices, using $\alpha = 0.01$. Assume that the samples are independent.

Gold						
1121.5	1128	1086.8	1098.25	1114	1104.25	
1123.5	1154.5	1185	1236	1227.75	1225	1234
1208						

Silver						
17.17	18.52	16.23	15.57	16.50	17.02	17.69
18.27	18.71	19.11	18.30	18.42	18.65	18.42

38. Runs Scored. The following data represent independent random samples of the number of total runs scored in the 2009 Major League Baseball season, for the American and National Leagues. amruns, natruns

American League team	Runs	National League team	Runs
New York Yankees	915	Florida Marlins	772
Boston Red Sox	872	Atlanta Braves	735
Chicago White Sox	724	Chicago Cubs	720
Tampa Bay Rays	803	New York Mets	707
Detroit Tigers	743	Arizona Diamondbacks	671
Texas Rangers	784	Philadelphia Phillies	820
Cleveland Indians	773	Los Angeles Dodgers	780

Source: ESPN.com: espn.go.com/mlb/standings//date/20091015.

Note: Normal probability plots indicate that the normality assumption is not violated. Test whether the population standard deviations of the two leagues' number of runs scored differ, using $\alpha = 0.05$.

39. Miles per Gallon. The following data represent the combined (city and highway) fuel efficiency in miles per gallon for independent random samples of models manufactured by Honda and Lexus.

Honda car	mpg	Lexus car	mpg
Accord	24	GX 470	15
Odyssey	18	LS 460	18
Civic Hybrid	42	RX 350	19
Fit	31	IS 350	20
CR-V	23	GS 450	23
Ridgeline	17	IS 250	24
S2000	21		

a. The boxplots represent the miles per gallon for each manufacturer. Based on this graph, would you expect that the standard deviations of the two manufacturers are the same or different? Why?

b. *Note:* Normal probability plots indicate that the normality assumption is not violated. Test whether the population standard deviations of the two manufacturers' fuel efficiency differ, using $\alpha = 0.10$.

Chapter 10 Formulas and Vocabulary

SECTION 10.1
- $100(1 - \alpha)\%$ confidence interval for μ_d (p. 506).

$$\bar{x}_d \pm t_{\alpha/2}(s_d/\sqrt{n})$$

- **Dependent samples** (p. 500)
- **Independent samples** (p. 500)
- **Matched-pair samples** (p. 500)
- **Test statistic for the paired sample t test** (p. 502).

$$t_{\text{data}} = \frac{\bar{x}_d}{s_d/\sqrt{n}}$$

SECTION 10.2
- $100(1 - \alpha)\%$ confidence interval for $\mu_1 - \mu_2$ (p. 518).

$$(\bar{x}_1 - \bar{x}_2) \pm t_{\alpha/2}\sqrt{\frac{s_1^2}{n_1} + \frac{s_2^2}{n_2}}$$

- **Margin of error E** (p. 518). For a $100(1 - \alpha)\%$ confidence interval for $\mu_1 - \mu_2$,

$$E = t_{\alpha/2} \cdot \sqrt{\frac{s_1^2}{n_1} + \frac{s_2^2}{n_2}}$$

- **Sampling distribution of $\bar{x}_1 - \bar{x}_2$** (p. 514)

SECTION 10.3
- $100(1 - \alpha)\%$ confidence interval for $p_1 - p_2$ (p. 535).

$$\hat{p}_1 - \hat{p}_2 \pm Z_{\alpha/2}\sqrt{\frac{\hat{p}_1 \cdot \hat{q}_1}{n_1} + \frac{\hat{p}_2 \cdot \hat{q}_2}{n_2}}$$

- **Margin of error E** (p. 535). For a $100(1 - \alpha)\%$ confidence interval for $p_1 - p_2$,

$$E = Z_{\alpha/2} \cdot \sqrt{\frac{\hat{p}_1 \cdot \hat{q}_1}{n_1} + \frac{\hat{p}_2 \cdot \hat{q}_2}{n_2}}$$

- **Pooled estimate of p** (p. 530).

$$\hat{p}_{\text{pooled}} = \frac{x_1 + x_2}{n_1 + n_2}$$

- **Sampling distribution of $\hat{p}_1 - \hat{p}_2$** (p. 530)
- **Test statistic for the independent samples Z test for $p_1 - p_2$** (p. 531).

$$Z_{\text{data}} = \frac{(\hat{p}_1 - \hat{p}_2)}{\sqrt{\hat{p}_{\text{pooled}} \cdot (1 - \hat{p}_{\text{pooled}})\left(\frac{1}{n_1} + \frac{1}{n_2}\right)}}$$

SECTION 10.4
- **F critical values** (p. 541).

$$F_{\alpha, n_1 - 1, n_2 - 1}$$

- **F critical values for a given area α to the left** (p. 542).

$$F_{1-\alpha, n_1 - 1, n_2 - 1} = \frac{1}{F_{\alpha, n_2 - 1, n_1 - 1}}$$

- **Test statistic for comparing two population standard deviations** (p. 540).

$$F_{\text{data}} = \frac{s_1^2}{s_2^2}$$

Chapter 10 Review Exercises

SECTION 10.1
1. Assume that a sample of differences for the matched pairs in the table follows a normal distribution, and carry out Steps **(a)** and **(b)**.

Subject	1	2	3	4	5	6	7	8
Sample 1	100.7	110.2	105.3	107.1	95.6	109.9	112.3	94.7
Sample 2	104.4	112.5	105.9	111.4	99.8	109.9	115.7	97.7

    a. Calculate $\bar{x}_d$ and s_d.
    b. Construct a 95% confidence interval for μ_d.
2. For the data in Exercise 1, test whether $\mu_d < 0$, using the critical-value method and level of significance $\alpha = 0.05$.
3. For the data in Exercise 1, test whether $\mu_d < 0$, using the p-value method and level of significance $\alpha = 0.05$.

SECTION 10.2
Refer to the following summary statistics for two independent samples for Exercises 4–7.

Sample 1	$n_1 = 36$	$\bar{x}_1 = 14.4$	$s_1 = 0.01$
Sample 2	$n_2 = 81$	$\bar{x}_2 = 14.3$	$s_2 = 0.02$

4. We are interested in constructing a 95% confidence interval for $\mu_1 - \mu_2$. Explain why it is appropriate to do so.
5. Provide the point estimate of the difference in population means $\mu_1 - \mu_2$.
6. Calculate the margin of error for a confidence level of 95%.
7. Construct and interpret a 95% confidence interval for $\mu_1 - \mu_2$.
8. A random sample of 49 young persons with college degrees had a mean salary of $30,000 with a standard deviation of $5000. An independent random sample of 36 young persons without college degrees had a mean salary of $25,000 and a standard deviation of $4000.

    a. Test at level of significance $\alpha = 0.10$ whether the population mean salary of college graduates μ_1 is greater than the population mean salary of those without a degree μ_2.
    b. Construct and interpret a 90% confidence interval for $\mu_1 - \mu_2$.

SECTION 10.3

9. The Web site www.internettrafficreport.com reports on the current state of Internet data flow around the world. On August 1, 2004, the packet loss from 32 Asian Web sites was 16%, while the packet loss from 125 North American Web sites was 4%.

    a. Perform a hypothesis test of whether the population proportion from Asian Web sites is greater, at level of significance $\alpha = 0.05$, using the p-value method.

    b. Find a 90% confidence interval for the difference in population proportions.

10. The Centers for Disease Control, in their Pregnancy Risk Assessment Monitoring System, reported that 641 of 823 new mothers living in Florida and 658 of 824 new mothers living in North Carolina took their babies in for a checkup within one week of delivery.

    a. Find a 99% confidence interval for the difference in population proportions.

    b. Perform a hypothesis test of whether the population proportions differ, at level of significance $\alpha = 0.01$, using the p-value method.

SECTION 10.4

For Exercises 11 and 12, assume that the populations are normally distributed. Perform the indicated hypothesis tests using the critical-value method.

11. $H_0: \sigma_1 = \sigma_2$ versus $H_a: \sigma_1 > \sigma_2$, $\alpha = 0.01$, $n_1 = 55$, $n_2 = 107$, $s_1 = 20.2$, $s_2 = 5.6$

12. $H_0: \sigma_1 = \sigma_2$ versus $H_a: \sigma_1 < \sigma_2$, $\alpha = 0.05$, $n_1 = 125$, $n_2 = 27$, $s_1 = 5.7$, $s_2 = 10.2$

For Exercises 13 and 14, assume that the populations are normally distributed. Perform the indicated hypothesis tests using the p-value method for each exercise.

13. $H_0: \sigma_1 = \sigma_2$ versus $H_a: \sigma_1 > \sigma_2$, $\alpha = 0.05$, $n_1 = 1050$, $n_2 = 250$, $s_1 = 10.4$, $s_2 = 4.6$

14. $H_0: \sigma_1 = \sigma_2$ versus $H_a: \sigma_1 < \sigma_2$, $\alpha = 0.01$, $n_1 = 150$, $n_2 = 80$, $s_1 = 25.1$, $s_2 = 35.8$

Chapter 10 QUIZ

TRUE OR FALSE

1. True or false: In a dependent sampling method the subjects in the first sample determine the subjects for selection in the second sample.

2. True or false: The pooled estimate of p, $\hat{p}_{pooled} = (x_1 + x_2)/(n_1 + n_2)$, always lies between $\hat{p}_1$ and $\hat{p}_2$.

3. True or false: The test statistic Z_{data} measures the size of the typical error in using $\hat{p}_1 - \hat{p}_2$ to estimate $p_1 - p_2$.

FILL IN THE BLANK

4. The conditions on paired sample data for performing a hypothesis test or constructing a confidence interval on paired sample data are that the population is _____ or the sample size is _____.

5. The notation E represents the _____ _____ _____ (three words).

6. _____ [notation] represents the sample mean of the set of n paired differences.

SHORT ANSWER

7. What is the notation used to indicate the difference in population means for two independent samples?

8. What statistic is used to estimate the common unknown population proportion?

9. If a $100(1 - \alpha)\%$ confidence interval for $\mu_1 - \mu_2$ contains 0, then with $100(1 - \alpha)\%$ confidence what can you conclude about the difference in the population means?

CALCULATIONS AND INTERPRETATIONS

10. Trying to quit smoking? Butt-Enders, a cigarette dependence reduction program, claims to lower the average number of cigarettes smoked for its participants. A sample of 10 participants consumed the following numbers of cigarettes on a randomly chosen day before and after attending Butt-Enders. Assume that the differences are normally distributed.

Participant	1	2	3	4	5
Before	40	20	60	30	50
After	20	0	40	30	20

Participant	6	7	8	9	10
Before	60	20	40	30	20
After	60	20	20	0	20

    a. Find a 90% confidence interval for the population mean difference in number of cigarettes smoked.

    b. Use your confidence interval to test at level of significance $\alpha = 0.10$ whether the population mean difference in number of cigarettes smoked differs from 0.

11. A family is trying to decide where to move. The choice has come down to Suburb A and Suburb B. A random sample of 40 households in Suburb A had a mean income of $50,000 and a standard deviation of $15,000. A random sample of 36 households in Suburb B had a mean income of $65,000 and a standard deviation of $20,000.

a. Test at level of significance $\alpha = 0.05$ whether the population mean income in Suburb A is less than the population mean income in Suburb B.
b. Construct and interpret a 95% confidence interval for $\mu_1 - \mu_2$.

Use this information for Exercises 12 and 13. A soft drink company recently performed a major overhaul of one of its bottling machines. Management is eager to determine whether the overhaul has resulted in an increase in productivity for the machine. One hundred "minute segments" are sampled at random from the updated machine (Sample 1) and a machine which was not updated (Sample 2), and the number of bottles processed is noted. The mean and standard deviation of the number of bottles processed by each machine is given in the table.

Updated machine	$n_1 = 100$	$\bar{x}_1 = 200$	$s_1 = 30$
Non-updated machine	$n_2 = 100$	$\bar{x}_2 = 190$	$s_2 = 25$

12. Construct and interpret a 95% confidence interval for $\mu_1 - \mu_2$.
13. Refer to the previous exercise.
   a. Test at level of significance $\alpha = 0.05$ whether μ_1 is greater than μ_2.
   b. Explain whether the confidence interval in Exercise 12 could have been used to perform the hypothesis test in (a). Why or why not?
14. The U.S. Census Bureau reported in 2002 that, for people 18–24 years old, the mean annual income for people who never married was $13,539 and for married people was $19,321. Suppose that this information came from a survey of 100 people from each group and that the sample standard deviations were $5000 for the people who never married and $8000 for the married people.
   a. Test at level of significance $\alpha = 0.10$ whether the population mean income for never married people differs from that of married people.

b. If we construct a 90% confidence interval for $\mu_1 - \mu_2$, will the interval include 0? Explain why or why not.
   c. Confirm your statements from (b).
15. The *2005 National Survey on Drug Use and Health* reported that, in 2004, 38.5% of 18–20 year olds reported having used an illicit drug within the past year, and 37.9% reported use in 2005. Assume $n_1 = n_2 = 1000$. Perform a hypothesis test of whether the population proportion of 18- to 20-year-olds who used an illicit drug decreased from 2004 to 2005, using level of significance $\alpha = 0.05$.
16. Are fewer people getting married? The U.S. Census Bureau reported that in 1990, 74.1% of people aged 35–44 were married, while in 2000, 69% of people aged 35–44 were married. Assume that the data are from random samples of size 1000 each. Test whether the population proportion of people aged 35–44 who were married was lower in 2000 than in 1990, using level of significance $\alpha = 0.05$.
17. Pollution in Beijing. The Chinese authorities made strong efforts to reduce the amount of air pollution in Beijing during the 2008 Summer Olympics. But did these improvements stay when the Olympians left? A comparison was made[18] between the amount of fine particulate pollution in taxicabs during the Olympics versus after the Olympics. A random sample of the air inside 11 closed taxicabs during the Olympics showed a mean level of fine particulate pollution of 45.2 milligrams per cubic meter with a sample standard deviation of 27. A random sample of the air inside 11 closed taxicabs after the Olympics showed a mean level of fine particulate pollution of 80.4 milligrams per cubic meter with a sample standard deviation of 72.5. Test whether the population standard deviation of the air during the Olympics is less than that of the air after the Olympics using $\alpha = 0.05$. Assume that the samples are independent and that the two populations are normally distributed.

11

Categorical Data Analysis

Introduction

Chapter 11 introduces the multinomial random variable. Students learn methods for performing hypothesis tests for this type of data using the χ^2 distribution.

Section 11.1 covers the multinomial random variable and the χ^2 goodness of fit test. In Section 11.2, students learn how to perform a χ^2 test for independence between two categorical variables and to test for differences in proportions among k populations. They also learn how to test whether the proportions from several populations are equal or not.

From the Author

- **Section 11.1 χ^2 Goodness of Fit Test**

  - Instructors may wish to review the chi-square distribution in Section 8.4 before starting Chapter 11.

  - The extended example in this section was rewritten to obtain a whole-number value for the test statistic. In this way, students can concentrate on the concepts and techniques, without the decimals and rounding getting in the way.

  - Instructors may wish to use the Developing Your Statistical Sense feature in this section to show how a goodness of fit test is a lot like trying on a new pair of gloves.

  - Instructors may wish to emphasize that, in a goodness of fit test, we are comparing two sets of frequencies: observed frequencies and expected frequencies. Large differences between them will likely lead to rejection of the null hypothesis, as indicated by the What Results Might We Expect feature in this section.

- **Section 11.2 χ^2 Tests for Independence and for Homogeneity of Proportions**

  - Instructors may point out that, even though the hypothesis tests and calculations in this section are different from Section 11.1, we are still comparing observed frequencies with expected frequencies.

  - Students may note that, in a test for the homogeneity of proportions, the proportions usually do not sum to 1.

Teaching Tips

Starting Example: Collect data from the class to see whether there is a difference in the majors of men and women or to see whether there is a difference in year in school between men and women.

In-Class Activities

1. Use the EESEE case study What Makes a Pre-Teen Popular? Let students use some of the variables in the data set to set up contingency tables. Apply the χ^2 test for independence to the variables in the table.

2. A χ^2 Goodness of Fit Test for the Proportions of Freshmen, Sophomores, Juniors, and Seniors at your College

(*Note to instructor:* The small sample sizes involved in the following activities may not meet the assumptions for the χ^2 test. You can alleviate this by taking a larger sample or by collapsing the categories with the smaller expected frequencies.)

a. What do you think are the proportions of freshmen, sophomores, juniors, and seniors at your college? Write out the hypotheses for the test to determine whether these proportions are correct.

b. Use a sample of 25 students to test this hypothesis. What are the expected frequencies for each category? Do you have any data yet to evaluate your claim in (a)?

c. Each student should generate a sample of 25 students from the class, using either (a) technology or (b) the *Random Sample* applet.

d. For each student in your sample, ask which class he or she belongs to. Then add up the counts for each class. Which type of frequencies are these?

e. You will use a level of significance of $\alpha = 0.10$ for this test. What is the critical value χ^2_{crit} for this test? Will it be the same for each student?

f. Carry out the χ^2 goodness of fit test using your sample data. Will the value of χ^2_{data} be the same for each student?

g. Record your name and your value for the test statistic χ^2_{data} calculated in (f) on a Post-It Note®.

h. Place your Post-It Note® on the number line that the instructor prepared on the blackboard, noting the location of the cutoff value χ^2_{crit}. We thus have a collection of values for the statistic χ^2_{data}, representing an approximation of the sampling distribution of χ^2_{data}. Can you make any comment on the shape of the distribution of χ^2_{data} values?

i. What proportion of students rejected the null hypothesis?

j. Reach a class consensus as to why most students either did or did not reject the null hypothesis.

Supplements

- StatTutor 6.1–6.2, 23.2–23.10
- EESEE case studies
  - Alcoholism in Twins (Question 5 on χ^2 test)
  - Cancer and Power Lines (Questions 2, 3(b), 4(d))

Videos

- *Against All Odds* **www.learner.org/resources/series65.html**
  - Program 24: Inference for Two-Way Tables

Web Sites

- The site Online Statistics: An Interactive Multimedia Course of Study has information on contingency tables and the χ^2 distribution, and it has a link to the Rice Virtual Lab in Statistics with simulation demonstrations and other topics related to statistics: **http://onlinestatbook .com/index.html**.

- This Web site lists other sites that do statistical calculations for contingency tables and the χ^2 distribution: **http://statpages.org/**.

- This site has an activity that deals with contingency tables and the χ^2 distribution: **www .amstat.org/publications/jse/v6n3/smith.html**.

Susan Wides/Getty Images

OVERVIEW

11

Categorical Data Analysis

CASE STUDY	## Online Dating

The Pew Internet and American Life Project reports that about 16 million people, representing 11% of the American Internet-using public, have visited a dating Web site, and 37% of Internet users who are currently seeking partners have gone to a dating Web site.[1] In this chapter, we apply the concepts and methodologies of categorical data analysis to investigate online dating. In Section 11.2, we examine whether women and men report different types of relationships, and whether women and men differ in how they self-report their physical appearance.

The Big Picture

Where we are coming from, and where we are headed . . .

- In Chapters 8–10, we learned how to perform inference for continuous variables.

- Here, in Chapter 11, we learn how to perform hypothesis tests for *multinomial data,* an extension of the binomial distribution. These methods rely on the χ^2 (chi-square) distribution, which we learned in Chapters 8 and 9.

- In later chapters, we will learn about *analysis of variance* and *regression,* which rank among the most commonly used data analytic methods in the world.

11.1 χ^2 Goodness of Fit Test

OBJECTIVES By the end of this section, I will be able to . . .

1   Explain what a multinomial random variable is and how to calculate expected frequencies.

2   Describe how a χ^2 goodness of fit test works.

3   Perform and interpret the results from the χ^2 goodness of fit test using the critical-value method, the *p*-value method, and the estimated *p*-value method.

According to **NetApplications.com**, the market share for the leading Internet browsers in May 2011 was as follows: Microsoft Internet Explorer, 55%; Firefox, 25%; others, 20%. Change is rapid in the online environment. Have these market shares changed since May 2011? How would we go about performing a hypothesis test to determine whether market shares have changed significantly? In Section 11.1, we examine this question using a new type of hypothesis test called a χ^2 *goodness of fit test*. We begin by first considering a new type of random variable that is used to represent categorical data.

1 The Multinomial Random Variable

Recall from Chapter 1 that *categorical* (qualitative) variables take values that can be classified into categories. In Chapter 6, we considered binomial random variables, for which there are only two possible outcomes. Now let's consider the following type of random variable, which can have more than two possible values. Suppose we choose a card from a deck of 52 playing cards at random and with replacement, and we define our random variable to be

$$X = \textit{suit of the card}$$

The random variable X has 4 possible outcomes (clubs, spades, hearts, diamonds). We say that X is a **multinomial random variable** because it satisfies the following properties:

> **Multinomial Random Variable**
>
> A random variable is *multinomial* if it satisfies each of the following conditions:
> - Each independent trial of the experiment has k possible outcomes, $k = 2, 3, 4, \ldots$
> - The ith outcome (category) occurs with probability p_i, where $i = 1, 2, \ldots, k$ (that is, p_i is the population proportion for category i)
> - $\sum_{i=1}^{k} p_i = 1$ (Law of Total Probability)
>
> Data from a **multinomial random variable** are said to follow a *multinomial distribution*.

Note: The binomial distribution may be considered a special case of the multinomial distribution, with $k = 2$.

The random variable $X = \textit{suit}$ of the card has 4 outcomes, and the probability of each outcome is

$$p_{\text{clubs}} = p_{\text{spades}} = p_{\text{hearts}} = p_{\text{diamonds}} = 1/4$$

Successive draws are independent since they are made at random and with replacement. Thus, since

$$\sum_{i=1}^{4} p_i = \frac{1}{4} + \frac{1}{4} + \frac{1}{4} + \frac{1}{4} = 1$$

the random variable $X = \textit{suit}$ is a multinomial random variable.

Next, recall from Chapter 6 that the formula for finding the expected value (mean) of a binomial random variable having n trials and probability of success p is

$$\text{expected value} = n \cdot p$$

Now You Can Do
Exercises 5–8.

> For a multinomial random variable, the **expected frequency** of the ith category is
>
> $$\text{expected frequency}_i = E_i = n \cdot p_i$$
>
> where n represents the number of trials, and p_i represents the population proportion for the ith category.

Example 11.1 Browser market share

According to **NetApplications.com**, the market share for the leading Internet browsers in May 2011 was as shown in Table 11.1. Let $X = \textit{browser}$ of a randomly selected Internet user.
a. Verify that $X = \textit{browser}$ is a valid multinomial random variable.
b. Find the expected frequency for each category in a series of 100 trials.

Table 11.1 Distribution of browser market share

Browser	Relative frequency
Microsoft Internet Explorer	0.55
Firefox	0.25
Other	0.20

Solution

a. There are $k = 3$ possible outcomes: Microsoft Internet Explorer, Firefox, and Other. Assigning probabilities using the relative frequency method, we have the following hypothesized proportions for each browser:

$$p_{\text{MS IE}} = 0.55, \quad p_{\text{Firefox}} = 0.25, \quad p_{\text{Other}} = 0.20$$

And

$$\sum_{i=1}^{3} p_i = 0.55 + 0.25 + 0.20 = 1$$

Therefore, $X = browser$ is a valid multinomial random variable.

b. We have $n = 100$ trials (sample size = 100), so the expected frequencies are as provided in Table 11.2.

Table 11.2 Expected frequencies for browser preference in sample of size 100

Category	Expected frequency$_i$ = E_i = $n \cdot p_i$
Microsoft Internet Explorer	$E_{\text{MS IE}} = 100 \cdot 0.55 = 55$
Firefox	$E_{\text{Firefox}} = 100 \cdot 0.25 = 25$
Other	$E_{\text{Other}} = 100 \cdot 0.20 = 20$

As a check on the calculations, we should have $\sum E_i = n$. In this case,

$$\sum E_i = 55 + 25 + 20 = 100 = n$$

Now You Can Do
Exercises 9a–12a.

What Do These Expected Frequencies Mean?

Recall that the expected value of a random variable refers to the long-run mean of that random variable after an arbitrarily large number of trials. For example, if we repeatedly took samples of 100 Internet users and asked about browser preference, the mean number of persons who preferred Firefox would approach 25 as the number of trials increased, *if the proportions given in Table 11.1 are correct.* Similarly, since 25% of the entire population of Internet users prefer Firefox, we would *expect* about 25% of any given sample of 100 Internet users to prefer Firefox, since the sample is a subset of the population. This of course begs the question: are the proportions in Table 11.1 still true? That is the type of question we will learn how to address here in Section 11.1.

2 What Is a χ^2 Goodness of Fit Test?

Do the 2011 market shares still hold true today? In other words, has the distribution of the multinomial random variable *browser* given in Table 11.1 changed since May 2011? To determine this, we introduce a new type of hypothesis test, called a **χ^2 goodness of fit test.**

> **χ^2 Goodness of Fit Test**
>
> A χ^2 **goodness of fit test** is a hypothesis test used to determine whether a random variable follows a particular distribution. In a goodness of fit test, the hypotheses are
> H_0 : The random variable follows a particular distribution.
> H_a : The random variable does not follow the distribution specified in H_0.

For Example 11.1, the null hypothesis completely specifies each of the probabilities in the relative frequency distribution, as follows:

$$H_0 : p_{\text{MS IE}} = 0.55, p_{\text{Firefox}} = 0.25, p_{\text{Other}} = 0.20$$

The alternative hypothesis simply denies the claim made by the null hypothesis:

$$H_a : \text{The random variable does not follow the distribution specified in } H_0.$$

In other words, H_a claims that the browser market shares have changed since May 2011.

Developing Your Statistical Sense

Fitting the Model to the Data

Now, a goodness of fit test sounds like something you do in a clothing store dressing room. Actually, the analogy to clothes is rather appropriate. Suppose winter is coming and you are in the market for a new pair of gloves. You find one pair that is especially attractive, but the gloves don't fit your hands. What do you do? You reject the ill-fitting gloves and search for a new pair. In statistics, the gloves represent the models and your hands represent the actual "hard data" observed in the sample.

The null hypothesis H_0 represents what is called a *model,* a working theory of how the population proportions are distributed. Our working model of how the market shares are distributed is stated in the null hypothesis:

$$\text{Model 1. } H_0 : p_{\text{MS IE}} = 0.55, p_{\text{Firefox}} = 0.25, p_{\text{Other}} = 0.20$$

Of course, we could also try other models if we think the market has changed, such as the following:

$$\text{Model 2. } H_0 : p_{\text{MS IE}} = 0.60, p_{\text{Firefox}} = 0.25, p_{\text{Other}} = 0.15$$
$$\text{Model 3. } H_0 : p_{\text{MS IE}} = 0.50, p_{\text{Firefox}} = 0.30, p_{\text{Other}} = 0.20$$

In hypothesis testing, we "try on" only one model at a time. ◢

In statistics, a goodness of fit test determines if the actual "hard data" observed in the sample are consistent with the proportions stated in the null hypothesis. Market researchers would collect data on the actual preferences of a sample of 100 real Internet users in order to determine whether or not the market shares have changed. The sample is summarized in a set of *observed frequencies* of Internet users who prefer the various browsers. The χ^2 goodness of fit test then *compares these observed frequencies with the expected frequencies* found in Example 11.1.

> **How a Goodness of Fit Test Works**
>
> The goodness of fit test is based on a comparison of the *observed frequencies* (sample data) with the *expected frequencies* when H_0 is true. That is, we compare what we actually see with what we would expect to see if H_0 were true. If the difference between the observed and expected frequencies is large, we reject H_0.

The difference between the observed and expected frequencies is measured by the test statistic, χ^2_{data}. As usual, it comes down to how large a difference is large.

Test Statistic for the χ^2 Goodness of Fit Test

For a multinomial random variable with k categories and n trials, let O_i represent the observed frequency for category i, and let E_i represent the expected frequency for category i. Then the **test statistic for a goodness of fit test**

$$\chi^2_{\text{data}} = \sum \frac{(O_i - E_i)^2}{E_i}$$

approximately follows a χ^2 (chi-square) distribution with $k - 1$ degrees of freedom, if the following conditions are satisfied:

a. None of the expected frequencies is less than 1.

b. At most 20% of the expected frequencies are less than 5.

Students may wish to review the characteristics of the χ^2 distribution (page 411) and the procedure for finding χ^2 critical values for a right-tailed test (page 480).

If the conditions are not satisfied, then it may be possible to combine two or more categories so that the conditions may then be fulfilled.

3 Performing the χ^2 Goodness of Fit Test

The χ^2 goodness of fit test may be performed using (a) the critical-value method or (b) the p-value method.

χ^2 Goodness of Fit Test: Critical-Value Method

Step 1 State the hypotheses and check the conditions.
- The null hypothesis states that the multinomial random variable follows a particular distribution.
- The alternative hypothesis states that the random variable does not follow that distribution.

The following conditions must be met:
a. None of the expected frequencies is less than 1.
b. At most 20% of the expected frequencies are less than 5.

The expected frequency for the ith category is $E_i = n \cdot p_i$ where n represents the number of trials and p_i represents the population proportion for the ith category.

Step 2 Find the χ^2 critical value χ^2_{crit} and state the rejection rule. Use Table E in the Appendix. Reject H_0 if $\chi^2_{\text{data}} \geq \chi^2_{\text{crit}}$.

Step 3 Calculate χ^2_{data}.

$$\chi^2_{\text{data}} = \sum \frac{(O_i - E_i)^2}{E_i}$$

where O_i = observed frequency, and E_i = expected frequency.

Step 4 State the conclusion and the interpretation. Compare χ^2_{data} with χ^2_{crit}.

Example 11.2 Critical-value method for the χ^2 goodness of fit test

Test whether the Internet browser market shares have changed since May 2011, using the observed frequencies of browser preference from a survey of 100 Internet users in Table 11.3, and level of significance $\alpha = 0.05$.

Table 11.3 Observed frequencies of browser preference in sample of 100 Internet users

Browser	Observed frequency
Microsoft Internet Explorer	55
Firefox	35
Other	10

Solution

Step 1 **State the hypotheses and check the conditions.** The hypotheses are:

$H_0 : p_{\text{MS IE}} = 0.55, p_{\text{Firefox}} = 0.25, p_{\text{Other}} = 0.20$
H_a : The random variable does not follow the distribution specified in H_0.

Checking the conditions, the expected frequencies from Table 11.2 are

$$E_{\text{MS IE}} = 55 \quad E_{\text{Firefox}} = 25 \quad E_{\text{Other}} = 20$$

Since none of these expected frequencies is less than 1, and none of the expected frequencies is less than 5, the conditions for performing the goodness of fit test are satisfied.

All hypothesis tests in this chapter are right-tailed tests, so that we need to find χ^2_{crit} for the area to the right of the critical value only.

Step 2 **Find the χ^2 critical value χ^2_{crit} and state the rejection rule.** We have degrees of freedom $k - 1 = 3 - 1 = 2$ and $\alpha = 0.05$. Turning to the χ^2 table (Table E in the Appendix) in the column labeled $\chi^2_{0.05}$ and the row containing df $= 2$, we find $\chi^2_{\text{crit}} = \chi^2_{0.05} = 5.991$, as shown in Figure 11.1. The rejection rule is "Reject H_0 if $\chi^2_{\text{data}} \geq 5.991$."

Chi-Square (χ^2) Distribution

Area to the Right of Critical Value

Degrees of freedom	0.995	0.99	0.975	0.95	0.90	0.10	0.05	0.025
1	—	—	0.001	0.004	0.016	2.706	3.841	5.024
2	0.010	0.020	0.051	0.103	0.211	4.605	5.991	7.378
3	0.072	0.115	0.216	0.352	0.584	6.251	7.815	9.348

FIGURE 11.1 Finding the χ^2 critical value for df $= k - 1 = 2$ and level of significance $\alpha = 0.05$.

Step 3 **Find the test statistic χ^2_{data}.** The observed frequencies O_i are found in Table 11.3 and the expected frequencies are given in Table 11.2. Then

$$\chi^2_{\text{data}} = \sum \frac{(O_i - E_i)^2}{E_i} = \frac{(55 - 55)^2}{55} + \frac{(35 - 25)^2}{25} + \frac{(10 - 20)^2}{20} = 0 + 4 + 5 = 9$$

Table 11.4 gives the quantities needed to calculate χ^2_{data}.

Table 11.4 Calculating χ^2_{data}

Category	p_i	O_i	E_i	$O_i - E_i$	$(O_i - E_i)^2$	$\dfrac{(O_i - E_i)^2}{E_i}$
MS IE	0.55	55	55	0	0	$\dfrac{(55 - 55)^2}{55} = 0$
Firefox	0.25	35	25	10	100	$\dfrac{(35 - 25)^2}{25} = 4$
Other	0.20	10	20	-10	100	$\dfrac{(10 - 20)^2}{20} = 5$

Step 4 **State the conclusion and the interpretation.** Compare χ^2_{data} with χ^2_{crit}. $\chi^2_{\text{data}} = 9$ is greater than $\chi^2_{\text{crit}} = 5.991$, as shown in Figure 11.2. Therefore, we reject H_0.

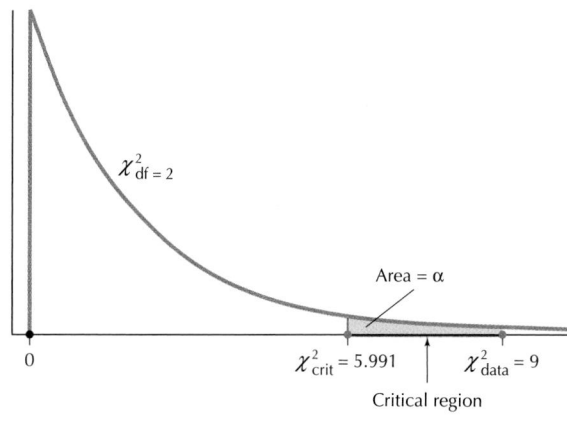

FIGURE 11.2 Reject H_0 when $\chi^2_{\text{data}} \geq \chi^2_{\text{crit}}$.

Now You Can Do
Exercises 19–22.

There is evidence that the random variable *browser* does not follow the distribution specified in H_0. In other words, there is evidence that the market shares for Internet browsers have changed. ∎

Developing Your
Statistical Sense

Be Careful How You Interpret the Conclusion

Note carefully what this conclusion says and what it doesn't say. The χ^2 goodness of fit test shows that there is evidence that the random variable does not follow the distribution specified in H_0. In particular, the conclusion does *not* state, for example, that Firefox's proportion is significantly greater. Informally, we can compare the observed frequency of 35 with the expected frequency of 25 for the Firefox browser and note that there appears to be evidence of an increase in market share for Firefox. But this is only informal and is not part of the hypothesis test. It is a common error in statistical analysis to form conclusions beyond what the hypothesis test is actually testing. ◢

Next we turn to the *p*-value method. Since the χ^2 goodness of fit test is a right-tailed test, the *p*-value for the χ^2 statistic is defined as the area under the χ^2 curve to the right of the test statistic χ^2_{data}, as shown in Figure 11.3. That is,

$$p\text{-value} = P(\chi^2 > \chi^2_{\text{data}})$$

We can use technology to find the exact *p*-value for a particular value of χ^2_{data}. Or, alternatively, the *p*-value may be estimated using the χ^2 table.

FIGURE 11.3
p-Value $= P(\chi^2 > \chi^2_{\text{data}})$.

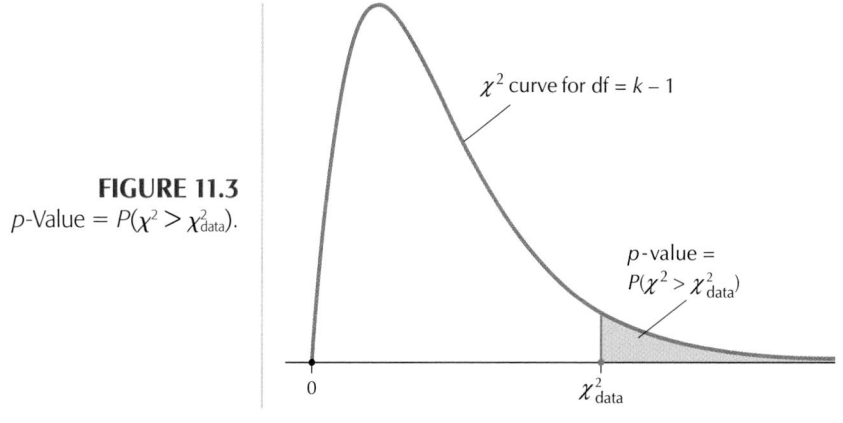

χ^2 Goodness of Fit Test: p-Value Method

Step 1   State the hypotheses and the rejection rule. Check the conditions.

- The null hypothesis states that the multinomial random variable follows a particular distribution.
- The alternative hypothesis states that the random variable does not follow that distribution.
- Reject H_0 if the p-value $\le \alpha$.

The following conditions must be met:

a. None of the expected frequencies is less than 1.

b. At most 20% of the expected frequencies are less than 5.

The expected frequency for the ith category is $E_i = n \cdot p_i$ where n represents the number of trials and p_i represents the population proportion for the ith category.

Step 2   Calculate χ^2_{data}.

$$\chi^2_{data} = \sum \frac{(O_i - E_i)^2}{E_i}$$

where O_i = observed frequency, and E_i = expected frequency.

Step 3   Find the p-value.

p-value $= P(\chi^2 > \chi^2_{data})$ (see Figure 11.3)

Step 4   State the conclusion and the interpretation. Compare the p-value with α.

Example 11.3 p-Value method for the χ^2 goodness of fit test using technology

Table 11.5 2006 broadband adoption survey

Cable modem	DSL	Wireless/Other
41%	50%	9%

Table 11.6 2009 broadband adoption survey

Cable modem	DSL	Wireless/Other
410	330	260

The Pew Internet and American Life Project released the report *Home Broadband Adoption 2009,* which updated figures on the market share of cable modem, DSL, and wireless broadband from a 2006 survey (Table 11.5). The 2009 survey (Table 11.6) was based on a random sample of 1000 home broadband users. Test whether the population proportions have changed since 2006, using the p-value method, and level of significance $\alpha = 0.05$.

Solution

[Step 1] **State the hypotheses and the rejection rule. Check the conditions.**

$H_0 : p_{Cable} = 0.41, p_{DSL} = 0.50, p_{Wireless/Other} = 0.09$
$H_a :$ The random variable does not follow the distribution specified in H_0.

Reject H_0 if the p-value ≤ 0.05.

First we need to find the expected frequencies. We have $n = 1000$, so the expected frequencies are as shown here.

Expected frequencies for broadband access preference in sample of size $n = 1000$

Category	Expected frequency$_i = E_i = n \cdot p_i$
Cable	$E_{Cable} = 1000 \cdot 0.41 = 410$
DSL	$E_{DSL} = 1000 \cdot 0.50 = 500$
Wireless/Other	$E_{Wireless/Other} = 1000 \cdot 0.09 = 90$

What Results Might We Expect?

Before we do the formal hypothesis test, let's try to figure out what the conclusion might be. Figure 11.4 is a clustered bar graph (see Section 2.1) of the observed and expected frequencies for each of the three categories. If H_0 were true, then, for each category, we would expect the green bars (observed frequencies) and yellow bars (expected frequencies) to have somewhat similar heights.

Note that the observed frequency for DSL is much lower than the expected frequency, while the observed frequency for wireless/other is much higher than the expected frequency. These both indicate evidence against the null hypothesis. Thus, we might expect to reject H_0. ◢

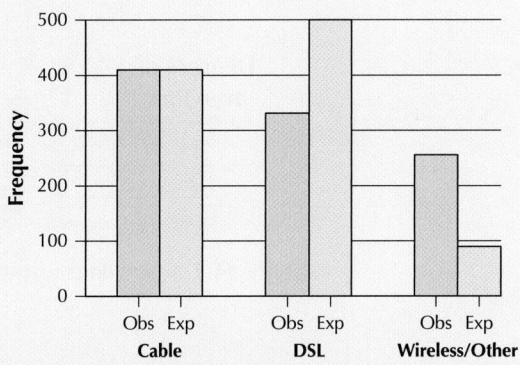

FIGURE 11.4 Graph indicates evidence against H_0.

Next check the requirements for this test. Since (a) none of the expected frequencies is less than 1 and (b) no more than 20% of the expected frequencies are less than 5, we may proceed. We use the instructions provided in the Step-by-Step Technology Guide at the end of this section.

Step 2 **Find the test statistic χ^2_{data}.** The TI-83/84 results in Figure 11.5 tell us that $\chi^2_{\text{data}} = 378.9111111 \approx 378.91$.

Step 3 **Find the p-value.** Figure 11.5 also tells us that

$$p\text{-value} = P(\chi^2 > 378.9111111) \approx 5.25409183\text{E}{-83} \approx 0$$

Figure 11.6 illustrates why the p-value is so small. There is essentially no area to the right of $\chi^2_{\text{data}} = 378.91$ in the $\chi^2_{\text{df}=2}$ distribution.

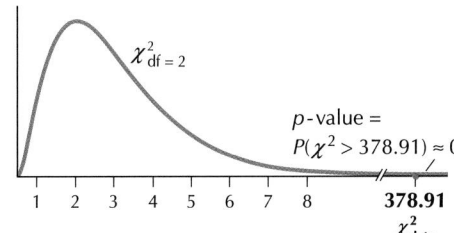

FIGURE 11.5 χ^2 test on TI-83/84.   **FIGURE 11.6** $\chi^2_{\text{data}} = 378.91$ is extreme.

Step 4 **State the conclusion and the interpretation.** Since the p-value is less than $\alpha = 0.05$, we reject H_0, which we expected. There is evidence at a level of significance $\alpha = 0.05$ that the proportions of broadband type in 2009 have changed since 2006. ■

Now You Can Do
Exercises 23–26.

Example 11.4 Estimated *p*-value method for the χ^2 goodness of fit test

Estimate the *p*-value from Example 11.3.

Solution

First find the row in the χ^2 table (Table E in the Appendix) for degrees of freedom $k - 1 = 3 - 1 = 2$. Then find where the value of χ^2_{data} would lie in relationship to the other χ^2 values in that row. Here, $\chi^2_{data} \approx 378.91$ is much greater than the largest value in that row, so the *p*-value must be much smaller than the area 0.005 associated with $\chi^2 = 10.597$ (Figure 11.7). ■

Degrees of freedom	Area to the Right of Critical Value			
	0.025	0.01	0.005	
1	5.024	6.635	7.879	
2	7.378	9.210	10.597	378.91

FIGURE 11.7 Estimating the *p*-value for the χ^2 goodness of fit test.

STEP-BY-STEP TECHNOLOGY GUIDE: The χ^2 Goodness of Fit Test

We illustrate the use of technology, once the observed and expected frequencies are known, for Example 11.3 (page 562).

TI-84

Step 1 Enter observed frequencies in list **L1** and expected frequencies in list **L2**.
Step 2 Press **STAT**, highlight **TESTS**, select **D: χ^2 GOF-Test**, and press **ENTER** (Figure 11.8).

Step 3 Highlight **df**, and enter degrees of freedom **2** (Figure 11.9).
Step 4 Highlight **Calculate** and press **ENTER**. The results are shown in Figure 11.10, including χ^2_{data} and the *p*-value.

FIGURE 11.8

FIGURE 11.9

FIGURE 11.10

TI-83/84

To find χ^2_{data}:
Step 1 Enter observed frequencies in list **L1** and expected frequencies in list **L2**. Press **2nd QUIT**.
Step 2 Press **2nd LIST**, highlight **MATH**, select **5: sum(**, and press **ENTER** (Figure 11.11).

Step 3 Type the following: (L1–L2)²/L2) (see Figure 11.5 in Example 11.3) and press **ENTER**.
Step 4 The TI-83/84 then displays 378.9111111 as χ^2_{data} (see Figure 11.5, in Example 11.3).

To find the *p*-value:
Step 1 Select **2nd DISTR**, then **χ^2 cdf(**, and press **ENTER**.
Step 2 To get the *p*-value, that is, the area to the right of 378.9111111, enter **305.7526652, comma, 1E99, comma, 2)**, as shown in Figure 11.5, in Example 11.3.

FIGURE 11.11

EXCEL

To find χ^2_{data}:
Step 1 Enter the observed and expected frequencies in rows 1 and 2 (Figure 11.12).
Step 2 In cell B3, enter: **=(B1-B2)^2/B2** (Figure 11.12).

	B3		f_x	=(B1-B2)^2/B2	
	A	B	C	D	E
1	Observed	410	330	260	
2	Expected	410	500	90	
3		0			

FIGURE 11.12

Step 3 Copy the contents of cell B3 to cells C3 and D3.
Step 4 Select an empty cell, enter **=SUM(B3:D3)**, and press **ENTER**. Excel then displays the value $\chi^2_{data} = 378.9111111$ (Figure 11.13).

MINITAB

To find χ^2_{data}:
Step 1 Enter the observed frequencies (**O**) into **C1** and the hypothesized proportions into **C2**.
Step 2 Click **Stat > Tables > Chi-Square Goodness of Fit Test** (one variable).

	E3		f_x	=SUM(B3:D3)	
	A	B	C	D	E
1	Observed	410	330	260	
2	Expected	410	500	90	
3		0	57.8	321.111111	378.911111

FIGURE 11.13

To find the _p_-value:
Step 1 Select a cell and enter **=CHITEST(B1:D1,B2:D2)** and press **ENTER**.
Step 2 Excel then provides the _p_-value (Figure 11.14).

	A5		f_x	=CHITEST(B1:D1,B2:D2)	
	A	B	C	D	E
1	Observed	410	330	260	
2	Expected	410	500	90	
3		0	57.8	321.111111	378.911111
4					
5	5.25409E-83				

FIGURE 11.14

Step 3 For observed counts, enter **C1**.
Step 4 Click **Specific Proportions** and enter **C2** in box.
Step 5 Click **OK**.

Section 11.1 Summary

1 A random variable is multinomial if (a) each independent trial has k possible outcomes, $k = 2,3,4, \cdots$; (b) the ith outcome (category) occurs with probability p_i, where $i = 1,2, \cdots, k$; and (c) $\sum_{i=1}^{k} p_i = 1$ (Law of Total Probability).

2 A goodness of fit test is a hypothesis test used to ascertain whether a random variable follows a particular distribution. In a goodness of fit test, the hypotheses are

H_0 : The random variable follows a particular distribution.
H_a : The random variable does not follow the distribution specified in H_0.

Compare the observed frequencies (actual data from the field) with the expected frequencies when H_0 is true. If the difference between the observed and expected frequencies is large, reject H_0.

3 The χ^2 goodness of fit test is performed using (a) the critical-value method or (b) the _p_-value method.

Section 11.1 Exercises

CLARIFYING THE CONCEPTS

1. What are the conditions required for a random variable to be multinomial?
2. Explain in your own words what is meant by a goodness of fit test.
3. Explain the meaning of the term _expected frequency_. (_Hint:_ Use the idea of the long-run mean in your answer.)
4. State the hypotheses for a χ^2 goodness of fit test.

PRACTICING THE TECHNIQUES

For Exercises 5–8, determine whether the random variable is multinomial.
5. We take a sample of 10 M&M's at random and with replacement and observe the color of each. Let X = color of the M&M's, where the possible values of X are green, blue, yellow, orange, red, and brown.

6. We select 5 students from a group of 25 statistics students at random and without replacement, and we define our random variable to be $X =$ student's class, where the possible values of X are freshman, sophomore, junior, and senior.

7. We choose 10 stocks at random and with replacement, and we define our random variable to be $X =$ the exchange that the stock is traded on. The possible values of X are New York Stock Exchange, NASDAQ, London Stock Exchange, and Shenzhen Stock Exchange.

8. We pick 10 stocks at random and with replacement, and we define our random variable to be $X =$ the amount that the stock price increased or decreased since the last trading day.

For Exercises 9–12, the alternative hypothesis takes the form

H_a: The random variable does not follow the distribution specified in H_0.

a. Find the expected frequencies.

b. Determine whether the conditions for performing the χ^2 goodness of fit test are met.

9. $H_0: p_1 = 0.50, p_2 = 0.25, p_3 = 0.25; n = 100$
10. $H_0: p_1 = 0.2, p_2 = 0.3, p_3 = 0.4, p_4 = 0.1; n = 10$
11. $H_0: p_1 = 0.9, p_2 = 0.05, p_3 = 0.04, p_4 = 0.01; n = 100$
12. $H_0: p_1 = 0.4, p_2 = 0.35, p_3 = 0.10, p_4 = 0.10, p_5 = 0.05; n = 200$

For Exercises 13–18, calculate the value of χ^2_{data}.

13.

O_i	E_i
10	12
12	12
14	12

16.

O_i	E_i
8	6
10	8
7	9
5	7

14.

O_i	E_i
15	10
20	25
25	25

17.

O_i	E_i
1	6
10	6
8	6
0	6
11	6

15.

O_i	E_i
20	25
30	25
40	30
40	50

18.

O_i	E_i
90	100
100	110
100	90
100	80
110	120

For Exercises 19–22, do the following.

a. Calculate the expected frequencies and verify that the conditions for performing the χ^2 goodness of fit test are met.

b. Find χ^2_{crit} for the χ^2 distribution with the given degrees of freedom. State the rejection rule.

c. Calculate χ^2_{data}.

d. Compare χ^2_{data} with χ^2_{crit}. State the conclusion and the interpretation.

19. $H_0: p_1 = 0.4, p_2 = 0.3, p_3 = 0.3; O_1 = 50, O_2 = 25, O_3 = 25;$ level of significance $\alpha = 0.05$
20. $H_0: p_1 = 1/3, p_2 = 1/3, p_3 = 1/3; O_1 = 40, O_2 = 30, O_3 = 20;$ level of significance $\alpha = 0.01$

21. $H_0: p_1 = 0.4, p_2 = 0.35, p_3 = 0.10, p_4 = 0.10, p_5 = 0.05; O_1 = 90, O_2 = 75, O_3 = 15, O_4 = 15, O_5 = 5;$ level of significance $\alpha = 0.10$
22. $H_0: p_1 = 0.3, p_2 = 0.2, p_3 = 0.2, p_4 = 0.2, p_5 = 0.1; O_1 = 63, O_2 = 42, O_3 = 40, O_4 = 38, O_5 = 17;$ level of significance $\alpha = 0.05$

For Exercises 23–26, do the following.

a. State the rejection rule for the p-value method, calculate the expected frequencies, and verify that the conditions for performing the χ^2 goodness of fit test are met.

b. Calculate χ^2_{data}.

c. Find the p-value.

d. Compare the p-value with level of significance α. State the conclusion and the interpretation.

23. $H_0: p_1 = 0.50, p_2 = 0.50; O_1 = 40, O_2 = 60;$ level of significance $\alpha = 0.05$
24. $H_0: p_1 = 0.50, p_2 = 0.25, p_3 = 0.25; O_1 = 52, O_2 = 23, O_3 = 25;$ level of significance $\alpha = 0.10$
25. $H_0: p_1 = 0.5, p_2 = 0.25, p_3 = 0.15, p_4 = 0.1; O_1 = 90, O_2 = 55, O_3 = 40, O_4 = 15;$ level of significance $\alpha = 0.10$
26. $H_0: p_1 = 0.4, p_2 = 0.2, p_3 = 0.2, p_4 = 0.1, p_5 = 0.1; O_1 = 90, O_2 = 45, O_3 = 40, O_4 = 15, O_5 = 10;$ level of significance $\alpha = 0.05$

APPLYING THE CONCEPTS

27. Adult Education. The National Center for Education Statistics reported on the percentages of adults who enrolled in personal-interest courses, by the highest education level completed.[2] Of these, 8% had less than a high school diploma, 23% had a high school diploma, 32% had some college, 24% had a bachelor's degree, and 13% had a graduate or professional degree. A survey taken of 200 randomly selected adults who enrolled in personal-interest courses showed the following numbers for the highest education level completed. Test whether the distribution of education levels has changed, using level of significance $\alpha = 0.05$.

Less than high school	High school diploma	Some college	Bachelor's degree	Graduate or professional degree
12	40	62	54	32

28. Mall Restaurants. Based on monthly sales data, the International Council of Shopping Centers reported that the proportions of meals eaten at food establishments in shopping malls were as follows: fast food, 30%; food court, 46%; and restaurants, 24%. A survey of 100 randomly selected meals eaten at malls showed that 32 were eaten at fast-food places, 49 were eaten at food courts, and the rest were eaten at restaurants. Test whether the population proportions have changed, using level of significance $\alpha = 0.10$.

29. Spinal Cord Injuries. A study found that, of the minority patients who suffered spinal cord injury, 30% had a private health insurance provider, 55.6% used Medicare or Medicaid, and 14.4% had other arrangements.[3] Suppose that a sample of 1000 randomly selected minority patients with spinal cord injuries found that 350 had a private health insurance provider, 500 used Medicare or Medicaid, and 150 had other arrangements. Test whether the proportions have changed, using level of significance $\alpha = 0.05$.

30. The College Experience. A 2007 *New York Times* poll of Americans with at least a four-year college degree asked them how they would rate their overall experience as an undergraduate student. The results were 54% excellent, 39% good, 6% only fair, and 1% poor. A survey held this year of 500 randomly selected Americans with at least a four-year college degree found 275 rated their overall experience as an undergraduate student as excellent, 200 as good, 20 as only fair, and 5 as poor. Test whether the proportions have changed since 2007, using level of significance $\alpha = 0.05$.

31. Dormitory Life. The U.S. Census Bureau reported in 2010 that 1 million males and 1.2 million females were living in college dormitories. Suppose that a survey taken this year indicates that 1027 males and 1406 females were living in college dormitories. Test whether the population proportions have changed, using level of significance $\alpha = 0.05$.

32. University Dining. The university dining service believes there is no difference in student preference among the following four entrees: pizza, cheeseburgers, quiche, and sushi. A sample of 500 students showed that 250 preferred pizza, 215 preferred cheeseburgers, 30 preferred quiche, and 5 preferred sushi. Test at level of significance $\alpha = 0.01$ whether or not there is a difference in student preference among the four entrees. (*Hint*: For the χ^2 test of no difference among the proportions, the null hypothesis states that all proportions are equal.)

33. Car Rentals. The Web site **www.consumerwebwatch.org** reported that the market shares held by the largest car rental agencies were as follows.

Hertz	Avis	National	Budget	Alamo	Dollar	All others
28%	21.4%	12.1%	10.5%	10.5%	8.5%	9%

A new survey showed that, out of every $100 spent on car rentals, $28 went to Hertz, $22 went to Avis, $12 went to National, $10 went to Budget, $10 went to Alamo, $8 went to Dollar, and $10 went to all others. Test whether the population proportions have changed, using level of significance $\alpha = 0.05$.

34. Census Data. According to the U.S. Census Bureau, the population of the United States in 2002 was 288,369,000. Of these, 232,647,000 were white, 36,746,000 were black, 2,752,000 were American Indian, 11,559,000 were Asian, 484,000 were Hawaiian or other Pacific Islander, and 4,181,000 were two or more races. A survey of 1000 randomly selected Americans taken this year showed 770 white, 130 black, 10 American Indian, 50 Asian, 1 Hawaiian, and 39 of two or more races. Test whether the population proportions have changed since 2002, using level of significance $\alpha = 0.10$.

35. Weekly Religious Services. A 2007 *New York Times* poll found that 31% of Americans attend religious services every week, 12% almost every week, 14% once or twice a month, 24% a few times a year, and 19% never. A survey

taken this year of 100 randomly selected Americans showed 32 who attend religious services every week, 10 almost every week, 15 once or twice a month, 25 a few times a year, and 18 never. Test whether the population proportions have changed since 2007, using level of significance $\alpha = 0.10$.

36. Community College Advising. In 2007, the Community College Survey of Student Engagement found that 50% of students had met with an adviser by the end of their first four weeks at college, while 41% did not do so and 9% did not recall. A survey this year of 1000 randomly selected community college students had the following results.

Met with adviser by the end of first four weeks at college	Yes	No	Do not recall
Frequency	550	370	80

Test whether the population proportions have changed since 2007, using level of significance $\alpha = 0.05$.

37. Believing in Angels. Do you believe in angels? A Gallup Poll found that 78% of respondents believed in angels, 12% were not sure or had no opinion, and 10% didn't believe in angels. Suppose that a survey taken this year of 1000 randomly selected people had the following results.

Believe in angels?	Yes	No	Not sure or no opinion
Frequency	820	110	70

Test whether the population proportions have changed, using level of significance $\alpha = 0.05$.

38. Diversity on Campus. The University Diversity Officer is interested in determining if the ethnic composition of the university faculty has changed since 2010. In 2010, 60% of the professors were Caucasian, 25% were Asian American, 10% were African American, and 5% were Hispanic. A sample of 100 randomly selected professors this year showed 57 Caucasian, 22 Asian American, 15 African American, and 6 Hispanic. Is there evidence at level of significance $\alpha = 0.05$ that the ethnic composition of the university faculty has changed since 1990?

39. U.S. Defense Budget. The Department of Defense reported that the 1985 defense budget included 24% for personnel costs, 28% for operations, and the remainder for other budget items. Former Secretary of Defense Donald Rumsfeld reported that, in 2004, the defense budget included $99 billion for personnel costs, $117 billion for operations, and $163.4 billion for other budget items. Test whether the population proportions changed from 1985 to 2004, using level of significance $\alpha = 0.05$.

40. U.S. Defense Budget. Refer to the previous exercise. *What if* the amount spent in 2004 on personnel costs was not $99 billion but some amount less than $99 billion. How would that affect the following, and why? Would the following increase, decrease, stay the same, or is there insufficient information to determine?
   a. χ^2_{data}
   b. *p*-Value
   c. Conclusion

χ^2 Tests for Independence and for Homogeneity of Proportions

OBJECTIVES By the end of this section, I will be able to . . .

1 Explain what a χ^2 test for the independence of two variables is.

2 Perform and interpret a χ^2 test for the independence of two variables using the critical-value method and the p-value method.

3 Perform and interpret a test for the homogeneity of proportions.

1 Introduction to the χ^2 Test for Independence

The term *contingency table* derives from the fact that the table covers all possible combinations of the values for the two variables, that is, all possible contingencies.

In Section 11.1, we learned that the χ^2 distribution could help us determine a model's goodness of fit to the data. Here, in Section 11.2, we will learn two more hypothesis tests that use the χ^2 distribution. Recall from Section 2.1 that a *contingency table*, also known as a *crosstabulation* or a *two-way table*, is a tabular summary of the relationship between two categorical variables. The categories of one variable label the rows, and the categories of the other variable label the columns. Each cell in the table contains the number of observations that fit the categories of that row and column. Table 11.7 is a contingency table based on the study *How Young People View Their Lives, Futures, and Politics: A Portrait of "Generation Next."*[4] The researchers asked 1500 randomly selected respondents, "How are things in your life?" Subjects were categorized by age and response. The researchers identified those aged 18–25 in 2007 as representing "Generation Next."

Table 11.7 Contingency table showing relative frequencies of variable categories

	Age Group			
Response	**Gen Nexter (18–25)**	**26+**	**Total**	**Relative frequency**
Very happy	180	330	**510**	$\frac{510}{1500} = 0.34$
Pretty happy	378	435	**813**	$\frac{813}{1500} = 0.542$
Not too happy	42	135	**177**	$\frac{177}{1500} = 0.118$
Total	**600**	**900**	**1500**	
Relative frequency	$\frac{600}{1500} = 0.4$	$\frac{900}{1500} = 0.6$		

We can use contingency tables like Table 11.7 to determine whether two random variables are independent. Recall that two random variables are *independent* if the value of one variable does not affect the probabilities of the values of the other variable. For example, is a "Gen Nexter" (someone aged 18–25 in 2007) less likely to report that he or she is "very happy" and more likely to report that he or she is "pretty happy" than someone older? If so, then the response depends on age, so the variables *age group* and *response* are dependent.

By "dependent" we simply mean that the variables are not independent.

To determine whether two categorical variables are independent, using the data in a contingency table, we use a χ^2 test for independence. Just like our χ^2 goodness of fit test from Section 11.1, the **χ^2 test for independence** is based on a comparison of the observed frequencies with the frequencies that are expected if the null hypothesis is assumed true.

χ^2 Test for Independence

To determine whether two categorical variables are independent, using the data from a contingency table, we use a χ^2 **test for independence.** The hypotheses take the form

H_0 : Variable A and Variable B are independent.

H_a : Variable A and Variable B are dependent.

We compare the observed frequencies with the frequencies that we expect if we assume that H_0 is correct. Large differences lead to the rejection of the null hypothesis.

Here, we are testing whether the variables *age group* and *response* are independent. Thus, the hypotheses are

H_0 : *Age group* and *response* are independent.

H_a : *Age group* and *response* are dependent.

H_0 states that a response to the survey question does not depend on the age group. H_a says that a response does depend on the age group. To calculate the expected frequencies, we begin by recalling the Multiplication Rule for Two Independent Events from Chapter 5 (page 230):

If A and B are any two independent events, $P(A \text{ and } B) = P(A)\, P(B)$.

To illustrate, let our events be defined as A = 18–25 age group, and B = reported "very happy." Then, on the assumption that these events are independent, we have

$$P(\text{Gen Nexter and very happy}) = P(A \text{ and } B) = P(A)P(B) = \frac{600}{1500} \cdot \frac{510}{1500}$$

$$= 0.4 \cdot 0.34 = 0.136$$

Thus, the probability that a randomly chosen young person is both a Gen Nexter and is very happy is 0.136. Then, to find the expected frequency of this cell (Gen Nexters who are very happy), we multiply this probability 0.136 by the total sample size $n = 1500$, using the result from Section 11.1 that the expected frequency is

$$E = \text{expected frequency} = n \cdot p = 1500 \cdot 0.136 = 204$$

In other words, if the random variables *age group* and *response* are independent, then the expected frequency of Gen Nexters who report being very happy is

$$\text{expected frequency}_{\text{Gen Nexter and very happy}} = 1500 \cdot \frac{600}{1500} \cdot \frac{510}{1500} = 204$$

But note that two of the 1500s cancel, providing us with the shortcut

$$\text{expected frequency}_{\text{Gen Nexter and very happy}} = \frac{(600)(510)}{1500} = 204$$

Generalizing, this provides us with the following shortcut method for finding expected frequencies.

Expected Frequencies for a χ^2 Test for Independence

The expected frequencies for the cells of a contingency table in a χ^2 test for independence are given by

$$\text{expected frequency} = \frac{(\text{row total})(\text{column total})}{\text{grand total}}$$

Example 11.5 Calculating expected frequencies using the shortcut method

Calculate the expected frequencies from Table 11.7 using the shortcut method.

Solution
Table 11.8 contains the expected frequencies calculated using the shortcut method. ■

Table 11.8 Expected frequencies using the shortcut method

Response	Age Group		Total
	Gen Nexter (18–25)	**26+**	
Very happy	$\frac{(510)(600)}{1500} = 204$	$\frac{(510)(900)}{1500} = 306$	510
Pretty happy	$\frac{(813)(600)}{1500} = 325.2$	$\frac{(813)(900)}{1500} = 487.8$	813
Not too happy	$\frac{(177)(600)}{1500} = 70.8$	$\frac{(177)(900)}{1500} = 106.2$	177
Total	**600**	**900**	**1500**

Now You Can Do
Exercises 5–10.

The χ^2 test for independence measures the difference between the observed frequencies and the expected frequencies using the following test statistic.

Test Statistic for the χ^2 Test for Independence

Let O_i represent the observed frequency in the ith cell, and E_i represent the expected frequency in the ith cell. Then the **test statistic for the independence of two categorical variables**

$$\chi^2_{data} = \sum \frac{(O_i - E_i)^2}{E_i}$$

approximately follows a χ^2 (chi-square) distribution with $(r - 1)(c - 1)$ degrees of freedom, where r is the number of categories in the row variable and c is the number of categories in the column variable, if the following conditions are satisfied:

a. None of the expected frequencies is less than 1.

b. At most 20% of the expected frequencies are less than 5.

---

2 Performing the χ^2 Test for Independence

The χ^2 test for independence may be performed using either the critical-value method or the p-value method. We provide examples of each.

χ^2 Test for Independence: Critical-Value Method

Step 1   State the hypotheses and check the conditions.

H_0 : Variable A and Variable B are independent.

H_a : Variable A and Variable B are dependent.

The following conditions must be met:

a. None of the expected frequencies is less than 1.

b. At most 20% of the expected frequencies are less than 5.

The expected frequency for a given cell is

$$\text{expected frequency} = \frac{(\text{row total}) \cdot (\text{column total})}{\text{grand total}}$$

Step 2 **Find the critical value χ^2_{crit} and state the rejection rule.** Reject H_0 if $\chi^2_{\text{data}} \geq \chi^2_{\text{crit}}$. Use $(r-1)(c-1)$ degrees of freedom, where r is the number of categories in the row variable and c is the number of categories in the column variable.

Step 3 **Calculate χ^2_{data}.**

$$\chi^2_{\text{data}} = \sum \frac{(O_i - E_i)^2}{E_i}$$

where O_i = observed frequency and E_i = expected frequency for each cell.

Step 4 **State the conclusion and the interpretation.** Compare χ^2_{data} with χ^2_{crit}.

Caution: Do not include the row or column totals when counting the categories.

Example 11.6 Performing the χ^2 test for independence using the critical-value method

Using Table 11.7, test whether *age group* is independent of *response*, using level of significance $\alpha = 0.05$.

Solution

Step 1 **State the hypotheses and check the conditions.**

H_0 : *Age group* and *response* are independent.

H_a : *Age group* and *response* are dependent.

We note from Table 11.8 that none of the expected frequencies are less than either 1 or 5. Therefore, the conditions are met, and we may proceed with the hypothesis test.

Step 2 **Find the critical value χ^2_{crit} and state the rejection rule.** The row variable, *response,* has three categories, so $r = 3$. The column variable, *age group,* has two categories, so $c = 2$. Thus,

$$\text{degrees of freedom} = (r-1)(c-1) = (3-1)(2-1) = 2$$

See Figure 11.1 (page 560) to review how to find χ^2_{crit}.

With level of significance $\alpha = 0.05$, this gives us $\chi^2_{\text{crit}} = 5.991$ from the χ^2 table. The rejection rule is therefore

$$\text{Reject } H_0 \text{ if } \chi^2_{\text{data}} \geq 5.991$$

Step 3 **Calculate χ^2_{data}.** The observed frequencies are found in Table 11.7 and the expected frequencies are found in Table 11.8. Then

$$\chi^2_{\text{data}} = \sum \frac{(O_i - E_i)^2}{E_i} = \frac{(180-204)^2}{204} + \frac{(330-306)^2}{306} + \frac{(378-325.2)^2}{325.2}$$

$$+ \frac{(435-487.8)^2}{487.8} + \frac{(42-70.8)^2}{70.8} + \frac{(135-106.2)^2}{106.2}$$

$$\approx 38.5192$$

Step 4 **State the conclusion and the interpretation.** Our χ^2_{data} of 38.5192 is greater than our χ^2_{crit} of 5.991 (see Figure 11.15), and so we reject H_0. The interpretation is: "There is evidence at level of significance $\alpha = 0.05$ that *age group* and *response* are dependent." ■

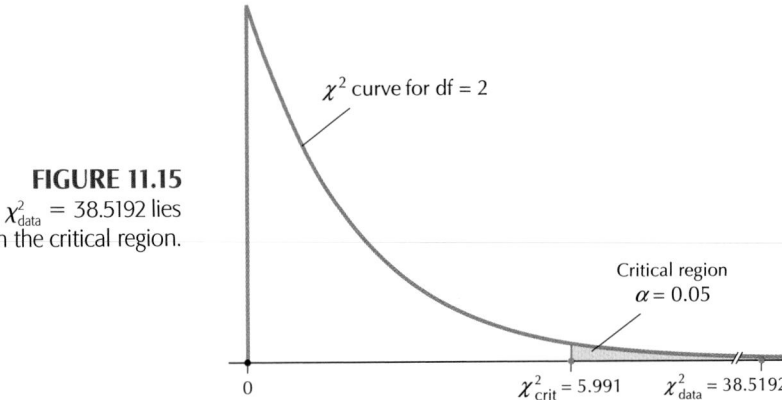

FIGURE 11.15
$\chi^2_{data} = 38.5192$ lies
in the critical region.

Now You Can Do
Exercises 11–14.

χ^2 Test for Independence: p-Value Method

Step 1   State the hypotheses and the rejection rule. Check the conditions.

H_0 : Variable A and Variable B are independent.

H_a : Variable A and Variable B are dependent.

Reject H_0 if the p-value $\leq \alpha$.

The following conditions must be met:

a. None of the expected frequencies is less than 1.

b. At most 20% of the expected frequencies are less than 5.

The expected frequency for a given cell is

$$\text{expected frequency} = \frac{(\text{row total})(\text{column total})}{\text{grand total}}$$

Step 2   Calculate χ^2_{data}.

$$\chi^2_{data} = \sum \frac{(O_i - E_i)^2}{E_i}$$

where O_i = observed frequency and E_i = expected frequency for each cell.

Step 3   Find the p-value.

$$p\text{-value} = P(\chi^2 > \chi^2_{data})$$

Step 4   State the conclusion and the interpretation. Compare the p-value with α.

Example 11.7 χ^2 test for independence using the p-value method and technology

homicideage

Table 11.9 contains the numbers of work-related homicides that took place in the United States in 2002, according to the Bureau of Labor Statistics, categorized by the age group of the victim and the type of homicide. Test whether homicide type and age group of victim are independent, using the TI-83/84, Minitab, the p-value method, and level of significance $\alpha = 0.01$.

Table 11.9 Contingency table of age group of victim versus type of homicide

Type of homicide	Age Group of Victim			Total
	Under 25	25 to 44	Over 44	
Shooting	31	258	180	469
Stabbing	5	21	37	63
Total	36	279	217	532

Solution

Step 1 **State the hypotheses and the rejection rule. Check the conditions.**

H_0 : Age group of victim and homicide type are independent.

H_a : Age group of victim and homicide type are dependent.

Reject H_0 if the p-value ≤ 0.01.

Note that Minitab provides the expected counts (frequencies) below the observed counts. We can then verify that none of the expected frequencies is less than 1. We do have 1 of the 6 expected frequencies (4.26) with a value less than 5. But this represents $1/6 \approx 0.1667$, which is less than 20%, as required. The conditions for the χ^2 hypothesis test are therefore met.

Step 2 **Calculate χ^2_{data}.** We use the instructions found in the Step-by-Step Technology Guide at the end of this section. The TI-83/84 results in Figure 11.16 tell us that $\chi^2_{data} = 10.76001797$. The Minitab results in Figure 11.17 round this to "Chi-Sq" = $\chi^2_{data} = 10.760$.

```
X²-Test
 X²=10.76001797
 P=.0046077805
 df=2
```

```
Expected counts are printed below observed counts
Chi-Square contributions are printed below expected counts
                      Age 25
          Age < 25    - 44  Age > 44  Total
      1         31     258       180    469
              31.74  245.96    191.30
              0.017   0.589     0.668

      2          5      21        37     63
               4.26   33.04     25.70
              0.127   4.387     4.971

Total          36     279       217    532

Chi-Sq = 10.760, DF = 2, P-Value = 0.005
1 cells with expected counts less than 5.
```

FIGURE 11.16 TI-83/84 χ^2 results.

FIGURE 11.17 Minitab χ^2 results.

Step 3 **Find the p-value.** From the TI-83/84 results in Figure 11.16, we have

$$p\text{-value} = P(\chi^2 > \chi^2_{data}) = 0.0046077805$$

The Minitab results in Figure 11.17 round this to p-value $= 0.005$.

Step 4 **State the conclusion and the interpretation.** Since p-value $\approx 0.0046 < 0.01$, we reject H_0. There is evidence that the age group and homicide type are dependent. ∎

Now You Can Do
Exercises 15–18.

3 Test for the Homogeneity of Proportions

Recall the two-sample Z test for $p_1 - p_2$ from Section 10.3, where we compared the proportions of two independent populations. When we extend that hypothesis test to k independent populations, we use a test statistic that follows a χ^2 distribution. Just as the null hypothesis for the two-sample test assumed no difference between the population proportions

- the null hypothesis for the k-sample test also assumes that all k proportions are equal, and

- the alternative hypothesis states that not all the population proportions are equal.

When performing the **test for the homogeneity of proportions,** we use the same steps as for the χ^2 test for independence.

Developing Your Statistical Sense

Difference Between χ^2 Test for Homogeneity and χ^2 Test for Independence

The difference between the test for homogeneity of proportions and the test for independence has to do with how the data are collected. If a single sample is taken and two variables are measured, then the test for independence is appropriate. If several (*k*) samples are taken and the sample proportion is measured for each sample, then the test for homogeneity of proportions is appropriate. ◢

Example 11.8 Airline on-time performance

flyontime

The Bureau of Transportation Statistics (**www.bts.gov**) reports on the proportion of airline passenger flights that are on time, for each major airline. The January–April 2007 statistics for the three busiest carriers are shown in Table 11.10. Test whether the population proportions of on-time flights are the same for the three airlines, using the *p*-value method, Minitab, and level of significance $\alpha = 0.05$.

Table 11.10 Observed on-time statistics for three major airlines, January–April 2007

	Southwest	American	Skywest	Total
Number of on-time flights	146,607	68,939	60,298	275,844
Number of flights not on time	36,697	35,688	32,497	104,882
Total flights	183,304	104,627	92,795	380,726

What Results Might We Expect?

The observed sample proportions of on-time flights are as follows:

$$p_{\text{Southwest}} = \frac{146,607}{183,304} \approx 0.80 \quad p_{\text{American}} = \frac{68,939}{104,627} \approx 0.66 \quad p_{\text{Skywest}} = \frac{60,298}{92,795} \approx 0.65$$

The 80% on-time proportion of Southwest Airlines does seem to be somewhat higher than the on-time proportions of the other airlines. Thus, we would not be surprised if the hypothesis test found evidence that not all the population proportions were equal. ◢

Solution

The Minitab results are shown here. We use the same steps as for the χ^2 test for independence.

```
Expected counts are printed below observed counts
Chi-Square contributions are printed below expected counts

          Southwest   American    Skywest     Total
    1        146607      68939      60298     275844
          132807.61   75804.46   67231.93
           1433.828    621.792    715.127

    2         36697      35688      32497     104882
           50496.39   28822.54   25563.07
           3771.027   1635.338   1880.815

Total        183304     104627      92795     380726

Chi-Sq = 10057.927, DF = 2, P-Value = 0.000
```

Step 1 **State the hypotheses and the rejection rule. Check the conditions.**

$$H_0 : p_{\text{Southwest}} = p_{\text{American}} = p_{\text{Skywest}}$$

$$H_a : \text{Not all the proportions in } H_0 \text{ are equal.}$$

Reject H_0 if the p-value ≤ 0.05.

None of the expected frequencies are less than either 1 or 5. Therefore, the conditions are met, and we may proceed with the hypothesis test.

Step 2 **Find the test statistic χ^2_{data}.** χ^2_{data} is shown as "Chi-Sq" = 10,057.927. There are $r = 2$ rows and $c = 3$ columns, so the degrees of freedom are $(r - 1)(c - 1) = (2 - 1)(3 - 1) = 2$.

Step 3 **Find the p-value.** Minitab provides the p-value, which is essentially 0.000.

Step 4 **State the conclusion and the interpretation.** The p-value of 0.000 is less than $\alpha = 0.05$. We therefore reject H_0, as expected. There is evidence at level of significance $\alpha = 0.05$ that not all population proportions of on-time flights are equal. ∎

Now You Can Do
Exercises 19–22.

onlinedata

CASE STUDY

Online Dating

We look at two tests for independence in this Case Study. The first examines whether the type of relationship reported by respondents depends on the gender of the respondent. The second investigates whether the self-reported physical appearance of online daters depends on the person's gender.

Does the Reported Type of Relationship Depend on Gender?

In its 2005 study, the Pew Internet and American Life Project examined whether single men and women differed with respect to their current relationships. The observed frequencies are given in Table 11.11.

Table 11.11 Observed frequencies, online dating study

Type of relationship	Gender	
	Single men	Single women
In committed relationship	115	138
Not in committed relationship and not looking for partner	162	391
Not in committed relationship but looking for partner	89	54
Don't know/refused	19	18

We are interested in whether the type of relationship reported depends on the gender of the respondent. In other words, we will test whether the type of relationship is independent of gender. We will use the p-value method, with level of significance $\alpha = 0.05$, and we will follow the TI-83/84 instructions in the Step-by-Step Technology Guide on page 578 for the calculations.

What Results Might We Expect?

Table 11.11 and Figure 11.18 indicate that the proportion of men who are "looking" is greater than the proportion of women who are "looking." Similarly, the proportion of women who are "not looking" is greater than for men. This is evidence that the type of relationship depends on gender and that we might expect to reject the null hypothesis of independence. ◢

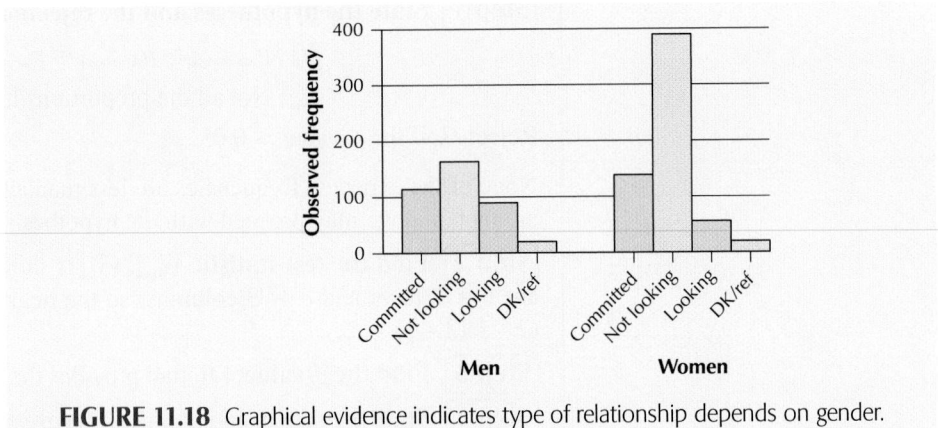

FIGURE 11.18 Graphical evidence indicates type of relationship depends on gender.

Step 1 **State the hypotheses and the rejection rule. Check the conditions.**

H_0 : *Type of relationship* and *gender* are independent.

H_a : *Type of relationship* and *gender* are dependent.

Reject H_0 if the *p*-value ≤ 0.05.

Figure 11.19 shows the expected frequencies, none of which are less than 5. Thus, the conditions are met.

Step 2 **Find χ^2_{data}.** The TI-83/84 results in Figure 11.20 tell us

$$\chi^2_{\text{data}} = 61.12955651$$

Step 3 **Find the *p*-value.** Figure 11.20 also gives us the *p*-value:

$$p\text{-value} = 3.372011\text{E-}13 \approx 0.0000000000003372011$$

FIGURE 11.19 Expected frequencies.

FIGURE 11.20 χ^2 results on TI-83/84.

Step 4 **State the conclusion and the interpretation.** Since the *p*-value $\leq \alpha = 0.05$, we reject H_0, as we expected. There is evidence that the type of relationship reported in the study depends on the gender of the respondent for level of significance $\alpha = 0.05$.

Does Self-Reported Physical Appearance of Online Daters Depend on Gender?

A master's thesis from the Massachusetts Institute of Technology examined the characteristics and behavior of online daters.[5] Table 11.12 contains the self-reported physical appearance and gender of 52,817 users of an online dating service.

 onlineappear

Table 11.12 Gender and self-reported physical appearance

	Physical Appearance				
	Very attractive	Attractive	Average	Prefer not to answer	Total
Female	3113	16,181	6093	3478	28,865
Male	1415	12,454	7274	2809	23,952
Total	4528	28,635	13,367	6287	52,817

Note from Table 11.12 that females seem to have higher proportions of those self-reporting as either attractive or very attractive, while males seem to have a higher proportion of those self-reporting as average. This is evidence that self-reported physical appearance does depend on gender and that we might expect to reject the null hypothesis of independence. We will test using the *p*-value method, with level of significance $\alpha = 0.01$, and Minitab. The hypotheses are

H_0 : *Self-reported physical appearance* and *gender* are independent.

H_a : *Self-reported physical appearance* and *gender* are dependent.

We reject H_0 if the *p*-value $\leq$ level of significance $\alpha = 0.01$.

The Minitab results in Figure 11.21 tell us

$$\chi^2_{\text{data}} = \text{``Chi-Sq''} = 847.702$$
$$p\text{-value} \approx 0$$

Figure 11.21 gives us the expected frequencies (highlighted in color), none of which are less than 5, allowing us to perform the hypothesis test. Since the *p*-value $\leq$ $\alpha = 0.01$, we reject H_0, as we expected. There is evidence at level of significance $\alpha = 0.01$ that the self-reported physical appearance depends on the gender of the online dater. ■

```
Expected counts are printed below observed counts
Chi-Square contributions are printed below expected counts

            VA       Att       Ave      PNTA   Total
   F       3113     16181      6093      3478   28865
         2474.60  15649.30   7305.19   3435.91
          164.698   18.065   201.147     0.516

   M       1415     12454      7274      2809   23952
         2053.40  12985.70   6061.81   2851.09
          198.480   21.770   242.406     0.621
Total      4528     28635     13367      6287   52817

Chi-Sq = 847.702, DF = 3, P-Value = 0.000
```

FIGURE 11.21 Minitab results showing expected frequencies, χ^2_{data} and the *p*-value.

STEP-BY-STEP TECHNOLOGY GUIDE: Test for Independence or Test for the Homogeneity of Proportions

We demonstrate using Example 11.7 (page 572).

TI-83/84

Entering Matrix Data
Step 1   Press **2nd**, then **MATRIX**.
Step 2   Highlight **EDIT**, and press **ENTER**.
Step 3   Set the dimensions of **MATRIX[A]** (number of rows × number of columns). Table 11.9 has 2 rows and 3 columns, so enter **2**, press **ENTER**, enter **3**, and press **ENTER**.
Step 4   Press the down-arrow key. Enter the first number in the first cell, **31**, and press **ENTER**.
Step 5   Continue entering the data row by row until the matrix is complete (Figure 11.22).

```
MATRIX[A] 2 ×3
[ 31    258   180  ]
[ 5     21    37   ]
```

FIGURE 11.22

χ^2 Test for Independence or Test for Homogeneity of Proportions
Step 1   Enter the data into **Matrix[A]**.
Step 2   Press **STAT**, highlight **TESTS**, select **C: χ^2 Test**, and press **ENTER**.
Step 3   The expected frequencies are automatically generated and put into **MATRIX[B]**. Highlight **Calculate**, and press **ENTER**. The results are shown in Figure 11.16 in Example 11.7.
Step 4   To view the expected frequencies, press **2ⁿᵈ MATRIX**, highlight **EDIT**, choose **2** for **MATRIX[B]**, and press **ENTER**.

EXCEL

χ^2 Test for Independence or Test for Homogeneity of Proportions Using the WHFStat Macros
Step 1   Enter the data from Table 11.9, *including row and column totals,* in cells A1 to D3.
Step 2   Load the **WHFStat Macros**.

Step 3   Select **Add-Ins > Macros > Tables > Two Way Tables/Chi Squared Test**.
Step 4   Select cells A1 to D3 as the **Dataset Range**.
Step 5   Select **Chi-squared Test**, and click **OK**.

MINITAB

χ^2 Test for Independence or Test for Homogeneity of Proportions
Step 1   Enter the observed frequencies from Table 11.9 into the Minitab worksheet, as shown here.
Step 2   Click **Stat > Tables > Chi-Square Test**.
Step 3   Choose each of columns C1, C2, and C3 as the **Columns containing the table**. Then click **OK**. The results are

shown in Figure 11.17 in Example 11.7.

C1	C2	C3
Age < 25	Age 25 - 44	Age > 44
31	258	180
5	21	37

CRUNCHIT!

Test for Independence
We will use the data from Example 11.7.

Step 1   Click **File . . .** then highlight **Load from Larose2e . . . Chapter 11 . . .** and click on **Example 11.7**.

Step 2   Click **Statistics** and select **Contingency tables . . . with counts**. For **Row Variable** select **Response**. For **Column Variable** select **Age Group**. For **Counts** select **Count**. Then click **Calculate**.

Section 11.2 Summary

1 To determine whether two categorical variables are independent, using the data from a contingency table, we use a χ^2 test for independence. The hypotheses take the form

H_0 : Variable A and Variable B are independent.

H_a : Variable A and Variable B are dependent.

2 The χ^2 test for independence is performed using the critical-value method, the exact p-value method, or the estimated p-value method. The observed frequencies are compared with the expected frequencies on the assumption that H_0 is correct. Large differences lead to the rejection of the null hypothesis.

3 The k-sample test, called the test for the homogeneity of proportions, determines whether all k population proportions are equal. The result uses a test statistic that follows a χ^2 distribution. The null hypothesis for the k-sample test assumes that all k population proportions are equal. The alternative hypothesis states that not all the population proportions are equal. When performing the test for the homogeneity of proportions, the same steps are used as for the χ^2 test for independence.

Section 11.2 Exercises

CLARIFYING THE CONCEPTS
1. Explain what a contingency table is.
2. Explain in your own words what is meant by a test for independence.
3. What is the difference between the χ^2 test for homogeneity of proportions and the two-sample Z test for the difference in proportions from Chapter 10?
4. Explain how the expected frequencies are calculated without using the shortcut method.

PRACTICING THE TECHNIQUES
For Exercises 5–10, the observed frequencies are provided in a contingency table of two categorical variables. Find the expected frequencies, on the assumption that the variables are independent.

5.

	A1	A2
B1	10	20
B2	12	18

6.

	C1	C2
D1	50	100
D2	60	90

7.

	E1	E2	E3
F1	30	20	10
F2	35	24	8

8.

	G1	G2
H1	10	8
H2	8	10
H3	9	9

9.

	I1	I2	I3
J1	100	90	105
J2	50	60	55
J3	25	15	20

10.

	K1	K2	K3	K4
L1	40	70	90	100
L2	20	40	60	70
L3	30	65	65	70

For Exercises 11–14, test whether or not the variables are independent.
  a. State the hypotheses.
  b. Verify that the conditions for performing the χ^2 test for independence are met.
  c. Find χ^2_{crit} and state the rejection rule.
  d. Calculate χ^2_{data}.
  e. Compare χ^2_{data} with χ^2_{crit}. State the conclusion and the interpretation.

11. Exercise 5, level of significance $\alpha = 0.05$
12. Exercise 7, level of significance $\alpha = 0.10$
13. Exercise 9, level of significance $\alpha = 0.01$
14. Exercise 9, level of significance $\alpha = 0.10$

For Exercises 15–18, test whether or not the variables are independent.
  a. State the hypotheses and the rejection rule for the p-value method, and verify that the conditions for performing the χ^2 test for independence are met.
  b. Find χ^2_{data}.
  c. Calculate the p-value.
  d. Compare the p-value with α. State the conclusion and the interpretation.

15. Exercise 6, level of significance $\alpha = 0.05$
16. Exercise 8, level of significance $\alpha = 0.10$
17. Exercise 10, level of significance $\alpha = 0.01$
18. Exercise 10, level of significance $\alpha = 0.10$

For Exercises 19–22, test whether or not the proportions of successes are the same for all populations.
  a. State the hypotheses.
  b. Calculate the expected frequencies and verify that the conditions for performing the χ^2 test for homogeneity of proportions are met.
  c. Find χ^2_{crit} and state the rejection rule. Use level of significance $\alpha = 0.05$.
  d. Find χ^2_{data}.
  e. Compare χ^2_{data} with χ^2_{crit}. State the conclusion and the interpretation.

19.

	Sample 1	Sample 2	Sample 3
Successes	10	20	30
Failures	20	45	62

20.

	Sample 1	Sample 2	Sample 3
Successes	50	50	100
Failures	200	210	425

21.

	Sample 1	Sample 2	Sample 3	Sample 4
Successes	10	15	20	25
Failures	15	24	32	40

22.

	Sample 1	Sample 2	Sample 3	Sample 4
Successes	100	150	200	250
Failures	150	240	320	400

For Exercises 23–26, test whether or not the proportions of successes are the same for all populations.

a. State the rejection rule for the p-value method using level of significance $\alpha = 0.05$, calculate the expected frequencies, and verify that the conditions for performing the χ^2 test for homogeneity of proportions are met.

b. Find χ^2_{data}.

c. Calculate the p-value.

d. Compare the p-value with α. State the conclusion and the interpretation.

23.

	Sample 1	Sample 2	Sample 3
Successes	30	60	90
Failures	10	25	50

24.

	Sample 1	Sample 2	Sample 3
Successes	100	120	140
Failures	20	25	30

25.

	Sample 1	Sample 2	Sample 3	Sample 4
Successes	10	12	24	32
Failures	6	10	15	30

26.

	Sample 1	Sample 2	Sample 3	Sample 4
Successes	100	200	300	400
Failures	30	70	150	300

APPLYING THE CONCEPTS

27. Conditioning Mice. A psychologist is conducting research using white mice, brown mice, a classical conditioning stimulus, and an operant conditioning stimulus. The psychologist is interested in whether type of stimulus is independent of the type of mouse. One hundred mice were tested. The following table shows the number of each type of mice that completed their assigned task satisfactorily, given the type of stimulus. Test at level of significance $\alpha = 0.10$ whether type of stimulus and type of mouse are independent. 🐾 **micecond**

	Type of Stimulus		
Type of mouse	**Classical**	**Operant**	**Total**
White	20	40	60
Brown	10	30	40
Total	30	70	100

28. Information Technology Jobs. In its report *The Digital Economy 2003*, the Economics and Statistics Administration of the U.S. Department of Commerce tracked the number of information technology–related jobs by year (1999 and 2002) and the level of education and training required (high, moderate, and low). Test whether year and level are independent, using level of significance $\alpha = 0.05$. 🐾 **techjob**

	High	**Moderate**	**Low**
1999	3435	1652	1151
2002	3512	1411	1080

29. Cable TV Content Restrictions. A June 2004 *Chicago Tribune* Poll asked, "Should government restrict violence and sexual content that appears on cable TV, or should government not impose restrictions?" The responses were categorized by political affiliation. Test whether the population proportion favoring restriction is the same for all three groups, using level of significance $\alpha = 0.05$. 🐾 **tvcontent**

	Restrict	**Not restrict/don't know**
Republicans	59	41
Independents	52	48
Democrats	53	47

30. History Course Preferences. A history professor teaches three types of history courses: American history, world history, and European history. The professor would like to assess whether student preference for these courses differs among four ethnic groups. A random sample of 600 students resulted in the following table of preferences. Test using level of significance $\alpha = 0.05$ whether type of course and ethnic group are independent. 🐾 **history**

	Type of History Course			
Ethnic group	**American history**	**World history**	**European history**	**Total**
Caucasian	100	40	60	200
African American	100	40	20	160
Asian American	50	60	30	140
Hispanic	50	20	30	100
Total	300	160	140	600

31. Gender Gap on Campus? Much has been written about the gender gap in the electoral process. Is there a gender gap on campus? A random sample of 500 students were selected from one campus, and their gender and political party preference were noted. Test using level of significance $\alpha = 0.01$ whether a gender gap exists on this campus (that is, whether or not gender and political party preference are independent). 🐾 **gendergap**

	Political Party Preference			
Gender	**Democrat**	**Republican**	**Independent**	**Total**
Female	100	50	100	250
Male	50	100	100	250
Total	150	150	200	500

32. Immigrant Origins and Preferences. Does the state where immigrants wish to settle depend on where the immigrant is coming from? The U.S. Department of Homeland Security tracks the continent of origin and the desired state of settlement for immigrants. Some of the 2002 data are shown here, in thousands. Test using the critical-value method whether continent of origin and state of settlement are independent, using level of significance $\alpha = 0.01$. 🏝 **immigrant**

	California	**Florida**	**New York**
Europe	24.0	9.8	23.2
Asia	112.6	9.0	31.3
South America	8.0	16.1	17.7

33. Email, Phone, or in Person? What is the most effective way to handle a task at work: by email, by phone, or in person? Well, you probably say, it depends on the task. The Pew Internet and American Life Project Email at Work Survey surveyed 1000 randomly selected work email users, who chose the following methods as the best for handling certain work tasks. Test whether the proportions who favor email differ between the two tasks, using level of significance $\alpha = 0.05$ and the estimated p-value method. 🏝 **worktask**

Task	By email	By phone or in person
Edit or review documents	670	330
Arrange meetings or appointments	630	370

34. Using Graphical Evidence. Sick of spam (unsolicited broadcast email)? Do you get more spam at your work, school, or home email address? The Pew Internet and American Life Project Email at Work Survey examined the proportion of spam in email users' work and home email accounts. Using only the information in the clustered bar graph below, would you conclude that the proportion of those who report "a lot of spam" is the same for work email and personal email? Why?

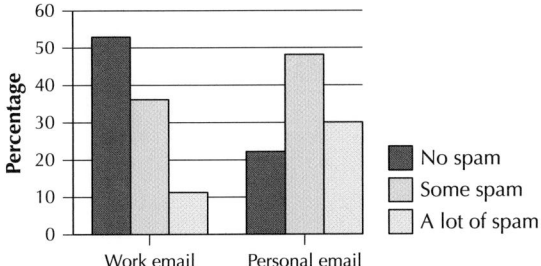

35. Spam, Spam, Spam. Continue your work from the previous exercise. The following contingency table shows the actual percentages in the graph above based on samples of size 100 for each of work email and personal email. Test whether the proportions who report "a lot of spam" are the same for work email and personal email, using level of significance $\alpha = 0.01$. Does your conclusion agree with your conjecture in the previous exercise?

	None	**Some**	**A lot**
Work email	53%	36%	11%
Personal email	22%	48%	30%

36. Gender Differences in Computer/Video/Online Gaming. The Pew Internet and American Life Project collected data on the College Students Gaming Survey. Among the questions they asked 1720 randomly selected college students was "Which one of the following do you play the most: video games, computer games, or online games?" The results are summarized by gender in the following contingency table. 🏝 **games**

	Video games	**Computer games**	**Internet games**
Male	616	221	139
Female	198	372	174

a. Before you carry out the hypothesis test, *what result might you expect?* Look over the data set carefully to see whether you can detect significant differences between the levels of the variables. Then see whether your hypothesis test bears out your intuition.

b. Test whether *gender* and *game type* are independent, using level of significance $\alpha = 0.01$.

37. Online Dating. A Pew Internet and American Life Project study reported that the proportion of urban residents who use online dating is 13%, while the proportion for suburban residents is 10% and the proportion for rural residents is 9%.[6] Test using level of significance $\alpha = 0.05$ whether there are differences among the population proportions of residents from the three categories who use online dating. Assume that each sample size was 1000. (*Hint:* The null hypothesis assumes that all proportions are equal.)

Use Minitab or Excel for each of Exercises 38–44. 🏝 **goals**

BRINGING IT ALL TOGETHER

Goals of Middle School Students. Open the **Goals** data set. The subjects are students in grades 4, 5, and 6, from three school districts in Michigan. The students were asked which of the following was most important to them: good grades, athletic ability, or popularity. Information about the students' age, gender, race, and grade was also gathered, as well as whether their school was in an urban, suburban, or rural setting.[7]

38. How many observations are in the data set? How many variables?

39. Comparing gender and goals.

a. Looking at the data, do you think that boys and girls at this age differ in what is most important to them: grades, popularity, or sports? In other words, do you think that the variables *gender* and *goals* are dependent or independent?

b. Perform the χ^2 test for independence, using level of significance $\alpha = 0.05$.

40. Comparing gender and grade.

a. Looking at the data, do you think that the ratio of females to males differs significantly from grade to grade? In other words, do you think that the variables *gender* and *grade* are dependent or independent?

b. Perform the χ^2 test for independence, using level of significance $\alpha = 0.05$.

41. Comparing goals and school setting.

    a. Looking at the data, do you think that the setting of the school (urban, suburban, or rural) affects the goals of the students? Or do you think that it has no effect? In other words, do you think that the variables *urb_rur* and *goals* are independent or dependent?

    b. Perform the χ^2 test for independence, using level of significance $\alpha = 0.10$.

42. Comparing grades and goals.

    a. One thing we know for sure is that, as students get older, they get more serious and grades get more important to them (don't they?). So we would expect that the variables *grade* and *goals* would be dependent, wouldn't we? Is this borne out by looking at the data?

    b. Perform the χ^2 test for independence, using level of significance $\alpha = 0.01$.

43. 1970 Military Draft. Is there evidence that the 1970 military draft, conducted at the height of the Vietnam War, was not truly random? For this exercise, birth dates were ranked from 1 (for the first date drawn) to 366 (the last date drawn). In 1970, only those young men with birth date rankings up to 195 were eventually drafted. Since 195 of the 366 dates were "drafted," the overall proportion of "drafted dates" is $195/366 \approx 0.5328$. Assuming the draft was truly random, we do not expect the proportion of "drafted dates" to vary significantly from month to month. In other words, the proportion of "drafted dates" should be about the same for each of the 12 months. We therefore define a multinomial random variable *drafted*, with the $k = 12$ months as categories. The monthly counts of dates not drafted and drafted are provided here. (For example, for April, 12 dates out of 30 were chosen to be drafted.) Test whether the proportions of "drafted dates" are equal for all months, using level of significance $\alpha = 0.01$. 🐌 **1970draft**

Month	Dates not drafted	Dates drafted	All
Jan.	17	14	31
Feb.	16	13	29
Mar.	21	10	31
Apr.	18	12	30
May	17	14	31
June	16	14	30
July	13	18	31
Aug.	12	19	31
Sept.	11	19	30
Oct.	17	14	31
Nov.	8	22	30
Dec.	5	26	31
All	171	195	366

44. 1971 Military Draft. Criticism of the 1970 draft lottery led the U.S. Selective Service Bureau to focus on making sure that the 1971 draft lottery was truly random. Were their efforts successful? The results of the 1971 draft lottery are shown here (365 days). The Selective Service reports that all birth dates with a rank of 125 or less were chosen for the draft. Perform a χ^2 test for homogeneity of proportions to determine whether the population proportions of "drafted dates" per month were all equal, using level of significance $\alpha = 0.10$. 🐌 **1971draft**

Month	Dates not drafted	Dates drafted
Jan.	19	12
Feb.	19	9
Mar.	21	10
Apr.	21	9
May	22	9
June	21	9
July	19	12
Aug.	18	13
Sept.	23	7
Oct.	19	12
Nov.	16	14
Dec.	22	9

Chapter 11 Formulas and Vocabulary

SECTION 11.1

- Conditions for performing a goodness of fit test (p. 559)
- χ^2 Goodness of fit test (p. 558)
- Multinomial random variable (p. 556)
- Test statistic for the goodness of fit test (p. 559).

$$\chi^2_{\text{data}} = \sum \frac{(O_i - E_i)^2}{E_i}$$

SECTION 11.2

- χ^2 test for independence (p. 569)
- Conditions for performing both the test for independence and the test for the homogeneity of proportions (p. 569)

- Test for the homogeneity of proportions (p. 573)
- Test statistic for both the test for independence and the test for the homogeneity of proportions (p. 570).

$$\chi^2_{\text{data}} = \sum \frac{(O_i - E_i)^2}{E_i}$$

Chapter 11 Review Exercises

SECTION 11.1

For Exercises 1–6, perform the χ^2 goodness of fit test.

1. Truck-Hauled Trade. According to the U.S. Census Bureau, 32% of North American international truck-hauled trade (in dollars) goes from the United States to Canada, 22% goes from the United States to Mexico, 31% goes from Canada to the United States, and 15% goes from Mexico to the United States. Suppose that a new survey showed that $25 billion went from the United States to Canada, $15 billion went from the United States to Mexico, $20 billion went from Canada to the United States, and $10 billion went from Mexico to the United States. Test whether the population proportions of truck-hauled trade have changed, using level of significance $\alpha = 0.05$.

2. Death Row Inmates. According to the report *Death Row, USA*, published by the National Association for the Advancement of Colored People, 42% of the people on death row are black, 46% are white, 10% are Hispanic, and 2% are other. Suppose that a later survey of randomly selected death row inmates found 1500 blacks, 1600 whites, 375 Hispanics, and 100 inmates otherwise classified. Test whether the population proportions have changed, using level of significance $\alpha = 0.10$.

3. College Radio Preferences. A college radio station claims that the music preferences of college students have changed since 1995. In 1995, 40% of the students preferred rock music, 25% preferred rap and hip-hop, 15% preferred country music, 8% preferred blues, 7% preferred jazz, and 5% preferred classical music. A random sample of 200 university students showed that 60 preferred rock music, 60 preferred rap and hip-hop, 35 preferred country music, 12 preferred blues, 18 preferred jazz, and 15 preferred classical. Is there evidence at level of significance $\alpha = 0.05$ that the music preferences of college students differs from the radio station's claim?

4. Alcohol Abuse and Dependence in College. A report found that 25% of college students had abused alcohol in the last 12 months, while a further 6% (not counted in the 25%) were alcohol-dependent.[8] Suppose that a new survey of 1000 randomly selected college students finds 275 who had abused alcohol in the last 12 months and a further 50 (not counted in the 275) who are alcohol-dependent. Test whether the population proportions have changed, using level of significance $\alpha = 0.10$.

5. Truly Random Lottery Drawing? Have you ever wondered whether lottery drawings are truly random? For example, the accompanying histogram shows the frequencies of the third digit in the Maryland lottery's Pick 3 game (218 drawings from September 1989 to April 1990). In a Pick 3 game, you choose a three-digit number between 000 and 999, and if your number comes up, you win the cash prize. Notice that 1 appears as the third digit least of all the digits, and quite a bit less often than some of the other digits. Does the relative scarcity of 1s indicate that the system is flawed?

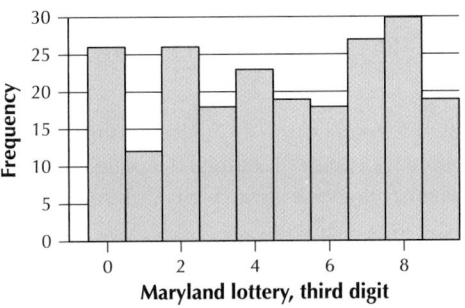

Frequency histogram of third digits in Maryland lottery's Pick 3 game.

The relative frequency distribution of the third digit is shown in the following table. We would, of course, expect each digit to show up 10% of the time. Test whether the population proportions of digits are all 0.10, using level of significance $\alpha = 0.05$. 🍎 **marylandlott**

Digit	Count	Percent
0	26	11.93
1	12	5.50
2	26	11.93
3	18	8.26
4	23	10.55
5	19	8.72
6	18	8.26
7	27	12.39
8	30	13.76
9	19	8.72
$N =$	218	

6. Alternative Medicine Use. A study examined the prevalence of alternative medicine usage by age group among persons with diabetes.[9] In the study, 5.7% of the subjects were aged 18–34 years, 20.7% were aged 35–49 years, 38.8% were aged 50–64 years, and 34.8% were age 65 or older. Suppose that a study conducted this year found that, of the 1000 randomly selected respondents with diabetes, 70 were 18–34 years old, 220 were 35–49 years old, 440 were 50–64 years old, and 270 were over age 65. Test using level of significance $\alpha = 0.05$ whether the proportions have changed.

SECTION 11.2

7. Grades and the SAT. In its "Profile of College-Bound Seniors," the College Board provided the following data on high school grade point average and gender for the students taking the SAT exam. We are interested in testing whether the proportion of females is the same across the six grade categories. 🐾 **highschoolgpa**

Gender	High School Grade Point Average					
	A+	A	A−	B	C	D–F
Female	60	62	59	53	43	43
Male	40	38	41	47	57	57

a. Before you perform any calculations, *what result might we expect*? Examine the table carefully to see whether you can identify any differences in the proportions of females.

b. Test whether the proportion of females is the same across the six grade categories, using level of significance $\alpha = 0.05$.

8. Homicide Victims by Race. The U.S. Bureau of Justice Statistics reported the following numbers of homicide victims, by gender and race, for the state of California in the year 2000. Test whether gender and race are independent, using level of significance $\alpha = 0.10$. **homiciderace**

Gender	White	Black	Other
Male	1089	516	64
Female	297	85	23

9. Pregnancy and HIV Testing. A study examined the proportions of pregnant women in the United States who have had an HIV test in the past 12 months.[10] The proportions for the Northeast, Midwest, South, and West were 56.8%, 49.3%, 58.5%, and 50.2%. Test whether the population proportions of pregnant women who have had an HIV test in the past 12 months are the same across all four regions, using level of significance $\alpha = 0.01$. Assume that each sample size equals 1000.

10. September 11 and Pearl Harbor. The terrorist attacks on New York City and Washington, D.C., on September 11, 2001, were often compared to the Japanese attack on Pearl Harbor on December 7, 1941. In an NBC News Terrorism Poll, the following question was asked: Would you say that Tuesday's attacks are more serious than, equal to, or not as serious as the Japanese attack on Pearl Harbor? This poll was conducted on September 12, 2001, and the results are given in the accompanying table. Were there systematic differences in the way men and women responded to this question? In other words, are the variables *poll response* and *gender* independent? Perform the χ^2 test for independence between *poll response* and *gender*, using level of significance $\alpha = 0.01$. **terroristpoll**

	Gender		Total
	Male	Female	
More serious	200	212	412
Equal	70	84	154
Not as serious	23	6	29
Not sure	11	12	23
Total	304	314	618

11. Radio-Listening Trends. The Arbitron Corporation tracks radio-listening trends among demographic groups. In a survey, 240 teens aged 12–17 listened to pop contemporary hit radio stations while 170 teens listened to alternative radio stations. Also, 250 young adults aged 18–24 listened to pop contemporary hit radio stations while 260 young adults listened to alternative radio stations. Test whether age and radio station type are independent, using level of significance $\alpha = 0.05$.

12. Happiness in Marriage. The General Social Survey tracks trends in American society. The accompanying crosstabulation shows the responses to a question that asked people to characterize their feelings about being married. Test whether happiness in marriage is independent of gender, using level of significance $\alpha = 0.05$. **happymarriage**

Respondents' gender	Happiness in Marriage			Total
	Very happy	Pretty happy	Not too happy	
Male	242	115	9	366
Female	257	149	17	423
Total	499	264	26	789

13. The Digital Divide: Accounting for Income. It is well known that a greater proportion of whites than blacks use the Internet. This is one aspect of what is known as the "digital divide." However, what if we control for income? That is, suppose that we consider only whites, blacks, and Hispanics of a certain annual income range, say, more than $50,000. The Pew Internet and American Life Project conducted a survey in which the following proportions of respondents with incomes above $50,000 were found to be using the Internet. Test whether the digital divide exists after accounting for income. That is, test whether or not there is a significant difference in Internet use levels among the races. Use level of significance $\alpha = 0.05$. Assume each sample size equals 400.

Whites	Blacks	Hispanics
82%	65%	82%

Chapter 11 QUIZ

TRUE OR FALSE

1. True or false: In a goodness of fit test, large differences between the observed frequencies and the expected frequencies lead to rejection of the null hypothesis.

2. True or false: In a test for independence, the degrees of freedom equals $k - 1$.

3. True or false: In the test for the homogeneity of proportions, the alternative hypothesis states that all the population proportions are different.

FILL IN THE BLANK

4. The conditions for performing a goodness of fit test are that none of the expected frequencies is less than ____, and, at most, 20% of the expected frequencies are less than ____.

5. In the test for the homogeneity of proportions, the null hypothesis states that all k population proportions are _____.

6. The _____ _____ [two words] of the ith category is given by the formula $n \cdot p_i$, where n is the number of trials, and p_i is the population proportion for the ith category.

SHORT ANSWER

7. Name the three methods for performing the χ^2 goodness of fit test.

8. In the test for the homogeneity of proportions, which hypothesis states that not all population proportions are equal?

9. How does one calculate the degrees of freedom for the χ^2 test for independence?

CALCULATIONS AND INTERPRETATIONS

For Exercises 10–13, perform the χ^2 goodness of fit test, where the alternative hypothesis takes the following form:

H_a : The random variable does not follow the distribution specified in H_0.

10. $H_0 : p_1 = 0.2, p_2 = 0.2, p_3 = 0.2, p_4 = 0.2, p_5 = 0.2$; $O_1 = 8, O_2 = 9, O_3 = 10, O_4 = 11, O_5 = 12$; $\alpha = 0.05$

11. $H_0 : p_1 = 0.3, p_2 = 0.25, p_3 = 0.20, p_4 = 0.15, p_5 = 0.06, p_6 = 0.04$; $O_1 = 50, O_2 = 40, O_3 = 30, O_4 = 20, O_5 = 10, O_6 = 10$; $\alpha = 0.05$

12. $H_0 : p_1 = 0.2, p_2 = 0.2, p_3 = 0.2, p_4 = 0.2, p_5 = 0.2$; $O_1 = 18, O_2 = 19, O_3 = 21, O_4 = 22, O_5 = 20$; $\alpha = 0.01$

13. $H_0 : p_1 = 0.3, p_2 = 0.25, p_3 = 0.20, p_4 = 0.15, p_5 = 0.06, p_6 = 0.04$; $O_1 = 65, O_2 = 55, O_3 = 30, O_4 = 25, O_5 = 15, O_6 = 10$; $\alpha = 0.05$

14. **Illicit Drug Use Among Young People.** Monitoring the Future (www.monitoringthefuture.org), at the University of Michigan, is an "an ongoing study of the behaviors, attitudes, and values of American secondary school students, college students, and young adults." They reported the lifetime prevalence of the use of any illicit drug among 8th-graders, 10th-graders, and 12th-graders, as shown in the table. **druguse**

	8th-graders	10th-graders	12th-graders
Have used an illicit drug	3,655	6,527	7,461
Have never used an illicit drug	13,345	9,873	7,139

  a. Before you carry out the hypothesis test, *what result might you expect?* Look over the data set carefully to see whether you can detect significant differences between the levels of the variables. Then see whether your hypothesis test bears out your intuition.

  b. Test using level of significance $\alpha = 0.01$ for differences among the proportions of children in those grades who have ever used an illicit drug.

15. **Sport Preference and Gender.** A student group would like to determine whether or not gender and participatory sport preference are independent on campus. A survey of 200 randomly selected college students showed the following sport preferences. Test at level of significance $\alpha = 0.05$ whether gender and sport preference are independent. **sportsgender**

Gender	Sport Preference			Total
	Basketball	Soccer	Swimming	
Female	30	20	50	100
Male	50	30	20	100
Total	80	50	70	200

16. **Beef Cattle and Farm Size.** The National Agricultural Statistics Service publishes data on farm products in the United States.[11] The accompanying table shows the number of beef cattle on smaller-scale operations (farms having fewer than 50 head) for three states. Test whether the proportions of cattle on smaller farms are the same across all three states, using level of significance $\alpha = 0.05$. **cattlefarm**

	Texas	Oklahoma	Pennsylvania
Beef cattle on smaller scale operations	103,000	3,600	11,400
Beef cattle on operations that are not smaller scale	28,000	44,400	600

12

Analysis of Variance

Introduction

Chapter 12 discusses analysis of variance (ANOVA), where we determine whether significant differences exist among the population means of several groups. Section 12.1 describes how ANOVA works and shows how to perform one-way ANOVA. In Section 12.2 we learn multiple comparisons, where we test for pairwise differences in means. Section 12.3 introduces the randomized block design, which can account for nuisance variables. Finally, Section 12.4 explains two-way ANOVA, where two factors can be tested at the same time.

From the Author

- **Section 12.1 One-Way Analysis of Variance (ANOVA)**
  - Instructors may ask students to carefully read Objective 1, How ANOVA Works, to get an intuitive sense of how ANOVA works by comparing variation among the groups to variation within the groups.
  - Instructors may wish to review the F distribution in Section 10.4 at some point.

- **Section 12.2 Multiple Comparisons**
  - New section.
  - The Bonferroni method and Tukey's method are provided. Instructors may choose which method to teach.
  - Students may wonder why they need to learn this material. The answer is that, even though ANOVA may reject the null hypothesis, we cannot determine which pairs of means are significantly different without performing a multiple comparisons test.
  - Some instructors do not have time to teach all the calculations in this section, and prefer simply to work with the Minitab output to determine which pairs of means are significantly different.

- **Section 12.3 Randomized Block Design**
  - New section.
  - Why should students learn this material? Because randomized block design increases the ability of the ANOVA to reject the null hypothesis, by accounting for a nuisance factor (or blocking factor).
  - Note that, in Example 12.9, one-way ANOVA is unable to find significance, while in Example 12.10 the randomized block design does find significance for the same data.

- **Section 12.4 Two-way ANOVA**
  - New section.
  - Why should students learn this material? Because two-way ANOVA allows us to account for the effects of two factors simultaneously. For example, we could test whether *major* and *gender* have a significant effect on student GPA.
  - Instructors may stress that, if interaction between the factors exists, then students should not perform the tests for Factor A or Factor B effects.

Teaching Tips

Starting Example: See whether different fraternities or sororities have different GPAs using analysis of variance. Other similar examples could be to see whether men and women athletes have different GPAs or whether athletes on different sport teams have different GPAs.

In-Class Activities

1. Ask students to collect information on the number of pennies, nickels, dimes, and quarters a person may have in a wallet or purse. Data can be collected from about 50 people. Students can create a table with four columns to record the data set. They can construct boxplots for the four columns and discuss what is being revealed, then use one-way ANOVA to test whether there is a significant difference in the averages for the four categories and whether these results support their observations from the boxplot. Also, students can use the appropriate technology to test the assumptions for a one-factor (coins in this case) experiment.

Analysis of Variance for the Mean Height of Freshmen, Sophomores, Juniors, and Seniors

2. You are going to test whether there are differences in the population mean height of freshmen, sophomores, juniors, and seniors. If the frequency of any class is too small, either eliminate that class or combine it with another class. However, do not go below three classes.

    a. State the appropriate hypotheses, and define your notation.

    b. Generate a sample of four students from each class, using either (a) technology or (b) the *Random Sample* applet.

c. Find out the height of each student in the sample and express the height in inches. Then find the sample mean height for each class.

d. The sample means you calculated in (c) were not all the same. Isn't this sufficient evidence to reject the null hypothesis that the population means are all the same? Why or why not?

e. Using the level of significance of $\alpha = 0.10$, what is the critical value F_{crit} for this test? Will it be the same for each student?

f. Carry out the analysis of variance using your sample data. Use $\alpha = 0.10$. Will the value of the test statistic F_{data} be the same for each student?

g. Record your name and the value for the test statistic F_{data} calculated in (f) on a Post-It Note®.

h. Place your Post-It Note® on the number line that the instructor has prepared on the board, noting the location of the cutoff value F_{crit}. You thus have a collection of the values for the statistic F_{data}. Can you make any comment on the shape of the distribution of F_{data} values?

i. What proportion of students rejected the null hypothesis?

j. Reach a class consensus as to why most student either did or did not reject the null hypothesis.

Supplements

- StatTutor 25.0–25.5
- EESEE case study:
  - Blinded Knee Doctors (Questions 5 and 6 on one-way ANOVA)

Applets

The *Analysis of Variance* applet is referenced in Chapter 12 for demonstrations and for Exercises 44 and 45 in Section 12.1.

Videos

- *Against All Odds* **www.learner.org/resources/series65.html**
  - Program 12: Experimental Design
  - Program 13: Blocking and Sampling

Web Sites

- The site Online Statistics: An Interactive Multimedia Course of Study has information on ANOVA, and it has a link to the Rice Virtual Lab in Statistics with demonstrations and other topics related to statistics: **http://onlinestatbook.com/index.html**.
- This Web site lists other sites that do statistical calculations for ANOVA: **http://statpages.org/**.
- This site has an activity that deals with ANOVA and F tests: **www.amstat.org/publications/jse/v6n3/smith.html**.

© Elena Elisseeva/SuperFusion/SuperStock

OVERVIEW

12

Analysis of Variance

CASE STUDY

Professors on Facebook

To improve communication with students, many instructors have been turning to computer-mediated interaction via online social networks. Online social networks serve as virtual meeting spots, where instructors and students can share information and interests outside the classroom. Examples of online social networks include Facebook, MySpace, and Second Life. Do you think that the amount of information a professor posts about himself or herself, that is, *self-disclosure*, has an effect on the motivation, affective learning, classroom climate, or other important instructional issues? A recently published research paper asked precisely this question.[1] The researchers' primary research tool was *analysis of variance (ANOVA)*, our topic here in Chapter 12. We investigate their results on page 599 in the Case Study "Professors on Facebook."

The Big Picture

Where we are coming from, and where we are headed . . .

- In Chapters 8–10 we learned statistical inference for continuous random variables, and in Chapter 11 we learned hypothesis tests for categorical variables.

- Here, in Chapter 12, we are introduced to *analysis of variance*, a way to compare the population means of several different groups, and determine whether significant differences exist between the means. For example, are there significant differences in mean grade point average among the freshmen, sophomores, juniors, and seniors at your school?

- There is only one more chapter in the text, Chapter 13, "Inference in Regression," where we extend our work from Chapter 4, "Correlation and Regression."

12.1 One-Way Analysis of Variance (ANOVA)

OBJECTIVES By the end of this section, I will be able to . . .

1 Explain how analysis of variance works.

2 Perform one-way analysis of variance.

1 How Analysis of Variance (ANOVA) Works

Analysis of variance (ANOVA) is a hypothesis test for determining whether three or more means of different populations are equal. ANOVA works by comparing the variability *between* the samples to the variability *within* the samples.

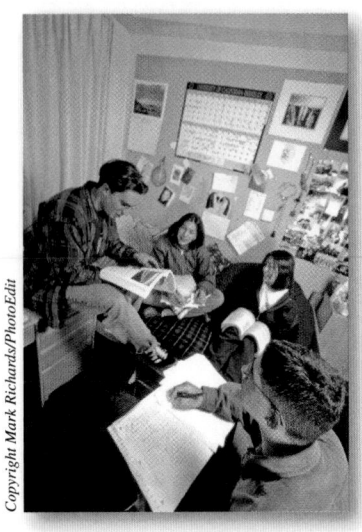

Suppose we are interested in determining whether there are significant differences in grade point averages (GPAs) among residents of three dormitories, A, B, and C. Table 12.1 displays three random samples of GPAs of ten residents from each dormitory.

Table 12.1 Sample GPAs from Dorms A, B, and C

A	0.60	3.82	4.00	2.22	1.46	2.91	2.20	1.60	0.89	2.30
B	2.12	2.00	1.03	3.47	3.70	1.72	3.15	3.93	1.26	2.62
C	3.65	1.57	3.36	1.17	2.55	3.12	3.60	4.00	2.85	2.13

The sample mean GPA for Dormitory A is

$$\bar{x}_A = \frac{0.60 + 3.82 + 4.00 + 2.22 + 1.46 + 2.91 + 2.20 + 1.60 + 0.89 + 2.30}{10} = 2.2$$

Similarly, we can find the sample mean GPAs for the other dormitories: $\bar{x}_B = 2.5$ and $\bar{x}_C = 2.8$. We note that the sample means are not equal. The question is, Are the population means equal? Let μ_A, μ_B, and μ_C represent the population mean GPAs for Dormitories A, B, and C, respectively. We are interested in the following hypotheses, where μ_i represents the population mean GPA for dormitory i:

$$H_0: \mu_A = \mu_B = \mu_C \quad \text{versus} \quad H_a: \text{not all the population means are equal}$$

Sufficient differences in the sample means would represent evidence that the population means were not equal. The question is, What represents "sufficiently" different? We need something to compare against, such as the *spread* of each sample. One measure of spread or variability is the *range*:

$$\text{range} = \text{max} - \text{min}$$

We have

$$\text{range (Dorm A)} = 4.00 - 0.60 = 3.40$$
$$\text{range (Dorm B)} = 3.93 - 1.03 = 2.90$$
$$\text{range (Dorm C)} = 4.00 - 1.17 = 2.83$$

These ranges are rather large spreads, and there is a considerable amount of overlap among the different dormitory GPAs, as shown in Figure 12.1.

Figure 12.1 shows the difference among the means for the three dorm GPAs compared with the spread of each dorm's GPAs, as measured by the range. The red triangles represent the sample means, $\bar{x}_A = 2.2$, $\bar{x}_B = 2.5$, and $\bar{x}_C = 2.8$. The spread of the sample means (shown by the red arrows) is much less than the spreads of the individual dorm GPAs (shown by the green arrows). Thus, the sample means $\bar{x}_A = 2.2$, $\bar{x}_B = 2.5$, and $\bar{x}_C = 2.8$ are not sufficiently different when compared against the spread of the GPAs. This graph would therefore not provide evidence to reject the null hypothesis that the population mean GPAs are all equal.

FIGURE 12.1
Comparison dotplot of GPAs for Dorms A, B, and C.

Now we make a similar comparison for the GPAs for Dormitories D, E, and F in Table 12.2.

Table 12.2 Sample GPAs from Dorms D, E, and F

D	2.16	2.23	2.09	2.17	2.25	2.19	2.24	2.28	2.25	2.14
E	2.45	2.34	2.58	2.49	2.60	2.42	2.55	2.62	2.45	2.50
F	2.80	2.75	2.93	2.68	2.88	2.75	2.87	2.81	2.73	2.80

The sample mean GPAs for Dormitories D, E, and F are the *same* as those for Dormitories A, B, and C, respectively: $\bar{x}_D = 2.2$, $\bar{x}_E = 2.5$, and $\bar{x}_F = 2.8$. Again we are interested in whether the population means are equal.

$$H_0 : \mu_D = \mu_E = \mu_F \quad \text{versus} \quad H_a : \text{not all the population means are equal}$$

Consider the comparison dotplot in Figure 12.2. There now seems to be better evidence for concluding that the three population means are not all equal. There is no overlap among the three samples because the spread *within* each dormitory is much smaller than for Dormitories A, B, and C.

$$\text{range (Dorm D)} = 2.28 - 2.09 = 0.19$$
$$\text{range (Dorm E)} = 2.62 - 2.34 = 0.28$$
$$\text{range (Dorm F)} = 2.93 - 2.68 = 0.25$$

Figure 12.2 shows the difference among the means for the three dorm GPAs compared with the range of each dorm's GPAs. The red triangles represent the sample means, $\bar{x}_D = 2.2$, $\bar{x}_E = 2.5$, and $\bar{x}_F = 2.8$. The spread of the sample means (red arrows) is much greater than the spreads of the individual dorm GPAs (green arrows). Thus, the sample means $\bar{x}_D = 2.2$, $\bar{x}_E = 2.5$, and $\bar{x}_F = 2.8$ are sufficiently different when compared against the range of the GPAs. This graph would, therefore, provide some evidence to reject the null hypothesis that the population mean GPAs are all equal.

FIGURE 12.2
Comparison dotplot of GPAs for Dorms D, E, F.

Note that we arrived at *opposite conclusions* for the two sets of dormitories, *even though the sample means of the first group are identical to the sample means of the second group.* Here is the key difference:

- The within-sample spreads of Dormitories A, B, and C are *large*. Compared to these large spreads, the difference in sample means did not seem large;

- The within-sample spreads of Dormitories D, E, and F are *small*. Compared to these small spreads, the difference in sample means did seem large.

These are the types of comparisons that the ANOVA method makes.

Instead of using the range as the measure of spread, analysis of variance uses the standard deviation of the individual samples. Recall that samples with larger spread have larger standard deviations, just as they have larger ranges.

Developing Your Statistical Sense

How Does Analysis of Variance Work?

The key to how analysis of variance works is the following comparison. Compare

a. the variability in the sample means—that is, how large the differences are between the sample means (indicated by the lengths of the red arrows in Figures 12.1 and 12.2)—with

b. the variability within each sample—that is, the within-sample spreads (indicated by the lengths of the green arrows in Figures 12.1 and 12.2).

When (a) is much larger than (b), this is evidence that the population means are not all equal and that we should reject the null hypothesis. Thus, our analysis depends on measuring variability. And hence the term *analysis of variance*. ◢

Just as for hypothesis-testing procedures from previous chapters, analysis of variance can be performed only if certain requirements are met.

> **Requirements for Performing Analysis of Variance**
> 1. Each of the k populations is normally distributed.
> 2. The variances (σ^2) of the populations are all equal.
> 3. The samples are independently drawn.

Note: In analysis of variance, the null hypothesis *always* states that all the population means are equal and the alternative hypothesis *always* states that not all the population means are equal. Note that H_a is *not* stating that the population means are all different. For H_a to be true, it is sufficient for a single population mean to be different, even though all the other population means may be equal.

Our hypotheses for testing for the equality of the population mean GPA for Dormitories A, B, and C are

$$H_0 : \mu_A = \mu_B = \mu_C \quad \text{versus} \quad H_a : \text{not all the population means are equal}$$

Let us stop for a moment to consider what these requirements and the hypotheses mean.

- If H_0 is true, then all three dormitories would have the same population mean GPA: $\mu_A = \mu_B = \mu_C = \mu$, where we denote the hypothesized common mean as μ.
- Requirement 1 states that each population is normally distributed.
- Requirement 2 states that all the population variances are equal. Let's call this common variance σ^2.

Putting all this together, H_0 assumes that the observations from each population come from the same normal distribution, with mean μ and variance σ^2.

Suppose we then take samples of size n from each group. Fact 3 in Chapter 7 states that the sampling distribution of $\bar{x}$ for a sample of size n taken from a normal population with mean μ and standard deviation σ (that is, variance σ^2) is also normal, with mean μ and standard deviation $\sigma/\sqrt{n}$ (that is, variance σ^2/n), as shown in Figure 12.3. Since each dormitory's GPA is assumed (under H_0) to come from the same sampling distribution, we would expect the sample means to be fairly close together.

On the other hand, if H_0 is not true, then not all the population means are equal (Figure 12.4). In this case, there is no sampling distribution common to all sample means, so we would not expect the sample means to be close together. Note in Figure 12.4 that each distribution nevertheless has the same shape (normal) and spread (i.e., variance) because of the requirements.

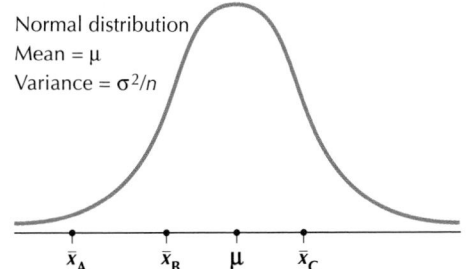

FIGURE 12.3 Common sampling distribution when H_0 is true.

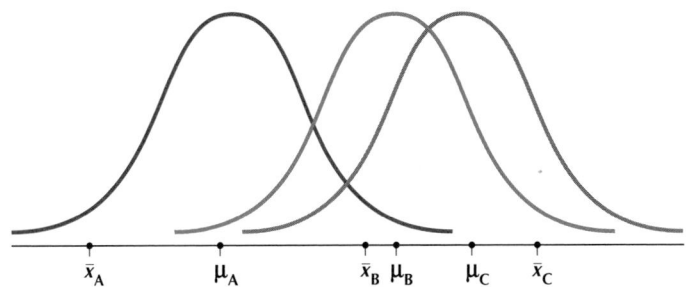

FIGURE 12.4 No common sampling distribution when H_0 is not true.

Note: Normal probability plots were introduced in Chapter 7.

Procedure for Verifying the Requirements for Analysis of Variance

Step 1 **Normality.** Check that the data from each group are normally distributed, using normality probability plots.

Step 2 **Equal Variances.** Compute the sample standard deviation for each group to verify that the largest standard deviation is not larger than twice the smallest standard deviation.

Step 3 **Independence.** Verify that the samples drawn from each group are independently drawn.

Example 12.1 | Verify the requirements for performing an analysis of variance

dormitory

Verify the requirements for performing an analysis of variance using the hypotheses

$$H_0 : \ \mu_A = \mu_B = \mu_C \quad \text{versus} \quad H_a : \ \text{not all the population means are equal}$$

where μ_i represents the population mean GPA for Dormitory i, using data from Table 12.1.

Solution

Step 1 **Normality.** To verify that each of the $k = 3$ populations is normally distributed, we examine normal probability plots of each sample, shown in Figure 12.5. Each plot indicates acceptable normality.

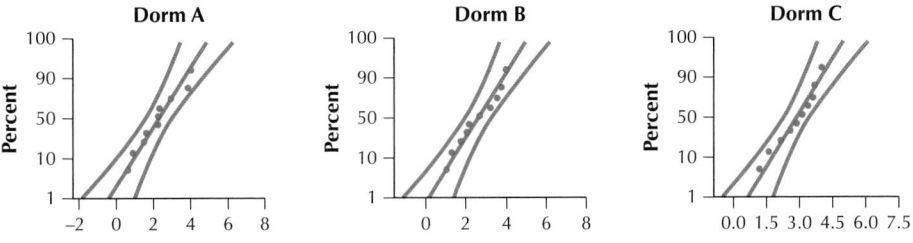

FIGURE 12.5 Normal probability plots verify normality requirement.

Step 2 **Equal Variances.** To find the standard deviation for Dorm A, we first find

$$\sum (x - \bar{x})^2 = (0.60 - 2.2)^2 + (3.82 - 2.2)^2 + (4.00 - 2.2)^2 + (2.22 - 2.2)^2$$
$$+ (1.46 - 2.2)^2 + (2.91 - 2.2)^2 + (2.20 - 2.2)^2 + (1.60 - 2.2)^2$$
$$+ (0.89 - 2.2)^2 + (2.30 - 2.2)^2$$
$$= 11.5626$$

Note: We retain many decimal places when calculating s_A, s_B, and s_C because these values are used to calculate other quantities later on.

Then

$$s_A = \sqrt{\frac{\sum(x - \bar{x})^2}{n - 1}} = \sqrt{\frac{11.5626}{10 - 1}} \approx 1.133460777$$

We similarly find $s_B \approx 1.030857248$ and $s_C \approx 0.9370284$. The largest, $s_A \approx 1.133460777$, is not larger than twice the smallest, $s_C \approx 0.9370284$. Thus, the equal variance requirement is satisfied.

Step 3 **Independence.** Since the students are randomly sampled from each dormitory, with the selection of students in one dormitory not affecting the selection of students sampled from the other dormitories, the independence assumption is also validated. ■

Now You Can Do
Exercises 23a–25a.

Assuming that H_0 is true, we estimate the common population mean μ using the **overall sample mean,** $\bar{\bar{x}}$:

Note: This form for $\bar{\bar{x}}$ is a weighted mean with the weights being the sample sizes.

$$\bar{\bar{x}} = \frac{(n_1\bar{x}_1 + n_2\bar{x}_2 + \cdots + n_k\bar{x}_k)}{n_t}$$

where there are k samples and n_t is the "total sample size" (sum of the k sample sizes). The overall sample mean $\bar{\bar{x}}$ is simply the mean of all the observations from all the samples. For the special case when all the sample sizes are equal, the overall sample mean $\bar{\bar{x}}$ is simply the mean of the k sample means,

$$\bar{\bar{x}} = \frac{(\bar{x}_1 + \bar{x}_2 + \cdots + \bar{x}_k)}{k}$$

Example 12.2 Calculating the overall sample mean $\bar{\bar{x}}$

For the sample GPA data given in Table 12.1 for Dorms A, B, and C, calculate the overall sample mean, $\bar{\bar{x}}$.

Solution

We have $k = 3$ dormitories, with sample mean GPAs $\bar{x}_A = 2.2$, $\bar{x}_B = 2.5$, $\bar{x}_C = 2.8$. Also, $n_A = n_B = n_C = 10$, and $n_t = 10 + 10 + 10 = 30$. Thus,

$$\bar{\bar{x}} = \frac{(10(2.2) + 10(2.5) + 10(2.8))}{30} = 2.5$$

Since all the sample sizes are equal, we can also calculate $\bar{\bar{x}}$ as follows:

Now You Can Do
Exercises 7b–10b.

$$\bar{\bar{x}} = \frac{(2.2 + 2.5 + 2.8)}{3} = 2.5$$

■

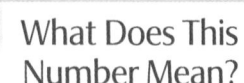
What Does This Number Mean?

$\bar{\bar{x}} = 2.5$ is the mean GPA for all 30 students from all three samples. We can use $\bar{\bar{x}}$ as our estimate of the common population mean μ assumed in H_0. ◢

Recall that analysis of variance works by comparing the variability in the sample means to the variability within each sample. We use the following statistics to measure these variabilities.

> The **mean square treatment (MSTR)** measures the variability in the sample means. MSTR is the sample variance of the sample means, weighted by sample size.
>
> $$\text{MSTR} = \frac{\sum n_i(\bar{x}_i - \bar{\bar{x}})^2}{k - 1}$$
>
> where n_i and $\bar{x}_i$ are the sample size and mean of the ith sample, $\bar{\bar{x}}$ is the overall sample mean, and there are k populations.
>
> The **mean square error (MSE)** measures the variability within the samples. MSE is the mean of the sample variances, weighted by sample size.
>
> $$\text{MSE} = \frac{\sum(n_i - 1)s_i^2}{n_t - k}$$
>
> where n_i and s_i^2 are the sample size and variance of the ith sample, n_t is the total sample size, and there are k populations.

The greater the distance between the sample means, the larger the MSTR.

The larger the standard deviation of the k samples, the larger the MSE.

We compare MSTR to MSE by taking the ratio of these two quantities. This ratio MSTR/MSE follows the F distribution that we learned about in Section 10.4.

The student may wish to review the characteristics of the F distribution in Section 10.4.

> The **test statistic for analysis of variance** is
>
> $$F_{\text{data}} = \frac{\text{MSTR}}{\text{MSE}}$$
>
> F_{data} measures the variability among the sample means, compared to the variability within the samples. F_{data} follows an F distribution with $\text{df}_1 = k - 1$ and $\text{df}_2 = n_t - k$, when the following requirements are met: (1) each of the k populations is normally distributed, (2) the variances of the populations are all equal, and (3) the samples are independently drawn.

The term *mean square* represents a weighted mean of quantities that are squared. Each mean square itself consists of two parts: the *sum of squares* in the numerator and the *degrees of freedom* in the denominator. The numerator for MSTR is called the **sum of squares treatment (SSTR),** and the numerator for MSE is called the **sum of squares error (SSE).**

$$\text{MSTR} = \frac{\text{sum of squares treatment}}{\text{df}_1} = \frac{\text{SSTR}}{\text{df}_1} = \frac{\sum n_i(\bar{x}_i - \bar{\bar{x}})^2}{k - 1}$$

$$\text{MSE} = \frac{\text{sum of squares error}}{\text{df}_2} = \frac{\text{SSE}}{\text{df}_2} = \frac{\sum(n_i - 1)s_i^2}{n_t - k}$$

The **total sum of squares (SST)** is found by adding SSTR and SSE:

$$\text{SST} = \text{SSTR} + \text{SSE}$$

The ANOVA table shown in Table 12.3 is a convenient way to display the various statistics calculated during an analysis of variance. Note that the quantities in the mean square column equal the ratio of the two columns to its left.

Table 12.3 ANOVA table

Source of variation	Sum of squares	Degrees of freedom	Mean square	F-test statistic
Treatment	SSTR	$\text{df}_1 = k - 1$	$\text{MSTR} = \dfrac{\text{SSTR}}{k - 1}$	$F_{\text{data}} = \dfrac{\text{MSTR}}{\text{MSE}}$
Error	SSE	$\text{df}_2 = n_t - k$	$\text{MSE} = \dfrac{\text{SSE}}{n_t - k}$	
Total	SST			

Example 12.3 Constructing the ANOVA table

Use the summary statistics in Table 12.4 for the sample GPAs for Dorms A, B, and C to construct the ANOVA table.

Table 12.4 Summary statistics for sample GPAs for Dorms A, B, and C

	Dorm A	Dorm B	Dorm C
Mean	$\bar{x}_A = 2.2$	$\bar{x}_B = 2.5$	$\bar{x}_C = 2.8$
Standard deviation	$s_A \approx 1.133460777$	$s_B \approx 1.030857248$	$s_C \approx 0.9370284$
Sample size	$n_1 = 10$	$n_2 = 10$	$n_3 = 10$

Solution

We have $k = 3$ dormitories, and total sample size $n_t = 10 + 10 + 10 = 30$. Thus,

- $\text{SSTR} = \sum n_i(\bar{x}_i - \bar{\bar{x}})^2 = 10(2.2 - 2.5)^2 + 10(2.5 - 2.5)^2 + 10(2.8 - 2.5)^2$
  $= 10[(-0.3)^2 + (0)^2 + (0.3)^2] = 1.8$

- $\text{SSE} \approx (10 - 1)(1.133460777)^2 + (10 - 1)(1.030857248)^2 + (10 - 1)(0.9370284)^2$
  ≈ 29.0288

- $\text{SST} = \text{SSTR} + \text{SSE} = 1.8 + 29.0288 = 30.8288$

- $\text{MSTR} = \dfrac{\text{SSTR}}{k - 1} = \dfrac{1.8}{3 - 1} = 0.9$

- $\text{MSE} = \dfrac{\text{SSE}}{n_t - k} = \dfrac{29.0288}{30 - 3} = 1.0751407407$

- $F_{\text{data}} = \dfrac{\text{MSTR}}{\text{MSE}} = \dfrac{0.9}{1.0751407407} = 0.8370997079 \approx 0.84$

Now You Can Do
Exercises 11d–14d, 19, and 20.

We summarize these calculations in the following ANOVA table with the results rounded for clarity. ■

Source of variation	Sum of squares	Degrees of freedom	Mean square	F-test statistic
Treatment	$\text{SSTR} = 1.8$	$df_1 = 3 - 1 = 2$	$\text{MSTR} = \dfrac{1.8}{2} = 0.9$	$F_{\text{data}} = \dfrac{0.9}{1.075} \approx 0.84$
Error	$\text{SSE} = 29.0288$	$df_2 = 30 - 3 = 27$	$\text{MSE} = \dfrac{29.0288}{27} \approx 1.075$	
Total	$\text{SST} = 30.8288$			

2 Performing One-Way ANOVA

Now that we know how it works, we next learn how to perform ANOVA.

> **One-Way Analysis of Variance**
>
> We have taken random samples from each of k populations and want to test whether the population means of the k populations are all equal.
> Required conditions:
>
> 1. Each of the k populations is normally distributed.
> 2. The variances (σ^2) of the populations are all equal.
> 3. The samples are independently drawn.

Remember: H_a is not stating that the population means are all different.

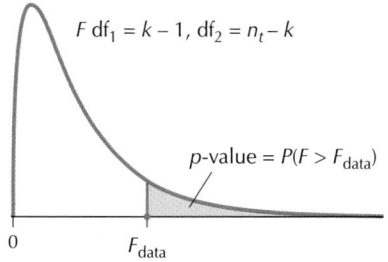

$F \; df_1 = k - 1, \; df_2 = n_t - k$

$p\text{-value} = P(F > F_{data})$

$0 \qquad F_{data}$

FIGURE 12.6 *p*-Value for the one-way ANOVA *F* test.

***Step 1* State the hypotheses, and state the rejection rule.**
$H_0 : \mu_1 = \mu_2 = \cdots = \mu_k$ versus $H_a :$ not all the population means are equal
where the μ's represent the population mean from each population. The rejection rule is
Reject H_0 if the p-value $\leq \alpha$.

***Step 2* Calculate F_{data}.**

$$F_{data} = \frac{\text{MSTR}}{\text{MSE}}$$

where

$$\text{MSTR} = \frac{\sum n_i(\bar{x}_i - \bar{\bar{x}})^2}{k - 1} \qquad \text{and} \qquad \text{MSE} = \frac{\sum (n_i - 1)s_i^2}{n_t - k}$$

F_{data} follows an F distribution with $df_1 = k - 1$ and $df_2 = n_t - k$ if the required conditions are satisfied, where n_t represents the total sample size.

***Step 3* Find the *p*-value.** Use technology to find the *p*-value $= P(F > F_{data})$, as shown in Figure 12.6.

***Step 4* State the conclusion and the interpretation.** Compare the *p*-value with α.

Example 12.4 Performing one-way ANOVA

Test using level of significance $\alpha = 0.05$ whether the population mean GPAs from Example 12.1 differ among the students in Dormitories A, B, and C.

◢ What Result Might We Expect?

Recall that the comparison dotplot in Figure 12.1 (page 588) showed a large amount of overlap in the GPAs among the three dormitories. The large ranges illustrate the large within-dormitory spread of the GPAs for these dorms. When compared against this large within-sample variability, the variability in sample means may not seem large. Therefore, we might expect that the null hypothesis of no difference will *not be rejected.* ◢

Solution

We already verified the requirements for performing the analysis of variance in Example 12.1.

Step 1 **State the hypotheses, and state the rejection rule.** Define the μ_i.

$$H_0 : \mu_A = \mu_B = \mu_C \quad \text{versus} \quad H_a : \text{not all the population means are equal}$$

where μ_i represents the population mean GPA of students from dormitory i. The rejection rule is *Reject H_0 if the p-value $\leq \alpha$.*

Step 2 **Calculate F_{data}.** From Example 12.3, we have MSTR = 0.9, MSE = 1.0751407407, and

$$F_{data} = \frac{\text{MSTR}}{\text{MSE}} = \frac{0.9}{1.0751407407} = 0.8370997079$$

F_{data} follows an F distribution with $df_1 = k - 1 = 3 - 1 = 2$ and $df_2 = n_t - k = 30 - 3 = 27$.

Step 3 **Find the *p*-value.** We use the instructions provided in the Step-by-Step Technology Guide at the end of this section (page 600). From Figures 12.7 and 12.8, we have

$$p\text{-value} = P(F > F_{data}) = P(F > 0.8370997079) = 0.4438929572 \approx 0.4439$$

CAUTION When calculating the *p*-value for analysis of variance, always retain as many decimal places in the value of F_{data} as you can. This will make the *p*-value as accurate as possible. Rounding F_{data} too much will make the *p*-value less accurate.

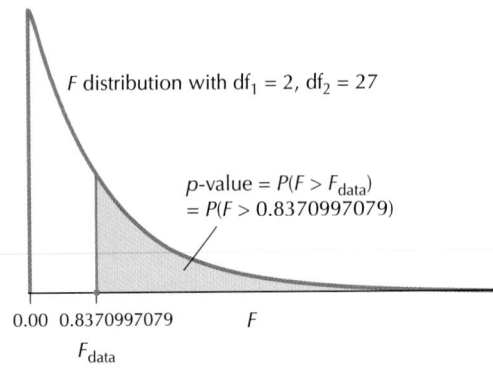

FIGURE 12.7 p-Value = $P(F > 0.8370997079)$.

FIGURE 12.8 TI-83/84 p-value.

Now You Can Do
Exercises 15–18.

Step 4 **State the conclusion and the interpretation.** Compare the p-value with α. Since the p-value of 0.4439 is not $\leq \alpha = 0.05$, we do not reject H_0. As expected, there is not enough evidence to conclude at level of significance $\alpha = 0.05$ that not all population mean GPAs are equal. ∎

Example 12.5 Performing one-way ANOVA using technology

Alamy

DATA FILE
micemaze

Researchers from the Institute for Behavioral Genetics at the University of Colorado investigated the effect that the enzyme protein kinase C (PKC) has on anxiety in mice. The genotype for a particular gene in a mouse (or a human) consists of two *alleles* (copies) of each chromosome, one each from the father and mother. The investigators in the study separated the mice into three groups. In Group 0, neither of the mice's alleles for PKC produced the enzyme. In Group 1, one of the two alleles for PKC produced the enzyme and the other did not. In Group 2, both PKC alleles produced the enzyme. To measure the anxiety in the mice, scientists measured the time (in seconds) the mice spent in the "open-ended" sections of an elevated maze. It was surmised that mice spending more time in open-ended sections exhibit decreased anxiety. The data are provided in Table 12.5. Use technology to test at $\alpha = 0.01$ whether the population mean time spent in the open-ended sections of the maze was the same for all three groups.

Table 12.5 Time spent in open-ended section of maze

Group 0		Group 1		Group 2	
15.8	14.4	5.2	7.6	10.6	9.2
16.5	25.7	8.7	10.4	6.4	14.5
37.7	26.9	0.0	7.7	2.7	11.1
28.7	21.7	22.2	13.4	11.8	3.5
5.8	15.2	5.5	2.2	0.4	8.0
13.7	26.5	8.4	9.5	13.9	20.7
19.2	20.5	17.2	0.0	0.0	0.0
2.5		11.9		16.5	

◢ **What Result Might We Expect?**

Figure 12.9 shows a plot of the time in open-ended sections for the mice in the three groups. Note that the Group 1 and Group 2 mice spent on average about the same amount of time in the open-ended sections but that Group 0 spent on average somewhat more time in the open-ended sections. This would tend to suggest that the null hypothesis that all three population means are equal should be rejected. Remember that to reject H_0, it is sufficient for just one of the population means to be different. ◢

FIGURE 12.9 Evidence that the population mean of Group 0 is larger than the others.

Solution

We use the instructions provided in the Step-by-Step Technology Guide at the end of this section (page 600). We first verify whether the requirements are met.

- The normal probability plots in Figure 12.10 indicate acceptable normality.
- The group standard deviations are $s_0 \approx 9.0$, $s_1 \approx 6.0$, and $s_2 \approx 6.4$. Thus, the largest standard deviation is not greater than twice the smaller, which verifies the equal variances requirement.
- The selection of a mouse to a particular group did not affect the selection of mice to the other groups, so that the samples are independent.

FIGURE 12.10 Normal probability plots.

Thus, we proceed with the one-way ANOVA.

H_0 : $\mu_{\text{Group 0}} = \mu_{\text{Group 1}} = \mu_{\text{Group 2}}$

H_a : Not all population means are equal

where the μ's represent the population mean time spent in the open-ended sections of the maze for each group.

Figure 12.11 contains the results from the TI-83/84, showing where each statistic corresponds to the ANOVA table structure in Table 12.3. We have $F_{\text{data}} = 10.906$, with a p-value of "1.5320224E-4" = 0.00015320224. Since this p-value is less than $\alpha = 0.01$, we reject H_0. There is evidence at level of significance $\alpha = 0.01$ that the population mean times in the open-ended sections of the maze are not equal for all three groups.

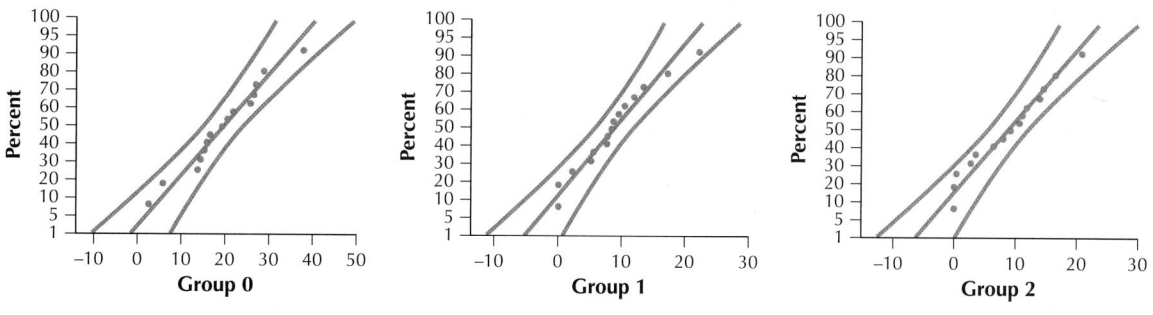

Source of variation	Sum of squares	Degrees of freedom	Mean square	F-test statistic
Treatment	SSTR $\approx$ 1154.92	$\text{df}_1 = 2$	MSTR $\approx$ 577.46	$F_{\text{data}} \approx 10.906$
Error	SSE $\approx$ 2223.84	$\text{df}_2 = 42$	MSE $\approx$ 52.95	
Total	SST $\approx$ 3378.75			

FIGURE 12.11 Correspondence between TI-83/84 ANOVA output and the ANOVA table.

Figure 12.12 contains the Excel ANOVA results, and Figure 12.13 contains the Minitab ANOVA results. Values differ slightly due to rounding. ∎

ANOVA						
Source of Variation	SS	df	MS	F	P-value	F crit
Between Groups	1154.92	2	577.4602	10.90607	0.000153	3.219938
Within Groups	2223.84	42	52.94851			
Total	3378.76	44				

Source	DF	SS	MS	F	P
Group	2	1154.9	577.5	10.91	0.000
Error	42	2223.8	52.9		
Total	44	3378.8			

FIGURE 12.12 Excel ANOVA results.

FIGURE 12.13 Minitab ANOVA results.

One-way ANOVA may also be conducted using the critical-value method. The conditions are the same as for the *p*-value method.

Example 12.6 Performing one-way ANOVA using the critical-value method

 micemaze

Use the data from Example 12.5 to test using the critical-value method and level of significance $\alpha = 0.01$ whether the population mean time spent in the open-ended sections of the maze was the same for all three groups.

Solution

The conditions for performing ANOVA were verified in Example 12.5.

Step 1 **State the hypotheses.**

$H_0 : \mu_{\text{Group 0}} = \mu_{\text{Group 1}} = \mu_{\text{Group 2}}$
$H_a :$ Not all population means are equal

where the μ's represent the population mean time spent in the open-ended sections of the maze for each group.

Step 2 **Find the critical value F_{crit} and state the rejection rule.** The one-way ANOVA test is a right-tailed test, so the *F*-critical value F_{crit} is the value of the *F* distribution for $\text{df}_1 = k - 1$ and $\text{df}_2 = n_t - k$ that has area α to the right of it (see Figure 12.14). Here, $\text{df}_1 = 3 - 1 = 2$ and $\text{df}_2 = 45 - 3 = 42$. To find F_{crit}, we may use the *F* tables or technology. To find our F_{crit} using Excel, enter **=FINV(0.01,2,42)** in cell **A1**, as shown in Figure 12.14. Thus, $F_{\text{crit}} = 5.149$. Since ANOVA is a right-tailed test, we will reject H_0 if $F_{\text{data}} \geq 5.149$.

FIGURE 12.14
Using Excel to find the *F* critical value.

	A1				f_x	=FINV(0.01,2,42)
	A	B	C	D	E	F
1	5.149					

Step 3 **Calculate F_{data}.** From Example 12.5 we have $F_{\text{data}} = 10.906$.

Step 4 **State the conclusion and interpretation.** Since $F_{\text{data}} = 10.906 \geq F_{\text{crit}} = 5.149$ (Figure 12.15), we reject H_0. There is evidence that not all population mean times spent in the open-ended sections of the maze are equal. ∎

FIGURE 12.15
$F_{\text{crit}} = 5.149$ has area of $\alpha = 0.01$ to the right of it.

<table>
<tr><td>Developing Your
Statistical Sense</td><td>

Do Not Draw the Wrong Conclusion

Note that we did not conclude that all three population means are different. As long as one mean is sufficiently different from the other two, we would reject H_0. Our conclusion was simply that the population means were not all equal.

Also, we cannot yet formally conclude that Group 0 has a larger population mean time than the other groups, even though Figure 12.9 seems to indicate so. All we can formally conclude at this point is that not all the population means are equal. In Section 12.2, we will learn *multiple comparisons,* which is the type of analysis needed to test whether the mean of Group 0 is larger than the others. ◢

</td></tr>
</table>

CASE STUDY   Professors on Facebook

A recent study investigated whether the amount of information a professor posts about himself or herself (that is, *self-disclosure*) on the online social network Facebook is related to student motivation. A professor constructed three different Facebook sites, one offering low self-disclosure, one offering medium self-disclosure, and one offering high self-disclosure. For example, the low-disclosure site offered information only about her position at the university. The medium-disclosure site also showed the professor's favorite movies, books, and quotes. On the high-disclosure site, fictitious comments from "friends" were posted on "the Wall," highlighting social gatherings.

Study participants (students not enrolled in the professor's courses) were then randomly assigned to access and browse one of the three Facebook sites, develop an impression of the professor, and complete the research questionnaire. Student motivation was measured using a set of 16 items, and the sum of the 16 items was calculated to form the total motivation score. The items measured student interest, involvement, stimulation, level of excitement, and whether the student was inspired or challenged. Use technology to test at $\alpha = 0.05$ whether the population mean motivation scores are equal for the three types of Facebook pages, low, medium, and high self-disclosure.

Solution

First we verify whether the requirements are satisfied.

- The normal probability plots in Figure 12.16 indicate acceptable normality.

FIGURE 12.16 Normal probability plots.

- The standard deviations are shown in the Minitab output in Figure 12.17. The largest, $s_{\text{medium}} = 14.70$, is not larger than twice the smallest, $s_{\text{low}} = 11.88$. Thus, the equal-variance requirement is satisfied.

```
Source    DF     SS     MS     F       P
Group      2   2712   1356   8.05   0.001
Error    127  21386    168
Total    129  24098


S = 12.98   R-Sq = 11.25%   R-Sq(adj) = 9.86%


                              Individual 95% CIs For Mean Based on
                              Pooled StDev
Level   N   Mean   StDev  -------+---------+---------+---------+--
High    43  81.09  12.12                        (-------*-------)
Medium  44  79.36  14.70                       (-------*------)
Low     43  70.63  11.88  (-------*-------)
                          -------+---------+---------+---------+--
                             70.0      75.0      80.0      85.0

Pooled StDev = 12.98
```

FIGURE 12.17 Minitab output for Facebook ANOVA.

- Since the student participants were randomly selected for each level of self-disclosure, the independence assumption is also validated.

We therefore proceed with the ANOVA. The hypotheses are

$$H_0 : \mu_{\text{high}} = \mu_{\text{medium}} = \mu_{\text{low}} \quad \text{versus} \quad H_a : \text{not all the population means are equal}$$

where μ_i represents a population mean motivation score for each self-disclosure level. Reject H_0 if the p-value is less than $\alpha = 0.05$.

From Figure 12.17, we get $F_{\text{data}} = 8.05$, with an associated p-value of approximately 0.001. Since this p-value is less than $\alpha = 0.05$, we reject H_0. There is evidence that not all population mean motivation scores are equal across all levels of self-disclosure. Informally, we may observe that the mean motivation score for the Facebook Web site with low self-disclosure seems lower than the other groups. We test this formally in Section 12.2. ∎

 The *Analysis of Variance* applet allows you to experiment with various values for the sample means and the sample variability in order to see how changes in these values affect F_{data} and the p-value.

STEP-BY-STEP TECHNOLOGY GUIDE: Analysis of Variance

TI-83/84

Performing ANOVA
(Example 12.4, page 595, is used to illustrate the procedure.)
Step 1 Enter the Dormitory A data in **L1**, the Dormitory B data in **L2**, and the Dormitory C data in **L3**.
Step 2 Press **STAT**, highlight **TESTS**, select **"ANOVA("** , and press **ENTER**.
Step 3 On the home screen, enter **"L1, L2, L3)"** and press **ENTER** (Figure 12.18).

Finding the *p*-Value for a Given F_{data}.
(Example 12.4, page 595, is used to illustrate the procedure.)
p-value $= P(F > F_{\text{data}}) = P(F > 0.8370997079)$, where $df_1 = 2$ and $df_2 = 27$.
Step 1 Press **2nd > DISTR**.
Step 2 Select **Fcdf(** and press **ENTER**.
Step 3 Enter **"0.8370997079, 1E99, 2, 27)"** and press **ENTER**. The results are shown in Figure 12.8 (page 596).

```
ANOVA(L₁,L₂,L₃)
```

FIGURE 12.18

EXCEL

Performing ANOVA
(Example 12.4, page 595, is used to illustrate the procedure.)
Step 1   Enter the Dormitory A data in column A, the Dormitory B data in column B, and the Dormitory C data in column C.
Step 2   Click **Data > Data Analysis > Anova: Single Factor**, and click **OK**.
Step 3   Select the input range of the data by clicking and dragging over the data in columns A, B, and C. Then click **OK**.

MINITAB

Performing ANOVA
(Example 12.4, page 595, is used to illustrate the procedure.)
    Minitab accepts data in two different forms for performing ANOVA, *stacked* or *unstacked*. *Unstacked* refers to the data of

ANOVA (Stacked)

Step 1   Enter the **GPA** data for all three groups in C1 and the values for the categorical variable **Dorm** in C2.
Step 2   Click on **Stat > ANOVA > One-Way**.

ANOVA (Unstacked)

Step 1   Enter the Dormitory A data in **C1**, the Dormitory B data in **C2**, and the Dormitory C data in **C3**.
Step 2   Click **Stat > ANOVA > One-Way (Unstacked)**.

Finding the *p*-Value for a Given F_{data}
(Example 12.4, page 595, is used to illustrate the procedure.)
p-value = $P(F > F_{data})$ = $P(F > 0.8370997079)$, where $df_1 = 2$ and $df_2 = 27$.
Step 1   Click **Calc > Probability Distributions > F**.
Step 2   Select **Cumulative Probability**, enter **2** for **Numerator degrees of freedom** and **27** for **Denominator degrees of freedom**.
Step 3   Select **Input Constant**, enter **0.8370997079**, and click **OK**.

CRUNCHIT!

One-Way ANOVA
We will use the data from Example 12.5.
Step 1   Click **File** . . . then highlight **Load from Larose 2e** . . . **Chapter 12** . . . and click on **Example 12.5**.

Finding the *p*-Value for a Given F_{data}.
(Example 12.4, page 595, is used to illustrate the procedure.)
p-value = $P(F > F_{data})$ = $P(F > 0.8370997079)$, where $df_1 = 2$ and $df_2 = 27$.
Step 1   Select cell **A1**. Click the **Insert Function** icon f_x.
Step 2   For **Search for a Function**, type **FDIST** and click **OK**.
Step 3   For **X**, enter **0.8370997079**, for **Deg_freedom 1**, enter **2**, and for **Deg_freedom 2**, enter **27**. Then click **OK**. The cell now contains the *p*-value: 0.4438929572.

each group being in a separate column. *Stacked* merges each group's data together in a single column, with the group numbers in a different column.

Step 3   Choose the quantitative variable **GPA** as your **response** and the categorical variable **Dorm** as your **factor**. Then click **OK**.

Step 3   For **Responses (in separate columns)**, select columns C1–C3 and click **OK**.

Step 4   Minitab then displays the cumulative probability $P(F < 0.8370997079) = 0.5561070428$. This cumulative probability represents the area to the left of 0.8370997079 (the unshaded area in Figure 12.7, page 596). Since the entire area under the curve equals 1, to get the *p*-value we need to subtract $P(F < 0.8370997079) = 0.5561070428$ from 1:

$$\text{\textit{p}-value} = P(F > 0.8370997079) = 1 - P(F < 0.8370997079)$$
$$= 1 - 0.5561070428 = 0.4438929572$$

Step 2   Click **Statistics** and select **ANOVA . . . One-way**. Choose the **Columns** tab. Select each of the available columns and click **Calculate**.

Section 12.1 Summary

1 Analysis of variance (ANOVA) is an inferential method for testing whether the means of different populations are equal. The null hypothesis always states that all the population means are equal, and the alternative hypothesis always states that not all the population means are equal. ANOVA works by comparing (a) the variability in the sample means and (b) the variability within each sample. If (a) is large *compared with* (b), this is evidence that the true means are not all equal and we should reject the null hypothesis.

2 ANOVA is usually performed using the *p*-value method and technology.

Section 12.1 Exercises

CLARIFYING THE CONCEPTS

1. Does the overall sample mean always equal the mean of the sample means? Explain.
2. What does MSTR measure? What does MSE measure?
3. In your own words, explain how ANOVA works.
4. What are the required conditions for performing an analysis of variance?
5. A comparison dotplot of the SAT scores of three sororities shows no overlap at all between the groups. Does this represent evidence for or against the null hypothesis that all population means are equal?
6. True or false: If we reject the null hypothesis in an analysis of variance, then there is evidence that all the population mean sizes are different. If the statement is false, explain why it is false.

PRACTICING THE TECHNIQUES

For Exercises 7–10, calculate the following measures.
  a. df_1 and df_2
  b. $\bar{\bar{x}}$
  c. SSTR
  d. SSE
  e. SST

7.

Sample A	Sample B	Sample C
$\bar{x}_A = 10$	$\bar{x}_B = 12$	$\bar{x}_C = 8$
$s_A = 1$	$s_B = 1$	$s_C = 1$
$n_A = 5$	$n_B = 5$	$n_C = 5$

8.

Sample A	Sample B	Sample C	Sample D
$\bar{x}_A = 10$	$\bar{x}_B = 12$	$\bar{x}_C = 8$	$\bar{x}_D = 14$
$s_A = 1$	$s_B = 1$	$s_C = 1$	$s_D = 1$
$n_A = 5$	$n_B = 5$	$n_C = 5$	$n_D = 5$

9.

Sample A	Sample B	Sample C	Sample D
$\bar{x}_A = 50$	$\bar{x}_B = 75$	$\bar{x}_C = 100$	$\bar{x}_D = 125$
$s_A = 5$	$s_B = 4$	$s_C = 6$	$s_D = 5$
$n_A = 100$	$n_B = 150$	$n_C = 200$	$n_D = 250$

10.

Sample A	Sample B	Sample C	Sample D
$\bar{x}_A = 0$	$\bar{x}_B = 10$	$\bar{x}_C = 20$	$\bar{x}_D = 10$
$s_A = 1.5$	$s_B = 2.25$	$s_C = 1.75$	$s_D = 2.0$
$n_A = 50$	$n_B = 100$	$n_C = 50$	$n_D = 100$

In Exercises 11–14, refer to the exercises cited and calculate the following measures.
  a. MSTR
  b. MSE
  c. F_{data}
  d. Construct the ANOVA table.

11. Exercise 7
12. Exercise 8
13. Exercise 9
14. Exercise 10

For Exercises 15–22, assume that the ANOVA assumptions are verified.
  For Exercises 15–18, test whether the population means differ, using $\alpha = 0.05$.
    a. State the hypotheses and the rejection rule.
    b. Calculate F_{data}. (*Hint:* You already calculated F_{data} in Exercises 11–14).
    c. Find the p-value.
    d. Compare the p-value with $\alpha = 0.05$. State the conclusion and the interpretation.

15. Data from Exercises 7 and 11
16. Data from Exercises 8 and 12
17. Data from Exercises 9 and 13
18. Data from Exercises 10 and 14
19. Part of an ANOVA table for an analysis of variance involving seven groups for a study follows. Each sample contained ten data values.

Source of variation	Sum of squares	Degrees of freedom	Mean square	F
Treatment	120	___	___	___
Error	315	___	___	
Total	___			

  a. Find all six missing values in the table and fill in the blanks.
  b. Perform the appropriate hypothesis test using $\alpha = 0.05$.

20. Part of an ANOVA table for an analysis of variance involving three groups follows. Each sample contained six data values.

Source of variation	Sum of squares	Degrees of freedom	Mean square	F
Treatment	___	___	___	___
Error	90	___	___	
Total	150			

  a. Find all six missing values in the table.
  b. Perform the appropriate hypothesis test using $\alpha = 0.01$.

21. Part of an ANOVA table follows.

Source of variation	Sum of squares	Degrees of freedom	Mean square	F
Treatment	___	4	10	1.0
Error	___	___	___	
Total	440			

a. Find all four missing values in the table and fill in the blanks.

b. Perform the appropriate hypothesis test using $\alpha = 0.10$.

22. Part of an ANOVA table follows.

Source of variation	Sum of squares	Degrees of freedom	Mean square	F
Treatment	___	2	___	2.0
Error	480	___	24	
Total	___			

a. Find all four missing values in the table and fill in the blanks.

b. Perform the appropriate hypothesis test using $\alpha = 0.05$.

APPLYING THE CONCEPTS

For Exercises 23–26, assume that the data are independently drawn random samples from normal populations.

a. Verify the equal-variance assumption.

b. Calculate the following measures.
   i. df_1 and df_2 ii. $\bar{\bar{x}}$ iii. SSTR iv. SSE
   v. SST vi. MSTR vii. MSE viii. F_{data}

c. Construct the ANOVA table.

d. Perform the appropriate one-way ANOVA using level of significance $\alpha = 0.05$.

23. Online, Hybrid, and Traditional Classrooms. A researcher randomly selected six students from each of three different treatment groups. The first group of students took elementary statistics online. The second group of students took the same course in the traditional in-class way. The third group of students took a hybrid course, which met once each week and also had an online component. The table shows the grade results. Researchers are interested in whether significant differences exist among the mean grades for the three groups. 🔊 **statclass**

Online grades	Traditional grades	Hybrid grades
70	75	95
75	75	60
60	95	90
90	60	75
85	60	85
50	80	75
$\bar{x} = 71.6667$	$\bar{x} = 74.1667$	$\bar{x} = 80$
$s = 15.0555$	$s = 13.1972$	$s = 12.6491$

24. Store Sales. The district sales manager would like to determine whether there are significant differences in the mean sales among the four franchise stores in her district. Sales (in thousands of dollars) were tracked over 5 days at each of the four stores. The resulting data are summarized in the following table. 🔊 **storesales**

Store A sales	Store B sales	Store C sales	Store D sales
10	20	3	30
15	20	7	25
10	25	5	30
20	15	10	35
20	20	4	30
$\bar{x} = 15$	$\bar{x} = 20$	$\bar{x} = 5.8$	$\bar{x} = 30$
$s = 5$	$s = 3.5355$	$s = 2.7749$	$s = 3.5355$

25. Education and Religious Background. The General Social Survey collected data on the number of years of education and the religious preference of the respondent. The summary statistics are shown here.

	n	Mean	Std. deviation
Protestant	1660	13.10	2.87
Catholic	683	13.51	2.74
Jewish	68	15.37	2.80
None	339	13.52	3.22
Other	141	14.46	3.18

26. The Full Moon and Emergency Room Visits. Is there a difference in emergency room visits before, during, and after a full moon? A study looked at the admission rate (number of patients per day) to the emergency room of a Virginia mental health clinic over a series of 12 full moons.[2] The data are provided in the table. Is there evidence of a difference in emergency room visits before, during, and after the full moon? 🔊 **fullmoon**

Before		During		After	
6.4	11.5	5	13	5.8	13.5
7.1	13.8	13	16	9.2	13.1
6.5	15.4	14	25	7.9	15.8
8.6	15.7	12	14	7.7	13.3
8.1	11.7	6	14	11.0	12.8
10.4	15.8	9	20	12.9	14.5

27. ANOVA Can Be Applied to Two Populations. Researchers are interested in whether the mean heart rates of women and men differ. The following table provides summary statistics of random samples of pulse rates drawn from groups of women and men.

a. Test using $\alpha = 0.05$ whether the population mean pulse rates differ.

b. Which method of inference from an earlier chapter could we also use to solve this problem?

	Females	Males
n	65	65
$\bar{x}$	98.384	98.104
s	0.743	0.699

Do Taller People Have Lower Voices? Use this information for Exercises 28 and 29. The heights of the members of the

New York Choral Society were recorded.[3] Choral singers are roughly divided into four groups, from highest-pitched voices to lowest: sopranos, altos (usually female), tenors, and basses (usually male). Assume that the assumptions are satisfied.

28. What Result Might We Expect? The comparison boxplot of the heights is shown here. Is there evidence for differences in the population mean heights?

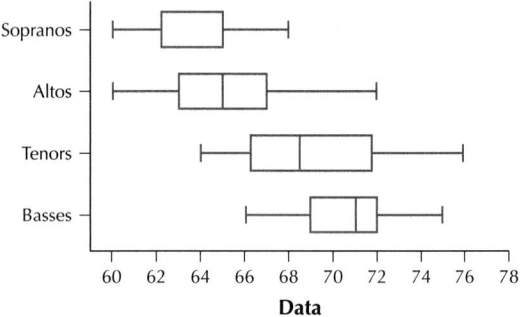

29. The summary statistics are shown here. Test at $\alpha = 0.01$ whether the population mean heights of the groups differ.

Variable	n	Mean	StDev
Sopranos	36	64.250	1.873
Altos	35	64.886	2.795
Tenors	20	69.150	3.216
Basses	39	70.718	2.361

Breakfast Cereals. Use this information for Exercises 30–33. Does the nutritional rating of breakfast cereals vary by manufacturer? The data set **breakfast cereals 2** contains information on the nutritional rating and manufacturer for 68 breakfast cereals.[4] Assume that the cereals were selected randomly from the manufacturers so that the selection of a cereal from one manufacturer did not affect the selection of cereals from other manufacturers. 🖲 **breakfastcereals2**

30. What Result Might We Expect? The comparison boxplot of the nutritional ratings is shown here. Assume that the normality condition is satisfied.

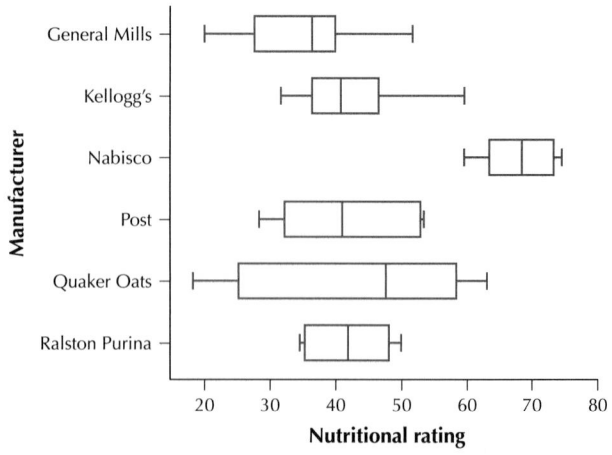

a. Explain whether the plot may be considered evidence for or against the null hypothesis that all population mean nutritional ratings were equal.

b. Would we expect the null hypothesis to be rejected or not to be rejected?

31. The largest standard deviation is $s_{\text{Quaker Oats}} = 10.603$, while the smallest is $s_{\text{Nabisco}} = 5.509$. State whether the equal-variance requirement is satisfied.

32. Is the independence assumption validated? Why?

33. The Minitab output shown here contains the ANOVA results. F_{data} and the p-value are in boldface. Test using level of significance $\alpha = 0.05$ whether all population mean nutritional ratings are equal across all manufacturers.

```
Source         DF       SS       MS       F      P
Manufacturer    5   5717.7   1143.5   15.71  0.000
Error          62   4511.7     72.8
Total          67  10229.4

S = 8.531    R-Sq = 55.89%    R-Sq(adj) = 52.34%

Level            N     Mean    StDev
General Mills   22   34.486    8.947
Kelloggs        17   41.761    8.102
Nabisco          6   67.969    5.509
Post             9   41.706   10.048
Quaker Oats      6   50.569   10.603
Ralston Purina   8   41.543    6.081
```

⟨?⟩ Online, Hybrid, and Traditional Classrooms. Refer to Exercise 23. Without redoing the calculations and without rerunning the ANOVA, answer **(a)** and **(b)** for Exercises 34 and 35.

a. How would each of the following changes affect each statistic in the ANOVA table? Would it increase the statistic, decrease it, or leave it unaffected. Why?

b. How would each change affect the conclusion and why? (If there is insufficient information in a particular case to respond properly, indicate so.)

34. *What if* the 50 recorded for the sixth online student should really be 100.

35. *What if* each of the online scores is 10 points lower than indicated.

⟨?⟩ 36. Store Sales. Refer to Exercise 24. *What if* the data are all wrong and all the stores actually have a sample mean sales of $30,000. Try to answer the following questions without touching your calculator.

a. Find the value of SSTR, MSTR, and F_{data}.

b. What would be the p-value of the ANOVA hypothesis test?

c. What would be the conclusion?

BRINGING IT ALL TOGETHER
Gas Mileage for European, Japanese, and American Cars. Use this information for Exercises 37–39. The following figure shows a comparison boxplot of

the vehicle mileage (in mpg) for random samples of automobiles manufactured in Europe, Japan, and the United States. The summary statistics are provided. We are interested in testing using $\alpha = 0.01$ whether population mean gas mileage differs among automobiles from the three regions. Assume that the assumptions are satisfied.

MPG	Sample 1: Europe	Sample 2: Japan	Sample 3: USA
Sample mean	$\bar{x}_1 = 27.603$	$\bar{x}_2 = 30.451$	$\bar{x}_3 = 20.033$
Sample standard deviation	$s_1 = 6.58$	$s_2 = 6.09$	$s_3 = 6.440$
Sample size	$n_1 = 68$	$n_2 = 79$	$n_3 = 245$

37. What Result Might We Expect?
   a. Based on the graphical evidence in the comparison boxplot, what might be the conclusion? Explain your reasoning.
   b. Perform the ANOVA, using whichever method you prefer.
   c. Is your intuition from (a) supported?

38. Confidence Intervals as Further Clues in ANOVA. Refer to Exercise 37. Suppose we construct a confidence interval for each of the population means. If at least one confidence interval does not overlap the others, then it is evidence against the null hypothesis.
   a. Use a *t* interval from Section 8.2 to construct a 99% confidence interval for the population mean gas mileage of
      i. European cars
      ii. Japanese cars
      iii. American cars
   b. Is there one confidence interval from (a) that does not overlap the other two? If so, what does this mean in terms of the null hypothesis that all the population means are equal?

39. Refer to the table of descriptive summaries of vehicle mileage. *What if* we discovered that we made a mistake in the data collection and that every Japanese vehicle tested actually had 1 mpg higher gas mileage than previously recorded. Explain how and why this change would affect the following measures—increase, decrease, or no change.

a. *n*   f. MSTR
b. *k*   g. MSE
c. SSTR   h. F_{data}
d. SSE   i. *p*-value
e. SST   j. Conclusion

For Exercises 40–43, use the **Crash** data set, which contains information about the severity of injuries sustained by crash dummies when the National Transportation Safety Board crashed automobiles into a wall at 35 miles per hour.

40. Head Injuries and Vehicle Size. The variable *head_inj* contains a measure of the severity of the head injury sustained by crash dummies. The variable *size2* categorizes the type of vehicle, such as light, medium, heavy, pickup truck, MPV (SUV), and so on. The values of the variable *size2* are as follows: 1 = compact car, 2 = light car, 3 = medium car, 4 = heavy car, 5 = minicompact car, 6 = van, 7 = pickup truck, and 8 = MPV (SUV). Would you expect the population mean severity of head injuries suffered by the dummies to be the same across all the size categories? Use technology to perform the analysis of variance, using $\alpha = 0.05$. Comment on the results. **crash**

41. Head Injuries and Vehicle Year. The variable *year* indicates the model year of the vehicle (1987–1991). Would you expect the population mean severity of head injuries suffered by the dummies to be the same across all model years? Use technology to perform the analysis of variance, using $\alpha = 0.05$. Comment on the results.

42. Chest Injury and Protection Device. The variable *chest_in* is a measure of the severity of the chest injury suffered by the crash dummy. The variable *protect2* categorizes the type of protection that the vehicle offers: 1 = manual seat belts, 2 = motorized seat belts, 3 = passive seat belts, 4 = dual air bags. Would you expect the population mean severity of chest injuries suffered by the dummies to be the same for all categories of protection? Use technology to perform the analysis of variance, using $\alpha = 0.01$. Comment on the results.

43. Refer to Exercise 42. Now use $\alpha = 0.05$. How does this affect your conclusion?

Use the *Analysis of Variance* applet for Exercises 44 and 45.

44. Move the group means so that they are about the same by clicking and dragging the black dots so that they are about even horizontally.
   a. What happens to the value of F (F_{data})?
   b. Explain why this happens, using the concept of between-sample variability and the statistics SSTR, MSTR, and F_{data}.

45. Click **Reset**. Increase the **Within-Sample Variability.**
   a. What happens to the value of F (F_{data})?
   b. Explain why this change happens, using the concept of within-sample variability and the statistics SSE, MSE, and F_{data}.

12.2 Multiple Comparisons

OBJECTIVES By the end of this section, I will be able to . . .

1 Perform multiple comparisons tests using the Bonferroni method.

2 Use Tukey's test to perform multiple comparisons.

3 Use confidence intervals to perform multiple comparisons for Tukey's test.

Recall Example 12.5, where we rejected the null hypothesis that the population mean time spent in the open-ended sections of a maze was the same for three groups of genetically altered mice. But so far we have not tested to find out which pairs of population means are significantly different.

Level	N	Mean	StDev
Group 0	15	19.387	9.029
Group 1	15	8.660	6.028
Group 2	15	8.620	6.402

FIGURE 12.19 Summary statistics for three groups of mice.

Figure 12.19 indicates that the sample mean time for Group 0 $\bar{x}_{Group\ 0} = 19.387$ was much larger than the sample means of the other groups $\bar{x}_{Group\ 1} = 8.660$ or $\bar{x}_{Group\ 2} = 8.620$. Since $\bar{x}_{Group\ 0} > \bar{x}_{Group\ 1}$, and since the ANOVA test produced evidence that the three population means are not equal, we are tempted to conclude that $\mu_{Group\ 0} > \mu_{Group\ 1}$. But we cannot formally draw such a conclusion based on the one-way ANOVA results alone. Instead, we need to perform **multiple comparisons.**

> **Multiple Comparisons**
>
> Once an ANOVA result has been found significant (the null hypothesis is rejected) **multiple comparisons** procedures seek to *determine which pairs of population means are significantly different.* Multiple comparisons are not performed if the ANOVA null hypothesis has not been rejected.

We shall learn three multiple comparisons procedures: the *Bonferroni method, Tukey's test,* and *Tukey's test using confidence intervals.*

1 Performing Multiple Comparisons Tests Using the Bonferroni Method

In Section 10.2, we learned about the independent sample t test for determining whether pairs of population means were significantly different. We shall do something similar here, except that (a) the formula for test statistic t_{data} is different from the one in Section 10.2, and (b) we need to apply the **Bonferroni adjustment** to the p-value.

Denote the number of population means as k. In general, there are

$$c = ({}_kC_2) = \frac{k!}{2!(k-2)!}$$

possible *pairs* of means to compare; that is, there are c **pairwise comparisons.** For $k = 3$ there are $c = ({}_3C_2) = \frac{3!}{2!(3-2)!} = 3$ comparisons, and for $k = 4$ means there are $c = ({}_4C_2) = \frac{4!}{2!(3-2)!} = 6$ comparisons. Since we rejected the null hypothesis in Example 12.5, we are interested in *which pairs of population means are significantly different.* There are $c = 3$ hypothesis tests:

- $H_0 : \mu_{Group\ 0} = \mu_{Group\ 1}$ versus $H_a : \mu_{Group\ 0} \neq \mu_{Group\ 1}$
- $H_0 : \mu_{Group\ 0} = \mu_{Group\ 2}$ versus $H_a : \mu_{Group\ 0} \neq \mu_{Group\ 2}$
- $H_0 : \mu_{Group\ 1} = \mu_{Group\ 2}$ versus $H_a : \mu_{Group\ 1} \neq \mu_{Group\ 2}$

Suppose each of these three *pairwise hypothesis tests* is carried out using a level of significance $\alpha = 0.05$. Then the **experimentwise error rate,** that is, the probability of making at least one Type I error in these three hypothesis tests is

$$\alpha_{EW} = 1 - (1 - \alpha)^3 = 0.142625$$

Recall that a Type I error is rejecting the null hypothesis when it is true.

which is approximately three times larger than $\alpha = 0.05$. The *Bonferroni adjustment* corrects for this as follows.

> **The Bonferroni Adjustment**
> - When performing multiple comparisons, the **experimentwise error rate** α_{EW} is the probability of making at least one Type I error in the set of hypothesis tests.
> - α_{EW} is always greater than the comparison level of significance α by a factor approximately equal to the number of comparisons being made.
> - Thus, the **Bonferroni adjustment** corrects for the experimentwise error rate by multiplying the *p*-value of each pairwise hypothesis test by the number of comparisons being made. If the Bonferroni-adjusted *p*-value is greater than 1, then set the adjusted value equal to 1.

For example, when we test $H_0 : \mu_{\text{Group 0}} = \mu_{\text{Group 1}}$ versus $H_a : \mu_{\text{Group 0}} \neq \mu_{\text{Group 1}}$, the Bonferroni adjustment says to multiply the resulting *p*-value by $c = 3$. Example 12.7 shows how to use Bonferroni method of multiple comparisons.

Example 12.7   Bonferroni method of multiple comparisons

Use the Bonferroni method of multiple comparisons to determine which pairs of population mean times differ, for the mice in Groups 0, 1, and 2 in Example 12.5. Use level of significance $\alpha = 0.01$.

Solution

The Bonferroni method requires that

- the requirements for ANOVA have been met, and
- the null hypothesis that the population means are all equal has been rejected.

In Example 12.5 we verified both requirements.

Step 1 **For each of the c hypothesis tests, state the hypotheses and the rejection rule.** There are $k = 3$ means, so there will be $c = 3$ hypothesis tests. Our hypotheses are

- Test 1: $H_0 : \mu_{\text{Group 0}} = \mu_{\text{Group 1}}$ versus $H_a : \mu_{\text{Group 0}} \neq \mu_{\text{Group 1}}$
- Test 2: $H_0 : \mu_{\text{Group 0}} = \mu_{\text{Group 2}}$ versus $H_a : \mu_{\text{Group 0}} \neq \mu_{\text{Group 2}}$
- Test 3: $H_0 : \mu_{\text{Group 1}} = \mu_{\text{Group 2}}$ versus $H_a : \mu_{\text{Group 1}} \neq \mu_{\text{Group 2}}$

where μ_i represents the population mean time spent in the open-ended sections of the maze, for the ith group. For each hypothesis test, reject H_0 if the *Bonferroni-adjusted p-value* $\leq \alpha = 0.01$.

Step 2 **Calculate t_{data} for each hypothesis test.** From Figure 12.11 on page 597, we have the mean square error from the original ANOVA as MSE $= 52.9485079$ and from Figure 12.19 we get the sample means and the sample sizes. Thus:

- Test 1:

$$t_{\text{data}} = \frac{\bar{x}_{\text{Group 0}} - \bar{x}_{\text{Group 1}}}{\sqrt{\text{MSE} \cdot \left(\dfrac{1}{n_{\text{Group 0}}} + \dfrac{1}{n_{\text{Group 1}}} \right)}} = \frac{19.387 - 8.660}{\sqrt{(52.9485079)\left(\dfrac{1}{15} + \dfrac{1}{15} \right)}} \approx 4.037$$

- Test 2:

$$t_{\text{data}} = \frac{\bar{x}_{\text{Group 0}} - \bar{x}_{\text{Group 2}}}{\sqrt{\text{MSE} \cdot \dfrac{1}{n_{\text{Group 0}}} + \dfrac{1}{n_{\text{Group 2}}}}} = \frac{19.387 - 8.620}{\sqrt{(52.9485079)\left(\dfrac{1}{15} + \dfrac{1}{15} \right)}} \approx 4.052$$

- Test 3:

$$t_{\text{data}} = \frac{\bar{x}_{\text{Group 1}} - \bar{x}_{\text{Group 2}}}{\sqrt{\text{MSE} \cdot \left(\frac{1}{n_{\text{Group 1}}} + \frac{1}{n_{\text{Group 2}}}\right)}} = \frac{8.660 - 8.620}{\sqrt{(52.9485079)\left(\frac{1}{15} + \frac{1}{15}\right)}} \approx 0.015$$

When the requirements are met, t_{data} follows a t distribution with $n_T - k = 45 - 3 = 42$ degrees of freedom, where n_T represents the total sample size.

f_x	=TDIST(4.037,42,2)
D	E
tdata	pvalue
4.037	0.000225
4.052	0.000215
0.015	0.988103

FIGURE 12.20 Unadjusted p-values from Excel.

Step 3 **Find the Bonferroni-adjusted p-value for each hypothesis test.** Figure 12.20 shows the *unadjusted* p-values for the values of t_{data} from Step 2, using the function **tdist (t_{data}, df, 2)**, where df $= 42$ and the 2 represents a two-tailed test. Then the *Bonferroni-adjusted p-value* $= c \cdot (p\text{-value}) = 3 \cdot (p\text{-value})$, for each hypothesis test.
- Test 1: Bonferroni-adjusted p-value $= 3 \cdot 0.000225 = 0.000675$.
- Test 2: Bonferroni-adjusted p-value $= 3 \cdot 0.000215 = 0.000645$.
- Test 3: Bonferroni-adjusted p-value $= 3 \cdot 0.988103 = 2.964309$, but since this value exceeds 1, we set this p-value equal to 1.

Step 4 **For each hypothesis test, state the conclusion and the interpretation.**
- Test 1: The adjusted p-value $= 0.000675$, which is ≤ 0.01; therefore, reject H_0. There is evidence at the 0.01 level of significance that the population mean time spent in the open-ended part of the maze differs between Group 0 and Group 1.
- Test 2: The adjusted p-value $= 0.000645$, which is ≤ 0.01; therefore, reject H_0. There is evidence at the 0.01 level of significance that the population mean time differs between Group 0 and Group 2.
- Test 3: The adjusted p-value $= 1$, which is not ≤ 0.01; therefore, do not reject H_0. There is insufficient evidence at the 0.01 level of significance that the population mean time differs between Group 1 and Group 2. ■

Now You Can Do
Exercises 9–16.

2 Tukey's Test for Multiple Comparisons

We may also use Tukey's test to determine which pairs of population means are significantly different. Tukey's test was developed by John Tukey, whom we met earlier as the developer of the stem-and-leaf display. We illustrate the steps for Tukey's method using an example.

Example 12.8 Tukey's test for multiple comparisons

In the Case Study on page 599, we tested whether the population mean student motivation scores were equal for the three types of professor self-disclosure on Facebook: high, medium, and low. Figure 12.17 on page 600 contains the ANOVA results, for which we rejected the null hypothesis of equal population mean scores. Use Tukey's method to determine which pairs of population means are significantly different, using level of significance $\alpha = 0.05$.

Solution

Tukey's method has the same requirements as the Bonferroni method:
- the requirements for ANOVA have been met, and
- the null hypothesis that the population means are all equal has been rejected.
In the Case Study, both requirements were verified.

Step 1 **For each of the c hypothesis tests, state the hypotheses.** There are $k = 3$ means, so there will be $c = 3$ hypothesis tests. Our hypotheses are:

- Test 1: $H_0: \mu_{High} = \mu_{Medium}$ versus $H_a: \mu_{High} \neq \mu_{Medium}$
- Test 2: $H_0: \mu_{High} = \mu_{Low}$ versus $H_a: \mu_{High} \neq \mu_{Low}$
- Test 3: $H_0: \mu_{Medium} = \mu_{Low}$ versus $H_a: \mu_{Medium} \neq \mu_{Low}$

where μ_i represents the population mean score, for the ith category.

Step 2 **Find the Tukey critical value q_{crit} and state the rejection rule.** The total sample size is $n_T = 43 + 44 + 43 = 130$. Use experimentwise error rate $\alpha_{EW} = 0.05$, degrees of freedom df $= n_T - k = 130 - 3 = 127$, and k = number of population means $= 3$. Using the table of Tukey critical values (Table H in the Appendix), we seek df $= 127$ on the left, but, not finding it, conservatively choose df $= 120$. Then, in the column for $k = 3$, we find the Tukey critical value $q_{crit} = 3.356$ (Figure 12.21). The rejection rule for the Tukey method is "Reject H_0 if $q_{data} \geq q_{crit}$," that is, Reject H_0 if $q_{data} \geq 3.356$.

Step 3 **Calculate the Tukey test statistic q_{data} for each hypothesis test.** From Figure 12.17 on page 600, we get the sample means, the sample sizes, and the mean square error MSE $= 168$. Thus:

- Test 1:

$$q_{data} = \frac{\bar{x}_{High} - \bar{x}_{Medium}}{\sqrt{\frac{MSE}{2} \cdot \left(\frac{1}{n_{High}} + \frac{1}{n_{Medium}}\right)}} = \frac{81.09 - 79.36}{\sqrt{\left(\frac{168}{2}\right)\left(\frac{1}{43} + \frac{1}{44}\right)}} \approx 0.880$$

- Test 2:

$$q_{data} = \frac{\bar{x}_{High} - \bar{x}_{Low}}{\sqrt{\frac{MSE}{2} \cdot \left(\frac{1}{n_{High}} + \frac{1}{n_{Low}}\right)}} = \frac{81.09 - 70.63}{\sqrt{\left(\frac{168}{2}\right)\left(\frac{1}{43} + \frac{1}{43}\right)}} \approx 5.292$$

- Test 3:

$$q_{data} = \frac{\bar{x}_{Medium} - \bar{x}_{Low}}{\sqrt{\frac{MSE}{2} \cdot \left(\frac{1}{n_{Medium}} + \frac{1}{n_{Low}}\right)}} = \frac{79.36 - 70.63}{\sqrt{\left(\frac{168}{2}\right)\left(\frac{1}{44} + \frac{1}{43}\right)}} \approx 4.442$$

Step 4 **For each hypothesis test, state the conclusion and the interpretation.**
- Test 1: $q_{data} = 0.880$, which is not $\geq q_{crit} = 3.356$; therefore, do not reject H_0. There is insufficient evidence at the 0.05 level of significance that the population mean student motivation scores differ between professors having high and medium self-disclosure on Facebook.
- Test 2: $q_{data} = 5.292$, which is $\geq q_{crit} = 3.356$; therefore, reject H_0. There is evidence at the 0.05 level of significance that the population mean scores differ between high and low professor self-disclosure on Facebook.
- Test 3: $q_{data} = 4.442$, which is $\geq q_{crit} = 3.356$; therefore, reject H_0. There is evidence at the 0.05 level of significance that the population mean scores differ between medium and low professor self-disclosure on Facebook.

This set of three hypothesis tests has an experimentwise error rate $\alpha_{EW} = 0.05$. ∎

$\alpha_{EW} = 0.05$			
df	k	2	3
1		17.97	26.98
2		6.085	8.331
120		2.800	3.356

FIGURE 12.21 Finding the Tukey critical value q_{crit}.

When calculating the numerator of q_{data} for each pairwise comparison, be sure to subtract the smaller value of $\bar{x}$ from the larger value of $\bar{x}$, so that the value of q_{data} is positive.

Now You Can Do
Exercises 17–26.

3 Using Confidence Intervals to Perform Tukey's Test

Tukey's test for multiple comparisons may also be performed using confidence intervals and technology. Recall that when using confidence intervals for hypothesis tests, H_0 is rejected if the hypothesized value of the population mean does not fall inside the confidence interval.

> **Rejection Rule for Using Confidence Intervals to Perform Tukey's Test**
>
> If a $100(1 - \alpha)\%$ confidence interval for $\mu_1 - \mu_2$ contains zero, then at level of significance α we do not reject the null hypothesis $H_0 : \mu_1 = \mu_2$. If the interval does not contain zero, then we do reject H_0.

We illustrate using confidence intervals to perform Tukey's test with an example using the Facebook data.

Example 12.9 Using confidence intervals to perform Tukey's test

Use the 95% confidence intervals for the differences in population means provided by Minitab to perform Tukey's test for multiple comparisons on the Facebook data.

Solution

We use the steps in the Step-by-Step Technology Guide provided at the end of this section. Figure 12.22 contains the output from Minitab showing 95% confidence intervals for the differences in population means for the high, medium, and low professor disclosure levels. The output states that "Group = Low" is being subtracted from the other two groups, meaning that, the first two confidence intervals are for $\mu_{\text{Medium}} - \mu_{\text{Low}}$ and $\mu_{\text{High}} - \mu_{\text{Low}}$. Later, "Group = Medium" is subtracted from the high group, indicating a confidence interval for $\mu_{\text{High}} - \mu_{\text{Medium}}$. The column headings "Lower" and "Upper" represent the lower and upper bounds of the confidence interval.

```
Tukey 95% Simultaneous Confidence Intervals
All Pairwise Comparisons among Levels of Group

Individual confidence level = 98.06%

Group = Low subtracted from:

Group   Lower   Center   Upper    --+---------+---------+---------+-----
Medium   2.14    8.74    15.33                    (-------*-------)
High     3.84   10.47    17.09                     (-------*-------)
                                   --+---------+---------+---------+-----
                                   -7.0      0.0       7.0      14.0

Group = Medium subtracted from:

Group   Lower   Center   Upper    --+---------+---------+---------+-----
High    -4.86    1.73     8.32              (-------*-------)
                                   --+---------+---------+---------+-----
                                   -7.0      0.0       7.0      14.0
```

FIGURE 12.22 Using Minitab confidence intervals to perform Tukey's test.

Thus, for our $c = 3$ hypothesis tests we have

- Test 1: $H_0 : \mu_{\text{Medium}} = \mu_{\text{Low}}$ versus $H_a : \mu_{\text{Medium}} \neq \mu_{\text{Low}}$
  - 95% confidence interval for $\mu_{\text{Medium}} - \mu_{\text{Low}}$ is (2.14, 15.33), which does not contain zero, so we reject $H_0 : \mu_{\text{Medium}} = \mu_{\text{Low}}$ for level of significance $\alpha = 0.05$.
- Test 2: $H_0 : \mu_{\text{High}} = \mu_{\text{Low}}$ versus $H_a : \mu_{\text{High}} \neq \mu_{\text{Low}}$
  - 95% confidence interval for $\mu_{\text{High}} - \mu_{\text{Low}}$ is (3.84, 17.09), which does not contain zero, so we reject $H_0 : \mu_{\text{High}} = \mu_{\text{Low}}$ for level of significance $\alpha = 0.05$.

- Test 3: $H_0 : \mu_{\text{High}} = \mu_{\text{Medium}}$ versus $H_a : \mu_{\text{High}} \neq \mu_{\text{Medium}}$
  - 95% confidence interval for $\mu_{\text{High}} - \mu_{\text{Medium}}$ is $(-4.86, 8.32)$, which does contain zero, so we do not reject $H_0 : \mu_{\text{High}} = \mu_{\text{Medium}}$ for level of significance $\alpha = 0.05$.

Now You Can Do
Exercises 31 and 32.

Note that these conclusions are exactly the same as the conclusions from Example 12.8. ∎

STEP-BY-STEP TECHNOLOGY GUIDE: Multiple Comparisons

Neither the TI-83/84 nor Excel performs multiple comparisons.

MINITAB

Step 1 Enter the data for ANOVA into columns C1, C2, etc., as shown in the Section 12.1 technology guide on page 601.
Step 2 Select **Stat**, then **ANOVA**, then either **One way** or **One way (unstacked)**, depending on how you entered your data in Step 1.

Step 3 Click **Comparisons**, check **Tukey's**, and enter the **familywise (experimentwise) error rate** (such as "5" for $\alpha_{\text{EW}} = 0.05$). Click **OK** twice.

Section 12.2 Summary

1 Once an ANOVA result has been found, significant multiple comparisons procedures are performed to determine which pairs of population means are significantly different. The Bonferroni method uses the Bonferroni adjustment, which multiplies the p-value of each pairwise hypothesis test by the number of comparisons being made.

2 Tukey's test may be performed using the critical-value method, where the test statistic q_{data} is compared to the critical value q_{crit} for each hypothesis test.

3 Tukey's test may also be performed using confidence intervals and technology.

Section 12.2 Exercises

CLARIFYING THE CONCEPTS

1. Explain why we cannot conclude, based on the ANOVA results alone, that one particular population mean differs from another.

2. Clarify why we do not perform multiple comparisons if we did not reject the null hypothesis in the original ANOVA.

3. What is a pairwise comparison? Explain how we calculate how many pairwise comparisons there are.

4. What do we mean by experimentwise error rate?

5. How does the Bonferroni adjustment correct for the greater size of the experimentwise error rate?

6. What do we do if the Bonferroni adjustment results in an adjusted p-value greater than 1? Why must we do this?

7. What are the requirements for performing multiple comparisons using either the Bonferroni method or Tukey's test?

8. What is the rejection rule for using confidence intervals to perform Tukey's test?

PRACTICING THE TECHNIQUES

For Exercises 9–14, use the summary statistics to calculate the value of the test statistic t_{data} for the Bonferroni method.

9. $\bar{x}_1 = 85, \bar{x}_2 = 75$, MSE $= 25, n_1 = 10, n_2 = 10$
10. $\bar{x}_1 = 85, \bar{x}_3 = 65$, MSE $= 25, n_1 = 10, n_3 = 10$
11. $\bar{x}_2 = 75, \bar{x}_3 = 65$, MSE $= 25, n_2 = 10, n_3 = 10$
12. $\bar{x}_1 = 100, \bar{x}_2 = 105$, MSE $= 100, n_1 = 8, n_2 = 8$
13. $\bar{x}_1 = 100, \bar{x}_3 = 85$, MSE $= 100, n_1 = 8, n_3 = 8$
14. $\bar{x}_2 = 105, \bar{x}_3 = 85$, MSE $= 100, n_2 = 8, n_3 = 8$

For Exercises 15 and 16, perform multiple comparisons using the Bonferroni method at level of significance $\alpha = 0.05$, for the data indicated. Assume the requirements are met. Do the following:
  a. For each hypothesis test, state the hypotheses and the rejection rule.
  b. Use the value of t_{data} from Exercises 9–14 for each hypothesis test.

c. Find the Bonferroni-adjusted p-value for each hypothesis test.

d. For each hypothesis test, state the conclusion and the interpretation.

15. The data from Exercises 9–11

16. The data from Exercises 12–14

For Exercises 17–22, use the summary statistics to calculate the value of the test statistic q_{data} for Tukey's test.

17. $\bar{x}_1 = 60, \bar{x}_2 = 61, MSE = 100, n_1 = 50, n_2 = 50$

18. $\bar{x}_1 = 60, \bar{x}_3 = 65, MSE = 100, n_1 = 50, n_3 = 50$

19. $\bar{x}_2 = 61, \bar{x}_3 = 65, MSE = 100, n_2 = 50, n_3 = 50$

20. $\bar{x}_1 = 220, \bar{x}_2 = 200, MSE = 450, n_1 = 25, n_2 = 25$

21. $\bar{x}_1 = 220, \bar{x}_3 = 210, MSE = 450, n_1 = 25, n_3 = 25$

22. $\bar{x}_2 = 200, \bar{x}_3 = 210, MSE = 450, n_2 = 25, n_3 = 25$

For Exercises 23 and 24, find the critical value q_{crit}.

23. Experimentwise error rate $\alpha_{EW} = 0.05, n_1 = 50, n_2 = 50, n_3 = 50$

24. Experimentwise error rate $\alpha_{EW} = 0.05, n_1 = 25, n_2 = 25, n_3 = 25$

For Exercises 25 and 26, perform multiple comparisons using Tukey's test at experimentwise error rate $\alpha_{EW} = 0.05$, for the data indicated. Assume the requirements are met. Do the following.

a. For each hypothesis test, state the hypotheses.

b. Use the value of q_{crit} from Exercises 23 and 24, and state the rejection rule.

c. Use q_{data} from Exercises 17–22 for each hypothesis test.

d. For each hypothesis test, state the conclusion and the interpretation.

25. The data from Exercises 17–19

26. The data from Exercises 20–22

For Exercises 27 and 28, assume the ANOVA requirements are met. If appropriate, perform multiple comparisons using the Bonferroni method with individual level of significance $\alpha = 0.01$ for the indicated data. If not appropriate to perform multiple comparisons, state why not.

27. The data from Exercise 15, Section 12.1

28. The data from Exercise 16, Section 12.1

For Exercises 29 and 30, assume the ANOVA requirements are met. If appropriate, perform multiple comparisons using Tukey's test with experimentwise error rate $\alpha_{EW} = 0.05$ for the indicated data. If not appropriate to perform multiple comparisons, state why not.

29. The data from Exercise 17, Section 12.1

30. The data from Exercise 18, Section 12.1

For Exercises 31 and 32, use the indicated output to perform Tukey's test using the confidence interval method to determine if significant pairwise differences exist among the population means.

31. Minitab output in Figure 12.23, for groups A, B, and C

FIGURE 12.23

32. Minitab output in Figure 12.24

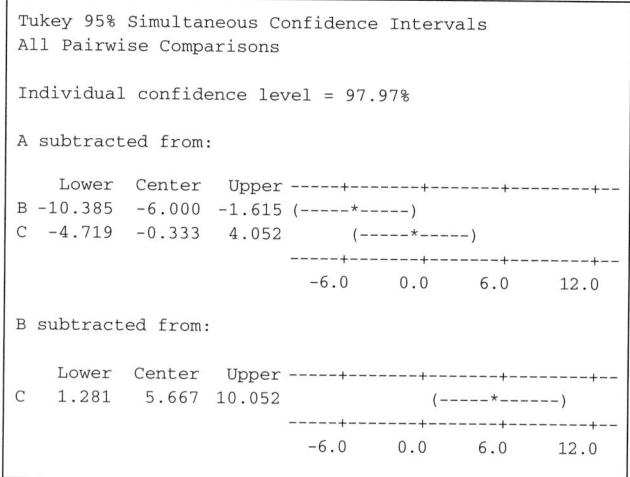

FIGURE 12.24

APPLYING THE CONCEPTS

For Exercises 33–36, assume the ANOVA requirements are met. If appropriate, perform multiple comparisons using the Bonferroni method with individual level of significance $\alpha = 0.01$ for the indicated data. If not appropriate to perform multiple comparisons, state why not.

33. The data from Exercise 23, Section 12.1

34. The data from Exercise 25, Section 12.1

35. The data from Exercise 29, Section 12.1

36. The data from Exercise 37, Section 12.1

For Exercises 37–40, assume the ANOVA requirements are met. If appropriate, perform multiple comparisons using Tukey's test with experimentwise error rate $\alpha_{EW} = 0.05$ for the indicated data. If not appropriate to perform multiple comparisons, state why not.

37. The data from Exercise 24, Section 12.1

38. The data from Exercise 26, Section 12.1

39. The data from Exercise 33, Section 12.1

40. The data from Exercise 40, Section 12.1

12.3   Randomized Block Design

OBJECTIVE   By the end of this section, I will be able to . . .

1   Explain the power of the randomized block design and perform a randomized block design ANOVA.

In the appropriate circumstances, we can use the **randomized block design** to improve the ability of the ANOVA to find significant differences among the treatment means. Suppose that a study was performed to determine whether significant differences existed among three types of educational methods: in-class learning, online learning, and the hybrid approach, which combines in-class and online learning. There were five courses taught in the study, and each course was taught using each method. For each course/method combination, the final exam average grade was calculated (see Table 12.6).

Table 12.6   Average final exam grade for five courses using three learning methods

| | | Learning Method | | |
		In-class	Online	Hybrid
Course	Statistics	75	70	69
	English	80	77	82
	Psychology	72	69	72
	Biology	73	60	66
	Communication	88	82	85

The researchers are not interested in the differences among the courses, only the difference in population mean performance among the learning methods. Thus, our *factor of interest* is the treatment variable learning methods, and our **blocking factor** is the variable course.

> Another common term for the blocking factor is *nuisance factor*, which may hint at why we are not interested in it.

A **blocking factor**, or **block**, is a variable that is not of primary interest to the researcher, but is included in the ANOVA in order to improve the ability of the ANOVA to find significant differences among the treatment means. In a **randomized block design ANOVA**, we test for differences among the treatment means, while accounting for the variability among the levels in the blocking factor.

Thus, in Table 12.6 the blocking factor *course* divides all the classes using a learning method into five blocks or courses.

We shall demonstrate the power of blocking by

1.   first performing a usual one-way ANOVA testing for differences among the learning methods, and then

2.   performing a *randomized block design* ANOVA, where we test for differences among the learning methods, while accounting for the variability among the courses (the blocks).

Example 12.10   One-way ANOVA unable to find significance

finalexam

Use technology to perform a one-way ANOVA using level of significance $\alpha = 0.05$ to determine whether the population mean test grades for the three learning methods are all the same.

Solution

If we ignore the blocking factor *course*, Table 12.6 becomes Table 12.7.

Table 12.7 Average final exam grade for the three learning methods without using the blocking factor *course*

	Learning Method	
In-Class	**Online**	**Hybrid**
75	70	69
80	77	82
72	69	72
73	60	66
88	82	85

Figure 12.25 shows acceptable normality, and the largest of the standard deviations in the ANOVA output in Figure 12.26 is not larger than twice the smallest.

FIGURE 12.25 Normal probability plots for the three learning methods.

Thus we may proceed with the ANOVA. The hypotheses are

$$H_0 : \mu_{\text{In-class}} = \mu_{\text{Online}} = \mu_{\text{Hybrid}} \quad \text{versus} \quad H_a : \text{not all the population means are equal}$$

Reject H_0 if the *p*-value ≤ 0.05.

```
One-way ANOVA: Grade versus Method

Source  DF       SS      MS      F      P
Method   2   90.133  45.067   0.74  0.497
Error   12  729.200  60.767
Total   14  819.333

S = 7.795   R-Sq = 11.00%   R-Sq(adj) = 0.00%

                              Individual 95% CIs For Mean
                              Based on Pooled StDev
Level  N    Mean   StDev  --+-------+-------+--------+----
1      5  77.600   6.580                (--------*----------)
2      5  71.600   8.385  (--------*----------)
3      5  74.800   8.289      (--------*--------)
                            --+-------+-------+--------+----
                            66.0    72.0    78.0     84.0
```

FIGURE 12.26
Minitab ANOVA output.

The *p*-value from Figure 12.26 is 0.497, which is not ≤ 0.05; therefore, we do not reject H_0. There is insufficient evidence at level of significance $\alpha = 0.05$ that the population mean test performance differs among the three learning methods. ■

Next, we use the randomized block design to account for the variability among the courses.

| Example 12.11 | Randomized block design uncovers the significant differences among the learning methods |

Use technology and the randomized block design (RBD) to test for differences among the population mean test grades, at level of significance $\alpha = 0.05$.

Solution

We use the Step-by-Step Technology Guide at the end of this section to run this analysis in Minitab. The hypotheses and the rejection rule are the same for RBD as they are for one-way ANOVA:

$$H_0: \mu_{\text{In-class}} = \mu_{\text{Online}} = \mu_{\text{Hybrid}} \quad \text{versus} \quad H_a: \text{ not all the population means are equal}$$

Reject H_0 if the p-value ≤ 0.05.

Figure 12.27 shows the Minitab output from the randomized block design. The factor of interest (that is, the treatment) is the learning method, while the blocking factor is the course. Note that there are two p-values, but we examine the p-value of the treatment only, not of the blocking factor.

Note that the p-value for the blocking factor is approximately zero, which means that the blocking factor is significant. But in the randomized block design we are not interested in the significance of the blocking factor. If we are interested in a second factor, we use *two-way ANOVA* in Section 12.4.

	Source	DF	SS	MS	F	P
Factor of Interest (Treatment) —— Method	2	90.133	45.067	6.95	0.018 ← *p*-value for treatment
Blocking Factor —— Course	4	677.333	169.333	26.12	0.000
	Error	8	51.867	6.483		
	Total	14	819.333			

FIGURE 12.27 Output for randomized block design.

Now You Can Do
Exercises 9–12.

The p-value for the factor of interest from Figure 12.27 is 0.018, which is ≤ 0.05; therefore, we reject H_0. There is evidence at level of significance $\alpha = 0.05$ that the population mean test grade differs among the three learning methods. ∎

Developing Your Statistical Sense

How Does Blocking Work?

Why did the randomized block design succeed in rejecting the null hypothesis, when the usual one-way ANOVA failed? From Section 12.1, we know that the following relationship exists among the three sums of squares:

$$\text{SST} = \text{SSTR} + \text{SSE}$$

Now, the sum of squares error (SSE) includes all unexplained variability, including random variation as well as the variability among the courses themselves. For example, note from Table 12.6 that the three values from the communication courses are all larger than the three values from the statistics courses. This represents variability, and becomes part of SSE when we perform the usual ANOVA. In other words, the variability in the courses makes SSE larger than it should be.

Why is a large SSE bad? Recall our F statistic from the ANOVA table (Table 12.3, page 593):

$$F = \frac{\text{MSTR}}{\text{MSE}} = \frac{\text{MSTR}}{\text{SSE}/df_2}$$

Recall that we reject H_0 when the p-value is small. Also note that

- The p-value is small only when F is large (see Figure 12.28);
- F is large when SSE is small.

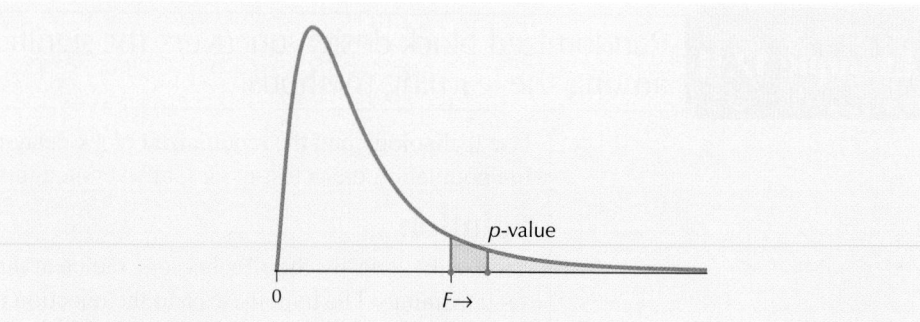

FIGURE 12.28 Larger $F \leftrightarrow$ smaller p-value.

So we would like to keep SSE small (as we would any type of error). The randomized block design reduces SSE by extracting the *sum of squares blocks* (SSB), which represents the variability among the groups in the blocking factor, such as the variability among the courses. This is done as follows. The SSE from the original one-way ANOVA is separated into the sum of two quantities:

$$\text{SSE}_{\text{one-way ANOVA}} = \text{SSB} + \text{SSE}_{\text{RBD}}$$

Since sums of squares are non-negative, the new SSE_{RBD} from the RBD will probably be smaller than the original $\text{SSE}_{\text{one-way ANOVA}}$, and thus F will become larger, leading to easier rejection of H_0. ◢

Example 12.12 Demonstrating how RBD works

Demonstrate how randomized block design works, using the results from Examples 12.10 and 12.11.

Solution

Figure 12.26 from Example 12.10 provides us with

$$\text{SSTR} = 90.133, \text{SSE}_{\text{one-way ANOVA}} = 729.2, \text{ and } \text{SST} = 819.333$$

The RBD from Example 12.11 (Figure 12.27) separates $\text{SSE}_{\text{one-way ANOVA}}$ into the sum of the following two quantities:

$$\text{SSE}_{\text{one-way ANOVA}} = \text{SSB} + \text{SSE}_{\text{RBD}} = 677.333 + 51.867 = 729.2$$

The new sum of squares error SSE_{RBD} is small enough that the resulting new F statistic is large, leading to a rejection of the null hypothesis. ■

Let k and b represent the number of treatments and the number of blocks, respectively. Then, the ANOVA table for the randomized block design is as shown in Table 12.8.

Table 12.8 ANOVA table for randomized block design

Source	Sum of squares	Degrees of freedom	Mean square	F
Treatments	SSTR	$k - 1$	$\text{MSTR} = \dfrac{\text{SSTR}}{k - 1}$	$F = \dfrac{\text{MSTR}}{\text{MSE}}$
Blocks	SSB	$b - 1$	$\text{MSB} = \dfrac{\text{SSB}}{b - 1}$	
Error	SSE	$(k - 1)(b - 1)$	$\text{MSE} = \dfrac{\text{SSE}}{(k - 1)(b - 1)}$	
Total	SST	$n_T - 1$		

Note the following facts about the ANOVA table for randomized block design.

- Notice that SSTR, its degrees of freedom $k - 1$, and MSTR are all the same quantities as in the one-way ANOVA Table 12.3 on page 593.

- SSE_{RBD} is denoted simply as SSE.

- Quantities in the "Mean square" column equal the ratio of the quantities in the "Sum of squares" column divided by their respective degrees of freedom.

- We have SST = SSTR + SSB + SSE, and the 3 degrees of freedom values sum to $n_T - 1$.

- Since we are not interested in the blocks and thus the *mean square blocks MSB*, there is no F statistics for blocks.

- In one-way ANOVA, the degrees of freedom for $SSE_{one-way ANOVA}$ is $n_T - k$. In RBD, this error degrees of freedom is broken down into the degrees of freedom for SSB, $b - 1$, and the degrees of freedom for the new SSE, $(k - 1)(b - 1)$. An exercise in this section asks the student to show that these two degrees of freedom sum to $n_T - k$.

Now You Can Do
Exercises 13a and 14.

STEP-BY-STEP TECHNOLOGY GUIDE: Randomized Block Design

Neither the TI-83/84 nor Excel performs randomized block design analysis.

MINITAB
We shall use the data from Examples 12.10 and 12.11.

Step 1 Enter the score (response) data into column **C1**, the method (treatment) in column **C2**, and the course (block) in column **C3** (see Figure 12.29).
Step 2 Select **Stat**, then **ANOVA**, and choose **Two-way . . .** (*Note:* Randomized block design is not a two-way ANOVA, which we cover in Section 12.4. This is just how Minitab does it.)
Step 3 For **Response**, select the score (response) variable; for **Row factor**, select the method (treatment) variable; and for the **column factor**, select the course (block) variable. Click **Fit additive model** (and optionally click **Display means** for further results), and click **OK**.

↓	C1 Score	C2 Method	C3 Course
1	75	1	1
2	80	1	2
3	72	1	3
4	73	1	4
5	88	1	5
6	70	2	1
7	77	2	2
8	69	2	3
9	60	2	4
10	82	2	5
11	69	3	1
12	82	3	2
13	72	3	3
14	66	3	4
15	85	3	5

FIGURE 12.29 Entering the RBD data into Minitab.

Section 12.3 Summary

1 A blocking factor, or block, is a variable that is not of primary interest to the researcher, but is included in the ANOVA in order to improve the ability of the ANOVA to find significant differences among the treatment means. We perform a randomized block design ANOVA, where we test for differences among the factor of interest (treatment), while accounting for the variability among the blocks.

Section 12.3 Exercises

CLARIFYING THE CONCEPTS

1. Explain the difference between the variable of interest and the blocking factor. What is another term for the variable of interest? For the blocking factor?
2. What do we do in a randomized block design ANOVA?
3. Explain why a large SSE is bad if we want to reject the null hypothesis in ANOVA.
4. Explain how a larger F statistic leads to a more likely rejection of the null hypothesis in ANOVA.

PRACTICING THE TECHNIQUES

For Exercises 5–8, use the following randomized block design ANOVA output. Answer the following questions.

  a. How many treatments are there? Blocks?
  b. Minitab reports two F statistics. Which one are we interested in? Verify that $F = \dfrac{\text{MSTR}}{\text{MSE}}$.
  c. Use technology to verify that the area to the right of F equals the p-value. (*Hint:* Using the TI-83/84, press **2nd DISTR**, then **Fcdf(F, 1E99, df$_1$, df$_2$)**, where df$_1 = k - 1$ and df$_2 = (k - 1)(b - 1)$.)

5.

Source	DF	SS	MS	F	P
Treatmt	3	44.5	14.833	7.03	0.010
Block	3	402.5	134.167	63.55	0.000
Error	9	19.0	2.111		
Total	15	466.0			

6.

Source	DF	SS	MS	F	P
Treatmt	2	19.600	9.8000	2.64	0.132
Block	4	387.067	96.7667	26.04	0.000
Error	8	29.733	3.7167		
Total	14	436.400			

7.

Source	DF	SS	MS	F	P
Treatmt	3	2.27344	0.757813	5.03	0.009
Block	7	0.99219	0.141741	0.94	0.497
Error	21	3.16406	0.150670		
Total	31	6.42969			

8.

Source	DF	SS	MS	F	P
Treatmt	3	0.81250	0.270833	1.70	0.204
Block	6	1.33929	0.223214	1.40	0.269
Error	18	2.87500	0.159722		
Total	27	5.02679			

For Exercises 9–12, use the indicated randomized block design ANOVA output to test using level of significance $\alpha = 0.05$ whether the treatment means differ.

  a. Provide the hypotheses and the rejection rule.
  b. Find the relevant p-value; provide the conclusion and the interpretation.
9. Output from Exercise 5
10. Output from Exercise 6
11. Output from Exercise 7
12. Output from Exercise 8

For Exercises 13 and 14, for the indicated partially completed randomized block ANOVA table, do the following.

  a. Provide the hypotheses.
  b. Complete the missing entries in the table.
  c. Use technology to find the p-value. For level of significance $\alpha = 0.05$, provide the conclusion and the interpretation.

13.

Source	Sum of squares	Degrees of freedom	Mean square	F
Treatments	90	___	45	___
Blocks	50	___	___	
Error	___	8	7.5	
Total	___	15		

14.

Source	Sum of squares	Degrees of freedom	Mean square	F
Treatments	___	3	___	___
Blocks	___	6	40	___
Error	216	___	___	
Total	636	___		

For Exercises 15 and 16, do the following.

  a. Reconstruct the corresponding one-way ANOVA table.
  b. Perform the one-way ANOVA using level of significance $\alpha = 0.05$. Provide the hypotheses, the conclusion, and the interpretation.
  c. Is the conclusion from the one-way ANOVA different from that of the RBD analysis? Did the RBD help to find significance?
15. The randomized block design ANOVA table in Exercise 13
16. The randomized block design ANOVA table in Exercise 14
17. Verify that, in general, $n_T - k$ equals the sum of $b - 1$ and $(k - 1)(b - 1)$. (*Hint:* $n_T = k \cdot b$.)

APPLYING THE CONCEPTS

18. **The Price of Strawberries.** Is there a difference in the mean price of strawberries from year to year? The table contains the price per pound for strawberries in four states. Test using the randomized block design at level of significance $\alpha = 0.05$ whether the population mean price is the same for all three years. 🍓 **strawberries**

	2006	2007	2008
California	0.65	0.76	0.76
New York	1.70	1.65	1.65
Wisconsin	1.34	1.36	1.45
Michigan	1.18	1.20	1.22

Source: U.S. Department of Agriculture.

19. Eighth-Grade Math Scores Worldwide. Have worldwide eighth-grade math scores been changing? The table contains the TIMMS average math score for eighth-graders in five countries, for the years 1995, 2003, and 2007. Test using the randomized block design at level of significance $\alpha = 0.10$ whether the population mean math score differs across the three years. 🦶 **worldmath**

	1995	2003	2007
Singapore	609	605	593
Japan	581	570	570
Russia	524	508	512
USA	492	504	508
Sweden	540	499	491

Source: National Center for Education Statistics.

20. Oregon Towns and Cities. The following table contains the number of people living in a sample of towns and cities in Oregon, for the years 1990, 2000, and 2005 (in hundreds of thousands). Test using the randomized block design at level of significance $\alpha = 0.10$ whether the population mean number of people living in the towns and cities in Oregon is the same for all three years. 🦶 **oregon**

	1990	2000	2005
Portland	485	529	533
Eugene	114	139	145
Salem	108	137	148
Corvallis	45	49	50
Lake Oswego	31	35	37

Source: U.S. Census Bureau.

21. The Price of Strawberries. Refer to Exercise 18.
   a. Test whether the population mean price is the same for all three years, using a one-way ANOVA and level of significance $\alpha = 0.05$.
   b. Compare your conclusions in Exercises 18 and 21(**a**). Did the randomized block design help us to find significance?

22. Eighth-Grade Math Scores Worldwide. Refer to Exercise 19.
   a. Test whether the population mean math score differs across the three years, using a one-way ANOVA and level of significance $\alpha = 0.10$.
   b. Compare your conclusions in Exercises 19 and 22(**a**). Did the randomized block design help us to reject the null hypothesis?

23. Oregon Towns and Cities. Refer to Exercise 20.
   a. Test whether the population mean number of people living in the towns and cities in Oregon is the same for all three years, using a one-way ANOVA and level of significance $\alpha = 0.10$.
   b. Compare your conclusions in Exercises 20 and 23(**a**). Did the randomized block design help us to find significance?

24. Economic Assistance for Children. The following table contains the amount the United States sent to five foreign countries in economic assistance earmarked for child survival and health, for the fiscal years (FY) 2005–2008 (in millions of dollars). 🦶 **economist**
   a. Use one-way ANOVA to test at level of significance $\alpha = 0.05$ whether the population mean assistance was the same across all four fiscal years.
   b. Notice how much more assistance some countries received than others. This indicates that there is *variability among the countries.* Let us account for this variability by using the countries as blocks. Test using the randomized block design at level of significance $\alpha = 0.05$ whether the population mean economic assistance was the same across all four fiscal years.
   c. Did accounting for the variability among the countries help us to find significant differences among the four fiscal years in the amount of economic assistance?

	FY 2005	FY 2006	FY 2007	FY 2008
Mexico	29	53	36	4
Russia	15	81	68	17
Bangladesh	239	228	276	5
Ghana	166	167	204	10
India	613	578	571	25

Source: U.S. Department of State.

25. Measures of Business Value. The following table contains three measures of the value of a business: the market capitalization, the firm value, and the business enterprise value (in millions of dollars). 🦶 **businessvalue**
   a. Use one-way ANOVA to test at level of significance $\alpha = 0.05$ whether the population mean values differ among the three measures.
   b. Notice how much some of the larger firms (like Caterpillar) differ from some of the smaller firms (like Abercrombie & Fitch) for all three measures. This indicates that there is *variability among the firms.* Let us account for this variability by using the firms as blocks, and testing using the randomized block design at level of significance $\alpha = 0.05$ whether the population mean values differ among the three measures.
   c. Did accounting for the variability among the firms help us to find significant differences among the three measures of firm value?

	Market cap	Firm value	Enterprise value
Abercrombie & Fitch	3.1	3.2	2.7
Caterpillar	36.3	71.9	69.1
CIGNA	10.0	12.1	10.7
Delta Air Lines	9.2	25.8	21.3
Nissan Motors	38.2	90.0	82.4
Repsol Petroleum	32.6	50.2	45.5

Source: U.S. Federal Trade Commission.

12.4 Two-Way ANOVA

OBJECTIVES By the end of this section, I will be able to . . .

1 Construct and interpret an interaction graph.

2 Perform a two-way ANOVA.

In Section 12.1, we analyzed the treatment means for a single factor in one-way ANOVA. Then, in Section 12.3, a second factor was introduced, but we were not interested in testing for this blocking factor (or nuisance factor). Finally, here is Section 12.4, we learn about *two-way ANOVA*, where we are interested in testing for the significance of two factors.

Consumer Reports publishes ratings of many different items, including cell phones and smartphones. Table 12.9 contains a random sample of the cell phone and smartphone ratings for three leading carriers, AT&T, T-Mobile, and Verizon, published November 15, 2010.

Table 12.9 Ratings of mobile phones showing type and carrier

Phone	Carrier	Type	Rating
Samsung Impression	AT&T	Cell	68
Pantech Breeze	AT&T	Cell	62
Samsung Gravity	T-Mobile	Cell	69
Sony Ericsson	T-Mobile	Cell	61
Nokia Twist	Verizon	Cell	66
LG Cosmos	Verizon	Cell	63
Apple iPhone 4	AT&T	Smart	76
Sony Experia	AT&T	Smart	68
Samsung Vibrant	T-Mobile	Smart	76
Blackberry Bold	T-Mobile	Smart	69
Motorola Droid	Verizon	Smart	75
Blackberry Storm	Verizon	Smart	70

Source: www.consumerreports.org/cro/electronics-computers/phones-mobile-devices/cell-phones-services/smart-phone-ratings/ratings-overview.htm.

Let us denote carrier as Factor A and type as Factor B, and rating as the response variable. Together, Factor A and Factor B are known as the *main effects*. We rearrange Table 12.9 into the 2×3 contingency table shown in Table 12.10. Each cell in the table contains two ratings of carrier/phone type combination as well as the mean of these ratings.

Table 12.10 *Consumer Reports* phone ratings, by type and carrier

		Factor A: Carrier		
		AT&T	**T-Mobile**	**Verizon**
Factor B: Type	Cell phone	68 62 Mean = 65	69 61 Mean = 65	66 63 Mean = 64.5
	Smartphone	76 68 Mean = 72	76 69 Mean = 72.5	75 70 Mean = 72.5

Informally, Table 12.10 shows that the cell means in a given row do not differ by much. For example, the means in the cell phone row are all roughly 65. In contrast, the cell means in a column do seem to differ somewhat. For example, the column AT&T has means 65 and 72. This hints that Factor A: *c*arrier may not be significant, while Factor B: *t*ype may have a significant effect on ratings. But we need to perform the actual two-way ANOVA to determine this beyond a reasonable doubt.

1 Constructing and Interpreting an Interaction Graph

Before we perform two-way ANOVA, however, we should ascertain whether factor interaction is present. If the two factors have substantial interaction, then we cannot safely draw conclusions about either factor. So it is important when performing two-way ANOVA to check for the presence of **interaction** between the factors.

> **Interaction** exists between two factors when the effect of one factor depends on the level of the other factor.

For example, suppose that the mean smartphone ratings for AT&T and T-Mobile were higher than their cell phone ratings, but for Verizon the cell phone ratings were higher. This would be an example of interaction, since the effect of the type factor (cell phone versus smartphone ratings) depended on the level of the carrier factor.

We investigate the presence of interaction using an **interaction plot.**

> An **interaction plot** is a graphical representation of the cell means for each cell in the contingency table. To construct an interaction plot:
>
> 1. Compute the cell means for all cells.
> 2. Construct an $x - y$ plot (Cartesian plane). Label the horizontal axis for each level of Factor A. The vertical axis represents the response variable.
> 3. For the first level of Factor A, insert a point at a height representing the cell means for the response variable, for each level of Factor B. Then do this for the other levels of Factor A.
> 4. Connect points that have a common Factor B level.

Example 12.13 Constructing an interaction plot

mobilephone

Construct the interaction plot for the data in Table 12.9.

Solution

We have already calculated the cell means in Table 12.10. We then use the instructions in the Step-by-Step Technology Guide to construct the interaction plot in Minitab, shown here in Figure 12.30.

FIGURE 12.30
Interaction plot for phone ratings.

Now You Can Do
Exercises 9–16.

Figure 12.30 contains some typical interaction plots, showing (a) no interaction, (b) some interaction, and (c) significant interaction, with three levels for each of Factor A and Factor B. In an interaction plot, we are looking to see if the lines are parallel, or nearly parallel, or not at all parallel. Parallel lines indicate no interaction (Figure 12.31a); nearly parallel lines indicate some interaction (Figure 12.31b); lines that are not at all parallel indicate substantial interaction (Figure 12.31c). ■

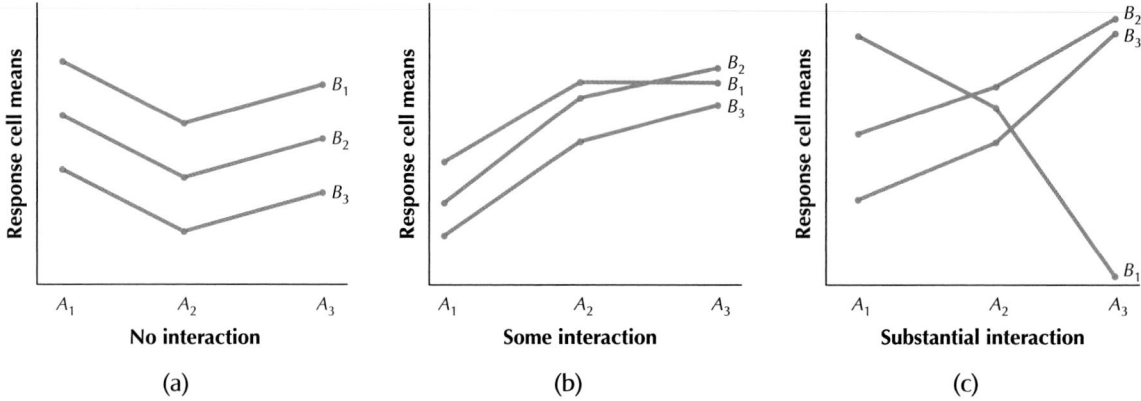

(a)	(b)	(c)
No interaction	Some interaction	Substantial interaction

FIGURE 12.31 Examples of interaction plots.

2 Performing a Two-Way ANOVA

Next we turn to performing the two-way ANOVA. The requirements are the same as for one-way ANOVA:

- Random samples are taken from each of k normally distributed populations.
- The variances (σ^2) of the populations are all equal.
- The samples are independently drawn.

These requirements may be checked as we did for the one-way ANOVA requirement. Two-way ANOVA actually involves a series of three hypothesis tests:

1. Test for interaction between the factors
2. Test for Factor A effect
3. Test for Factor B effect

> **Warning!**
> If *there is interaction between the factors*, then we *cannot* draw conclusions about the main effects. If the test for interaction *produces evidence that* interaction is present, then *do not perform* the test for either Factor A or Factor B.

The steps involved in performing a two-way ANOVA are illustrated using the following example.

Example 12.14   Performing a two-way ANOVA

 cellsmartphone

Perform a two-way ANOVA for the cell phone and smartphone ratings data in Table 12.10, using level of significance $\alpha = 0.05$. Assume the requirements are met.

Solution

The Minitab results are provided in Figure 12.32.

```
Two-way ANOVA: Rating versus Carrier, Type
Source        DF      SS        MS      F       P
Carrier        2    0.167     0.083   0.00   0.996
Type           1  168.750   168.750   8.20   0.029
Interaction    2    0.500     0.250   0.01   0.988
Error          6  123.500    20.583
Total         11  292.917
```

The null hypothesis H_0 in the test for interaction always states that there is no interaction between the factors.

Step 1 **Test for interaction.** The hypotheses are:

H_0 : There is no interaction between carrier (Factor A) and type (Factor B).
H_a : There is interaction between carrier and type.

Reject H_0 if the p-value $\leq \alpha = 0.05$. The p-value in the Interaction row in Figure 12.32 is 0.988, which is not ≤ 0.05; therefore, do not reject H_0. There is insufficient evidence of interaction between carrier and type at level of significance $\alpha = 0.05$. Therefore, we may proceed with the tests for the main effects.

Step 2 **Test for Factor A.** The hypotheses are:

H_0 : There is no carrier (Factor A) effect. That is, the population mean ratings do not differ by carrier.
H_a : There is a carrier (Factor A) effect. The population mean ratings do differ by carrier.

Reject H_0 if the p-value ≤ 0.05. According to the two-way ANOVA table in Figure 12.32:

p-value in the Carrier (Factor A) row = 0.996, which is not ≤ 0.05

Therefore, we do not reject H_0. There is insufficient evidence for a carrier (Factor A) effect. Thus we do not find a statistically significant difference in *Consumer Reports* ratings among the three carriers, AT&T, T-Mobile, and Verizon.

Step 3 **Test for Factor B.** The hypotheses are

H_0 : There is no type (Factor B) effect. That is, the population mean ratings do not differ by phone type.
H_a : There is a type (Factor B) effect. The population mean ratings do differ by phone type.

Reject H_0 if the p-value ≤ 0.05. The p-value in the type (Factor B) row in Figure 12.32 is 0.029, which is ≤ 0.05; therefore, reject H_0. There is evidence for a type (Factor B) effect. Thus we can conclude that there is significant difference in *Consumer Reports* ratings between the types: cell phones versus smartphones. ∎

Now You Can Do
Exercises 17–20.

The next example illustrates what happens when interaction is present.

Example 12.15 Two-Way ANOVA when interaction is present

computerrating

Consumer Reports provides ratings for computers as well. A random sample of laptop computers and desktop computers from three leading manufacturers, together with the *Consumer Reports* rating, is shown in Table 12.11. Table 12.12 organizes this information into a 2×3 contingency table, with three levels of Factor A (company) and two levels of Factor B (type), along with the ratings for each company/type combination, and the cell mean ratings. If appropriate, perform a two-way ANOVA for this data, using level of significance $\alpha = 0.01$. Assume that the requirements are met.

Table 12.11 *Consumer Reports* ratings of six laptops and six desktops

Computer	Company	Type	Rating
MacBook MC372	Apple	Laptop	78
MacBook MC024	Apple	Laptop	80
Studio 15	Dell	Laptop	72
Inspiron 1545	Dell	Laptop	62
Pavillion DV6	HP	Laptop	64
G60	HP	Laptop	58
iMac MC510	Apple	Desktop	73
iMac MC024	Apple	Desktop	67
XPS 8100	Dell	Desktop	84
XPS 7100	Dell	Desktop	80
Pavillion HPE	HP	Desktop	89
Pavillion Elite	HP	Desktop	83

Table 12.12 Contingency table organization of *Consumer Reports* computer ratings

		Factor A: Company		
		Apple	**Dell**	**HP**
Factor B: Type	Laptop	78 80 Mean = 79	72 62 Mean = 67	64 58 Mean = 61
	Desktop	73 67 Mean = 70	84 80 Mean = 82	89 83 Mean = 86

What Result Might We Expect?

The interaction plot in Figure 12.33 indicates the presence of substantial interaction. We would therefore expect that the test for interaction will find that interaction is present. ◢

FIGURE 12.33
Interaction plot shows evidence of interaction.

Step 1   **Test for interaction.** The hypotheses are:

H_0 : There is no interaction between company (Factor A) and type (Factor B).
H_a : There is interaction between company and type.

Reject H_0 if the p-value ≤ 0.01. The results of the two-way ANOVA are provided in Figure 12.34.

FIGURE 12.34
Two-way ANOVA results for the computer ratings data.

```
Two-way ANOVA: Rating versus Company, Type
Source       DF      SS       MS      F      P
Company       2     2.67    1.333   0.07  0.933
Type          1   320.33  320.333  16.86  0.006
Interaction   2   610.67  305.333  16.07  0.004
Error         6   114.00   19.000
Total        11  1047.67
```

The presence of interaction between the effects makes it problematical to draw conclusions about the factors company and type.

The p-value in the Interaction row in Figure 12.34 is 0.004, which is ≤ 0.01; therefore, reject H_0. As expected, there is evidence of interaction between company and type at level of significance $\alpha = 0.01$. Therefore, we may not proceed with the tests for the main effects. ∎

STEP-BY-STEP TECHNOLOGY GUIDE: Two-Way ANOVA

MINITAB
We illustrate using the data from Example 12.14.

Performing Two-Way ANOVA
Step 1   Enter the carrier (Factor A) data in column **C1**, the type (Factor B) data in column **C2**, and the rating data (response) in column **C3**, as shown in Figure 12.35.
Step 2   Select **Stat**, highlight **ANOVA**, and choose **Two-way . . . .**
Step 3   For **Response**, select the **Rating** data; for **Row factor**, select **Carrier**; and for **Column factor**, select **Type**. Leave the **Fit additive model** option unchecked. Click **OK**.

Constructing an Interaction Plot
Step 1   Enter the data just like in Step 1 above. Select **Stat**, highlight **ANOVA**, and choose **Interaction plots . . . .**
Step 2   For **Responses**, select *rating*. For **Factors**, select **Type**, then select **Carrier**. Click **OK**.

↓	C1-T	C2-T	C3
	Carrier	Type	Rating
1	AT&T	Cell	68
2	AT&T	Cell	62
3	T-Mobile	Cell	69
4	T-Mobile	Cell	61
5	Verizon	Cell	63
6	Verizon	Cell	66
7	AT&T	Smart	76
8	AT&T	Smart	68
9	T-Mobile	Smart	76
10	T-Mobile	Smart	69
11	Verizon	Smart	75
12	Verizon	Smart	70

FIGURE 12.35 Entering the two-way ANOVA data into Minitab.

CRUNCHIT!
Two-Way ANOVA
We will use the data from Example 12.13.

Step 1   Click **File . . .** then highlight **Load from Larose2e . . . Chapter 12 . . .** and click on **Example 12.13**.

Step 2   Click **Statistics** and select **ANOVA . . . Two-way**.
Step 3   For **Factor 1** select **Carrier**. For **Factor 2** select **Type**. For **Values** select **Rating**. Then click **Calculate**.

Section 12.4 Summary

1 In two-way ANOVA, we are interested in testing for the significance of two factors. There is interaction between the two factors of a two-way ANOVA if the effect of one factor depends on the level of the other factor. If the two factors have substantial interaction, then we will not be able to safely draw conclusions regarding either of the factors. An interaction plot is a graphical representation of the cell means for each cell in the contingency table.

2 Two-way ANOVA actually involves a series of three hypothesis tests: (a) test for interaction between the factors, (b) test for Factor A effect, and (c) test for Factor B effect. If interaction exists between the factors, then it becomes problematical to try to draw conclusions about the main effects. Therefore, if the test for interaction concludes that interaction is present, then we do not proceed to perform the test for either Factor A or Factor B.

Section 12.4 Exercises

CLARIFYING THE CONCEPTS

1. State two differences between the randomized block design and two-way ANOVA.
2. Together, Factor A and Factor B are known as what?
3. Before we perform two-way ANOVA, what should we check for the presence of?
4. Provide an example of interaction between two factors.
5. What is an interaction plot? What is it used for?
6. What do the following indicate in an interaction plot:
   a. Lines that are not at all parallel
   b. Parallel lines
   c. Nearly parallel lines
7. What are the three hypothesis tests involved in a two-way ANOVA?
8. What should we do if the test for interaction between the factors reveals evidence for the presence of interaction? Why do we do this?

PRACTICING THE TECHNIQUES

For Exercises 9–12, use the interaction plot to determine whether there is no interaction, some interaction, or substantial interaction between Factor A and Factor B.

9.

10.

11.

12.

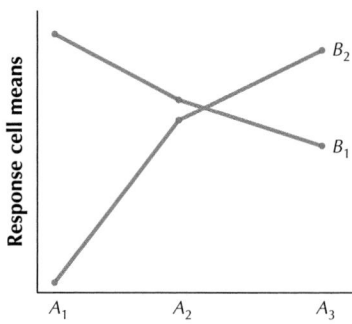

For the data in Exercises 13–16, draw an interaction plot and determine whether there exists no interaction, some interaction, or substantial interaction.

13.

Factor B	Factor A					
	A_1		A_2		A_3	
B_1	3.0	3.5	4.0	3.5	2.5	3.0
B_2	2.5	2.0	2.5	3.0	2.0	1.5

14.

Factor B	Factor A					
	A_1		A_2		A_3	
B_1	11	12	26	25	13	12
B_2	15	17	20	21	16	14

15.

Factor B	Factor A					
	A_1		A_2		A_3	
B_1	11	12	20	21	13	12
B_2	15	17	26	25	16	14

16.

Factor B		Factor A					
		A_1		A_2		A_3	
	B_1	100	105	95	100	110	100
	B_2	80	85	85	90	80	90

For Exercises 17–20, use level of significance $\alpha = 0.05$ to do the following for the indicated data.

    a. Test for interaction. Confirm that the result agrees with the interaction plot you constructed.

    b. If appropriate, test for the Factor A effect.

    c. If appropriate, test for the Factor B effect.

17. Data in Exercise 13

18. Data in Exercise 14

19. Data in Exercise 15

20. Data in Exercise 16

APPLYING THE CONCEPTS

21. Researchers at Harvard measured the cardiac output in liters per minute of patients involved in a cardiogenomics study.[5] A random sample of 8 patients is summarized here. Use level of significance $\alpha = 0.05$ to do the following. 🐢 **cardiac**

    a. Test for interaction.

    b. If appropriate, test whether cardiac output differs between those who have hypertension (high blood pressure) and those who do not.

    c. If appropriate, test whether cardiac output differs between the genders.

Factor B: Gender	Factor A: Hypertension			
	Yes		No	
Female	1.90	1.68	2.70	4.20
Male	2.60	2.20	4.30	5.50

22. Statistics and algebra instructors tested different types of problems for course assessment: multiple choice, short answer, and word problems, with the data provided here. Use level of significance $\alpha = 0.05$ to do the following. 🐢 **assessment**

    a. Test for interaction.

    b. If appropriate, test for the problem type effect.

    c. If appropriate, test for the course effect.

Factor B: Course	Factor A: Problem type					
	Multiple choice		Short answer		Word problems	
Statistics	70	75	73	77	75	79
Algebra	68	76	75	74	80	77

23. The following table contains a random sample of breakfast cereals, along with their brand, whether or not they are high in fiber (at least 3 grams), and their nutritional rating. Use level of significance $\alpha = 0.05$ to perform the two-way ANOVA. 🐢 **fibercereal**

Cereal	Brand	Fiber	Rating
Shredded Wheat	Kellogg's	High	68.2
All Bran	Kellogg's	High	59.4
Wheaties	General Mills	High	51.6
Total	General Mills	High	46.7
Nut'n Honey	Kellogg's	Low	29.9
Corn Flakes	Kellogg's	Low	45.9
Lucky Charms	General Mills	Low	26.7
Cocoa Puffs	General Mills	Low	22.7

24. A financial consultant is interested in differences in stock prices between industries and stock exchanges. She has collected a random sample of the stock prices of companies trading on the New York Stock Exchange and on NASDAQ, in the defense industry, the apparel industry, and the chemicals industry. Use level of significance $\alpha = 0.01$ to do the following. 🐢 **stockindustry**

    a. Test for interaction.

    b. If appropriate, test for difference in mean stock price among the industries.

    c. If appropriate, test for difference in mean stock price between the exchanges.

    d. For the results in **(b)** and **(c)**, would anything change if we used level of significance $\alpha = 0.05$ instead?

Company	Industry	Exchange	Stock price
Lockheed Martin	Defense	NYSE	75.35
General Dynamics	Defense	NYSE	68.17
Guess, Inc.	Apparel	NYSE	42.30
Van Heusen	Apparel	NYSE	40.68
Monsanto	Chemicals	NYSE	81.75
3M Company	Chemicals	NYSE	82.67
Argon ST	Defense	NASDAQ	21.71
Elbit Systems	Defense	NASDAQ	65.05
Iconix Group	Apparel	NASDAQ	12.67
Perry Ellis	Apparel	NASDAQ	15.06
Gulf Resources	Chemicals	NASDAQ	11.66
Hawkins, Inc.	Chemicals	NASDAQ	21.83

Source: Federal Trade Commission, November 17, 2009.

25. The table contains random samples of infielders and outfielders for the 2007 New York Yankees and Los Angeles Angels. Perform a two-way ANOVA using level of significance $\alpha = 0.05$. 🐢 **inoutfielder**

Player	Position	Team	Batting average
Derek Jeter	Infield	NY Yankees	.322
Alex Rodriguez	Infield	NY Yankees	.314
Hideki Matsui	Outfield	NY Yankees	.285
Bobby Abreu	Outfield	NY Yankees	.283
Chone Figgins	Infield	LA Angels	.330
Vladimir Guerrero	Infield	LA Angels	.324
Howie Kendrick	Outfield	LA Angels	.322
Garrett Anderson	Outfield	LA Angels	.297

Chapter 12 Formulas and Vocabulary

SECTION 12.1
- **Analysis of variance (ANOVA)** (p. 587)
- F_{crit} (p. 598)
- F_{data} (p. 593).

$$F_{data} = \frac{MSTR}{MSE}$$

- **Hypotheses for analysis of variance** (p. 590).

$$H_0: \mu_1 = \mu_2 = \cdots = \mu_k$$

versus

$$H_a: \text{ not all the population means are equal}$$

- **Mean square error (MSE)** (p. 593).

$$MSE = \frac{\sum(n_i - 1)s_i^2}{n_t - k}$$

- **Mean square treatment (MSTR)** (p. 593).

$$MSTR = \frac{\sum n_i(\bar{x}_i - \bar{\bar{x}})^2}{k - 1}$$

- **Overall sample mean,** $\bar{\bar{x}}$ (p. 592).

$$\bar{\bar{x}} = \frac{(n_1\bar{x}_1 + n_2\bar{x}_2 + \cdots + n_k\bar{x}_k)}{n_t}$$

- *p*-**Value** (p. 595)
- **Sum of squares error (SSE)** (p. 593).

$$SSE = \sum(n_i - 1)s_i^2$$

- **Sum of squares treatment (SSTR)** (p. 593).

$$SSTR = \sum n_i(\bar{x}_i - \bar{\bar{x}})^2$$

- **Total sum of squares (SST)** (p. 593).

$$SST = SSTR + SSE$$

SECTION 12.2
- **Bonferroni adjustment** (p. 606)
- **Experimentwise error rate** α_{EW} (p. 606)
- **Multiple comparisons** (p. 606)
- **Number of pairwise comparisons** (p. 606).

$$c = \left(_kC_2\right) = \frac{k!}{2!(k - 2)!}$$

- **Rejection rule for using confidence intervals to perform Tukey's test** (p. 610)
- **Test statistic for Bonferroni method** (p. 607).

$$t_{data} = \frac{\bar{x}_1 - \bar{x}_2}{\sqrt{MSE \cdot \left(\frac{1}{n_1} + \frac{1}{n_2}\right)}}$$

- **Test statistic for Tukey method** (p. 609).

$$q_{data} = \frac{\bar{x}_1 - \bar{x}_2}{\sqrt{\frac{MSE}{2} \cdot \left(\frac{1}{n_1} + \frac{1}{n_2}\right)}}$$

- **Tukey critical value** q_{crit} (p. 609)

SECTION 12.3
- **Blocking factor, or block** (p. 613)
- **Randomized block design** (p. 613)

SECTION 12.4
- **Interaction** (p. 621)
- **Interaction plot** (p. 621)

Chapter 12 Review Exercises

SECTION 12.1

1. For the following data, assume that the ANOVA assumptions are met, and calculate the measures in **(a)–(h)**.

Sample A	Sample B	Sample C	Sample D
$\bar{x}_A = 0$	$\bar{x}_B = 10$	$\bar{x}_C = 20$	$\bar{x}_D = 10$
$s_A = 1.5$	$s_B = 2.25$	$s_C = 1.75$	$s_D = 2.0$
$n_A = 50$	$n_B = 100$	$n_C = 50$	$n_D = 100$

a. df_1 and df_2

b. $\bar{\bar{x}}$

c. SSTR

d. SSE

e. SST

f. MSTR

g. MSE

h. F_{data}

2. Construct the ANOVA table for the statistics in Exercise 1.

For Exercises 3–5, assume that the ANOVA assumptions are met and perform the appropriate analysis of variance using $\alpha = 0.05$.

3. Diversity Awareness Test Scores. A corporate multicultural affairs officer would like to assess whether there are differences in the diversity awareness test scores for new employee training at three corporate locations, Branches A, B, and C. She randomly selects eight new employees from each of the three different branches. The following table provides the test score results. Test whether significant differences exist in the mean diversity awareness test scores for the three branches. **branchABC**

Branch A	Branch B	Branch C
50	80	85
90	90	95
60	95	90
90	60	75
85	60	85
50	80	75
60	70	65
70	75	80

4. Differences in Medical Treatments. A psychologist is interested in investigating whether differences in mean client improvement exist for three medical treatments. Seven clients undergoing each medical treatment were asked to rate their level of satisfaction on a scale of 0 to 100. The data are provided in the following table. **medicaltreatmt**

Medical treatment 1	Medical treatment 2	Medical treatment 3
75	75	100
100	100	100
0	25	50
50	75	90
50	50	75
40	75	75
25	60	90

5. Customer Satisfaction. The district sales manager of a local chain store would like to determine whether there are significant differences in the mean customer satisfaction among the four franchise stores in her district. Customer satisfaction data were gathered over seven days at each of the four stores. The resulting data are summarized in Table 12.13. **customersatisfy**

TABLE 12.13 Customer satisfaction in four stores

Store A	Store B	Store C	Store D
50	60	25	75
40	45	30	60
60	70	50	80
60	70	30	90
50	60	40	70
45	65	25	85
55	70	45	95
$\bar{x}_A = 51.43$	$\bar{x}_B = 62.86$	$\bar{x}_C = 35.00$	$\bar{x}_D = 79.29$
$s_A = 7.48$	$s_B = 9.06$	$s_C = 10.00$	$s_D = 12.05$

SECTION 12.2

For Exercises 6–8, use the summary statistics to calculate the value of the test statistic t_{data} for the Bonferroni method.

6. $\bar{x}_1 = 50, \bar{x}_2 = 75$, MSE $= 1250, n_1 = 25, n_2 = 25$

7. $\bar{x}_1 = 50, \bar{x}_3 = 65$, MSE $= 1250, n_1 = 25, n_2 = 25$

8. $\bar{x}_2 = 75, \bar{x}_3 = 65$, MSE $= 1250, n_1 = 25, n_2 = 25$

9. Perform multiple comparisons using the Bonferroni method at level of significance $\alpha = 0.05$ for the data in Exercises 6–8. Assume the requirements are met. Do the following.

a. For each hypothesis test, state the hypotheses and the rejection rule.

b. Use the value of t_{data} from Exercises 6–8 for each hypothesis test.

c. Find the Bonferroni-adjusted p-value for each hypothesis test.

d. For each hypothesis test, state the conclusion and the interpretation.

For Exercises 10–12, use the summary statistics to calculate the value of the test statistic q_{data} for Tukey's test.

10. $\bar{x}_1 = 200$, $\bar{x}_2 = 224$, MSE $= 14{,}400$, $n_1 = 100$, $n_2 = 100$

11. $\bar{x}_1 = 200$, $\bar{x}_3 = 248$, MSE $= 14{,}400$, $n_1 = 100$, $n_2 = 100$

12. $\bar{x}_2 = 224$, $\bar{x}_3 = 248$, MSE $= 14{,}400$, $n_1 = 100$, $n_2 = 100$

13. Find the Tukey critical value q_{crit} for experimentwise error rate $\alpha_{EW} = 0.05$, $n_1 = 100$, $n_2 = 100$, $n_3 = 100$.

14. Perform multiple comparisons using Tukey's test at experimentwise error rate $\alpha_{EW} = 0.05$, for the data in Exercises 10–12. Assume the requirements are met. Do the following.

   a. For each hypothesis test, state the hypotheses.
   b. Use the value of q_{crit} from Exercise 13, and state the rejection rule.
   c. Use q_{data} from Exercises 10–12 for each hypothesis test.
   d. For each hypothesis test, state the conclusion and the interpretation.

SECTION 12.3

15. For the partially completed randomized block ANOVA table, do the following.

   a. Provide the hypotheses.
   b. Complete the missing entries in the table.
   c. Use technology to find the p-value. For level of significance $\alpha = 0.05$, provide the conclusion and the interpretation.

Source	Sum of squares	Degrees of freedom	Mean square	F
Treatments	____	____	____	2
Blocks	420	5	____	
Error	200	20	10	
Total	700	____		

16. The following table represents an excerpt from a U.S. Census Bureau report on the numbers of small businesses owned by females and males in four industries. Perform

the randomized block design ANOVA using level of significance $\alpha = 0.05$. **genderindustry**

		Factor of interest: Gender of owner	
		Female	Male
Block: Industry	Retail	9	11
	Real estate	5	11
	Health care	20	10
	Entertainment	3	5

SECTION 12.4

For the data in Exercises 17–18, draw an interaction plot and determine whether there exists no interaction, some interaction, or substantial interaction.

17.

		Factor A					
		A_1		A_2		A_3	
Factor B	B_1	100	95	120	115	85	80
	B_2	120	125	150	155	100	95

18.

		Factor A					
		A_1		A_2		A_3	
Factor B	B_1	10	8	3	2	12	9
	B_2	3	4	11	7	5	2

For Exercises 19–20, use level of significance $\alpha = 0.05$ to do the following for the indicated data.

   a. Test for interaction. Confirm that the result agrees with the interaction plot you constructed.
   b. If appropriate, test for the Factor A effect.
   c. If appropriate, test for the Factor B effect.

19. Data in Exercise 17.
20. Data in Exercise 18.

Chapter 12 QUIZ

TRUE OR FALSE
1. True or false: The F curve is symmetric.
2. True or false: The total area under the F curve equals 1.
3. True or false: If we reject the null hypothesis in an ANOVA, we conclude that there is evidence that all the population means are different.

FILL IN THE BLANK
4. A weighted average (mean) of quantities that are squared is called a _____ _____ [two words].
5. The _____ _____ _____ [three words] measures the variability in the sample means.
6. The _____ _____ _____ [three words] measures the variability within the samples.

SHORT ANSWER
7. What do we use for an estimate of the overall population mean?
8. In the ANOVA table, what is the relationship between the quantities in the mean square column with respect to the quantities in the sum of squares column and the degrees of freedom column?
9. For analysis of variance, the p-value represents the area to the right of what?

CALCULATIONS AND INTERPRETATIONS
For Exercises 10–12, assume that the requirements for ANOVA have been met and test using level of significance $\alpha = 0.05$ whether the population means are equal.
10. **Gas Mileage and Number of Cylinders.** When it comes to getting good gas mileage, does the number of cylinders in your engine make a difference? The following table provides the summary statistics regarding miles per gallon for 4-cylinder, 6-cylinder, and 8-cylinder cars.

	4 cylinders	6 cylinders	8 cylinders
n	199	83	103
$\bar{x}$	29.3	20.0	15.0
s	5.7	3.8	2.9

11. **Hours Worked and Marital Status.** The General Social Survey tracks demographic trends. Here we are interested in whether the mean number of hours worked differs by marital status. The summary statistics are shown here.

	N	Mean	Std. Deviation
MARRIED	964	42.76	14.08
WIDOWED	72	40.13	14.28
DIVORCED	342	43.69	13.93
SEPARATED	79	41.66	15.71
NEVER MARRIED	478	41.03	14.03

12. **Calories in Breakfast Cereals.** A dietary researcher in interested in whether differences exist in the mean number of calories in breakfast cereals made by different manufacturers. The summary statistics for the samples from three manufacturers appear in the following table.

	Kellogg's	Quaker	Ralston Purina
n	23	8	8
$\bar{x}$	109	95	115
s	22	29	23

13

Regression Analysis

Introduction

Chapter 13 continues the development of the topic of regression analysis begun in Chapter 4, with emphasis on inference. In Section 13.1 we learn about hypothesis tests and confidence intervals about the slope of the regression line. Section 13.2 introduces confidence intervals and prediction intervals. Finally, Section 13.3 covers multiple regression and model building.

From the Author

- **Section 13.1 Inference About the Slope of the Regression Line**
  - Instructors may want to review Section 4.2, "Introduction to Regression," and Section 4.3, "Further Topics in Regression Analysis," before doing Section 13.1.
  - Example 13.1 is a review of several of the regression topics covered in Sections 4.2 and 4.3. Note that the regression coefficients are fairly round numbers, allowing students to concentrate on the concepts and techniques.
  - Students may not understand the difference between the regression equation and the population regression equation. The regression equation comes from a single sample, so, like $\bar{x}$, the values for b_0, and b_1 will vary from sample to sample. But the population regression equation comes from the entire population, so, like μ, the values for β_0 and β_1 are constants.
  - Instructors may wish to point out the importance of the value 0 for β_0. If $\beta_1 = 0$, then there is no linear relationship between x and y. If the confidence interval for β_2 contains zero, again there is no linear relationship between x and y.
- **Section 13.2 Confidence Intervals and Prediction Intervals**
  - New section.
  - Students may confuse the confidence interval learned in this section with the confidence interval from Section 13.1. Point out that, in Section 13.1, the confidence interval was for the slope β_1, while in Section 13.2, the confidence interval is for the mean value of y for a given value of x.
  - The calculations in this section are rather challenging. Instructors who are pressed for time may prefer to work with the confidence intervals and prediction intervals calculated by the software, and focus on the interpretation of the results.

Section 13.3 Multiple Regression

- New section.

- Instructors may point out that multiple regression is simply an extension of the regression model from Section 13.1 to include more than one x variable. Many concepts in Section 13.3 are similar to those in Section 13.1.

- Because of the widespread use of multiple regression (including my own consulting work), I was excited to write this new section. If we can offer students a taste of model building, then some of them will surely catch "statistics fever," and go on to become data analysts like us!

Teaching Tips

Starting Example: The example of high school GPA (x) and college GPA (y) used in Chapter 4 can also be used for this chapter. All the sums of squares can be calculated for this example as well as the confidence interval for the slope of the regression line. The t test for the slope of the regression line may also be performed for this example.

In-Class Activities

1. Ask students to collect data on two variables, such as the average daily temperature for their town and the number of soft drinks consumed during the day of the observed average temperature. This can be assigned to the students before the analysis is to be done in class, so that they can observe for a specified number of days (possibly 7). Since the students will be observing the same days, an average for the number of soft drinks consumed for each day should be used as well as the average daily temperature. The activity should include scatterplots for the data and modeling of the data. Students can use the average number of soft drinks consumed as the y variable and the average daily temperature as the x variable. **Note:** Use appropriate technology if available.

Regression Activity for Distance and Time to Class

2. In this activity we discuss whether the amount of time it takes a student to get to class depends on how far away the student lives.

a. Generate a sample of 15 students from your class, using either (a) technology or (b) the *Random Sample* applet. Each student's sample should be different.

b. Find out how long it takes each student in your sample to get to class and how far away the student lives. If the student lives on campus, get the data regarding the student's permanent residence (home mailing address).

    i. Construct a scatterplot of the time in minutes against the distance in miles. Will everyone's scatterplot look exactly the same? Will everyone's scatterplot look somewhat similar?

    ii. Draw a straight line that you think best approximates the relationship between time and distance.

    iii. Estimate the slope and y intercept of the line you drew in (ii).

    iv. Now calculate the regression equation using the data from your sample in (a). Draw the regression line on your scatterplot.

c. Explore the regression results.

    i. Clearly describe the meaning of the slope b_1.

    ii. Does the literal meaning of the y intercept b_0 make sense? What is its literal meaning? What is wrong with interpreting it this way?

    iii. Are your estimates in b(iii) close to the least-squares results in b(iv)?

    iv. Are time and distance positively correlated? Compute the correlation coefficient.

d. Make a prediction, and find the prediction error.

    i. Choose one student from your scatterplot and calculate the predicted time for the student. Then calculate the prediction error for the student.

    ii. What is the typical difference between the predicted amount of time and the actual amount of time? Do you want this statistic (*Hint: s*) to be large or small?

Supplements

- StatTutor 5.0–5.8, 24.1–24.8
- Stats@Work Simulations
  - Picture This, Scatterplots and Correlation; Jan Pepperoni
  - Picture This, Scatterplots and Correlation; Justine Red
- EESEE case studies
  - Brain Size and Intelligence (Questions 1, 2, 3, 4, and 5)
  - Is Old Faithful Faithful? (Questions 1, 2, 3, and 4)

Applets

This Web site has an applet for correlation and regression: **http://wise.cgu.edu/**.

Videos

- *Against All Odds* **www.learner.org/resources/series65.html**
  - Program 8: Describing Relationships
  - Program 9: Correlation
  - Program 25: Inference for Relationships

Web Sites

- The site Online Statistics: An Interactive Multimedia Course of Study has information on regression and correlation, and it has a link to the Rice Virtual Lab in Statistics with simulation demonstrations and other topics related to statistics: **http://onlinestatbook.com/index.html**
- This site lists other sites that do statistical calculations for correlation and regression analysis: **http://statpages.org/**.
- This site has an activity that deals with correlation and regression: **http://www.amstat.org/publications/jse/v6n3/smith.html**.

BEW Authors/AgeFotostock

OVERVIEW

13

Inference in Regression

CASE STUDY

How Fair Is the Scoring in Scrabble?

Scrabble is a game in which the players choose letters randomly from a pool of letter tiles and take turns building words. Each letter tile is worth a specific number of points. For example, the letter A is worth 1 point, and the letter Z is worth 10 points. Do you think the way the various letters are valued is fair? Do you dread picking up the letter Z so much that you think it should be worth 25 points rather than 10? Do you think there are too many I's, perhaps, and not enough T's?

We can use *regression analysis,* the topic of this chapter, to help us find out why it often seems that there are too many I's and not enough T's. Regression can also help us understand why we would rather pick up an H tile rather than a V tile, even though each tile is worth 4 points. We can compare the distribution of letter points in Scrabble to the number of letter tiles in the game and to the frequency distribution of letters in the English language. To see more, check out this chapter's Case Study, How Fair Is the Scoring in Scrabble? (page 644).

The Big Picture

Where we are coming from, and where we are headed . . .

- In the later chapters of *Discovering Statistics*, we have been studying more advanced methods in statistical inference. In Chapter 12, "Analysis of Variance," we studied how to compare the means of several different populations.

- Here, in Chapter 13, "Inference in Regression," we return to regression analysis, first discussed in Chapter 4. At that time we learned descriptive methods for regression analysis; now it is time to learn how to perform statistical inference in regression, such as the *t* test for the relationship between *x* and *y*.

- Where do you go from here? That's up to you. The world is overflowing with data and needs people like you who understand the statistical techniques and methods for uncovering the knowledge locked in the data. This course in statistics has tried to provide you with these tools. Here's hoping that your new expertise as a data analyst will help you achieve success in the Information Age.

13.1 Inference About the Slope of the Regression Line

OBJECTIVES By the end of this section, I will be able to . . .

1 Explain the regression model and the regression model assumptions.

2 Perform the hypothesis test for the slope β_1 of the population regression equation.

3 Construct confidence intervals for the slope β_1.

4 Use confidence intervals to perform the hypothesis test for the slope β_1.

1 The Regression Model and the Regression Assumptions

Before we learn about the regression model and assumptions, let us review the correlation and regression topics that we learned in Chapter 4. Recall that the regression line approximates the relationship between two continuous variables and is described by the regression equation $\hat{y} = b_1 x + b_0$, where b_1 is the *slope* of the regression line, b_0 is the *y intercept*, x represents the *predictor variable*, y represents the *response variable*, and $\hat{y}$ represents the *estimated or predicted y-value*.

Example 13.1 Review of regression topics

 textms

You may wish to refer to Section 4.1 for (a) and (b), and Section 4.2 for (c) and (d).

The Nielsen company has reported that the number of text messages that a person sends tends to decrease with age. Table 13.1 contains a random sample of 10 people, along with their age and the number of text messages they sent on the previous day.

a. Construct and interpret a scatterplot of the response variable y versus the predictor variable x.

b. Calculate and interpret the correlation coefficient r.

c. Compute the regression equation $\hat{y} = b_1 x + b_0$. Interpret the meaning of the y intercept b_0 and the slope b_1 of the regression equation.

d. Predict the number of text messages sent by a 20-year-old person, and calculate the prediction error (residual).

Table 13.1 Age and number of text messages

x = Age	y = Text messages	x = Age	y = Text messages
18	35	28	16
20	29	30	19
22	27	32	12
24	28	34	8
26	19	36	8

Solution

a. Since the number of messages depends on age, and not vice versa, the predictor variable x is age and the response variable y is messages. Also, note that in **(d)** we are trying to predict the number of text messages, which tells us that messages is the response variable y since we never try to predict the known value of x. The

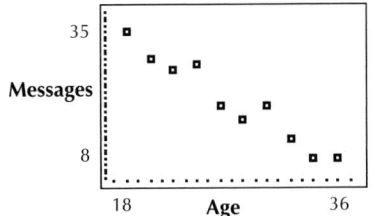

FIGURE 13.1 TI-83/84 scatterplot of messages versus age.

FIGURE 13.2 TI-83/84 correlation and regression results.

TI-83/84 scatterplot is shown in Figure 13.1. As age increases, the number of messages tends to decrease.

b. Figure 13.2 shows the correlation coefficient $r \approx -0.9701$, calculated by the TI-83/84. Age and messages are negatively correlated. An increase in age is associated with a decrease in the number of messages.

c. Figure 13.2 shows that $a = b_1 = -1.5$ and $b = b_0 = 60.6$, and thus the regression equation is

$$\hat{y} = b_1 x + b_0 = (-1.5) \, (\text{age}) + 60.6$$

We can interpret b_0 and b_1 as follows:
- The y intercept $b_0 = 60.6$ is the estimated number of text messages sent by someone aged $x = 0$, which does not make sense because this value $x = 0$ lies far below the minimum value of x and therefore represents extrapolation.
- The slope $b_1 = -1.5$ means there is an estimated *decrease* of 1.5 in the number of text messages for each additional year of age.

d. For a 20-year-old person, the estimated number of daily text messages is

$$\hat{y} = b_1 x + b_0 = (-1.5)(20) + 60.6 = 30.6$$

The actual number of text messages sent by our 20-year-old in Table 13.1 is $y = 29$. Our prediction from **(c)** is $\hat{y} = 30.6$. Thus, our prediction error (or residual) is: $(y - \hat{y}) = (29 - 30.6) = -1.6$. Our 20-year-old sent slightly fewer text messages than expected. ∎

Example 13.1 and our work in Chapter 4 on regression represented descriptive statistics. Next we turn to learning about *inference in regression*.

Note that the regression equation $\hat{y} = b_1 x + b_0 = (-1.5)(\text{age}) + 60.6$ depends on the sample. It is likely that a second sample will differ from the first, giving us a different regression line and different values for b_0 and b_1. In fact, for every different sample, b_0 and b_1 take different values since b_0 and b_1 are sample statistics. However, every sample comes from a population. Since we do not have data on the entire population, we are not able to calculate the population regression equation. The y intercept β_0 and slope β_1 of the population regression equation are unknown population parameters, just as μ and p are parameters in other contexts. Since the values of β_0 and β_1 are unknown, we need to perform inference to learn about them.

The **regression model** may be used to approximate the relationship between the predictor variable x and the response variable y for the *entire population* of (x, y) pairs.

Note that there is no "hat" on the y in the population regression equation because the equation represents a model of the relationship between the actual values of x and y, not an estimate of y.

Regression Model

The **population regression equation** is defined as

$$y = \beta_1 x + \beta_0 + \varepsilon$$

where β_0 is the y intercept of the population regression line, β_1 is the slope of the population regression line, and ε is the error term.

The 20-year-old in Table 13.1 sent 29 text messages. Suppose another 20-year-old sent 30 messages, so that both texters had age $x = 20$, but different values of y: $y = 29$ and $y = 30$. Then it would be impossible to draw a single regression line to pass through both $(x = 20, y = 29)$ and $(x = 20, y = 30)$. Thus, any linear approximation of the true relationship between x and y will introduce a certain amount of error. This is why the error term ε is needed.

Regression Model Assumptions

The regression model operates under a set of four assumptions that must be valid in order to perform the inference in this section.

> **Regression Model Assumptions**
> 1. **Zero-mean assumption.** The error term ε is a random variable, with a mean of 0. That is, the expected value of the random variable ε is 0: $E(\varepsilon) = 0$.
> 2. **Constant variance assumption.** The variance of ε, which is denoted as σ^2, is the same regardless of the value of x.
> 3. **Independence assumption.** The values of ε are independent of each other.
> 4. **Normality assumption.** The error term ε is a normal random variable.

To summarize, for each value of x, the values of y come from a normally distributed population with a mean on the population regression line $E(y) = \beta_1 x + \beta_0$ and constant standard deviation σ^2. Figure 13.3 illustrates how y is distributed for each value of x. Note that each normal curve has the same shape, indicating constant variance for each x.

FIGURE 13.3
Illustrating the regression assumptions.

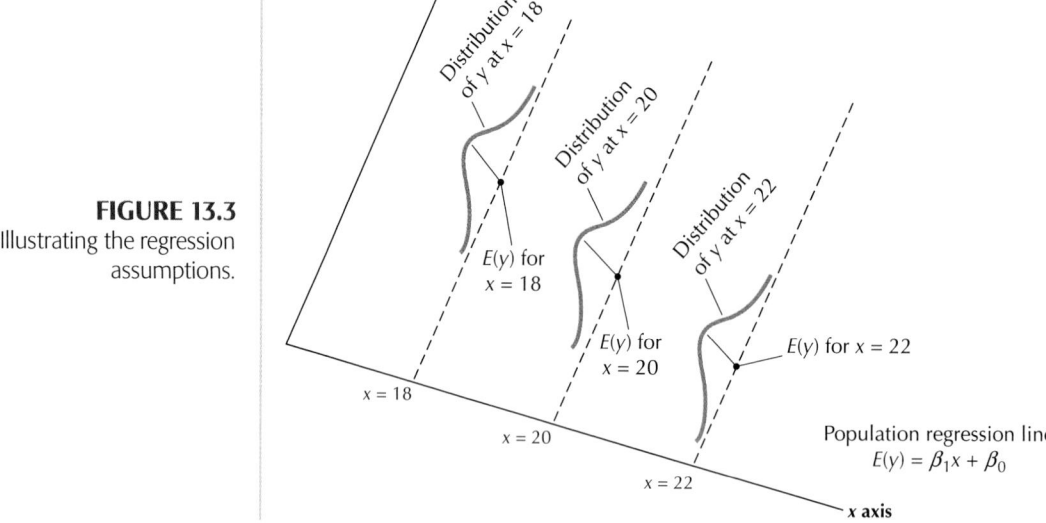

Verifying the Regression Assumptions

To check the regression model assumptions, we construct two graphs:

1. Scatterplot of the residuals (prediction errors $y - \hat{y}$) against the fitted values (**fitted values** refers to the predicted values, $\hat{y}$)

2. Normal probability plot of the residuals

Figure 13.4 shows four types of patterns that might be observed in the residuals versus fitted values plots.

- Plot (a) is a "healthy" plot, displaying no noticeable patterns.

- In plot (b) we see a curve, which indicates a violation of the independence assumption. Independence implies that knowing the value of a particular y does not help to predict the value of a different y. However, a curve suggests that knowing the value of a previous y helps in knowing the value of the next y.

- Plot (c) shows a "funnel" pattern, which contradicts the constant variance assumption. The residuals on the left are close together vertically (small variability), while the residuals on the right are far apart vertically (large variability).

- In plot (d) we see an increasing pattern, that violates the zero-mean assumption. The residuals on the left are all below the midline, so $E(y) < \beta_1 x + \beta_0$, while the residuals on the right are all above the midline, so $E(y) > \beta_1 x + \beta_0$.

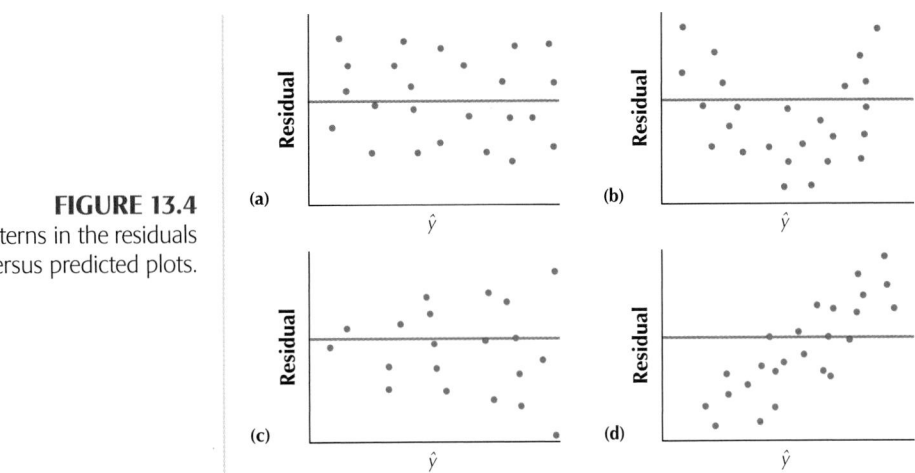

FIGURE 13.4
Patterns in the residuals
versus predicted plots.

> ### Developing Your Statistical Sense
>
> ### Verifying the Regression Assumptions
>
> With small data sets, it is difficult to ascertain whether or not patterns really exist. Be wary of seeing patterns where none exist. If one or more regression assumptions are violated, we should not proceed with inferential methods such as hypothesis tests or confidence intervals. However, even if one or more regression assumptions are violated, we can still report and interpret the descriptive regression statistics that we learned in Sections 4.2 and 4.3. ◢

Example 13.2   Calculating the residuals and verifying the regression assumptions

For the data in Example 13.1, do the following:
a.   Calculate the residuals $y - \hat{y}$.
b.   Verify the regression assumptions.

Solution

a.   Table 13.2 contains the x and y data from Table 13.1, the fitted (predicted) values $\hat{y}$, and the residuals $y - \hat{y}$.

Table 13.2 Calculating the residuals

x = Age	y = Text messages	Fitted (predicted) values $\hat{y} = (-1.5)(\text{age}) + 60.6$	Residuals $y - \hat{y}$
18	35	33.6	1.4
20	29	30.6	−1.6
22	27	27.6	−0.6
24	28	24.6	3.4
26	19	21.6	−2.6
28	16	18.6	−2.6
30	19	15.6	3.4
32	12	12.6	−0.6
34	8	9.6	−1.6
36	8	6.6	1.4

b. The scatterplot in Figure 13.5 of the residuals versus fitted values shows no strong evidence of the unhealthy patterns shown in Figure 13.3. Thus, the independence assumption, the constant variance assumption, and the zero-mean assumption are verified. Also, the normal probability plot of the residuals in Figure 13.6 indicates no evidence of departures from normality in the residuals. Therefore we conclude that the regression assumptions are verified. ■

Now You Can Do
Exercises 7–14.

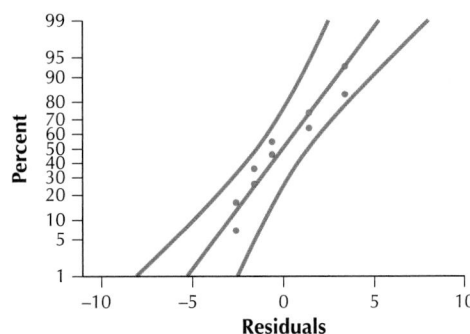

FIGURE 13.5 Scatterplot of residuals versus fitted values.

FIGURE 13.6 Normal probability plot of the residuals.

Once the regression assumptions have been verified, we may (a) perform hypothesis tests, and (b) construct confidence intervals for the population slope β_1.

2 Hypothesis Tests for Slope β_1

Suppose for a moment that, for the population regression equation $y = \beta_1 x + \beta_0 + \varepsilon$, the slope β_1 equals zero. Then the population regression equation would be

$$y = (0)x + \beta_0 + \varepsilon = \beta_0 + \varepsilon$$

That is,

- *If β_1 equals zero, then there is no relationship between x and y* because changing x in the equation $y = \beta_0 + \varepsilon$ does not affect y.

- If β_1 equals any other value, then there does exist a linear relationship between x and y.

This idea forms the basis for our inference in this section. To test whether there is a relationship between x and y, we begin with the hypothesis test to determine whether or not β_1 equals 0. The hypotheses are

$H_0 : \beta_1 = 0$ There is no linear relationship between x and y.
$H_a : \beta_1 \neq 0$ There is a linear relationship between x and y.

Assuming $H_0 : \beta_1 = 0$ is true, the test statistic t_{data} for this hypothesis test takes the following form.

CAUTION   Here, *s* refers to the standard error of the estimate, *not* the sample standard deviation.

Test Statistic t_{data}

$$t_{\text{data}} = \frac{b_1 - \beta_1}{s / \sqrt{\sum(x - \bar{x})^2}} = \frac{b_1 - 0}{s / \sqrt{\sum(x - \bar{x})^2}} = \frac{b_1}{s / \sqrt{\sum(x - \bar{x})^2}}$$

where b_1 represents the slope of the regression line, $s = \sqrt{\dfrac{SSE}{n - 2}}$ represents the standard error of the estimate (from Section 4.3), and $\sqrt{\sum(x - \bar{x})^2}$ represents the numerator of the sample variance of the x data (see page 110).

t_{data} consists of three quantities: b_1, s, and $\sqrt{\sum(x - \bar{x})^2}$. The next example shows how to calculate t_{data} by finding these three quantities.

Example 13.3 Calculating t_{data}

Table 13.3 Calculating SSE

Residuals $y - \hat{y}$	Squared residuals $(y - \hat{y})^2$
1.4	1.96
−1.6	2.56
−0.6	0.36
3.4	11.56
−2.6	6.76
−2.6	6.76
3.4	11.56
−0.6	0.36
−1.6	2.56
1.4	1.96
	Sum = 46.4

All calculations up to the final result are expressed to nine decimal places.

```
1-Var Stats
 x̄=27
 Σx=270
 Σx²=7620
 Sx=6.055300708
 σx=5.744562647
↓n=10
```

FIGURE 13.7 Summary statistics for the x (age) data.

Now You Can Do
Parts (b)–(d) of Exercises 15–18 and parts (a)–(c) of Exercises 19–22.

Use the following steps to calculate the test statistic $t_{data} = \dfrac{b_1}{s/\sqrt{\sum(x - \bar{x})^2}}$ for the data in Table 13.1:

a. Find b_1, the slope of the regression line.
b. Calculate s, the standard error of the estimate.
c. Compute $\sqrt{\sum(x - \bar{x})^2}$, the numerator of the sample variance of the x data.

Solution

a. From Example 13.1, the slope of the regression line is $b_1 = -1.5$.
b. Recall from Section 4.3 (page 187) that

$$s = \sqrt{\frac{SSE}{n - 2}} = \sqrt{\frac{\sum(y - \hat{y})^2}{n - 2}} = \sqrt{\frac{\sum(\text{residual})^2}{n - 2}}$$

is the *standard error of the estimate*. Squaring each residual from Table 13.2 gives us the squared residuals in Table 13.3, and the sum of squared residuals, or sum of squares error, equal to

$$SSE = \sum(y - \hat{y})^2 = 46.4$$

Then the standard error of the estimate is $s = \sqrt{\dfrac{SSE}{n - 2}} = \sqrt{\dfrac{46.4}{8}} \approx 2.408318916$.

c. To compute $\sum(x - \bar{x})^2$, we note from page 110 that the sample variance of x is

$$s_x^2 = \frac{\sum(x - \bar{x})^2}{n - 1}$$

Multiplying each side of the equation by $n - 1$, we obtain an equation for the quantity $\sum(x - \bar{x})^2$:

$$\sum(x - \bar{x})^2 = (n - 1) \cdot s_x^2$$

The TI-83/84 output from Figure 13.7 shows that $s_x = 6.055300708$, and, since $n = 10$,

$$\sum(x - \bar{x})^2 = (n - 1) \cdot s_x^2 = (9)(6.055300708)^2 = 330$$

Therefore,

$$t_{data} = \frac{b_1}{s/\sqrt{\sum(x - \bar{x})^2}} = \frac{-1.5}{2.408318916/\sqrt{330}} \approx -11.3 \quad \blacksquare$$

Now that we have t_{data}, we can perform the hypothesis test for the slope β_1, as the next example shows using the critical-value method.

Example 13.4 Hypothesis test for slope β_1 using the critical-value method

Test whether a linear relationship exists between age and text messages, using the data from Table 13.1 at level of significance $\alpha = 0.01$.

Solution

The regression assumptions were shown to be valid in Example 13.2. We may thus proceed with the hypothesis test.

Step 1 **State the hypotheses.**

$H_0 : \beta_1 = 0$ There is no linear relationship between age and text messages.
$H_a : \beta_1 \neq 0$ There is a linear relationship between age and text messages.

Step 2 **Find the t critical value t_{crit} and the rejection rule.** To find t_{crit}, use the t distribution table (Table D in the Appendix) for a two-tailed test and degrees of freedom df $= n - 2$. The rejection rule is

$$\text{Reject } H_0 \text{ if } t_{\text{data}} \geq t_{\text{crit}} \text{ or } t_{\text{data}} \leq -t_{\text{crit}}.$$

Here, $n = 10$, so df $= 8$. For level of significance $\alpha = 0.01$, the t table gives us $t_{\text{crit}} = 3.355$. We will reject H_0 if $t_{\text{data}} \geq 3.355$ or $t_{\text{data}} \leq -3.355$.

Step 3 **Calculate t_{data}.** From Example 13.3, we have

$$t_{\text{data}} = \frac{b_1}{s/\sqrt{\sum(x - \bar{x})^2}} \approx -11.3$$

Now You Can Do
Exercises 15–18.

Step 4 **State the conclusion and the interpretation.** Since $t_{\text{data}} \approx -11.3 \leq -3.355$, we reject H_0. There is evidence at level of significance $\alpha = 0.01$ that $\beta_1 \neq 0$ and that there is a linear relationship between age and text messages. ■

The next example illustrates the steps for performing the hypothesis test for the slope β_1 using the p-value method.

Example 13.5 **Hypothesis test for the slope β_1 using the p-value method and technology**

shortmemory

In Section 4.3 we considered a study on short-term memory. Ten subjects were given a set of nonsense words to memorize within a certain amount of time and were later scored on the number of words they could remember. The results are repeated here in Table 13.4. Use the p-value method and technology to test using level of significance $\alpha = 0.01$ whether a linear relationship exists between time and score.

Solution

We begin by verifying the regression assumptions. The scatterplot of the residuals versus the fitted values in Figure 13.8 shows no strong evidence that the independence assumption, the constant variance assumption, or the zero-mean assumption is violated. Also, the normal probability plot of the residuals in Figure 13.9 offers evidence of the normality of the results. Therefore we conclude that the regression assumptions are verified, and proceed with the hypothesis test.

Table 13.4

Time (x)	Score (y)
1	9
1	10
2	11
3	12
3	13
4	14
5	19
6	17
7	21
8	24

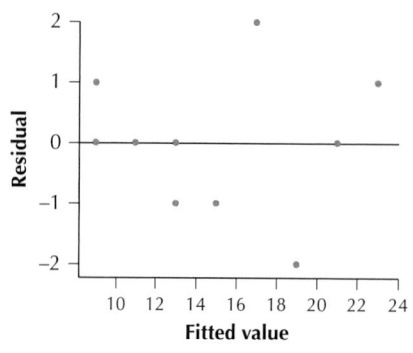

FIGURE 13.8 Residuals versus fitted values plot.

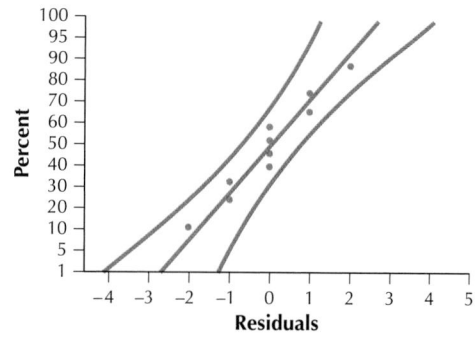

FIGURE 13.9 Normal probability plot of the residuals.

Step 1 **State the hypotheses and the rejection rule.**

$H_0 : \beta_1 = 0$ There is no linear relationship between time and score.
$H_a : \beta_1 \neq 0$ There is a linear relationship between time and score.

Reject H_0 if the p-value ≤ 0.01.

Step 2 **Calculate t_{data}.**

$$t_{\text{data}} = \frac{b_1}{s/\sqrt{\sum(x - \bar{x})^2}}$$

From page 185 in Section 4.3 we have $b_1 = 2$. From Example 4.14 on page 187 we have

$$s = \sqrt{\frac{12}{8}} \approx 1.224744871$$

From the TI-83/84 summary statistics, we have the standard deviation of the x (time) data to be $s_x = 2.449489743$. Thus, from Example 13.3:

$$\sum(x - \bar{x})^2 = (n - 1) \cdot s_x^2 \approx (9)2.449489743^2 = 54$$

Therefore,

$$t_{\text{data}} = \frac{b_1}{s/\sqrt{\sum(x - \bar{x})^2}} \approx \frac{2}{1.224744871/\sqrt{54}} = 12$$

Step 3 **Find the p-value.** For instructions, see the Step-by-Step Technology Guide on page 646. The regression results (including the p-value) for the TI-83/84, Excel, and Minitab are shown in Figures 13.10, 13.11, and 13.12. (Differing results are due to rounding.)

TI-83/84 summary statistics for x (time) data.

Regression equation $\hat{y} = b_1 x + b_0$
(TI-83/84 expresses as $y = a + bx$)
$t_{\text{data}} = 12$
p-value of 2.1438667E-6 = 0.0000021439
Degrees of freedom, $n - 2 = 8$
$a = b_0 = 7$
$b = b_1 = 2$
Standard error of the estimate $s \approx 1.2247$
Coefficient of determination $r^2 \approx 0.9474$
Correlation coefficient $r \approx 0.9733$

```
LinRegTTest
 y=a+bx
 β≠0 and ρ≠0
 t=12
 p=2.1438667ε-6
 df=8
↓a=7
■
```

```
LinRegTTest
 y=a+bx
 β≠0 and ρ≠0
↑b=2
 s=1.224744871
 r²=.9473684211
 r=.9733285268
■
```

FIGURE 13.10 TI-83/84 regression results.

Regression Statistics	
Multiple R	0.9733
R Square	0.9474
Adjusted R Square	0.9408
Standard Error	1.2247
Observations	10

Correlation coefficient $r = 0.9733$
Coefficient of determination $r^2 = 0.9474$
Standard error of the estimate $s = 1.2247$
Sample size $n = 10$

	Coefficients	Standard Error	t Stat	P-value
Intercept	7	0.7710	9.0791	0.00001738
X Variable - Time	2	0.1667	12.0000	0.00000214

$b_0 = 7$
$b_1 = 2$
$t_{\text{data}} = 12$
p-value = 0.00000214

FIGURE 13.11 Excel regression results.

FIGURE 13.12 Minitab regression results.

The regression equation is
Score = 7.00 + 2.00 Time

Predictor	Coef	SE Coef	T	P
Constant	7.0000	0.7710	9.08	0.000
Time	2.0000	0.1667	12.00	0.000

$b_0 = 7$
$b_1 = 2$
$t_{data} = 12$
$p\text{-value} \approx 0$

S = 1.22474   R-Sq = 94.7%   R-Sq(adj) = 94.1%

Now You Can Do
Exercises 19–22,
parts (a)–(c).

Step 4 Since the p-value of about 0.000 is $\leq \alpha = 0.01$, we reject H_0. There is evidence at level of significance $\alpha = 0.01$ for a linear relationship between time and score. ■

3 Confidence Interval for Slope β_1

Recall that in Chapter 8 we constructed a confidence interval estimate for a population parameter, consisting of an interval of numbers that contain the parameter with a certain confidence level. Similarly, we can construct a confidence interval for the slope of the population regression equation β_1.

Confidence Interval for β_1

When the regression assumptions are met, a $100(1 - \alpha)\%$ confidence interval for β_1 is given by

$$b_1 \pm t_{\alpha/2} \cdot \frac{s}{\sqrt{\sum(x - \bar{x})^2}}$$

where b_1 is the point estimate of the slope β_1 of the population regression equation, s is the standard error of the estimate, and $t_{\alpha/2}$ has $n - 2$ degrees of freedom.

Margin of Error E

The margin of error for a $100(1 - \alpha)\%$ confidence interval for β_1 is given by

$$E = t_{\alpha/2} \cdot \frac{s}{\sqrt{\sum(x - \bar{x})^2}}$$

Thus, the confidence interval for β_1 takes the form $b_1 \pm E$.

Example 13.6 Confidence interval for the slope β_1

Construct a 95% confidence interval for the slope β_1 of the population regression equation for the memory-test data in Example 13.5.

Solution

The regression assumptions were verified in Example 13.5, where we found:
- $b_1 = 2$,
- $s = 1.224744871$, and
- $\sum(x - \bar{x})^2 = 54$.

From the t table (Appendix Table D), we find that, for 95% confidence, $t_{\alpha/2}$ for $n - 2 = 10 - 2 = 8$ degrees of freedom is $t_{\alpha/2} = 2.306$. So, our margin of error E is

$$E = t_{\alpha/2} \cdot \frac{s}{\sqrt{\sum(x - \bar{x})^2}} = (2.306)\left(\frac{1.224744874}{\sqrt{54}}\right) \approx 0.3843$$

Now You Can Do
Exercises 23–30.

The 95% confidence interval for β_1 is then given by

$$b_1 \pm E = 2 \pm 0.3843 = (1.6157, 2.3843)$$ ■

What Do These Numbers Mean?	• The margin of error $E = 0.3843$ means that, when we repeatedly take samples from this population, 95% of the time the sample estimate b_1 will be within $E = 0.3843$ of the unknown value of the slope β_1 of the population regression line. • Thus, we are 95% confident that the interval (1.6157, 2.3843) captures the slope β_1 of the population regression line. • Since β_1 is the increase in memory-test score per added minute of memorization, *we are 95% confident that, for each additional minute of memorization, the increase in memory-test score will lie between 1.6157 and 2.3843 points.* ◢

4 Using Confidence Intervals to Perform the *t* Test for the Slope β_1

As in earlier sections, we may use a $100(1 - \alpha)\%$ *t* confidence interval for the slope β_1 to perform the *t* test for β_1, which is a two-tailed test.

> **Equivalence of a Two-Tailed *t* Test About β_1 and a *t* Confidence Interval for β_1**
> • If a $100(1 - \alpha)\%$ *t* confidence interval for β_1 does not contain zero, then we would reject $H_0 : \beta_1 = 0$ for level of significance α, and conclude that a linear relationship exists between *x* and *y*.
> • If a $100(1 - \alpha)\%$ *t* confidence interval for β_1 does contain zero, then we would not reject $H_0 : \beta_1 = 0$ for level of significance α.

Example 13.7 Using confidence intervals to perform the *t* test for the slope β_1

 textms

a. Construct and interpret a 99% confidence interval for the slope β_1 for the text messaging data in Table 13.1.

b. Use the confidence interval in **(a)** to test whether a linear relationship exists between age and text messages, using level of significance $\alpha = 0.01$.

Solution

a. The regression assumptions were verified in Example 13.2. Also,
   • In Example 13.1, we found $b_1 = -1.5$.
   • In Example 13.3, we calculated $s = 2.408318916$, and $\Sigma(x - \bar{x})^2 = 330$.

From the *t* table, we find that, for 99% confidence, $t_{\alpha/2}$ for $n - 2 = 10 - 2 = 8$ degrees of freedom is $t_{\alpha/2} = 3.355$. So, our margin of error E is

$$E = t_{\alpha/2} \cdot \frac{s}{\sqrt{\Sigma(x - \bar{x})^2}} = (3.355)\left|\frac{2.408318916}{\sqrt{330}}\right| \approx 0.4448$$

The 99% confidence interval for β_1 is then given by

$$b_1 \pm E = -1.5 \pm 0.4448 = (-1.9448, -1.0552)$$

We are 99% confident that the interval $(-1.9448, -1.0552)$ captures the slope β_1 of the population regression line. That is, we are 99% confident that, for each additional year of age, the *decrease* in the number of text messages lies between 1.9448 and 1.0552.

b. The hypotheses are

$H_0 : \beta_1 = 0$ There is no linear relationship between age and text messages.
$H_a : \beta_1 \neq 0$ There is a linear relationship between age and text messages.

Since the confidence interval from **(a)** does not contain zero, we may conclude that a linear relationship exists between age and text messages, at level of significance $\alpha = 0.01$. ∎

CASE STUDY

How Fair Is the Scoring in Scrabble?

In this Case Study, we consider the frequency and point values of Scrabble tiles. Table 13.5 shows the relative frequency in the English language, the frequency (number of tiles) in Scrabble, and the point value in Scrabble.

Table 13.5 Frequency in English, frequency in Scrabble, and Scrabble point value of the letters in the alphabet

Letter	Rel. freq. in English language	Frequency in Scrabble	Point value in Scrabble	Letter	Rel. freq. in English language	Frequency in Scrabble	Point value in Scrabble
A	0.073	9	1	N	0.078	6	1
B	0.009	2	3	O	0.074	8	1
C	0.030	2	3	P	0.027	2	3
D	0.044	4	2	Q	0.003	1	10
E	0.130	12	1	R	0.077	6	1
F	0.028	2	4	S	0.063	4	1
G	0.016	3	2	T	0.093	6	1
H	0.035	2	4	U	0.027	4	1
I	0.074	9	1	V	0.013	2	4
J	0.002	1	8	W	0.016	2	4
K	0.003	1	5	X	0.005	1	8
L	0.035	4	1	Y	0.019	2	4
M	0.025	2	3	Z	0.001	1	10

First of all, what is the relationship between the tile frequencies in Scrabble and the letter frequencies in the English language? Figure 13.13 shows a scatterplot of the tile frequencies in Scrabble against the letter frequencies in the English language. There appears to be a positive relationship between the two variables. That is, as the English frequencies increase, game frequencies also tend to increase.

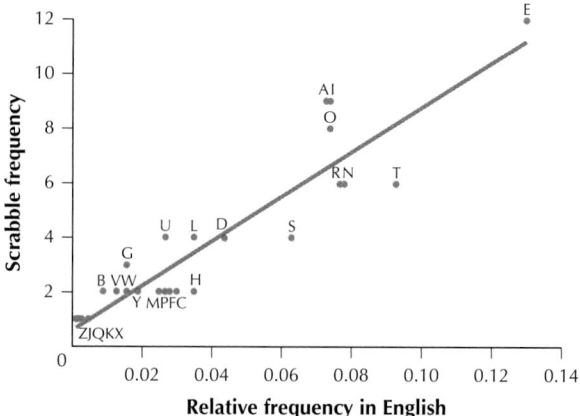

FIGURE 13.13
Scatterplot of Scrabble frequency versus English frequency of letters, with regression line.

Note that the letters above the regression line occur "too frequently" in the game, whereas the letters below the line occur "not frequently enough." Playing typical English words during a game of Scrabble would tend to leave you with a rack of letters similar to those above the regression line. Note that S is one of the letters that is rarer in the game than in the language.

Figure 13.14 displays the Minitab results from a regression of the tile frequencies against the English language relative frequencies. The regression equation is

$$\hat{y} = 81.5(\text{relative frequency in English}) + 0.636$$

The slope is positive, which concurs with the scatterplot in Figure 13.13.

Next we turn to the hypothesis test:

$H_0: \beta_1 = 0$ There is no linear relationship between Scrabble frequency and English relative frequency.

$H_a: \beta_1 \neq 0$ There is a linear relationship between Scrabble frequency and English relative frequency.

FIGURE 13.14
Minitab regression output.

```
The regression equation is
Scrabble Freq = 0.636 + 81.5 Rel Freq Eng

Predictor        Coef  SE Coef      T      P
Constant       0.6362   0.3484   1.83  0.080
Rel Freq Eng   81.458    6.856  11.88  0.000


S = 1.16096    R-Sq = 85.5%   R-Sq(adj) = 84.9%


Analysis of Variance

Source          DF       SS      MS       F      P
Regression       1   190.27  190.27  141.17  0.000
Residual Error  24    32.35    1.35
Total           25   222.62
```

The 0.000 in red represents the p-value for the t test. Since this p-value is smaller than any α, we reject the null hypothesis that there is no linear relationship between the game frequencies and the English frequencies. Does the model fit the data well? The coefficient of determination r^2 is 0.855, which is good, and the correlation coefficient r equals 0.924, which indicates that the variables are positively correlated.

But the fit really could be better. Look at the value of s, the standard error of the estimate: $s \approx 1.16$. This means that, given the English language frequency of a letter, the estimate of the tile frequency will typically differ from the actual tile frequency by more than one tile.

Next, what is the relationship between the Scrabble point values and the English relative frequencies? Figure 13.15 shows a scatterplot of these two variables. The first

FIGURE 13.15
Scatterplot of Scrabble frequency versus English frequency. Linear regression would not be appropriate.

thing you might notice about this relationship is that it is not linear. Therefore, it would not be appropriate to perform linear regression on this data set.

We can, nevertheless, make some descriptive remarks.

- What is a "good" Scrabble tile to pick up? In the best case, it would be a letter with high English frequency worth lots of Scrabble game points. Unfortunately, the two do not go together. The high-frequency letters like E and T have low point values, and the high point-value letters like Q and Z have low frequencies. But we can still make comparisons.

- Which would you rather pick up, a D or a G? It would seem that D would be preferable since it has the same point value as G with much higher English frequency.

- Which do you prefer between J and X? They are worth the same points, but X has a higher frequency in English, so it is easier to make words with it in the game. The letter H seems to have a good combination of high points and moderate frequency. ■

STEP-BY-STEP TECHNOLOGY GUIDE: Regression Analysis

Data from Example 13.5 (page 640) are used to illustrate the steps.

TI-83/84

Step 1 Enter the **X (Time)** data in **L1** and the **Y (Score)** data in **L2**.
Step 2 Press **STAT**, highlight **CALC**, and press **4** to choose **LinReg(ax+b)**. On the home screen, the following command appears: **LinReg(ax+b)**.
Step 3 Press **ENTER**. The output shows **y = ax+b**, **a=7**, **b=2**. The TI-83/84 denotes the slope β_1 as **a** and the **y** intercept b_0 as **b**. Thus the TI-83/84 is telling you that the estimated regression equation is $\hat{y} = 2x+7$.
Step 4 Now Press **STAT** again and press the right arrow key until **TESTS** is highlighted.

Step 5 Press the **down arrow** key until **E** is highlighted (for **LinRegTTest**).
Step 6 Press **ENTER**. The LinRegTTest menu appears.
Step 7 For **Xlist**, enter **L1** (or whichever list you entered the X data in).
Step 8 For **Ylist**, enter **L2** (or whichever list you entered the Y data in).
Step 9 For **Freq**, enter **1**, and for β & ρ highlight "$\neq$ 0".
Step 10 Move the cursor over **Calculate**, make sure all your entries are correct, and press **ENTER**. The results are as shown in Figure 13.10 (page 641).

EXCEL

Step 1 Enter the "Time" variable in column **A** and the "Score" variable in column **B**.
Step 2 Click on **Data > Data Analysis > Regression** and click **OK**.
Step 3 For **Input Y Range**, select cells **B1 − B10**. For **Input X Range**, select cells **A1 − A10**.

Step 4 If you would like to verify the regression assumptions, then select **Residual Plots** and **Normal Probability Plots**.
Step 5 Click **OK**. The results are as shown in Figure 13.11 (page 641).

MINITAB

Step 1 Enter the "Time" variable in **C1** and the "Score" variable in **C2**.
Step 2 Click on **Stat > Regression > Regression**.
Step 3 Select "Score" as your **Response Variable** and "Time" as your **Predictor Variable**.

Step 4 If you would like to verify the regression assumptions, click the button labeled **Graphs** and select **Four in One**.
Step 5 Click **OK** twice. The results are as shown in Figure 13.12 (page 642).

Section 13.1 Summary

1 This section examines inferential methods for regression analysis. The regression model, or the (population) regression equation, is $y = \beta_1 x + \beta_0 + \varepsilon$, where β_0 is the y intercept of the population regression line, β_1 is the slope of the population regression line, and ε is the error term.

2 A hypothesis test may be performed to determine whether a linear relationship exists between x and y.

3 We can construct confidence intervals for the true value of the population regression slope β_1 since it is unknown.

Section 13.1 Exercises

CLARIFYING THE CONCEPTS

1. What is the difference between the regression equation (calculated using the sample) and the population regression equation?

2. What are the four regression model assumptions?

3. How do we go about verifying the regression model assumptions?

4. What is the difference between b_0 and b_1 on the one hand and β_0 and β_1 on the other hand?

5. What does it mean for the relationship between x and y when β_1 equals 0?

6. What is the difference between s and s_x?

PRACTICING THE TECHNIQUES

For Exercises 7–14, you are given the regression equation.

    a. Calculate the predicted values.

    b. Compute the residuals.

    c. Construct a scatterplot of the residuals versus the predicted values.

    d. Use technology to construct a normal probability plot of the residuals.

    e. Verify that the regression assumptions are valid.

7.

x	y
1	15
2	20
3	20
4	25
5	25

$\hat{y} = 2.5x + 13.5$

8.

x	y
0	10
5	20
10	45
15	50
20	75

$\hat{y} = 3.2x + 8$

9.

x	y
−5	0
−4	8
−3	8
−2	16
−1	16

$\hat{y} = 4x + 21.6$

10.

x	y
−3	−5
−1	−15
1	−20
3	−25
5	−30

$\hat{y} = -3x - 16$

11.

x	y
10	100
20	95
30	85
40	85
50	80

$\hat{y} = -0.5x + 104$

12.

x	y
0	11
20	11
40	16
60	21
80	26

$\hat{y} = 0.2x + 9$

13.

x	y
1	1
2	1
3	2
4	3
5	3

$\hat{y} = 0.6x + 0.2$

14.

x	y
1	6
2	5
2	4
2	3
3	2

$\hat{y} = -2x + 8$

For Exercises 15–18, follow these steps. Assume that the regression model assumptions are valid.

    a. Find t_{crit} for a two-tailed test with $\alpha = 0.05$ and df $= n - 2$.

    b. Calculate s.

c. Compute $\Sigma (x - \bar{x})^2$.

d. Calculate t_{data}.

e. Perform the hypothesis test for the linear relationship between x and y, using the critical-value method and $\alpha = 0.05$.

15. Data in Exercise 7, where $b_1 = 2.5$
16. Data in Exercise 8, where $b_1 = 3.2$
17. Data in Exercise 9, where $b_1 = 4.0$
18. Data in Exercise 10, where $b_1 = -3$

For Exercises 19–22, follow these steps. Assume that the regression model assumptions are valid.

a. Calculate s.

b. Compute $\Sigma (x - \bar{x})^2$.

c. Calculate t_{data}.

d. Find p-value $= 2 \cdot P(t > |t_{\text{data}}|)$.

e. Perform the hypothesis test for the linear relationship between x and y using the p-value method and $\alpha = 0.05$.

19. Data in Exercise 11, where $b_1 = -0.5$
20. Data in Exercise 12, where $b_1 = 0.2$
21. Data in Exercise 13, where $b_1 = 0.6$
22. Data in Exercises 14, where $b_1 = -2$

For Exercises 23–30, follow these steps. Assume that the regression model assumptions are valid.

a. Find $t_{\alpha/2}$ for a 95% confidence interval for β_1.

b. Find the margin of error E.

c. Construct a 95% confidence interval for β_1.

d. Use the confidence interval from (c) to perform the t test for β_1 at level of significance $\alpha = 0.05$.

23. Data in Exercise 7
24. Data in Exercise 8
25. Data in Exercise 9
26. Data in Exercise 10
27. Data in Exercise 11
28. Data in Exercise 12
29. Data in Exercise 13
30. Data in Exercise 14

APPLYING THE CONCEPTS

For Exercises 31–36, follow steps (a) and (b).

a. Verify the regression model assumptions. (*Hint:* You can use either Excel or Minitab; see the Step-by-Step Technology Guide on page 646.)

b. Perform the hypothesis test for the linear relationship between x and y, using level of significance $\alpha = 0.05$.

31. **Volume and Weight.** The following table contains the volume (x, in cubic meters) and weight (y, in kilograms) of five randomly chosen packages shipped to a local college. 🏔 **volweight**

Volume (x)	Weight (y)
4	10
8	16
12	25
16	30
20	35

32. **Family Size and Pets.** Shown in the accompanying table are the number of family members (x) in a random sample taken from a suburban neighborhood, along with the number of pets (y) belonging to each family. 🏔 **familypet**

Family size (x)	Pets (y)
2	1
3	2
4	2
5	3
6	3

33. **World Temperatures.** Listed in the following table are the low (x) and high (y) temperatures for a particular day, measured in degrees Fahrenheit, for a random sample of cities worldwide. 🏔 **worldtemp**

City	Low (x)	High (y)
Kolkata	57	77
London	36	45
Montreal	7	21
Rome	39	55
San Juan	70	83
Shanghai	34	45

34. **NCAA Power Ratings.** The accompanying table shows the team's winning percentage (x) and power rating (y) for the 2011 NCAA Basketball Tournament, according to www.teamrankings.com. 🏔 **ncaa**

School	Win%(x)	Rating (y)
Ohio State	91.9	121.0
Kansas	92.1	119.5
San Diego State	91.4	118.1
Duke	86.5	117.8
Connecticut	77.5	117.5
Pittsburgh	82.4	116.9
Kentucky	76.3	116.6
Notre Dame	79.4	116.3

35. **Midterm Exams and Overall Grade.** Can you predict how you will do in a course based on the result of the midterm exam only? The midterm exam score and the overall grade were recorded for a random sample of 10 students in an elementary statistics course. The results are shown in the following table. 🏔 **midexam**

Student	Midterm exam score (x)	Overall grade (y)
1	50	65
2	90	80
3	70	75
4	80	75
5	60	45
6	90	95
7	90	85
8	80	80
9	70	65
10	70	70

36. Stock Prices. Would you expect there to be a relationship between the price (x) of a stock and its change in price (y) on a particular day? The table provides stock price and stock price change for June 1, 2011, for a random sample of 8 stocks. 🌐 **stocks**

Stock	Price (x)	Change (y)
Bank of America	11.38	−0.36
Sirius XM Radio	2.3	−0.05
Microsoft	24.49	−0.52
General Electric	19.35	−0.28
Intel	22.34	−0.17
Pfizer	21.17	−0.28
Dell	15.75	−0.34
Lucent	5.69	0.02

For Exercises 37–42, do the following for the indicated data.
   a. Calculate the margin of error E for a 95% confidence interval for β_1.
   b. Construct a 95% confidence interval for β_1.
   c. Interpret the confidence interval.
37. Data from Exercise 31
38. Data from Exercise 32
39. Data from Exercise 33
40. Data from Exercise 34
41. Data from Exercise 35
42. Data from Exercise 36

BRINGING IT ALL TOGETHER
SAT Reading and Math Scores. Use this information for Exercises 43–47. The table shows the SAT scores for five states as reported by the College Board. We are interested in whether a linear relationship exists between the SAT Reading score (x) and the SAT Math score (y). 🌐 **statesat**

State	SAT Reading	SAT Math
New York	497	510
Connecticut	515	515
Massachusetts	518	523
New Jersey	501	514
New Hampshire	522	521

43. What Result Might We Expect? Consider the accompanying scatterplot of Math score versus Reading score. Is there evidence for or against the null hypothesis that no linear relationship exists? Explain.

44. Consider the following graphics. Is there strong evidence that the regression assumptions are violated?

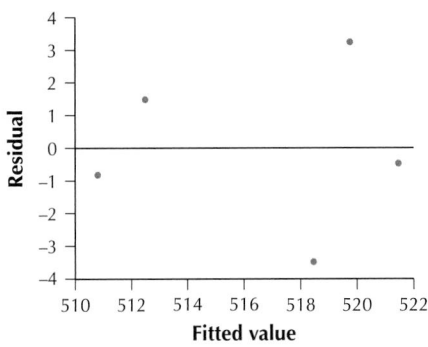

Plot of residuals versus fitted values.

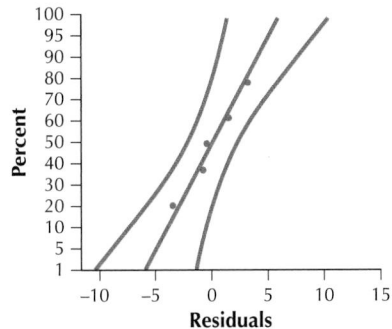

Normality plot of residuals.

45. Test whether a linear relationship exists between the SAT reading score and the SAT Math score using level of significance $\alpha = 0.10$.
46. Construct and interpret a 90% confidence interval for a slope β_1.
47. Do your inferences in Exercises 45 and 46 agree with each other? Explain.
48. Batting Average and Runs Scored. The table shows the top ten hitters in Major League Baseball for 2007. We are interested in estimating the number of runs scored (y) using the player's batting average (x).

Player	Team	Batting average (x)	Runs scored (y)
M. Ordonez	Detroit Tigers	.363	117
I. Suzuki	Seattle Mariners	.351	111
P. Polanco	Detroit Tigers	.341	105
M. Holliday	Colorado Rockies	.340	120
J. Posada	New York Yankees	.338	91
C. Jones	Atlanta Braves	.337	108
D. Ortiz	Boston Red Sox	.332	116
H. Ramirez	Florida Marlins	.332	125
E. Renteria	Atlanta Braves	.332	87
C. Utley	Philadelphia Phillies	.332	104

   a. Construct a residuals versus predicted values plot. What type of pattern do you see?
   b. Which regression assumption is violated?
   c. Should we construct a confidence interval or perform a hypothesis test for the slope of the regression line?
   d. Is it still appropriate to report the descriptive statistics we learned in Sections 4.2 and 4.3? Why?

49. Suppose we have a regression equation whose slope was not significant (that is, the null hypothesis was not rejected). *What if* we add five new data values to the original data set, and all five data values are identical, $(\bar{x}, \bar{y})$. How and why will this affect the following statistics? Will the statistic increase, decrease, or remain unchanged, or is there insufficient information to determine? (*Hint:* The data point $(\bar{x}, \bar{y})$ always lies on the estimated regression line.)

a. *n*
b. SSE
c. SST
d. SSR
e. MSE
f. MSR

50. Refer to Exercise 49. How and why will the change affect the following items?

a. t_{data}
b. r^2
c. *s*
d. *p*-value
e. Conclusion

51. Suppose a regression analysis of *y* on *x* was found to be significant (that is, the null hypothesis was rejected). *What if* we get ten new data values, all with different values of *x* and *all of which can be found on the estimated regression line of the original model.* How and why will this change affect the following statistics? Will the statistic increase, decrease, or remain unchanged, or is there insufficient information to determine?

a. *n*
b. SSE
c. SST
d. SSR
e. MSE
f. MSR

52. Refer to Exercise 51. How and why will this change affect the following measures?

a. t_{data}
b. r^2
c. *s*
d. *p*-value
e. Conclusion

53. Challenge Exercise. Suppose a regression analysis of *y* on *x* was found to be significant (that is, the null hypothesis was rejected) and the slope $b_1 > 0$. Consider the observation (max *x*, *y*), which represents the (*x*, *y*) data value for the maximum value of *x* in the data set. Suppose the residual for (max *x*, *y*) is negative. *What if* we increase max *x* by an arbitrary amount *c* so that the new data value is (max *x* + *c*, *y*). (All other data values in the data set are unchanged.) How will this increase affect the following measures? Will they increase, decrease, or remain unchanged, or is there insufficient information to determine the effect?

a. *n*
b. SSE
c. SST
d. SSR
e. MSE
f. MSR
g. *F*

54. Challenge Exercise. Refer to Exercise 53. How and why will the change affect the following measures?

a. t_{data}
b. r^2
c. *s*
d. *p*-value
e. Conclusion

For Exercises 55–57, you can use Excel, Minitab, or some other statistical computing software to solve the following problems.

a. Verify the regression model assumptions.
b. Construct and interpret a 95% confidence interval for β_1.

c. Based on the confidence interval constructed in **(b)**, would you expect the hypothesis test to reject the null hypothesis that $\beta_1 = 0$?
d. Test at $\alpha = 0.05$ whether a linear relationship exists between *x* and *y*.

55. Open the **Darts** data set, which we used for the Chapter 3 Case Study. Use the Dow Jones Industrial Average (*x*) to estimate the pros' performance (*y*). **Darts**

56. Open the **Nutrition** data set. Estimate the number of calories per gram (*y*) using the amount of fat per gram (*x*). **Nutrition**

57. Open the **PulseandTemp** data set. Estimate body temperature (*y*) using heart rate (*x*). **PulseandTemp**

Crash Tests. Use Excel, Minitab, or some other statistical computing software for Exercises 58–61. Open the **Crash** data set, which contains information about the severity of injuries sustained by crash dummies when the National Transportation Safety Board crashed automobiles into a wall at 35 miles per hour. **Crash**

58. The variable *head_inj* contains a measure of the severity of the head injury sustained by the dummies. The variable *chest_in* is a measure of the severity of the chest injury suffered by the crash dummies.

a. Would you expect there to be a linear relationship between the severity of head injuries and chest injuries?
b. Construct a scatterplot of the *head_inj* against *chest_in*. Describe the relationship between the variables.
c. If we were to perform a regression analysis using these two variables, is it clear which of the two variables we should label as the predictor and which we should label as the response? Explain.

59. Perform a regression of the head injury severity (*y*) on the chest injury severity (*x*).

a. What is the regression equation? Write it out in words and numbers so that a nonstatistician would understand it.
b. Perform the appropriate hypothesis test using $\alpha = 0.01$.
c. Clearly interpret the meaning of the slope estimate b_1.
d. Construct and interpret a 99% confidence interval for the true slope β_1 of the relationship between severity of head injury and severity of chest injury. How does your confidence interval support your conclusion in **(b)**?

60. The variable *lleg_inj* contains a measure of the severity of the injury sustained by the dummies' left legs. The variable *weight* contains the weight of the vehicles.

a. Would you expect there to be a linear relationship between the severity of left leg injuries and the weight of the vehicles?
b. Construct a scatterplot of the *lleg_inj* against weight. Describe the relationship between the variables.
c. If we were to perform a regression analysis using these two variables, is it clear which of the two variables we should label as the predictor and which we should label as the response? Explain.

61. Perform a regression of the leg injury severity (y) on the vehicle weight (x).

    a. What is the regression equation? Write it out in words and numbers so that a nonstatistician would understand it.

    b. Is the relationship significant? Perform the appropriate hypothesis test using level of significance $\alpha = 0.5$.

    c. Construct and interpret a 95% confidence interval for the true slope β_1 of the relationship between vehicle weight and severity of left leg injury. How does your confidence interval support your conclusion in **(b)**?

13.2   Confidence Intervals and Prediction Intervals

OBJECTIVES By the end of this section, I will be able to . . .

1   Construct confidence intervals for the mean value of y for a given value of x.

2   Construct prediction intervals for a randomly chosen value of y for a given value of x.

1 Construct Confidence Intervals for the Mean Value of y for a Given x

Suppose a cell phone company would like to increase sales to 20-year-olds, and therefore wants to estimate the number of text messages sent by 20-year-old men and women. In earlier sections we learned how to calculate the predicted value $\hat{y}$ using the regression equation $\hat{y} = b_1 x + b_0$. For example, in Example 13.1 (page 634), we saw that the predicted number of text messages for the 20-year-old texter is $\hat{y} = (-1.5)(20) + 60.6 = 30.6$ messages. However, this estimate of 30.6 messages is only a point estimate, similar to using the sample mean $\bar{x}$ alone to estimate the unknown population mean μ. We learned in Section 8.1 about the pitfalls of point estimates, such as the lack of a measure of confidence associated with the estimate. So, just as we learned about confidence intervals for μ in Chapter 8, in this section we will learn how to construct:

* confidence intervals for the mean value of y for a given value of x, and

* prediction intervals for a randomly chosen value of y for a given value of x.

Refer to Figure 13.3 (reproduced here from page 636), which illustrates the regression assumptions. Note that, for $x = 20$, there is assumed to be an entire population of y-values. The cell phone company is interested in this population, and would like to construct a confidence interval for the mean number of text message sent by all 20-year-olds.

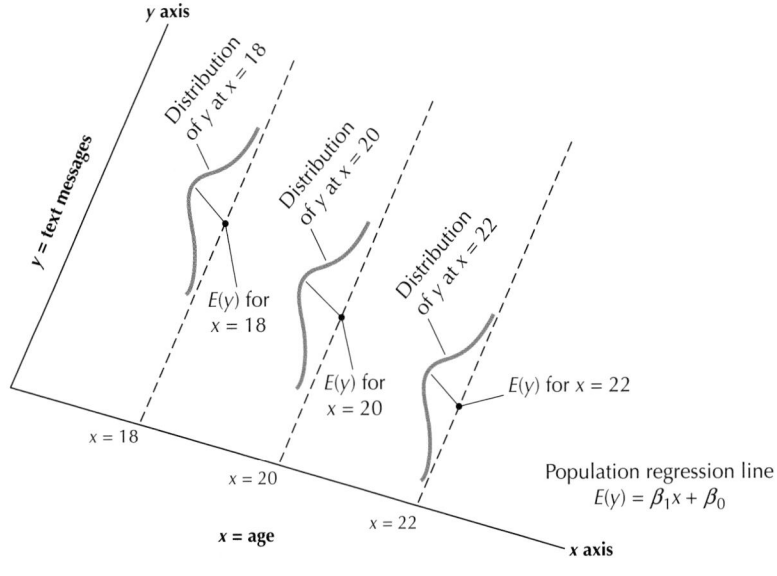

FIGURE 13.3
For $x = 20$ years old, there is an entire population of y = number of text messages.

> **Confidence Interval for the Mean Value of y for a Given x**
>
> A $100(1 - \alpha)\%$ confidence interval for the mean response, that is, for the population mean of all values of y, given a value of x, may be constructed using the following lower and upper bounds:
>
> $$\text{Lower bound:} \quad \hat{y} - t_{\alpha/2} \cdot s \sqrt{\frac{1}{n} + \frac{(x^* - \bar{x})^2}{\sum(x_i - \bar{x})^2}}$$
>
> $$\text{Upper bound:} \quad \hat{y} + t_{\alpha/2} \cdot s \sqrt{\frac{1}{n} + \frac{(x^* - \bar{x})^2}{\sum(x_i - \bar{x})^2}}$$
>
> where x^* represents the given value of the predictor variable x, $s = \sqrt{\dfrac{MSE}{n - 2}}$ represents the standard error of the estimate, n is the number of observations, $\bar{x}$ is the sample mean of the x-values, and $t_{\alpha/2}$ is the critical value with $n - 2$ degrees of freedom. The requirements for the confidence interval are met if the regression assumptions are met.

Let's look at an example of constructing and interpreting such a confidence interval.

Example 13.8	Constructing and interpreting a confidence interval for the mean value of *y* for a given *x*

Construct and interpret a 95% confidence interval for the population mean number of text message sent for all 20-year-olds.

Solution

Example 13.2 showed that the regression assumptions for this data set are met, thus allowing us to construct this confidence interval.

- Using our given value $x^* = 20$, we calculate the point estimate as follows: $\hat{y} = (-1.5)(20) + 60.6 = 30.6$.
- The data set in Table 13.1 shows that there are $n = 10$ people, so that the degrees of freedom for the t critical value is $n - 2 = 8$. From the t table (Appendix Table D in the Appendix), the t critical value for confidence level 95% is $t_{\alpha/2} = 2.306$.
- In Example 13.3 we calculated $\sum(x_i - \bar{x})^2 = 330$ and the standard error of the estimate to be $s \approx 2.4083$.
- The Minitab output in Figure 13.16 shows that $\bar{x} = 27$ years of age.

```
Descriptive Statistics: age
Variable        Mean
age             27.00
```

FIGURE 13.16 Minitab shows $\bar{x} = 27$.

Thus,

$$\text{Lower bound:} \quad \hat{y} - t_{\alpha/2} \cdot s \sqrt{\frac{1}{n} + \frac{(x^* - \bar{x})^2}{\sum(x_i - \bar{x})^2}}$$

$$\approx 30.6 - (2.306) \cdot 2.4083 \sqrt{\frac{1}{10} + \frac{(20 - 27)^2}{330}} \approx 27.8317$$

$$\text{Upper bound:} \quad \hat{y} + t_{\alpha/2} \cdot s \sqrt{\frac{1}{n} + \frac{(x^* - \bar{x})^2}{\sum(x_i - \bar{x})^2}}$$

$$= 30.6 + (2.306) \cdot 2.4083 \sqrt{\frac{1}{10} + \frac{(20 - 27)^2}{330}} \approx 33.3683$$

We are 95% confident that the population mean number of text messages for all 20-year-olds lies between 27.8317 and 33.3683 messages. ∎

CAUTION Extrapolation (page 178) continues to be a danger for confidence intervals and prediction intervals. For example, it would not have been wise to ask for a confidence interval for the population mean number of text messages sent by all 50-year-old people because $x = 50$ lies outside the range of x.

Now You Can Do
Exercises 3–8.

2 Construct Prediction Intervals for an Individual Value of y for a Given x

The formula for constructing a prediction interval for an individual random value of y is similar to that for the confidence interval for the mean y, except that the margin of error is larger. We talk about why this is so later on in this section.

Prediction Interval for a Randomly Selected Value of y for a Given x

A $100(1 - \alpha)\%$ prediction interval for a randomly selected value of y given a value of x may be constructed using the following lower and upper bounds:

$$\text{Lower bound: } \hat{y} - t_{\alpha/2} \cdot s\sqrt{1 + \frac{1}{n} + \frac{(x^* - \bar{x})^2}{\sum(x_i - \bar{x})^2}}$$

$$\text{Upper bound: } \hat{y} + t_{\alpha/2} \cdot s\sqrt{1 + \frac{1}{n} + \frac{(x^* - \bar{x})^2}{\sum(x_i - \bar{x})^2}}$$

where x^* represents the given value of the predictor variable x, $s = \sqrt{\frac{MSE}{n - 2}}$ represents the standard error of the estimate, n is the number of observations, $\bar{x}$ is the sample mean of the x values, and $t_{\alpha/2}$ is the critical value with $n - 2$ degrees of freedom. The requirements for the confidence interval are met if the regression assumptions are met.

Example 13.9 Constructing and interpreting a prediction interval for a randomly selected value of y for a given x

Construct and interpret a 95% prediction interval for the number of text messages sent by a randomly selected 20-year-old.

Solution

Since the requirements for the prediction interval are the same as for the confidence interval, we know from Example 13.8 that the requirements for constructing the prediction interval are met. Using the values obtained in Example 13.8, we calculate the lower and upper bounds as follows:

$$\text{Lower bound: } \hat{y} - t_{\alpha/2} \cdot s\sqrt{1 + \frac{1}{n} + \frac{(x^* - \bar{x})^2}{\sum(x_i - \bar{x})^2}}$$

$$\approx 30.6 - (2.306) \cdot 2.4083\sqrt{1 + \frac{1}{10} + \frac{(20 - 27)^2}{330}} \approx 24.3947$$

$$\text{Upper bound: } \hat{y} + t_{\alpha/2} \cdot s\sqrt{1 + \frac{1}{n} + \frac{(x^* - \bar{x})^2}{\sum(x_i - \bar{x})^2}}$$

$$= 30.6 + (2.306) \cdot 2.4083\sqrt{1 + \frac{1}{10} + \frac{(20 - 27)^2}{330}} \approx 36.8053$$

Now You Can Do
Exercises 9–14.

We are 95% confident that the number of text messages sent by a randomly selected 20-year-old lies between 24.3947 and 36.8053. ∎

Developing Your
Statistical Sense

Why Are Prediction Intervals Wider?

The prediction interval (24.3947, 36.8053) from Example 13.9 is *wider* than the corresponding confidence interval from Example 13.8. This is true is general, but why? Note that the only difference in the formulas for the prediction interval, compared to the confidence interval, is the "1 +" inside the radical in the formula for the prediction interval. This ensures that the prediction interval always has a larger margin of error than the confidence interval for a given x. This larger margin of error reflects the greater variability of individual responses compared to the mean response.

To see how individual values have greater variability than their means, consider that you would probably stand a better chance of guessing the class mean height to within 2 inches rather than the height of a randomly chosen student. This is because the variability of the randomly selected y is larger than that of the mean y. In the one-sample case, this is because the standard deviation σ of a particular value of x is always larger than the standard deviation of the sample mean $\bar{x}$ is $\sigma_{\bar{x}} = \sigma/\sqrt{n}$. Similarly, the prediction interval for a randomly chosen y is wider than the confidence interval for the mean value of y, for a given value of x. ◢

Now You Can Do
Exercises 15 and 16.

Finally, we illustrate the use of technology to construct confidence intervals and prediction intervals.

Example 13.10   Confidence intervals and prediction intervals using technology

Use Minitab to construct a 95% confidence interval for the population mean number of text messages sent by all 20-year-olds, and to construct a 95% prediction interval for the number of text messages sent by a randomly selected 20-year-old.

Solution

We use the instructions provided in the Step-by-Step Technology Guide below. Figure 13.17 shows the Minitab results. ■

```
Predicted Values

Fit     SE Fit       95% CI            95% PI
30.6    1.201    (27.832, 33.368    (24.395, 36.805)
```

FIGURE 13.17 Minitab results for confidence interval and prediction interval.

STEP-BY-STEP TECHNOLOGY GUIDE: Confidence Intervals and Prediction Intervals

MINITAB

Step 1   Enter the x data into column **C1** and the y data into column **C2**.
Step 2   Select the **Stat** menu, highlight **Regression**, and select **Regression** . . . .
Step 3   For **Response**, enter the y data from column **C2**. For **Predictors**, enter the x data from column **C1**.

Step 4   Click **Options** . . . . In the space for **Prediction intervals for new observations**, enter the desired value x^*. Then enter the desired **Confidence level**. Then click **OK** and click **OK** again.

Section 13.2 Summary

1 A confidence interval may be constructed for the mean response y for a given value of x. The confidence interval takes the form *point estimate* $\pm$ *margin of error*, where the point estimate is $\hat{y}$.

2 A prediction interval may be constructed for a random value of y for a given value of x. This prediction interval is similar to the confidence interval for the mean response y, except that the margin of error is always larger. Thus, the prediction interval is always wider than the confidence interval.

Section 13.2 Exercises

CLARIFYING THE CONCEPTS

1. Explain the difference between the confidence interval and the prediction interval we learned about in this section.

2. True or false: For a given value of x, the confidence interval is always wider than the prediction interval.

PRACTICING THE TECHNIQUES

For Exercises 3–8, use the data provided to construct a 95% confidence interval for the mean value of y for the given value of x. The regression equation is provided; assume the regression assumptions are met.

3.

x	y
1	15
2	20
3	20
4	25
5	25

$\hat{y} = 2.5x + 13.5$; $x = 3$

4.

x	y
0	10
5	20
10	45
15	50
20	75

$\hat{y} = 3.2x + 8$; $x = 10$

5.

x	y
−5	0
−4	8
−3	8
−2	16
−1	16

$\hat{y} = 4x + 21.6$; $x = -4$

6.

x	y
−3	−5
−1	−15
1	−20
3	−25
5	−30

$\hat{y} = -3x - 16$; $x = 3$

7.

x	y
10	100
20	95
30	85
40	85
50	80

$\hat{y} = -0.5x + 104$; $x = 10$

8.

x	y
0	11
20	11
40	16
60	21
80	26

$\hat{y} = 0.2x + 9$; $x = 20$

For Exercises 9–14, use the data from the indicated exercise to construct a 95% prediction interval for a randomly chosen value of y for the given value of x. Assume the regression assumptions are met.

9. The data in Exercise 3

10. The data in Exercise 4

11. The data in Exercise 5

12. The data in Exercise 6

13. The data in Exercise 7

14. The data in Exercise 8

15. Compare the width of the intervals you constructed in Exercises 3 and 9. Which interval is wider? Why?

16. Compare the width of the intervals you constructed in Exercises 4 and 10. Which interval is wider? Why?

APPLYING THE TECHNIQUES

For Exercises 17–26, use the regression equations that you calculated in the Section 13.1 exercises.

17. Volume and Weight. The table contains the volume (x, in cubic meters) and weight (y, in kilograms) of 5 randomly chosen packages shipped to a local college. **volweight**

Volume (x)	Weight (y)
4	10
8	16
12	25
16	30
20	35

a. Predict the weight of a package that has a volume of 4 cubic meters.

b. Construct a 95% confidence interval for the population mean weight of all packages that have a volume of 4 cubic meters.

18. Family Size and Pets. Shown in the table are the number of family members (x) in a random sample taken from a suburban neighborhood and the number of pets (y) belonging to each family. 🐾 **familypet**

Family size (x)	Pets (y)
2	1
3	2
4	2
5	3
6	3

a. Predict the population mean number of pets for a family of size 5.

b. Construct a 95% confidence interval for the population mean number of pets for all families of size 5.

19. SAT Reading and Math Scores. The College Board reported the SAT Reading scores (x) and SAT Math scores (y) for five states. 🏫 **statesat**

State	Reading (x)	Math (y)
New York	497	510
Connecticut	515	515
Massachusetts	518	523
New Jersey	501	514
New Hampshire	522	521

a. Predict the population mean SAT Math score for a state with a SAT Reading score of 500.

b. Construct a 90% confidence interval for the population mean SAT Math score for all states with a SAT Reading score of 500.

20. World Temperatures. Listed in the table are the low (x) and high (y) temperatures for a particular day in 2006, measured in degrees Fahrenheit, for a random sample of cities worldwide. 🌡 **worldtemp**

City	Low (x)	High (y)
Kolkata	57	77
London	36	45
Montreal	7	21
Rome	39	55
San Juan	70	83
Shanghai	34	45

a. Predict the population mean high temperature for a city with a low temperature of 30 degrees.

b. Construct a 99% confidence interval for the population mean high temperature for all cities with a low temperature of 30 degrees.

21. Volume and Weight. Refer to the data from Exercise 17.

a. Construct a 95% prediction interval for the weight of a randomly selected package that has a volume of 4 cubic meters.

b. Compare the intervals from Exercise 17(**b**) and Exercise 21(**a**). Which interval is wider, and why?

22. Family Size and Pets. Refer to the data from Exercise 18.

a. Construct a 95% prediction interval for the number of pets for a randomly selected family of size 5.

b. Compare the intervals from Exercise 18(**b**) and Exercise 22(**a**). Which interval is wider, and why?

23. SAT Reading and Math Scores. Refer to the data from Exercise 19.

a. Construct a 90% prediction interval for the SAT Math score for a randomly selected state with a SAT Reading score of 500.

b. Which of the intervals you constructed in Exercise 19(**b**) and Exercise 23(**a**) is wider, and why?

24. World Temperatures. Refer to the data from Exercise 20.

a. Construct a 99% prediction interval for the high temperature for a randomly chosen city with a low temperature of 30 degrees.

b. Which of the intervals you constructed in Exercise 20(**b**) and Exercise 24(**a**) is wider, and why?

25. NCAA Power Rankings. Use the data from Exercise 34 in Section 13.1 to do the following.

a. Construct a 95% confidence interval for the population mean power rating for all schools with a winning percentage of 90%.

b. Construct a 95% prediction interval for the power rating for a randomly selected school with a winning percentage of 90%.

26. Midterm Exams and Overall Grade. Use the data from Exercise 35 in Section 13.1 to do the following.

a. Construct a 99% confidence interval for the population mean overall grade for all students with a midterm exam grade of 50.

b. Construct a 99% prediction interval for all overall grade for a randomly selected student with a midterm exam grade of 50.

c. Suppose we were asked to provide a prediction interval for the overall grade for a randomly selected student with a midterm exam grade of 40. Explain what the danger would be in constructing such a prediction interval.

27. Stock Prices. Use the data from Exercise 36 in Section 13.1 to do the following.

a. Construct a 95% confidence interval for the population mean change for all stocks with a price of $10.

b. Construct a 95% prediction interval for the change for a randomly selected stock with a price of $10.

c. Suppose we were asked to construct a confidence interval for the population mean change for all stocks with a price of $50. Explain what the danger would be in constructing such a confidence interval.

28. **Refer to Exercise 27.** *What if* we increased the confidence level from 95% to some unspecified higher confidence level. How would that affect the width of the following? Explain your answer.
   a. The confidence interval from Exercise 27(**a**)
   b. The prediction interval from Exercise 27(**b**)
29. **Open the PulseandTemp data set.** Select the females data only. Use technology to do the following. **PulseandTemp**
   a. Construct a 95% confidence interval for the population mean body temperature for all females with a heart rate of 72.
   b. Construct a 95% prediction interval for the body temperature for a randomly selected female with a heart rate of 72.

30. **Open the Nutrition data set.** Use technology to do the following. **Nutrition**
   a. Construct a 95% confidence interval for the population mean number of calories per gram (y) for all foods with the amount of fat per gram (x) of 0.5.
   b. Construct a 95% prediction interval for the number of calories per gram for a randomly selected food with the amount of fat per gram (x) of 0.5.

13.3 Multiple Regression

OBJECTIVES By the end of this section, I will be able to . . .

1   Find the multiple regression equation, interpret the multiple regression coefficients, and use the multiple regression equation to make predictions.

2   Calculate and interpret the adjusted coefficient of determination.

3   Perform the F test for the overall significance of the multiple regression.

4   Conduct t tests for the significance of individual predictor variables.

5   Explain the use and effect of dummy variables in multiple regression.

6   Apply the strategy for building a multiple regression model.

1 Finding the Multiple Regression Equation, Interpreting the Coefficients, and Making Predictions

Regression analysis using a single y variable and a single x variable is called simple linear regression.

Thus far we have examined the relationship between the response variable y and a single predictor variable x. In our data-filled world, however, we often encounter situations where we can use more than one x variable to predict the y variable. This is called **multiple regression.**

> **Multiple regression** describes the linear relationship between one response variable y and more than one predictor variable, $x_1, x_2, x_3, \ldots$. The **multiple regression equation** is an extension of the regression equation
>
> $$\hat{y} = b_0 + b_1 x_1 + b_2 x_2 + \cdots b_k x_k$$
>
> where k represents the number of x variables in the equation, and $b_0, b_1, b_2, \ldots b_k$ represent the **multiple regression coefficients.**

The interpretation of the regression coefficients is similar to the interpretation of the slope b_1 in simple linear regression, except that we also state that the other x variables are held constant. The interpretation of the y intercept b_0 is similar to the simple linear regression case. The next example illustrates the multiple regression equation, and shows how to interpret the multiple regression coefficients.

Example 13.11 Multiple regression equation, coefficients, and prediction

Breakfast Cereals

In the data set **Breakfast Cereals,** there are several predictor variables and one response variable, y = (nutritional) rating.

a. Use technology to find the multiple regression equation for predicting y = rating using x_1 = fiber and x_2 = sugar. State the equation using a sentence.

b. State the values of the multiple regression coefficients.

c. Interpret the multiple regression coefficients for using x_1 = fiber and x_2 = sugar.

d. Use the multiple regression equation to predict the rating of a breakfast cereal with 5 mg of fiber and 10 mg of sugar.

Solution

Using the instructions in the Step-by-Step Technology Guide at the end of this section, we open the **Breakfast Cereals** data set and perform a multiple regression of y = rating on x_1 = fiber and x_2 = sugar.

When we perform a multiple regression of one variable *on* (or *against* or *versus*) a set of other variables, the first variable is always the y variable, and the set of variables following the word *on* are the x variables.

a. A partial Minitab printout is shown in Figure 13.18. The multiple regression equation is

$$\hat{y} = b_0 + b_1 x_1 + b_2 x_2 = 51.6 + 2.87 \text{ (fiber)} - 2.18 \text{ (sugar)}$$

The estimated nutritional rating equals 51.6 points plus 2.87 times the number of grams of fiber minus 2.18 times the number of grams of sugar.

FIGURE 13.18
Multiple regression equation in Minitab.

```
Regression Analysis: rating versus fiber, sugar

The regression equation is
rating = 51.6 + 2.87 fiber - 2.18 sugar
```

b. The values of the multiple regression coefficients are $b_0 = 51.6$, $b_1 = 2.87$, and $b_2 = -2.18$.

c. The multiple regression coefficients are interpreted as follows:
- $b_0 = 51.6$ (y intercept). The estimated nutritional rating when there are zero grams of fiber and zero grams of sugar is 51.6.
- $b_1 = 2.87$. For every increase of one gram of fiber, the estimated increase in nutritional rating is 2.87 points, *when the amount of sugar is held constant.*
- $b_2 = -2.18$. For every increase of one gram of sugar, the estimated *decrease* in nutritional rating is 2.18 points, *when the amount of fiber is held constant.*

d. To find the predicted rating for a breakfast cereal with x_1 = fiber = 5 and x_2 = sugar = 10, we plug these values into the multiple regression equation from part (a):

$$\hat{y} = 51.6 + 2.87(5) - 2.18(10) = 44.15$$

Now You Can Do
Exercises 9–11 and 14.

The predicted nutritional rating for a breakfast cereal with 5 mg of fiber and 10 mg of sugar is 44.15. ∎

When making predictions in multiple regression, beware of the pitfalls of extrapolation, just like those for simple linear regression. Further, in multiple regression, the values for *all* predictor variables must lie within their respective ranges. Otherwise, the prediction represents extrapolation, and may be misleading.

2 The Adjusted Coefficient of Determination

Recall from Section 4.3 that we measure the goodness of a regression equation using the coefficient of determination r^2 = SSR/SST. In multiple regression, we use the same formula for the coefficient of determination (though the letter r is promoted to a capital R).

> **Multiple Coefficient of Determination R^2**
>
> The multiple coefficient of determination is given by:
>
> $$R^2 = \frac{SSR}{SST} \qquad 0 \leq R^2 \leq 1$$
>
> where SSR is the sum of squares regression, and SST is the total sum of squares. The multiple coefficient of determination R^2 represents the proportion of the variability in the response y that is explained by the multiple regression equation.

Unfortunately, when a new x variable is added to the multiple regression equation, the value of R^2 always increases, even when the variable is not useful for predicting y. So, we need a way to *adjust* the value of R^2 as a penalty for having too many unhelpful x variables in the equation. This is the **adjusted coefficient of determination, R^2_{adj}.**

> **Adjusted Coefficient of Determination R^2_{adj}**
>
> The adjusted coefficient of determination is given by the formula
>
> $$R^2_{adj} = 1 - (1 - R^2)\left(\frac{n-1}{n-k-1}\right)$$
>
> where n is the number of observations, k is the number of x variables, and R^2 is the multiple coefficient of determination. R^2_{adj} is always smaller than R^2.

R^2_{adj} is preferable to R^2 as a measure of the goodness of a regression equation, because R^2_{adj} will decrease if an unhelpful x variable is added to the regression equation. The interpretation of R^2_{adj} is similar to R^2.

Example 13.12 Calculating and interpreting the adjusted coefficient of determination R^2_{adj}

For the multiple regression in Example 13.11, we have SSR $= 12,134.8$ and SST $= 14,996.8$.
a. Calculate the multiple coefficient of determination for R^2.
b. There are $n = 77$ observations. Compute and interpret the adjusted coefficient of determination R^2_{adj}.

Solution
a.
$$R^2 = \frac{SSR}{SST} = \frac{12,134.8}{14,996.8} \approx 0.8092$$

b.
$$R^2_{adj} = 1 - (1 - R^2)\left(\frac{n-1}{n-k-1}\right) = 1 - (1 - 0.8092)\left(\frac{77-1}{77-2-1}\right) \approx 0.8040$$

Now You Can Do
Exercises 12 and 13.

80.4% of the variability in nutritional rating is accounted for by the multiple regression equation. ∎

Thus far in this section we have used descriptive methods for multiple regression. Next we learn how to perform inference in multiple regression.

3 The *F* Test for the Overall Significance of the Multiple Regression

The multiple regression model is an extension of the regression model from Section 13.1, and approximates the relationship between y and the collection of x variables.

> **Multiple Regression Model**
>
> The **population multiple regression equation** is
>
> $$y = \beta_0 + \beta_1 x_1 + \beta_2 x_2 + \cdots + \beta_k x_k + \varepsilon$$
>
> where $\beta_0, \beta_1, \beta_2, \cdots \beta_k$ are the parameters of the population regression equation, k is the number of x variables, and ε represents the random error term that follows a normal distribution with mean 0 and constant variance σ^2.

The population parameters $\beta_0, \beta_1, \beta_2, \cdots \beta_k$ are unknown, and so we must perform inference to learn about them. We begin by asking, *is our multiple regression useful?* To answer this question, we perform the *F test for the overall significance of the multiple regression.*

Our multiple regression will not be useful if all of the population parameters equals zero, for this will result in no relationship at all between the y variable and the set of x variables. Thus the hypotheses for the *F test* are

- $H_0: \beta_1 = \beta_2 = \cdots = \beta_k = 0$. There is no linear relationship between y and the set of x variables. The overall multiple regression is not significant.

H_a states that at least one of the β's $\neq 0$, not that all of the β's $\neq 0$.

- H_a: At least one of the β's $\neq 0$. There is a linear relationship between y and the set of x variables. The overall multiple regression is significant.

The *F test* is not valid if there is strong evidence that the regression assumptions have been violated. The multiple regression assumptions are similar to those for simple linear regression. We illustrate the steps for the *F test* using the following example.

Example 13.13 | *F test for the overall significance of the multiple regression*

For the breakfast cereal data, we are interested in determining whether there is a linear relationship between y = (nutritional) rating, and x_1 = vitamins and x_2 = sodium.
a. Determine whether the regression assumptions have been violated.
b. Perform the *F test* for the overall significance of the multiple regression of rating on vitamins and sodium, using level of significance $\alpha = 0.01$.

Solution

a. Figure 13.19, a scatterplot of the residuals versus fitted values, contains no strong evidence of unhealthy patterns. Although the two cereals, All-Bran with Extra Fiber and Product 19, are unusual, the vast majority of the data suggest that the independence, constant variance, and zero-mean assumptions are satisfied. Figure 13.20 indicates the normality assumption is satisfied.

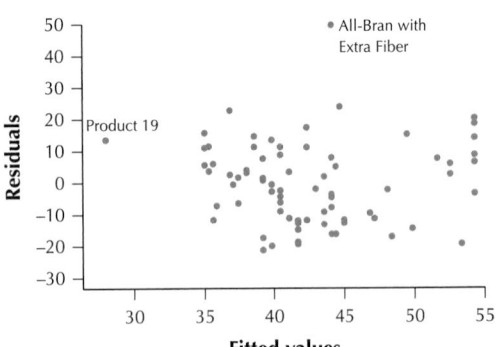

FIGURE 13.19 Scatterplots of residuals versus fitted values.

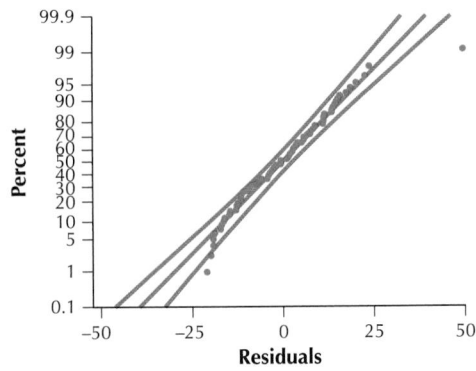

FIGURE 13.20 Normal probability plot of the residuals.

b. The Minitab multiple regression results are provided in Figure 13.21.

FIGURE 13.21
Minitab results for
regression of rating on
vitamins and sodium.

```
Regression Analysis: Rating versus vitamins, sodium

The regression equation is
rating = 54.3 - 0.0691 vitamins - 0.0606 sodium

Predictor      Coef   SE Coef       T      P
Constant     54.291     3.322   16.34  0.000
Vitamins   -0.06906   0.07135   -0.97  0.336
Sodium     -0.06059   0.01902   -3.19  0.002

S = 12.9576   R-Sq = 17.2%   R-Sq(adj) = 14.9%

Analysis of Variance

Source           DF       SS      MS      F      P
Regression        2   2572.3  1286.2   7.66  0.001
Residual Error   74  12424.5   167.9
Total            76  14996.8
```

Step 1 **State the hypotheses and the rejection rule.** We have $k = 2$ x variables, so the hypotheses are

- $H_0: \beta_1 = \beta_2 = 0$. There is no linear relationship between rating and the set of vitamins and sodium. The overall multiple regression is not significant.
- H_a: At least one of β_1 and $\beta_2 \neq 0$. There is a linear relationship between rating and the set of vitamins and sodium. The overall multiple regression is significant.

Reject H_0 if the p-value $\leq \alpha = 0.01$.

Step 2 **Find the F statistic and the p-value.** These are located in the ANOVA table portion of the printout, denoted *Analysis of Variance*. From Figure 13.21 we have $F = 7.66$ and p-value $= 0.001$. The p-value represents $P(F > 7.66)$.

Step 3 **Conclusion and interpretation.** The p-value 0.001 is $\leq \alpha = 0.01$, so we reject H_0. There is evidence at level of significance $\alpha = 0.01$ for a linear relationship between rating and the set of vitamins and sodium. The overall multiple regression is significant. ■

The ANOVA table is a convenient way to organize a set of statistics, which can be used to perform multiple regression as well as ANOVA.

Now You Can Do
Exercises 23 and 30.

Once we find that the overall multiple regression is significant, we may ask: Which of the individual x variables have a significant linear relationship with the response variable y?

4 The t Test for the Significance of Individual Predictor Variables

To determine whether a particular x variable has a significant linear relationship with the response variable y, we perform the t test that was used in Section 13.1 to test for the significance of that x variable. One may perform as many such t tests as there are x variables in the model, which is k. We illustrate the steps for performing a set of t tests using the following example.

Example 13.14 Performing a set of t tests for the significance of a set of individual x variables

Using the results from Example 13.13, do the following using level of significance $\alpha = 0.05$.
- Test 1: Test whether a significant linear relationship exists between rating and vitamins.
- Test 2: Test whether a significant linear relationship exists between rating and sodium.

Solution

The regression assumptions were verified in Example 13.13.

Step 1 **For each hypothesis test, state the hypotheses and the rejection rule.**
Vitamins is x_1, and sodium is x_2, so the hypotheses are
- Test 1:
  - $H_0: \beta_1 = 0$.   There is no linear relationship between rating and vitamins.
  - $H_a: \beta_1 \neq 0$.   There is a linear relationship between rating and vitamins.
  - Reject H_0 if the p-value $\leq \alpha = 0.05$
- Test 2:
  - $H_0: \beta_2 = 0$.   There is no linear relationship between rating and sodium.
  - $H_a: \beta_2 \neq 0$.   There is a linear relationship between rating and sodium.
  - Reject H_0 if the p-value $\leq \alpha = 0.05$

Step 2 **For each hypothesis test, find the t statistic and the p-value.** Figure 13.22 is an excerpt of the Minitab results from Figure 13.21, with the relevant t statistics and p-values highlighted. For Test 1, the p-value represents $P(t < -0.97) + P(t > 0.97)$, since it is a two-tailed test. For Test 2, the p-value represents $P(t < -3.19) + P(t > 3.19)$.

Predictor	Coef	SE Coef	T	P
Constant	54.291	3.322	16.34	0.000
Vitamins	-0.06906	0.07135	-0.97	0.336
Sodium	-0.06059	0.01902	-3.19	0.002

FIGURE 13.22 t statistics and p-values for the t test for the significance of the x variables vitamins and sodium.

- Test 1: $t = -0.97$, with p-value 0.336.
- Test 2: $t = -3.19$, with p-value 0.002.

Step 3 **For each hypothesis test, state the conclusion and interpretation.**
- Test 1: The p-value = 0.336, which is not $\leq \alpha = 0.05$. Therefore we do not reject H_0. There is insufficient evidence of a linear relationship between rating and vitamins when sodium is held constant. Perhaps surprisingly, the x variable vitamins is *not significant*, meaning that amount of vitamins in the breakfast cereal is not helpful in predicting nutritional rating.
- Test 2: The p-value = 0.002, which is $\leq \alpha = 0.05$. Therefore we reject H_0. There is evidence of a linear relationship between rating and sodium when vitamins is held constant. The x variable sodium is *significant*, meaning that amount of sodium in the breakfast cereal is helpful in predicting nutritional rating. ∎

Now You Can Do
Exercises 24 and 31.

So far, all of our x variables have been continuous. But what if we would like to include a categorical variable as a predictor?

5 Dummy Variables in Multiple Regression

The data set **PulseandTemp** contains the heart rate, body temperature, and sex of 130 men and women. We would like to use x_1 = heart rate and x_2 = sex to predict y = body temperature. However, sex is a categorical variable, so we must *recode* the values of x_2 as follows:

$$x_2: \text{Let "female"} = 1 \text{ and let "male"} = 0.$$

The variable x_2 is called a **dummy variable,** since it recodes the values of the binomial (categorical) variable sex into values of 0 and 1.

> A **dummy variable** is a predictor variable used to recode a binomial categorical variable in regression, and taking values 0 or 1.

This recoding will provide us with two different regression equations, one for the females ($x_2 = 1$) and one for the males ($x_2 = 0$), shown here:

- Females: $\hat{y} = b_0 + b_1 x_1 + b_2 x_2 = b_0 + b_1 x_1 + b_2(1) = (b_0 + b_2) + b_1 x_1$
- Males: $\hat{y} = b_0 + b_1 x_1 + b_2 x_2 = b_0 + b_1 x_1 + b_2(0) = b_0 + b_1 x_1$

Note that these two regression equations have the *same slope* b_1, but different y intercepts. The females have y intercept $(b_0 + b_2)$ while the males have y intercept b_0. See Figure 13.26 on page 664. The *difference in y intercepts* is $(b_0 + b_2) - b_0 = b_2$, which is the coefficient of the dummy variable x_2. Let us illustrate with an example.

Example 13.15 Dummy variables in multiple regression

a. Verify that the regression assumptions are met.
b. Perform a multiple regression of y = body temperature on x_1 = heart rate and x_2 = sex, using level of significance $\alpha = 0.05$. Find the two regression equations, one for females and the other for males.
c. Construct a scatterplot of y = body temperature versus x_1 = heart rate, using different-shaped points to show the different sexes. Place the two regression equations on the scatterplot.
d. Interpret the coefficient of the dummy variable x_2 = sex.

Solution

a. Figures 13.23 and 13.24 contain no evidence of unhealthy patterns. We therefore conclude that the regression assumptions are verified.

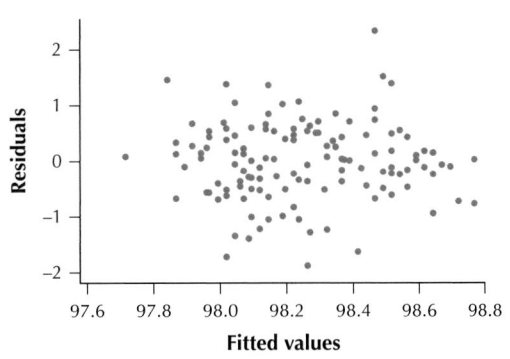

FIGURE 13.23 Scatterplot of residuals versus fitted values.

FIGURE 13.24 Normal probability plot of the residuals.

b. Figure 13.25 contains the multiple regression results. The *p*-value for the F test is 0.001, which is $\leq \alpha = 0.05$, so we conclude that the overall regression is significant. The regression results tell us that $b_0 = 96.3$, $b_1 = 0.0253$, and $b_2 = 0.270$. Thus, our two regression equations are:
- Females: $\hat{y} = (b_0 + b_2) + b_1 x_1 = (96.3 + 0.27) + 0.0253 x_1$
$$= 96.57 + 0.0253 x_1$$
- Males: $\hat{y} = b_0 + b_1 x_1 = 96.3 + 0.0253 x_1$
c. Figure 13.26 contains the scatterplot of y = body temperature versus x_1 = heart rate, with the orange dots representing females and the blue dots representing males. The regression lines are shown, orange for females, blue for males. *Note that the regression lines are parallel, because they each have the same slope $b_1 = 0.0253$. So the only difference in the lines is the y intercepts.*
  - For females, the y intercept is $b_0 + b_2 = 96.3 + 0.27 = 96.57$.
  - For males, the y intercept is simply $b_0 = 96.3$.

```
Regression Analysis: Body Temp versus Heart Rate, Sex

The regression equation is
Body Temp = 96.3 + 0.0253 Heart Rate + 0.270 Sex

Predictor      Coef   SE Coef      T      P
Constant     96.2511    0.6487  148.37  0.000
Heart Rate  0.025260  0.008762    2.88  0.005
Sex           0.2695    0.1233    2.19  0.031

S = 0.701701   R-Sq = 9.8%   R-Sq(adj) = 8.4%

Analysis of Variance

Source          DF       SS      MS      F      P
Regression       2   6.8130  3.4065   6.92  0.001
Residual Error 127  62.5328  0.4924
Total          129  69.3458
```

FIGURE 13.25 Results for multiple regression of y = body temperature on x_1 = heart rate and x_2 = sex.

FIGURE 13.26 Scatterplot showing parallel regression lines when using dummy variables.

d. The vertical distance between the parallel regression lines equals $b_2 = 0.27$, as shown in Figure 13.26. Thus, we interpret the coefficient b_2 of the dummy variable x_2 as the estimated increase in y = body temperature for those observations with $x_2 = 1$ (females), as compared to those with $x_2 = 0$ (males), when heart rate is held constant. That is, for the same heart rate, females have a body temperature that is higher than that of males, by an estimated 0.27 degrees. ■

Now You Can Do
Exercises 28 and 29.

6 Strategy for Building a Multiple Regression Model

In order to bring together all you have learned of multiple regression, we now present a general strategy for building a multiple regression model.

Strategy for Building a Multiple Regression Model

Step 1   The F Test.
Construct the multiple regression equation using all relevant predictor variables. Apply the F test for the significance of the overall regression, in order to make sure that a linear relationship exists between the response y and at least one of the predictor variables.

Step 2   The t Tests.
Perform the t tests for the individual predictors. If at least one of the predictors is not significant (that is, its p-value is greater than level of significance α), then eliminate the x variable with the largest p-value from the model. Ignore the p-value of β_0. *Repeat Step 2 until all remaining predictors are significant.*

We eliminate only one variable at a time. It may happen that eliminating one nonsignificant variable will nudge a second, formerly nonsignificant, variable into significance.

Step 3   Verify the Assumptions.
For your *final model*, verify the regression assumptions.

Step 4   Report and Interpret Your Final Model.
   a. Provide the multiple regression equation for your final model.
   b. Interpret the multiple regression coefficients so that a nonstatistician could understand.
   c. Report and interpret the standard error of the estimate s and the adjusted coefficient of determination R^2_{adj}.

We illustrate this strategy, known as **backward stepwise regression,** in the following example.

Example 13.16 Strategy for building a multiple regression model — **Baseball2007**

Suppose a baseball researcher is interested in predicting y = runs scored, using the data set **Baseball2007** and the following predictor variables:

- x_1 = Hits, the number of hits (of all kinds) the player makes
- x_2 = Doubles, the number of doubles the player makes
- x_3 = Triples, the number of triples the player makes
- x_4 = Home Runs, the number of home runs the player makes
- x_5 = RBIs, the number of runs batted in (runs scored by other players, but caused by this player)
- x_6 = Walks, the number of walks issued to the player
- x_7 = Batting Average, the number of hits divided by the number of at-bats
- x_8 = Yankees, a dummy variable equal to 1 if the player plays for the New York Yankees, and 0 otherwise

Use the Strategy for Building a Multiple Regression Model to build the best multiple regression model for predicting the number of runs scored using these predictor variables, at level of significance $\alpha = 0.05$.

Solution

The data set **Baseball2007** contains the batting statistics of the $n = 127$ players in the American League who had at least 300 at-bats during the 2007 season.

Step 1 **The F Test.** Figure 13.27 shows the Minitab results of a regression of y = runs scored on the set of predictor variables $x_1, x_2, x_3, \ldots, x_8$. The p-value for the F test is significant, so we know that a linear relationship exists between y = runs scored and at least one of the x variables.

```
Regression Analysis: Runs Scored versus Hits, Doubles,...

The regression equation is
Runs Scored = -6.68 + 0.438 Hits + 0.002 Doubles + 1.24 Triples
              + 0.758 Home Runs - 0.204 RBIs + 0.284 Walks + 12.7 Batting Ave
              + 9.19 Yankees

Predictor       Coef    SE Coef       T       P
Constant      -6.677      8.359   -0.80   0.426
Hits         0.43799    0.04871    8.99   0.000
Doubles       0.0019     0.1428    0.01   0.990   Step 2: p-value for t test
Triples       1.2368     0.2910    4.25   0.000
Home Runs     0.7578     0.1740    4.35   0.000
RBIs        -0.20360    0.07534   -2.70   0.008
Walks        0.28355    0.04382    6.47   0.000
Batting Ave    12.65      38.82    0.33   0.745
Yankees        9.194      3.330    2.76   0.007

S = 8.62287   R-Sq = 87.0%   R-Sq(adj) = 86.1%

Analysis of Variance

Source           DF       SS      MS       F        P
Regression        8  58617.7  7327.2   98.55    0.000   Step 1: p-value for F test
Residual Error  118   8773.8    74.4
Total           126  67391.4
```

FIGURE 13.27 Step 1: F test is significant.

Step 2 **The t test (the first time).** In Figure 13.27, the p-values for Doubles and Batting Ave are each greater than level of significance $\alpha = 0.05$. Of these, we eliminate the variable with the largest p-value, which is Doubles, with a p-value of 0.990. The number of doubles a player hits is evidently not helpful in predicting the number of runs that player will score when all other predictors are held constant.

Step 2 **The t test (the second time).** We repeat Step 2 as long as there are x variables with p-values greater than level of significance $\alpha = 0.05$. Figure 13.28 shows the

The author of this book first became interested in the field of statistics through the enjoyment of sports statistics, especially baseball, which is packed with interesting statistics. Today, professional sports teams are seeking competitive advantage through the analysis of data and statistics, such as *Sabermetrics* (Society of American Baseball Research, **www.sabr.org**).

Ronald C. Modra/Sports Imagery/Getty Images

results of performing the multiple regression of y = Runs Scored on all the x variables except Doubles. We note that the p-value for Batting Ave is the largest p-value above $\alpha = 0.05$, and so we must omit this variable from the model.

```
Regression Analysis: Runs Scored versus Hits, Triples,...

The regression equation is
Runs Scored = - 6.67 + 0.438 Hits + 1.24 Triples + 0.758 Home Runs
              - 0.203 RBIs + 0.284 Walks + 12.6 Batting Ave + 9.19 Yankees

Predictor        Coef   SE Coef       T       P
Constant       -6.672     8.316   -0.80   0.424
Hits          0.43830   0.04253   10.30   0.000
Triples        1.2366    0.2894    4.27   0.000
Home Runs      0.7578    0.1733    4.37   0.000
RBIs         -0.20339   0.07333   -2.77   0.006
Walks         0.28352   0.04358    6.51   0.000
Batting Ave     12.63     38.62    0.33   0.744
Yankees         9.191     3.307    2.78   0.006

S = 8.58657   R-Sq = 87.0%   R-Sq(adj) = 86.2%

Analysis of Variance

Source          DF        SS       MS       F       P
Regression       7   58617.6   8373.9  113.58   0.000
Residual Error 119    8773.8     73.7
Total          126   67391.4
```

FIGURE 13.28   Batting average is not significant and should be omitted from the model.

[Step 2] **The t test (the third time).** Figure 13.29 shows the results of performing the multiple regression of y = Runs Scored on all the x variables except Doubles and Batting Aver. Finally all x variables are significant and no further variables need to be removed. In other words, we have our final model.

```
Regression Analysis: Runs Scored versus Hits, Triples,...

The regression equation is
Runs Scored = - 4.14 + 0.446 Hits + 1.23 Triples + 0.751 Home Runs
              - 0.203 RBIs + 0.283 Walks + 9.23 Yankees

Predictor        Coef   SE Coef       T       P
Constant       -4.135     2.978   -1.39   0.168
Hits          0.44647   0.03430   13.02   0.000
Triples        1.2253    0.2863    4.28   0.000
Home Runs      0.7510    0.1714    4.38   0.000
RBIs         -0.20312   0.07305   -2.78   0.006
Walks         0.28284   0.04337    6.52   0.000
Yankees         9.233     3.292    2.80   0.006

S = 8.55456   R-Sq = 87.0%   R-Sq(adj) = 86.3%

Analysis of Variance

Source          DF        SS       MS       F       P
Regression       6   58609.8   9768.3  133.48   0.000
Residual Error 120    8781.7     73.2
Total          126   67391.4
```

FIGURE 13.29   All x variables are significant; we have our final model.

[Step 3] **Verify the assumptions.** For our final model, we now verify the regression assumptions. Figures 13.30 and 13.31 show no patterns that would indicate a violation of the regression assumptions. We therefore conclude that the regression assumptions are verified.

[Step 4] **Report and interpret your final model.**
a.   The multiple regression equation for the final model is shown here.

$$\hat{y} = -4.14 + 0.446 \text{ Hits} + 1.23 \text{ Triples} + 0.751 \text{ Home Runs}$$
$$-0.203 \text{ RBIs} + 0.283 \text{ Walks} + 9.23 \text{ Yankees}$$

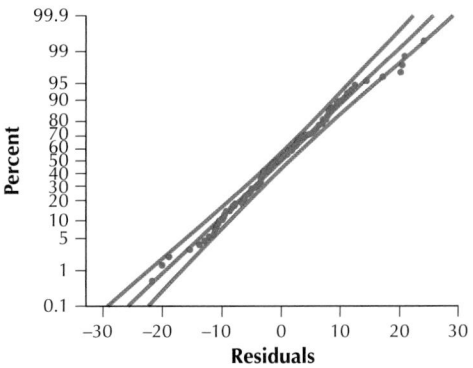

FIGURE 13.30 Scatterplot of residuals versus fitted values.

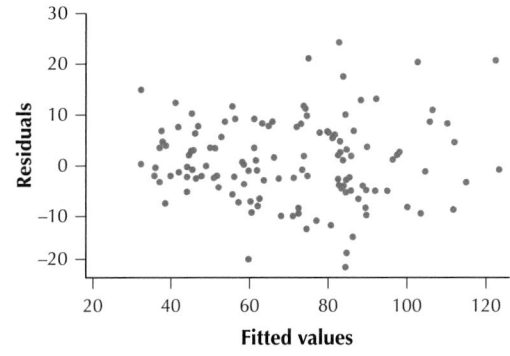

FIGURE 13.31 Normal probability plots of the residuals.

b. We interpret the coefficient for Hits, and leave to the exercises the interpretation of the other multiple regression coefficients. "For each additional hit that a player makes, the estimated increase in the number of runs that player will score is 0.446, when all the other x variables are held constant."

c. The standard error of the estimate for the final model is $s = 8.55456 \approx 8.55$. That is, using the multiple regression equation in (a), the size of the typical prediction error will be about 8.55 runs. The value of the adjusted coefficient of determination is $R^2_{adj} = 86.3\%$. In other words, 86.3% of the variability in the number of runs scored is accounted for by this multiple regression equation. ∎

Now You Can Do
Exercises 25–27.

STEP-BY-STEP TECHNOLOGY GUIDE: Multiple Regression

TI-83/84
The TI-83/84 calculators do not perform the calculations for multiple regression.

EXCEL
Step 1 Load the response variable y into column **A**, and the predictor variables into columns **B**, **C**, and so on.
Step 2 Click on **Data**, then **Data Analysis**, then **Regression**, and click **OK**.
Step 3 For **Input Y Range**, select the cells in column **A**. For **Input X Range**, select the cells in columns **B**, **C**, etc.

Step 4 If you would like to verify the regression assumptions, select **Residual Plots** and **Normal Probability Plots**.
Step 5 Click **OK**.
Note: Excel does not construct prediction intervals and confidence intervals for multiple regression.

MINITAB
Step 1 Load the response variable y into **C1** and the predictor variables into **C2**, **C3**, and so on.
Step 2 Click on **Stat**, highlight **Regression**, and then select **Regression . . .**
Step 3 Select **C1** as your **Response Variable**, and select **C2**, **C3**, etc. as your **Predictor Variables**.

Step 4 If you would like to verify the regression assumptions, click the button labeled **Graphs**, select **Four in One**, and click **OK**.
Step 5 Click **OK**.
Note: See the Guide on page 654 for instructions on how to construct confidence intervals and prediction intervals for multiple regression.

Section 13.3 Summary

1 Multiple regression describes the linear relationship between one response variable y and more than one predictor variable, x_1, $x_2, x_3, \ldots$. The multiple regression equation is an extension of the regression equation: $\hat{y} = b_0 + b_1x_1 + b_2x_2 + \cdots b_kx_k$, where k represents the number of x variables in the equation, and $b_1, b_2, b_3, \ldots b_x$ represent the multiple regression coefficients.

2 The multiple coefficient of determination R^2 represents the proportion of the variability in the response y that is explained by the multiple regression equation. The adjusted coefficient of determination R^2_{adj} adjusts the value of R^2 as a penalty for having too many unhelpful x variables in the equation.

3 The multiple regression model is an extension of the regression model from Section 13.1. The population multiple regression equation is $y = \beta_0 + \beta_1 x_1 + \beta_2 x_2 + \cdots + \beta_k x_k + \varepsilon$. The F test is performed to assess the significance of the overall model.

4 To determine whether a particular x variable has a significant linear relationship with the response variable y, we perform the t test for the significance of that x variable. One may perform as many such t tests as there are x variables in the model, which is k.

5 Dummy variables are 0/1 variables which allow, via recoding, categorical variables to be included in the multiple regression model.

6 The Strategy for Building a Multiple Regression Model brings together all we have learned about multiple regression modeling.

Section 13.3 Exercises

CLARIFYING THE CONCEPTS
1. Write the multiple regression equation for $k = 3$ predictor variables.
2. Which is preferable, R^2 or R^2_{adj}, and why?
3. Which test do we perform if we want to determine whether our multiple regression is useful?
4. If we conclude from the F test that our multiple regression is useful, is it still possible that one of the β's equals zero? Explain.
5. Explain the difference between the F test and the t test we learned in this section.
6. How many t tests may we perform for a multiple regression model?
7. How do we interpret the coefficient for a dummy variable. (*Hint:* Consider Figure 13.26.)
8. What are the four steps of the Strategy for Building a Multiple Regression Model.

PRACTICING THE TECHNIQUES
Use the following information for Exercises 9–14. A multiple regression model has been produced for a set of $n = 20$ observations with multiple regression equation $\hat{y} = 10 + 5x_1 - 8x_2$, with multiple coefficient of determination $R^2 = 0.5$. Assume the regression assumptions are met.
9. Interpret the value of the coefficient for x_1.
10. Explain what the value of b_2 means.
11. Interpret the value of b_0.
12. How should the value of R^2 be interpreted?
13. Calculate R^2_{adj}.
14. Find point estimates of y for the following values of x_1 and x_2:
    a. $x_1 = 6, x_2 = 4$
    b. $x_1 = 10, x_2 = 8$

Use the following information for Exercises 15–20. A multiple regression model has been produced for a set of $n = 50$ observations with multiple regression equation $\hat{y} = 0.5 - 0.1x_1 + 0.9x_2$, with multiple coefficient of determination $R^2 = 0.75$. Assume the regression assumptions are met.

15. Interpret the value of the coefficient for x_1.
16. Explain what the value of b_2 means.
17. Interpret the value of b_0.
18. How should the value of R^2 be interpreted?
19. Calculate R^2_{adj}.
20. Find point estimates of y for the following values of x_1 and x_2.
    a. $x_1 = 5, x_2 = 6$
    b. $x_1 = 4, x_2 = 3$

Use the following data set for Exercises 21–27.

y	x_1	x_2	x_3
0.6	1	10	1.3
4.0	2	10	-3.2
3.2	3	8	-1.0
9.0	4	8	0.9
1.8	5	6	-2.5
8.4	6	6	0.9
9.8	7	4	1.0
10.4	8	4	2.0
8.8	9	2	0.2
14.7	10	2	-2.2

21. Perform the multiple regression of y on x_1, x_2, and x_3 and write the multiple regression equation.
22. Interpret the coefficients b_0, b_1, b_2, and b_3.
23. Assuming the regression assumptions are met, perform the F test for the significance of the overall regression, using level of significance $\alpha = 0.05$. Do the following:
    a. State the hypotheses and the rejection rule.
    b. Find the F statistic and the p-value.
    c. State the conclusion and interpretation.
24. Perform the t test for the significance of the individual predictor variables, using level of significance $\alpha = 0.05$. Do the following:
    a. For each hypothesis test, state the hypotheses and the rejection rule.

b. For each hypothesis test, find the t statistic and the p-value.
c. For each hypothesis test, state the conclusion and interpretation.

25. Identify any predictors that have corresponding p-values greater than the level of significance $\alpha = 0.05$. Of these, discard the variable with the largest p-value. Then redo Exercise 24, omitting this predictor. Repeat if necessary.

26. Verify the regression assumptions for your final model from Exercise 25.

27. Report and interpret your final model from Exercise 25, by doing the following:
  a. Provide the multiple regression equation for your final model.
  b. Interpret the multiple regression coefficients so that a nonstatistician could understand.
  c. Report and interpret the standard error of the estimate s and the adjusted coefficient of determination R^2_{adj}.

Use the following data set for Exercises 28–34. Note that x_3 is a dummy variable.

y	x_1	x_2	x_3
−0.7	2	0.1	0
6.4	4	−2.5	1
2.8	6	2.7	0
9.4	8	2.8	1
8.6	10	−1.6	0
13.1	12	1.0	1
12.2	14	−1.4	0
19.1	16	−0.5	1
18.8	18	1.0	0
23.2	20	−2.3	1

28. Perform the multiple regression of y on x_1, x_2, and x_3 and write the multiple regression equation.

29. Interpret the coefficients b_0, b_1, b_2, and b_3.

30. Assuming the regression assumptions are met, perform the F test for the significance of the overall regression, using level of significance $\alpha = 0.01$. Do the following:
  a. State the hypotheses and the rejection rule.
  b. Find the F statistic and the p-value.
  c. State the conclusion and interpretation.

31. Perform the t test for the significance of the individual predictor variables, using level of significance $\alpha = 0.01$. Do the following:
  a. For each hypothesis test, state the hypotheses and the rejection rule.
  b. For each hypothesis test, find the t statistic and the p-value.
  c. For each hypothesis test, state the conclusion and interpretation.

32. Identify any predictors that have corresponding p-values greater than the level of significance $\alpha = 0.01$. Of these, discard the variable with the largest p-value. Then redo Exercise 31, omitting this predictor. Repeat if necessary.

33. Verify the regression assumptions for your final model from Exercise 32.

34. Report and interpret your final model from Exercise 32, by doing the following:
  a. Provide the multiple regression equation for your final model.
  b. Interpret the multiple regression coefficients so that a nonstatistician could understand.
  c. Report and interpret the standard error of the estimate s, and the adjusted coefficient of determination R^2_{adj}.

APPLYING THE CONCEPTS

For Exercises 35–42, apply the Strategy for Building a Multiple Regression Model by performing the following steps. Use level of significance $\alpha = 0.05$.
  a. *Step 1* Perform the F test for significance of the overall regression.
  b. *Step 2* Perform the t tests for the individual predictors. If at least one of the predictors is not significant, then eliminate the x variable with the largest p-value from the model. Repeat Step 2 until all remaining predictors are significant.
  c. *Step 3* Verify the assumptions.
  d. *Step 4* Report and interpret your final model. Report and interpret the coefficients, the standard error of the estimate s, and the adjusted coefficient of determination R^2_{adj}.

35. Best Places for Dating. Sperling's Best Places published the list of best places for dating in America for 2010. Table 13.6 shows the top ten places, along with the overall dating score (y) and a set of predictor variables. 🌎 **bestdating**

TABLE 13.6 Best places for dating in America

City	y = Overall dating score	Percentage 18–24 years old	Percentage 18–24 years and single	Online dating score
Austin	100.00	13.40%	81.20%	77.8
Colorado Springs	88.7	10.50%	74.20%	88.9
San Diego	84.0	11.30%	79.40%	77.4
Raleigh	80.7	11.60%	82.90%	79.2
Seattle	78.7	9.00%	83.90%	100.0
Charleston	78.7	11.20%	82.70%	66.9
Norfolk	77.0	11.20%	75.60%	82.9
Ann Arbor	75.5	12.90%	90.30%	51.1
Springfield	75.2	11.70%	89.80%	63.5
Honolulu	75.2	10.10%	82.30%	50.2

36. Ease of Doing Business. DoingBusiness.org publishes statistics on how easy or difficult different countries make it to do business. Table 13.7 shows the top 12 countries for ease of doing business, with y = easiness score along with a set of predictor variables. 🐦 **bestbusiness**

TABLE 13.7   Best countries for ease of doing business

Country	Easiness score	Starting a business	Employing workers	Paying taxes
Singapore	100	10	1	5
New Zealand	99	1	14	12
United States	98	6	1	46
Hong Kong	97	15	20	3
Denmark	96	16	10	13
U.K.	95	8	28	16
Ireland	94	5	38	6
Canada	93	2	18	28
Australia	92	3	8	48
Norway	91	33	99	18
Iceland	90	17	62	32
Japan	89	64	17	112

37. Virginia Weather. Table 13.8 contains data on weather in a sample of cities in the state of Virginia. We are interested in predicting y = heating degree days using the other predictor variables. 🐦 **vaweather**

TABLE 13.8   Data on the weather in Virginia

City	Heating degree-days	Avg. Jan. temp.	Avg. July temp.	Cooling degree-days
Alexandria	4055	34.9	79.2	1531
Arlington	4055	34.9	79.2	1531
Blacksburg	5559	30.9	71.1	533
Charlottesville	4103	35.5	76.9	1212
Chesapeake	3368	40.1	79.1	1612
Danville	3970	36.6	78.8	1418
Hampton	3535	39.4	78.5	1432
Harrisonburg	5333	30.5	73.5	758
Leesburg	5031	31.5	75.2	911
Lynchburg	4354	34.5	75.1	1075
Manassas	4925	31.7	75.7	1075
Newport News	3179	41.2	80.3	1682
Norfolk	3368	40.1	79.1	1612
Petersburg	3334	39.7	79.6	1619
Portsmouth	3368	40.1	79.1	1612
Richmond	3919	36.4	77.9	1435
Roanoke	4284	35.8	76.2	1134
Suffolk	3467	39.6	78.5	1427
Virginia Beach	3336	40.7	78.8	1482

Source: National Oceanic and Atmospheric Administration.

38. Health Insurance Coverage. We are interested in estimating y = the number of people covered by health insurance, using x_1 = the number of adults not covered and x_2 = the number of children not covered. Use the data in Table 13.9, containing a random sample of U.S. states. All data are in thousands. 🐦 **healthinsurance**

TABLE 13.9   Health insurance coverage

State	Persons covered	Adults not covered	Children not covered
Alabama	3,843	689	82
Arizona	4,958	1311	283
Colorado	3,977	826	176
Georgia	7,688	1659	314
Illinois	10,867	1776	302
Kentucky	3,467	639	98
Maryland	4,836	776	137
Massachusetts	5,678	657	103
Michigan	8,928	1043	116
Minnesota	4,675	475	104
Missouri	5,028	772	127
New Jersey	7,319	1341	277
North Carolina	7,266	1585	307
Ohio	10,181	1138	157
Pennsylvania	11,108	1237	203
South Carolina	3,553	672	112
Tennessee	5,111	809	94
Virginia	6,532	1006	185
Washington	5,572	746	105
Wisconsin	4,995	481	63

39. Regression in Accounting. We are interested in estimating y = current ratio using x_1 = price–earnings ratio, x_2 = total assets, and x_3 = total liabilities. Use the data in Table 13.10, containing a random sample of large technology companies in 2010. Total assets and total liabilities are in billions of dollars. 🐦 **accounting**

   a. Build the final multiple regression model using level of significance $\alpha = 0.10$.
   b. Comment on your results from (a).
   c. Redo your work from (a), this time using level of significance $\alpha = 0.13$.
   d. Report and interpret your final model from (c).

TABLE 13.10   Accounting data for large technology companies

Company	Current ratio	Price-earning ratio	Assets	Liabilities
Microsoft	1.82	12.51	77.9	38.3
Intel	2.79	18.44	53.1	11.4
Dell	1.28	10.95	33.7	28.0
Apple	1.88	24.57	53.9	26.0
Google	10.62	18.87	40.5	4.5

Source: Lexis-Nexis.

40. Fuel Efficiency. Open the data set **Fuel Efficiency.** We would like to estimate y = combined fuel efficiency, based on x_1 = engine displacement, x_2 = number of cylinders, x_3 = city fuel efficiency, and x_4 = highway fuel efficiency. Apply the Strategy for Building a Multiple Regression Model, using level of significance $\alpha = 0.10$. 🐾 **fuelefficiency**

41. Blood Pressure. Open the data set **Systolic**. We are interested in estimating y = systolic blood pressure, based on the other predictor variables. Apply the Strategy for Building a Multiple Regression Mode, using level of significance $\alpha = 0.05$. 🐾 **Systolic**

42. Baseball. In Example 13.16, interpret the coefficients for Triples, Hits, Home Runs, RBIs, Walks, and Yankees.

Chapter 13 Formulas and Vocabulary

SECTION 13.1
- **Confidence interval for slope β_1** (p. 642).

$$b_1 \pm t_{\alpha/2} \cdot \frac{s}{\sqrt{\Sigma(x - \bar{x})^2}}$$

- **Fitted values** (p. 636)
- **Margin of error E** (p. 642)
- **Population regression equation** (p. 635)
- **Regression model** (p. 635)
- **Regression model assumptions** (p. 636)
- **Test statistic t_{data}** (p. 638).

$$t_{\text{data}} = \frac{b_1}{s/\sqrt{\Sigma(x - \bar{x})^2}}$$

SECTION 13.2
- **Confidence interval for the mean of the values of y for a given x** (p. 652)
- **Prediction interval for a randomly selected value of y for a given x** (p. 653)

SECTION 13.3
- **Adjusted coefficient of determination R^2_{adj}** (p. 659).

$$R^2_{\text{adj}} = 1 - (1 - R^2)\left(\frac{n - 1}{n - k - 1}\right)$$

- **Backward, stepwise regression** (p. 664)
- **Dummy variable** (p. 662)
- **Multiple coefficient of determination R^2** (p. 659).

$$R^2 = \frac{\text{SSR}}{\text{SST}}$$

- **Multiple regression** (p. 657)
- **Multiple regression coefficients** (p. 657)
- **Multiple regression equation** (p. 657)
- **Multiple regression model** (p. 660)
- **Population multiple regression equation** (p. 660)
- **Strategy for Building a Multiple Regression Model** (p. 664)

Chapter 13 Review Exercises

SECTION 13.1
For Exercises 1–3, test whether there is a linear relationship between x and y, using level of significance $\alpha = 0.05$.

1. Education and Earnings. The U.S. Census Bureau reports the mean annual earnings of American citizens according to the number of years of education. We are interested in the relationship between earnings (y, in thousands of dollars) and years of education (x). 🐾 **eduearn**

Education (x)	Annual earnings (y)
8	18.6
10	18.9
12	27.3
13	29.7
14	34.2
16	51.2
18	60.4

2. High School GPA and College GPA. The college admissions office would like to determine if there is a relationship between the high school grade point average and the first-year college grade point average of first-year college students, using the data in the following table. 🐾 **gpa**

Student	High school GPA (x)	First-year college GPA (y)
1	2.4	2.6
2	2.5	1.9
3	2.9	2.7
4	2.7	2.5
5	3.0	2.4
6	3.5	2.9
7	3.0	2.7
8	3.6	3.1
9	3.4	3.0
10	3.9	3.3

3. Used Cars: Price versus Age. Do you think you can predict the price of a used car based on how old it is? The table shows the price (in thousands of dollars) and the age (in years) of 10 previously owned vehicles of the same make and model. 🔊 **ageprice**

Car	Age (x)	Price (y)
1	1	18.0
2	2	16.0
3	3	15.5
4	4	13.5
5	4	14.5
6	5	10.5
7	5	12.0
8	6	9.5
9	7	8.5
10	8	7.0

For Exercises 4–6, construct and interpret a 95% confidence interval for β_1.

4. Data in Exercise 1
5. Data in Exercise 2
6. Data in Exercise 3

SECTION 13.2
For Exercises 7–9, do the following, for the indicated data.
 a. Find the point estimate of y, for the given x.
 b. Calculate and interpret a 95% confidence interval for the mean value of y for the given x.
 c. Compute and interpret a 95% prediction interval for a randomly chosen value of y for the given x.

7. Data in Exercise 1, for 10 years of education
8. Data in Exercise 2, for a high school GPA of 3.0
9. Data in Exercise 3, for a used car 8 years old

SECTION 13.3
Use the following data set for Exercises 10–13.

y	x_1	x_2	x_3
18.7	2	100	4.1
18.4	4	90	5.0
21.8	6	90	3.8
22.0	8	70	5.2
25.2	10	70	3.8
25.7	12	50	5.3
26.9	14	50	5.4
28.3	16	30	5.4
28.6	18	30	4.3
31.8	20	10	4.9

10. Assuming the regression assumptions are met, perform the F test for the significance of the overall regression, using level of significance $\alpha = 0.05$. Do the following.
 a. State the hypotheses and the rejection rule.
 b. Find the F statistic and the p-value.
 c. State the conclusion and interpretation.

11. Perform the t test for the significance of the individual predictor variables, using level of significance $\alpha = 0.05$. Do the following.
 a. For each hypothesis test, state the hypotheses and the rejection rule.
 b. For each hypothesis test, find the t statistic and the p-value.
 c. For each hypothesis test, state the conclusion and interpretation.

12. Identify any predictors that have corresponding p-values greater than the level of significance $\alpha = 0.05$. Of these, discard the variable with the largest p-value. Then redo Exercise 11, omitting this predictor. Repeat if necessary.

13. Verify the regression assumptions for your final model from Exercise 12.

Chapter 13 QUIZ

TRUE OR FALSE
1. True or false: We may check all the regression assumptions using a scatterplot of the residuals versus the fitted values.
2. True or false: When $\beta_1 = 0$, there is no relationship between the predictor variable and the response variable.
3. True or false: For a given value of x, the prediction interval for a randomly chosen value of y is always wider than the confidence interval for the mean value of y.

FILL IN THE BLANK
4. Two other terms for the fitted values of a regression are the (a) _____ and the (b) _____ values.
5. The point estimate of the slope _____ of the population regression equation in Section 13.1 is _____.

6. A predictor variable used to recode a binomial categorical variable in regression, and taking values 0 or 1, is called a _____ variable.

SHORT ANSWER
7. What are the four regression assumptions?
8. What other form of inference is the $100(1 - \alpha)\%$ confidence interval for β_1 equivalent to?
9. Why is R^2_{adj} preferable to R^2 in multiple regression?

CALCULATIONS AND INTERPRETATIONS
10. **Men's Heights and Weights.** The university medical unit is collecting data on the heights and weights of the male students on campus. A random sample of ten male students showed the following heights (in inches) and weights (in pounds). Test for a linear relationship between height and weight using level of significance $\alpha = 0.01$. 🔊 **heightweight**

Student	Height (x)	Weight (y)
1	66	150
2	68	145
3	69	160
4	70	165
5	70	165
6	71	180
7	72	175
8	72	180
9	73	195
10	75	210

11. For the data in Problem 10, answer the following.
  a. Will a 99% confidence interval for β_1 include zero? Why or why not?
  b. Verify your statement in **(a)** by constructing and interpreting a 99% confidence interval for β_1.

12. Using the data in Problem 10, do the following.
  a. Find the point estimate of the height of a man 70 inches tall.
  b. Calculate and interpret a 95% confidence interval for the mean height of all men 70 inches tall.
  c. Compute and interpret a 95% prediction interval for a randomly chosen man 70 inches tall.

For Exercise 13, refer to the data in Review Exercises 10–13 (page 672).

13. Report and interpret your final model from Exercise 12, by doing the following.
  a. Provide the multiple regression equation for your final model.
  b. Interpret the multiple regression coefficients so that a nonstatistician could understand.
  c. Report and interpret the standard error of the estimate s and the adjusted coefficient of determination R^2_{adj}.

Answers to Exercises and Chapter Quizzes

Chapter 1

Section 1.1

1. **(a)** "No car." **(b)** "I did not have a car or a way to leave."
2. **(a)** The table **(b)** It would have used too much space.
3. Answers will vary.
4. Answers will vary.
5. Note the large differences in the comparative heights of the rectangles that measure responses of sadness, anger, and disbelief.
6. The rectangles for men and women for the emotions of fear and vulnerability have similar heights.
7. **(a)** About 36,000,000 **(b)** About 7600
8. **(a)** About 23,000,000 **(b)** About 900
9. About 5400
10. About 3500

Section 1.2

1. Answers will vary.
2. False
3. Elements
4. A *qualitative variable* is usually classified into categories; a *quantitative variable* takes on numerical values.
5. Categorical variable
6. True
7. A population is the collection of all elements (persons, items, or data) of interest in a particular study. A sample is a subset of the population from which the information is collected.
8. A *statistic* is a characteristic of a sample.
9. The value of a parameter is constant but usually unknown. The value of a statistic may vary from sample to sample but is usually known.
10. Collection of data from every element in the population
11. Students Michael, Ashley, Christopher, and Jessica
12. Gender, height, class rank, siblings, and math SAT
13. Freshman, sophomore, junior, and senior
14. Female, 66, freshman, 3, 550
15. Hospitals City, Memorial, Children's, Eldercare, and County
16. Type, number of floors, HMO ranking, number of patients per nurse, and year opened
17. General and specialized
18. Specialized, 3, 1st, 5.9, 2005
19. Height, siblings, and Math SAT
20. Gender and class rank
21. Number of floors, HMO ranking, number of patients per nurse, year opened
22. Type
23. Siblings, Math SAT
24. Height
25. Number of floors, HMO ranking, year opened
26. Number of patients per nurse
27. Gender
28. Class rank
29. Math SAT
30. Height and siblings
31. Type
32. HMO ranking
33. Year opened
34. Number of floors and number of patients per nurse
35. **(a)** Quantitative **(b)** Interval
36. **(a)** Qualitative **(b)** Nominal
37. **(a)** Quantitative **(b)** Ratio
38. **(a)** Quantitative **(b)** Interval
39. **(a)** Quantitative **(b)** Ratio
40. **(a)** Qualitative **(b)** Nominal
41. **(a)** Qualitative **(b)** Ordinal
42. **(a)** Quantitative **(b)** Ratio
43. **(a)** Qualitative **(b)** Nominal
44. **(a)** Quantitative **(b)** Ratio
45. **(a)** Qualitative **(b)** Nominal
46. **(a)** Quantitative **(b)** Ratio
47. **(a)** Quantitative **(b)** Ratio
48. **(a)** Qualitative **(b)** Nominal
49. Population: all home sales in Tarrant County, Texas; sample: 100 home sales selected
50. Population: all veterans returning from war; sample: the 20 veterans selected
51. Population: all 4-H clubs in Maricopa County, Arizona: Sample: ten selected 4-H clubs.
52. Population: all older women; sample: the physical therapist's 10 selected patients
53. Population: all students at Portland Community College; sample: 50 selected Portland Community College students.
54. Population: all companies that recently underwent a merger; sample: the 50 selected companies that recently underwent a merger
55. Descriptive statistics; the variable describes a sample.
56. Inferential statistics; the sample was used to draw a conclusion about the entire population.
57. Statistical inference; the sample was used to draw a conclusion about the entire population.
58. Descriptive statistics; the variable describes a sample.
59. Descriptive statistics; the variable describes a sample.
60. Inferential statistics; the sample was used to draw a conclusion about the entire population.
61. Descriptive statistics; the variable describes a sample.
62. Inferential statistics; the sample was used to draw a conclusion about the entire population.
63. **(a)** Elements: Endangered species Pygmy rabbit, Florida panther, Red wolf, and West-Indian manatee; Variables: Year listed as endangered, Estimated number remaining, and Range. **(b)** Qualitative variables: Range; Quantitative variables: Year listed as endangered and estimated number remaining. **(c)** Year listed as endangered—interval; estimated number remaining—ratio, range—nominal. **(d)** Year listed as endangered—discrete, Estimated number remaining—discrete. **(e)** 1973, 50, Florida.
64. **(a)** Elements: Companies City of Santa Monica, St. John's Health Center, The Macerich Company, Fremont General Corp., and Entravision Corp.; Variables: Employees and industry. **(b)** Qualitative variables: Industry; Quantitative variables: Employees. **(c)** Employees—ratio; Industry—nominal **(d)** Employees—discrete **(e)** 1892, government
65. **(a)** Elements: States Texas, Missouri, Minnesota, Ohio, and South Dakota; Variables: Proportion of GE corn and most prevalent type. **(b)** Qualitative variables: Most

prevalent type; Quantitative variables: Proportion of GE corn **(c)** Proportion of GE corn—ratio; most prevalent type—nominal **(d)** Proportion of GE corn—continuous **(e)** 79%, Herbicide-tolerant

66. (a) Elements: Crime types robberies, assaults, burglaries, larceny/thefts, and motor vehicle thefts; Variables: 2005 total, per 100,000 people, national per 100,000 people, compared to national average **(b)** Qualitative variables: Compared to national average; Quantitative variables: 2005 total, per 100,000 people, national per 100,000 people **(c)** 2005 total—ratio; per 100,000 people—ratio; national per 100,000 people—ratio, compared to national average—nominal **(d)** 2005 total—discrete; per 100,000 people—continuous; national per 100,000 people—continuous **(e)** 55, 134.1, 526.5, Better

67. (a) Elements: Hospital names Hardy Wilson, Humphreys County, Jefferson County, Lackey Memorial, Leake Memorial, Madison County, Monfort Jones, and Rankin Medical Center; Variables: Beds, City, and Zip **(b)** Qualitative variables: City and zip; Quantitative variables: Beds **(c)** Beds—ratio; City—nominal; Zip—nominal **(d)** Beds—discrete **(e)** 134, Brandon, 39042

68. (a) Elements: Hospitals Briarcliff Manor, Buchanan, Cortlandt, Croton-on-Hudson, Mount Pleasant, Ossining 1, Ossining 2, Peekskill, Pleasantville, and Sleepy Hollow; Variables: Births and average maternal age **(b)** Qualitative variables: There are no qualitative variables; Quantitative variables: Births and average maternal age **(c)** Births—ratio; average maternal age—ratio **(d)** Births—discrete; average maternal age—continuous **(e)** 134, 29.2

69. (a) Elements: Commodities oil, gold, and coffee; Variables: Price per share and percent change **(b)** Qualitative variables: There are no qualitative variables; Quantitative variables: Price per share and percent change **(c)** Price per share—ratio; percent change—ratio **(d)** Price per share—continuous; percent change—continuous **(e)** $393.70, +3.90%

70. (a) Elements: Years 1910, 1986, 2004, 1981, 1962, 1996, 1972, 1980, 1963, and 1951. Variables: Deaths **(b)** Qualitative variables: There are no qualitative variables. Quantitative variables: Deaths **(c)** Deaths—ratio **(d)** Deaths—discrete **(e)** 16

71. (a) Elements are the types of music that *all* radio listeners listened to in the winter of 2004; we can only list Mainstream AC, Hot AC, Mod AC, and Soft AC—other elements are not given. **(b)** Percentage of listeners for each type; quantitative. **(c)** The proportion is (% Mainstream AC ÷ % AC) *100% = (7.8/14)100% = 55.71%.

72. (a) Sample **(b)** No, these companies are relatively large and there are probably many more small companies than larger companies.

73. (a) Sample **(b)** No; years were not selected randomly.

74. They compared the average lifetime of a sample of their own light bulb to the reported average lifetimes of other current models of light bulbs.

75. (a) Statistic **(b)** An estimate of the average lifetime of all new light bulbs is the average lifetime of the sample of 100 light bulbs, which is 2000 hours.

76. (a) Campuses Arizona State, Ohio State, Central Florida, University of Minnesota, and University of Texas **(b)** Location, enrollment, and rank **(c)** Location **(d)** Enrollment and rank **(e)** Location—nominal; enrollment—ratio; rank—ordinal

77. (a) Sample **(b)** No, they are the university campuses with the largest enrollment. **(c)** Tempe, 55,552,1 **(d)** Ohio State University is located in Columbus, Ohio, and it had the second highest enrollment of university campuses in 2009 with 55,014 students.

Section 1.3

1. Convenience sampling usually only includes a select group of people. For example, surveying people at a mall on a workday during working hours would probably include few if any people who work full time.

2. Answers will vary.

3. Answers will vary; could have chosen a random sample of houses and apartments and surveying the people door to door, for instance.

4. No.

5. A sample for which every element has an equal chance of being included.

6. Observational study—observes association between explanatory and response variables; experimental study—investigates how varying the explanatory variable affects the response by placing subjects into treatment and control groups.

7. Cluster sampling

8. Systematic sampling

9. Convenience sampling

10. Cluster sampling

11. Target population: All college students; Potential population: All students working out at the gymnasium on the Monday night Brandon was there.

12. Yes. Students working out at the gymnasium are more likely to be physically fit than the rest of the students.

13. Target population: All small businesses; Potential population: Small businesses near the state university.

14. Yes. Businesses near the state university are more likely to employ college students than businesses farther away.

15. Vague terminology

16. Leading question

17. Neither simple nor clear

18. Asking two questions in one

19. (a) Observational **(b)** response variable: how often they attend religious services; predictor variable: whether or not the family is large (at least four children)

20. (a) Observational **(b)** response variable: stock price; predictor variable: whether or not the company gives large bonuses to its CEOs

21. (a) Experimental **(b)** response variable: performance of the electronics equipment; predictor variable: whether or not a piece of equipment has a new computer processor

22. (a) Experimental **(b)** response variable: whether or not the person's blood pressure is lowered; predictor variable: whether or not the person is taking the new drug

23. Answers will vary.

24. Answers will vary.

25. Answers will vary.

26. Answers will vary.

27. Level of insect damage to crops

28. Whether or not the new pesticide was used

29. The new pesticide

30. The traditional pesticide

31. LDL cholesterol level in the bloodstream

32. Whether person is given new medication or placebo

33. New medication

34. Placebo

35. Randomization

36. A person who has a high HDL cholesterol level may have a much larger decrease in HDL cholesterol level than the average person. This might result in a higher mean decrease in cholesterol level than would have been obtained if the people in the treatment and control groups were randomly assigned.

37. Answers will vary. For instance, the poll by Ann Landers was extremely biased. Only people who read the Ann Landers column and felt strongly about the poll responded to this poll. The *Newsday* poll was done professionally, and therefore the sample used was more likely to be representative of the population.

38. Target population: all high schools in New England; potential population: all high schools in greater Boston. Potential population is not a random sample of all high schools in New England; dropout rate for target population may differ from potential population.

39. Target population: all the people living in Chicago; potential population: people who have phones and who have their phone number listed in the Chicago phone directory. Reasons for potential selection bias vary; for instance, many of the people living below the poverty level in Chicago may not have phones.

40. Desired response type is open to interpretation: preference or yes/no.

41. The survey question is a leading question.

42. No; the conclusion leaves out the details of the survey question

43. (a) No, different random samples may contain different lowest stock prices. (b) Answers will vary. (c) No; see answer (a). (d) Answers will vary.

44. (a) No; no. We don't know which two companies will be selected. (b)–(c) Answers will vary.

45. It is a variable that may vary from sample to sample.

46. Predictor variable: patient diet, Mediterranean or Western; response variable: risk for a second heart attack.

47. (a) Forcing the parents of a treatment group to smoke tobacco will increase the occurrence of respiratory illnesses of their children. This is not very ethical. (b) Observational study

48. (a) The 305 subjects that wore the placebo bracelet (b) The subjects were randomly assigned to wear either the placebo bracelet or the ionized bracelet. (c) There are 305 subjects in both the treatment and the control groups.

49. (a) Type of bracelet worn, placebo or ionized (b) Wearing the ionized bracelet (c) Measure of pain

50. This study is an experimental study because the subjects were randomly assigned to either a treatment or a control.

51. Answers will vary.

52. Answers will vary.

53. (a) Answers will vary. (b) No. (c) Answers will vary. (d) We cannot tell in advance.

Chapter 1 Review

1. (a) Cars Subaru Forester, Honda CR-V, Nissan Rogue, and Mitsubishi Outlander (b) Cylinders, passengers, base price, and customer satisfaction (c) Customer satisfaction (d) Cylinders, passengers, and base price (e) Cylinders—ratio; passengers—ratio; base price—ratio; customer satisfaction—ordinal

2. (a) Subaru Forester, Honda CR-V (b) The base price

3. 4, 5, $20,295, above average

4. (a) Elements are the states; variables are Pop (1960, in 1000s), Pop (2005, in 1000s), and Increase. (b) Quantitative (c) Population of 4,952,000 in 1960 and population of 17,790,000 in 2005, which was an increase of 12,838,000 people (d) California, Texas, and Florida; New York and Illinois

5. (a) Turn on all 1 million light bulbs, leave them all on until they burn out, compute the average of all bulb lifetimes. (b) Use the average lifetime of a sample to estimate the average lifetime of the population.

6. (a) All registered voters in the United States (b) People on the lists of people who owned cars and had telephones (c) All people on the lists of people who owned cars and had telephones (d) Not similar; answers will vary.

7. (a) Observational study (b) It would be impractical to randomly reassign people to a statistics class after classes have started.

8. (a) Replication (b) Surveying only four dentists is not likely to get a sample representative of the population of all dentists.

9. Observational; it would be impossible to randomly assign a child to come from a single-parent family or a two-parent family.

10. No; there may be other factors that determine a child's cognitive skills.

Chapter 1 Quiz

1. False

2. False

3. collecting

4. observation

5. sample

6. Observational study

7. Experimental study

8. Predictor variable: drug given to an elderly patient with Alzheimer's, new or placebo; response variable: whether or not the patient's Alzheimer's symptoms are reduced.

9. (a) All statistics students (b) The students in the statistics class who were selected for the sample (c) Left-handed or not; qualitative (d) No; not likely to be very far away from the population proportion since enrollment in a specific statistics class is not dependent on being left-handed or not.

10. Different people have different interpretations of the words *often, occasionally, sometimes,* and *seldom.*

Chapter 2

Section 2.1

1. We use graphical and tabular form to summarize data in order to organize it in a format where we can better assess the information. If we just report the raw data, it may be extremely difficult to extract the information contained in the data.

2. A frequency distribution is a listing of all the values with the corresponding frequencies for each value of a variable; a relative frequency distribution lists the relative frequencies for the values.

3. True.

4. False

5. The sample size, n.

6. 1.00

7. The row totals, the column totals

8. The grand total, the sample size

9. When the sample sizes are substantially different

10. The headings of the columns and the rows of a crosstabulation are categories, not numbers. We could recode the variables in order to use crosstabulation by dividing the numbers up into classes, as we did for grouped frequency distributions. Then we could code each class as a category.

11.

Variable: political party affiliation	Frequency
Democrat	7
Independent	6
Republican	7
Total	20

12.

Variable: political party affiliation	Relative frequency
Democrat	0.35
Independent	0.30
Republican	0.35
Total	1.00

13.

14.

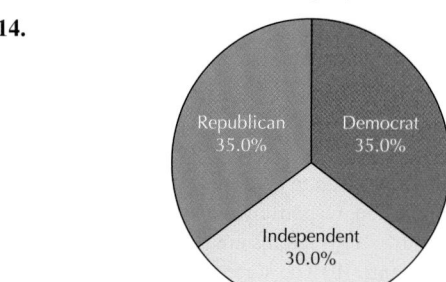

15.

Variable: blood type	Frequency
A	11
AB	1
B	3
O	10
Total	25

16.

Variable: blood type	Relative frequency
A	0.44
AB	0.04
B	0.12
O	0.40
Total	1.00

17.

18.

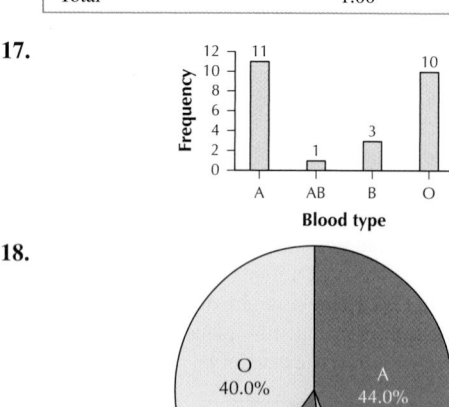

19.

Variable: major	Frequency
Business	4
Math	4
Psychology	4
Total	12

20.

Variable: major	Relative frequency
Business	0.3333
Math	0.3333
Psychology	0.3333
Total	1.00

21.

22.

23.

Variable: gender	Frequency
Female	7
Male	5
Total	12

24.

Variable: gender	Relative frequency
Female	0.5833
Male	0.4167
Total	1.00

25.

26.

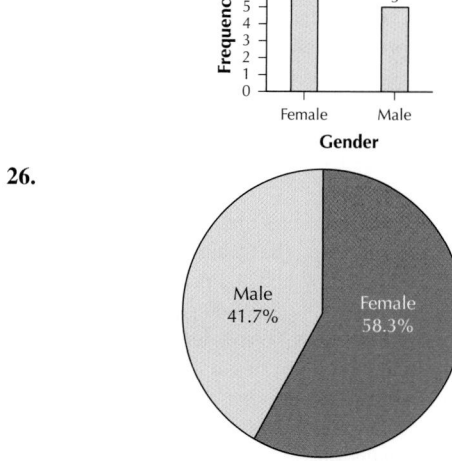

27.

	Female	Male	Total
Business	2	2	4
Math	3	1	4
Psychology	2	2	4
Total	7	5	12

28.

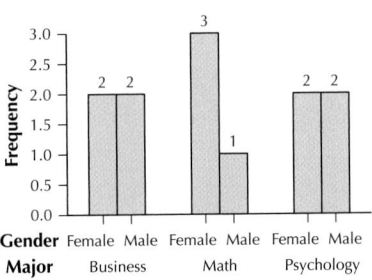

29.

Variable: class	Frequency
Freshman	3
Sophomore	4
Junior	3
Senior	4
Total	14

30.

Variable: class	Relative frequency
Freshman	0.2143
Sophomore	0.2857
Junior	0.2143
Senior	0.2857
Total	1.00

31.

32.

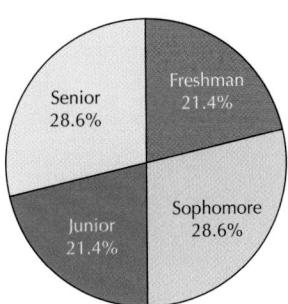

33.

Variable: handedness	Frequency
Left	4
Right	10
Total	14

34.

Variable: handedness	Relative frequency
Left	0.2857
Right	0.7143
Total	1.00

35.

36.

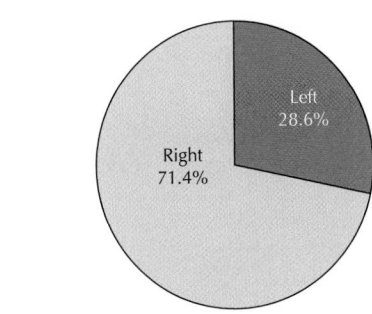

37.

	Freshman	Sophomore	Junior	Senior	Total
Left	1	1	1	1	4
Right	2	3	2	3	10
Total	3	4	3	4	14

38.

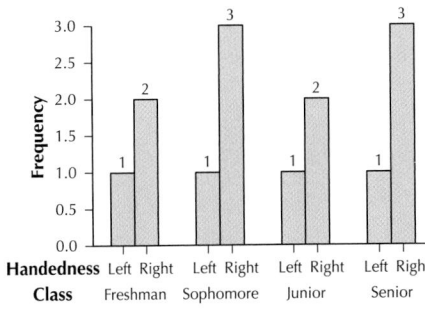

39. No. There are actually two categorical variables—*level of education* and *whether or not the person owns a cell phone*. The percents are percents of each category of level of education who own cell phones and not the percent of the whole group who own cell phones.

40. No. There are actually two categorical variables—*level of education* and *whether or not the person owns a cell phone*. The percents are percents of each category of level of education who own cell phones and not the percent of the whole group who own cell phones. Also, the categories are arranged in order from lowest percent to highest percent and not in order from highest percent to lowest percent.

41. (a) Several times a day; 43.4% (b) Every few weeks; 5.1%

42. (a) 12.1% (b) 12.1%

43. (a) Fractures; 26% (b) Traumatic brain injury; 9% (c) Yes. It would have to be one of the injuries included in the category "Other injuries."

44. (a) 25% (b) 16%

45. (a)–(b)

Continent	Frequency	Relative frequency
Africa	1	0.10
Asia	5	0.50
Europe	1	0.10
North America	2	0.20
South America	1	0.10

(c)

(c)

(d)

(d)

(e)

(e)

(f)

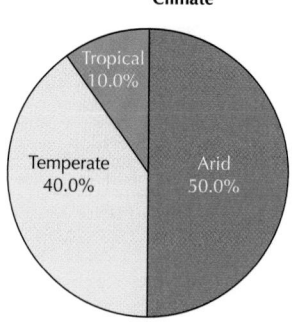

47. (a)–(b)

Main use	Frequency	Relative frequency
Industry	2	0.20
Irrigation	6	0.60
Not reported	2	0.20

(c)

(f)

(d)

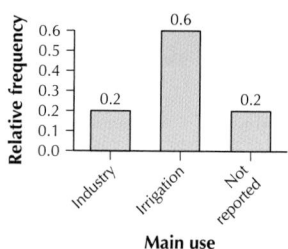

46. (a)–(b)

Climate	Frequency	Relative frequency
Arid	5	0.50
Temperate	4	0.40
Tropical	1	0.10

(e)

(f)

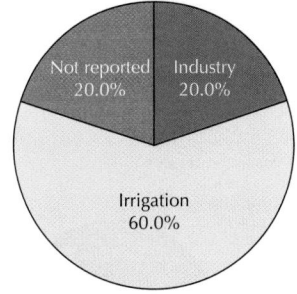

48. The countries are the elements.

49.

	Arid	**Temperate**	**Tropical**	**Total**
Africa	0	0	1	1
Asia	4	1	0	5
Europe	0	1	0	1
North America	0	2	0	2
South America	1	0	0	1
Total	5	4	1	10

50.

	Industry	**Irrigation**	**Not reported**	**Total**
Africa	0	1	0	1
Asia	0	4	1	5
Europe	0	0	1	1
North America	2	0	0	2
South America	0	1	0	1
Total	2	6	2	10

51.

	Industry	**Irrigation**	**Not reported**	**Total**
Arid	0	5	0	5
Temperate	2	0	2	4
Tropical	0	1	0	1
Total	2	6	2	10

52.

53.

54.

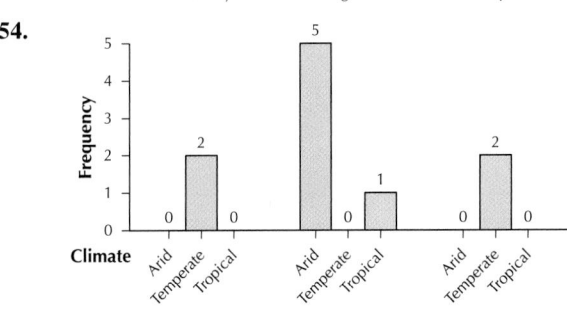

55. (a)

End-use sector	**Relative frequency**
Residential	0.2049
Commercial	0.1746
Industrial	0.2931
Transportation	0.3274

(b)

(c)

(d)

(e)

(d)

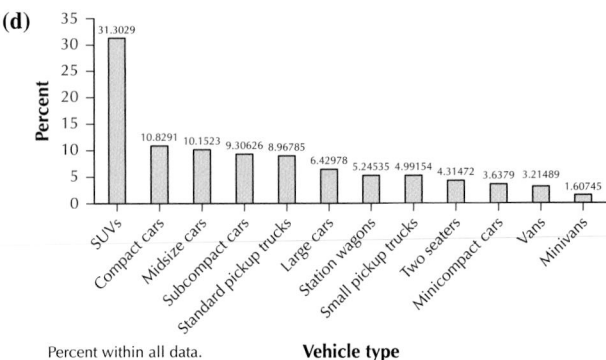

Percent within all data. **Vehicle type**

56. (a) Relative frequency distribution of *vehicle type*

Variable: vehicle type	Relative frequency
SUVs	0.3130
Compact cars	0.1083
Midsize cars	0.1015
Subcompact cars	0.0931
Standard pickup trucks	0.0897
Large cars	0.0643
Station wagons	0.0525
Small pickup trucks	0.0499
Two seaters	0.0431
Minicompact cars	0.0364
Vans	0.0321
Minivans	0.0161
Total	1.00

(e)

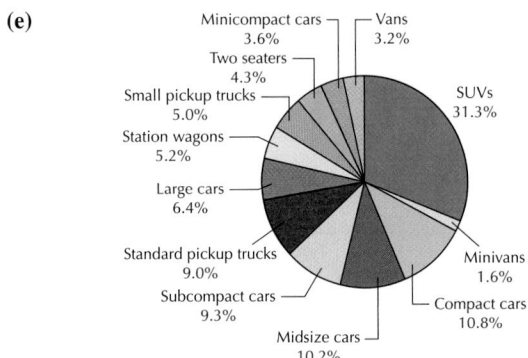

57. The sample may be a representative sample of all U.S. teenagers if one assumes that teenagers of all walks of life visit this particular Web site and participate in the survey. If only teenagers of a particular social class visit this Web site, then although the sample is "large" it will not be a representative sample. Bias may be introduced if only teenagers of a particular social standing, region, ethnicity, and so on visit this Web site.

(b)

Vehicle type

58.

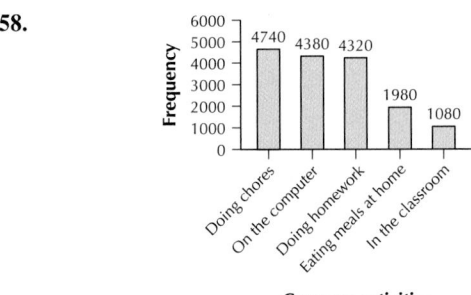

Common activities

59. A pie chart cannot be constructed for the data since the percentages for the different classes do not add up to 100%. Respondents could select more than one category.

60. Yes; e.g., "I don't know" or "Other factors."

(c)

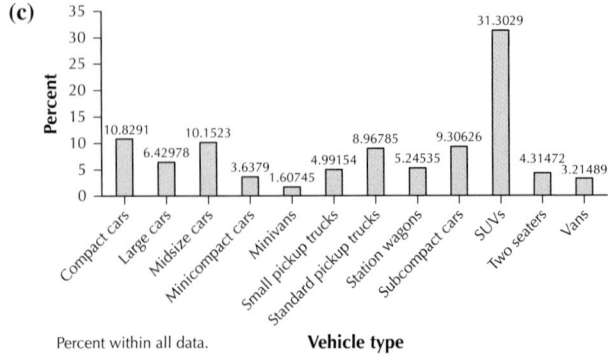

Percent within all data. **Vehicle type**

61.

Response	Frequency
Yes	1860
No	2700
I've never thought about it.	1440

62.

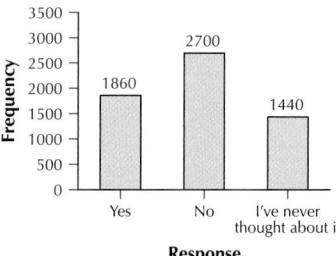

63. Relative frequencies are expressed as percentages.

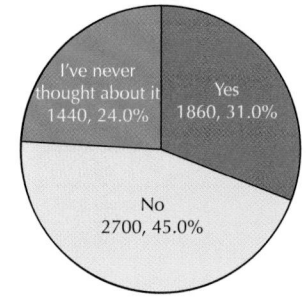

64. (a) Virgo (b) Aries

65. (a)

(b)

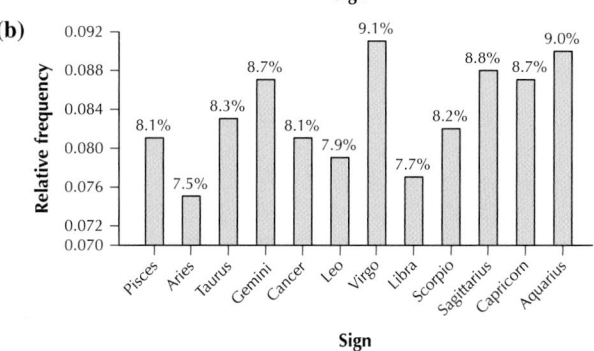

The graph in (b) uses an adjusted scale, which is misleading. Use this graph to magnify the small variability in percentages.

66. Virgo occurs the most and Aries occurs the least.

Sign	Relative frequency	Frequency
Pisces	0.081	118
Aries	0.075	110
Taurus	0.083	121
Gemini	0.087	127
Cancer	0.081	118
Leo	0.079	116
Virgo	0.091	133
Libra	0.077	113
Scorpio	0.082	120
Sagittarius	0.088	129
Capricorn	0.087	127
Aquarius	0.090	132

67. Categories are qualitative; interpretation will vary.

68. Yes.

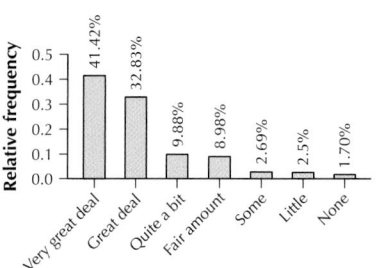

69. Yes.

70.

Investor	Frequency	Relative frequency
Intel Capital Corp.	41	0.299
New Enterprise Associates	22	0.161
Sequoia Capital	19	0.139
Venrock Associates	19	0.139
Canaan Partners	18	0.131
Draper Fisher Jurvetson	18	0.131

71. (a)

(b)

72.

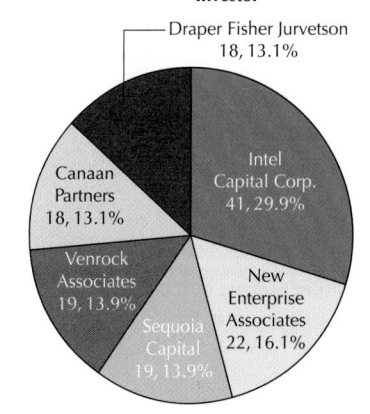

73. (a)–(c) Unchanged

74. Distribution for under 65 years

Type of insurance	Frequency	Relative frequency
Private	126,800,000	0.6967
Medicaid	13,700,000	0.0753
Other	5,700,000	0.0313
Uninsured	35,800,000	0.1967

75.

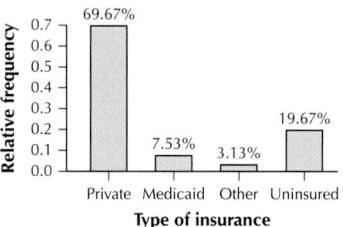

76. Yes ≈ 85%; No ≈ 15%

Response	Frequency
Yes	≈ 794
No	≈ 140

77.

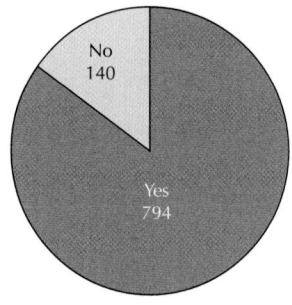

78. No, you would just have to relabel the slices with percents instead of frequencies.

79.

	Beverages	Food	Household	Tobacco	All
Glass	2	0	0	0	2
Metal	0	0	2	0	2
Paper	0	0	1	3	4
Plastic	1	2	1	0	4
All	3	2	4	3	12

80.

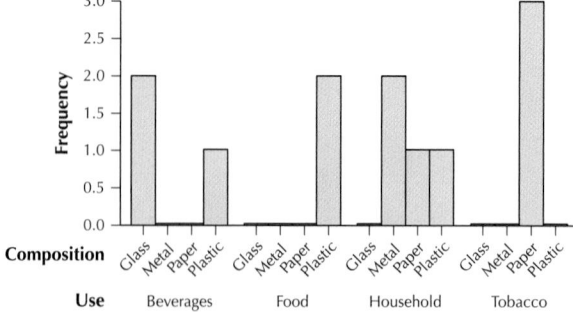

81. The composition of most of the litter from tobacco use is paper, the composition of most of the litter from food is plastic, the composition of most of the litter from beverages is paper or plastic, and the composition of most of the litter from household use is metal, paper, or plastic.

82. Missing values are in red

"How much do you enjoy shopping?"	Gender		
	Male	Female	Total
A lot	388	950	1338
Some	528	673	1255
Only a little	662	497	1159
Not at all	497	220	717
Don't know/refused	20	25	45
Total	2149	2365	4514

83.

"How much do you enjoy shopping?"	Gender		
	Male	Female	Total
A lot	29.00%	71.00%	100%
Some	46.37%	53.63%	100%
Only a little	57.12%	42.88%	100%
Not at all	69.32%	30.68%	100%
Don't know/refused	44.44%	55.56%	100%
Total	47.61%	52.39%	100%

84. (a) Women **(b)** Women **(c)** Men **(d)** Men

85. 0.5239

86. (a) .7100 **(b)** .5363 **(c)** .4288 **(d)** .3068

87.

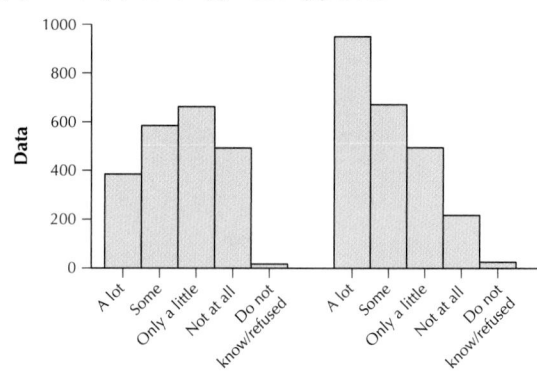

88. Missing values are in red

	Exciting	Routine	Dull	Total
Protestant	264	326	33	623
Catholic	107	128	6	241
Jewish	12	8	0	20
None	38	29	2	69
Other	9	5	0	14
Total	430	496	41	967

89.

	Exciting	Routine	Dull
Protestant	61.40%	65.73%	80.49%
Catholic	24.88%	25.81%	14.63%
Jewish	2.79%	1.61%	0%
None	8.84%	5.85%	4.88%
Other	2.09%	1.01%	0%
Total	100.00%	100.01%	100.00%

90. Protestant
91. Protestant

92. Protestant

93. **(a)** Girls: 0.525; boys: 0.475

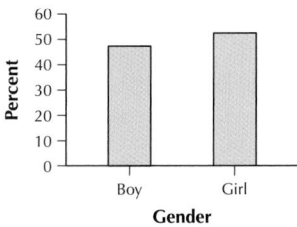

Gender

(b) Grades: 51.67%; popular: 29.50%; sports: 18.83%

Goals

94. **(a)**

```
Tally for Discrete Variables: GENDER

      GENDER   Percent
         boy    47.49
        girl    52.51
```

(b)

```
Tally for Discrete Variables: GOALS

       GOALS   Percent
      Grades    51.67
     Popular    29.50
      Sports    18.83
```

95. There are 51 observations and 8 variables.

96. Qualitative: State; Quantitative: Tot_hhld, Fam_tpc, Fam_mpc, Fam_fpc, Nfm_tpc, Nfm_lpc, and Ave_size.

97. Each relative frequency in the relative frequency distribution would be the same, each slice in the pie chart would be the same size, and each rectangle in the bar graph would be the same height.

98. **(a)** and **(b)**

Class	Frequency	Relative frequency
Freshman	5	0.25
Sophomore	5	0.25
Junior	5	0.25
Senior	5	0.25

99. Answers will vary.

100. Answers will vary.

Section 2.2

1. Both: frequency distribution, relative frequency distribution; quantitative data only: histograms, frequency polygons, stem-and-leaf displays, dotplot.

2. Answers will vary.

3. Between 5 and 20

4. We would be unable to use such summary information in constructing histograms.

5. Answers will vary.

6. Answers will vary; of a symmetric shape; circle; of a nonsymmetric shape; scalene triangle.

7. Answers will vary.

8. No (excluding the Pareto chart). Symmetry and skewness are not relevant in dealing with qualitative data.

9.

Number of game consoles	Frequency
0	9
1	10
2	5
Total	24

10.

Number of game consoles	Relative frequency
0	0.375
1	0.4167
2	0.2083
Total	1.00

11.

Age	Frequency
18	2
19	4
20	6
21	4
22	2
Total	18

12.

Age	Relative frequency
18	0.1111
19	0.2222
20	0.3333
21	0.2222
22	0.1111
Total	1.00

13.

Age	Frequency
18–19	6
20–21	10
22–23	2
Total	18

14.

Age	Relative frequency
18–19	0.3333
20–21	0.5556
22–23	0.1111
Total	1.00

15. Using 6 classes: Range = 87 − 61 = 26. Use 6 classes, so the class width = $\frac{26}{6}$ = 4.33. Use class width = 5.

Pulse rate	Frequency
60–64	2
65–69	4
70–74	3
75–79	5
80–84	5
85–89	1
Total	20

Using 5 classes: Range $= 87 - 61 = 26$. Use 5 classes, so the class width $= \frac{26}{5} = 5.2$. Use class width $= 6$.

Pulse rate	Frequency
60–65	3
66–71	3
72–77	5
78–83	7
84–89	2
Total	20

16. Using 6 classes:

Pulse rate	Relative frequency
60–64	0.10
65–69	0.20
70–74	0.15
75–79	0.25
80–84	0.25
85–89	0.05
Total	1.00

Using 5 classes:

Pulse rate	Relative frequency
60–65	0.15
66–71	0.15
72–77	0.25
78–83	0.35
84–89	0.10
Total	1.00

17. Using 6 classes:

Using 5 classes:

18. Using 6 classes:

Using 5 classes:

19. Using 6 classes:

Using 5 classes:

20. Stem-and-leaf display using split stems.

```
6 | 12
6 | 5999
7 | 234
7 | 57889
8 | 01234
8 | 7
```

Stem-and-leaf display.

```
6 | 125999
7 | 23457889
8 | 012347
```

21.

22. Using 6 classes: Range $= 95 - 62 = 33$. Use 6 classes, so the class width $= \frac{33}{6} = 5.5$. Use class width $= 6$.

Quiz grades	Frequency
60–65	2
66–71	3
72–77	7
78–83	3
84–89	2
90–95	3
Total	20

Using 5 classes: Range $= 95 - 62 = 33$. Use 5 classes, so the class width $= \frac{33}{5} = 6.6$. Use class width $= 7$.

Quiz grades	Frequency
62–68	2
69–75	8
76–82	5
83–89	2
90–96	3
Total	20

23. Using 6 classes:

Quiz grades	Relative frequency
60–65	0.10
66–71	0.15
72–77	0.35
78–83	0.15
84–89	0.10
90–95	0.15
Total	1.00

Using 5 classes:

Quiz grades	Relative frequency
62–68	0.10
69–75	0.40
76–82	0.25
83–89	0.10
90–96	0.15
Total	1.00

24. Using 6 classes:

Using 5 classes:

25. Using 6 classes:

Using 5 classes:

26. Using 6 classes:

Using 5 classes:

27.

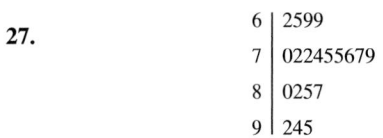

```
6 | 2599
7 | 022455679
8 | 0257
9 | 245
```

28.

29. (a) 4 (b) 1 and 6 (c) 15 times (d) 15% of the times
30. (a) 35 (b) 1 (c) 10; approximately 115 (d) Right-skewed
31. (a) 46 (b) 33 (not including a frequency of 0) (c) highest: 49; lowest: 33. (d) left-skewed
32. (a) 10 (b) 2.5; yes (c) Frequency histogram
33. (a) Divide the frequency values by the total frequency—classes not affected (b) change the scale along the relative frequency (vertical) axis by multiplying the relative frequency values by the total frequency—shape of distribution not affected (c) 19
34. (a) 2 (b) 0.1053 (c) 5 (d) 0.2632
35. (a) 0 (b) 0 (c) \$25 to \$27.5 has the largest relative frequency, $4/19 = 0.2105$. (d) 3 (e) 0
36. (c) Tending to be left-skewed
37. Data set: 23 24 25 26 27 28 28 29 30 31 31 32 32 32 33 35 36 37 39 40

38.

Classes	Frequency	Relative frequency
22–25	3	3/20 = 0.15
26–29	5	5/20 = 0.25
30–33	7	7/20 = 0.35
34–37	3	3/20 = 0.15
38–41	2	2/20 = 0.10

39. Histogram with five classes

40.

41. **(a)** 15 **(b)** 37.5 **(c)** 52.5 **(d)** 67.5 to 82.5 **(e)** 22.5 to 37.5
42. **(a)** Approximately 35 **(b)** Approximately 11 **(c)** No, because this interval does not contain only values in the 90s.
43. **(a)** 2000 **(b)** 1000 **(c)** 1000 to 3000 **(d)** 17,000 to 19,000
44. **(a)** Approximately 72 **(b)** Approximately 2 **(c)** Approximately 18
45. **(a)** and **(b)**

Continent	Frequency	Relative frequency
Africa	1	0.1
Asia	5	0.5
Europe	1	0.1
North America	2	0.2
South America	1	0.1

(c) Cannot construct because the variable is qualitative.
(d) Cannot construct because the variable is qualitative.
(e) We cannot construct because the variable is qualitative.

46.

Classes	Frequency	Relative frequency
550–599	1	$1/12 \approx 0.0833$
600–649	1	$1/12 \approx 0.0833$
650–699	1	$1/12 \approx 0.0833$
700–749	0	$0/12 = 0.0000$
750–799	3	$3/12 = 0.2500$
800–849	3	$3/12 = 0.2500$
850–899	1	$1/12 \approx 0.0833$
900–949	2	$2/12 \approx 0.1667$

47. Highest: Class 750 to 799 and Class 800 to 849.
Lowest: Class 550 to 599, Class 600 to 649, Class 650 to 699, and Class 850 to 899 (disregarding a frequency of zero)

48.

49.

50. Fairly symmetrical
51. 62%; middle.
52. $n \approx 690$.
53. No. We need the original data to construct a stem-and-leaf display. Since the data are grouped with a class width of 2, we only know how many observations are in each class, not the actual numbers.
54. **(a)** Range $= 98 - 57 = 41$. Use 6 classes, so the class width $= \dfrac{41}{6} = 6.833$. Use class width $= 7$.

Exam score	Frequency
57–63	3
64–70	2
71–77	7
78–84	4
85–91	2
93–98	2
Total	20

(b)

Exam score	Relative frequency
57–63	0.15
64–70	0.10
71–77	0.35
78–84	0.20
85–91	0.10
92–98	0.10
Total	1.00

(c)

55. **(a)**

(b)

(c)

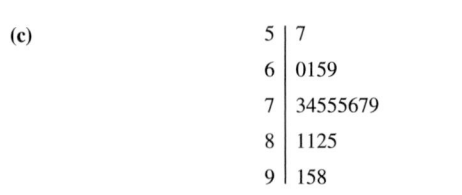

```
5 | 7
6 | 0159
7 | 34555679
8 | 1125
9 | 158
```

56.

	Dotplot	Histogram	Stem-and-leaf	Frequency polygon
(a) Symmetry and skewness	Appropriate to use for small ranges of data	Appropriate to use	Appropriate to use for small ranges of data	Appropriate to use
(b) Construct using pencil and paper	Easily done for small ranges of data	Easily done for small ranges of data	Easily done for small ranges of data	Easily done for small ranges of data
(c) Retain complete knowledge of the data	Appropriate	Appropriate only if the data are ungrouped	Appropriate	Appropriate only if the data are ungrouped
(d) Presentation in front of non-statisticians	Appropriate	Appropriate	Appropriate	Appropriate

57. (a) The horizontal scale would shift to the left. The vertical scale and size of the rectangles will be the same. **(b)** The horizontal scale would shift to the left. The vertical scale and the number of dots in each column will remain the same. **(c)** The numbers in the stem-and-leaf display will all be less by the same amount. This may change the number of numbers in each row, depending on the increments of the leaves. **(d)** The horizontal scale would shift to the left. The vertical scale and the height of the graph will remain the same.

58. 961; 22

59. The histogram is right-skewed.

60. Yes; fats and oils.

61. The histogram is right-skewed.

62. One whole cheesecake (2053 grams of cholesterol)

63. (a) 9 **(b)** 0.30

64. (a) 2 **(b)** 4.00, 4.30

65. (a) Decreases **(b)** Increases

66. (a) Increases **(b)** Decreases

67. (a) 3 **(b)** 57. There are 57 observations in the data set.

68. (a) 6 **(b)** 57 **(c)** Split stems

69. Answers will vary.

70. Answers will vary.

Section 2.3

1. A frequency distribution gives the frequency counts for each class (grouped or ungrouped). A cumulative frequency distribution gives the number of values which are less than or equal to the upper limit of a given class for grouped data or it gives the number of values which are less than or equal to a given number for ungrouped data.

2. A cumulative frequency distribution gives the number of values that are less than or equal to the upper limit of a given class for grouped data or it gives the number of values that are less than or equal to a given number for ungrouped data. A cumulative relative frequency distribution gives the proportion of values that are less than or equal to the upper limit of a given class for grouped data or it gives the proportion of values that are less than or equal to a given number for ungrouped data.

3. Ogive.

4. Plot the upper class limits along the x axis and the cumulative frequency or cumulative relative frequency along the y axis and connect the points with line segments.

5. Time series data.

6. Plot the values of the variable along the y axis and the time points (hours, days, months, years) along the x axis. Connect these points with line segments.

7. and 8.

Age	Frequency	Relative frequency	Cumulative frequency	Cumulative relative frequency
17.0–18.9	4	0.2	4	0.2
19.0–20.9	10	0.5	14	0.7
21.0–22.9	6	0.3	20	1.00
	$n = 20$	1.0		

9.

10.

11. and 12.

Height (inches)	Frequency	Relative frequency	Cumulative frequency	Cumulative relative frequency
60.0–63.9	3	0.12	3	0.12
64.0–67.9	10	0.40	13	0.52
68.0–71.9	10	0.40	23	0.92
72.0–75.9	2	0.08	25	1.00
	$n = 25$	1.00		

13.

14.

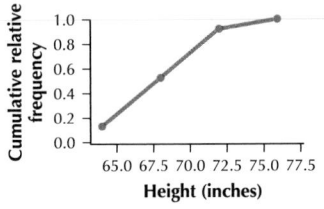

15. and **16.**

Value of single die roll	Frequency	Relative frequency	Cumulative frequency	Cumulative relative frequency
1	13	0.13	13	0.13
2	20	0.20	33	0.33
3	15	0.15	48	0.48
4	24	0.24	72	0.72
5	15	0.15	87	0.87
6	13	0.13	100	1.00
Total	100	1.00		

17.

18.

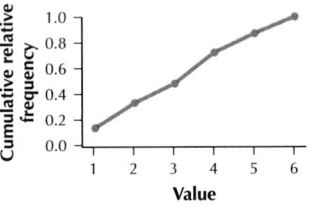

19. and **20.**

Stock prices (dollars)	Frequency	Relative frequency	Cumulative frequency	Cumulative relative frequency
5.00–7.49	1	0.0526	1	0.0526
7.50–9.99	1	0.0526	2	0.1052
10.00–12.49	2	0.1053	4	0.2105
12.50–14.99	1	0.0526	5	0.2631
15.00–17.49	2	0.1053	7	0.3684
17.50–19.99	0	0	7	0.3684
20.00–22.49	3	0.1579	10	0.5263
22.50–24.99	3	0.1579	13	0.6842
25.00–27.49	4	0.2105	17	0.8947
27.50–29.49	2	0.1053	19	1.0000
Total	$n = 19$	1.0000		

21.

22.

23. and **24.** Using 6 classes:

Pulse rate	Frequency	Relative frequency	Cumulative frequency	Cumulative relative frequency
60–64	2	0.10	2	0.10
65–69	4	0.20	6	0.30
70–74	3	0.15	9	0.45
75–79	5	0.25	14	0.70
80–84	5	0.25	19	0.95
85–89	1	0.05	20	1.00
	20	1.00		

Using 5 classes:

Pulse rate	Frequency	Relative frequency	Cumulative frequency	Cumulative relative frequency
60–65	3	0.15	3	0.15
66–71	3	0.15	6	0.30
72–77	5	0.25	11	0.55
78–83	7	0.35	18	0.90
84–89	2	0.10	20	1.00
	20	1.00		

25. Using 6 classes:

Using 5 classes:

26. Using 6 classes:

Using 5 classes:

27. and **28.** Using 6 classes:

Quiz score	Frequency	Relative frequency	Cumulative frequency	Cumulative relative frequency
60–65	2	0.10	2	0.10
66–71	3	0.15	5	0.25
72–77	7	0.35	12	0.60
78–83	3	0.15	15	0.75
84–89	2	0.10	17	0.85
90–95	3	0.15	20	1.00
	20	1.00		

Using 5 classes:

Quiz score	Frequency	Relative frequency	Cumulative frequency	Cumulative relative frequency
62–68	2	0.10	2	0.10
69–75	8	0.40	10	0.50
76–82	5	0.25	15	0.75
83–89	2	0.10	17	0.85
90–96	3	0.15	20	1.00
	20	1.00		

29. Using 6 classes:

Using 5 classes:

30. Using 6 classes:

Using 5 classes:

31.

32.

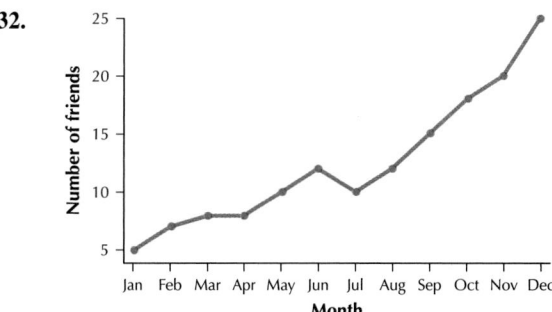

33. (a) 0.8 (b) 2.39 (c) 1.99
34. (a) Approximately 120 (b) Approximately 300
(c) Approximately 67
35. (a) Approximately 950 (b) Approximately 50
36. (a) Between 1996 and 1997 (b) Encouraging news
37.

Agricultural exports (in billions of dollars)	Frequency	Cumulative frequency
$0–$1.9	3	3
$2.0–$3.9	9	12
$4.0–$5.9	6	18
$6.0–$7.9	1	19
$8.0–$9.9	0	19
$10.0–$11.9	0	19
$12.0–$13.9	1	20
Total	20	

(a) 12
(b) 18
(c) 2
38. (a) 0.60 (b) 0.90 (c) 0.10

Agricultural exports (in billions of dollars)	Frequency	Relative frequency	Cumulative relative frequency
$0–$1.9	3	0.15	0.15
$2.0–$3.9	9	0.45	0.60
$4.0–$5.9	6	0.30	0.90
$6.0–$7.9	1	0.05	0.95
$8.0–$9.9	0	0	0.95
$10.0–$11.9	0	0	0.95
$12.0–$13.9	1	0.05	1.00
Total	20	1.00	

39.

40. (a)

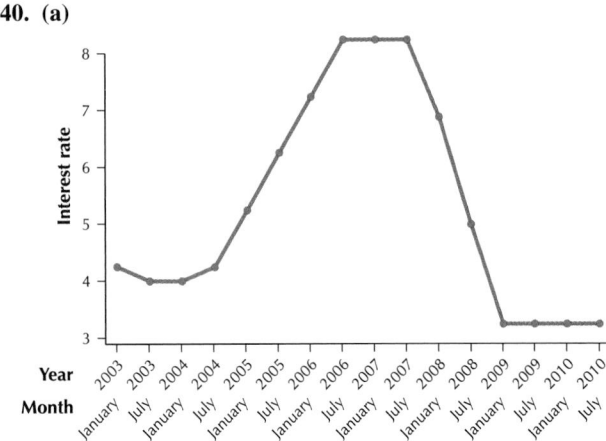

(b) Interest rates decreased from January 2003 to July 2003, remained the same from July 2003 to January 2004, increased from January 2004 to July 2006, remained the same from July 2006 to July 2007, decreased from July 2007 to January 2009, and remained the same from January 2009 to July 2010.

41. (a)

(b) Summer

42. The only change would be that the entire time series graph would shift up 3 units. The horizontal scale would stay the same and the shape of the graph would stay the same.

43. (a)

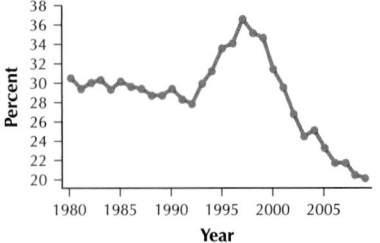

(b) The percent of 12th-graders who smoked cigarettes was relatively constant from 1980 to 1992, it increased from 1992 to 1997, and then it decreased from 1997 to 2009.

44. (a)

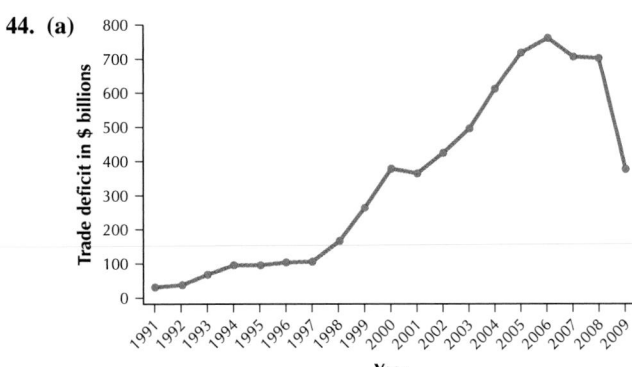

(b) From 1991 to 2006 the general trend in the trade deficit is that it increased and then it decreased from 2006 to 2009.

Section 2.4

1. Answers will vary.
2. False
3. Figure 2.33 visually reinforces the magnitude of the differences.
4. By factoring the "number of cars per country," we can compute the number of cars stolen per 1000 cars in each population. This would give more useful statistics than the per capita statistics.
5. Table 2.23 gives the actual number of cars stolen.
6. (a) Bar graph **(b)** Omitting the zero on the relevant scale; biased distortion or embellishment; inaccuracy in relative lengths of bars in a bar chart. **(c)** We can use a Pareto chart or pie chart.
7. (a) Biased distortion or embellishment; omitting the zero on the relevant scales; inaccuracy in relative lengths of bars in a bar chart. **(b)** A Pareto chart or pie chart can be used.
8. (a) Biased distortion or embellishment; omitting the zero on the relevant scales; inaccuracy in relative lengths of bars in a bar chart; careless combination of categories. **(b)** We can use a Pareto chart. **Note:** we cannot split the categories.
9. (a) The number of people living with AIDS is increasing.
(b) Using two dimensions (area) to emphasize a one-dimensional difference.
(c)

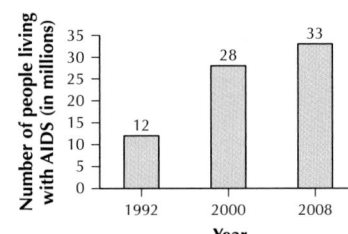

10. (a) Omitting the zero on the vertical scale.
(b)

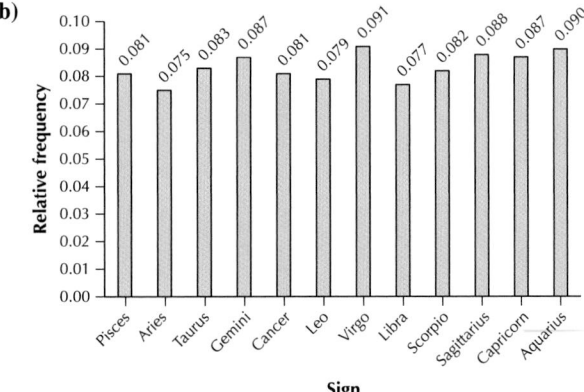

11. (a) Manipulating the scale **(b)** We can use a bar chart.

12. (a)

(b) Manipulating the scale, omitting the 0 on the vertical scale

(c)

(d) Manipulating the scale

13. (a)

(b)

(c)

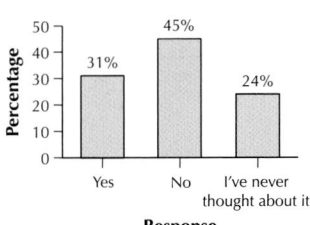

14. Answers will vary.
15. Answers will vary.
16. Answers will vary.

Chapter 2 Review
1. No, because the variable is categorical.

2.

3. and **4.**

Part of speech	Frequency	Relative frequency
Adjective	1	0.0323
Adverb	2	0.0645
Article	3	0.0968
Conjunction	3	0.0968
Preposition	9	0.2903
Pronoun	7	0.2258
Verb	6	0.1935
Total	31	$31/31 = 1.000$

5.

6.

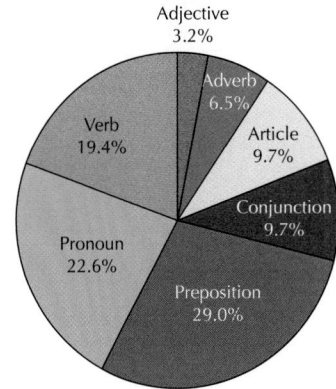

7. 0.6612
8. 0.6076
9. 0.0246
10. 0.0402
11. Answers will vary. May have clustered bar graph by happiness of marriage or clustered bar graph by sex.

12.

Percentage	Frequency	Cumulative frequency	Relative frequency	Cumulative relative frequency
34–35	2	2	0.0025	0.0025
36–37	0	2	0	0.0025
38–39	0	2	0	0.0025
40–41	0	2	0	0.0025
42–43	0	2	0	0.0025
44–45	3	5	0.0038	0.0063
46–47	0	5	0	0.0063
48–49	3	8	0.0038	0.0101
50–51	4	12	0.0051	0.0152
52–53	20	32	0.0253	0.0405
54–55	48	80	0.0608	0.1013
56–57	109	189	0.1380	0.2393
58–59	114	303	0.1443	0.3836
60–61	118	421	0.1494	0.5330
62–63	129	550	0.1633	0.6963
64–65	123	673	0.1557	0.8520
66–67	59	732	0.0747	0.9267
68–69	22	754	0.0278	0.9545
70–71	14	768	0.0177	0.9722
72–73	2	770	0.0025	0.9747
74–75	2	772	0.0025	0.9772
76–77	5	777	0.0063	0.9835
78–79	0	777	0	0.9835
80–81	2	779	0.0025	0.9860
82–83	3	782	0.0038	0.9898
84–85	3	785	0.0038	0.9936
86–87	2	787	0.0025	0.9961
88–89	1	788	0.0013	0.9974
90–91	1	789	0.0013	0.9987
92–93	1	790	0.0013	1

13. Around a value of 62.
14. Approximately 0.0165 (1.65%)
15. and **16.**

Average size of household	Frequency	Relative frequency
2.25–2.34	1	0.0196
2.35–2.44	0	0
2.45–2.54	12	0.2353
2.55–2.64	23	0.4510
2.65–2.74	10	0.1961
2.75–2.84	3	0.0588
2.85–2.94	0	0
2.95–3.04	1	0.0196
3.05–3.14	0	0
3.15–3.24	1	0.0196
Total	51	1.0

17.

18.

19.

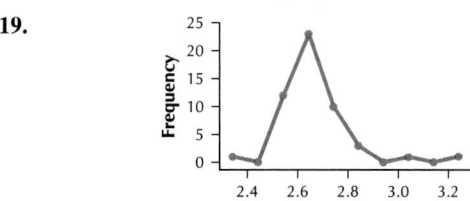

20. Shape would not be affected. The scale would move 0.5 unit to the right
21. (a)–(b) Cannot be done because the variable is qualitative.
22. (a)

(b)

23.

24. (a) Pareto chart or bar graph **(b)** It gives the impression that the NFL category is significantly larger than the rest because of the width of the bar and the fact that other graphics are on that bar. **(c)** Omitting the zero on the *y* scale; inaccuracy in relative lengths of bars; biased distortion or embellishments **(d)** We can use a Pareto chart.

25. (a)

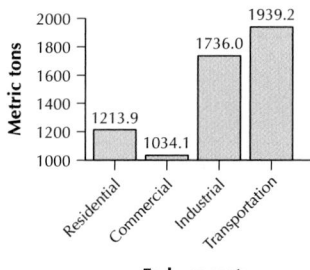

(b) Manipulating the scale.

(c)

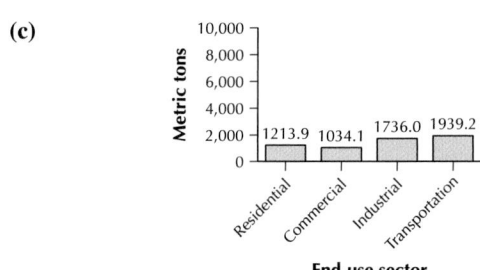

(d) Manipulating the scale.

(e)

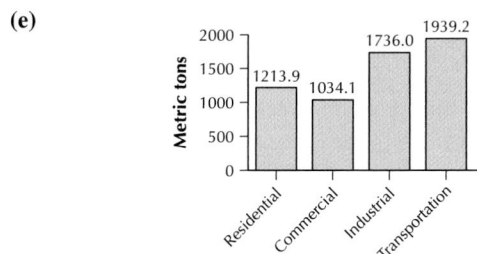

Chapter 2 Quiz

1. False
2. True
3. sample size.
4. frequency distribution
5. Symmetric
6. Right skewed
7–10.

Vowels	Frequency	Cumulative frequency	Relative frequency	Cumulative relative frequency
a	73	73	0.1931	0.1931
e	130	203	0.3439	0.5370
i	74	277	0.1958	0.7328
o	74	351	0.1958	0.9286
u	27	378	0.0714	1.0000

11.

12.

13.

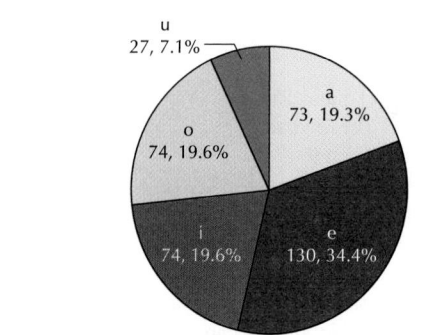

14. and 15. Can't construct because variable is qualitative.

Chapter 3

Section 3.1

1. A value that locates the center of the data set
2. Mean; answers will vary.
3. Because the mean depends in part on the sum of all data values, an outlier will skew the mean (pull it in one direction or another). Since the median simply depends on position in an ordered list, it is not sensitive to outliers.
4. Mean, the median, and the mode
5. Sample size (n)
6. Population size (N)
7. x_i
8. Σ
9. Sample mean ($\bar{x}$)
10. Population mean (μ)
11. Median
12. Mode
13. (a) 5 **(b)** 18
14. (a) 6 **(b)** 0
15. (a) 7 **(b)** 81.429
16. (a) 5 **(b)** 131.6
17. (a) 7 **(b)** 75
18. (a) 6 **(b)** 0
19. (a) 5 **(b)** 1576.8
20. (a) 11 **(b)** 8

21. 17
22. 0
23. 80
24. 133
25. No mode
26. 0
27. 75
28. 155
29. $6.12
30. $21.07
31. $25
32. 2 Mb
33. 25
34. 16
35. 8
36. Mean = 3.5
37. Median = 3
38. Mode = 3
39. (a) 6 cylinders (b) 5 cylinders (c) 4 cylinders
40. (a) 3.317 liters (b) 2.75 liters (c) No mode
41. (a) 24 mpg (b) 21.5 mpg (c) 18 mpg
42. USA
43. (a) 16.6 (b) 17 (c) 5 and 15
44. (a) Mean = 18.8 (b) Median = 19 (c) No mode
45. (a) 7 (b) 7.5 (c) 4 and 9
46. (a) Mean = 59.8 (b) Median = 57.5 (c) Mode = 55
47. (a) 624.667 (b) 614.5
48. (a) 604.5 (b) 601.5
49. (a) 604.167 (b) 602.5
50. No. All of the test scores for each test are different.
51. (a) English; no. (b) No, the data are qualitative.
(c) Economics does not occur with the highest frequency.
52. Mean = $15.17, median = $15, mode = $15.95. A typical
book on the best-seller list would not cost less than $14 since the
mean, median, and mode are all greater than $14.
53. (a) $25.17 (b) The new mean is $10 more than the original
mean. (c) If a positive number of d is added to each value of a
data set, the mean of the resulting data set will be greater than the
mean of the original data set by d.
54. (a) $75.85 (b) The new mean is 5 times the original
mean. (c) If each value of a data set is multiplied by a positive
number m, then the mean of the resulting data set will be m times
the mean of the original data set.
55. (a) $15.95 (b) Stieg Larsson
56. It does not make sense to find the mean and the median
of the variable author because the variable author is a categorical
variable.
57. Mean = 2009.5, median = 2010, mode = 2011
58. (a) Mode = 1 year (b) Mean = 2.5 years, median =
2 years
59. Mean = 5.5 years, median = 5 years, mode = 4 years
60. (a) Mean < Median < Mode (b) Mode < Median < Mean
(c) Mean = Median = Mode
61. (a) $n = 59$ (b) Sample mean = 45.46 (c) Sample median =
42; (d) Highest ratings = 93.7, lowest ratings = 22.4
62. The mean is larger than the median, which implies the
distribution is positively skewed.
63. New mean = 40.46; new median = 37; new mode = old
mode − 5. Each statistic will be affected equally.
64. The mean, median and mode will all be halved. Each statistic
will be affected equally.

65. (a) Female (b) Approximately 73 (c) Approximately 74
(d) Female; yes
66. (a) 73 (b) 76 (c) Females; yes
67. (a) 78 (b) 79 (c) Females; yes
68. (a) Decrease (b) Unchanged (c) Unchanged
69. (a) 74.9 (b) 75.25 (c) 75.417
70. (a) Smaller (b) Larger (c) Same
71. (a) $14.98 (b) 2009
72. 2.190 mph
73. Since she walked the first mile at a speed of 5 mph for the first
mile, her time for walking the first mile was $\frac{1}{5}$ hours. Similarly, her
time to walk the second, third, fourth, and fifth miles was $\frac{1}{4}, \frac{1}{3}$,
$\frac{1}{2}$, and $\frac{1}{1}$ hours, respectively. Thus the total time it took Emily to
walk 5 miles is $\frac{1}{5} + \frac{1}{4} + \frac{1}{3} + \frac{1}{2} + \frac{1}{1} = \Sigma\frac{1}{x}$ hours. Therefore her
average speed is $\frac{\text{distance}}{\text{time}} = \frac{n}{\Sigma\frac{1}{x}}$, which is the harmonic mean. The
arithmetic mean is just the average of the 5 rates.
74. Geometric mean = 1.0664, 6.64% growth
75. Answers will vary.
76. Answers will vary.
77. Answers will vary.
78. Answers will vary.
79. (a) Answers will vary. (b) The mean increases. (c) The
median remains the same.
80. Answers will vary.

Section 3.2
1. Deviation for a data value gives the distance the value is from
the mean.
2. A distance from the mean that is representative for that
data set
3. Less variance is better because it means that the delivery times
are more consistent.
4. Benefit—simple to calculate, Drawbacks—quite sensitive to
extreme values, does not use all of the data values.
5. Sensitive. It is calculated from the difference of the two most
extreme values in the data set.
6. 0
7. False
8. Benefit—uses all of the numbers in a data set. Drawback—can
be time-consuming to calculate.
9. Population variance
10. True
11. Never
12. When all of the data values are the same
13. 33
14. 102
15. 702
16. 5
17. 25
18. 0
19. 5
20. 10
21. 35
22. 60
23. 15
24. 0
25. (a) 127.714 (b) 11.301
26. (a) 2375.333 (b) 48.737
27. (a) 56,993.36 (b) 238.733

28. (a) 2.545 (b) 1.595
29. (a) 66 (b) 8.124
30. (a) 0 (b) 0
31. (a) 4.5 (b) 2.121
32. (a) 13.6 (b) 3.688
33. (a) 130.952 (b) 11.443
34. (a) 642.8 (b) 25.354
35. (a) 41.667 (b) 6.455
36. (a) 0 (b) 0
37. (a) 8 cylinders (b) 9.6 cylinders^2 (c) 3.098 cylinders
38. (a) 4.9 liters (b) 3.078 liters^2 (c) 1.754 liters
39. (a) 30 mpg (b) 116 mpg^2 (c) 10.770 mpg
40. No. The standard deviation.
41. (a) 24 victories (b) 55.822 victories^2 (c) 7.471 victories
42. (a) 46 victories (b) 202.4 victories^2 (c) 14.227 victories
43. (a) 8 victories (b) 8 victories^2 (c) 2.828 victories
44. No. Standard deviation.
45. The Short Tracks variable has the greater variability.
46. The Super Speedways variable has the greater variability.

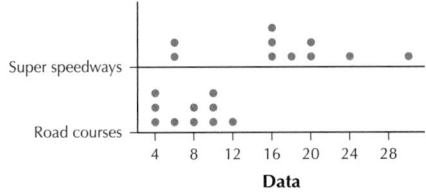

47. Super Speedway variable: 24, Road Courses: 8; Super Speedway has greater variability.
48. Variance for Super Speedway = 55.82; variance for Road Courses = 8; standard deviation for Super Speedway = 7.47; standard deviation for Road Courses = 2.828. Super Speedway.
49. (i)—(d); (ii)—(b); (iii)—(c); (iv)—(a)
50. (i)—(b); (ii)—(d); (iii)—(a); (iv)—(c)
51. Zooplankton: 6.86, phytoplankton: 9.96 (a) phytoplankton (b) phytoplankton
52. Zooplankton: 1.992; phytoplankton: 2.819.
(a) Phytoplankton (b) Phytoplankton because this variable has the larger standard deviation. (c) Phytoplankton because it has the larger standard deviation.
53. Range for Colony A = 73; range for Colony B = 91
(a) Colony B (b) Colony B
54. Colony A = 480.04; Colony B = 694.49. (a) Colony B
(b) Colony B; yes (c) Colony B, because it has the larger variance.
55. Math. The range of numbers on the scale is larger.

56. SAT Mathematics test: Range = 89, Variance = 1104.267;
SAT Reading test: Range = 23, Variance = 89.9; SAT Writing test:
Range = 25, Variance = 88.567; Yes.

57. (a) SAT Mathematics test (b) SAT Writing test
58. (a) It would decrease all three measures of spread for both tests. (b) SAT Mathematics test: Range = 70, Variance = 650.2, Standard deviation = 25.499; SAT Writing test: Range = 14, Variance = 35.5, Standard deviation = 5.958
59. (a) 6 inches (b) 2 inches
60. (a) WMU: 5.48 inches; NCU: 2.45 inches (b) The heights for the WMU team typically differ from the mean of 69 inches by only 5.48 inches; the heights for the NCU team typically differ from the mean of 69 inches by only 2.45 inches. (c) WMU
61. (a) Increase the range, variance, and standard deviation.
(b) New range = 10. New variance = 15.2. New standard deviation = 3.9. Yes, the judgment in (a) was supported.
62. (a) Increase because the contribution of a value of 84 to the computation is greater than the contribution of a value of 72.
(b) 7.27; yes.
63. (a) Range = 15; standard deviation = 5.48.
(b) Adding a positive constant to each value in a data set will not change the value of the original range or standard deviation.
64. (a) Range = 12; standard deviation = 4.9
(b) Multiplying each value in a data set by a constant will increase the value of the original range or standard deviation by a factor of the constant.
65. (a) Cylinders: CV = 51.64%; Engine size: CV = 52.89%; City mpg: CV = 44.88% (b) Engine size, City mpg
66. (a) SAT Mathematics test: CV = 5.32%; SAT Reading test: CV = 1.57%; SAT Writing test: CV = 1.56% (b) SAT Mathematics test
67. (a) Cylinders: MAD = 2; Engine size: MAD = 1.189; City mpg: MAD = 8.333 (b) City mpg, Engine size
68. (a) SAT Mathematics test: MAD = 26.556; SAT Reading test: MAD = 7.667; SAT Writing test: MAD = 7.167
(b) SAT Mathematics test
69. (a) Skewness = 0 (b) Skewness = 3 (c) Skewness = −3
(d) Skewness = −1.5 (e) Skewness = 0 (f) Skewness = 0.6
70. 0
71. (a) Pros: Skewness = 0.182; Darts: Skewness = 0.197; DJIA: Skewness = −0.077 (b) Pros and Darts are slightly right-skewed, DJIA are slightly left-skewed.
72. (a)

	Range	Sample variance	Sample standard deviation	Coefficient of variation	Mean absolute deviation
Cylinders	8	9.6	3.098	51.64%	2
Engine size	4.9	3.078	1.754	52.89%	1.189
City mpg	30	116	10.770	44.88%	8.333

(b) City mpg: Range, Sample variance, Sample standard deviation, Mean absolute deviation. Engine size: Coefficient of variation; Cylinders: None of them. (c) City mpg, Engine size
73. (a) SAT Mathematics test: s = 33.231; SAT Reading test: s = 9.482; SAT Writing test: s = 9.411

(b)

	Range	Sample variance	Sample standard deviation	Coefficient of variation	Mean absolute deviation
SAT Mathematics	89	1104.267	33.231	5.32%	26.556
SAT Reading	23	89.9	9.482	1.57%	7.667
SAT Writing	25	88.567	9.411	1.56%	7.167

(c) Yes **(d)** The variability of the scores on the SAT Mathematics test is greater than the variability of the scores on the other two tests.
74. Answers will vary.
75. Answers will vary.
76. Answers will vary.
77. Answers will vary.
78. Answers will vary.

Section 3.3
1. These formulas will provide only estimates because we will not know the exact data values.
2. The "hat" notation indicates that the statistic is an estimate for a corresponding parameter.
3. Population mean
4. 60
5. 69
6. 118.5714
7. 3.2
8. 83
9.

Class limits	Midpoints
0–1.99	1
2–3.99	3
4–5.99	5
6–7.99	7
8–9.99	9

10.

Class limits	Midpoints
0–4.99	2.5
5–9.99	7.5
10–14.99	12.5
15–19.99	17.5
20–29.99	25
30–49.99	40
50–99.99	75
100–199.99	150

11. 14.2857
12. 6.25
13. Estimated standard deviation = 6.226998; estimated variance = 38.7755.
14. Estimated standard deviation = 7.310096; estimated variance = 53.4375.

15. (a)

Age	Frequency	Midpoints
0–4.99	63,422	2.5
5–17.99	240,629	11.5
18–64.99	540,949	41.5

(b) Estimated mean = 30.0298 years **(c)** Estimated standard deviation = 15.455909 years; estimated variance = 238.8851 years squared
16. 61
17. (a)

Dollar value	Housing units (frequency)	Midpoints
$0–$49,999	5,430	25,000
$50,000–$99,000	90,605	75,000
$100,000–$149,999	90,620	125,000
$150,000–$199,999	54,295	175,000
$200,000–$299,000	34,835	250,000
$300,000–$499,999	15,770	400,000
$500,000–$999,999	5,595	750,000

(b) Estimated mean = $158,079.25 **(c)** Estimated standard deviation = $116,223.13; estimated variance = 13,507,815,862.70 (dollars squared)
18. Estimated mean = 135.5224; estimated standard deviation = 95.6874
19. 82.8%
20. $58.72
21. $70,940
22. If $w_i = 1$ for all i, then the weighted mean formula will be equivalent to the formula for the sample mean.

Section 3.4
1. Positive z-score: the data value is above the mean. Negative z-score: the data value is below the mean. z-score of zero: the data value is equal to the mean.
2. Answers will vary.
3. Answers will vary.
4. No more than 100% of the data values can be less than or equal to any value in the data set.
5. It is possible for the 1st percentile to equal the 99th percentile if all of the data values are the same.
6. A percentile is a data value while a percentile rank is a percentage.
7. False
8. All numbers between Q1 and Q2 would be the same; median line and line for Q1 would be the same.
9. Right-skewed with a few values much larger than the rest; median line of box plot closer to the line for Q3 than the line for Q1.
10. Can't do. The 50th percentile of a data set can never be smaller than the 25th percentile.
11. Not possible. Q1, the 25th percentile, will always be less than or equal to Q3, the 75th percentile. Thus the IQR = Q3 − Q1 is always greater than or equal to zero.
12. 1
13. 3.5

14. (a) The standard deviation, which is 10 mg/dl.
(b) 2.5 **(c)** Chelsea's blood sugar level lies 2.5 standard deviations above the mean blood sugar level of 100 mg/dl.
15. (a) -1.5 **(b)** David's blood sugar level lies 1.5 standard deviations below the mean blood sugar level of 100 mg/dl.
16. 110 mg/dl
17. 80 mg/dl
18. Elizabeth: $z = 1$; Fiona: $z = 2$; Fiona did better.
19. Juan: $z = 1$; Luis: $z = 1$; They both did the same.
20. Not an outlier
21. Outlier
22. Moderately unusual
23. Not an outlier
24. $11
25. $14.50
26. $7.50
27. $5
28. $4
29. $20
30. 67%
31. 100%
32. 25%
33. 8%
34. 92%
35. 17%
36. $7.50
37. $11
38. $14.50
39. $7.00
40. (a) -1.304 **(b)** 1.477 **(c)** -0.261
41. (a) 4.599 **(b)** 6.325 **(c)** 7.476
42. No outliers
43. Lady Gaga has the highest number of Twitter followers, and Kim Kardashian has the lowest number of Twitter followers.
44. (a) 5.75 **(b)** 6.1 **(c)** 5.3
45. (a) 17% **(b)** 33% **(c)** 100%
46. (a) 5.3 **(b)** 5.75 **(c)** 6.1 **(d)** 0.8
47. The middle 50%, or half of the number of Twitter followers each celebrity has ranges over 0.8 million followers.
48. (a) -0.79 **(b)** 1.79 **(c)** -1.65 **(d)** 0.93
49. (a) 109.167 calories **(b)** 120.812 calories **(c)** 97.522 calories **(d)** 114.989 calories
50. No outliers
51. (a) 105 **(b)** 110 calories **(c)** 115 calories **(d)** 130
52. (a) 17% **(b)** 92% **(c)** 75% **(d)** 25%
53. (a) 105 calories **(b)** 110 calories **(c)** 115 calories **(d)** 10 calories
54. The middle 50%, or half of the number of calories in 12 breakfast cereals ranges over 10 calories.
55. (a) 90 calories **(b)** Bran Chex and Bran Flakes
56. (a) 2.87 **(b)** -0.91 **(c)** -0.89 **(d)** 1.11
57. (a) 5.073 million **(b)** 15.151 million **(c)** -5.005 million **(d)** 8.433 million
58. Echinacea with 14.7 million users is moderately unusual.
59. (a) Valerian with 2.1 million **(b)** Ginseng with 8.8 million **(c)** 2 million **(d)** 14.7 million
60. (a) 100% **(b)** 7% **(c)** 93% **(d)** 13%
61. (a) Bee pollen with 2.8 million **(b)** Fish oil with 4.2 million **(c)** Garlic with 7.1 million **(d)** 4.3 million

62. The middle 50%, or half of the usage of dietary supplements ranges over 4.3 million.
63. (a) 7.7 million **(b)** Ginkgo biloba
64. (a)

(b)

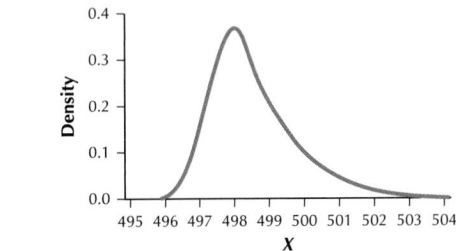

(c) 498
65. (a) Right-skewed **(b)** Greater than, since the distribution is right-skewed.
(c)

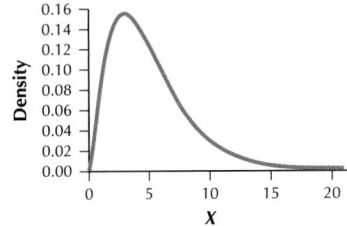

Section 3.5
1. False
2. The boxplot is a graphical display of the five-number summary.
3. (a) The median will be about the same distance from Q1 and Q3, and the upper and lower whiskers will be about the same length. **(b)** The median is closer to Q1 than to Q3, and the upper whisker is much longer than the lower whisker. **(c)** The median is closer to Q3 than to Q1, and the lower whisker is much longer than the upper whisker.
4. Never
5. Any data value located 1.5 (IQR) or more below Q1 or 1.5 (IQR) or more above Q3 is considered an outlier.
6. The z-score is sensitive to the outliers themselves while the IQR is not. The IQR method is more robust.
7. Q1 = 65 inches, Q2 = median = 68 inches, Q3 = 70 inches
8. 5 inches
9. Minimum = 64 inches, Q1 = 65 inches, Q2 = median = 68 inches, Q3 = 70 inches, maximum = 78 inches
10. Not an outlier
11. Outlier
12.

Student heights (in inches)

13. Q1 = 15 minutes, Q2 = median = 15 minutes, Q3 = 22.5 minutes

14. 7.5 minutes

15. Minimum = 10 minutes, Q1 = 15 minutes, Q2 = median = 15 minutes, Q3 = 22.5 minutes, maximum = 50 minutes

16. Not an outlier

17. Outlier

18.

Commuting times (in minutes)

19. Q1 = 68, Q2 = median = 76, Q3 = 85.5

20. 17.5

21. Min = 51, Q1 = 68, median = 76, Q3 = 85.5, max = 98

22. Outlier

23. Not an outlier

24.

Final exam scores

25. (a) Right-skewed **(b)** Minimum = 0, Q1 = 1, Q2 = median = 3, Q3 = 7.5, maximum = 12

26. (a) Symmetric **(b)** Minimum = 1, Q1 = 2, Q2 = median = 3, Q3 = 4, maximum = 5

27. (a) Right-skewed **(b)** Minimum = 5, Q1 = 10, Q2 = median = 15, Q3 = 25, maximum = 45

28. (a) Symmetric **(b)** Minimum = 15, Q1 = 20, Q2 = median = 25, Q3 = 30, maximum = 35

29. x

30. x

31. For WMU: min = 60, Q1 = 70, median = 70, Q3 = 70, max = 75. For NCU: min = 66, Q1 = 67, median = 70, Q3 = 70, max = 72; probably not.

32. WMU: IQR = 0; NCU: IQR = 3. For WMU, the spread of the middle 50% of the data is 0, and for NCU, the spread of the middle 50% of the data is 3.

33. The boxplots look so unusual because each data set only has 5 numbers.

34. Min = 8.33, Q1 = 13.69, median = 23.375, Q3 = 37.79, max = 55.46

35. IQR = 24.1, which is the spread of the middle 50% of the data.

36. Q1 − 1.5 * IQR = −22.46 and Q3 + 1.5 * IQR = 73.94. There are no values outside this interval, so there are no outliers.

37.

Price

38. Min = −4.09, Q1 = −0.14, median = −0.015, Q3 = 0.08, max = 0.1.

39. IQR = 0.22, which is the spread of the middle 50% of the data.

40. Q1 − 1.5 * IQR = −0.47 and Q3 + 1.5 * IQR = 0.41. The change −4.09 is an outlier.

41.

Change

42. Min = 2,000,000; Q1 = 2,800,000; median = 4,200,000; Q3 = 7,100,000; max = 14,700,000

43. IQR = 4,300,000, which is the spread of the middle 50% of the data.

44. Q1 − 1.5 * IQR = −3.65 and Q3 + 1.5 * IQR = 13.55. Usage of 14,700,000 is the only outlier.

45.

Usage (in millions)

46. Mean: 5,073,000; standard deviation: 3,359,300

47. The z-score is 2.87, so echinacea usage is moderately unusual but not an outlier. The robust method indicates that echinacea usage is an outlier.

48. Zooplankton: Minimum = −6.6, Q1 = −3, Q2 = median = −1.54, Q3 = −0.64, maximum = 0.26; phytoplankton: minimum = 0.65, Q1 = 1.57, Q2 = median = 2.55, Q3 = 3.04, maximum = 10.61

49.

Effect size

50. Zooplankton: left-skewed; phytoplankton: right-skewed

51. Zooplankton: smaller; phytoplankton: larger

52. Zooplankton: mean = −2.048; phytoplankton: mean = 3.123. They concur.

53. Since the box for the zooplankton effect sizes lies below zero, the majority of the zooplankton effect sizes lie below zero. Since the box for the phytoplankton effect sizes lies above zero, the majority of the phytoplankton effect sizes lie above zero. Phytoplankton, yes

54. Zooplankton: IQR = 2.36; phytoplankton: IQR = 1.47. Zooplankton more variable

55. Zooplankton: −6.60 is an outlier; phytoplankton: 5.67 and 10.61 are outliers

56. Zooplankton: −6.60 is moderately unusual; phytoplankton: 10.61 is moderately unusual.

57. (a) 961 **(b)** 25

58. Mean = 1.784 mg, standard deviation = 3.138 mg, min = 0.000 mg, Q1 = 0.300 mg, median = 0.800 mg, Q3 = 1.700 mg, max = 37.600 mg. Range = 37.600 mg − 0.000 mg = 37.600 mg. IQR = 1.700 mg − 0.300 mg = 1.400 mg

59. Homemade dark fruitcake (1 cake)

60. The boxplot is very right-skewed.

Section 3.6

1. When $k \le 1$ or when the data set is not continuous
2. The interval between the mean minus 2 standard deviations and the mean plus 2 standard deviations.
3. True
4. When the distribution is bell-shaped
5. (a) At least 75% (b) At least 88.9%
6. (a) About 95% (b) About 99.7%
7. (a) Between 80 and 120 (b) 120 (c) 80
8. (a) 68% of all values lie between 400 and 600 (b) 600
(c) 400
9. (a) At least 75% (b) At least 88.9% (c) Can't find since $k = 1$.
10. (a) Cannot be found since $k = 1$ (b) At least 55.6%
(c) At most 44%
11. (a) About 95% (b) About 99.7% (c) About 68%
12. (a) About 68% (b) Between 68% and 95% (c) Between 2.5% and 16%
13. (a) (i) 102,000,000 (ii) He is very truthful. (b) The day corresponding to the 25th percentile. (c) At least 75%
14. (a) Between 65.5 and 85.5 years old (b) Between 53 and 98 years old. The Empirical Rule is more precise.
15. (a) Cannot be done since $k = 1$. (b) At least 75%
(c) At most 25%
16. (a) About 68% (b) About 95% (c) About 2.5%
17. Answers in Exercise 16 are more precise; the distribution is bell-shaped.
18. No, because 4.0 is only 0.8 standard deviation above the mean.
19. Lower-performing school z-score 0.8, so 4.0 GPA is not considered unusual; higher-performing school z-score 2.8, so a GPA of 4.0 is considered moderately unusual.

Chapter 3 Review

1. 3.1227
2. 2.55
3. 2.55
4. The median and the mode are both the same and are both the largest. From the histogram, the mode is 110 calories. Also from the histogram, there are three cereals with less than 110 calories and three cereals with more than 110 calories. Thus the median is 110 calories. Looking at the histogram, the data are slightly right-skewed. Thus the mean is slightly less than the median and the mode.

5. The mode, since the value with the largest frequency is unaffected by the deletion of values 90 or less.
6. Each will be increased by 10 calories.
7. Mean = 396.8; range = 803
8. About 300.
9. 276.2
10. Standard deviation = 276.2. (a) 24 (b) The frequency counts for the syllables typically differ from the mean of 396.8 by only 276.2.

11. 3.3133
12. Estimated mean = 41.2055. Estimated standard deviation = 10.7061
13. 39.5
14. 57.5
15. 80
16. 0.013
17. 1.516
18. −1.554
19. There are no moderately unusual values or outliers.
20. 10%
21. 50%
22. 100%
23. Q1 = 25, Q2 = 34.5, Q3 = 48
24. IQR = 23, which is the spread of the middle 50% of the data set
25. No outliers
26. (a) Min = 8, Q1 = 25, median = 34.5, Q3 = 48, max = 60

(b)

(c) Close to symmetric, slightly right-skewed. **(d)** The mean should be close to the median or a little above the median.
(e) Mean = 36.30, standard deviation = 16.51. The value of the mean is slightly above the median of 34.50.
27. No outliers, yes
28. Unchanged; robustness
29. At least 75%
30. About 95%
31. 75 mph

Chapter 3 Quiz

1. False
2. False
3. False
4. outlier
5. center
6. mean
7. robust measures
8. mode
9. Zero
10. Class midpoint
11. (a) Mean = 87,453 (b) Median = 98,008
12. (a) Range = 86,910 (b) Standard deviation = 33,857
13. Estimated mean = 61.6527; estimated standard deviation = 18.4518.
14. (a) 1.5 (b) −1 (c) 1 (d) −1.5 (e) 0
15. (a) 60 (b) Between 34% and 81.5% (c) No, furthermore we must assume that one of the values of k is less than 1. (d) Between 2.5% and 16%.
16. (a) 501.5 (b) 512 (c) 518
17. IQR = 16.5
18. Min = 499, Q1 = 501.5, median = 512, Q3 = 518, max = 523.
19. Q1 − 1.5 * IQR = 476.75 and Q3 + 1.5 * IQR = 542.75. All the SAT scores lie between 476.75 and 542.75, so there are no outliers.

20.

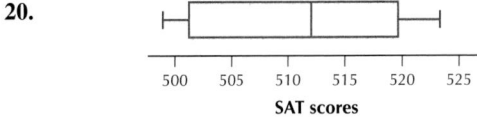

Chapter 4

Section 4.1

1. Scatterplot
2. It measures the strength and direction of the linear relationship between two variables; r.
3. Between –1 and 1, inclusive
4. (a) The variables are positively correlated. **(b)** The variables are negatively correlated. **(c)** The variables are not correlated.
5. Often, the value of the x variable can be used to predict or estimate the value of the y variable.
6. They increase.
7. They decrease.
8. No. It means that x and y don't have a linear relationship. They may have another type of relationship.

9.

10.

11.

12.
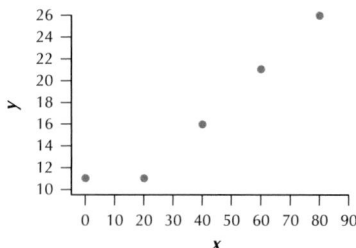

13. (a) Strong negative linear relationship **(b)** They decrease.
14. (a) No apparent linear relationship **(b)** They remain unchanged.
15. (a) Perfect positive linear relationship **(b)** They increase.
16. (a) Moderate positive linear relationship **(b)** They increase.
17. (a) Strong positive linear relationship **(b)** They increase.
18. (a) Moderate negative linear relationship **(b)** They decrease.
19. (a) Perfect negative linear relationship **(b)** They decrease.
20. (a) Nonlinear relationship but no linear relationship **(b)** First they decrease, then they increase.
21. 0.9487
22. −0.9707
23. −0.9686

24. 0.9701
25. The variables x and y are strongly positively correlated. As x increases, y increases.
26. The variables x and y are strongly negatively correlated. As x increases, y decreases.
27. The variables x and y are strongly negatively correlated. As x increases, y decreases.
28. The variables x and y are strongly positively correlated. As x increases, y increases.
29. x and y are positively correlated.
30. x and y are negatively correlated.
31. x and y are negatively correlated.
32. x and y are positively correlated.
33. i
34. ii
35. iii
36. iv
37. (a) (1,1), (2,3), (3,3), (4,4), (5,6), (6,6), (7,7), (8,7), (9,9), (10,11) **(b)** Minitab: Pearson correlation of x and y = 0.978. TI-83/84: $r = 0.9781316853$
38. (a) (6,8), (7,7), (8,7), (9,8), (10,8), (11,8), (12,7), (13,8), (14,8), (15,7) **(b)** Minitab: Correlations: x, y; Pearson correlation of x and y = 0.000. TI-83/84: $r = 0$
39. (a) (1,7), (2,8), (3,7), (4,6), (5,6), (6,5), (7,6), (8,5), (9,7), (10,6) **(b)** Minitab: Pearson correlation of x and y = −0.522. TI-83/84: $r = -0.5222329679$
40. (a) (1,11), (2,9), (3,7), (4,7), (5,6), (6,6), (7,4), (8,3), (9,3), (10,1) **(b)** Minitab: Correlations: x, y; Pearson correlation of x and y = −0.978. TI-83/84: $r = -0.9781316853$
41. x and y are positively correlated.
42. No apparent linear relationship
43. Weakly negatively correlated
44. x and y are negatively correlated.

45. (a)
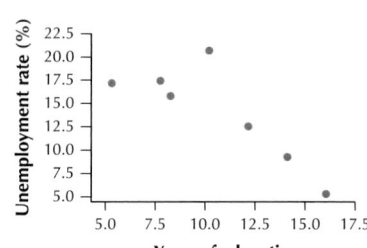

(b) Negative
46. $r = -0.8261$. The variables *years of education* and *unemployment rate* are strongly negatively correlated. As the years of education increase, the unemployment rate decreases.
47. Negatively correlated
48. Yes. Since years of education and unemployment rate are negatively correlated, the more years of education a person has, the lower the unemployment rate.
49. Not correlated

50. Minitab: Correlations: Body Weight (kg), Brain Weight (g); Pearson correlation of body weight (kg) and brain weight (g) = 0.099. TI-83/84: $r = 0.0992032294$
51. Brain weight and body weight are not correlated. As body weight increases, brain weight tends to remain the same. Yes
52. Near 0
53. A player's age and a player's batting average are not correlated. As a player's age increases, the player's batting average tends to remain unchanged.

54. (a)

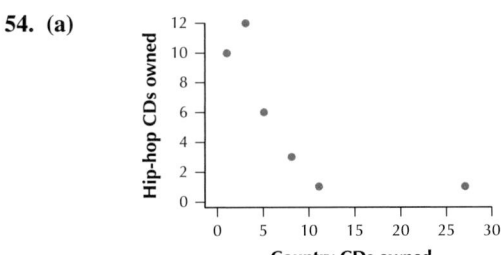

(b) Negative **(c)** Negative.
55. (a) $\bar{x} = 9.16666667$; $\bar{y} = 5.5$; $s_x = 9.432214303$; $s_y = 4.679743583$; $r = -0.7453498716$. Minitab: Correlations: Hip-Hop CDs owned, Country CDs owned; Pearson correlation of Hip-Hop CDs owned and Country CDs owned = -0.745. TI-83/84: $r = -0.7453498716$. **(b)** Yes **(c)** The variables number of Hip-Hop CDs owned and number of Country CDs owned are negatively correlated. As the number of Country CDs owned increases, the number of Hip-Hop CDs owned decreases.
56. $|r| = |-0.7453| = 0.7453$, which is less than the critical value of 0.811 for $n = 6$. We thus cannot formally conclude that the variables are correlated.
57. (a) The dots form the same pattern. The only difference is that the dots are shifted 5 units up.

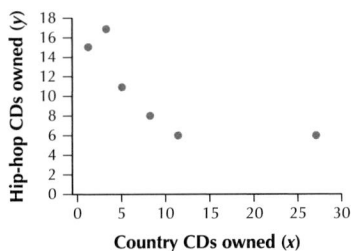

(b) $r = -0.7453$ **(c)** They are the same. **(d)** The correlation coefficient remains unchanged when a constant is added to each y data value.
58. (a) The dots form the same pattern. The dots would just move to the right the number of units that was added to each x value if the constant is positive, and to the left the absolute value of the number of units that was added to each x value if the constant is negative. **(b)** It will remain the same. **(c)** The correlation coefficient remains unchanged when a constant is added to each x data value.
59. Positively correlated

60. (a) $\bar{x} = 510.6$; $\bar{y} = 516.6$
(b)

x	y	$x - \bar{x}$	$(x - \bar{x})^2$	$y - \bar{y}$	$(y - \bar{y})^2$	$(x - \bar{x})(y - \bar{y})$
497	510	-13.6	184.96	-6.6	43.56	89.76
515	515	4.4	19.36	-1.6	2.56	-7.04
518	523	7.4	54.76	6.4	40.96	47.36
501	514	-9.6	92.16	-2.6	6.76	24.96
522	521	11.4	129.96	4.4	19.36	50.16
			$\sum(x - \bar{x})^2$ $= 481.2$		$\sum(y - \bar{y})^2$ $= 113.2$	$\sum(x - \bar{x})(y - \bar{y})$ $= 205.2$

(c) $s_x = 10.96813567$; $s_y = 5.319774431$ **(d)** $r = 0.8792073976$
(e) Minitab: Pearson correlation of SAT Reading and SAT Math $= 0.879$. TI-83/84: $r = 0.8792073978$
61. SAT Reading scores and SAT Math scores are positively correlated. As the SAT Reading score increases, the SAT Math score increases. Yes.
62. Answers will vary.
63. Answers will vary.
64. (a)–(c) Answers will vary.
65. (a) Positively correlated **(b)** Negatively correlated
(c) Not correlated
66. (a)–(c) Answers will vary.

Section 4.2
1. To approximate the relationship between two numerical variables using the regression line and the regression equation
2. $\hat{y} = b_1 x + b_0$, where $b_1 = \dfrac{\sum(x - \bar{x})(y - \bar{y})}{\sum(x - \bar{x})^2}$ and $b_0 = \bar{y} - (b_1 \cdot \bar{x})$
3. We can find the predicted value of y by plugging a given value of x into the regression equation and simplifying.
4. y is the actual value of the response variable for a given x, and $\hat{y}$ is the value of the response variable predicted from the regression equation.
5. Extrapolation is the process of making predictions based on x-values that are beyond the range of the x-values in our data set.
6. The slope of the regression line and the correlation coefficient always have the same sign.
7. Negative
8. Near zero
9. Positive
10. Positive
11. Positive
12. Negative
13. (a) $b_1 = 3.4$ **(b)** $b_0 = -1.5$ **(c)** $\hat{y} = 3.4x - 1.5$
14. (a) $b_1 = -0.2$ **(b)** $b_0 = 5.6$ **(c)** $\hat{y} = -0.2x + 5.6$
15. (a) $b_1 = 4$ **(b)** $b_0 = 21.6$ **(c)** $\hat{y} = 4x + 21.6$
16. (a) $b_1 = -3$ **(b)** $b_0 = -16$ **(c)** $\hat{y} = -3x - 16$
17. (a) $b_1 = 0.01$ **(b)** $b_0 = 2.47$ **(c)** $\hat{y} = 0.01x + 2.47$
18. (a) $b_1 = 0$ **(b)** $b_0 = 4$ **(c)** $\hat{y} = 0x + 4 = 4$
19. (a) $b_1 = 0.5$ **(b)** $b_0 = 5$ **(c)** $\hat{y} = 0.5x + 5$
20. (a) $b_1 = -1.41$ **(b)** $b_0 = 44.19$ **(c)** $\hat{y} = -1.41x + 44.19$
21. (a) For each increase of 1 unit in x, the estimated value of y increases by 3.4 units. **(b)** When x equals 0, the estimated value of y is -1.5.
22. (a) For each increase of 1 unit in x, the estimated value of y decreases by 0.2 unit. **(b)** When x equals 0, the estimated value of y is 5.6.

23. (a) For each increase of 1 unit in x, the estimated value of y increases by 4 units. **(b)** When x equals 0, the estimated value of y is 21.6.

24. (a) For each increase of 1 unit in x, the estimated value of y decreases by 3 units. **(b)** When x equals 0, the estimated value of y is -16.

25. (a) For each increase of 1 unit in x, the estimated value of y increases by 0.01 unit. **(b)** When x equals 0, the estimated value of y is 2.47.

26. (a) For each increase of 1 unit in x, the estimated value of y increases by 0 units. **(b)** When x equals 0, the estimated value of y is 4.

27. (a) For each increase of 1 unit in x, the estimated value of y increases by 0.5 unit. **(b)** When x equals 0, the estimated value of y is 5.

28. (a) For each increase of 1 unit in x, the estimated value of y decreases by 1.41 units. **(b)** When x equals 0, the estimated value of y is 44.19.

29. 8.7

30. 5.6

31. 13.6

32. -40

33. 2.57

34. 4

35. 5

36. -12.21

37. (a) 0.3 **(b)** The data point lies above the regression line, so the actual value of y is larger than predicted given $x = 3$.

38. (a) -0.6 **(b)** The data point lies below the regression line, so the actual value of y is smaller than predicted given $x = 0$.

39. (a) 2.4 **(b)** The data point lies above the regression line, so the actual value of y is larger than predicted given $x = 2$.

40. (a) 0.43 **(b)** The data point lies above the regression line, so the actual value of y is larger given $x = 10$.

41. Can't do since prediction represents extrapolation.

42. (a) 0 **(b)** The data point lies on the regression line, so the actual value of y is the same as predicted given $x = 0$.

43. Does not represent extrapolation

44. Does not represent extrapolation

45. Does not represent extrapolation

46. Represents extrapolation

47. Does not represent extrapolation

48. Represents extrapolation

49. Does not represent extrapolation

50. Represents extrapolation.

51. (a) $b_1 = -1.24$, $b_0 = 26.19$ **(b)** The estimated unemployment rate is -1.24 times the number of years of education plus 26.19. **(c)** For each increase of 1 year of education, the estimated unemployment rate decreases by 1.24%. **(d)** When the number of years of education equals 0, the estimated unemployment rate is 26.19%.

52. (a) $b_1 = 0.03$; $b_0 = 18.25$ **(b)** $\hat{y} = b_1x + b_0 = 0.03x + 18.25$. The estimated value of the number of super speedways won is 0.03 times the number of short tracks won plus 18.25. **(c)** The estimated number of super speedway wins increases by 0.03 (slope b_1) for each additional short track win. **(d)** The predicted number of super speedway wins when no short tracks have been won is $18.25 \approx 18$ (y intercept b_0).

53. (a) 0.43; 298.86 **(b)** $\hat{y} = 0.43x + 298.86$. The estimated SAT Math score is equal to 0.43 times the SAT Reading score plus 298.86. **(c)** The slope $b_1 = 0.43$ means that the estimated SAT Math score increases by 0.43 point for every increase of 1 point in

the SAT Reading score. **(d)** The y intercept $b_0 = 298.86$ means that the estimated SAT Math score is 298.86 when the SAT Reading score is 0.

54. (a) $b_1 = 1.595$, $b_2 = 193.5$ **(b)** The estimated brain weight of a mammal is 193.5 grams plus 1.595 times the body weight. **(c)** The estimated brain weight increases by 1.595 grams (slope b_1) for each 1 kilogram increase in body weight. **(d)** The y intercept $b_0 = 193.5$ is the predicted brain weight in grams of a mammal with a body weight of 0 kilograms.

55. (a) 13.79 **(b)** 7.59 **(c)** 20 years is outside of the range of the data set. **(d)** The result in part **(a)** is the predicted unemployment rate for individuals with 10 years of education while 20.6 is the actual unemployment rate for individuals with 10 years of education. **(e)** 6.81, above the regression line. The observed unemployment rate of 20.6 is greater than the predicted unemployment rate of 13.79 for 10 years of education.

56. (a) 19.15 super speedway wins **(b)** 19.66 super speedway wins **(c)** 50 short track wins is outside of the range of the data set. **(d)** 19.66 super speedway wins is the predicted number of super speedway wins for Darrell Waltrip and 18 super speedway wins is the actual number of super speedway wins for Darrell Waltrip. **(e)** -1.66 super speedway wins, below. The observed number of 18 super speedway wins for Darrell Waltrip is less than the predicted number of 19.66 super speedway wins.

57. (a) 514.29 **(b)** The SAT Reading score can't be 0, so this situation will never happen. **(c)** No, a mean SAT Reading score of 400 is out of the range of the data set. **(d)** The mean SAT Math score of 514.29 is the predicted mean SAT Math score for New Jersey, and 514 is the actual mean SAT Math score for New Jersey. **(e)** -0.29. The observed mean SAT Math score of 514 for New Jersey is less than the predicted mean SAT Math score of 514.29.

58. (a) 353 g. **(b)** No, there are no mammals with a body weight of 0 kg. **(c)** Dangerous, a mammal with a body weight of 5 kg is outside of the range of the data set so the predicted brain weight would represent extrapolation. **(d)** The brain weight of 157 g is the actual brain weight of a mammal with a body weight of 100 kg, and the brain weight of 353 g is the predicted brain weight of a mammal with a body weight of 100 kg. **(e)** -196 g. The observed brain weight of 157 g for a mammal with a body weight of 100 kg is less than the predicted brain weight of 353 g.

59. Negative

60. Curved

61. No; curved

62. (a) 10.5. In a state with 0 households, 10.5% of the households are headed by women. Since all states have households, the value $x = 0$ would not occur. **(b)** This estimate would be considered extrapolation since the value of $x = 0$ is outside the range of x-values in the data set. **(c)** 0.000000282. For each increase of one household, the percentage of households headed by women increases by 0.000000282. **(d)** (Percentage of households headed by women) $= 10.5 + 0.000000282$ (Total number of households). The estimated percentage of households headed by women equals 10.5 plus 0.000000282 times the total number of households. **(e)** Positive since the slope is positive.

63. (a) Then State A has 0.282% more households headed by women than State B. **(b)** Then State C has 1.41% fewer households headed by women than State D.

64. (a) 12.474% **(b)** $x = 100{,}000$ is not in the range of the x-values in the data set.

65. (a) Darts is the y variable and DJIA is the x variable. **(b)** -2.49 **(c)** When the Dow Jones Industrial Average changes 0%, the portfolios chosen by the Darts decreases by 2.49%. Since the Dow

Jones Industrial Average is based on a different set of stocks than the stock portfolio selected by the Darts, this situation makes sense. **(d)** The estimate in **(c)** would be considered extrapolation since a value of $x = 0$ is outside the range of the x-values of the data set.
66. (a) 1.032. The estimated percent change in the stock prices selected by the Darts increases by 1.032% for each unit percent increase in the Dow Jones Industrial Average. **(b)** Darts = $-2.49 + 1.032$ DJIA. The estimated percent change in the stock prices selected by the Darts is equal to -2.49 plus 1.032 times the percent change in the Dow Jones Industrial Average. **(c)** Positive since the slope of the regression line is positive.
67. (a) The percent change in the stocks selected by the Darts for Contest A is 1.032 (10) = 10.32% more than the percent change in the stocks selected by the Darts for Contest B. **(b)** The percent change in the stocks selected by the Darts for Contest C is 1.032 (5) = 5.16% less than the percent change in the stocks selected by the Darts for Contest D.
68. (a) 20.214% **(b)** -12.81% **(c)** $x = -22$ is not in the range of the x-values of the data set.
69. (a) Decrease **(b)** No change **(c)** Increases if slope is positive, decreases if slope is negative **(d)–(e)** No change
70. (a) It decreases.
(b)

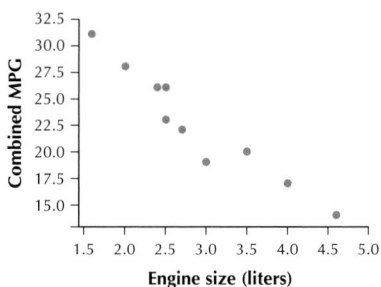

(c) Engine size and combined mpg are negatively correlated. Yes.
71. (a) Negative **(b)** -0.9, the dots lie in a pattern that is close to a straight line **(c)** Yes **(d)** Negative, the dots lie in a pattern that is close to a straight line with a negative slope.
72. (a) $r = -0.9585$; yes **(b)** Engine size is negatively correlated with combined mpg; yes **(c)** As the engine size of a car increases the combined mpg decreases.
73. (a) $b_1 = -5.49$; yes **(b)** $b_0 = 38.41$ **(c)** The slope of $b_1 = -5.49$ means that the combined mpg will decrease by 5.49 mpg for each 1 liter increase in engine size. The y intercept of $b_0 = 38.41$ is the predicted combined mpg for an engine size of 0 liters.
74. (a) 21.94 mpg **(b)** -2.94, below. The observed combined mpg of 19 for the Chevrolet Equinox is less than the predicted combined mpg of 21.94. **(c)** The result obtained in part **(a)** of 21.94 mpg is the predicted combined mpg for the Chevrolet Equinox. It is obtained using the regression equation. The combined mpg of 19 is the observed combined mpg for the Chevrolet Equinox. **(d)** No, 6 liters is outside the range of the data set.
75. Answers will vary.
76. Answers will vary.
77. Answers will vary.
78. Answers will vary.

Section 4.3
1. The standard error of the estimate s is a measure of the size of the typical difference between the predicted value of y and the observed value of y.
2. Out of all possible straight lines, the least-squares criterion chooses the line with the smallest SSE.

3. SSE measures the prediction errors. SSE is the sum of the squared prediction errors. Since we want our prediction errors to be small, we want SSE to be as small as possible.
4. It measures the amount of improvement in the accuracy of our estimate when using the regression equation compared with relying only on the y-values and ignoring the x information. We want SSR to be large, since SSR measures the amount of improvement in the accuracy of our estimate when using the regression equation compared with relying only on the y-values and ignoring the x information.
5. Measure of the variability in y. The variance s^2 of the y's.
6. A value of r^2 close to 1 indicates that the regression equation fits the data extremely well. A value of r^2 close to 0 indicates that the regression equation fits the data extremely poorly.
7. No
8. No, we don't have enough information to determine the sign of r.
9. 64% of the variability in the variable y is accounted for by the linear relationship between x and y.
10. False

11. (a) and (b)

x	y	$\hat{y} = 3.4x - 1.5$	$(y - \hat{y})$	$(y - \hat{y})^2$
1	2	1.9	0.1	0.01
2	5	5.3	-0.3	0.09
3	9	8.7	0.3	0.09
4	12	12.1	-0.1	0.01
				SSE = 0.2

12. (a) and (b)

x	y	$\hat{y} = -0.2x + 5.6$	$(y - \hat{y})$	$(y - \hat{y})^2$
0	5	5.6	-0.6	0.36
2	6	5.2	0.8	0.64
4	5	4.8	0.2	0.04
6	4	4.4	-0.4	0.16
				SSE = 1.2

13. (a)

x	y	Predicted value $\hat{y} = 21.6 + 4x$	Residual $(y - \hat{y})$	(Residual)^2 $(y - \hat{y})^2$
-5	0	1.6	-1.6	2.56
-4	8	5.6	2.4	5.76
-3	8	9.6	-1.6	2.56
-2	16	13.6	2.4	5.76
-1	16	17.6	-1.6	2.56

(b) SSE = 19.2

14. (a)

x	y	Predicted value $\hat{y} = -216 - 3x$	Residual $(y - \hat{y})$	(Residual)^2 $(y - \hat{y})^2$
-3	-5	-7	2	4
-1	-15	-13	-2	4
1	-20	-19	-1	1
3	-25	-25	0	0
5	-30	-31	1	1

(b) SSE = 10

15. (a) and (b)

x	y	$\hat{y} = 0.01x + 2.47$	$(y - \hat{y})$	$(y - \hat{y})^2$
5	2	2.52	−0.52	0.2704
10	3	2.57	0.43	0.1849
15	3	2.62	0.38	0.1444
20	3	2.67	0.33	0.1089
25	2	2.72	−0.72	0.5184
30	3	2.77	0.23	0.0529
				SSE = 1.2799

16. (a) and (b)

x	y	$\hat{y} = 4$	$(y - \hat{y})$	$(y - \hat{y})^2$
6	4	4	0	0
7	4	4	0	0
8	4	4	0	0
9	4	4	0	0
11	4	4	0	0
13	4	4	0	0
				SSE = 0

17. $s = 0.3162$
18. $s = 0.7746$
19. The typical error in prediction is 2.5298.
20. The typical error in prediction is 1.8257.
21. 0.5657; TI-83/84: 0.5648
22. $s = 0$
23. (a) $s^2 = 19.33333333$ **(b)** SST = 58 **(c)** SSR = 57.8
24. (a) $s^2 = 0.666666667$ **(b)** SST = 2 **(c)** SSR = 0.8
25. (a) $s^2 = 44.8$ **(b)** SST = 179.2 **(c)** SSR = 160
26. (a) $s^2 = 92.5$ **(b)** SST = 370 **(c)** SSR = 360
27. (a) $s^2 = 0.2666666667$ **(b)** SST = 1.3333 **(c)** SSR = 0.0534
28. (a) $s^2 = 0.0$ **(b)** SST = 0.0 **(c)** SSR = 0.0
29. (a) $r^2 = 0.9966$ **(b)** 99.66% of the variability in the variable y is accounted for by the linear relationship between x and y. **(c)** $r = 0.9983$
30. (a) $r^2 = 0.4$ **(b)** 40% of the variability in the variable y is accounted for by the linear relationship between x and y. **(c)** $r = -0.6325$
31. (a) $r^2 = 0.8929$ **(b)** 89.29% of the variability in the variable y is accounted for by the linear relationship between x and y. **(c)** $r = 0.9449$
32. (a) $r^2 = 0.9730$ **(b)** 97.30% of the variability in the variable y is accounted for by the linear relationship between x and y. **(c)** $r = -0.9864$
33. (a) $r^2 = 0.0401$, from the TI-83/84: $r^2 = 0.0429$ **(b)** 4.01% (4.29%) of the variability in the variable y is accounted for by the linear relationship between x and y. **(c)** $r = 0.2001$; TI-83/84: $r = 0.2070$
34. (a) r^2 is undefined. **(b)** Not applicable since r^2 is undefined. **(c)** r is undefined.
35. (a) and (b)

x = Years of education	y = Unemployment rate	$\hat{y} = -1.24x + 26.19$	$(y - \hat{y})$	$(y - \hat{y})^2$
5	16.8	19.99	−3.19	10.1761
7.5	17.1	16.89	0.21	0.0441
8	15.3	16.27	−0.97	0.9409
10	20.6	13.79	6.81	46.3761
12	11.7	11.31	0.39	0.1521
14	8.1	8.83	−0.73	0.5329
16	3.8	6.35	−2.55	6.5025
				SSE = 64.7247

36. (a) and (b)

x = Short track wins	y = Super speedway wins	$\hat{y} = 0.03x + 18.25$	$(y - \hat{y})$	$(y - \hat{y})^2$
47	18	19.66	−1.66	2.7556
27	29	19.06	9.94	98.8036
15	15	18.7	−3.7	13.69
29	15	19.12	−4.12	16.9744
23	19	18.94	0.06	0.0036
				SSE = 132.2272

37. (a) and (b)

x = Mean SAT Reading score	y = Mean SAT Math score	$\hat{y} = 0.43x + 298.86$	$(y - \hat{y})$	$(y - \hat{y})^2$
497	510	512.57	−2.57	6.6049
515	515	520.31	−5.31	28.1961
518	523	521.6	1.4	1.96
501	514	514.29	−0.29	0.0841
522	521	523.32	−2.32	5.3824
				SSE = 42.2275

38. (a) and (b)

x = Body weight (kg)	y = Brain weight (g)	$\hat{y} = 1.59x + 193.51$	$(y - \hat{y})$	$(y - \hat{y})^2$
52.16	440	276.4444	163.5556	26,750.43429
60	81	288.91	−207.91	43,226.5681
27.66	115	237.4894	−122.4894	15,003.65311
85	325	328.66	−3.66	13.3956
36.33	119.5	251.2747	−131.7747	17,364.57156
100	157	352.51	−195.51	38,224.1601
35	56	249.16	−193.16	37,310.7856
62	1320	292.09	1027.91	1,056,598.968
83	98.2	325.48	−227.28	51,656.1984
55.5	175	281.755	−106.755	11,396.63003
				SSE = 1,297,545.365

39. (a) $s^2 = 33.96952381$; SST = 203.8171429 **(b)** SSR = 139.0924429 **(c)** $r^2 = 0.6837$, TI-83/84: $r^2 = 0.6824$, 68.24% (68.37%) of the variability in the variable y = the unemployment rate is accounted for by the linear relationship between x = years of education and y = the unemployment rate. **(d)** $r = -0.8269$. TI-83/84: $r = -0.8269$. TI-83/84: $r = 0.8261$.
40. (a) $s^2 = 33.2$; SST = 132.8 **(b)** SSR = 0.5728 **(c)** $r^2 = 0.0043$, TI-83/84: $r = 0.0048$, 0.43% (0.48%) of the variability in the variable y = super speedway wins is accounted for by the linear relationship between x = short track wins and y = super speedway wins. **(d)** $r = 0.0657$; TI-83/84: $r = 0.0691$
41. (a) $s^2 = 28.3$; SST = 113.2 **(b)** SSR = 70.9725 **(c)** $r^2 = 0.6270$; TI-83/84: $r^2 = 0.7730$, 62.70% (77.30%) of the variability in the variable y = mean SAT Math score is accounted for by the linear relationship between x = mean SAT Reading score and y = mean SAT Math score. **(d)** $r = 0.7918$; TI-83/84: $r = 0.8792$.
42. (a) $s^2 = 145,604.5334$; SST = 1,310,440.801 **(b)** SSR = 12,895.436 **(c)** $r^2 = 0.0098$, 0.98% of the variability in the variable

y = brain weight is accounted for by the linear relationship between x = body weight and y = brain weight. **(d)** $r = 0.0992$

43. (a)

Volume (x)	Weight (y)	$\hat{y} = 1.6x + 4$	$(y - \hat{y})$	$(y - \hat{y})^2$
4	10	10.4	−0.4	0.16
8	16	16.8	−0.8	0.64
12	25	23.2	1.8	3.24
16	30	29.6	0.4	0.16
20	35	36	−1	1
				SSE = 5.2

(b) $s = 1.3166$. If we know the volume (x) of a package, then our estimate of the weight (y) of the package will typically differ from the actual weight of the package by 1.3166 kg. **(c)** $s^2 = 103.7$; SST = 414.8 **(d)** SSR = 409.6 **(e)** $r^2 = 0.9875$, 98.75% of the variability in the variable y = weight is accounted for by the linear relationship between x = volume and y = weight. **(f)** $r = 0.9937$

44. (a)

Low (x)	High (y)	$\hat{y} = 1.05x + 11.9$	$(y - \hat{y})$	$(y - \hat{y})^2$
57	77	71.75	5.25	27.5625
36	45	49.7	−4.7	22.09
7	21	19.25	1.75	3.0625
39	55	52.85	2.15	4.6225
70	83	85.4	−2.4	5.76
34	45	47.6	−2.6	6.76
				SSE = 69.8575

(b) $s = 4.1790$; TI-83/84: $s = 4.1767$. If we know the low temperature (x) for a particular day in 2006, then our estimate of the high temperature (y) for that day will typically differ from the actual high temperature by 4.1790 (4.1767) degrees Fahrenheit. **(c)** $s^2 = 524.2666667$; SST = 2621.333333 **(d)** SSR = 2551.475833 **(e)** $r^2 = 0.9734$, 97.34% of the variability in the variable y = high temperature is accounted for by the linear relationship between x = low temperature and y = high temperature. **(f)** $r = 0.9866$

45. (a)

Win % (x)	Rating (y)	$\hat{y} = 0.117x + 85.1$	$(y - \hat{y})$	$(y - \hat{y})^2$
84	96.0	94.928	1.072	1.149184
94	95.5	96.098	−0.598	0.357604
85	95.5	95.045	0.455	0.207025
88	95.3	95.396	−0.096	0.009216
86	94.5	95.162	−0.662	0.438244
74	93.1	93.758	−0.658	0.432964
				SSE = 2.594237

(b) $s = 0.8053$; TI-83/84: $s = 0.7992$. If we know a team's winning percentage (x) for the 2004 NCAA Basketball Tournament, then our estimate of the team's rating (y) will typically differ from the actual rating by 0.8053 (0.7992). **(c)** $s^2 = 1.089666667$; SST = 5.448333333 **(d)** SSR = 2.854096333 **(e)** $r^2 = 0.5238$; TI-83/84: $r^2 = 0.5311$, 52.38% (53.11%) of the variability in the variable y = team's rating is accounted for by the linear relationship between x = winning percentage and y = team's rating. **(f)** $r = 0.7238$; TI-83/84: $r = 0.7288$

46. (a)

Overall birth rate (x)	Teenage birth rate (y)	$\hat{y} = 5.39x - 34.3$	$(y - \hat{y})$	$(y - \hat{y})^2$
15.2	39.5	47.628	−8.128	66.064384
12.5	42.4	33.075	9.325	86.955625
15.7	53.4	50.323	3.077	9.467929
13.0	26.9	35.77	−8.87	78.6769
13.0	38.5	35.77	2.73	7.4529
11.7	30.5	28.763	1.737	3.017169
17.0	62.6	57.33	5.27	27.7729
13.9	35.2	40.621	−5.421	29.387241
				SSE = 308.795048

(b) $s = 7.1740$, TI-83/84: $s = 7.1739$. If we know the overall birth rate of a state (x), then our estimate of the teenage birth rate of the state (y) will typically differ from the actual teenage birth rate for the state by 7.1740 (7.1739). **(c)** $s^2 = 139.0507143$; SST = 973.355 **(d)** SSR = 664.559952 **(e)** $r^2 = 0.6828$, 68.28% of the variability in the variable y = teenage birth rate is accounted for by the linear relationship between x = overall birth rate and y = teenage birth rate. **(f)** $r = 0.8263$.

47. (a)

Height (x)	Weight (y)	$\hat{y} = 4.99x - 189$	$(y - \hat{y})$	$(y - \hat{y})^2$
60	100	110.4	−10.4	108.16
60	115	110.4	4.6	21.16
62	110	120.38	−10.38	107.7444
63	125	125.37	−0.37	0.1369
63	135	125.37	9.63	92.7369
64	145	130.36	14.64	214.3296
66	140	140.34	−0.34	0.1156
67	145	145.33	−0.33	0.1089
68	150	150.32	−0.32	0.1024
70	155	160.3	−5.3	28.09
				SSE = 572.6847

(b) $s = 8.4608$; TI-83/84: $s = 8.4593$. If we know the height of a female student (x), then our estimate of the student's weight (y) will typically differ from the student's actual weight by 8.4608 (8.4593) pounds. **(c)** $s^2 = 345.5555556$; SST = 3110 **(d)** SSR = 2537.3153 **(e)** $r^2 = 0.8159$, 81.59% of the variability in the variable y = weight is accounted for by the linear relationship between x = height and y = weight. **(f)** $r = 0.9033$

48. (a)

Price (x)	Change (y)	$\hat{y} = 0.01x - 0.112$	$(y - \hat{y})$	$(y - \hat{y})^2$
3.86	+0.04	−0.0734	0.1134	0.01285956
3.41	−0.56	−0.0779	−0.4821	0.23242041
3.04	−0.03	−0.0816	0.0516	0.00266256
10.36	−0.82	−0.0084	−0.8116	0.65869456
14.74	+1.62	0.0354	1.5846	2.51095716
33.19	+0.03	0.2199	−0.1899	0.03606201
39.15	+0.46	0.2795	0.1805	0.03258025
33.05	−0.21	0.2185	−0.4285	0.18361225
				SSE = 3.66984876

(b) $s = 0.7821$. If we know the price of a stock (x), then our estimate of the change in price (y) will typically differ from the actual change in price by 0.7821. **(c)** $s^2 = 0.5477696429$; SST = 3.8343875 **(d)** SSR = 0.16453874 **(e)** $r^2 = 0.0429$, 4.29% of the variability in the variable y = change in price is accounted for by the linear relationship between x = price and y = change in price. **(f)** $r = 0.2072$

49. (a) $x = 10$ years of education; $y = 20.6$ = unemployment rate. It doesn't follow the trend of the higher the number of years of education, the lower the unemployment rate. **(b)** Since $r^2 = 0.6824$, 68.24% of the variability in the variable y = unemployment rate is accounted for by the linear relationship between x = years of education and y = unemployment rate. Hence the statement is not true. **(c)** Since the absolute values of the residuals for 5, 10, and 16 years of education are more than 1%, this claim is not always true. **(d)** Since $b_1 = -1.24$, we can say that each additional year of education drops the predicted unemployment rate by 1.24%.

50. The y intercept would increase and the slope would increase in absolute value (decrease since it is negative). This is because an increase in the y-value of the point closest to the y axis would pull the left side of the regression line higher up, increasing the y intercept and making the slope more negative.

51. (a) Massachusetts. This means that the actual mean SAT Math score for Massachusetts lies above the regression line. **(b)** Connecticut. This means that the actual mean SAT Math score for Connecticut lies below the regression line. **(c)** No, because the y intercept is the predicted mean SAT Math score for a state with a mean SAT Reading score of zero, and it is impossible to have a score of zero on the SAT Reading test.

52. (a) Since $b_1 = 0.43$, for every additional point increase in the mean SAT Reading score, you could expect an increase of 0.43 point in the predicted mean SAT Math score. Hence the statement is not true. **(b)** Since $r = 0.8792 > 0.878$, the variables are strongly positively correlated. Therefore the statement is not true. **(c)** Since one of the residuals is greater than 3 in absolute value, the statement is not true. **(d)** Since $r^2 = 0.7730$, 77.30% of the variability in the variable y = mean SAT Math score is accounted for by the linear relationship between x = mean SAT Reading score and y = mean SAT Math score. Thus, the statement is true.

53. The y intercept would increase and the slope would decrease. This is because an increase in the y-value of the point closest to the y axis would pull the left side of the regression line higher up, increasing the y intercept and decreasing the slope.

54. (a) Since $r = 0.0992 < 0.632$, the variables are not linearly correlated. Therefore the statement is not true. **(b)** Since one of the residuals is greater than 402 grams, the statement is not true. **(c)** Since $b_1 = 1.59$, for every additional kilogram increase in body weight, you could expect an increase of 1.59 grams in brain weight. Therefore, the statement is not true. **(d)** The regression equation is only valid for body weights between 27.66 grams and 100 grams, inclusive. Since $x = 0$ is not in this range, the prediction from the regression equation is not valid.

55. $x = 62$ kg. The brain weight is much higher than all of the other brain weights. Humans.

56. $b_1 = 1.07$, $b_0 = 110.61$, $s = 132.4691$, $r^2 = 0.0449$, $r = 0.2120$ **(a)** Increases: r^2, r; decreases: b_1, b_0, s **(b)** Since $r = 0.2120 < 0.666$, the variables are not correlated.

57. b_0 increases; b_1, s, r^2, and r all remain the same. The increase in the y-values by a fixed positive amount will shift the regression line up by that fixed amount. This will increase the y intercept by that fixed amount but leave the slope, s, r^2, and r unchanged.

58. (a)

x = Engine size (liters)	y = Combined (city/highway) gas mileage (MPG)	$\hat{y} = -5.49x + 38.41$	$(y - \hat{y})$	$(y - \hat{y})^2$
1.6	31	29.626	1.374	1.887876
2.0	28	27.43	0.57	0.3249
2.5	26	24.685	1.315	1.727925
2.5	23	24.685	-1.685	2.839225
2.4	26	25.234	0.766	0.586756
2.7	22	23.587	-1.587	2.518569
3.0	19	21.94	-2.94	8.6436
3.5	20	19.195	0.805	0.648025
4.0	17	16.45	0.55	0.3025
4.6	14	13.156	0.844	0.712336
			SSE =	20.193012

(b) SSE is the sum of the squared residuals. Since we know that $\hat{y} = -5.49x + 38.41$ is the regression line, according to the least-squares criterion, no other possible straight line would result in a smaller SSE. **(c)** Chevrolet Equinox. It has much less combined mpg than expected. **(d)** Since the residual for the Suburu Forester is negative, the actual combined mpg is lower than expected.

59. (a) $s = 1.5887$ **(b)** If we know car's engine size (x), then our estimate of the combined mpg will typically differ from the actual mpg by 1.5887 mpg. **(c)** Since one of the absolute residuals is greater than 2 mpg, the statement is not always true.

60. (a) $s^2 = 27.6$, SST = 248.4 **(b)** SSR = 228.206988, SSR measures the amount of improvement in the accuracy of our estimates using the regression equation compared with relying only on the y-values and ignoring the x information. **(c)** $r^2 = 0.9187$, 91.87% of the variability in the variable y = combined mpg is accounted for by the linear relationship between x = engine size and y = combined mpg. **(d)** Since $r^2 = 0.9187$, 91.87% of the variability in the variable y = combined mpg is accounted for by the linear relationship between x = engine size and y = combined mpg. Therefore the statement is true.

61. (a) $r = -0.9585$ **(b)** Since $|r| = |-0.9585| = 0.9585 > 0.632$ and r is negative, the variables engine size and combined mpg are negatively correlated. **(c)** From **(b)**, the results are true.

62. Since $(\bar{x}, \bar{y})$ is on the regression line, the slope and the y intercept would remain the same.

63. The slope would increase and the y intercept would decrease.

64. 38.1744186 mpg

65. Since $b_1 = 0$, the regression equation is $\hat{y} = \bar{y} = 25.02$. Thus $\hat{y} - \bar{y} = 0$ for all of the $\hat{y} - \bar{y}$'s. Hence SSR = 0, so SSR would decrease. Since SST = SSR + SSE and SSR = 0, SSE = SST = 358.5622634, so both SSE and SST increase. Since the regression line doesn't include any information from the x-values, SSR = 0, $r^2 = 0$, and $r = 0$. Since SSR = 0, $r^2 = \dfrac{\text{SSR}}{\text{SST}}$, and $r = \sqrt{r^2}$, $r^2 = 0$ and $r = 0$. Since $s = \sqrt{\dfrac{\text{SSE}}{n-2}} = 6.6948$ and SSE increases, s increases.

66. (a) y intercept $b_1 = 97.1$ **(b)** A breakfast cereal with 0 grams of fat will have 97.1 calories per serving. Yes, because there are other ingredients in cereal besides fat and they have calories. **(c)** No, since $x = 0$ is an x-value in the data set. **(d)** The number of calories in a serving of breakfast cereal increases by 9.65 calories for every increase of 1 gram of fat. **(e)** Calories = $97.1 + 9.65$ fat. The estimated number of calories in a serving of breakfast cereal equals 97.1 plus 9.65 times the number of grams of fat. **(f)** Positive, since the slope of the regression line is positive.

67. (a) Cereal A has 2 (9.65) = 19.3 more calories per serving than Cereal B has. **(b)** Cereal C has 3 (9.65) = 28.95 fewer calories per serving than Cereal D has.

68. (a)

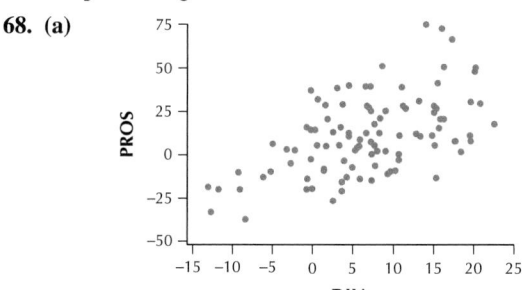

(b) $\hat{y} = 1.49x + 0.83$. The estimated increase (in percent) in the Pros stock portfolio equals 1.49 times the increase in the DJIA plus 0.83. **(c)** $r^2 = 0.289$, so 28.9% of the variability in the Pros price increase is accounted for by the linear relationship between the Pros price increase and the DJIA. **(d)** $s = 18.8545$. The typical difference between the predicted Pros price increase and the actual Pros price increase is 18.8545%. **(e)** $r = \sqrt{r^2} = \sqrt{0.289} = 0.5376$

69. (a)

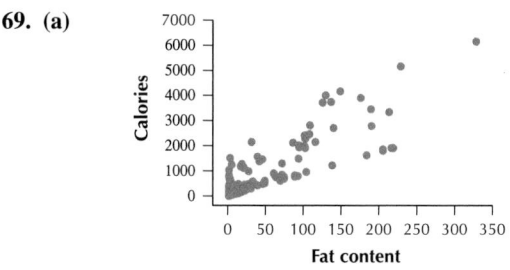

(b) $\hat{y} = 8.12x + 1.28$. The estimated calories per gram equals 8.12 times the amount of fat per gram, plus 1.28. **(c)** $r^2 = 0.736$, so 73.6% of the variability in the number of calories per gram is accounted for by the linear relationship between calories per gram and fat per gram. **(d)** $s = 0.9944$. The typical difference between the predicted number of calories per gram and the actual calories per gram is 0.9944. **(e)** $r = \sqrt{r^2} = \sqrt{0.736} = 0.8579$

70. (a)

(b) $\hat{y} = 0.0263x + 96.3$. The estimated body temperature equals 0.0263 times the heart rate, plus 96.3. **(c)** $r^2 = 0.064$, so 6.4% of the variability in body temperature is accounted for by the linear relationship between body temperature and heart rate. **(d)** $s = 0.7120$. The typical difference between the predicted body temperature and the actual body temperature is 0.7120. **(e)** $r = \sqrt{r^2} = \sqrt{0.064} = 0.2530$

71. Answers will vary.

72. Answers will vary.
73. Answers will vary.
74. Answers will vary.
75. Answers will vary.
76. Answers will vary.
77. (a) Answers will vary. **(b)** That your adjusted line matches the least squares regression line **(c)** Yes
78. Answers will vary.

Chapter 4 Review

1.

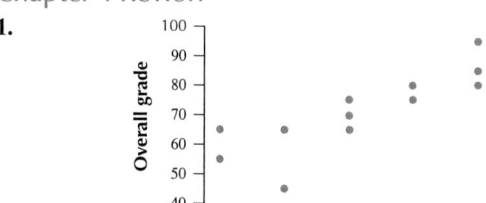

2. (a) Positive. **(b)** As midterm exam score increases, overall grade tends to increase.
3. $r = 0.838$.
4. $r = 0.838 > 0.576$, so the variables are positively correlated.
5. Midterm exam scores and overall grades are positively correlated. Low (high) midterm exam scores are associated with low (high) overall grades.

6.

7. Positive
8. (a) Close to 1 **(b)** $r = 1$ **(c)** Yes **(d)** Since $r = 1 > 0.878$ and r is positive, the variables are positively correlated. **(e)** The variables are positively correlated. As x increases, y increases. Low values of x are associated with low values of y, and high values of x are associated with high values of y.
9. $b_0 = 15.99$, $b_1 = 0.77$, $\hat{y} = 0.77x + 15.99$
10. The predicted overall grade ($\hat{y}$) in elementary statistics is 0.77 times the midterm exam score (x) plus 15.99.
11. For each 1-point increase in the midterm exam score, the student's predicted overall grade increases by 0.77 point.
12. The predicted overall grade in elementary statistics for a student with a midterm grade of 0 is 15.99.
13. (a) 54.49 **(b)** 92.99
14. Two students have a midterm exam score of 50. The prediction error for the overall grade of 65 is 10.51 and the prediction error for the overall grade of 55 is 0.51. In both instances the predicted value is less than the actual value. Since no student had a midterm exam score of 100, we can't calculate the prediction error for $x = 100$.
15. For $x = 50$, the prediction does not represent extrapolation. For $x = 100$, the prediction represents extrapolation.
16. SSE = 598.9
17. $s = 7.7392$. The typical difference between the actual predicted overall grade and the actual overall grade is 7.7392 points.

18. SST = 2006.3. SSR = 1407.3.

19. $r^2 = 0.701$, meaning that 70.1% of the variability in overall grade is accounted for by the midterm exam scores.

20. $r = 0.8373$. Midterm exam scores and overall grades are positively correlated.

Chapter 4 Quiz

1. False

2. False

3. estimate

4. unit

5. extrapolation

6. negative

7.

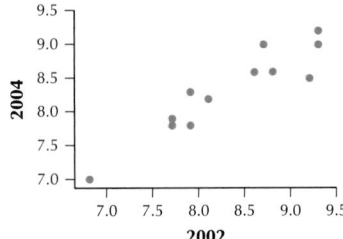

8. Positive

9. $\hat{y} = 0.75x + 2.04$

10. SSR = 3.7726, SSE = 0.5899, SST = 4.3625.

11. $s = 0.2429$. The typical difference between the predicted 2004 percentage and the actual 2004 percentage is 0.2429 percentage points.

12. $r^2 = 0.865$, meaning that 86.5% of the variability in 2004 percentage is accounted for by the 2002 percentage.

13. $r = 0.9300$. The 2002 percentage and the 2004 percentage are positively correlated.

14. **(a)** $-0.1980, 0.3020$. **(b)** $0.1456, -0.0544$. **(c)** 0.0511.

Chapter 5

Section 5.1

1. Answers will vary; chance, likelihood.

2. A numerical value for probability is more definite and is interpreted the same way by everyone.

3. Answers will vary.

4. Classical method, relative frequency method, and subjective method

5. The experiment has equally likely outcomes.

6. When we have prior knowledge about the relative frequency of an outcome

7. We consider all available information, tempered by our experience and intuition, and then assign a probability value that expresses our estimate of the likelihood that the outcome will occur.

8. The classical and relative frequency methods

9. First find out how many students are at your college and find out how many of them like hip-hop music. Then calculate the relative frequency of students who like hip-hop music. Use the relative frequency method.

10. **(a)** Outcome or event is very unlikely.

(b) Outcome or event cannot occur.

(c) Outcome or event is nearly certain to occur.

(d) Outcome or event is certain to occur. It's "a sure thing."

11. No, probability for females is greater than 1.

12. It is not a probability model since the probability of a tenor is negative.

13. No, sum of probabilities is greater than 1.

14. Not a probability model. The sum of the probabilities is greater than 1.

15. It is a probability model.

16. No, sum of probabilities is less than 1.

17. 1/13

18. 1/4

19. 1/52

20. 1/2

21. 1/6

22. 1/2

23. 1/2

24. 1/3

25. 1/3

26. 0

27. outcome; event; event; event; event; event

28. 3 is only one of the outcomes in the event 3 or 5.

29.

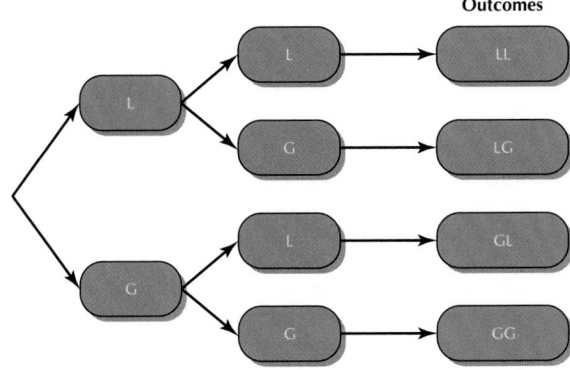

30. {(Even, Even), (Even, Odd), (Odd, Even), (Odd, Odd)}

31. $1/4 = 0.25$

32. $2/4 = 1/2 = 0.5$

33. $1/4 = 0.25$

34.

Number of even numbers	Probability
Zero even numbers	0.25
One even number	0.5
Two even numbers	0.25

35. Let L = tossing a number less than 4 and G = tossing a number greater than or equal to 4.

36. {LL, LG, GL, GG}

37. $1/4 = 0.25$

38. $1/4 = 0.25$

39.

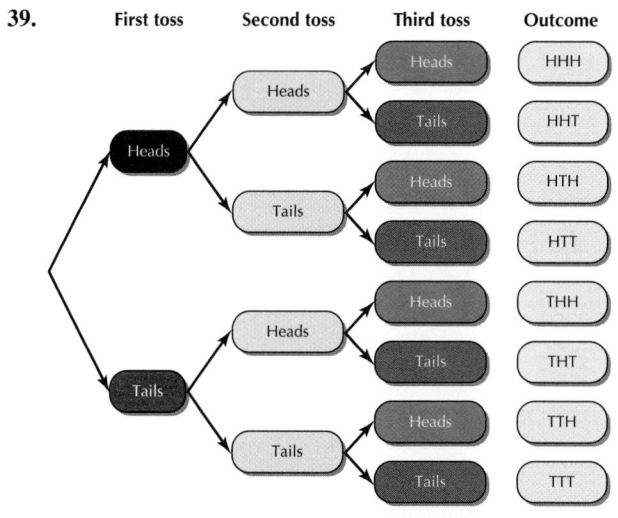

40. {HHH, HHT, HTH, THH, TTH, THT, HTT, TTT}

41. We can follow the branches to get all possible outcomes.

42. Choose a branch for the first toss, then choose a branch for the second toss, then choose a branch for the third toss. This will give one of the possible outcomes. If we follow all possible choices of branches for each toss, we get all the outcomes in the sample space.

43. $1/8 = 0.125$

44. $3/8 = 0.375$

45. $3/8 = 0.375$

46. $1/8 = 0.125$

47.

Number of heads	Probability
0	$1/8 = 0.125$
1	$3/8 = 0.375$
2	$3/8 = 0.375$
3	$1/8 = 0.125$

48. The classical method.

49. $4/36 = 1/9$

50. $1/6$

51. $1/36$

52. $1/6$

53. 0

54.

Sum of dice	Probability
2	$1/36$
3	$2/36 = 1/18$
4	$3/36 = 1/12$
5	$4/36 = 1/9$
6	$5/36$
7	$6/36 = 1/6$
8	$5/36$
9	$4/36 = 1/9$
10	$3/36 = 1/2$
11	$2/36 = 1/18$
12	$1/36$

55. Sum of 7

56. Sum of 2 and sum of 12

57. $40/100 = 2/5 = 0.4$

58. $25/100 = 1/4 = 0.25$

59. $20/100 = 1/5 = 0.2$

60. $15/100 = 3/20 = 0.15$

61. The relative frequency method

62.

Hot caffeinated beverage	Probability
Regular coffee	$40/100 = 0.4$
Latte	$25/100 = 0.25$
Cappuccino	$20/100 = 0.2$
Tea	$15/100 = 0.15$

63. $100/200 = 1/2 = 0.5$

64. $60/200 = 3/10 = 0.3$

65. $40/200 = 2/10 = 0.2$

66.

Where student lives	Probability
On campus	$100/200 = 0.5$
With family off-campus	$60/200 = 0.3$
In an apartment off-campus	$40/200 = 0.2$

67.

Favorite color	Probability
Red	$30/100 = 0.3$
Blue	$25/100 = 0.25$
Green	$20/100 = 0.2$
Black	$10/100 = 0.1$
Violet	$10/100 = 0.1$
Yellow	$5/100 = 0.05$

68.

Favorite season	Probability
Summer	$80/200 = 0.4$
Spring	$60/200 = 0.3$
Autumn	$40/200 = 0.2$
Winter	$20/200 = 0.1$

69. (a)

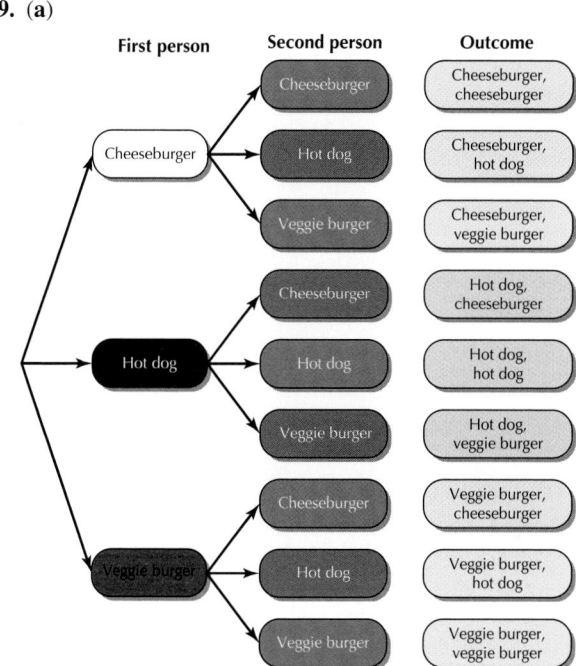

(b) {Cheeseburger and cheeseburger, Cheeseburger and hot dog, Cheeseburger and veggie burger, Hot dog and cheeseburger, Hot dog and hot dog, Hot dog and veggie burger, Veggie burger and cheeseburger, Veggie burger and hot dog, Veggie burger and veggie burger}

70. (a)

Outcomes

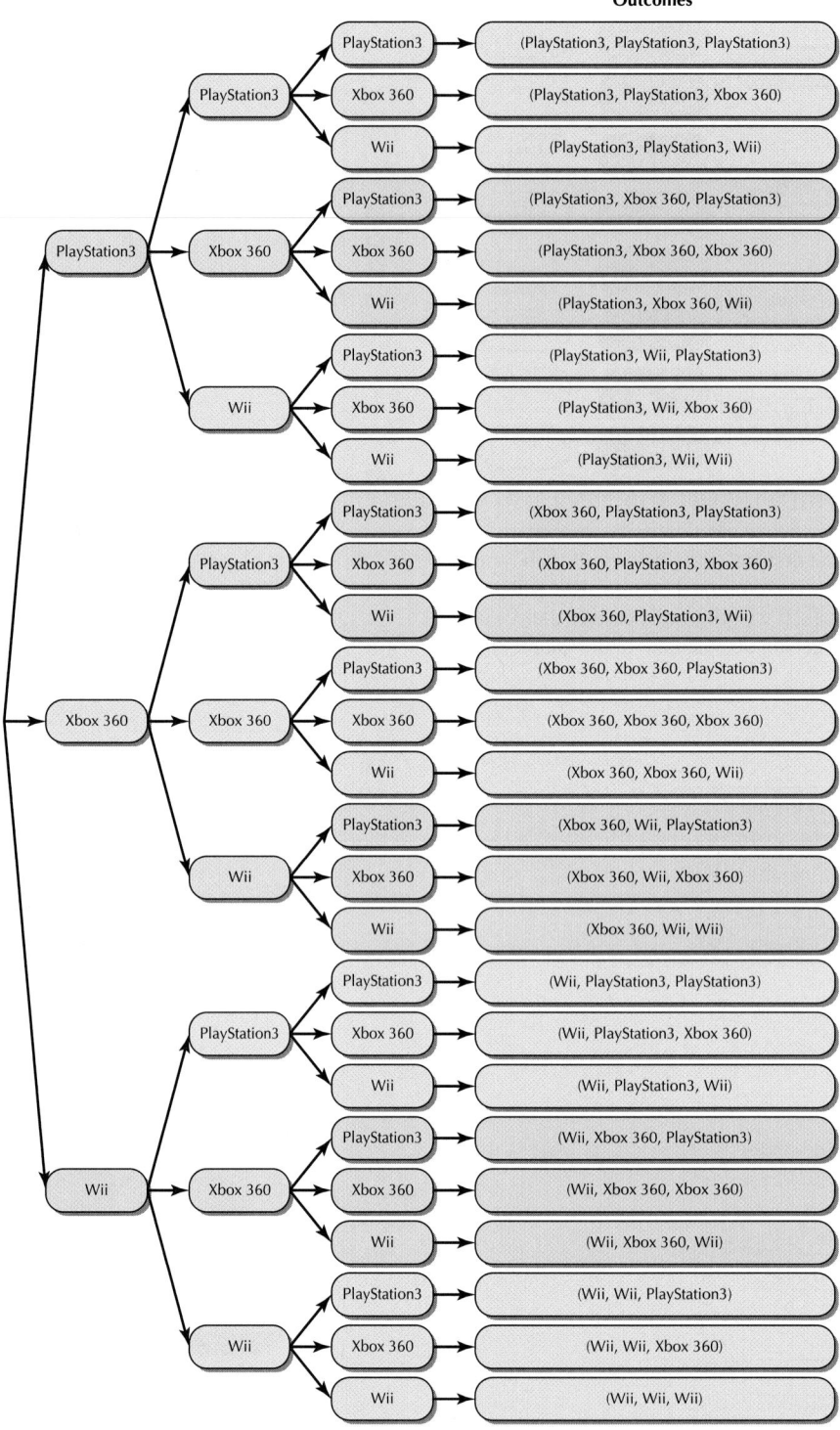

(b) {{PlayStation3, PlayStation3, PlayStation3}, {PlayStation3, PlayStation3, Xbox 360}, {PlayStation3, PlayStation3, Wii}, {PlayStation3, Xbox 360, PlayStation3}, {PlayStation3, Xbox 360, Xbox 360}, {PlayStation3, Xbox 360, Wii}, {PlayStation3, Wii, PlayStation3}, {PlayStation3, Wii, Xbox 360}, {PlayStation3, Wii, Wii}, {Xbox 360, PlayStation3, PlayStation3}, {Xbox 360, PlayStation3, Xbox 360}, {Xbox 360, PlayStation3, Wii}, {Xbox 360, Xbox 360, PlayStation3}, {Xbox 360, Xbox 360, Xbox 360}, {Xbox 360, Xbox 360, Wii}, {Xbox 360, Wii, PlayStation3}, {Xbox 360, Wii, Xbox 360}, {Xbox 360, Wii, Wii}, {Wii, PlayStation3, PlayStation3},

{Wii, PlayStation3, Xbox 360}, {Wii, PlayStation3, Wii}, {Wii, Xbox 360, PlayStation3}, {Wii, Xbox 360, Xbox 360}, {Wii, Xbox 360, Wii}, {Wii, Wii, PlayStation3}, {Wii, Wii, Xbox 360}, {Wii, Wii, Wii}}

71. (a) 0.33 **(b)** 0.67 **(c)** Relative frequency method

72. (a) No, because the outcomes parked illegally and not parked illegally are not equally likely. **(b)** 1/5; relative frequency method

73. (a) 0.025 **(b)** Relative frequency method **(c)** The events "cutting class" and "not cutting class" are not equally likely.

74. (a)–(c) Answers will vary.

75. (a)

	Frequency	Relative frequency
Girls	18	18/44 = 0.4091
Boys	26	26/44 = 0.5909
Total	44	44/44 = 1.0000

(b)

Outcome	Probability
Girl	18/44 = 0.4091
Boy	26/44 = 0.5909

(c) Both P (Girl) = 18/44 = 0.4091 and P (Boy) = 26/44 = 0.5909 are between 0 and 1. P (Girl) + P (Boy) = 18/44 + 26/44 = 0.4091 + 0.5909 = 44/44 = 1.0000.
76. (a) See Instructor's Guide with Solutions for chart.
(b) {Cognitive performance increased and cognitive performance increased, Cognitive performance increased and cognitive performance decreased, Cognitive performance increased and cognitive performance remained unchanged, Cognitive performance decreased and cognitive performance increased, Cognitive performance decreased and cognitive performance decreased, Cognitive performance decreased and cognitive performance remained unchanged, Cognitive performance remained unchanged and cognitive performance increased, Cognitive performance remained unchanged and cognitive performance decreased, Cognitive performance remained unchanged and cognitive performance remained unchanged} **(c)** 1 **(d)** The outcomes Cognitive performance increased, Cognitive performance decreased, and Cognitive performance remained unchanged are not equally likely.
77. Answers will vary.
78. (a) consonant **(b)** 5/26 **(c)** 1/2
79. (a) Half of the most popular letters are vowels, but only 5/26 of all of the letters are vowels. **(b)** T, N, R, S, D
80. (a) 1/52 **(b)** $1.92
81. (a) 5/18 **(b)** 13/18 **(c)** $1.39
82. The sum of the percents is greater than 100%.

83. (a)

Type of music	Probability
Hip-hop/rap	0.27
Pop	0.23
Rock/punk	0.17
Alternative	0.07
Christian/gospel	0.06
R&B	0.06
Country	0.05
Techno/house	0.04
Jazz	0.01
Other	0.04

(b) Yes. **(c)** Answers will vary. **(d)** As the sample size increases, the relative frequencies approach the probabilities.
84. (a) Answers will vary. **(b)** As the sample size increases, the relative frequencies approach the probabilities.
85. (a) $(1/2)^8$ **(b)** $(1/2)^9$ **(c)** 1/2 **(d)** $(1/2)^k$
86. (a) Greater **(b)** Greater
87. p^k

88.

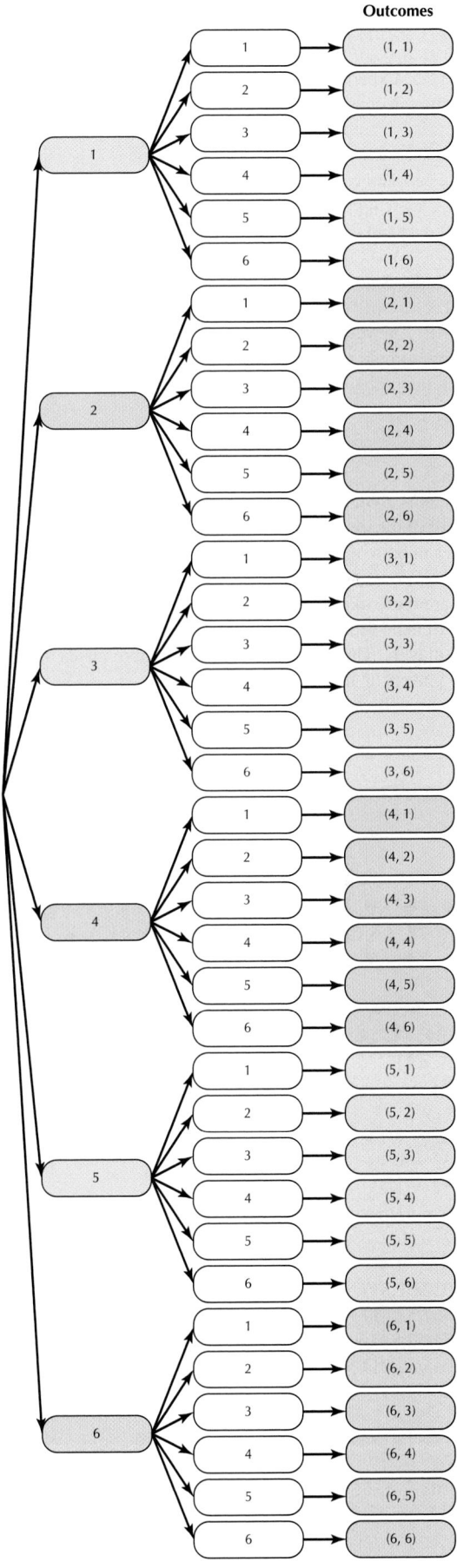

89. $\begin{cases} (1,1), (1,2), (1,3), (1,4), (1,5), (1,6), (2,1), (2,2), (2,3), (2,4), (2,5), (2,6), \\ (3,1), (3,2), (3,3), (3,4), (3,5), (3,6), (4,1), (4,2), (4,3), (4,4), (4,5), (4,6), \\ (5,1), (5,2), (5,3), (5,4), (5,5), (5,6), (6,1), (6,2), (6,3), (6,4), (6,5), (6,6) \end{cases}$
Example 5.5, Experiment is tossing 2 fair dice.

90. Events can consist of more than one outcome, but outcomes can't consist of more than one event.

91. 1/36. Classical probability method; have the sample space but no actual data and can assume outcomes are equally likely

92. 1/9. Classical probability method; have the sample space but no actual data and can assume outcomes are equally likely

93. 1/4

94. 1/2, order is not important

95. **(a)** 1/9 **(b)** 4/9 **(c)** 4/9 **(d)** 5/9 **(e)** 8/9

96. **(a)–(d)** Answers will vary.

97. As the sample size increases, the relative frequencies approach the probabilities.

Section 5.2

1. Two events are mutually exclusive if they have no outcomes in common.

2. It contains no outcomes.

3. It is all of the outcomes in each of the events. There are no outcomes in both.

4. Yes

5. You are more likely to select a male than a male football player. All male football players are males, but most males are not football players. Therefore, there are many more males than male football players at any college or university.

6. Answers will vary; $1 - P$ (will rain); they are complementary events.

7. 5/6

8. 5/6

9. 1/2

10. 2/3

11. 1/2

12. 1/2

13. $\{K\spadesuit, K\clubsuit, K\heartsuit, K\diamondsuit, A\heartsuit, 2\heartsuit, 3\heartsuit, 4\heartsuit, 5\heartsuit, 6\heartsuit, 7\heartsuit, 8\heartsuit, 9\heartsuit, 10\heartsuit, J\heartsuit, Q\heartsuit, A\diamondsuit, 2\diamondsuit, 3\diamondsuit, 4\diamondsuit, 5\diamondsuit, 6\diamondsuit, 7\diamondsuit, 8\diamondsuit, 9\diamondsuit, 10\diamondsuit, J\diamondsuit, Q\diamondsuit\}$

14. $\{K\spadesuit, K\clubsuit, K\heartsuit, K\diamondsuit, A\heartsuit, 2\heartsuit, 3\heartsuit, 4\heartsuit, 5\heartsuit, 6\heartsuit, 7\heartsuit, 8\heartsuit, 9\heartsuit, 10\heartsuit, J\heartsuit, Q\heartsuit\}$

15. $\{A\heartsuit, 2\heartsuit, 3\heartsuit, 4\heartsuit, 5\heartsuit, 6\heartsuit, 7\heartsuit, 8\heartsuit, 9\heartsuit, 10\heartsuit, J\heartsuit, Q\heartsuit, K\heartsuit, A\diamondsuit, 2\diamondsuit, 3\diamondsuit, 4\diamondsuit, 5\diamondsuit, 6\diamondsuit, 7\diamondsuit, 8\diamondsuit, 9\diamondsuit, 10\diamondsuit, J\diamondsuit, Q\diamondsuit, K\diamondsuit\}$

16. $\{K\heartsuit, K\diamondsuit\}$

17. $\{K\heartsuit\}$

18. $\{A\heartsuit, 2\heartsuit, 3\heartsuit, 4\heartsuit, 5\heartsuit, 6\heartsuit, 7\heartsuit, 8\heartsuit, 9\heartsuit, 10\heartsuit, J\heartsuit, Q\heartsuit, K\heartsuit\}$

19. 28/52 = 7/13

20. 16/52 = 4/13

21. 26/52 = 1/2

22. 2/52 = 1/26

23. 1/52

24. 13/52 = 1/4

25. 23,952/52,817 ≈ 0.4535

26. 13,367/52,817 ≈ 0.2531

27. 7,274/52,817 ≈ 0.1377

28. 30,045/52,817 ≈ 0.5689

29. 4,528/52,817 ≈ 0.0857

30. 3,113/52,817 ≈ 0.0589

31. 1,415/52,817 ≈ 0.0268

32. 6,287/52,817 ≈ 0.1190

33. 1

34. 1

35. 5/6

36. 4/6 = 2/3

37. 4/6 = 2/3

38. 5/6

39. 0

40. 0

41. 1/6

42. 2/6 = 1/3

43. 2/6 = 1/3

44. 1/6

45. 5/18

46. 25/36

47. 1/18

48. 0

49. 1/3

50. 25/36

51. 2/52 = 1/26

52. 28/52 = 7/13

53. 6/13

54. 1/2

55. 0

56. 51/52

57. 3/13

58. 1/2

59. 10/13

60. 9/52

61. 11/26

62. 3/52

63. 1/8

64. 7/8

65. 3/8

66. 5/8

67. {BBB, BBG, BGB, GBB, GGB, GBG, BGG, GGG}

68. 3/8

69. 3/8

70. 3/4

71. 3/4

72. 1/8

73. 2/9

74. **(a)** 1/3 **(b)** 2/3

75. **(a)** 1/4 **(b)** 7/20

76. **(a)** 3/5 **(b)** 3/4 **(c)** 2/5

77. **(a)** Yellow light, red light **(b)** 1/3, classical **(c)** 2/3

78. **(a)** 1/9 **(b)** 1/18 **(c)** 1/6

79. **(a)** 5/36 **(b)** 1/6 **(c)** 1/9 **(d)** 5/12

80. **(a)** 1/2 **(b)** 7/10 **(c)** 9/10

81. **(a)** 0.8 **(b)** We would get P (chocolate bars or peanut butter cups) = 1.3, which is greater than 1.

82. **(a)** 1/2 **(b)** 7/13 **(c)** 11/26 **(d)** 0 **(e)** 3/4

83. **(a)** 0.85 **(b)** 0.50 **(c)** 0.65 **(d)** 0

84. **(a)** 5/6 **(b)** No, we would not know the probability of someone ordering both chicken and a bacon cheeseburger.

85. **(a)** 0.57 **(b)** 0.55

86. **(a)** 0.1190 **(b)** 0.0532 **(c)** 0.5193

87. (a) $1966/3691 \approx 0.5326$ **(b)** $2104/3691 \approx 0.5700$
(c) $1220/3691 \approx 0.3305$ **(d)** $2850/3691 \approx 0.7721$
88. (a) 0.2727 **(b)** 0.7273
89. (a) 0 **(b)** 0.5022
90. Yes
91. (a) 1/3 **(b)** $8/12 = 2/3$; $1 - 1/3 = 2/3$
92. (a) 1/4 **(b)** $9/12 = 3/4$; $1 - 1/4 = 3/4$
93. (a) 1/4 **(b)** 1/3

Section 5.3

1. (a) Yes. **(b)** The probability of winning the football game depends on whether or not the star quarterback can play in the game.
2. Answers will vary.
3. For $P(A \mid B)$, we assume that the event B has occurred, and now need to find the probability of event A, given event B. On the other hand, for $P(A \cap B)$, we do not assume that event B has occurred, and instead need to determine the probability that both events occurred.
4. Answers will vary.
5. Answers will vary.
6. $A \cap B$ is a subset of A, $P(A \cap B) \leq P(A)$, and $A \cap B$ is a subset of B, $P(A \cap B) \leq P(B)$. Therefore, $P(A \cap B)$ cannot equal 0.30 if $P(A) = 0.25$ and $P(B) = 0.25$.
7. (a) Independent; sampling with replacement **(b)** Dependent; sampling without replacement
8. (a) Independent. The probability of selecting any particular card is not influenced by the outcome of the coin toss. The probability of heads or tails is not influenced by which card is selected. **(b)** Dependent, since we are sampling without replacement.
9. $50/200 = 1/4 = 0.25$
10. $150/200 = 3/4 = 0.75$
11. $100/200 = 1/2 = 0.5$
12. $100/200 = 1/2 = 0.5$
13. $40/200 = 1/5 = 0.2$
14. $10/200 = 1/20 = 0.05$
15. $60/200 = 3/10 = 0.3$
16. $90/200 = 9/20 = 0.45$
17. $40/100 = 2/5 = 0.4$
18. $10/100 = 1/10 = 0.1$
19. $60/100 = 3/5 = 0.6$
20. $90/100 = 9/10 = 0.9$
21. $40/50 = 4/5 = 0.8$
22. $10/50 = 1/5 = 0.2$
23. $60/150 = 2/5 = 0.4$
24. $90/150 = 3/5 = 0.6$
25. $178/288 \approx 0.6181$
26. $240/288 \approx 0.8333$
27. $161/178 \approx 0.9045$
28. $161/240 \approx 0.6708$
29. Dependent
30. Dependent
31. Independent
32. Dependent
33. Dependent
34. Independent

35. 0.27
36. 0.05
37. 0.125
38. 0.24
39. 0.2
40. 0.1
41. 0.05
42. 0.08
43. 0.04
44. 0.02
45. $1/4 = 0.25$
46. $1/16 = 0.0625$
47. $25/102 \approx 0.2451$
48. $1/17 \approx 0.0588$
49. 2 is 0.1% of 2000, so we can use the 1% Guideline to approximate the probabilities.
50. 0.0625
51. 0.015625
52. 0.00390625
53. Dependent
54. Dependent
55. Dependent
56. Dependent
57. They are independent only if $P(X) = 0$ or $P(Y) = 0$. Otherwise they are dependent.
58. No. If A occurs, B can't occur and vice versa.
59. If the intersection of W and Z is empty, then $P(W \cap Z) = 0$. They are independent only if $P(W) = 0$ or $P(Z) = 0$. Otherwise they are dependent.
60. No. If W occurs W^C can't occur and vice versa.
61. $(1/3)^3$
62. $(1/3)^4$
63. $(1/3)^5$
64. $(1/3)^{10}$
65. $1 - (1/3)^3$
66. $1 - (1/3)^4$
67. $1 - (1/3)^5$
68. $1 - (1/3)^{10}$
69. $(1/2)^5$
70. $(1/2)^{10}$
71. 0.24
72. 0.6
73. 0.4
74. 0.76
75. 0.1
76. 0.5
77. 0.2
78. 0.6
79. 0.1667
80. 0.54
81. 0.2
82. 0.4
83. 0.5
84. 0.7
85. 0.8
86. 0.3

87. 0.7
88. 0.3
89. Yes. $P(C \text{ and } D) = 0.21 = (0.7)(0.3) = P(C) P(D)$, $P(C \mid D) = 0.7 = P(C)$, and $P(D \mid C) = 0.3 = P(D)$.
90. No. $P(C \text{ and } D) \neq 0$.
91. $P(E \text{ and } F)$
92. $P(E \text{ and } F)$
93. 1/6
94. 1/2
95. 1/2
96. They are independent.
97. (a) 0.0016 (b) 0.0000001024 (c) 0.15065344
98. (a) 1/6 (b) 1/3 (c) P (rolling a 6) = 1/6; P(rolling a 6 | odd number) = 0
99. (a) 16/49 (b) 2/7
100. (a) Without replacement; the only way to make sure that we sample two different computers is to sample without replacement. (b) 1/10 (c) 1/11 (d) 109/110 (e) 1/110 (f) Either reject the batch if at least one computer is defective or increase the sample size.
101. (a) 0.000361 (b) 0.962361 (c) 0.9085 (d) 0.0559
102. (a) 3/29 (b) 57/203 (c) 1/3, yes, sampling with replacement (d) 9/29, no, sampling without replacement
103. (a) 0.055 (b) 0.3025 (c) 0.55 (d) 0.55 (e) 0.003025 (f) It is not possible since we are given only the percent of female students that are business majors, not the percent of all students that are business majors.
104. (a) 1/2 (b) 9/19 (c) 4/9
105. (a) 3/5 (b) 2/5 (c) 1/3 (d) 5/9 (e) 1/3
106. (a) 0.5081 (b) 0.4919 (c) 0.6667
107. (a) 0.3430 (b) 0.3236
108. (a) 0.6752 (b) 0.6579
109. No, P (more serious than Pearl Harbor | female) = 0.6752 ≠ 0.6667 = P (more serious than Pearl Harbor) and P (more serious than Pearl Harbor | male) = 0.6579 ≠ 0.6667 = P (more serious than Pearl Harbor).
110. (a) 3/5 (b) 2/5 (c) 1/2 (d) 1/6
111. (a) 1/3 (b) 1/10 (c) 1/6 (d) 1/15
112. (a) 5/9 (b) 5/12 (c) 1/6 (d) 1/6
113. No; $P(C) = 1/2 \neq 5/9 = P(C \mid F)$, $P(C) = 1/2 \neq 5/12 = P(C \mid M)$, $P(F \text{ and } C) = 1/3 \neq 3/10 = P(F) P(C)$, and $P(M \text{ and } C) = 1/6 \neq 1/5 = P(M) P(C)$.
114. Women's magazines since P (Cat | Female) $= \frac{5}{9} > \frac{5}{12} = P$ (Cat | Male)

Section 5.4
1. Tree diagram
2. Multiply all the numbers from 5 down to 1 together. $5! = 5 \cdot 4 \cdot 3 \cdot 2 \cdot 1 = 120$
3. In a permutation, order is important. In a combination, order is not important.
4. No; this symbol represents the number of ways to select and order 9 objects from 8 different objects, which is not possible.

5. Answers will vary.
6. (a) Classical (b) All outcomes in the sample space are equally likely.
7.

8.

9.

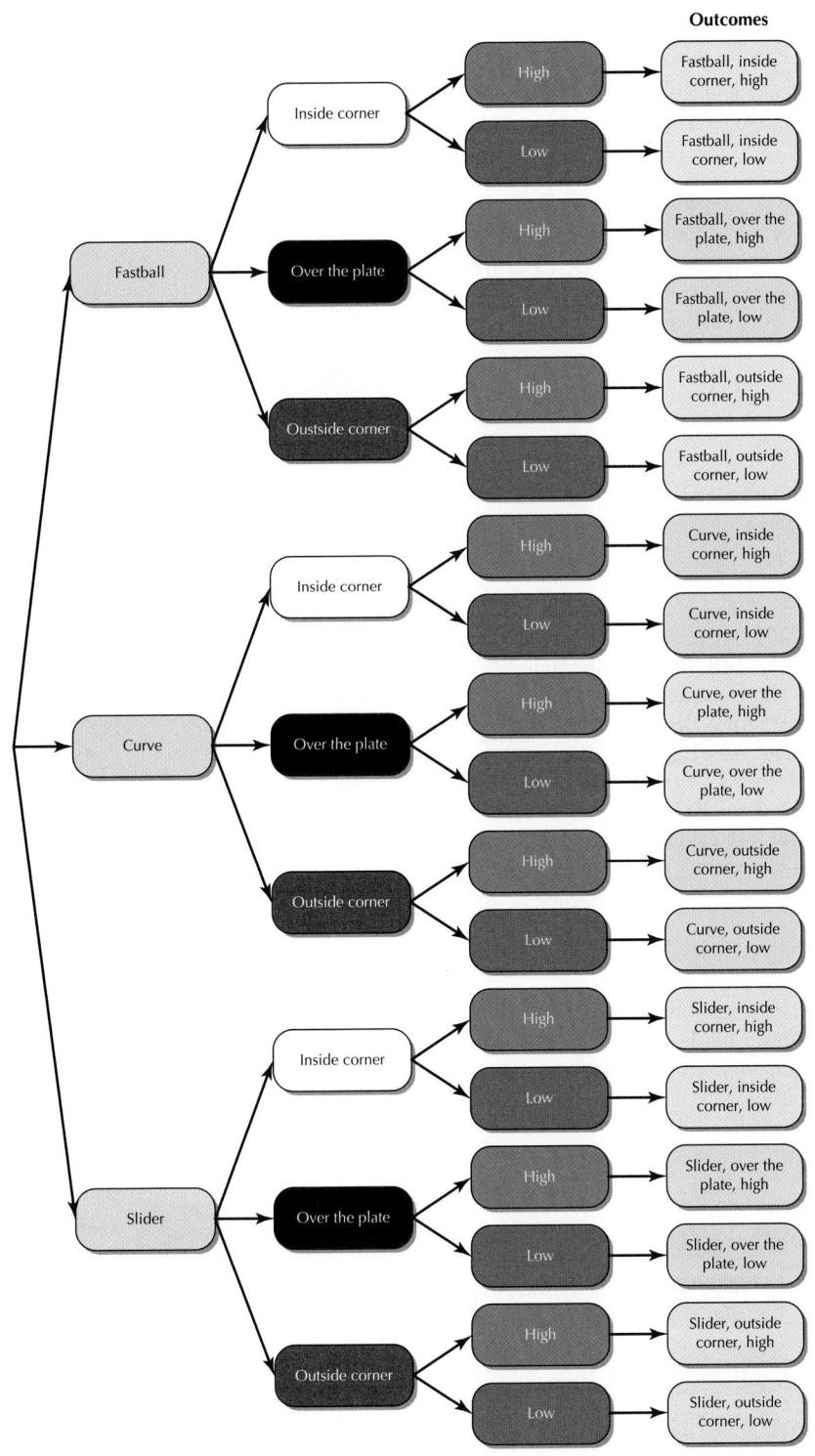

10. See the Instructor's Guide with Solutions.
11. 26^4
12. $3^5 = 243$
13. 20
14. 15
15. 24
16. 720
17. 720
18. 362,880

19. 1
20. 39,916,800
21. 1
22. 1,307,674,368,000
23. 12
24. 360
25. 210
26. 840
27. 6720

28. 336
29. 100
30. 1
31. 93,326,215,443,944,152,681,699,238,856,266,700,490,715,
968,264,381,621,468,592,963,895,217,599,993,229,915,608,941,
463,976,156,518,286,253,697,920,827,223,758,251,185,210,916,
864,000,000,000,000,000,000,000,000
32. 93,326,215,443,944,152,681,699,238,856,266,700,490,715,
968,264,381,621,468,592,963,895,217,599,993,229,915,608,941,
463,976,156,518,286,253,697,920,827,223,758,251,185,210,916,
864,000,000,000,000,000,000,000,000
33. 35
34. 35
35. 165
36. 55
37. 11
38. 1
39. 1
40. 100
41. $5!/(2!1!1!1!) = 60$
42. $9!/(3!2!1!1!1!1!) = 30,240$
43. $_7C_3 = 7!/3!\cdot4! = 7!/4!\cdot3! = {}_7C_4$
44. $_{11}C_8 = 11!/8!\cdot3! = 11!/3!\cdot8! = {}_{11}C_3$
45. {Amy, Bob, Chris}, {Amy, Chris, Bob}, {Bob, Amy,
Chris}, {Bob, Chris, Amy}, {Chris, Amy, Bob}, {Chris, Bob,
Amy}, {Amy, Bob, Danielle}, {Amy, Danielle, Bob}, {Bob,
Amy, Danielle}, {Bob, Danielle, Amy}, {Danielle, Amy,
Bob}, {Danielle, Bob, Amy}, {Amy, Chris, Danielle}, {Amy,
Danielle, Chris}, {Chris, Amy, Danielle}, {Chris, Danielle,
Amy}, {Danielle, Amy, Chris}, {Danielle, Chris, Amy}, {Bob,
Chris, Danielle}, {Bob, Danielle, Chris}, {Chris, Bob, Danielle},
{Chris, Danielle, Bob}, {Danielle, Bob, Chris}, {Danielle, Chris,
Bob}. $_4P_3 = 24$
46. {Amy, Bob, Chris}, {Amy, Bob, Danielle}, {Amy, Chris,
Danielle}, {Bob, Chris, Danielle}
47. {Amy, Bob, Chris}, {Amy, Chris, Bob}, {Chris, Amy, Bob},
{Chris, Bob, Amy}, {Bob, Amy, Chris}, and {Bob, Chris, Amy}
are all different permutations but the same combination.
48. 3!
49. $r!$
50. (a)

(b) 6

51. (a)

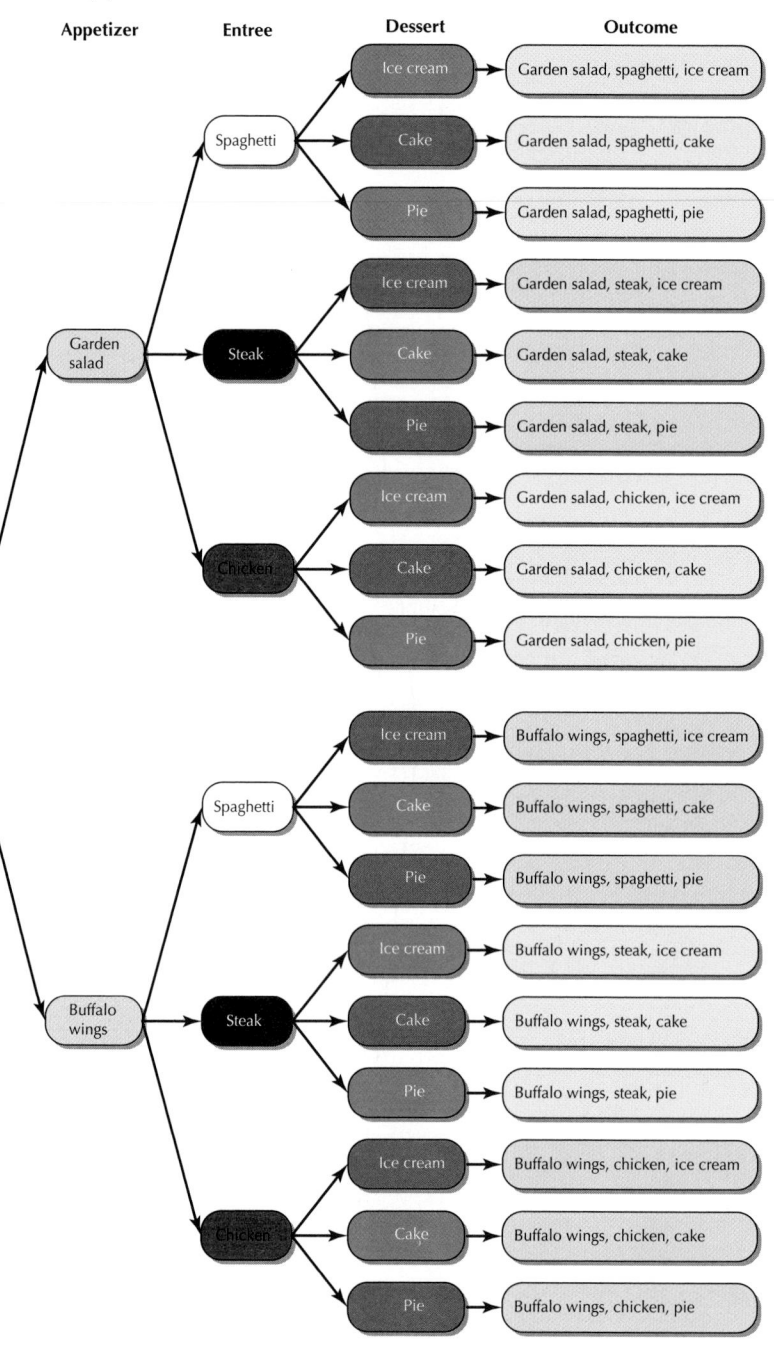

(b) 18
52. 576
53. 362,880
54. 3,628,800
55. 120
56. 1,307,674,368,000
57. 720
58. 360
59. 20
60. 30
61. 300
62. 455
63. 20
64. 1

65. 184,756
66. 4,989,600
67. 6720
68. 91
69. (a) Combination; order is unimportant. (b) 260 (c) 0.0640
70. (a) Combination. We are interested only in which two PDAs are selected, not in the order in which they are selected. (b) 3 (c) 0.01
71. (a) 0.0265 (b) 0.0013 (c) 0.2652 (d) 0.4419

Chapter 5 Review

1. 3/8
2. 1/2
3. 0
4. 3/8
5. 1/2
6. (a) 0.75 (b) The relative frequency method was used because there is prior knowledge of the relative frequencies of the sonnets.
7. (a) 0.213 (b) 0.656 (c) 0
8. (a) 0.013028169 (b) 0.0090140845 (c) 0.016 (d) 0.006
9. (a) Yes, since no student in the sample repeated 12th grade. (b) 0.0290 (c) 0.0150
10. (a) No, someone could have used Ecstasy and methamphetamine in the past 30 days. (b) We don't know how many students used both Ecstasy and methamphetamine in the past 30 days.
11. (a) 0.9269 (b) 0 (c) 1
12. (a) 0.2704 (b) 0.5300 (c) 0.5300
13. (a) 0.3729 (b) 0.6271
14. 0
15. (a) 1/2 (b) 1/3
16. (a) 1/6 (b) 1/6
17. (a) 5/18 (b) 5/12
18. Men's TV channel, since $P(\text{Dog} \mid \text{Male}) = 5/12 > 5/18 = P(\text{Dog} \mid \text{Female})$
19. 34,650
20. 60
21. (a) Combination; order is not important. (b) 3 (c) 0.0196.

Chapter 5 Quiz

1. False
2. True
3. 0, 1
4. or, and
5. 0.5
6. 1
7. With replacement
8. Intersection of A and B.
9. (a) 1/9 (b) 8/9 (c) 5/18 (d) 1/18 (e) 1/3
10. 0.2
11. 0.2125
12. (a) 1/4 (b) 3/13 (c) 1/13 (d) 1/2 (e) 1/52 (f) 1/26
13. (a) 0.5361 (b) 0.4639 (c) 0.0330
14. (a) 0.0215 (b) 0.0114

15. No, $P(\text{Not too happily married}) = 0.0330 \neq 0.0402 = P(\text{Not too happily married} \mid \text{Female})$ and $P(\text{Not too happily married}) = 0.0330 \neq 0.0246 = P(\text{Not too happily married} \mid \text{Male})$
16. 4
17. (a) Permutation; the order in which the numbers are selected is important. (b) 6840 (c) 1/6840

Chapter 6

Section 6.1

1. Answers will vary.
2. Your individual height is not a random variable. But if your height were "drawn from a hat" consisting of the heights of randomly selected people, your height would be considered a random variable.
3. Discrete: takes finite or a countable number of values that can be graphed as separate points on the number line; continuous takes infinitely many values that form an interval on the number line.
4. A discrete random variable can take either a finite or a countable number of values. Each value can be graphed as a separate point on the number line with space between each point. A probability distribution of a discrete random variable provides all the possible values that the random variable can assume, together with the probability associated with each value.
5. $\sum P(X) = 1$ and $0 \leq P(X) \leq 1$.
6. The mean μ of a discrete random variable represents the mean result when the experiment is repeated an indefinitely large number of times. It is the mean of the results from the population of all possible repetitions of the experiment. The sample mean $\bar{x}$ is simply the arithmetic mean of a finite set of sample values.
7. Discrete
8. Continuous
9. Continuous
10. Continuous
11. Discrete
12. Discrete
13. {0, 1, 2, 3, 4, 5, 6, 7, 8, 9, 10, 11, 12, 13, 14, 15}
14. {0, 1, 2, 3, 4, 5, 6, 7, 8, 9, 10}
15. {0, 1, 2, 3, 4}
16. {0, 1, 2, 3}

17.

X = Number of CDs	0	1	2	3	4
P(X)	0.06	0.24	0.38	0.22	0.10

18.

X = Number of goals	0	1	2	3
P(X)	0.25	0.35	0.25	0.15

19.

X = Money gained	−$10,000	$10,000	$50,000
P(X)	1/3	1/2	1/6

20.

X = Number of pets	0	1	2	3
P(X)	0.5	0.3	0.1	0.1

21. No, the probabilities don't add up to 1.
22. Yes
23. No, $P(X = 1)$ is negative.
24. No, $P(X = 100{,}000)$ is greater than 1.
25.

26.

27.

28.

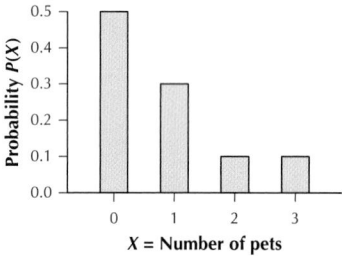

29. 0.32
30. 0.30
31. 0
32. 0.94
33. 0.40
34. 0.60
35. 0
36. 0.75
37. 2/3
38. 1/3
39. 0
40. 0
41. 0.5

42. 0.8
43. 0.2
44. 0.4
45. (a) 2 (b) 0
46. (a) 1 (b) 3
47. (a) \$10,000 (b) \$50,000
48. (a) 0 pets (b) 2 and 3 pets
49. $\mu = 2.06$ CDs
50. $\mu = 1.3$ goals
51. $\mu = \$10{,}000$
52. $\mu = 0.8$ pet
53. $\sigma^2 = 1.0964$ CDs squared, $\sigma = 1.0471$ CDs
54. $\sigma^2 = 1.01$ goals squared, $\sigma = 1.0050$ goals
55. $\sigma^2 = 400{,}000{,}000$ dollars squared, $\sigma = \$20{,}000$
56. $\sigma^2 = 0.96$ pet squared, $\sigma = 0.9798$ pet
57. No outliers, no moderately unusual values
58. No outliers, no moderately unusual values
59. No outliers, \$50,000 is moderately unusual.
60. No outliers, 3 pets is moderately unusual.
61. (a) We don't know the number of games that will be played in the finals before the finals begin. This introduces an element of chance into the experiment, thereby making the number of games a random variable. (b) There are only a finite number of possibilities for the number of games that can be played in the finals.

(c)

X = Games	4	5	6	7
$P(X)$	0.25	0.2	0.25	0.3

(d)

(e) 0.45 (f) Most likely: 7 games; Least likely: 5 games
62. (a) We don't know the number of vehicles a person owns before the person is selected. This introduces an element of chance into the experiment, thereby making the number of vehicles a random variable. (b) There are only a finite number of possibilities for the number of cars that a Florida resident can own.

(c)

(d) 0.88 (e) Most likely: 1 vehicle; Least likely: 0 vehicles

63. (a)

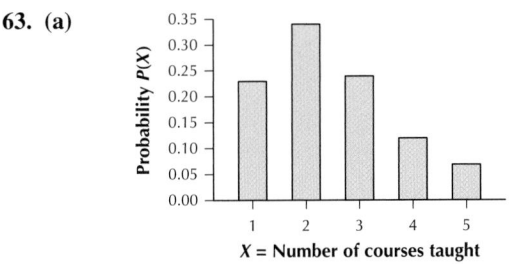

(b) 0.43 **(c)** 0.19 **(d)** The answer to **(b)** includes the probability that $X = 3$ and the answer to **(c)** does not. **(e)** Most likely: 2 courses; Least likely: 5 courses

64. (a)

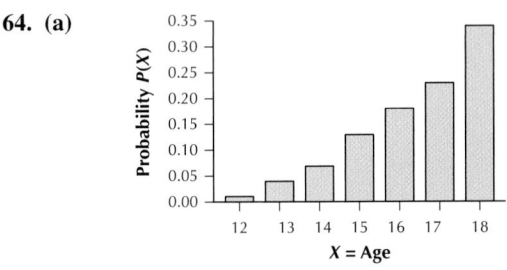

(b) 0.43 **(c)** 0.25 **(d)** The answer to **(b)** includes the probability that $X = 16$ and the answer to **(c)** does not. **(e)** Most likely: 18 years; Least likely: 12 years

65. (a) $\mu = 5.6$ games. If we were to consider an infinite number of Stanley Cup playoffs, the mean number of games played would be 5.6 games. **(b)** $\sigma^2 = 1.34$ games squared, $\sigma = 1.1576$ games **(c)** $Z = -1.3822$, not unusual

66. (a) $\mu = 1.54$ vehicles. If we were to consider an infinite number of Florida residents, the mean number of vehicles owned would be 1.54 vehicles. **(b)** $\sigma^2 = 0.6484$ vehicles squared, $\sigma = 0.8052$ vehicle **(c)** $Z = -1.9126$, not unusual

67. (a) $\mu = 2.46$ courses. If we were to consider an infinite number of faculty at all degree-granting institutions of higher

learning in the United States in the fall 2010 semester, the mean number of courses taught would be 2.46 courses.
(b) $\sigma^2 = 1.3684$ courses squared, $\sigma = 1.1698$ courses
(c) $Z = 2.1713$, moderately unusual

68. (a) $\mu = 16.48$ years. If we were to consider an infinite number of young people aged 12–18, the mean age of the young people who had tried tobacco products in the previous month would be 16.48 years. **(b)** $\sigma^2 = 2.2896$ years squared, $\sigma = 1.5131$ years **(c)** 12-year-old: $Z = -2.9608$, moderately unusual; 13-year-old: $Z = -2.2999$, moderately unusual

69. (a)

$X =$ Median age at first marriage	24	25	26	27	28
$P(X)$	$4/51 \approx$ 0.0784	$10/51 \approx$ 0.1961	$22/51 \approx$ 0.4314	$10/51 \approx$ 0.1961	$5/51 \approx$ 0.0980

(b) $14/51 \approx 0.2745$ **(c)** Most likely: 26 years; Least likely: 24 years **(d)** $\mu = 26.0392$ years. If we were to consider an infinite number of states, the mean median age of first marriage for females would be 26.0392 years.

(e)

70. If we were to consider an infinite number of states, the mean median age at first marriage for females would be 26.0392 years.

71. (a)

$X =$ Number of goals	0	1	2	3	4	5	6	7	8	9
$P(X)$	$\frac{161}{2638} \approx$ 0.0610	$\frac{407}{2638} \approx$ 0.1543	$\frac{602}{2638} \approx$ 0.2282	$\frac{603}{2638} \approx$ 0.2286	$\frac{455}{2638} \approx$ 0.1725	$\frac{249}{2638} \approx$ 0.0944	$\frac{108}{2638} \approx$ 0.0409	$\frac{40}{2638} \approx$ 0.0152	$\frac{11}{2638} \approx$ 0.0042	$\frac{2}{2638} \approx$ 0.0008

(b) $161/2638 \approx 0.0610$

(c) Most likely: 3 goals; Least likely: 9 goals

(d)

(e) $\sigma = \mathbf{1.6324}$ **goals** **(f)** Moderately unusual: 7 goals; Outliers: 8 goals and 9 goals

72. (a)

$X =$ Sum of dice	2	3	4	5	6	7	8	9	10	11	12
$P(X)$	1/36	1/18	1/12	1/9	5/36	1/6	5/36	1/9	1/12	1/18	1/36

(b) The mean is about 7.

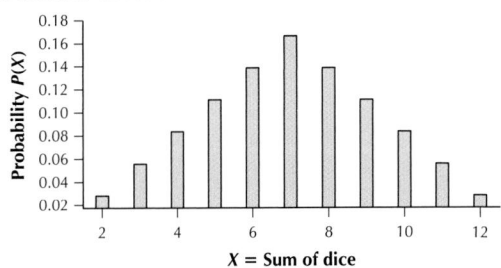

(c) $\mu = 7$. If we were to consider tossing two dice an infinite number of times, the mean sum of the dice would be 7.
(d) 7. The estimate is equal to the actual value.
(e)

X = Sum of dice

73. Z-score is -2.07; moderately unusual. By symmetry, so is $X = 12$.
74. (a) No. The mean is 2 but the most likely value is 0.

X	0	2	8
P(X)	0.6	0.2	0.2

(b) Symmetric, one mode
75. (a) Increases by k **(b)** Remains unchanged

Section 6.2

1. (i) Each trial of the experiment has only two possible mutually exclusive outcomes (or is defined in such a way that the number of outcomes is reduced to two). One outcome is denoted a success and the other a failure. **(ii)** There is a fixed number of trials, known in advance of the experiment. **(iii)** The experimental outcomes are independent of each other. **(iv)** The probability of observing a success remains the same from trial to trial.
2. A *success* denotes simply the outcomes we are interested in, without necessarily implying that the outcome is desirable.
3. If you perform an experiment n times, you can't have more than n successes. For example, if you flip a coin 10 times you can't get 11 heads.
4. $P(X) = (_nC_X)(P(\text{success}))^{\text{number of successes}} (P(\text{failures}))^{\text{number of failures}}$
5. Not binomial; the events "Person A comes to party" and "Person B comes to party" may not be independent.
6. Not binomial; more than two possible total number of spots.
7. Binomial, $X =$ number of correct answers, $n = 8$, $p = 1/4 = 0.25$, $1 - p = 3/4 = 0.75$
8. Binomial; $n = 3$, $X =$ number of sixes, $p = 1/6$, $1 - p = 5/6$
9. Not binomial; not a fixed number of trials
10. Binomial, $X =$ number of queens, $n = 4$, $p = 4/52 = 1/13$, $1 - p = 48/52 = 12/13$
11. Not binomial, trials are not independent, sample is more than 1% of the population.
12. Not binomial, more than 2 possible outcomes.
13. Binomial; $n = 2$, $X =$ number of games won, $p = 0.25$, $1 - p = 0.75$
14. Not binomial; not a fixed number of trials.
15. 0.3955
16. 0.2373
17. 0.1172
18. 0.0439
19. 0.2301
20. 0.3766
21. 0.6328

22. 0.7627
23. 0.1611
24. 0
25. 0.8891
26. 0.1109
27. 0.9744
28. 0.9957
29. $1/8 = 0.125$
30. $3/8 = 0.375$
31. $3/8 = 0.375$
32. $7/8 = 0.875$
33. $7/8 = 0.875$
34. $7/8 = 0.875$
35. 0.0154
36. 0.0162
37. 0.4823
38. 0.8681
39. 0.5177
40. 0
41. 0.0778
42. 0.9222
43. 0.6826
44. 0.8352
45. 0 (TI-83/84: 0.00001139)
46. 1 (TI-83/84: 0.99998861)
47. 0.0059
48. 0.0474 (TI-83/84: 0.0473)
49. (a) $\mu = 1.5$ heads. If we repeat the experiment of tossing a fair coin 3 times an infinite number of times, record the number of heads in each performance of the experiment, and take the mean of all of the performances of this experiment, the mean number of heads will equal $\mu = 1.5$. **(b)** $\sigma^2 = 0.75$ head squared **(c)** $\sigma = 0.8660$ head
50. (a) $\mu = 0.6667$ double. If we repeat the experiment of rolling a pair of dice 4 times an infinite number of times, record the number of doubles in each performance of the experiment, and take the mean of all of the performances of this experiment, the mean number of doubles will equal $\mu = 0.6667$. **(b)** $\sigma^2 = 0.5556$ double squared **(c)** $\sigma = 0.7454$ double
51. (a) $\mu = 2$ vehicles. If we repeat this experiment an infinite number of times, record the number of vehicles obeying the speed limit in each sample, and take the mean of all of these samples, the mean number of vehicles obeying the speed limit will equal $\mu = 2$. **(b)** $\sigma^2 = 1.2$ vehicles squared **(c)** $\sigma = 1.0954$ vehicles
52. (a) $\mu = 0.9$ voter. If we repeat this experiment an infinite number of times, record the number of voters who would support an Independent for president in each sample, and take the mean of all of these samples, the mean number of voters who would support an Independent for president will equal $\mu = 0.9$. **(b)** $\sigma^2 = 0.765$ voter squared **(c)** $\sigma = 0.8746$ voter

53. (a)

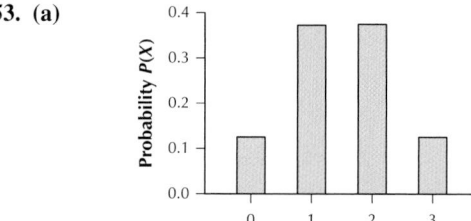

X = Number of heads

(b) 1 and 2 heads

54. (a)

(b) 0 doubles

55. (a)

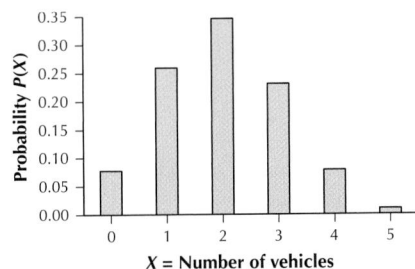

(b) 2 vehicles

56. (a)

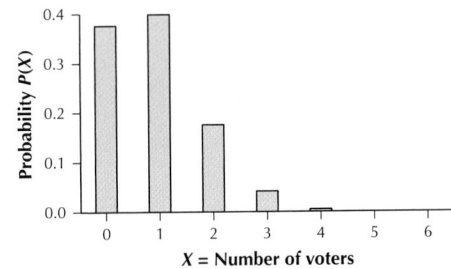

(b) 1 voter

57. (a) It fulfills the requirements: (i) There are only two possible outcomes for each trial: correct answer or incorrect answer. (ii) We know in advance that the quiz will have 5 questions. (iii) Since you are randomly guessing the answer to each question, the trials are independent. (iv) Since each question has 4 responses, the probability of guessing correctly remains the same from question to question. **(b)** $n = 5, p = 1/4 = 0.25$ **(c)** 0.1035 **(d)** 0.8965

58. (a) 0.2581 **(b)** 0.6488 **(c)** 3 users **(d)** 0.2581

59. (a) $p = 0.378$ is not in the table **(b)** 0.0313 **(c)** 0.0395

60. (a) 0.1171 **(b)** 0.0005 **(c)** 0.4565 (TI-83/84: 0.4566)

61. (a) $\mu = 1.25$ correct answers. If we repeat this experiment an infinite number of times, record the number of correct answers for each quiz taken, and take the mean of all of the quizzes, the mean number of correct answers will equal $\mu = 1.25$. $\sigma^2 = 0.9375$ correct answer squared, $\sigma = 0.9682$ correct answer **(b)** Five correct answers is considered an outlier; 4 correct answers is considered moderately unusual. **(c)** Mode is 1 correct answer.

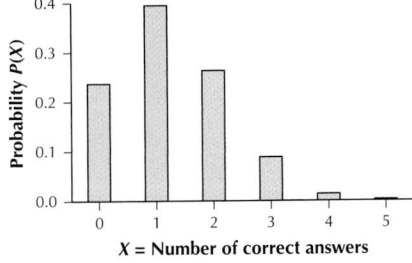

62. (a) $\mu = 3$ users. If we repeat this experiment an infinite number of times, record the number of users who had abandoned

their landlines in each survey, and take the mean of all of the surveys, the mean number of users who had abandoned their landlines will equal $\mu = 3$. $\sigma^2 = 2.25$ users squared, $\sigma = 1.5$ users **(b)** $Z = -2$, so moderately unusual

63. (a) $\mu = 5.67$ vowels. If we repeat this experiment an infinite number of times, record the number of vowels for each sample, and take the mean of all of the samples, the mean number of vowels will equal $\mu = 5.67$. $\sigma^2 = 3.5267$ vowels squared, $\sigma = 1.8780$ vowels **(b)** $Z = -1.4217$, not unusual

64. (a) $\mu = 8$ women. If we repeat this experiment an infinite number of times, record the number of women in each sample, and take the mean of all of the samples, the mean number of women will equal $\mu = 8$. $\sigma^2 = 4.8$ women squared, $\sigma = 2.1909$ women **(b)** $Z = -0.9129$, not unusual

65. (a) $\mu = 469$ spinal cord injuries caused by car accidents. If we repeat this experiment an infinite number of times, record the number of spinal cord injuries caused by vehicle accidents in each sample, and take the mean of all of the samples, the mean number of spinal cord injuries caused by vehicle accidents will equal $\mu = 469$. **(b)** 0.0253 **(c)** $\sigma = 15.7810$ spinal cord injuries caused by car accidents **(d)** $Z = 3.2317$, outlier **(e)** Outlier. 521 lies farther from the mean than 520 and 520 is an outlier.

66. (a) $\mu = 3.48$ women. If we repeat this experiment an infinite number of times, record the number of women reporting "Music I Like" as the biggest factor in deciding which radio station to listen to in each sample, and take the mean of all of the samples, the mean number of women reporting "Music I Like" as the biggest factor in deciding which radio station to listen to will equal $\mu = 3.48$. **(b)** Not possible. The expected value of X is not an integer.

(c)

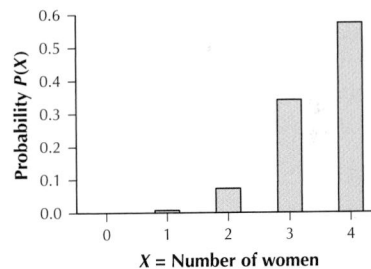

(d) 4 women **(e)** 0.5729

67. (a) $\mu = 2.25$ jobs. If we repeat this experiment an infinite number of times, record the number of new jobs added to the economy that are provided by small businesses for each sample, and take the mean of all of the samples, the mean number of new jobs added to the economy that are provided by small businesses will equal $\mu = 2.25$. **(b)** Not possible. The expected value of X is not an integer.

(c)

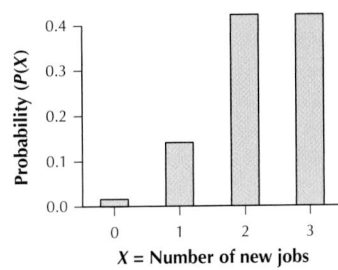

(d) 2 and 3 new jobs **(e)** $P(X = 2) = P(X = 3) = 0.4219$, $P(X = 2 \text{ or } X = 3) = P(X = 2) + P(X = 3) = 0.4219 + 0.4219 = 0.8438$

68. **(a)** $\mu = 15.6$ males. If we repeat this experiment an infinite number of times, record the number of males living with AIDS contracted through intravenous drug use for each sample, and take the mean of all of the samples, the mean number of males living with AIDS contracted through intravenous drug use will equal $\mu = 15.6$. **(b)** Not possible. The expected value of X is not an integer. **(c)** $\sigma^2 = 13.572$ males squared, $\sigma = 3.6840$ males **(d)** $Z = -0.9772$. Neither an outlier nor moderately unusual. **(e)** $X = 13$ is neither an outlier nor moderately unusual because $X = 12$ is neither an outlier nor moderately unusual and $X = 13$ lies closer to the mean than $X = 12$ does. **(f)** It increased.
69. **(a)** $\mu = 0.6$ women. If we repeat this experiment an infinite number of times, record the number of women affected by a depressive disorder for each sample, and take the mean of all of the samples, the mean number of women living with a depressive disorder will equal $\mu = 0.6$. **(b)** Not possible. The expected value of X is not an integer.
(c) $X = 0$ women

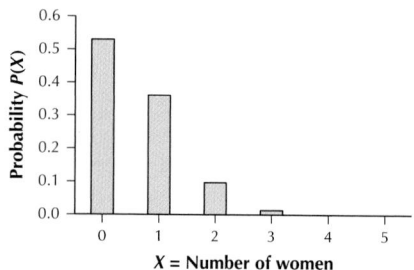

(d) 0.5277
70. **(a)** $\mu = 0.33$ men. If we repeat this experiment an infinite number of times, record the number of men affected by a depressive disorder for each sample, and take the mean of all of the samples, the mean number of men living with a depressive disorder will equal $\mu = 0.33$. **(b)** Not possible. The expected value of Y is not an integer.
(c) $Y = 0$ men

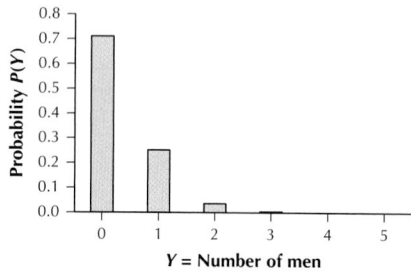

(d) 0.7108
71. **(a)** $\mu = 68$ music downloaders, $\sigma^2 = 56.44$ music downloaders squared, $\sigma = 7.5127$ music downloaders **(b)** 0.0530 **(c)** $Z = -3.7270$. Outlier. **(d)** It increased.
72. **(a)** 10 students **(b)** 10 students **(c)** 10 students
73. **(a)** 0.7 **(b)** 0.21 **(c)** 0.063
74. **(a)** $\mu = 1.4286$ households, $\sigma^2 = 0.6122$ household squared, $\sigma = 0.7825$ household. If we repeat this experiment an infinite number of times, record the number of households that were surveyed until a household that has access to the Internet is found, and take the mean of all of the sample sizes, the mean number of households that were surveyed until one was found that has access to the Internet will equal $\mu = 1.4286$.
(b) $Z = 13.5098$, outlier **(c)** Outlier, since $X = 12$ is an outlier and $X = 13$ lies farther from the mean. **(d)** The first success can't occur if there are no trials. You need at least one trial to have a first success.

75. **(a)** 0.7 **(b)** 0.21 **(c)** 0.49 **(d)** $\mu = 2.8571$ car safety seats, $\sigma^2 = 1.2245$ car safety seats squared, $\sigma = 1.1066$ car safety seats. If we repeat this experiment an infinite number of times, record the number of car safety seats sampled before finding the second incorrectly installed one, and take the mean of all of the repetitions of this experiment, the mean number of car safety seats sampled before finding the second incorrectly installed one will equal $\mu = 2.8571$. **(e)** $Z = 2.8401$, moderately unusual **(f)** You can't have more successes than the number of trials.
76. **(a)** $1287/2{,}598{,}960 \approx 0.0005$ **(b)** $27{,}885/2{,}598{,}960 \approx 0.0107$ **(c)** $29{,}172/2{,}598{,}960 \approx 0.0112$ **(d)** $211{,}926/2{,}598{,}960 \approx 0.0815$ **(e)** $2{,}357{,}862/2{,}598{,}960 \approx 0.9072$
77. **(a)** 0.0784 **(b)** 0.0588 **(c)** 0.0588

Section 6.3
1. When observing the number of occurrences of an event within a fixed interval of space and time
2. The number of occurrences of the event in the interval
3. The occurrences must be random, independent, and uniformly distributed over the given interval.
4. $n \geq 100$ and $np \leq 10$
5. Does not follow a Poisson distribution
6. Does not follow a Poisson distribution
7. Follows a Poisson distribution
8. Does not follow a Poisson distribution
9. 0.1126
10. 0.1251
11. 0.6472
12. 0.3528
13. 0.2381
14. 0.7619
15. **(a)** 4.4721 **(b)** 11.0558, 28.9442, any values less than or equal to 11 or greater than or equal to 29 will be considered moderately unusual
16. **(a)** 5 **(b)** 15, 35, any values less than or equal to 15 or greater than or equal to 35 will be considered moderately unusual
17. **(a)** 3.1623 **(b)** 3.6754, 16.3246, any values less than or equal to 3 or greater than or equal to 17 will be considered moderately unusual
18. **(a)** 1.4142 **(b)** -0.8284, 4.8284, any values that are greater than or equal to 5 will be considered moderately unusual
19. **(a)** $n = 200 \geq 100$ and $np = 10 \leq 10$ **(b)** 0.0948
20. **(a)** $n = 120 \geq 100$ and $np = 3.6 \leq 10$ **(b)** 0.1912
21. **(a)** $n = 200 \geq 100$ and $np = 8 \leq 10$ **(b)** 0.0993
22. **(a)** $n = 120 \geq 100$ and $np = 6 \leq 10$ **(b)** 0.1606
23. **(a)** 0.0399 **(b)** 0.0360 **(c)** 0.0395
24. **(a)** 0.0967 **(b)** 0.1224 **(c)** 0.0116 **(d)** 0.0033 **(e)** 0.0149
25. **(a)** $n = 247{,}000{,}000 \geq 100$ and $np = 5.2858 \leq 10$ **(b)** 5.2858 **(c)** 0.0051 **(d)** 0.9949
26. **(a)** $n = 142 \geq 100$ and $np = 5.68 \leq 10$ **(b)** 5.68 **(c)** 0.0551 **(d)** 0.9966
27. **(a)** 0.1704 **(b)** 0.1532 **(c)** 0.0038 **(d)** 0
28. **(a)** 0.0827 **(b)** 0.0803 **(c)** 0 **(d)** 0
29. **(a)** 0.2046 **(b)** 0.1615 **(c)** 0.0224 **(d)** 0.5625
30. **(a)** $n = 100 \geq 100$ and $np = 0.05 \leq 10$ **(b)** 0.05 **(c)** 0.0476 **(d)** 0.0488
31. **(a)** $n = 100 \geq 100$ and $np = 10 \leq 10$ **(b)** 10 **(c)** 0.1251 **(d)** 0.3336
32. **(a)** (i) 0, 11, 12; (ii) 13, 14, 15, . . . **(b)** (i) 9, 10, 11, 12, 13, 33, 34, 35, 36, 37; (ii) 0, 1, 2, 3, 4, 5, 6, 7, 8, 38, 39, 40, . . . **(c)** (i) 8, 9; (ii) 10, 11, 12, . . . **(d)** (i) None; (ii) 1, 2, 3, . . .

Section 6.4

1. The probability that X equals some particular value is zero.
2. X values
3. Area under the normal distribution curve above an interval.
4. Any real number; any positive real number
5. False
6. No difference. They are the same number.
7. 0.5
8. 0.5
9. 0.65
10. 0.2
11. 0.01
12. 0
13. 0.5
14. 1
15. 0.1
16. 0.6
17. About 0.68
18. About 0.95
19. About 0.025
20. About 0.16
21. About 0.997
22. About 0.975
23. About 0.0235
24. About 0.16
25. 0
26. 0.5
27. 0.5
28. Less than 0.5. Since $X = 4285$ is greater than the mean of 3285 and the area to the right of $\mu = 3285$ is 0.5, the area to the right of $X = 4285$ is less than the area to the right of $X = 3285$.
29. Greater than 0.5. Since $X = 4285$ is greater than the mean of 3285 and the area to the left of $\mu = 3285$ is 0.5, the area to the left of $X = 4285$ is greater than the area to the left of $X = 3285$.
30. About 0.68
31. About 0.997
32. Between 0.997 and 1
33. A has mean 10; B has mean 25. The peak of a normal curve is at the mean; from the graphs we see that the mean of A is less than the mean of B.
34. A: standard deviation 3; B: standard deviation 6. B is more spread out than A, so B has a larger standard deviation than A.
35. $\mu = 0, \sigma = 1$
36. $\mu = 100, \sigma = 5$
37. $\mu = -10, \sigma = 10$
38. $\mu = 1000, \sigma = 100$
39. $\mu = 100, \sigma = 12.5$
40. $\mu = 10, \sigma = 2$
41. $\mu = 0, \sigma = 2$
42. $\mu = 10, \sigma = 2$
43. (a) 0.25 (b) 0.25 (c) 0
44. (a) 0.3 (b) 0.65 (c) 0
45. (a)

(b) About 0.68

46. (a)

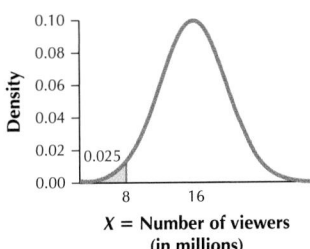

(b) About 0.025

47. (a)

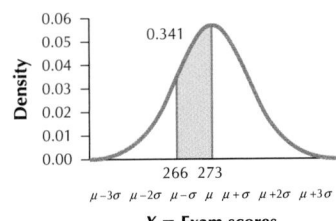

(b) About 0.34
48. About 0.95
49. About 0.16
50. (a) About 0.135 (b) About 0.84
51. (a) About 0.815

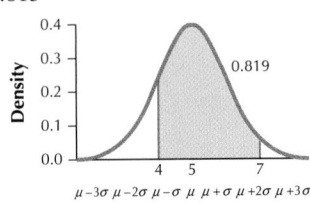

(b) About 0.16
52. (a) About 0.025 (b) About 0.68
53. (a) Increase. The majority of the area underneath the normal curve is close to the mean. Since an increase in the mean will result in $80,201 being closer to the mean, there will be an increase in the area underneath the normal distribution curve to the right of $80,201. Thus there will be an increase in $P(X > \$80{,}201)$.
(b) Decrease. The majority of the area underneath the normal curve is close to the mean. Since an increase in the mean will result in $32,201 being farther from the mean, there will be a decrease in the area underneath the normal distribution curve to the left of $32,201. Thus there will be an decrease in $P(X < \$32{,}201)$.
(c) Decrease. The majority of the area underneath the normal curve is close to the mean. Since an increase in the mean will result in $64,201 being closer to the mean and $32,301 being farther from the mean, there will be a decrease in the area underneath the normal distribution curve between the mean and $64,000 and an increase in the area underneath the normal distribution curve between $32,201 and the mean. Because of the shape of the normal distribution curve, the increase in the area underneath the normal distribution curve between $32,201 and the mean will be less than the decrease in the area underneath the normal distribution curve between the mean and $64,201. This results in a net decrease in $P(\$32{,}201 < X < \$64{,}201)$.
54. (a) 9.5 minutes (b) 9 minutes (c) 9.75 minutes
(d) 0.5 minute (e) 1 minute (f) 0.25 minute
55. (a) The distribution is symmetric, so the balance point (mean) is the midpoint of the bottom side of the rectangle.

(b) The distribution is rectangular shaped, so a line connecting the midpoints of the top side and bottom divides the rectangle; 50% of the area of the rectangle is left of this line and 50% of the area of the rectangle is right of this line. Thus the midpoint of the bottom side of the rectangle is the median. From part **(a)**, this is also the mean of the distribution.

Section 6.5

1. $\mu = 0$
2. $\sigma = 1$
3. True
4. True
5. 0.9750
6. 0.8997
7. 0.4821
8. 0.4641
9. 0.0179
10. 0.0446
11. 0.8020
12. 0.1359
13. 0.1832
14. 0.1253
15. 0.9641
16. 0.4772
17. (a)

(b) 0.8413

18. (a)

(b) 0.9772

19. (a)

(b) 0.9987

20. (a)

(b) 0.6915

21. (a)

(b) 0.0047

22. (a)

(b) 0.1841

23. (a)

(b) 0.4207

24. (a)

(b) 0.1151

25. (a)

(b) 0.1020

26. (a)

(b) 0.0170

27. (a)

(b) 0.9987

28. (a)

(b) 0.7549

29. (a)

(b) 0.3413

30. (a)

(b) 0.1359

31. (a)

(b) 0.0214

32. (a)

(b) 0.0753

33. (a)

(b) 0.3413

34. (a)

(b) 0.1359

35. (a)

(b) 0.0214

36. (a)

(b) 0.0753

37. (a)

(b) 0.7994

38. (a)

(b) 0.9689

39. (a)

(b) 0

40. (a)

(b) 0.5

41. (a)

(b) 1

42. (a)

(b) 0.0985

43. (a)

(b) 0.0150

44. (a)

(b) 0.7157

45. (a)

(b) 0.9500

46. (a)

(b) 0.6580

47. (a)

(b) 0.1725

48. (a)

(b) 0.0479

49. (a)

(b) 0.5000

50. (a)

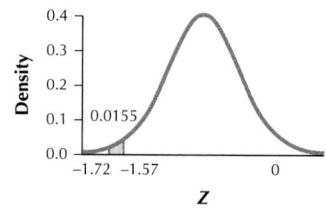

(b) 0.0155

51. Less than 0; $Z = -0.43$; -0.43 is less than 0

52.

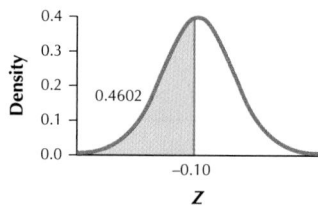

Less than 0, $Z = -0.10$, -0.10 is less than 0.

53. Less than 0; $Z = -0.45$; -0.45 is less than 0

54.

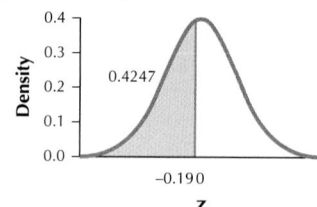

Less than 0, $Z = -0.19$, -0.19 is less than 0.

55. 1.65 (TI-83/84: 1.645)

56. 1.96

57. 2.05

58. 2.33

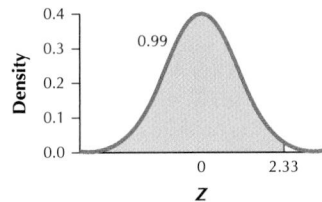

59. Less than 0; $Z = -0.87$; -0.87 is less than 0.

60.

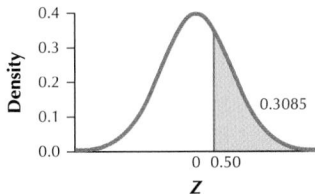

Greater than 0, $Z = 0.50$, 0.50 is greater than 0.

61. Less than 0; $Z = -2.03$; -2.03 is less than 0

62.

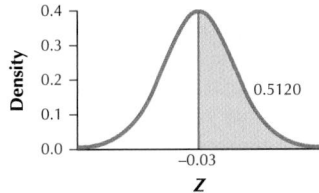

Less than 0, $Z = -0.03$, -0.03 is less than 0.

63. -1.28

64. -1.96

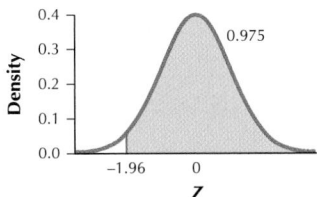

65. -3.036 (Using the table, both -3.03 and -3.04 have area to left of them equal to 0.0012 and area to the right of them as 0.9988.)

66. -3.49

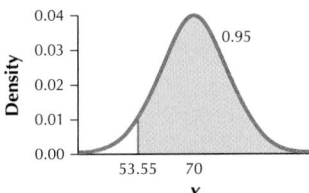

67. -1.28 and 1.28
68. -1.96 and 1.96

69. -2.33 and 2.33
70. -1.44 and 1.44
71. $Z = 0$
72. 0.67
73. $Z = 2.58$
74. -2.58
75. The area between $Z = -2$ and $Z = 2$ is 0.9544. By the Empirical Rule, the area between $Z = -2$ and $Z = 2$ is about 0.95.
76. The area between $Z = -3$ and $Z = 3$ is 0.9974. By the Empirical Rule, the area between $Z = -3$ and $Z = 3$ is about 0.997.
77. **(a)** 0.0668 **(b)** 0.9332 **(c)** 0.8664
78. **(a)** 0.9965 **(b)** 0.0035 **(c)** 0.9930
79. $Z = -2.58$ and $Z = 2.58$.
80. $Z = -1.645$ and $Z = 1.645$
81. -0.67; 0; 0.67
82. **(a)** 0.8997 **(b)** 0.4821 **(c)** 0.8413 **(d)** 0.9772 **(e)** 0.7549 **(f)** 0.3413

Section 6.6

1. To standardize things means to make them all the same, uniform, or equivalent. To standardize a normal random variable X, we transform X into the standard normal random variable Z using the formula $Z = \dfrac{X - \mu}{\sigma}$. We do this so that we can use the standard normal table to find the probabilities.
2. The Z-value is for the standard normal distribution and we want the value for the original normal distribution.
3. 0.5
4. 0.1587
5. 0.8413
6. 0.0062
7. 0.0062
8. 0.8413
9. 0.9332
10. 0.8400
11. 0.8400
12. 0.0214 using technology or 0.0215 using the table
13. 0.0049
14. 0.3413
15. $X = 86.45$
16. 53.55

17. 89.6

18. 50.4

19. 46.7

20. 93.3

21. 44.2

22. 95.8

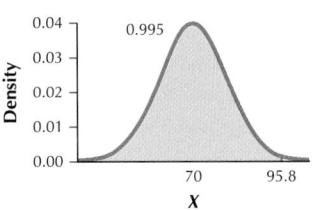

23. $X = 53.55$ and $X = 86.45$
24. $X = 50.4$ and $X = 89.6$
25. 46.7 and 93.3

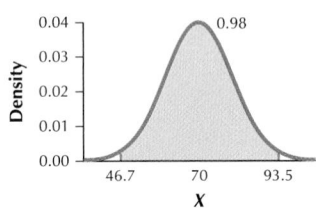

26. $X = 44.2$ and $X = 95.8$
27. (a) 0.5 (b) 0.1587 (c) 0.1359
28. (a) 0.1587 (b) 0.8413 (c) 0.3413
29. (a) 0.1423 (b) 0.1423 (c) 26.67% (d) $X = 27.6$ mph
(e) Z-score is -2.27; moderately unusual
30. (a) 0.3085 (b) 0.0928 (c) 0.5987 (d) $X = 14.70$ million
viewers (e) Yes, $Z = 4$
31. (a) 18.29 ounces (b) 11.71 ounces (c) 11.71 ounces and
18.29 ounces
32. (a) 4.765 million contracts (TI-83/84: 4.763 million)
(b) 2.435 million contracts (TI-83/84: 2.437 million) (c) 2.435
(2.437) million contracts and 4.765 (4.763) million contracts
33. (a) 21.28 mph (TI-83/84: 21.29 mph) (b) 5.92 mph
(TI-83/84: 5.91 mph) (c) 5.92 (5.91) mph and 21.28 (21.29) mph
(d) Z-score is -2.27; moderately unusual
34. (a) 5.42 million viewers (b) 18.58 million viewers
(c) 5.42 million viewers and 18.58 million viewers
(d) Z-score is 3; unusual
35. (a) 0.2420 (b) 0.0705 (c) 266.55 (d) Moderately unusual,
$Z = -2.5$

36. (a) 0.9772 (b) 4.75% (c) $X = 134.95$ years (d) Z-score is
3.33; unusual
37. (a) 0.0139 (b) 0.5249 (c) 4.87 days; the mean equals the
median. (d) The Z-score for $X = 8$ days is 3.23. Since $3.23 \geq 3$,
a hospital stay of 8 days is unusual.
38. (a) 0.6915 (b) 3.66 million tobacco-related deaths
(TI-83/84: 3.65 million) (c) The 25th percentile is $5 - 3.66 = 1.34$
$(5 - 3.65 = 1.35)$ million tobacco-related deaths below the mean.
By symmetry, the 75th percentile is 1.34 (1.35) million tobacco-
related deaths above the mean. Therefore, the 75th percentile is
$5 + 1.34 = 6.34$ $(5 + 1.35 = 6.35)$ million tobacco-related
deaths. (d) Z-score is 1.5; not unusual
39. (a) 0.0228 (b) 21.19% (c) $X = 1.78$ (d) The Z-score for
$X = 4.0$ is 2.8. Since $2 \leq 2.8 < 3$, a GPA of 4.0 is moderately
unusual.
40. (a) 0.1635 (TI-83/84: 0.1627) (b) 0.3113 (TI-83/84:
0.3124) (c) -5.86 yards and 17.66 yards (d) Outlier, $Z = 4.0167$
41. (a) 0.0013 (b) 0.3989 (TI-83/84: 0.4004) (c) 0.702 million
shares (TI-83/84: 0.704 million) (d) Outlier, $Z = 41.5$
42. (a) 0.0062 (b) 0.0228 (c) 0.7506 (d) 0.2963 (e) 0.7734
(f) \$24,880 (g) \$26,640 and \$33,360
43. (a) 0.5 (b) 0.0026 (c) 0.2313 (d) 80.40 and 119.60
44. (a) -1.04 calories per gram (b) No, food cannot have
negative calories per gram. (c) Yes (d) The distribution of the
number of calories per gram is right-skewed, so it is not normal.
45. (a) 0.0062 (b) 0.0228 (c) 0.7506 (d) 0.2963
46. (a) 0.0026 (b) 0.2313 (c) 80.40 and 119.60

Section 6.7
1. For certain values of n and p, it may be inconvenient to
calculate probabilities for the binomial distribution. For example,
if $n = 100$ and $p = 0.5$, it may be tedious to calculate $P(X > 57)$,
which, in the absence of technology, would involve 44
applications of the binomial probability formula.
2. $n \cdot p \geq 5$ and $n \cdot (1 - p) \geq 5$
3. Appropriate
4. Not appropriate
5. Not appropriate
6. Appropriate
7. Not appropriate
8. Appropriate
9. 0.1272
10. 0.5636
11. 0.4364
12. 0.5636
13. 0.4364
14. 0.5704
15. 0.3616
16. 0.4660
17. 0.0992
18. 0.7764
19. 0.6772
20. 0.1423
21. 0.0853
22. 0.2981
23. 0.0992
24. 0.2168
25. (a) 0.0558 (b) 0.5279
26. (a) 0.7157 (b) 0.0548
27. (a) 0.0037 (b) 1

28. (a) 0.1350 (b) 0.5675
29. (a) 1 (b) 0
30. (a) 0.4721 (b) 0.5387
31. (a) 0.0003 (b) 0.0951
32. (a) 0.5517 (b) 0
33. (a) 0.4325 (b) 0.5675 (c) 0.4325
34. (a) 0 (b) 0.7257
35. (a) No (b) The normal distribution is not a good approximation to the binomial distribution ($n \cdot p = 2 < 10$), so not appropriate.
36. (a) Yes (b) The normal distribution is a good approximation to the binomial distribution. (c) $n p = 10.08 \geq 5$ and $n (1 - p) \geq 5$, so it is appropriate to use the normal approximation to the binomial probability distribution.

Chapter 6 Review
1. (a) 0.95 (b) 2 games (c) 0.60
2. (a) 0.15 (b) 0.60 (c) More than three friends
3. (a) $\mu = \$1500$, $Var(X) = 60,250,000$, $SD(X) = \$7762.09$

(b)

(c) This value for the mean makes sense as the point where the distribution balances.

4. (a)

X	0	2	50	2000	2,600,000
P (X)	0.9746625583	0.02381	0.001495	0.0000323	0.0000001417

(b) $E(X) = \$0.56$. $0.44 is less than the $1 it costs to play.
5. (a) 0.1887 (b) 0.8113 (c) 0.7880
6. (a) 0.0036 (b) 0.9964 (c) 0.1236
7. (a) 0.2123 (b) 0.1792 (c) 0.5025
8. $\mu = 1.6$, $Var(X) = 1.472$, $SD(X) = 1.2133$. The expected number of pregnancies in which gestational diabetes occurs in a random sample of 20 pregnancies is 1.6.
9. $\mu = 5.7$, $Var (X) = 2.451$, $SD(X) = 1.5656$. The expected number of females in a random sample of 10 students from the College of DuPage is 5.7.
10. $\mu = 5.25$, $Var(X) = 3.4125$, $SD(X) = 1.8473$. The expected number of Americans who said that the price of gasoline was the news story they followed more closely than any other news story in a random sample of 15 Americans is 5.25.
11. 0.1755
12. 0.4913
13. 0.1247
14. 0.6160
15. (a) 0.3169 (b) 0.1920 (c) 0.7703 (d) 0.2297
16. 0
17. 0.5
18. 0.5

19. Less than 0.5. Since the area to the right of the mean $\mu = 106$ mm is 0.5 and $X = 110$ mm is greater than the mean $\mu = 106$ mm, the area to the right of $X = 110$ mm is less than the area to the right of the mean $\mu = 106$.
20. Greater than 0.5. Since the area to the left of $\mu = 106$ mm is 0.5 and $X = 110$ mm is greater than the mean $\mu = 106$ mm, the area to the left of $X = 110$ mm is greater than the area to the left of the mean $\mu =106$.
21. About 0.68
22. About 0.95
23. About 0.997
24. (a)

(b) 0.9821
25. (a)

(b) 0.9981
26. (a)

(b) 0.9861
27. (a)

(b) 0.9881
28. (a)

(b) 0.7995
29. (a)
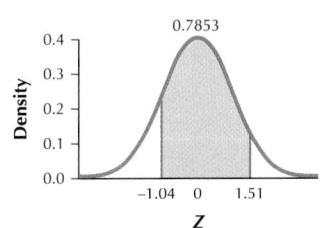

(b) 0.7853

30. (a) 0.7967 **(b)** 1.88% **(c)** 0.2967 **(d)** $X = 72.46$ mph
(e) The Z-score for $X = 55$ mph is -3.33. Since $-3.33 \le -3$, a driver from South Dakota who never drives faster than 55 mph on the Interstate is unusual.
31. (a) 0.0013 **(b)** 0.4287 **(c)** $X = 78.910$ deaths **(c)** The Z-score for $X = 60$ deaths is 1. Since $-2 < 1 < 2$, 60 people in the United States who are killed by drunk driving in a particular day is not unusual.
32. (a) 0.1587 **(b)** 0.2018 **(c)** $X = 17$ **(d)** Z-score is -3; unusual. The producer will have to file a report.
33. (a) 0.0736 **(b)** 0.3821 **(c)** 0.3085 **(d)** 0.6915 **(e)** 0.6179 **(f)** 0.3557
34. (a) 0.1192 **(b)** 0.0003 **(c)** 0.4404 **(d)** 0.5596 **(e)** 0.4404 **(f)** 0.6157

Chapter 6 Quiz

1. True
2. False
3. False
4. 0.5
5. 0
6. 0
7. discrete
8. binomial
9. $\mu = 0$, $\sigma = 1$
10. (a)

X = Amount won	0	5
P(X)	13/18	5/18

(b) $1.39 **(c)** $1.39
11. (a) 0.0962 **(b)** 19 CEOs **(c)** $\mu = 19$ CEOs, $Var(X) = 15.39$, $SD(X) = 3.9230$. The expected number of CEOs who drive luxury cars in a random sample of 100 CEOs is 19. **(d)** Z-score is 5.35; unusual
12. (a) 0.1003 **(b)** 33.22% **(c)** $4329.50 **(d)** Z-score is -2.05; moderately unusual
13. (a) 0.0257 **(b)** 0.0074 **(c)** For cats, $\mu = 314$ households, $Var(X) = 215.404$, $SD(X) = 14.6766$. The expected number of American households that have a cat in a random sample of 1000 households is 314. For dogs, $\mu = 343$ households, $Var(X) = 225.351$, $SD(X) = 15.0117$. The expected number of American households that have a dog in a random sample of 1000 households is 343. **(d)** Z-score is -1.64; not unusual
14. (a) 0.4207 **(b)** 0.2358 **(c)** $X = 50,800$ visitors **(d)** Z-score is -2.3; moderately unusual

Chapter 7

Section 7.1

1. Statistical inference refers to learning about population characteristics by studying the same characteristics in a sample.
2. It consists of the sample statistics of all possible samples of size n from the population. Sampling distributions can tell us about the expected location and variability of a statistic.
3. For a given sample size n, it is normal with mean μ and standard deviation $\sigma_{\bar{x}} = \sigma/\sqrt{n}$.
4. True
5. $\mu_{\bar{x}} = 100$, $\sigma_{\bar{x}} = 4$
6. $\mu_{\bar{x}} = 100$, $\sigma_{\bar{x}} = 2$
7. $\mu_{\bar{x}} = 0$, $\sigma_{\bar{x}} = 3.3333$
8. $\mu_{\bar{x}} = 0$, $\sigma_{\bar{x}} = 2$

9. $\mu_{\bar{x}} = -10$, $\sigma_{\bar{x}} = 0.5$
10. $\mu_{\bar{x}} = -10$, $\sigma_{\bar{x}} = 0.25$
11. 0.1587
12. 0.1587
13. 0.6826
14. 0.9772
15. 0.9772
16. 0.9544
17. 112.34
18. 87.66
19. 114.7
20. 85.3
21. 87.66 and 112.34
22. 85.3 and 114.7
23. Normal (50, 2)
24. 0.1587
25. 0.1587
26. 0.6826
27. 53.29
28. 46.71
29. 46.71 and 53.29
30. 0.1
31. Normal with mean $\mu = 10$ and standard deviation $\sigma_{\bar{x}} = 1$
32. 0.1587
33. 0.1587
34. 0.6826
35. 11.96
36. 8.04
37. 8.04 and 11.96
38. 0.05
39. (a) $\mu_{\bar{x}} = 1.7$ seconds, $\sigma_{\bar{x}} = 0.1$ second **(b)** 0.1587 **(c)** 0.1587
40. (a) $\mu_{\bar{x}} = 68$ inches, $\sigma_{\bar{x}} = 1$ inch **(b)** 0.0228 **(c)** 0.0013
41. (a) 0.1056 **(b)** 0.1359 **(c)** 0.4013
42. (a) 0.0228 **(b)** 0.0013 **(c)** 0.0215
43. (a) 1.86 seconds **(b)** 1.54 seconds **(c)** 1.54 seconds and 1.86 seconds
(d)

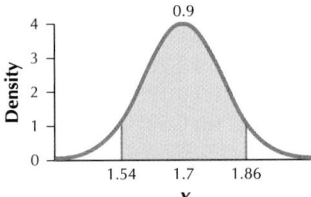

44. (a) 69.96 inches **(b)** 66.04 inches **(c)** 66.04 inches and 69.96 inches
(d)

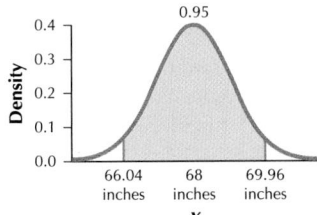

45. (a) $151.6 million; TI-83/84: $151.52 million
(b) $48.4 million; TI-83/84: $48.48 million **(c)** $48.4 million and $151.6 million; TI-83/84: $48.48 million and $151.52 million

(d)

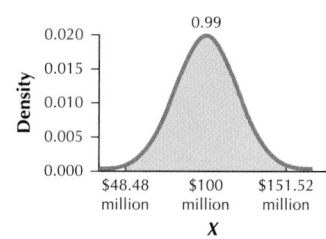

46. (a) $51,280 **(b)** $48,720 **(c)** $48,720 and $51,280
(d)

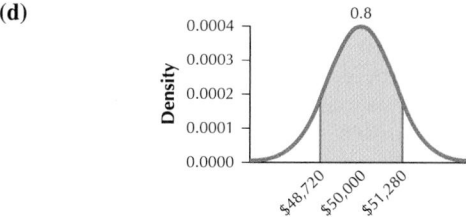

53. (a)

Sample	Cambodia China Egypt	Cambodia China Indonesia	Cambodia China Vietnam	Cambodia Egypt Indonesia	Cambodia Egypt Vietnam	Cambodia Indonesia Vietnam	China Egypt Indonesia	China Egypt Vietnam	China Indonesia Vietnam	Egypt Indonesia Vietnam
Data	1	1	1	1	1	1	1	1	1	13
	1	1	1	13	13	7	13	13	7	7
	13	7	2	7	2	2	7	2	2	2
$\bar{x}$	5	3	1.3333	7	5.3333	3.3333	7	5.3333	3.3333	7.3333

(b)

(c) $\mu_{\bar{x}} = 4.8$ deaths **(d)** They are the same.
54. (a) 3.5 **(b)** 0.4270
55. 0.2514
56. (a) $4 **(b)** $2 **(c)** The sampling distribution of the $\bar{x}$ is normal with a mean of $\mu_{\bar{x}} = \$4$ and a standard deviation of $\sigma_{\bar{x}} = \$2$ by Fact 4.
57. (a) 0.0228 **(b)** Sample means are less variable than individual observations, so $X = 0$ is more standard deviations below $\mu_{\bar{x}}$ than below μ. **(c)** The probability of a sample mean showing a net loss would look better on the broker's resume.
58. (a–b) Unchanged **(c)** Decrease in σ will result in a decrease in $P(X < 0)$. **(d)** Unchanged **(e)** Decrease
59. (a) Would still be normal with a mean of $\mu_{\bar{x}} = \mu = \$4$.
(b) Decrease
60. 0.4483
61. (a) $\mu_{\bar{x}} = 515$ **(b)** $\sigma_{\bar{x}} = 29$ **(c)** Since the sampling distribution of math SAT scores is normal with mean $\mu = 515$ and standard deviation $\sigma = 116$, the sampling distribution of the sample mean is normal with a mean of $\mu_{\bar{x}} = 515$ and a standard deviation of $\sigma_{\bar{x}} = 29$, by Fact 4.
62. (a) 0.3015 **(b)** Sample means are less variable than individual observations, so 500 is more standard deviations below $\mu_{\bar{x}}$ than below μ.
63. (a) Increase **(b)** Unchanged **(c)** Increase **(d)** Would still be normal with a mean of $\mu_{\bar{x}} = \mu = \$4$.
64. (a–b) Increase **(c)** Decrease

47. (a) 0.1587 **(b)** 0.9974 **(c)** 0.1587 **(d)** 404.20 **(e)** 325.80
(f) The middle 95% of sample mean carbon dioxide concentrations of samples of size $n = 25$.
48. (a) 0.0062 **(b)** 0.6826 **(c)** 0.1056 **(d)** 7.39 bits **(e)** 6.61 bits
(f) 6.61 bits and 7.39 bits
49. (a) $_5C_2 = 10$ **(b)** $\mu = 6.9$ **(c)** $\sigma = 0.7483$
50. (a)

Data	7.9	7.9	7.9	7.9	7.7	7.7	7.7	6.5	6.5	6.3
	7.7	6.5	6.3	6.1	6.5	6.3	6.1	6.3	6.1	6.1
$\bar{x}$	7.8	7.2	7.1	7	7.1	7	6.9	6.4	6.3	6.2

(b) and (c)

(d) 6.9
51. (a) $\mu_{\bar{x}} = 6.9$ **(b)** Yes. Fact 1: $\mu_{\bar{x}} = \mu$
52. (a) $_5C_2 = 10$ **(b)** $\mu = 4.8$ deaths **(c)** $\sigma = 4.6648$ deaths

Section 7.2
1. To determine whether or not the data are normally distributed. If the points either cluster around a straight line or nearly all fall within the curved bounds, then it is likely that the data set is normal. If there are systematic deviations off the straight line, then that is evidence against the claim that the data set is normal.
2. It becomes approximately normal (μ, $\sigma/\sqrt{n}$).
3. $n = 30$
4. Normal, approximately normal, or unknown
5. 4 times as large
6. The population is either non-normal or of unknown distribution and the sample size is less than 30.
7. Not acceptable
8. Acceptable
9. Acceptable
10. Not acceptable
11. (a) 516 **(b)** 38.6667, Normal
12. (a) 516 **(b)** 19.3333; Approximately normal
13. (a) 80 **(b)** 1; Approximately normal
14. (a) 80 **(b)** 1.6; Normal
15. (a) 50 miles per gallon **(b)** 1.5 miles per gallon; Unknown
16. (a) 50 miles per gallon **(b)** 0.75 mile per gallon; Approximately normal
17. 0.2676 (TI-83/84: 0.2674)
18. 0.2033 (TI-83/84: 0.2040)
19. 0.9772
20. Not possible. The variable is not normally distributed and the sample size is less than 30.

21. Not possible. The variable is not normally distributed and the sample size is less than 30.

22. 0.9962

23. 8.08

24. Not possible since the pollen count distribution for Los Angeles in September is not normally distributed and the sample size of $n = 16$ is small ($n < 30$). Case 3 applies and the sampling distribution of $\bar{x}$ is unknown.

25. $3.00

26. Since the 2007 prices for boned trout are not normally distributed and the sample size of $n = 16$ is small ($n < 30$), Case 3 applies and the sampling distribution of $\bar{x}$ is unknown. Thus the $\bar{x}$ that is smaller than 90% of all of the sample mean accountant incomes cannot be found.

27. $58,355

28. $61,645

29. **(a)** 0.0918 (TI-83/84: 0.0912) **(b)** 0.8164 (TI-83/84: 0.8176)

30. **(a)** 0.7995 **(b)** 0.1256 (TI-83/84: 0.1255)

31. **(a)** 0.0026 **(b)** 0.4974 **(c)** Since $n \geq 30$, the distribution of the sample mean is approximately normal by the Central Limit Theorem.

32. **(a)** Not possible. The distribution of the variable is unknown and the sample size is less than 30. **(b)** 0

33. **(a)** 214.34 **(b)** 189.66

(c)
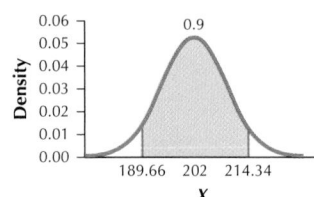

34. **(a)** 41.87° **(b)** 35.33°

(c)
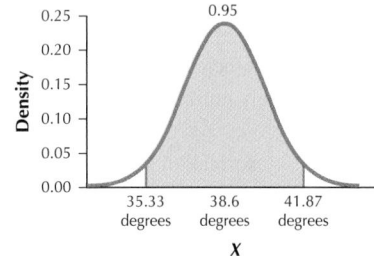

35. **(a)** 111.1 computers **(b)** 136.9 computers

(c)
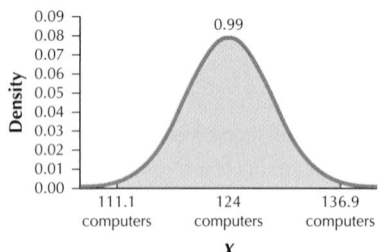

36. **(a)** $5.28 **(b)** $2.72

(c)
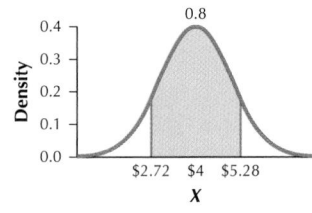

37. In favor of normality. All of the points are between the curved lines and most of the points are close to the center line.

38. 0.0359

39. 0 (TI-83/84: 0.0001592)

40. Against normality. There are several points outside of the curved lines and most of the points are close to the upper curved line.

41. Not possible. The variable is not normally distributed and the sample size is less than 30.

42. 0.9544 (TI-83/84: 0.9545)

43. **(a)** Remain unchanged. From Fact 1 in Section 7.1, $\mu_{\bar{x}} = \mu$. Thus $\mu_{\bar{x}}$ does not depend on the sample size n. **(b)** Decrease. Since $\sigma_{\bar{x}} = \sigma/(\sqrt{n})$, an increase in the sample size n results in a decrease in $\sigma_{\bar{x}}$. **(c)** Insufficient information to tell. If $\bar{x} > 50,000$, then $\bar{x} - 50,000 > 0$. Since $\sigma_{\bar{x}}$ decreases and is positive, $Z = x - \mu_x/(\sigma_x)$ will increase. If $\bar{x} = 50,000$, then $\bar{x} - 50,000 = 0$. Thus $Z = x - \mu_x/(\sigma_x)$ will remain 0. If $\bar{x} < 50,000$, then $\bar{x} - 50,000 < 0$. Since $\sigma_{\bar{x}}$ decreases and is positive, $Z = x - \mu_x/(\sigma_x)$ will decrease. **(d)** Increase. From part **(c)**, $Z = x - \mu_x/(\sigma_x) = 60,000 - 50,000/\sigma_x$ will increase and $Z = x - \mu_x/(\sigma_x) = 40,000 - 50,000/(\sigma_x)$ will decrease. Thus the area between these two values will increase. Since $P(\$40,000 < \bar{x} < \$60,000)$ is the area between these two values of Z, $P(\$40,000 < \bar{x} < \$60,000)$ will increase.

44. 0.0456

45. **(a)** 0.1067 gram **(b)** 1.067 grams **(c)** About 0.997

46. **(a)** 0.9803 **(b)** 0.9803, 0.0197 **(c)** The values found in **(b)** favor the Master of the Mint.

47. **(a)** 0.0002 **(b)** 0.0002, 0.9998 **(c)** The value found in the original case study in the text favors the Master of the Mint.

48. $\mu = 127.751946$ grams

49. **(a)** $n = 2$

(b) $n = 5$

(c) $n = 30$

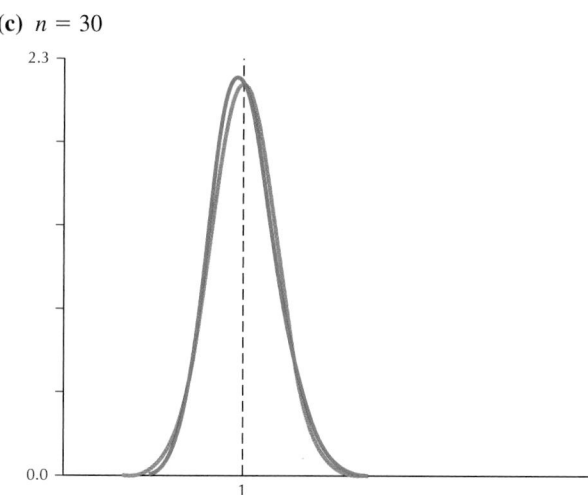

50. $n = 30$

Section 7.3

1. If we take a sample of size n, the sample proportion $\hat{p}$ is $\hat{p} = x/n$, where x represents the number of individuals in the sample that have the particular characteristic. Examples will vary.
2. The mean of the sampling distribution of $\hat{p}$ is $\mu_{\hat{p}} = p$.
3. $\sigma_{\hat{p}} = \sqrt{p \cdot (1 - p)/n}$
4. Both (1) $np \geq 5$ and (2) $n(1 - p) \geq 5$.
5. It decreases by a factor of $1/\sqrt{2} \approx 0.7071$.
6. **(a)** $\hat{p} = 1/4 = 0.25$ **(b)** $\hat{p} = 1/3 \approx 0.3333$ **(c)** $\hat{p} = 1/2 = 0.5$
(d) $\hat{p} = 1/1000 = 0.001$
7. **(a)** 0.5 **(b)** 0.05 **(c)** Approximately normal
8. **(a)** $\mu_{\hat{p}} = 0.5$ **(b)** $\sigma_{\hat{p}} = 0.2236$ **(c)** Unknown
9. **(a)** 0.01 **(b)** 0.0099 **(c)** Unknown
10. **(a)** $\mu_{\hat{p}} = 0.01$ **(b)** $\sigma_{\hat{p}} = 0.0044$ **(c)** Approximately normal
11. **(a)** 0.9 **(b)** 0.0474 **(c)** Unknown
12. **(a)** $\mu_{\hat{p}} = 0.9$ **(b)** $\sigma_{\hat{p}} = 0.0424$ **(c)** Approximately normal
13. **(a)** $\mu_{\hat{p}} = 0.02$ **(b)** $\sigma_{\hat{p}} \approx 0.0099$ **(c)** Unknown
14. **(a)** $\mu_{\hat{p}} = 0.02$ **(b)** $\sigma_{\hat{p}} \approx 0.0089$ **(c)** Approximately normal.
15. **(a)** $\mu_{\hat{p}} = 0.98$ **(b)** $\sigma_{\hat{p}} \approx 0.0089$ **(c)** Approximately normal
16. **(a)** $\mu_{\hat{p}} = 0.98$ **(b)** $\sigma_{\hat{p}} \approx 0.0099$ **(c)** Unknown

17. **(a)** $\mu_{\hat{p}} = 0.99$ **(b)** $\sigma_{\hat{p}} \approx 0.0044$ **(c)** Approximately normal
18. **(a)** $\mu_{\hat{p}} = 0.99$ **(b)** $\sigma_{\hat{p}} \approx 0.0099$ **(c)** Unknown
19. 10
20. 20
21. 50
22. 100
23. 500
24. 5000
25. 0.1587
26. We have $np = (5)(0.5) = 2.5 < 5$, so the sampling distribution of $\hat{p}$ is unknown. Hence $P(\hat{p} > 0.55)$ cannot be found.
27. Not possible; sampling distribution of $\hat{p}$ is unknown.
28. 0.4129
29. Not possible; sampling distribution of $\hat{p}$ is unknown.
30. 0.2756
31. Not possible since $np = (200)(0.02) = 4 < 5$.
32. 0.5438 (TI-83/84: 0.5450)
33. 0.564
34. 0.532
35. 0.962
36. 0.941
37. 0.052
38. 0.068
39. **(a)** $\mu_{\hat{p}} = 0.25$, $\sigma_{\hat{p}} \approx 0.0722$ **(b)** Approximately normal (0.25, 0.0722)
(c) 0.4443 (TI-83/84: 0.4449)
40. **(a)** $\mu_{\hat{p}} = 0.503$, $\sigma_{\hat{p}} \approx 0.0707$ **(b)** Approximately normal (0.503, 0.0707) **(c)** 0.0853 (TI-83/84: 0.0850)
41. **(a)** $\mu_{\hat{p}} = 0.75$, $\sigma_{\hat{p}} \approx 0.0968$ **(b)** 0.7324 (TI-83/84: 0.7323) **(c)** 0.0959 (TI-83/84: 0.0954)
42. **(a)** $\mu_{\hat{p}} = 0.13$, $\sigma_{\hat{p}} \approx 0.0480$ **(b)** 0.0301 (TI-83/84: 0.0304) **(c)** 0.3985 (TI-83/84: 0.3956)
43. **(a)** 0.1312, 0.3688
(b)

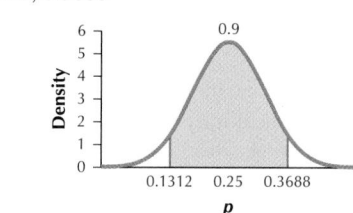

(c) For $\hat{p} = 2/36 \approx 0.0556$, $Z = -2.69$. Thus $\hat{p} = 2/36$ is considered moderately unusual. **(d)** Sample proportions between 0 and 0.0334 inclusive and between 0.4666 and 1 inclusive would be considered outliers.
44. **(a)** 0.3644, 0.6416

(b)

(c) $Z = 2.0792$, moderately unusual **(d)** $Z = -2.1641$, moderately unusual
45. **(a)** 0.5003, 0.9997 (TI-83/84: 0.5007, 0.9993)

(b)

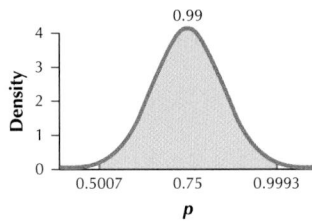

(c) For $\hat{p} = 14/20 = 0.7$, $Z = -0.5165$. Thus $\hat{p} = 0.7$ is neither moderately unusual nor an outlier.
46. (a) 0.0359, 0.2241

(b)

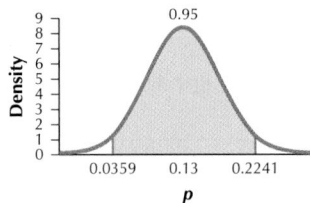

(c) 0.4168 (TI-83/84: 0.4175) **(d)** No
47. (a) Remain unchanged. Since $\mu_{\hat{p}} = p$, $\mu_{\hat{p}}$ does not depend on the sample size. Therefore an increase in the sample size would not affect $\mu_{\hat{p}}$. **(b)** Decrease. Since $\sigma_{\hat{p}} = \sqrt{p \cdot (1 - p)/n}$, an increase in the denominator would result in a decrease in the fraction, which would result in a decrease in $\sigma_{\hat{p}}$. **(c)** Decrease. Since $0.04 - 0.13 = -0.09$ is negative, and $\sigma_{\hat{p}}$ is positive and decreases, $Z = 0.04 - 0.13/\sigma_{\hat{p}}$ will decrease. Therefore the area to the left of $Z = 0.04 - 0.13/\sigma_{\hat{p}}$ will decrease. Since $P(\hat{p} < 0.04)$ is equal to this area, $P(\hat{p} < 0.04)$ will decrease. **(d)** Increase. Since $0.10 - 0.13 = -0.03$ is negative, $0.15 - 0.13 = 0.02$ is positive, and $\sigma_{\hat{p}}$ is positive and decreases, $Z = 0.10 - 0.13/\sigma_{\hat{p}}$ will decrease and $Z = 0.15 - 0.13/\sigma_{\hat{p}}$ will increase. Thus the area between these two values will increase. Since $P(0.10 < \hat{p} < 0.15)$ is equal to this area, $P(0.10 < \hat{p} < 0.15)$ will increase. **(e)** Decrease. Since $0.49 - 0.13 = 0.36$ is positive, $0.45 - 0.13 = 0.32$ is positive, and $\sigma_{\hat{p}}$ is positive and decreases, both $Z = 0.49 - 0.13/\sigma_{\hat{p}}$ and $Z = 0.45 - 0.13/\sigma_{\hat{p}}$ will increase. Both of these values will be farther out on the right tail of the standard normal distribution, where the curve is closer to the Z axis. Therefore, the area between these two values of Z will decrease. Since $P(0.45 < \hat{p} < 0.49)$ is equal to this area, it will decrease. **(f)** Increase. Since $\sigma_{\hat{p}}$ decreases, $1.96 \, \sigma_{\hat{p}}$ decreases. Since the 2.5th percentile is $0.13 - 1.96 \, \sigma_{\hat{p}}$, the 2.5th percentile increases. **(g)** Decrease. Since $\sigma_{\hat{p}}$ decreases, $1.96 \, \sigma_{\hat{p}}$ decreases. Since the 97.5th percentile is $0.13 + 1.96 \, \sigma_{\hat{p}}$, the 97.5th percentile decreases.
48. (a) $\mu_{\hat{p}} = 0.65$, $\sigma_{\hat{p}} \approx 0.0477$ **(b)** $\mu_{\hat{p}} = 0.41$, $\sigma_{\hat{p}} \approx 0.0492$
49. (a) 0.5 **(b)** 0 **(c)** 0 **(d)** 0.5
50. (a) 0.5565, 0.7435 **(b)** 0.3136, 0.5064
51. The results of Exercises 49 and 50 do not support this claim. The 97.5th percentile for the males is less than the 2.5th percentile for the females. Also $P(p < 0.41)$ and $P(p > 0.65)$ are both very different for males and females.

Chapter 7 Review
1. $\mu_{\bar{x}} = 10$, $\sigma_{\bar{x}} = 1$
2. $\mu_{\bar{x}} = 10$, $\sigma_{\bar{x}} = 5/6 \approx 0.8333$
3. $\mu_{\bar{x}} = 10$, $\sigma_{\bar{x}} = 5/7 \approx 0.7143$
4. $\mu_{\bar{x}} = 50$ and $\sigma_{\bar{x}} = 20$
5. $\mu_{\bar{x}} = 50$ and $\sigma_{\bar{x}} = 10$.

6. Normal (10, 0.8)
7. 0.1056
8. 0.1056
9. 0.7888
10. Not possible, since scores on a psychological test are not normally distributed and the sample size of $n = 25$ is small ($n < 30$). Solution 3 applies, so the sampling distribution of $\bar{x}$ is unknown.
11. 0.8185
12. Not possible, since scores on a psychological test are not normally distributed and the sample size of $n = 25$ is small ($n < 30$). Solution 3 applies, so the sampling distribution of $\bar{x}$ is unknown.
13. 100
14. (a) 47.18 years **(b)** 40.82 years **(c)** 40.82 years and 47.18 years

(d)

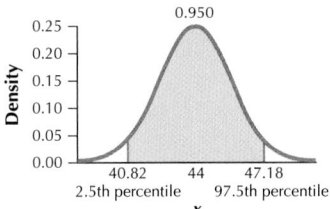

15. We have $np = (40)(0.1) = 4 < 5$, so the sampling distribution of $\hat{p}$ is unknown. Thus $P(\hat{p} < 0.12)$ can't be found.
16. 0.6808
17. 0.0153
18. 0.0162
19. (a) 0.2578 (TI-83/84: 0.2590) **(b)** 0.2422 (TI-83/84: 0.2410) **(c)** 0.7422 (TI-83/84: 0.7410) **(d)** 0.0437, 0.1963

Chapter 7 Quiz
1. True
2. False
3. Sampling error
4. Approximately normal
5. No
6. $np \geq 5$ and $n(1 - p) \geq 5$
7. (a) 0.1587 **(b)** 0.9500 **(c)** 0.1056
8. (a) 45.15 grams **(b)** 34.85 grams **(c)** 34.85 grams and 45.15 grams
9. (a) 0.0228 **(b)** 0.0228 **(c)** 0.9544
10. (a) 68.77 inches **(b)** 67.23 inches **(c)** 67.23 and 68.77 inches
11. (a) 0.5 **(b)** 0.2422 (TI-83/84: 0.2406) **(c)** 0.0174, 0.1146

Chapter 8

Section 8.1
1. A range of values is more likely to contain μ than a point estimate is to be exactly equal to μ. We have no measure of confidence that our point estimate is close to μ. A confidence level for a confidence interval means that if we take sample after sample for a very long time, then in the long run, the percent of intervals that will contain the population mean μ will equal the confidence level.
2. $\bar{x} + Z_{\alpha/2}(\sigma/\sqrt{n})$, and $(\bar{x} - Z_{\alpha/2}(\sigma/\sqrt{n}), \bar{x} + Z_{\alpha/2}(\sigma/\sqrt{n}))$
Point estimate $\pm$ margin of error and (point estimate $-$ margin of error, point estimate $+$ margin of error)

3. We are 95% confident that the population mean football score lies between 15 and 25.
4. True
5. $\bar{x} \pm E$ is shorthand for writing the two values $\bar{x} - E$ and $\bar{x} + E$. $\pm$ is shorthand notation for writing two numbers.
6. A *confidence interval estimate* of a parameter consists of an interval of numbers generated by a point estimate, together with an associated *confidence level* specifying the probability that the interval contains the parameter.
7. (a) $Z_{\alpha/2}$ increases. (b) Since the confidence level is $(1 - \alpha) \times 100\%$, as the confidence level increases, $1 - \alpha$ increases. Thus α and $\alpha/2$ will decrease. Since $\alpha/2$ is the area underneath the standard normal curve to the right of $Z_{\alpha/2}$, a decrease in $\alpha/2$ will result in an increase in $Z_{\alpha/2}$.
8. Increase the sample size.
9. Increases, Decreases
10. Decreases, Increases
11. $\bar{x} = 2$
12. $\bar{x} = 6$
13. $\bar{x} = 14$
14. $\bar{x} = 100$
15. No
16. Yes
17. Yes
18. We can use the Z interval.
19. We can use the Z interval.
20. We cannot use the Z interval.
21. $Z_{\alpha/2} = 2.576$
22. $Z_{\alpha/2} = 1.96$
23. $Z_{\alpha/2} = 1.96$
24. $Z_{\alpha/2} = 1.96$
25. $Z_{\alpha/2} = 1.645$
26. $Z_{\alpha/2} = 2.576$
27. (a) 0.5 (b) $Z_{\alpha/2} = 1.96$ (c) (34.02, 35.98). We are 95% confident that the true mean μ lies between 34.02 and 35.98.
28. (a) 1 (b) $Z_{\alpha/2} = 1.96$ (c) (48.04, 51.96). We are 95% confident that the true mean μ lies between 48.04 and 51.96.
29. (a) 2 (b) $Z_{\alpha/2} = 1.96$ (c) (11.08, 18.92). We are 95% confident that the true mean μ lies between 11.08 and 18.92.
30. (a) 0.5 (b) $Z_{\alpha/2} = 1.96$ (c) (9.02, 10.98). We are 95% confident that the true mean μ lies between 9.02 and 10.98.
31. (a) 1 (b) $Z_{\alpha/2} = 1.96$ (c) (18.04, 21.96). We are 95% confident that the true mean μ lies between 18.04 and 21.96.
32. (a) 2 (b) $Z_{\alpha/2} = 1.96$ (c) (96.08, 103.92). We are 95% confident that the true mean μ lies between 96.08 and 103.92.
33. (a) 0.98 (b) We can estimate μ to within 0.98 with 95% confidence.
34. (a) 1.96 (b) We can estimate μ to within 1.96 with 95% confidence.
35. (a) 3.92 (b) We can estimate μ to within 3.92 with 95% confidence.
36. (a) 0.98 (b) We can estimate μ to within 0.98 with 95% confidence.
37. (a) 1.96 (b) We can estimate μ to within 1.96 with 95% confidence.
38. (a) 3.92 (b) We can estimate μ to within 3.92 with 95% confidence.
39. (a) (9.342, 10.658). We are 90% confident that the true mean μ lies between 9.342 and 10.658. (b) (9.216, 10.784). We are 95% confident that the true mean μ lies between 9.216 and

10.784. (c) (8.9696, 11.0304). We are 99% confident that the true mean μ lies between 8.9696 and 11.0304. (d) The confidence interval for a given sample size becomes wider as the confidence level increases.
40. (a) (48.712, 51.288). We are 99% confident that the true mean μ lies between 48.712 and 51.288. (b) (49.02, 50.98). We are 95% confident that the true mean μ lies between 49.02 and 50.98. (c) (49.1775, 50.8225). We are 90% confident that the true mean μ lies between 49.1775 and 50.8225. (d) Decreases.
41. 1
42. 2
43. 5
44. As the margin of error is halved while σ and the confidence level stay fixed, the required sample size increases by a factor of approximately 4.
45. 5
46. 7
47. 11
48. As the confidence level increases while the margin of error and σ stay fixed, the required sample size increases.
49. (a) 69 gallons (b) 3.65 gallons (c) $Z_{\alpha/2} = 1.96$ (d) (61.84, 76.16). We are 95% confident that μ lies between 61.84 gallons and 76.16 gallons.
50. (a) $\bar{x} = 2$ billion shares (b) 83,333,333.33 shares (c) $Z_{\alpha/2} = 1.96$ (d) (1836.667, 2163.333); TI-83/84: (1836.7, 2163.3). We are 95% confident that the population mean number of shares traded daily on the New York Stock Exchange lies between 1836.667 (1836.7) million shares and 2163.333 (2163.3) million shares.
51. (a) 107 seconds (b) 19.5 seconds (c) $Z_{\alpha/2} = 1.96$ (d) (68.78, 145.22). We are 95% confident that the true mean length of time that boys remain engaged with a science exhibit at a museum μ lies between 68.78 seconds and 145.22 seconds.
52. (a) \$177 (b) 25 (c) 1.645 (d) (135.87, 218.13). We are 90% confident that μ lies between \$135.87 and \$218.13.
53. (a) 7.16 gallons. We can estimate μ to within 7.16 gallons with 95% confidence. (b) 3 (c) 62
54. (a) 163,333,333.33 shares. We can estimate μ to within 163,333,333.33 shares with 95% confidence. (b) 97 (c) 9604
55. (a) $E = 38.22$ seconds. We can estimate μ, the mean length of time that boys remain engaged with a science exhibit at a museum, to within 38.22 seconds with 95% confidence.
(b) 59 (c) 9604 days, approximately 26.31 years
56. (a) \$41.13. We can estimate μ to within \$41.13 with 90% confidence. (b) 35 (c) 865
57. (a) The normal probability plot indicates an acceptable level of normality.

(b) (415.067, 709.333); TI-83/84: (415.08, 709.32). We are 90% confident that the population mean carbon emissions lies between

415.067 (415.08) million tons and 709.333 (709.32) million tons. **(c)** $E = 147.133$ million tons. We can estimate the population mean emissions level of all nations to within 147.133 million tons with 90% confidence. **(d)** 44 nations

58. (a) The normal probability plot indicates an acceptable level of normality.

(b) (0.562, 1.122). We are 95% confident that the population mean cleanup costs in Florida counties for the BP oil spill lies between 0.562 million dollars and 1.122 million dollars. **(c)** $E = 0.280$ million dollars. We can estimate the population mean cleanup costs in Florida counties for the BP oil spill to within 0.280 million dollars with 95% confidence. **(d)** 189 counties

59. (a) The normal probability plot indicates an acceptable level of normality.

(b) (27.510, 82.240); TI-83/84: (27.554, 82.196). We are 99% confident that the population mean number of Wii games that are sold in the United States each week lies between 27.510 (27.554) thousand games and 82.240 (82.196) thousand games. **(c)** $E = 27.365$ thousand games. We can estimate the population mean number of Wii games sold to within 27.365 thousand games with 99% confidence. **(d)** 239 games

60. (a) The normal probability plot indicates an acceptable level of normality.

(b) (3.393, 4.187). We are 95% confident that the population mean rainfall in Georgia lies between 3.393 inches and 4.187 inches. **(c)** $E = 0.397$ inch. We can estimate the population mean rainfall in Georgia to within 0.397 inch with 95% confidence. **(d)** 158 locations

61. (a) 7 bits **(b)** 2 bits **(c)** $Z_{\alpha/2} = 1.96$ **(d)** 1 bit **(e)** $\bar{x} \pm E = 7 \pm 2 = (5, 9)$. We are 95% confident that μ lies between 5 bits and 9 bits.

62. (a) 2600 people **(b)** 141.42 people **(c)** $Z_{\alpha/2} = 2.576$ **(d)** $E = 364.30$ people. We can estimate μ, the mean number of members in a Roman Catholic church parish, to within 364.30 people with 99% confidence. **(e)** (2235.70, 2964.30). We are 99% confident that the true mean number of members in a Roman Catholic church parish μ lies between 2235.70 people and 2964.30 people.

63. (a) 97 **(b)** 385

64. (a) 97 **(b)** 166 **(c)** Larger. The higher the confidence level, the larger $Z_{\alpha/2}$ is. Therefore, the larger $n = (Z_{\alpha/2} \, \sigma/E)^2$ is.

65. (a) $E = 1.05$ miles. We can estimate μ, the mean commuting distance, to within 1.05 miles with 95% confidence. **(b)** (8.88, 11.00). We are 95% confident that the true mean commuting distance μ lies between 8.86 miles and 11.00 miles.

66. (a) $E = 3.70$ ng/g. We can estimate μ, the mean concentration of the herbicide dicamba in Iowa homes, to within 3.70 ng/g with 95% confidence. **(b)** (176.30, 183.70). We are 95% confident that the true mean concentration of the herbicide dicamba in Iowa homes μ lies between 176.30 ng/g and 183.70 ng/g. **(c)** 113 homes. This is only one more home than the original sample size. The margin of error for the 95% confidence interval is 3.7041 homes, which is close to 3.7 homes. **(d)** 194 homes

67. (a) $Z_{\alpha/2} = 1.96$ **(b)** 5.91 **(c)** 3.1948. We can estimate the true mean quality of life score within 3.1948 with 95% confidence. **(d)** 9.78

68. (a) $Z_{\alpha/2} = 1.96$ **(b)** 144 steps **(c)** 132 steps. We can estimate the true mean number of fewer steps for each additional hour of television viewing within 132 steps with 95% confidence. **(d)** 673.5

69. (a) Unchanged. **(b)–(d)** Decrease **(e)** Unchanged

70. (a) Since σ is a population characteristic, it stays constant and is unaffected by a decrease in confidence level. **(b)** The quantity $\sigma/\sqrt{n}$ is unaffected by a decrease in confidence level. **(c)** A decrease in the confidence level will result in a decrease in $Z_{\alpha/2}$. The width of the confidence interval $= 2 \cdot E = 2 \cdot Z_{\alpha/2}(\sigma/\sqrt{n})$. Thus a decrease in $Z_{\alpha/2}$ will result in a decrease in the width of the confidence interval. **(d)** The quantity $\bar{x}$ depends only on the sample taken, so it will remain unaffected by a decrease in the confidence level. **(e)** A decrease in the confidence level will result in a decrease in $Z_{\alpha/2}$. Since the margin of error is $E = Z_{\alpha/2}(\sigma/\sqrt{n})$, a decrease in $Z_{\alpha/2}$ will result in a decrease in the margin of error.

71. (a) 6199 small firms **(b)** See the histogram in **(e)**.
(c)

Since the majority of the points lie outside of the curved lines, the normality assumption is not valid.

(d) (3188.95, 9209.05). We are 95% confident that the average number of small firms per metropolitan area lies between 3188.95 and 9209.05.

(e)

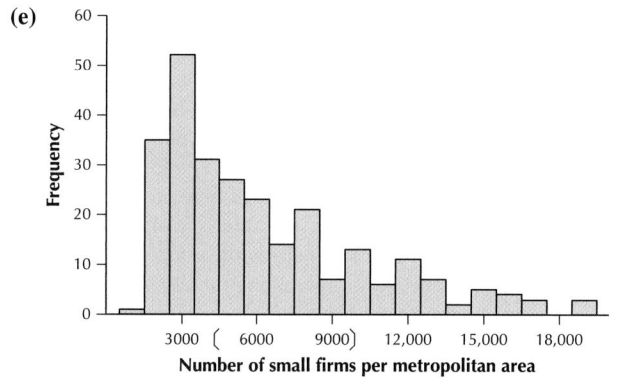

Number of small firms per metropolitan area

72. Answers will vary.

73. **(a)** The 99% confidence intervals are wider. **(b)** The higher the confidence level, the larger the margin of error. Since the width of the confidence level is twice the margin of error, a higher confidence level results in a wider confidence level.

74. Answers will vary.

75. **(a)** 1.28 **(b)** 1.44 **(c)** 2.33

Section 8.2

1. In most real-world problems, the population standard deviation σ is unknown, so we can't use the Z interval.

2. Yes. With even moderate sample sizes, reporting the t interval rather than the Z interval may offer peace of mind to the data analyst.

3. The t curve approaches closer and closer to the Z curve.

4. $E = t_{\alpha/2} (s/\sqrt{n})$

5. **(a)** $t_{\alpha/2} = 1.833$ **(b)** $t_{\alpha/2} = 2.262$ **(c)** $t_{\alpha/2} = 3.250$

6. **(a)** 2.262 **(b)** 2.145 **(c)** 2.093

7. **(a)** The value of $t_{\alpha/2}$ increases as the confidence level increases. **(b)** The larger the value of $1 - \alpha$, the larger the value of $t_{\alpha/2}$ will have to be in order to have an area of $1 - \alpha$ between $-t_{\alpha/2}$ and $t_{\alpha/2}$. $t_{\alpha/2} = 1.833$ for a 90% confidence interval with 9 degrees of freedom; $t_{\alpha/2} = 2.262$ for a 95% confidence interval with 9 degrees of freedom; $t_{\alpha/2} = 3.250$ for a 99% confidence interval with 9 degrees of freedom.

8. **(a)** Decreases **(b)** See the Instructor's Guide with Solutions for graphs. $t_{\alpha/2} = 2.262$ for $\alpha = 0.05$ and df = 9; $t_{\alpha/2} = 2.145$ for $\alpha = 0.05$ and df = 14; $t_{\alpha/2} = 2.093$ for $\alpha = 0.05$ and df = 19

9. **(a)** $\bar{x} = 2$, $s = 1$ **(b)** $t_{\alpha/2} = 2.776$ **(c)** (0.759, 3.241); TI-83/84: (0.758, 3.242). We are 95% confident that the population mean lies between 0.759 (0.758) and 3.241 (3.242).

10. **(a)** $\bar{x} = 6$, $s = 2$ **(b)** $t_{\alpha/2} = 2.776$ **(c)** (3.517, 8.483). We are 95% confident that the population mean lies between 3.517 and 8.483.

11. **(a)** $\bar{x} = 14$, $s = 3$ **(b)** $t_{\alpha/2} = 2.776$ **(c)** (10.276, 17.724); TI-83/84: (10.275, 17.725). We are 95% confident that the population mean lies between 10.276 (10.275) and 17.724 (17.725).

12. **(a)** $\bar{x} = 100$, $s = 4$ **(b)** $t_{\alpha/2} = 2.776$ **(c)** (95.034, 104.966); TI-83/84: (95.033, 104.970). We are 95% confident that the population mean lies between 95.034 (95.033) and 104.966 (104.970).

13. **(a)** $t_{\alpha/2} = 2.064$ **(b)** (7.936, 12.064)

(c)

14. **(a)** 1.860 **(b)** (20.140, 23.860)

(c)

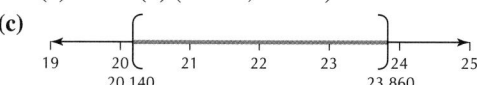

15. **(a)** $t_{\alpha/2} = 3.182$ **(b)** (40.454, 59.546)

(c)

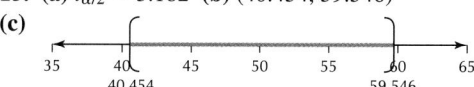

16. **(a)** 2.947 **(b)** (−5.894, 5.894)

(c)

17. **(a)** $t_{\alpha/2} = 1.860$ **(b)** (−23.720, −16.280)

(c)

18. **(a)** 2.064 **(b)** (−6.192, 6.192)

(c)

19. **(a)** $t_{\alpha/2} = 1.987$ **(b)** (98.013, 101.987)

(c)

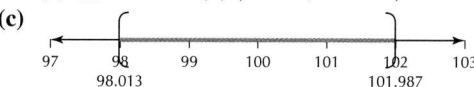

20. **(a)** 1.671 **(b)** (245.8225, 254.1775)

(c)

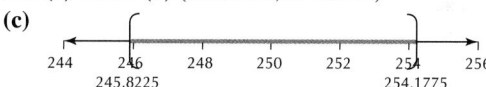

21. **(a)** $t_{\alpha/2} = 2.660$ **(b)** (32.340, 37.660)

(c)

22. **(a)** 1.984 **(b)** (41.008, 42.992)

(c)

23. **(a)** $t_{\alpha/2} = 1.664$ **(b)** (−21.1093, −18.8907)

(c)

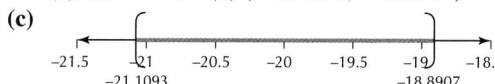

24. **(a)** 1.984 **(b)** (−1.984, 1.984)

(c)

25. **(a)** $t_{\alpha/2} = 2.009$ **(b)** $t_{\alpha/2} = 2.0054$

26. **(a)** $t_{\alpha/2} = 2.626$ **(b)** $t_{\alpha/2} = 2.6252$

27. **(a)** $t_{\alpha/2} = 1.684$ **(b)** $t_{\alpha/2} = 1.68$

28. **(a)** $t_{\alpha/2} = 2.021$ **(b)** $t_{\alpha/2} = 2.015$

29. **(a)** (95.937, 104.063). We are 95% confident that the population mean lies between 95.937 and 104.063. **(b)** (95.944, 104.056). We are 95% confident that the population mean lies between 95.944 and 104.056.

30. **(a)** (96.358, 103.642). We are 99% confident that the population mean lies between 96.358 and 103.642. **(b)** (96.360, 103.640). We are 99% confident that the population mean lies between 96.360 and 103.640.

31. **(a)** (9.503, 10.497). We are 90% confident that the population mean lies between 9.503 and 10.497. **(b)** (9.505, 10.495). We are 90% confident that the population mean lies between 9.505 and 10.495.

32. **(a)** (9.404, 10.596). We are 95% confident that the population mean lies between 9.404 and 10.596. **(b)** (9.406, 10.594). We are 95% confident that the population mean lies between 9.406 and 10.594.

33. Since the distribution of the population is unknown, Case 1 does not apply. Since the sample size of $n = 25$ is small ($n < 30$), Case 2 does not apply. Thus we cannot construct the indicated confidence interval.

34. Since the distribution of the population is unknown, Case 1 does not apply. Since the sample size of $n = 16$ is small ($n < 30$), Case 2 does not apply. Thus we cannot construct the indicated confidence interval.

35. Case 1 (9.3387, 10.6613)

36. (21.4453, 22.5547)

37. Since the distribution of the population is unknown, Case 1 does not apply. Since the sample size of $n = 16$ is small ($n < 30$), Case 2 does not apply. Thus we cannot construct the indicated confidence interval.

38. (37.872, 46.128)

39. Case 2 (47.97, 52.03)

40. (-2.660, 2.660)

41. $E = 1.241$. We can estimate the population mean to within 1.241 with 95% confidence.

42. $E = 2.483$. We can estimate the population mean to within 2.483 with 95% confidence.

43. $E = 3.724$. We can estimate the population mean to within 3.724 with 95% confidence.

44. $E = 4.966$. We can estimate the population mean to within 4.966 with 95% confidence.

45. $E = 2.064$. We can estimate the population mean to within 2.064 with 95% confidence.

46. $E = 1.860$. We can estimate the population mean to within 1.860 with 90% confidence.

47. $E = 9.546$. We can estimate the population mean to within 9.546 with 95% confidence.

48. $E = 5.894$. We can estimate the population mean to within 5.894 with 99% confidence.

49. (a) $t_{\alpha/2} = 1.987$ (b) (3.790, 6.810); TI-83/84: (3.792, 6.808). We are 95% confident that the population mean length of stay in hospital for sickle-cell anemia patients lies between 3.790 (3.792) days and 6.810 (6.808) days.

50. (a) $t_{\alpha/2} = 1.660$ (b) ($13,765, $17,085); TI-83/84: ($13,776, $17,074). We are 90% confident that the population mean student loan amount for students obtaining a bachelor's degree lies between $13,765 ($13,776) and $17,085 ($17,074).

51. (a) $t_{\alpha/2} = 1.994$ (b) (113.09, 126.91). We are 95% confident that the true mean revenue collected from all parking meters μ lies between $113.09 and $126.91.

52. (a) 1.690 (b) (2.9775, 3.8225). We are 90% confident that μ lies between 2.9775 points and 3.8225 points.

53. (a) $E = 1.510$ days. We can estimate the population mean length of stay in hospital for sickle-cell anemia to within 1.510 days with 95% confidence. (b) It will decrease.

54. (a) $E = 1660. We can estimate the population mean student loan amount for students obtaining a bachelor's degree to within $1660 with 90% confidence. (b) It will increase.

55. (a) $E = 6.91. We can estimate μ, the true mean revenue collected from all parking meters, to within $6.91 with 95% confidence. (b) Increasing the sample size and decreasing the confidence level. Increasing the sample size is more desirable. A lower confidence level means we are less confident that the population mean lies in our interval.

56. (a) 0.4225 points. We can estimate μ to within 0.4225 points with 90% confidence. (b) Increasing the sample size

and decreasing the confidence level. Increasing the sample size is more desirable. A lower confidence level means we are less confident that the population mean lies in our interval.

57. (a) (376.455, 747.945); TI-83/84: (376.47, 747.93). We are 90% confident that the population mean carbon emissions lies between 376.455 (376.47) million tons and 747.945 (747.93) million tons. (b) $E = 185.745$ million tons. We can estimate the population mean carbon emissions to within 185.745 million tons with 90% confidence. (c) Increasing the sample size and decreasing the confidence level. Increasing the sample size is more desirable. A lower confidence level means we are less confident that the population mean lies in our interval.

58. (a) (0.476, 1.207). We are 95% confident that the population mean amount of money disbursed by BP in Florida for cleanup of the *Deepwater Horizon* oil spill lies between 0.476 million dollars and 1.207 million dollars. (b) $E = 0.366$ million dollars. We can estimate the population mean amount of money disbursed by BP in Florida for cleanup of the *Deepwater Horizon* oil spill per county to within 0.366 million dollars with 95% confidence. (c) Increasing the sample size and decreasing the confidence level. Increasing the sample size is more desirable. A lower confidence level means we are less confident that the population mean lies in our interval.

59. (a) (19.380, 90.370); TI-83/84: (19.375, 90.375). We are 99% confident that the population mean number of units sold per Wii in the United States lies between 19.380 (19.375) thousand games and 90.370 (90.375) thousand games. (b) $E = 35.495$ thousand Wii games. We can estimate the population mean number of units sold per Wii game in the United States to within 35.495 thousand Wii games with 99% confidence. (c) Increase the sample size.

60. (a) (3.335, 4.245). We are 95% confident that the population mean rainfall for February in Georgia lies between 3.335 inches and 4.245 inches. (b) $E = 0.455$ inches. We can estimate the population mean rainfall for February in Georgia to within 0.455 inches with 95% confidence. (c) Increase the sample size.

61. (a) See the graph. All the data points lie between the curved lines. In fact all the points lie close to the center line. Thus the distribution appears to be normal. (b) $t_{\alpha/2} = 2.015$ (c) $E = 3.276$ miles per gallon. We can estimate μ, the true mean city gas mileage for hybrid cars, within 3.276 miles per gallon with 90% confidence. (d) (27.057, 33.609). We are 90% confident that the true mean city gas mileage for hybrid cars μ lies between 27.057 miles per gallon and 33.609 miles per gallon.

62. (a)

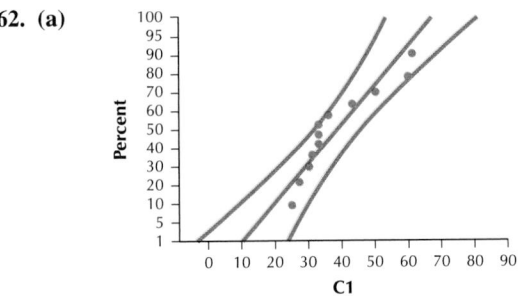

(b) Yes (c) Since the data do not appear to be normal, Case 1 does not apply. Since the sample size of $n = 12$ is small ($n < 30$), Case 2 does not apply. Thus a t interval cannot be used.

63. (a)

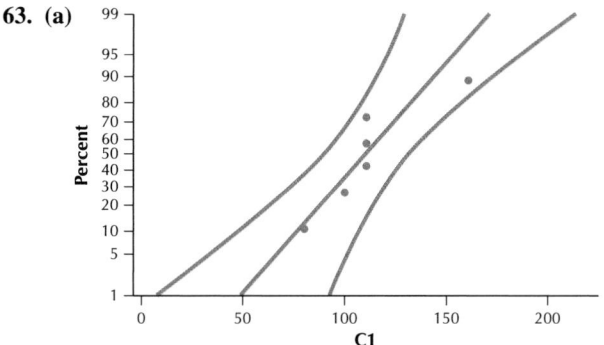

(b) Yes, the points do not appear to lie in a straight line. **(c)** Since the data do not appear to be normal, Case 1 does not apply. Since the sample size of $n = 6$ is small ($n < 30$), Case 2 does not apply. Thus a t interval cannot be used.
64. (a) $t_{\alpha/2} = 2.045$ **(b)** $E = 1.1003$ miles. We can estimate μ, the true mean commuting distance, to within 1.1003 miles with 95% confidence. **(c)** (8.3330, 11.0336). We are 95% confident that the true mean commuting distance lies between 8.3330 miles and 11.0336 miles.
65. (a) (14.0694, 15.9306). We are 90% confident that the true mean number of colors used in van Gogh's palette lies between 14.0694 colors and 15.9306 colors. **(b)** (13.8799, 16.1201). We are 95% confident that the true mean number of colors used in van Gogh's palette lies between 13.8799 colors and 16.1201 colors. **(c)** (13.4905, 16.5095). We are 99% confident that the true mean number of colors used in van Gogh's palette lies between 13.4905 colors and 16.5095 colors. **(d)** As the confidence level increases, the width of the confidence interval increases. **(e)** The only 100% confidence interval is the whole number line.
66. (a) t interval: (29.6671, 54.3329). Z interval = (32.2248, 51.7752). We are 99% confident that the population mean weekly number of HIV-related deaths in all large American cities lies between 29.6671 and 54.3329. **(b)** Lower the confidence level or increase the sample size.
67. (a) The data appear to be highly left-skewed and therefore not acceptably normal. **(b)** No. Since the population is not normally distributed, Case 1 does not apply. Since the sample size of $n = 20$ is small ($n < 30$), Case 2 does not apply. **(c)** The data set can be made more normal by increasing the sample size to at least 30. **(d)** The larger the sample size, the shorter and more precise the confidence interval. **(e)** The sample standard deviation can be used to estimate the population standard deviation. To construct a confidence interval for σ, the data must be normal.
68. (a) The histogram indicates that the data are left-skewed and therefore not normally distributed. The normal probability plot indicates that the data points all lie between the curved bounds but do not all lie along a straight line, so the normality assumption may not be valid. **(b)** $n = 10$, $\bar{x} = -0.306$, $s = 0.3435$ **(c)** $t_{\alpha/2} = 2.262$ **(d)** $(-0.5517, -0.0603)$ **(e)** $E = 0.2457$. We can estimate μ, the true mean net change of all NYSE stocks, within 0.2457 with 95% confidence.
69. (a) In the probability plot, all points lie between the curved lines except one. The histogram indicates that the data are right-skewed and not normal. **(b)** The number 59.40 is an outlier. We will omit 59.40 from the sample. **(c)** (43.679, 46.969). We are 90% confident that the true mean salary of assistant professors lies between $43,679 and $46,969.
70. (a) The graph is symmetric about the middle value with the values with the highest frequency in the middle. This indicates that the normality assumption is valid. Since the normality assumption appears

to be valid and σ is unknown, Case 1 applies, so we can use the t interval. **(b)** 2392.25 **(c)** 274.5910 **(d)** 1.895 **(e)** 183.9715 cigarettes per capita. We can estimate μ within 183.9715 cigarettes with 90% confidence. **(f)** (2208.2785, 2576.2215). We are 90% confident that μ lies between 2208.2785 and 2576.2215 cigarettes per capita.
71. (a) An increase in the sample size will result in a decrease in $t_{\alpha/2}$. **(b)** Since the margin of error is $E = t_{\alpha/2}(s/\sqrt{n})$ and the sample size n occurs in the denominator, an increase in the sample size will result in a decrease in $t_{\alpha/2}$ and a decrease in the margin of error. **(c)** Since the width of the confidence interval is $2E$, an increase in the sample size will result in a decrease in E, which will result in a decrease in the width of the confidence interval.
72. (a)–(c) Increase.

Section 8.3
1. No, unless there is some reason to suspect that the value of p has changed.
2. National pollsters almost always use 95% as their confidence level and plus or minus 3 percentage points as their margin of error.
3. $\hat{p} = 2/5 = 0.4$
4. $\hat{p} = 1/5 = 0.2$
5. $\hat{p} = 14/25 = 0.56$
6. $\hat{p} = 2057/10{,}000 = 0.2057$
7. (a) $Z_{\alpha/2} = 1.96$ **(b)** $n\hat{p} = (100)(0.2) = 20 \geq 5$ and $n(1 - \hat{p}) = (100)(1 - 0.2) = 80 \geq 5$. Thus the conditions for constructing a confidence interval for p are met. **(c)** (0.1216, 0.2784). We are 95% confident that the population proportion lies between 0.1216 and 0.2784.
(d)

```
 ├────┬────┬──┬─┬──┬────┬─┬────┬────┤
 0   0.05 0.1 0.15 0.2 0.25 0.3 0.35 0.4
            0.1216        0.2784
```

8. (a) $Z_{\alpha/2} = 1.96$ **(b)** $n\hat{p} = (100)(0.1) = 10 \geq 5$ and $n(1 - \hat{p}) = (100)(1 - 0.1) = 90 \geq 5$. Thus the conditions for constructing a confidence interval for p are met. **(c)** (0.0412, 0.1588). We are 95% confident that the population proportion lies between 0.0412 and 0.1588.
(d)

```
 ├──────┬──────────┬──────────┬──────┤
 0    0.05        0.1       0.15    0.2
     0.0412                0.1588
```

9. (a) $Z_{\alpha/2} = 1.96$ **(b)** $n\hat{p} = (100)(0.05) = 5 \geq 5$ and $n(1 - \hat{p}) = (100)(1 - 0.05) = 95 \geq 5$. Thus the conditions for constructing a confidence interval for p are met. **(c)** (0.0073, 0.0927). We are 95% confident that the population proportion lies between 0.0073 and 0.0927
(d)

```
 ├──┬──────┬──────┬──────┬──────┬──┤
 0   0.02  0.04   0.06   0.08  0.1
  0.0073                     0.0927
```

10. (a) $Z_{\alpha/2} = 1.96$ **(b)** $n\hat{p} = (100)(0.04) = 4 < 5$. Thus the conditions for constructing a confidence interval for $\hat{p}$ are not met. **(c)** Not applicable **(d)** Not applicable
11. (a) $Z_{\alpha/2} = 1.645$ **(b)** $n\hat{p} = (25)(0.2) = 5 \geq 5$ and $n(1 - \hat{p}) = (25)(1 - 0.2) = 20 \geq 5$. Thus the conditions for constructing a confidence interval for p are met. **(c)** (0.0684, 0.3316). We are 90% confident that the population proportion lies between 0.0684 and 0.3316.
(d)

```
 ├────┬────┬────┬────┬────┬────┬────┤
-0.05 0.05 0.15 0.25 0.35 0.45
     0.0684           0.3316
```

12. (a) $Z_{\alpha/2} = 1.96$ **(b)** $n\hat{p} = (25)(0.2) = 5 \geq 5$ and $n(1 - \hat{p}) = (25)(1 - 0.2) = 20 \geq 5$. Thus the conditions for constructing a confidence interval for p are met. **(c)** (0.0432, 0.3568). We are

95% confident that the population proportion lies between 0.0432 and 0.3568.

(d)

13. (a) $Z_{\alpha/2} = 2.576$ **(b)** $n\hat{p} = (25)(0.2) = 5 \geq 5$ and $n(1 - \hat{p}) = (25)(1 - 0.2) = 20 \geq 5$. Thus the conditions for constructing a confidence interval for p are met. **(c)** $(-0.0061, 0.4061)$. We are 99% confident that the population proportion lies between -0.0061 and 0.4061.

(d)

14. (a) $Z_{\alpha/2} = 1.96$ **(b)** $n\hat{p} = (25)(0.16) = 4 < 5$. Thus the conditions for constructing a confidence interval for $\hat{p}$ are not met. **(c)** Not applicable. **(d)** Not applicable
15. (a) $Z_{\alpha/2} = 1.96$ **(b)** $\hat{p} = X/n = 12/25 = 0.48$, $n\hat{p} = (25)(0.48) = 12 \geq 5$ and $n(1 - \hat{p}) = (25)(1 - 0.48) = 13 \geq 5$. Thus the conditions for constructing a confidence interval for p are met. **(c)** $(0.2842, 0.6758)$. We are 95% confident that the population proportion lies between 0.2842 and 0.6758.

(d)

16. (a) $Z_{\alpha/2} = 1.645$ **(b)** $\hat{p} = X/n = 8/81 \approx 0.0988$, $n\hat{p} = (81)(0.0988) = 8.0028 \geq 5$ and $n(1 - p) = (81)(1 - 0.0988) = 72.9972 \geq 5$. Thus the conditions for constructing a confidence interval for p are met. **(c)** $(0.0443, 0.1533)$; TI-83/84: $(0.0442, 0.1533)$. We are 90% confident that the population proportion lies between 0.0043 (0.0442) and 0.1533.

(d)

17. (a) $Z_{\alpha/2} = 2.576$ **(b)** $\hat{p} = X/n = 50/100 = 0.5$, $n\hat{p} = (100)(0.5) = 50 \geq 5$ and $n(1 - \hat{p}) = (100)(1 - 0.50) = 50 \geq 5$. Thus the conditions for constructing a confidence interval for p are met. **(c)** $(0.3712, 0.6288)$. We are 99% confident that the population proportion lies between 0.3712 and 0.6288.

(d)

18. (a) $Z_{\alpha/2} = 2.576$ **(b)** $\hat{p} = X/n = 1/20 = 0.05$, $n\hat{p} = (20)(0.05) = 1 < 5$. Thus the conditions for constructing a confidence interval for p are not met. **(c)** Not applicable **(d)** Not applicable
19. (a) $Z_{\alpha/2} = 1.96$ **(b)** $\hat{p} = X/n = 26/64 = 0.40625$, $np = (64)(0.40625) = 26 \geq 5$ and $n(1 - p) = (64)(1 - 0.40625) = 38 \geq 5$. Thus the conditions for constructing a confidence interval for p are met. **(c)** $(0.2859, 0.5266)$. We are 95% confident that the population proportion lies between 0.2859 and 0.5266.

(d)

20. (a) $Z_{\alpha/2} = 2.576$ **(b)** $\hat{p} = X/n = 80/144 \approx 0.5556$, $n\hat{p} = (144)(0.5556) = 80.0064 \geq 5$ and $n(1 - \hat{p}) = (144)(1 - 0.5556) = 63.9936 \geq 5$. Thus the conditions for constructing a confidence interval for p are met. **(c)** $(0.4489, 0.6623)$; TI-83/84: $(0.4489, 0.6622)$. We are 99% confident that the population proportion lies between 0.4489 (0.4489) and 0.6623 (0.6622).

(d)

21. (a) $Z_{\alpha/2} = 1.645$ **(b)** $\hat{p} = X/n = 18/49 \approx 0.3673$, $n\hat{p} = (49)(0.3673) = 17.9977 \geq 5$ and $n(1 - \hat{p}) = (49)(1 - 0.3673) = 31.0023 \geq 5$. Thus the conditions for constructing a confidence interval for p are met. **(c)** $(0.2540, 0.4806)$; TI-83/84: $(0.2541, 0.4806)$. We are 90% confident that the population proportion lies between 0.2540 (0.2541) and 0.4806.

(d)

22. (a) $Z_{\alpha/2} = 1.96$ **(b)** $\hat{p} = X/n = 26/15 \approx 1.7333 \geq 1$. Thus the conditions are not met. **(c)** Not applicable **(d)** Not applicable
23. $E = 0.0784$
24. $E = 0.0588$
25. $E = 0.0427$
26. (a) As the sample proportion decreases while the sample size and confidence level stay the same, the margin of error decreases. **(b)** The width decreases.
27. $E = 0.1316$
28. $E = 0.1568$
29. $E = 0.2061$
30. (a) As the confidence level increases while the sample size and the sample proportion stay the same, the margin of error increases. **(b)** The width increases.
31. (a) 0.3099 **(b)** 0.098 **(c)** 0.0310 **(d)** 0.0098
32. (a) 0.0588 **(b)** 0.0784 **(c)** 0.0898 **(d)** 0.0960 **(e)** 0.098
33. (a) Since the margin of error is $E = Z_{\alpha/2} \cdot \sqrt{\hat{p}(1 - \hat{p})/n}$, an increase in the sample size while $\hat{p}$ remains constant results in a decrease in the margin of error. **(b)** Since the width of the confidence interval is $2E$, an increase in the sample size while $\hat{p}$ remains constant results in a decrease in the width of the confidence interval.
34. (a) Since the margin of error is $E = Z_{\alpha/2} \cdot \sqrt{\hat{p}(1 - \hat{p})/n}$, the margin of error increases as the sample proportion approaches 0.5 while the sample size remains constant. **(b)** Increases
35. 897
36. 897
37. 385
38. 43
39. 5
40. Decreases
41. 752
42. 1068
43. 1844
44. 4269
45. 17,074
46. 68,296
47. Increases
48. Increases by about a factor of 4.
49. (a) $Z_{\alpha/2} = 2.576$ **(b)** $\hat{p} = X/n = 183/830 \approx 0.2205$, $np = (830)(0.2205) = 183.015 \geq 5$ and $n(1 - p) = (830)(1 - 0.2205) = 646.985 \geq 5$. Thus the conditions for constructing a confidence interval for p are met. **(c)** $(0.1834, 0.2576)$. We are 99% confident that the population proportion of millennials who are married lies between 0.1834 and 0.2576.

(d)

50. (a) 1.96 **(b)** $np = (100)(0.38) = 38 \geq 5$ and $n(1 - p) = (100)(1 - 0.38) = 62 \geq 5$. Thus the conditions for constructing a confidence interval for p are met. **(c)** (0.2849, 0.4751). We are 95% confident that the population proportion of people from Minnesota who go fishing lies between 0.2849 and 0.4751.

51. (a) 1.645 **(b)** We have $n\hat{p} = 25(0.83) = 20.75 \geq 5$, but $n(1 - \hat{p}) = 25(1 - 0.83) = 4.25 < 5$, so we cannot use the Z interval for p. **(c)** We have $n\hat{p} = 25(0.83) = 20.75 \geq 5$, but $n(1 - \hat{p}) = 25(1 - 0.83) = 4.25 < 5$, so we cannot use the Z interval for p.

52. (a) $Z_{\alpha/2} = 1.96$ **(b)** Yes **(c)** (0.3696, 0.4304). We are 95% confident that the true proportion of NASCAR racing attendees who own a pickup truck lies between 0.3696 and 0.4304.

53. (a) $E = 0.0371$ **(b)** We can estimate the proportion of American millennials who are married to within 0.0371 with 99% confidence.

54. (a) $E = 0.0951$. **(b)** We can estimate the population proportion of people from Minnesota who go fishing to within 0.0951 with 95% confidence.

55. (a)–(b) It is not appropriate to calculate the margin of error.

56. (a) $E = 0.0304$ **(b)** We can estimate p, the true proportion of NASCAR racing attendees who own a pickup truck, within 0.0304 with 95% confidence.

57. (a) $E = 0.0295$. We can estimate the population proportion of all Hawaiians who are thriving to within 0.0295 with 95% confidence. **(b)** (0.6255, 0.6845). We are 95% that the true population proportion of Hawaiians who are thriving lies between 0.6255 and 0.6845.

58. (a) Yes. **(b)** $E = 0.0353$. We can estimate p, the true proportion of all white twelfth-graders who are using Ecstasy, to within 0.0353 with 99% confidence. **(c)** (0.0037, 0.0743). We are 99% confident that the true proportion of all white twelfth-graders who are using Ecstasy lies between 0.0037 and 0.0743.

59. 13,080

60. (a) 271 **(b)** 6766

61. 1770

62. 0.0303

63. (a) 0.0318. We can estimate p to within 0.0318 with 99% confidence. **(b)** (0.1838, 0.2474)

64. (a) Decrease **(b)** Unchanged **(c)** Unchanged

65. (0.5565, 0.7435)

66. We have $\hat{p} = x/n = 482/1005 = 0.4796$. We have $n\hat{p} = 1005(0.4796) = 481.998 \geq 5$ and $n(1 - \hat{p}) = 1005(1 - 0.48796) = 523.002 \geq 5$. Thus we can use the Z interval for p. **(a)** (0.4537, 0.5055) **(b)** (0.4390, 0.5202)

67. (a)–(c) Increases

68. (a) Decrease **(b)** Unchanged **(c)** Decrease

69. (a) Decrease **(b)** Decrease **(c)** Decrease

70. We have $n\hat{p} = 40(0.975) = 39 \geq 5$ but $n(1 - \hat{p}) = 40(1 - 0.975) = 1 < 5$. Thus we cannot use the Z interval for p.

71. (0.7198, 0.8694)

72. (a) Decrease in $Z_{\alpha/2}$ from 1.96 to 1.645. **(b)** Decrease in margin of error from 0.0748 to 0.0628. **(c)** Decrease in the width of the confidence interval from 0.1496 to 0.1256.

Section 8.4

1. The population must be normal.

2. The difference between σ^2 and s^2 is that σ^2 is the population variance and s^2 is the sample variance.

3. To use this method, the distribution has to be symmetric and the χ^2 curve is not symmetric.

4. Answers will vary.

5. False. The χ^2 curve is *not* symmetric. It is right-skewed.

6. True

7. True

8. True

9. $\chi^2_{1-\alpha/2} = \chi^2_{0.95} = 13.848$ and $\chi^2_{\alpha/2} = \chi^2_{0.05} = 36.415$.

10. $\chi^2_{1-\alpha/2} = \chi^2_{0.975} = 12.401$ and $\chi^2_{\alpha/2} = \chi^2_{0.025} = 39.364$

11. $\chi^2_{1-\alpha/2} = \chi^2_{0.995} = 9.886$ and $\chi^2_{\alpha/2} = \chi^2_{0.005} = 45.559$.

12. $\chi^2_{1-\alpha/2} = \chi^2_{0.975} = 2.700$ and $\chi^2_{\alpha/2} = \chi^2_{0.025} = 19.023$

13. $\chi^2_{1-\alpha/2} = \chi^2_{0.975} = 5.629$ and $\chi^2_{\alpha/2} = \chi^2_{0.025} = 26.119$.

14. $\chi^2_{1-\alpha/2} = \chi^2_{0.975} = 8.907$ and $\chi^2_{\alpha/2} = \chi^2_{0.025} = 32.852$

15. For a given sample size, $\chi^2_{1-\alpha/2}$ decreases and $\chi^2_{\alpha/2}$ increases as the confidence level increases.

16. As the sample size increases, both $\chi^2_{1-\alpha/2}$ and $\chi^2_{\alpha/2}$ increase.

17. Lower bound = 6.59, upper bound = 17.33

18. Lower bound = 6.10, upper bound = 19.35

19. Lower bound = 5.27, upper bound = 24.28

20. Lower bound = 2.57, upper bound = 4.16

21. Lower bound = 2.47, upper bound = 4.40

22. Lower bound = 2.30, upper bound = 4.93

23. As the confidence level increases but the sample size stays the same, the lower bound for the confidence interval for σ^2 decreases and the upper bound for the confidence interval for σ^2 increases.

24. As the confidence level increases but the sample size stays the same, the lower bound for the confidence interval for σ decreases and the upper bound for the confidence interval for σ increases.

25. Lower bound = 4.73, upper bound = 33.33

26. Lower bound = 5.36, upper bound = 24.87

27. Lower bound = 5.78, upper bound = 21.33

28. Lower bound = 2.18, upper bound = 5.77

29. Lower bound = 2.32, upper bound = 4.99

30. Lower bound = 2.40, upper bound = 4.62

31. As the sample size increases but the confidence level stays the same, the lower bound of a confidence interval for σ^2 increases and the upper bound of a confidence interval for σ^2 decreases.

32. As the sample size increases but the confidence level stays the same, the lower bound of a confidence interval for σ increases and the upper bound of a confidence interval for σ decreases.

33. (a) $\chi^2_{1-\alpha/2} = \chi^2_{0.975} = 0.484$ and $\chi^2_{\alpha/2} = \chi^2_{0.025} = 11.143$. **(b)** Lower bound = 154.82, upper bound = 3564.46. We are 95% confident that the population variance σ^2 lies between 154.82 prisoners squared and 3564.46 prisoners squared. **(c)** Lower bound = 12.44, upper bound = 59.70. We are 95% confident that the population standard deviation σ lies between 12.44 prisoners and 59.70 prisoners.

34. (a) $\chi^2_{1-\alpha/2} = \chi^2_{0.975} = 2.700$ and $\chi^2_{\alpha/2} = \chi^2_{0.025} = 19.023$ **(b)** Lower bound = 0.056, upper bound = 0.393. We are 95% confident that the population variance σ^2 lies between 0.056 dollars squared and 0.393 dollars squared.

35. (a) Prisoners squared **(b)** Prisoners **(c)** Yes

36. (a) Dollars squared **(b)** No **(c)** Dollars **(d)** Lower bound = 0.236, upper bound = 0.627. We are 95% confident that the population standard deviation σ lies between \$0.236 and \$0.627.

37. (a) $\chi^2_{1-\alpha/2} = \chi^2_{0.975} = 8.907$ and $\chi^2_{\alpha/2} = \chi^2_{0.025} = 32.852$. **(b)** Lower bound = 0.95, upper bound = 3.49. We are 95% confident that the population variance σ^2 lies between 0.95 centimeter squared and 3.49 centimeters squared. **(c)** Lower bound = 0.97, upper bound = 1.87. We are 95% confident that the population standard deviation σ lies between 0.97 centimeter and 1.87 centimeters. **(d)** The interpretation in **(c)** is easier to understand since it is in the same units as our data.

38. (a) $\chi^2_{1-\alpha/2} = \chi^2_{0.975} = 10.982$ and $\chi^2_{\alpha/2} = \chi^2_{0.025} = 36.781$. **(b)** Lower bound = 1983.18, Upper bound = 6640.29. We are 95% confident that the population variance σ^2 lies between 1983.18 calories squared and 6640.29 calories squared.

(c) Lower bound $= 44.53$, Upper bound $= 81.49$. We are 95% confident that the population standard deviation σ lies between 44.53 calories and 81.49 calories. **(d)** The interpretation in (c) is easier to understand since it is in the same units as our data.
39. (a) $\chi^2_{1-\alpha/2} = \chi^2_{0.995} = 1.735$ and $\chi^2_{\alpha/2} = \chi^2_{0.005} = 23.589$.
(b) Lower bound $= 1.85$, upper bound $= 6.81$. We are 99% confident that the population standard deviation σ lies between 1.85 trillion BTUs and 6.81 trillion BTUs.
40. $(0.218, 0.855)$. We are 95% confident that the population standard deviation σ lies between 0.218 million dollars and 0.855 million dollars.
41. $(18.971, 58.395)$. We are 95% confident that the population standard deviation σ lies between 18.971 thousand Wii games and 58.395 thousand Wii games.

Chapter 8 Review

1. (a) $\sigma/\sqrt{n} = 2$ **(b)** $Z_{\alpha/2} = 1.96$ **(c)** $E = 3.92$. We can estimate μ to within 3.92 with 95% confidence. **(d)** $(46.08, 53.92)$. We are 95% confident that the true mean μ lies between 46.08 and 53.92.
2. (a) $\sigma/\sqrt{n} = 1$ **(b)** $Z_{\alpha/2} = 1.96$ **(c)** $E = 1.96$. We can estimate μ to within 1.96 with 95% confidence. **(d)** $(48.04, 51.96)$. We are 95% confident that the true mean μ lies between 48.04 and 51.96.
3. (a) 7 points **(b)** 0.2981 point **(c)** 1.645 **(d)** 0.4904 point. We can estimate μ to within 0.4904 point with 90% confidence. **(e)** $(6.5096, 7.4904)$. We are 90% confident that the true mean increase in IQ points for all children after listening to a Mozart piano sonata for about 10 minutes μ lies between 6.5106 points and 7.4904 points.
4. (a) \$45,000 **(b)** $\sigma/\sqrt{n} = \$1200$ **(c)** $Z_{\alpha/2} = 2.576$ **(d)** $E = \$3091.20$. We can estimate μ, the mean income of all working women in California, to within \$3091.20 with 99% confidence. **(e)** $(41,908.80, 48,091.20)$. We are 99% confident that the true mean income of all working women in California μ lies between \$41,908.80 and \$48,091.20.
5. 97
6. 35
7. 4
8. 68
9. Since the population is not normal, Case 1 does not apply. Since the sample size of $n = 25$ is small ($n < 30$), Case 2 does not apply. Thus we cannot use the t interval.
10. $(20.289, 23.711)$
11. $(21.169, 22.831)$
12. (a) $(2162.65, 2621.85)$ **(b)** $(2052.56, 2731.94)$ **(c)** The interval in (a) is more precise than the interval in (b) but the interval in (b) has higher confidence of containing μ.
13. (a) $t_{\alpha/2} = 1.667$ **(b)** $E = \$5.77$. We can estimate μ, the true mean amount of money collected by all parking meters, to within \$5.77 with 90% confidence. **(c)** $(114.23, 125.77)$. We are 90% confident that the true mean amount of money collected by all parking meters lies between \$114.23 and \$125.77.
14. (a) 1.96 **(b)** We have $n\hat{p} = 100(0.1) = 10 \geq 5$ and $n(1 - \hat{p}) = 100(1 - 0.1) = 90 \geq 5$. Thus we can use the Z interval for p. **(c)** 0.0588. We can estimate p to within $E = 0.0588$ with 95% confidence. **(d)** $(0.0412, 0.1588)$
15. (a) 1.96 **(b)** We have $n\hat{p} = 500(0.99) = 495 \geq 5$ and $n(1 - \hat{p}) = 500(1 - 0.99) = 5 \geq 5$. Thus we can use the Z interval for p. **(c)** 0.0087. We can estimate p to within $E = 0.0087$ with 95% confidence. **(d)** $(0.9813, 0.9987)$. Thus we are 95% confident that the true proportion lies between 0.9813 and 0.9987.
16. (a) 0.0583. We can estimate p to within $E = 0.0583$ with 95% confidence. **(b)** $(0.7117, 0.8283)$. We are 95% confident that the true proportion of all emergency room patients mentioning MDMA (Ecstasy) as a factor in their admission who are age 25 and under lies between 0.7117 and 0.8283.

17. (a) The margin of error is $E = 0.0255$. We can estimate p, the true proportion of all erasures that resulted in a correct answer, within $E = 0.0255$ with 99% confidence. **(b)** $(0.8645, 0.9155)$ **(c)** Since 0.70 does not lie in our confidence interval and none of the values below 0.70 lie in our confidence interval, we are 99% confident that no number less than or equal to 0.70 is a plausible value for p. All numbers less than or equal to 0.70 lie below our confidence interval. This is an indication that tampering may have occurred.
18. 664
19. 43
20. 5
21. 271
22. 752
23. 6766
24. Lower bound $= 70.278$, upper bound $= 155.798$
25. Lower bound $= 65.786$, upper bound $= 170.159$
26. Lower bound $= 8.383$, upper bound $= 12.482$
27. Lower bound $= 8.111$, upper bound $= 13.044$
28. Lower bound $= 30.537$, upper bound $= 104.367$. We are 95% confident that σ, the population standard deviation of total union membership per state, lies between 30.537 and 104.367 thousand.

Chapter 8 Quiz

1. False
2. True
3. 4
4. less
5. α is a probability.
6. Either the population is normal or the sample size is large ($n \geq 30$).
7. (a) $E = \$705$. We can estimate μ, the mean cost of a college education, to within \$705 with 90% confidence. **(b)** $(29,795, 31,205)$. We are 90% confident that the true mean cost of a college education lies between \$29,795 and \$31,205.
8. (a) $E = 49.35$ pounds. We can estimate μ, the mean femur load number in a frontal crash for the passenger in a 2005 Ford Equinox SUV, to within 49.35 pounds with 90% confidence. **(b)** $(953.65, 1052.35)$. We are 90% confident that the true mean femur load number in a frontal crash for the passenger in a 2005 Ford Equinox SUV lies between 953.65 pounds and 1052.35 pounds.
9. $(55.15, 58.85)$. We are 90% confident that the true mean day count of wolves in Isle Royale lies between 55.15 wolves and 58.85 wolves.
10. $(9.30, 9.70)$. We are 95% confident that the true mean fog index for all the books of this horror author lies between 9.30 and 9.70.
11. (a) $E = 0.0142$. We can estimate p, the true proportion of all Americans who attended a religious service in response to the attacks on the World Trade Center and the Pentagon, to within 0.0142 with 95% confidence. **(b)** $(0.2513, 0.2797)$. We are 95% confident that the true proportion of all Americans who attended a religious service in response to the attacks on the World Trade Center and the Pentagon lies between 0.2513 and 0.2797.
12. (a) $E = 0.0386$. We can estimate p, the true proportion of all Québecois who favor independence for the Province of Quebec, to within 0.0386 with 99% confidence. **(b)** $(0.3014, 0.3786)$
13. (a) $(1.863, 4.944)$. We are 95% confident that the population standard deviation of Amanda's delivery times lies between 1.8623 minutes and 4.941 minutes. **(b)** $(6.083, 16.147)$. We are 95% confident that the population standard deviation of Bethany's delivery times lies between 6.083 minutes and 16.147 minutes.
14. 363
15. 554
16. 752

Chapter 9

Section 9.1

1. The null hypothesis is assumed to be true unless the sample evidence indicates that the alternative hypothesis is true instead. It represents what has been tentatively assumed about the value of the parameter. It is the status quo hypothesis. The alternative hypothesis represents an alternative claim about the value of the parameter. The researcher concludes that the alternative hypothesis is true only if the evidence provided by the sample data indicates that it is true.

2. μ_0 is a specified value for the unknown mean μ.

3.

Form	Null hypothesis		Alternative hypothesis
1	$H_0 : \mu = \mu_0$	vs.	$H_a : \mu > \mu_0$
2	$H_0 : \mu = \mu_0$	vs.	$H_a : \mu < \mu_0$
3	$H_0 : \mu = \mu_0$	vs.	$H_a : \mu \neq \mu_0$

4. (1) Finding the defendant guilty when in reality he did not commit the crime (a Type I error) and (2) finding the defendant not guilty when in reality he did commit the crime (a Type II error).

5. A Type I error occurs when one rejects H_0 when H_0 is true. A Type II error occurs when one does not reject H_0 when H_0 is false.

6. The two ways of making the correct decision are to not reject H_0 when H_0 is true and to reject H_0 when H_0 is false.

7. No. It depends on how many standard deviations the sample mean of 90 is below the population mean of 100 and the level of significance of the test.

8. False

9. $H_0 : \mu = 10$ vs. $H_a : \mu > 10$

10. $H_0 : \mu = 100$ vs. $H_a : \mu < 100$

11. $H_0 : \mu = 0$ vs. $H_a : \mu \neq 0$

12. $H_0 : \mu = 4.0$ vs. $H_a : \mu \neq 4.0$

13. $H_0 : \mu = 36$ vs. $H_a : \mu \neq 36$

14. $H_0 : \mu = -4$ vs. $H_a : \mu > -4$

15. (a) $H_0 : \mu = 43.9$ vs. $H_a : \mu > 43.9$ (b) A Type II error was made.

16. (a) $H_0 : \mu = 15$ vs. $H_a : \mu > 15$ (b) A Type I error was made.

17. (a) $H_0 : \mu = 700$ vs. $H_a : \mu < 700$ (b) No error was made.

18. (a) $H_0 : \mu = 3$ vs. $H_a : \mu < 3$ (b) A correct decision was made.

19. (a) $H_0 : \mu = 1,602,000,000$ vs. $H_a : \mu > 1,602,000,000$ (b) Conclude that the mean is greater than 1.602 billion when the population mean is actually greater than 1.602 billion, and conclude that the mean is equal to 1.602 billion when the population is actually equal to 1.602 billion. (c) Concluding that the mean is greater than 1.602 billion when the population mean is actually equal to 1.602 billion (d) Concluding that the mean is equal to 1.602 billion when the population mean is actually greater than 1.602 billion

20. (a) $H_0 : \mu = 339.1$ vs. $H_a : \mu \neq 339.1$ (b) (1) The mean number of fatal and injury collisions is different from 339.1 per year when the population mean number of fatal and injury collisions is actually different than 339.1 per year and (2) the average number of fatal and injury collisions is equal to 339.1 per year when in actuality the population mean number of fatal and injury collisions is equal to 339.1 per year. (c) The mean number of fatal and injury collisions is different from 339.1 per year when the population mean

number of fatal and injury collisions is actually equal to 339.1 per year. (d) The mean number of fatal and injury collisions is equal to 339.1 per year when actually the population mean number of fatal and injury collisions is not equal to 339.1 per year.

21. (a) $H_0 : \mu = 3.24$ vs. $H_a : \mu > 3.24$ (b) Conclude that the mean is greater than \$3.24 when it actually is greater than \$3.24, and conclude that the mean is equal to \$3.24 when it actually is equal to \$3.24. (c) Concluding that the mean is greater than \$3.24 when it actually is equal to \$3.24 (d) Concluding that the mean is equal to \$3.24 when it actually is greater than \$3.24

22. (a) $H_0 : \mu = 175$ vs. $H_a : \mu \neq 175$ (b) (1) The mean height of Americans this year has changed from 175 centimeters when it actually is different from 175 centimeters and (2) the mean height of Americans has not changed from 175 centimeters when it actually is equal to 175 centimeters. (c) The mean height of Americans this year has changed from 175 centimeters when it actually is equal to 175 centimeters. (d) The mean height of Americans has not changed from 175 centimeters when it actually is not equal to 175 centimeters.

23. (a) $H_0 : \mu = 673$ vs. $H_a : \mu < 673$ (b) Conclude that the mean is less than 673 when it actually is less than 673, and conclude that the mean is equal to 673 when it actually is equal to 673. (c) Concluding that the mean is less than 673 when it actually is equal to 673 (d) Concluding that the mean is equal to 673 when it actually is less than 673.

24. (a) $H_0 : \mu = 52,200$ vs. $H_a : \mu > 52,200$ (b) (1) The mean salary of college graduates is actually greater than \$52,200 when it actually is greater than \$52,200 and (2) the mean salary of college graduates is equal to \$52,200 when it actually is equal to \$52,200. (c) The mean salary of college graduates is greater than \$52,200 when it actually is equal to \$52,200. (d) The mean salary of college graduates is equal to \$52,200 when it is actually greater than \$52,200.

Section 9.2

1. When the observed value of $\bar{x}$ is unusual or extreme in the sampling distribution of $\bar{x}$ that assumes H_0 is true, we should reject H_0. Otherwise, we should not reject H_0.

2. The number of standard deviations that the sample mean $\bar{x}$ lies above or below the hypothesized value of the mean μ_0 from H_0.

3. A statistic generated from a data set for the purpose of testing a statistical hypothesis

4. The critical region consists of the range of values of the test statistic Z_{data} for which we reject the null hypothesis. The noncritical region consists of the range of values of the test statistic Z_{data} for which we do not reject the null hypothesis.

5. The value of Z that separates the critical region from the noncritical region

6. There is evidence at level of significance α that the population mean is less than 5.

7. The critical region for a right-tailed test lies in the right (upper) tail.

8. True

9. $Z_{data} = 1$

10. $Z_{data} = 2$

11. $Z_{data} = 2.5$

12. $Z_{data} = -1$

13. $Z_{data} = -1.5$

14. $Z_{data} = -3$

15. $Z_{data} = -5$

16. $Z_{data} = -3$

17. (a) $Z_{\text{crit}} = 1.28$
(b)
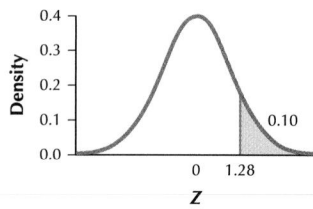

(c) Reject H_0 if $Z_{\text{data}} \geq 1.28$.
18. (a) $Z_{\text{crit}} = 1.645$
(b)
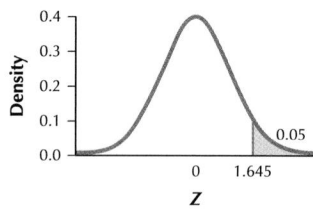

(c) Reject H_0 if $Z_{\text{data}} \geq 1.645$.
19. (a) $Z_{\text{crit}} = 2.33$
(b)
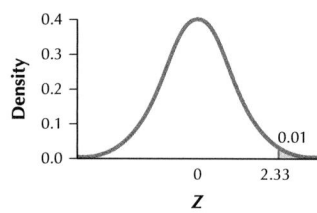

(c) Reject H_0 if $Z_{\text{data}} \geq 2.33$.
20. (a) $Z_{\text{crit}} = -1.28$
(b)
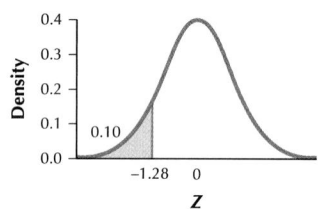

(c) Reject H_0 if $Z_{\text{data}} \leq -1.28$.
21. (a) $Z_{\text{crit}} = -1.645$
(b)
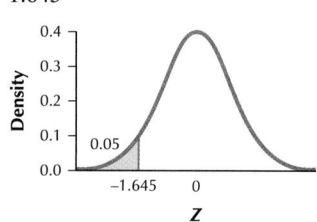

(c) Reject H_0 if $Z_{\text{data}} \leq -1.645$.
22. (a) $Z_{\text{crit}} = -2.33$
(b)
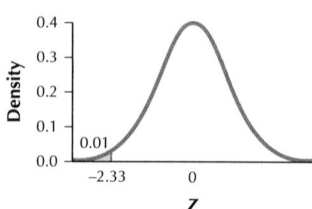

(c) Reject H_0 if $Z_{\text{data}} \leq -2.33$.

23. (a) $Z_{\text{crit}} = 1.96$
(b)
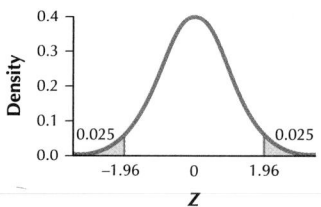

(c) Reject H_0 if $Z_{\text{data}} \leq -1.96$ or $Z_{\text{data}} \geq 1.96$
24. (a) $Z_{\text{crit}} = 2.58$
(b)
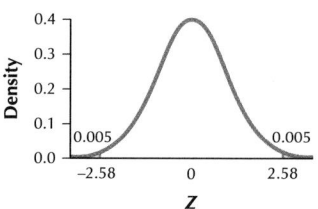

(c) Reject H_0 if $Z_{\text{data}} \leq -2.58$ or $Z_{\text{data}} \geq 2.58$.
25. (a) It increases. **(b)** It becomes smaller.
26. (a) It decreases. **(b)** It becomes smaller.
27. (a) $H_0 : \mu = 10$ vs. $H_a : \mu > 10$ **(b)** $Z_{\text{crit}} = 1.28$. Reject H_0 if $Z_{\text{data}} \geq 1.28$. **(c)** $Z_{\text{data}} = 1$ **(d)** Since $Z_{\text{data}} = 1$ is not ≥ 1.28, the conclusion is do not reject H_0. There is insufficient evidence at the 0.10 level of significance that the population mean is greater than 10.
28. (a) $H_0 : \mu = 10$ vs. $H_a : \mu > 10$ **(b)** $Z_{\text{crit}} = 1.645$. Reject H_0 if $Z_{\text{data}} \geq 1.645$. **(c)** $Z_{\text{data}} = 2$ **(d)** Since $Z_{\text{data}} = 2$ is ≥ 1.645, the conclusion is reject H_0. There is evidence at the 0.05 level of significance that the population mean is greater than 10.
29. (a) $H_0 : \mu = 10$ vs. $H_a : \mu > 10$ **(b)** $Z_{\text{crit}} = 2.33$. Reject H_0 if $Z_{\text{data}} \geq 2.33$. **(c)** $Z_{\text{data}} = 2.5$ **(d)** Since $Z_{\text{data}} = 2.5$ is ≥ 2.33, the conclusion is reject H_0. There is evidence at the 0.01 level of significance that the population mean is greater than 10.
30. (a) $H_0 : \mu = 7$ vs. $H_a : \mu < 7$ **(b)** $Z_{\text{crit}} = -1.28$. Reject H_0 if $Z_{\text{data}} \leq -1.28$. **(c)** $Z_{\text{data}} = -1$ **(d)** Since $Z_{\text{data}} = -1$ is not ≤ -1.28, the conclusion is do not reject H_0. There is insufficient evidence at the 0.10 level of significance that the population mean is less than 7.
31. (a) $H_0 : \mu = 7$ vs. $H_a : \mu < 7$ **(b)** $Z_{\text{crit}} = -1.645$. Reject H_0 if $Z_{\text{data}} \leq -1.645$. **(c)** $Z_{\text{data}} = -1.5$ **(d)** Since $Z_{\text{data}} = -1.5$ is not ≤ -1.645, the conclusion is do not reject H_0. There is insufficient evidence at the 0.05 level of significance that the population mean is less than 7.
32. (a) $H_0 : \mu = 7$ vs. $H_a : \mu < 7$ **(b)** $Z_{\text{crit}} = -2.33$. Reject H_0 if $Z_{\text{data}} \leq -2.33$. **(c)** $Z_{\text{data}} = -3$ **(d)** Since $Z_{\text{data}} = -3$ is ≤ -2.33, the conclusion is reject H_0. There is evidence at the 0.01 level of significance that the population mean is less than 7.
33. (a) $H_0 : \mu = 100$ vs. $H_a : \mu \neq 100$ **(b)** $Z_{\text{crit}} = 1.96$. Reject H_0 if $Z_{\text{data}} \leq -1.96$ or if $Z_{\text{data}} \geq 1.96$. **(c)** $Z_{\text{data}} = -5$ **(d)** Since $Z_{\text{data}} = -5$ is ≤ -1.96, the conclusion is reject H_0. There is evidence at the 0.05 level of significance that the population mean differs from 100.
34. (a) $H_0 : \mu = -50$ vs. $H_a : \mu \neq -50$ **(b)** $Z_{\text{crit}} = 2.58$. Reject H_0 if $Z_{\text{data}} \leq -2.58$ or if Z data ≥ 2.58. **(c)** $Z_{\text{data}} = -3$ **(d)** Since $Z_{\text{data}} = -3$ is ≤ -2.58, the conclusion is reject H_0. There is evidence at the 0.01 level of significance that the population mean differs from -50.

35. (a) $H_0 : \mu = 80$ vs. $H_a : \mu > 80$ **(b)** $Z_{crit} = 1.645$. Reject H_0 if $Z_{data} \geq 1.645$. **(c)** $Z_{data} = 1$.

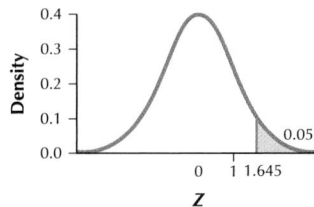

(d) Since $Z_{data} = 1$ is not ≥ 1.645, the conclusion is do not reject H_0. There is insufficient evidence at the 0.05 level of significance that the population mean number of connections to community pages, groups, and events is greater than 80.

36. (a) $H_0 : \mu = 80,000$ vs. $H_a : \mu < 80,000$ **(b)** $Z_{crit} = -2.33$. Reject H_0 if $Z_{data} \leq -2.33$. **(c)** $Z_{data} = -2.5$.

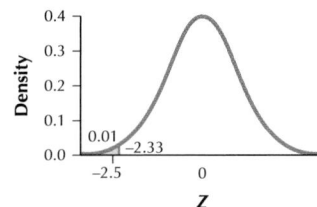

(d) Since $Z_{data} = -2.5$ is ≤ -2.33, the conclusion is reject H_0. There is evidence at the 0.01 level of significance that the population mean salary for marketing managers is less than \$80,000. Thus we can conclude at the 0.01 level of significance that the population mean salary for marketing managers fell during the recession.

37. (a) $H_0 : \mu = 10$ vs. $H_a : \mu \neq 10$ **(b)** $Z_{crit} = 2.58$. Reject H_0 if $Z_{data} \leq -2.58$ or if $Z_{data} \geq 2.58$. **(c)** $Z_{data} = 1$.

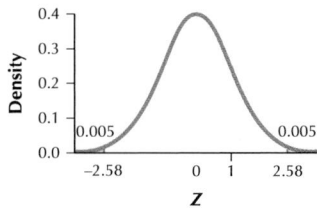

(d) Since $Z_{data} = 1$ is not ≤ -2.58 and not ≥ 2.58, the conclusion is do not reject H_0. There is insufficient evidence at the 0.01 level of significance that the population mean number of text messages per day differs from 10.

38. (a) $H_0 : \mu = 37$ vs. $H_a : \mu < 37$ **(b)** $Z_{crit} = -1.645$. Reject H_0 if $Z_{data} \leq -1.645$. **(c)** $Z_{data} = -1$.

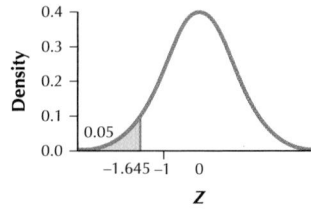

(d) Since $Z_{data} = -1$ is not ≤ -1.645, the conclusion is do not reject H_0. There is insufficient evidence at the 0.05 level of significance that the population mean age of video gamers is less than 37.

39. (a) $H_0 : \mu = 3.70$ vs. $H_a : \mu > 3.70$ **(b)** $Z_{crit} = 1.645$. Reject H_0 if $Z_{data} \geq 1.645$. **(c)** $Z_{data} = 2$.

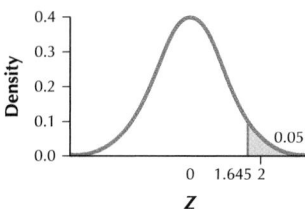

(d) Since $Z_{data} = 2$ is ≥ 1.645, the conclusion is reject H_0. There is evidence at the 0.05 level of significance that the population mean price of regular gasoline is greater than \$3.70 per gallon. Therefore we can conclude at the 0.05 level of significance that the population mean price for a gallon of regular gasoline has risen since June 2011.

40. (a) $H_0 : \mu = 2.58$ vs. $H_a : \mu < 2.58$ **(b)** $Z_{crit} = -1.28$. Reject H_0 if $Z_{data} \leq -1.28$. **(c)** $Z_{data} = -1$.

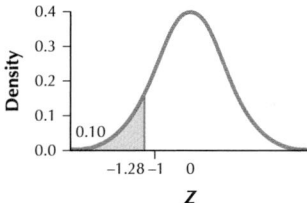

(d) Since $Z_{data} = -1$ is not ≤ -1.28, the conclusion is do not reject H_0. There is insufficient evidence at the 0.10 level of significance that the population mean household size this year is less than 2.58 persons.

41. (a) $H_0 : \mu = 175$ vs. $H_a : \mu \neq 175$ **(b)** $Z_{crit} = 1.645$. Reject H_0 if $Z_{data} \leq -1.645$ or if $Z_{data} \geq 1.645$. **(c)** $Z_{data} = 8$.

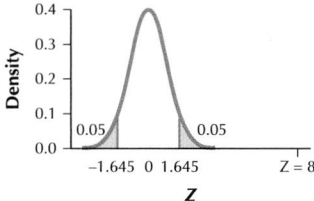

(d) Since $Z_{data} = 8$ is ≥ 1.645, the conclusion is reject H_0. There is evidence at the 0.10 level of significance that the population mean height of Americans has changed from 175 centimeters.

42. (a) $H_0 : \mu = 3.34$ vs. $H_a : \mu > 3.34$ **(b)** $Z_{crit} = 1.645$. Reject H_0 if $Z_{data} \geq 1.645$. **(c)** $Z_{data} = 2$.

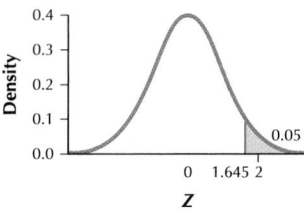

(d) Since $Z_{data} = 2$ is ≥ 1.645, the conclusion is reject H_0. There is evidence at the 0.05 level of significance that the population mean price for milk this year is greater than \$3.34 per gallon. Therefore we can conclude that the population mean price of milk this year has increased from the 2011 value.

43. The histogram indicates that the data are extremely right-skewed and therefore not normally distributed. Thus Case 1 does not apply. Since the sample size of $n = 16$ is small ($n < 30$), Case 2 does not apply. Thus it is not appropriate to apply the Z test.

44. **(a)** The histogram indicates acceptable normality, so we can apply the Z test. **(b)** $H_0 : \mu \le 30$ vs. $H_a : \mu > 30$. $Z_{\text{crit}} = 1.28$; Reject H_0 if $Z_{\text{data}} > 1.28$. $Z_{\text{data}} = 5.37$. Since $Z_{\text{data}} > 1.28$, we reject H_0. There is evidence that the population mean gas mileage of the Honda Civic is greater than 30 mpg. **(c)** We reject H_0 for both $\alpha = 0.10$ and $\alpha = 0.05$.

45. **(a)** Decrease **(b)** Unchanged **(c)** Depends on new value of $\bar{x}$.

46. **(a)** Since the sample size of $n = 100$ is large ($n \ge 30$), Case 2 applies, so it is appropriate to apply the Z test. **(b)** Even though the sample mean $\bar{x} = 6.2$ cents per mile is greater than the hypothesized mean $\mu_0 = 5.9$ cents per mile, this is not enough by itself to reject the null hypothesis. It also depends on the variability of the data and on α. **(c)** Since $\bar{x} = 6.2$ cents per mile is 2 standard errors above $\mu_0 = 5.9$ cents per mile, it is mildly extreme.

47. **(a)** $H_0 : \mu \le 60$ vs. $H_a : \mu > 60$ **(b)** $t_{\text{crit}} = 1.771$. Reject H_0 if $t_{\text{data}} > 1.771$ **(c)** $t_{\text{data}} = 2.50$ **(d)** Since $t_{\text{data}} > 1.771$, we reject H_0. There is evidence that the population mean response time is greater than 60 milliseconds.

48. **(a)** 961, 25

(b)

```
Descriptive Statistics: CALORIES

Variable        N      N*      Mean   SE Mean   StDev   Minimum     Q1
CALORIES      961       0     270.4      17.5   542.9       0.0   65.0

            Median      Q3  Maximum
             125.0   230.0   6175.0
```

(c)

```
One-Sample Z: CALORIES

Test of mu = 300 vs not = 300
The assumed standard deviation = 540

Variable        N    Mean   StDev   SE Mean        95% CI
CALORIES      961   270.4   542.9      17.4   (236.3, 304.6)

                Z       P
            -1.70   0.090
```

$H_0 : \mu = 300$ vs. $H_a : \mu \ne 300$. $Z_{\text{crit}} = 1.96$. Reject H_0 if $Z_{\text{data}} \le -1.96$ or if $Z_{\text{data}} \ge 1.96$. $Z_{\text{data}} = -1.70$. Since $Z_{\text{data}} = -1.70$ is not ≤ -1.96 and is not ≥ 1.96, the conclusion is do

not reject H_0. There is insufficient evidence at the 0.05 level of significance that the population mean number of calories per food differs from 300.

(d)

```
One-Sample Z: CALORIES

Test of mu = 320 vs not = 320
The assumed standard deviation = 540

Variable        N    Mean   StDev   SE Mean        95% CI
CALORIES      961   270.4   542.9      17.4   (236.3, 304.6)

                Z       P
            -2.84   0.004
```

$H_0 : \mu = 320$ vs. $H_a : \mu \ne 320$. $Z_{\text{crit}} = 1.96$. Reject H_0 if $Z_{\text{data}} \le -1.96$ or if $Z_{\text{data}} \ge 1.96$. $Z_{\text{data}} = -2.84$. Since $Z_{\text{data}} = -2.84$ is ≤ -1.96, the conclusion is reject H_0. There is evidence at the 0.05 level of significance that the population mean number of calories per food differs from 320.

49. **(a)** Graphs will vary.

```
Descriptive Statistics: SODIUM

Variable        N      N*      Mean   SE Mean   StDev   Minimum     Q1
SODIUM        961       0     320.4      20.2   625.7       0.0    7.0

            Median      Q3  Maximum
              75.0   313.5   8142.0
```

(b)

```
One-Sample Z: SODIUM

Test of mu = 280 vs > 280
The assumed standard deviation = 625

Variable        N    Mean   StDev   SE Mean   95% Lower Bound
SODIUM        961   320.4   625.7      20.2             287.3

                Z       P
             2.01   0.022
```

$H_0 : \mu = 280$ vs. $H_a : \mu > 280$. $Z_{\text{crit}} = 1.645$. Reject H_0 if $Z_{\text{data}} \ge 1.645$. $Z_{\text{data}} = 2.01$. Since $Z_{\text{data}} = 2.01$ is ≥ 1.645, the conclusion is reject H_0. There is evidence at the 0.05 level of significance that the population mean amount of sodium is greater than 280 mg.

(c)

```
One-Sample Z: SODIUM

Test of mu = 290 vs > 290
The assumed standard deviation = 625

Variable        N    Mean   StDev   SE Mean   95% Lower Bound
SODIUM        961   320.4   625.7      20.2             287.3

                Z       P
             1.51   0.065
```

$H_0 : \mu = 290$ vs. $H_a : \mu > 290$. $Z_{\text{crit}} = 1.645$. Reject H_0 if $Z_{\text{data}} \ge 1.645$. $Z_{\text{data}} = 1.51$. Since $Z_{\text{data}} = 1.51$ is not ≥ 1.645, the conclusion is do not reject H_0. There is insufficient evidence at the 0.05 level of significance that the population mean amount of sodium is greater than 290 mg.

Section 9.3

1. False

2. Reject H_0 if the p-value $\leq \alpha$, the level of significance. Otherwise, do not reject H_0.

3. It gives us extra information about whether H_0 was barely rejected or not rejected or whether it was a no-brainer decision to reject or not reject H_0.

4. If a certain value for μ_0 lies outside the corresponding $100(1 - \alpha)\%$ Z confidence interval for μ, then the null hypothesis specifying this value for μ_0 would be rejected for level of significance α. Alternatively, if a certain value for μ_0 lies inside the corresponding $100(1 - \alpha)\%$ Z confidence interval for μ, then the null hypothesis specifying this value for μ_0 would not be rejected for level of significance α.

5. False

6. (a) Not a probability (b) A probability (c) A probability

7. 0.1587

8. 0.0228

9. 0.0013

10. 0.0062

11. 0.0062

12. 0.0038 (TI-83/84: 0.0037)

13. 0.0038 (TI-83/84: 0.0037)

14. 0.2040 (TI-83/84: 0.2041)

15. It decreases.

16. They are the same.

17. (a) $H_0 : \mu = 98.6$ vs. $H_a : \mu > 98.6$. Reject H_0 if the p-value $\leq \alpha = 0.05$. (b) $Z_{\text{data}} = 0.5$. (c) 0.3085 (d) Since the p-value $= 0.3085$ is not ≤ 0.05, we therefore do not reject H_0. There is insufficient evidence at level of significance $\alpha = 0.05$ that the population mean is greater than 98.6.

18. (a) $H_0 : \mu = 32$ vs. $H_a : \mu < 32$. Reject H_0 if the p-value $\leq \alpha = 0.05$. (b) $Z_{\text{data}} = -1.25$. (c) 0.1056 (d) Since the p-value $= 0.1056$ is not ≤ 0.05, we therefore do not reject H_0. There is insufficient evidence at level of significance $\alpha = 0.05$ that the population mean is less than 32.

19. (a) $H_0 : \mu = -0.1$ vs. $H_a : \mu > -0.1$. Reject H_0 if the p-value $\leq \alpha = 0.05$. (b) $Z_{\text{data}} = 2$. (c) 0.0228 (d) Since the p-value $= 0.0228$ is ≤ 0.05, we therefore reject H_0. There is evidence at level of significance $\alpha = 0.05$ that the population mean is greater than -0.1.

20. (a) $H_0 : \mu = 100$ vs. $H_a : \mu \neq 100$. Reject H_0 if p-value $\leq \alpha = 0.05$. (b) $Z_{\text{data}} = 1.5333$. (c) 0.1252 (d) Since the p-value $= 0.1252$ is not ≤ 0.05, we therefore do not reject H_0. There is insufficient evidence at level of significance $\alpha = 0.05$ that the population mean differs from 100.

21. (a) $H_0 : \mu = -50$ vs. $H_a : \mu \neq -50$. Reject H_0 if p-value $\leq \alpha = 0.05$ (b) $Z_{\text{data}} = 2.6667$. (c) 0.0077 (d) Since the p-value $= 0.0077$ is ≤ 0.05, we therefore reject H_0. There is evidence at level of significance $\alpha = 0.05$ that the population mean differs from 50.

22. $H_0 : \mu = 0$ vs. $H_a : \mu \neq 0$. Reject H_0 if p-value $\leq \alpha = 0.05$ (b) $Z_{\text{data}} = -3.4$. (c) 0.0006 (TI-83/84: 0.0007) (d) Since the p-value $= 0.0006$ is ≤ 0.05, we therefore reject H_0. There is evidence at level of significance $\alpha = 0.05$ that the population mean differs from 0.

23. No evidence

24. Slight evidence

25. Solid evidence

26. Slight evidence

27. Very strong evidence

28. Extremely strong evidence

29.

	Value of μ_0	Form of hypothesis test, with $\alpha = 0.05$	Where μ_0 lies in relation to 95% confidence interval (2.7, 6.9)	Conclusion of hypothesis test
(a)	-3	$H_0 : \mu = -3$ vs. $H_a : \mu \neq -3$	Outside	Reject H_0
(b)	-2	$H_0 : \mu = -2$ vs. $H_a : \mu \neq -2$	Inside	Do not reject H_0
(c)	0	$H_0 : \mu = 0$ vs. $H_a : \mu \neq 0$	Inside	Do not reject H_0
(d)	5	$H_0 : \mu = 5$ vs. $H_a : \mu \neq 5$	Inside	Do not reject H_0
(e)	7	$H_0 : \mu = 7$ vs. $H_a : \mu \neq 7$	Outside	Reject H_0

30.

	Value of μ_0	Form of hypothesis test, with $\alpha = 0.01$	Where μ_0 lies in relation to 99% confidence interval (45, 55)	Conclusion of hypothesis test
(a)	0	$H_0 : \mu = 0$ vs. $H_a : \mu \neq 0$	Outside	Reject H_0
(b)	44	$H_0 : \mu = 44$ vs. $H_a : \mu \neq 44$	Outside	Reject H_0
(c)	50	$H_0 : \mu = 50$ vs. $H_a : \mu \neq 50$	Inside	Do not reject H_0
(d)	54	$H_0 : \mu = 54$ vs. $H_a : \mu \neq 54$	Inside	Do not reject H_0
(e)	56	$H_0 : \mu = 56$ vs. $H_a : \mu \neq 56$	Outside	Reject H_0

31.

	Value of μ_0	Form of hypothesis test, with $\alpha = 0.10$	Where μ_0 lies in relation to 90% confidence interval $(-10, -5)$	Conclusion of hypothesis test
(a)	-3	$H_0 : \mu = -3$ vs. $H_a : \mu \neq -3$	Outside	Reject H_0
(b)	-8	$H_0 : \mu = -8$ vs. $H_a : \mu \neq -8$	Inside	Do not reject H_0
(c)	-11	$H_0 : \mu = -11$ vs. $H_a : \mu \neq -11$	Outside	Reject H_0
(d)	0	$H_0 : \mu = 0$ vs. $H_a : \mu \neq 0$	Outside	Reject H_0
(e)	7	$H_0 : \mu = 7$ vs. $H_a : \mu \neq 7$	Outside	Reject H_0

32.

	Value of μ_0	Form of hypothesis test, with $\alpha = 0.05$	Where μ_0 lies in relation to 95% confidence interval (1024, 2056)	Conclusion of hypothesis test
(a)	1000	$H_0 : \mu = 1000$ vs. $H_a : \mu \neq 1000$	Outside	Reject H_0
(b)	2000	$H_0 : \mu = 2000$ vs. $H_a : \mu \neq 2000$	Inside	Do not reject H_0
(c)	3000	$H_0 : \mu = 3000$ vs. $H_a : \mu \neq 3000$	Outside	Reject H_0
(d)	0	$H_0 : \mu = 0$ vs. $H_a : \mu \neq 0$	Outside	Reject H_0
(e)	1025	$H_0 : \mu = 1025$ vs. $H_a : \mu \neq 1025$	Inside	Do not reject H_0

33.

	Value of μ_0	Form of hypothesis test, with $\alpha = 0.05$	Where μ_0 lies in relation to 95% confidence interval (0, 1)	Conclusion of hypothesis test
(a)	1.5	$H_0 : \mu = 1.5$ vs. $H_a : \mu \neq 1.5$	Outside	Reject H_0
(b)	-1	$H_0 : \mu = -1$ vs. $H_a : \mu \neq -1$	Outside	Reject H_0
(c)	0.5	$H_0 : \mu = 0.5$ vs. $H_a : \mu \neq 0.5$	Inside	Do not reject H_0
(d)	0.9	$H_0 : \mu = 0.9$ vs. $H_a : \mu \neq 0.9$	Inside	Do not reject H_0
(e)	1.2	$H_0 : \mu = 1.2$ vs. $H_a : \mu \neq 1.2$	Outside	Reject H_0

34.

	Value of μ_0	Form of hypothesis test, with $\alpha = 0.05$	Where μ_0 lies in relation to 95% confidence interval (1.3275, 1.4339)	Conclusion of hypothesis test
(a)	1.3	$H_0 : \mu = 1.3$ vs. $H_a : \mu \neq 1.3$	Outside	Reject H_0
(b)	1.35	$H_0 : \mu = 1.35$ vs. $H_a : \mu \neq 1.35$	Inside	Do not reject H_0
(c)	1.4	$H_0 : \mu = 1.4$ vs. $H_a : \mu \neq 1.4$	Inside	Do not reject H_0
(d)	1.45	$H_0 : \mu = 1.45$ vs. $H_a : \mu \neq 1.45$	Outside	Do not reject H_0
(e)	1.3275	$H_0 : \mu = 1.3275$ vs. $H_a : \mu \neq 1.3275$	Inside	Do not reject H_0

35. (a) $H_0 : \mu \leq 43.9$ vs. $H_a : \mu > 43.9$. Reject H_0 if the p-value ≤ 0.10. (b) 19.61 (c) ≈ 0 (d) Since the p-value $\leq \alpha$, reject. H_0. There is evidence that the population mean referral rate is greater than 43.9 per 1000 children.
36. (a) $H_0 : \mu \leq 2$ vs. $H_a : \mu > 2$. Reject H_0 if the p-value ≤ 0.05. (b) 24 (c) p-value ≈ 0 (d) Since the p-value $\leq \alpha$, reject

H_0. There is evidence that the population mean temperature increase in California is greater than 2 degrees.
37. (a) $H_0 : \mu \geq 700$ vs. $H_a : \mu < 700$. Reject H_0 if the p-value ≤ 0.10. (b) -20 (c) ≈ 0 (d) Since the p-value $\leq \alpha$, reject H_0. There is evidence that the population mean number of meals prepared and eaten at home is less than 700.
38. (a) $H_0 : \mu \leq 47.2$ vs. $H_a : \mu > 47.2$. Reject H_0 if the p-value ≤ 0.01. (b) 16.60 (c) p-value ≈ 0. (d) Since the p-value $\leq \alpha$, reject H_0. There is evidence that the population mean DDT level in the breast milk of Hispanic women in the Yakima valley is greater than 47.2 parts per billion.
39. (a) $H_0 : \mu = 2$ vs. $H_a : \mu \neq 2$. Reject H_0 if p-value $\leq \alpha = 0.05$. (b) $Z_{\text{data}} = 1.2$ (c) 0.2302 (TI-83/84: 0.2301) (d) Since the p-value $= 0.2302$ is not ≤ 0.05, we therefore do not reject H_0. There is insufficient evidence at level of significance $\alpha = 0.05$ that the population mean daily number of shares traded differs from 2 billion shares.
40. (a) $H_0 : \mu \geq 1.4261$ vs. $H_a : \mu < 1.4261$. Reject H_0 if the p-value ≤ 0.05. (b) -17.32 (c) ≈ 0 (d) Since the p-value $\leq \alpha$, reject H_0. There is evidence that the population mean annual ring growth in the tree's later years is less than 1.4261 mm per year.
41. (a) $H_0 : \mu \geq 3$ vs. $H_a : \mu < 3$. Reject H_0 if the p-value ≤ 0.01. (b) -13.5 (c) p-value ≈ 0 (d) Since the p-value $\leq \alpha$, reject H_0. There is evidence that the population mean time hybrid cars take to recoup their initial cost is less than 3 years.
42. (a) $H_0 : \mu = 175$ vs. $H_a : \mu \neq 175$. Reject H_0 if the p-value ≤ 0.01. (b) -1 (c) 0.3174 (d) Since the p-value $\geq \alpha$, do not reject H_0. There is insufficient evidence that the population mean height of Americans this year has changed from 175 centimeters.
43. (a) (23,160, 24,840) (b) (i) Since $\mu_0 = 24,000$ lies in the confidence interval, we do not reject H_0. (ii) Since $\mu_0 = 23,000$ does not lie in the confidence interval, we reject H_0. (iii) Since $\mu_0 = 23,200$ lies in the confidence interval, we do not reject H_0. (iv) Since $\mu_0 = 25,000$ does not lie in the confidence interval, we reject H_0.
44. $H_0 : \mu = 13,100$ vs. $H_a : \mu > 13,100$. Reject H_0 if the p-value $\leq \alpha = 0.05$. $Z_{\text{data}} = 2$. p-value $= 0.0228$. Since the p-value $= 0.0228$ is ≤ 0.05, we therefore reject H_0. There is evidence at level of significance $\alpha = 0.05$ that the population mean annual premium for a family of four is greater than $13,100.
45. (a) Remains the same (b) Remains the same (c) Remains the same (d) Increases (e) Remains the same
46. $H_0 : \mu = 13,100$ vs. $H_a : \mu > 13,100$. Reject H_0 if p-value $\leq \alpha = 0.01$. $Z_{\text{data}} = 2$. p-value $= 0.0228$. Since the p-value $= 0.0228$ is ≤ 0.01, we therefore do not reject H_0. There is insufficient evidence at level of significance $\alpha = 0.01$ that the population mean annual premium for a family of four is greater than $13,100. The decrease in the level of significance α from 0.05 to 0.01 resulted in the conclusion changing from reject H_0 to do not reject H_0.
47. (a) $H_0 : \mu = 3.14$ vs. $H_a : \mu < 3.14$. (b) $Z_{\text{data}} = -1.35$ (c) 0.0885 (d) Since the p-value $= 0.0885$ is not ≤ 0.05, we therefore do not reject H_0. There is insufficient evidence at level of significance $\alpha = 0.05$ that the population mean family size is less than 3.14 persons.
48. (a) $H_0 : \mu = 3.14$ vs. $H_a : \mu < 3.14$. (b) $Z_{\text{data}} = -1.35$ (c) 0.0885 (d) Since the p-value $= 0.0885$ is ≤ 0.10, we therefore reject H_0. There is evidence at level of significance $\alpha = 0.10$ that the population mean family size is less than 3.14

persons. The increase in the level of significance from $\alpha = 0.05$ to $\alpha = 0.10$ resulted in the conclusion changing from do not reject H_0 to reject H_0.

To resolve this dilemma, we could just report that, based on the p-value, there is moderate evidence against the null hypothesis or we could obtain more data.

49. (a) 0.0885 **(b)** The assumption $\sigma = 1$ person seems valid. This value would have been obtained from the sample standard deviation. **(c)** Type II error; Type I error **(d)** This headline is not supported by the data and our hypothesis test.

50. (a) Unchanged **(b)** Decrease from -1.5 to -2.25 **(c)** Decrease from 0.0668 to 0.0122 **(d)** Since the p-value is less than α, we reject H_0. There is evidence that the true mean family size in America is less than 3.15 persons. **(e)** As the sample mean becomes more extreme, $\sigma_{\bar{x}}$ remains unchanged, Z_{data} and the p-value decrease, and the conclusion becomes "Reject H_0."

51. (a) Yes, the normal probability plot indicates acceptable normality. **(b)** $H_0 : \mu \geq 78$ vs. $H_a : \mu < 78$. Reject H_0 if p-value ≤ 0.05. $Z_{\text{data}} = -1.03$. p-value $= 0.1515$. Since p-value $\geq \alpha$, do not reject H_0. There is insufficient evidence that the population mean heart rate for all women is less than 78 beats per minute. **(c)** $H_0 : \mu = 78$ vs. $H_a : \mu \neq 78$. Reject H_0 if p-value ≤ 0.05. $Z_{\text{data}} = -1.03$. p-value $= 0.303$. Since p-value ≥ 0.05, do not reject H_0. There is insufficient evidence that the population mean heart rate for all women is different from 78 beats per minute.

52. (a) There is insufficient evidence that the true mean heart rates for all women is less than 78 beats per minute and there is insufficient evidence that the true mean heart rate for all woman is different than 78 beats per minute. **(b)** The p-value for **(c)** is twice the p-value in **(b)**. If α is between these two p-values, then the conclusion for the one-tailed test will be "Reject H_0" and the conclusion for the two-tailed test will be "Do not reject H_0." **(c)** There is no evidence against the null hypothesis in **(b)** and **(c)**.

53. (a) Yes, the normal probability plot indicates acceptable normality. **(b)** $H_0 : \mu \geq 210$ vs. $H_a : \mu < 210$. Reject H_0 if p-value ≤ 0.01. $Z_{\text{data}} = -1.69$. p-value $= 0.0455$. Since p-value $\geq \alpha$, do not reject H_0. There is insufficient evidence that the population mean sodium content per serving of breakfast cereal is less than 210 grams.

54. (a) Decrease **(b)** Decrease **(c)** Decrease **(d)** Depends on new value of σ.

55. (a) $H_0 : \mu \geq 210$ vs. $H_a : \mu < 210$. Reject H_0 if p-value $\leq$ 0.05. $Z_{\text{data}} = -1.69$. p-value $= 0.0455$. Since p-value $\leq \alpha$, reject H_0. There is evidence that the population mean sodium content per serving of breakfast cereal is less than 210 grams. **(b)** The data have not changed; α was increased to a value greater than the p-value. **(c)** Report the p-value and assess the strength of the evidence against the null hypothesis; obtain more data.

56. There is solid evidence against the null hypothesis.

57. (a) p-value $= 0.0853$ **(b)** Since p-value ≥ 0.05, we would not reject H_0.

58. (a) p-value $= 0.0571$ **(b)** Since the p-value ≥ 0.05, we would not reject H_0.

59. (a) p-value $= 0.0384$ **(b)** Since p-value ≤ 0.05, we would reject H_0.

60. As sample size increases, the p-value decreases.

61. (a) 254 observations, 7 variables **(b)** $\bar{x} = 23{,}901$, $s = 88{,}421$. The distribution is right-skewed. **(c) Critical-value method:** $H_0 : \mu = 40{,}000$ vs. $H_a : \mu \neq 40{,}000$. For a two-tailed test with

$\alpha = 0.05$, $Z_{\text{crit}} = 1.96$. Reject H_0 if $Z_{\text{data}} \leq -1.96$ or $Z_{\text{data}} \geq 1.96$. From the Minitab output, $Z_{\text{data}} = -2.90$. Since $Z_{\text{data}} = -2.90$ is ≤ -1.96, we reject H_0. There is evidence that the population mean total occupied housing units for these counties in Texas differs from 40,000. *p-value method:* $H_0 : \mu = 40{,}000$ vs. $H_a :$ $\mu \neq 40{,}000$. Reject H_0 if p-value ≤ 0.05. From the Minitab output, $Z_{\text{data}} = -2.90$. From the Minitab output, p-value $= 0.004$. Since p-value $= 0.004$ is ≤ 0.05, we reject H_0. There is evidence that the population mean total occupied housing units for these counties in Texas differs from 40,000.

One-Sample Z: TOT_OCC

```
Test of mu = 40000 vs not = 40000
The assumed standard deviation = 88400

Variable      N    Mean   StDev   SE Mean      95% CI
TOT_OCC     254   23901   88421      5547   (13030, 34773)

              Z       P
          -2.90   0.004
```

Section 9.4

1. The population standard deviation σ is known.

2. Sample standard deviation s

3. (a) $H_0 : \mu = 22$ vs. $H_a : \mu < 22$ **(b)** $t_{\text{crit}} = -1.697$. Reject H_0 if $t_{\text{data}} \leq -1.697$.

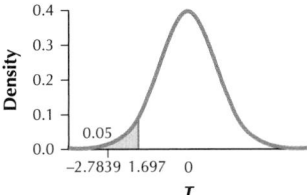

(c) $t_{\text{data}} = -2.7839$ **(d)** Since $t_{\text{data}} = -2.7839$ is ≤ -1.697, the conclusion is reject H_0. There is evidence at the 0.05 level of significance that the population mean is less than 22.

4. (a) $H_0 : \mu = 3$ vs. $H_a : \mu < 3$ **(b)** $t_{\text{crit}} = -1.303$. Reject H_0 if $t_{\text{data}} \leq -1.303$.

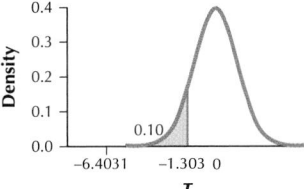

(c) $t_{\text{data}} = -6.4031$ **(d)** Since $t_{\text{data}} = -6.4031$ is ≤ -1.303, the conclusion is reject H_0. There is evidence at the 0.10 level of significance that the population mean is less than 3.

5. (a) $H_0 : \mu = 11$ vs. $H_a : \mu \leq 11$ **(b)** $t_{\text{crit}} = 2.602$. Reject H_0 if $t_{\text{data}} \geq 2.602$.

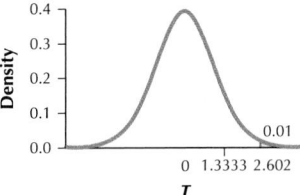

(c) $t_{data} = 1.3333$ (d) Since $t_{data} = 1.3333$ is not ≥ 2.602, the conclusion is do not reject H_0. There is insufficient evidence at the 0.01 level of significance that the population mean is greater than 11.
6. (a) $H_0 : \mu = 80$ vs. $H_a : \mu > 80$ (b) $t_{crit} = 1.860$. Reject H_0 if $t_{data} \geq 1.860$.

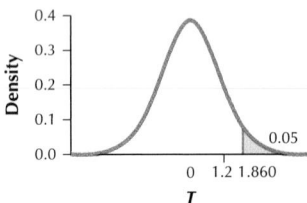

(c) $t_{data} = 1.2$ (d) Since $t_{data} = 1.2$ is not ≥ 1.860, the conclusion is do not reject H_0. There is insufficient evidence at the 0.05 level of significance that the population mean is greater than 80.
7. (a) $H_0 : \mu = 100$ vs. $H_a : \mu > 100$ (b) $t_{crit} = 2.492$. Reject H_0 if $t_{data} \geq 2.492$.

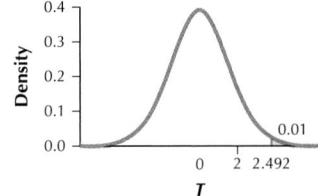

(c) $t_{data} = 2$ (d) Since $t_{data} = 2$ is not ≥ 2.492, the conclusion is do not reject H_0. There is insufficient evidence at the 0.01 level of significance that the population mean is greater than 100.
8. (a) $H_0 : \mu = -4$ vs. $H_a : \mu < -4$ (b) $t_{crit} = -1.662$. Reject H_0 if $t_{data} \leq -1.662$.

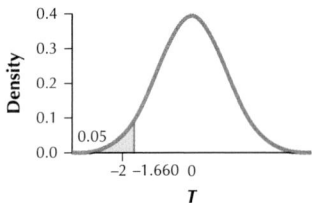

(c) $t_{data} = -2$ (d) Since $t_{data} = -2$ is ≤ -1.662, the conclusion is reject H_0. There is evidence at the 0.05 level of significance that the population mean is less than -4.
9. (a) $H_0 : \mu = 102$ vs. $H_a : \mu \neq 102$ (b) $t_{crit} = 1.990$. Reject H_0 if $t_{data} \leq -1.990$ or if $t_{data} \geq 1.990$.

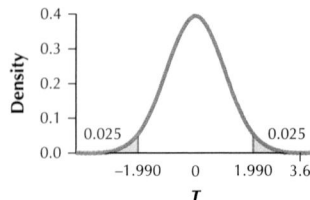

(c) $t_{data} = 3.6$ (d) Since $t_{data} = 3.6$ is ≥ 1.990, the conclusion is reject H_0. There is evidence at the 0.05 level of significance that the population mean differs from 102.

10. (a) $H_0 : \mu = 95$ vs. $H_a : \mu \neq 95$ (b) $t_{crit} = 2.750$. Reject H_0 if $t_{data} \leq -2.750$ or if $t_{data} \geq 2.750$.

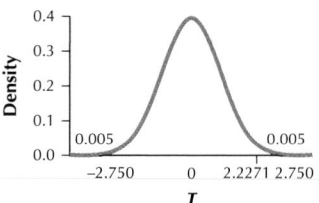

(c) $t_{data} = 2.2271$ (d) Since $t_{data} = 2.2271$ is not ≤ -2.750 and not ≥ 2.750, the conclusion is do not reject H_0. There is insufficient evidence at the 0.01 level of significance that the population mean differs from 95.
11. (a) $H_0 : \mu = 1000$ vs. $H_a : \mu \neq 1000$ (b) $t_{crit} = 1.711$. Reject H_0 if $t_{data} \leq -1.711$ or if $t_{data} \geq 1.711$.

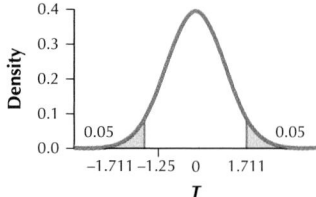

(c) $t_{data} = -1.25$ (d) Since $t_{data} = -1.25$ is not ≤ -1.711 and not ≥ 1.711, the conclusion is do not reject H_0. There is insufficient evidence at the 0.10 level of significance that the population mean differs from 1000.
12. (a) $H_0 : \mu = -10$ vs. $H_a : \mu \neq -10$ (b) $t_{crit} = 2.064$. Reject H_0 if $t_{data} \leq -2.064$ or if $t_{data} \geq 2.064$.

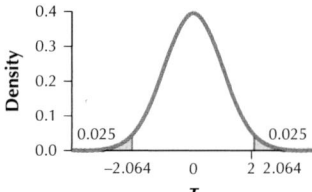

(c) $t_{data} = 2$ (d) Since $t_{data} = 2$ is not ≤ -2.064 and not ≥ 2.064, the conclusion is do not reject H_0. There is insufficient evidence at the 0.05 level of significance that the population mean differs from -10.
13. (a) $H_0 : \mu = 9$ vs. $H_a : \mu \neq 9$ (b) $t_{crit} = 1.690$. Reject H_0 if $t_{data} \leq -1.690$ or if $t_{data} \geq 1.690$.

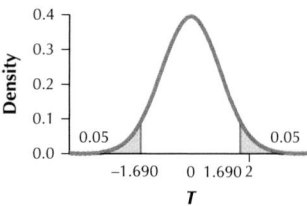

(c) $t_{data} = 2$ (d) Since $t_{data} = 2$ is ≥ 1.690, the conclusion is reject H_0. There is evidence at the 0.10 level of significance that the population mean differs from 9.

14. (a) $H_0 : \mu = 1000$ vs. $H_a : \mu \neq 1000$ **(b)** $t_{crit} = 2.947$. Reject H_0 if $t_{data} \leq -2.947$ or if $t_{data} \geq 2.947$.

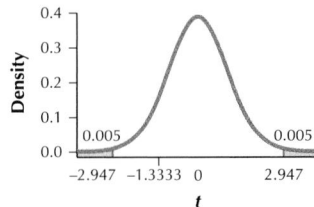

(c) $t_{data} = -1.3333$ **(d)** Since $t_{data} = -1.3333$ is not ≤ -2.947 and not ≥ 2.947, the conclusion is do not reject H_0. There is insufficient evidence at the 0.01 level of significance that the population mean differs from 1000.

15. (a) $H_0 : \mu = 10$ vs. $H_a : \mu < 10$. Reject H_0 if the p-value $\leq \alpha = 0.01$. **(b)** $t_{data} = -5.4$ **(c)** 0 **(d)** Since the p-value = 0 is $\leq \alpha = 0.01$, the conclusion is reject H_0. There is evidence at the 0.01 level of significance that the population mean is less than 10.

16. (a) $H_0 : \mu = 50$ vs. $H_a : \mu < 50$. Reject H_0 if the p-value $\leq \alpha = 0.05$. **(b)** $t_{data} = -6.4031$ **(c)** 0 **(d)** Since the p-value = 0 is $\leq \alpha = 0.05$, the conclusion is reject H_0. There is evidence at the 0.05 level of significance that the population mean is less than 50.

17. (a) $H_0 : \mu = 100$ vs. $H_a : \mu > 100$. Reject H_0 if the p-value $\leq \alpha = 0.10$. **(b)** $t_{data} = 2$ **(c)** 0.0285 **(d)** Since the p-value = 0.0285 is $\leq \alpha = 0.10$, the conclusion is reject H_0. There is evidence at the 0.10 level of significance that the population mean is greater than 100.

18. (a) $H_0 : \mu = 3.0$ vs. $H_a : \mu > 3.0$. Reject H_0 if the p-value $\leq \alpha = 0.05$. **(b)** $t_{data} = 2$ **(c)** 0.0285 **(d)** Since the p-value = 0.0285 is $\leq \alpha = 0.05$, the conclusion is reject H_0. There is evidence at the 0.05 level of significance that the population mean is greater than 3.0.

19. (a) $H_0 : \mu = 200$ vs. $H_a : \mu > 200$. Reject H_0 if the p-value $\leq \alpha = 0.05$. **(b)** $t_{data} = 120$ **(c)** 0 **(d)** Since the p-value = 0 is $\leq \alpha = 0.05$, the conclusion is reject H_0. There is evidence at the 0.05 level of significance that the population mean is greater than 200.

20. (a) $H_0 : \mu = 28$ vs. $H_a : \mu < 28$. Reject H_0 if the p-value $\leq \alpha = 0.05$. **(b)** $t_{data} = -1$ **(c)** 0.1599 **(d)** Since the p-value = 0.1599 is not $\leq \alpha = 0.05$, the conclusion is do not reject H_0. There is insufficient evidence at the 0.05 level of significance that the population mean is less than 28.

21. (a) $H_0 : \mu = 25$ vs. $H_a : \mu \neq 25$. Reject H_0 if the p-value $\leq \alpha = 0.01$. **(b)** $t_{data} = 0$ **(c)** 1 **(d)** Since the p-value = 1 is not $\leq \alpha = 0.01$, the conclusion is do not reject H_0. There is insufficient evidence at the 0.01 level of significance that the population mean differs from 25.

22. (a) $H_0 : \mu = 98.6$ vs. $H_a : \mu \neq 98.6$. Reject H_0 if the p-value $\leq \alpha = 0.05$. **(b)** $t_{data} = 0.36$ **(c)** 0.7198 **(d)** Since the p-value = 0.7918 is not $\leq \alpha = 0.05$, the conclusion is do not reject H_0. There is insufficient evidence at the 0.05 level of significance that the population mean differs from 98.6.

23. (a) $H_0 : \mu = 3.14$ vs. $H_a : \mu \neq 3.14$. Reject H_0 if the p-value $\leq \alpha = 0.10$. **(b)** $t_{data} = 0.18$ **(c)** 0.8616 **(d)** Since the p-value = 0.8616 is not $\leq \alpha = 0.10$, the conclusion is do not reject H_0. There is insufficient evidence at the 0.10 level of significance that the population mean differs from 3.14.

24. (a) $H_0 : \mu = 2.72$ vs. $H_a : \mu \neq 2.72$. Reject H_0 if the p-value $\leq \alpha = 0.05$. **(b)** $t_{data} = -7.5$ **(c)** 0 **(d)** Since the p-value = 0

is $\leq \alpha = 0.05$, the conclusion is reject H_0. There is evidence at the 0.05 level of significance that the population mean differs from 2.72.

25. (a) $H_0 : \mu = 0$ vs. $H_a : \mu \neq 0$. Reject H_0 if the p-value $\leq \alpha = 0.05$. **(b)** $t_{data} = 6$ **(c)** 0.0003 **(d)** Since the p-value = 0.0003 is $\leq \alpha = 0.05$, the conclusion is reject H_0. There is evidence at the 0.05 level of significance that the population mean differs from 0.

26. (a) $H_0 : \mu = 2.0$ vs. $H_a : \mu \neq 2.0$. Reject H_0 if the p-value $\leq \alpha = 0.01$. **(b)** $t_{data} = 2.6667$ **(c)** 0.0176 **(d)** Since the p-value = 0.0176 is not $\leq \alpha = 0.01$, the conclusion is do not reject H_0. There is insufficient evidence at the 0.01 level of significance that the population mean differs from 2.0.

27. p-value < 0.005

28. p-value < 0.005

29. p-value < 0.01

30. $0.02 < p$-value < 0.05

31.

	Value of μ_0	Form of hypothesis test, with $\alpha = 0.05$	Where μ_0 lies in relation to 95% confidence interval (1, 4)	Conclusion of hypothesis test
(a)	0	$H_0 : \mu = 0$ vs. $H_a : \mu \neq 0$	Outside	Reject H_0
(b)	2	$H_0 : \mu = 2$ vs. $H_a : \mu \neq 2$	Inside	Do not reject H_0
(c)	5	$H_0 : \mu = 5$ vs. $H_a : \mu \neq 5$	Outside	Reject H_0

32.

	Value of μ_0	Form of hypothesis test, with $\alpha = 0.01$	Where μ_0 lies in relation to 99% confidence interval (57, 58)	Conclusion of hypothesis test
(a)	55.5	$H_0 : \mu = 55.5$ vs. $H_a : \mu \neq 55.5$	Outside	Reject H_0
(b)	59.5	$H_0 : \mu = 59.5$ vs. $H_a : \mu \neq 59.5$	Outside	Reject H_0
(c)	57.5	$H_0 : \mu = 57.5$ vs. $H_a : \mu \neq 57.5$	Inside	Do not reject H_0

33.

	Value of μ_0	Form of hypothesis test, with $\alpha = 0.10$	Where μ_0 lies in relation to 90% confidence interval $(-20, -10)$	Conclusion of hypothesis test
(a)	-21	$H_0 : \mu = -21$ vs. $H_a : \mu \neq -21$	Outside	Reject H_0
(b)	-5	$H_0 : \mu = -5$ vs. $H_a : \mu \neq -5$	Outside	Reject H_0
(c)	-12	$H_0 : \mu = -12$ vs. $H_a : \mu \neq -12$	Inside	Do not reject H_0

34.

	Value of μ_0	Form of hypothesis test, with $\alpha = 0.05$	Where μ_0 lies in relation to 95% confidence interval (2010, 2015)	Conclusion of hypothesis test
(a)	2012	$H_0 : \mu = 2012$ vs. $H_a : \mu \neq 2012$	Inside	Do not reject H_0
(b)	2007	$H_0 : \mu = 2007$ vs. $H_a : \mu \neq 2007$	Outside	Reject H_0
(c)	2014	$H_0 : \mu = 2014$ vs. $H_a : \mu \neq 2014$	Inside	Do not reject H_0

35.

	Value of μ_0	Form of hypothesis test, with $\alpha = 0.05$	Where μ_0 lies in relation to 95% confidence interval $(-1, 1)$	Conclusion of hypothesis test
(a)	1.5	$H_0 : \mu = 1.5$ vs. $H_a : \mu \neq 1.5$	Outside	Reject H_0
(b)	-1.5	$H_0 : \mu = -1.5$ vs. $H_a : \mu \neq -1.5$	Outside	Reject H_0
(c)	0	$H_0 : \mu = 0$ vs. $H_a : \mu \neq 0$	Inside	Do not reject H_0

36.

	Value of μ_0	Form of hypothesis test, with $\alpha = 0.05$	Where μ_0 lies in relation to 95% confidence interval (19,570, 20,105)	Conclusion of hypothesis test
(a)	20,000	$H_0 : \mu = 20,000$ vs. $H_a : \mu \neq 20,000$	Inside	Do not reject H_0
(b)	21,000	$H_0 : \mu = 21,000$ vs. $H_a : \mu \neq 21,000$	Outside	Reject H_0
(c)	19,571	$H_0 : \mu = 19,571$ vs. $H_a : \mu \neq 19,571$	Inside	Do not reject H_0

37. Critical-value method: $H_0 : \mu = 15,200$ vs. $H_a : \mu > 15,200$. $t_{crit} = 1.660$. Reject H_0 if $t_{data} \geq 1.660$. $t_{data} = 3.2$. Since $t_{data} = 3.2$ is ≥ 1.660, the conclusion is reject H_0. There is evidence at the 0.05 level of significance that the population mean cost of a stay in the hospital for women aged 18–44 is greater than $15,200. Therefore we can conclude at level of significance 0.05 that the population mean cost of a stay in the hospital for American women aged 18–24 has increased since 2010. **p-value method:** $H_0 : \mu = 15,200$ vs. $H_a : \mu > 15,200$. Reject H_0 if the p-value $\leq \alpha = 0.05$. $t_{data} = 3.2$. p-value $= 0.0007$. Since the p-value $= 0.0007$ is $\leq \alpha = 0.05$, the conclusion is reject H_0. There is evidence at the 0.05 level of significance that the population mean cost of a stay in the hospital for women aged 18–44 is greater than $15,200. Therefore we can conclude at level of significance 0.05 that the population mean cost of a stay in the hospital for American women aged 18–24 has increased since 2010.

38. Critical-value method: $H_0 : \mu = 40$ vs. $H_a : \mu > 40$. $t_{crit} = 1.306$. Reject H_0 if $t_{data} \geq 1.306$. $t_{data} = 1.25$. Since $t_{data} = 1.25$ is not ≥ 1.306, the conclusion is do not reject H_0. There is insufficient evidence at the 0.10 level of significance that the population mean number of apps downloaded by iPhone users is

greater than 40. **p-value method:** $H_0 : \mu = 40$ vs. $H_a : \mu > 40$. Reject H_0 if p-value $\leq \alpha = 0.10$. $t_{data} = 1.25$. p-value $= 0.1098$. Since the p-value $= 0.1098$ is not $\leq \alpha = 0.10$, the conclusion is do not reject H_0. There is insufficient evidence at the 0.10 level of significance that the population mean number of apps downloaded by iPhone users is greater than 40.

39. Critical-value method: $H_0 : \mu = 130$ vs. $H_a : \mu < 130$. $t_{crit} = -1.662$. Reject H_0 if $t_{data} \leq -1.662$. $t_{data} = -4$. Since $t_{data} = -4$ is ≤ -1.662, the conclusion is reject H_0. There is evidence at the 0.05 level of significance that the population mean number of Facebook friends is less than 130. **p-value method:** $H_0 : \mu = 130$ vs. $H_a : \mu < 130$. Reject H_0 if p-value $\leq \alpha = 0.05$. $t_{data} = -4$. p-value $= 0$. Since the p-value $= 0$ is $\leq \alpha = 0.05$, the conclusion is reject H_0. There is evidence at the 0.05 level of significance that the population mean number of Facebook friends is less than 130.

40. Critical-value method: $H_0 : \mu = 16.1$ vs. $H_a : \mu \neq 16.1$. $t_{crit} = 2.704$. Reject H_0 if $t_{data} \leq -2.704$ or if $t_{data} \geq 2.704$. $t_{data} = -0.308$. Since $t_{data} = -0.308$ is not ≤ -2.704 and not ≥ 2.704, the conclusion is do not reject H_0. There is insufficient evidence at the 0.01 level of significance that the population mean number of employees in a small business is different from 16.1. **p-value method:** $H_0 : \mu = 16.1$ vs. $H_a : \mu \neq 16.1$. Reject H_0 if p-value $\leq \alpha = 0.01$. $t_{data} = -0.308$. p-value $= 0.7594$. Since the p-value $= 0.7594$ is not $\leq \alpha = 0.01$, the conclusion is do not reject H_0. There is insufficient evidence at the 0.01 level of significance that the population mean number of employees in a small business is different from 16.1.

41. No. The distribution of the variable is not normal and the sample size is less than 30.

42. (a) Yes. Most of the points in the normal probability plot lie close to the center line and all of the points lie between the two curved lines. **(b) Critical-value method:** $H_0 : \mu = 60$ vs. $H_a : \mu < 60$. $t_{crit} = -1.771$. Reject H_0 if $t_{data} \leq -1.771$. $t_{data} = -0.0816$. Since $t_{data} = -0.0816$ is not ≤ -1.771, the conclusion is do not reject H_0. There is insufficient evidence at the 0.05 level of significance that the population mean response time to Asia is less than 60 milliseconds. **p-value method:** $H_0 : \mu = 60$ vs. $H_a : \mu < 60$. Reject H_0 if p-value $\leq \alpha = 0.05$. $t_{data} = -0.0816$. p-value $= 0.4681$. Since the p-value $= 0.4681$ is not $\leq \alpha = 0.05$, the conclusion is do not reject H_0. There is insufficient evidence at the 0.05 level of significance that the population mean response time to Asia is less than 60 milliseconds. **(c)** The population standard deviation is unknown.

43. (a) Yes. Since the prices per bottle for Obsession by Calvin Klein are normally distributed, Case 1 applies. **(b)** No, a sample mean that is greater than the hypothesized mean is not enough to reject H_0. **(c) Critical-value method:** $H_0 : \mu = 46.42$ vs. $H_a : \mu > 46.42$. $t_{crit} = 2.624$. Reject H_0 if $t_{data} \geq 2.624$. $t_{data} = 3.87$. Since $t_{data} = 3.87$ is ≥ 2.624, we reject H_0. There is evidence at the $\alpha = 0.01$ level of significance that the population mean retail price for Obsession this year is greater than $46.42 per bottle. **p-value method:** $H_0 : \mu = 46.42$ vs. $H_0 : \mu > 46.42$. Reject H_0 if the p-value ≤ 0.01. $t_{data} = 3.87$. p-value $= 0.0008$. Since the p-value $= 0.0008$ is ≤ 0.01, we reject H_0. There is evidence at the $\alpha = 0.01$ level of significance that the population mean retail price for Obsession this year is greater than $46.42 per bottle.

44. (a) There is extremely strong evidence against the null hypothesis. **(b)** α would have to be less than or equal to the p-value $= 0.0008446364914$. **(c)** The strength of the evidence against the null hypothesis will remain the same for any value of α we choose.

45. (a) Decrease **(b)** Increase **(c–d)** Decrease **(e)** Unchanged
(f) Stronger **(g)** Unchanged
46. (a) Case 1 applies, so we can apply the t test. **(b)** $H_0 : \mu = 30$ vs. $H_a : \mu > 30$. Reject H_0 if p-value ≤ 0.01. $t_{\text{data}} = 3.54$. p-value $= 0.0031570524$. Since p-value ≤ 0.01, we reject H_0. There is evidence that the population mean gas mileage is greater than 30 mpg.
47. (a) $H_0 : \mu = 30$ vs. $H_a : \mu > 30$. Reject H_0 if p-value ≤ 0.001. $t_{\text{data}} = 3.54$. p-value $= 0.0031570524$. Since the p-value ≥ 0.001, we do not reject H_0. There is insufficient evidence that the population mean gas mileage is greater than 30 mpg. **(b)** We could turn to a direct assessment of the strength of the evidence against H_0 or we could obtain more data. **(c)** Since $0.001 \leq p$-value ≤ 0.01, there is very strong evidence against the null hypothesis that the population mean gas mileage is less than or equal to 30 mpg. This does not change for any value of α we use.
48. (a) Decrease **(b)** Unchanged **(c)** Increase **(d)** We don't know what the conclusion will be. **(e)** Will result in a conclusion of "Do not reject H_0." **(f)** We don't know what the strength of the evidence against the null hypothesis will be.
49. (a) Yes. Since all the points lie within the curved lines, the normal probability plot indicates acceptable normality. Case 1 applies. **(b)** $n = 10$, $\bar{x} = \$2538.92$, $s = \$404.75$ **(c)** $s_{\bar{x}} = \$404.75/\sqrt{10} = \$127.99$ **(d)** $t_{\text{data}} = 2.09$. Therefore, the sample mean fees and tuition at community colleges nationwide $\bar{x} = \$2538.92$ is 2.09 standard errors above the hypothesized mean fees and tuition at community colleges nationwide $\mu_0 = \$2272$. This is mildly extreme. **(e)** It says, "Test of mu = 2272 vs. not = 2272" across the top of the printout. The researchers wanted to test the hypotheses "$H_0 : \mu = 2272$ vs. $H_a : \mu > 2272$."
50. (a) There is evidence that the population mean tuition and fees at community colleges this year is greater than $2272. **(b)** We would not reject H_0. This is a Type II error. Answers will vary. **(c)** Answers will vary.
51. (a) Since the p-value for the two-tailed test is twice the p-value for the one-tailed test, it is possible to conclude that there is insufficient evidence that the population mean cost has changed but there is evidence that the population mean cost has increased if α is between the two p-values. **(b)** Since $0.01 \leq p$-value ≤ 0.05, there is solid evidence against the null hypothesis that the population mean tuition and fees at community colleges is less than or equal to $2272. **(c)** Since the test was done only for community colleges, not all colleges, our data and the hypothesis test do not support the headline.
52. (a) Case 2 applies, so it is appropriate to apply the t test. **(b)** There is insufficient evidence that the population mean age at first marriage is not equal to 26 years.
53. $H_0 : \mu = 26$ vs. $H_a : \mu > 26$. $t_{\text{crit}} = 1.290$: Reject H_0 if $t_{\text{data}} \geq 1.290$. $t_{\text{data}} = 1.57$. Since $t_{\text{data}} \geq 1.290$, reject H_0. There is evidence that the population mean age at first marriage is greater than 26 years.
54. (a) There is insufficient evidence that the population mean marriage age has changed, but there is evidence that the population mean marriage age has increased. **(b)** Two-tailed test
55. (a) p-value $= 0.1184412114$ **(b)** Since $0.10 \leq p$-value ≤ 0.15, there is slight evidence against the null hypothesis that the population mean marriage age is 26 years. **(c)** 0.10. Since the p-value is greater than 0.10, it is closer to 0.10 than it is to 0.05. **(d)** This headline is not supported by the data and the hypothesis test.

56. (a)

```
Descriptive Statistics: TOT_POP

Variable    N   N*    Mean   SE Mean    StDev   Minimum    Q1
Median   Q3   Maximum
TOT_POP   790   0   18305             9284   260938      1000   1901
4013   9059   7322564
```

(b)

```
One-Sample T: TOT_POP

Test of mu = 50000 vs not = 50000

Variable     N    Mean    StDev   SE Mean        95% CI          T
TOT_POP    790   18305   260938      9284   (81, 36529)    -3.41
P
0.001
```

Section 9.5

1. $\hat{p}$ is the sample proportion and p is population proportion.
2. Both $np_0 \geq 5$ and $n(1 - p_0) \geq 5$
3. Answers will vary.
4. It is the hypothesized value of the population proportion.
5. Between 0 and 1 inclusive: $0 \leq p_0 \leq 1$
6. p represents the population proportion of successes for a binomial experiment and is a population parameter. The p-value is roughly a measure of how extreme the value of Z_{data} is.
7. 2.8868
8. 5.7735
9. 7.2169
10. It increases.
11. -4.47
12. -2.24
13. 0
14. As $\hat{p}$ approaches p_0, the value of Z_{data} approaches 0.
15. (a) We have $np_0 = 225(0.5) = 112.5 \geq 5$ and $n(1 - p_0) = 225(1 - 0.5) = 112.5 \geq 5$, so we can use the Z test for proportions. **(b)** $H_0 : p = 0.5$ vs. $H_a : p < 0.5$ **(c)** $Z_{\text{crit}} = -1.645$. Reject H_0 if $Z_{\text{data}} \leq -1.645$. **(d)** -1.67 **(e)** Since $Z_{\text{data}} \leq -1.645$, we reject H_0. There is evidence that the population proportion is less than 0.5.
16. (a) $np_0 = 100 (0.3) = 30 \geq 5$ and $n(1 - p_0) = 100(1 - 0.3) = 70 \geq 5$, so we may use the Z test for proportions. **(b)** $H_0 : p = 0.3$ vs. $H_a : p \neq 0.3$. **(c)** $Z_{\text{crit}} = 2.58$. Reject H_0 if $Z_{\text{data}} \leq -2.58$ or $Z_{\text{data}} \geq 2.58$. **(d)** $Z_{\text{data}} = -1.09$. **(e)** Since Z_{data} is not ≤ -2.58 and Z_{data} is not ≥ 2.58, we do not reject H_0. There is insufficient evidence that the population proportion is not equal to 0.3.
17. (a) We have $np_0 = 400(0.6) = 240 \geq 5$ and $n(1 - p_0) = 400(1 - 0.6) = 160 \geq 5$, so we can use the Z test for proportions. **(b)** $H_0 : p = 0.6$ vs. $H_a : p > 0.6$ **(c)** $Z_{\text{crit}} = 1.645$. Reject H_0 if $Z_{\text{data}} \geq 1.645$. **(d)** 2.04 **(e)** Since $Z_{\text{data}} \geq 1.645$, we reject H_0. There is evidence that the population proportion is greater than 0.6.
18. (a) $np_0 = 900(0.4) = 360 \geq 5$ and $n(1 - p_0) = 900(1 - 0.4) = 540 \geq 5$, so the normality conditions are met. **(b)** $H_0 : p = 0.4$ vs. $H_a : p \neq 0.4$ **(c)** $Z_{\text{crit}} = 1.645$. Reject H_0 if $Z_{\text{data}} \leq -1.645$ or if $Z_{\text{data}} \geq 1.645$. **(d)** $\hat{p} = 400/900 = 0.4444444$, $Z_{\text{data}} = 2.7217$ **(e)** Since $Z_{\text{data}} = 2.7217$ is ≥ 1.645, the conclusion is reject H_0. There is evidence at the 0.10 level of significance that the population proportion differs from 0.4.
19. (a) We have $np_0 = 100(0.4) = 40 \geq 5$ and $n(1 - p_0) = 100(1 - 0.4) = 60 \geq 5$, so we can use the Z test for proportions. **(b)** $H_0 : p = 0.4$ vs. $H_a : p > 0.4$. Reject H_0 if the p-value ≤ 0.05. **(c)** 0.82 **(d)** p-value $= 0.2061$ **(e)** Since the

p-value is not ≤ 0.05, we do not reject H_0. There is insufficient evidence that the population proportion is greater than 0.4.
20. (a) $np_0 = 400(0.2) = 80 \geq 5$ and $n(1 - p_0) = 400(1 - 0.2) = 320 \geq 5$, so we may use the Z test for proportions. **(b)** $H_0 : p = 0.2$ vs. $H_a : p < 0.2$. Reject H_0 if p-value ≤ 0.05. **(c)** $Z_{\text{data}} = -0.63$. **(d)** p-value $= 0.2643$. **(e)** Since p-value is not ≤ 0.05, we do not reject H_0. There is insufficient evidence that the population proportion is less than 0.2.
21. (a) We have $np_0 = 900(0.5) = 450 \geq 5$ and $n(1 - p_0) = 900(1 - 0.5) = 450 \geq 5$, so we may use the Z test for proportions. **(b)** $H_0 : p = 0.5$ vs. $H_a : p \neq 0.5$. Reject H_0 if the p-value ≤ 0.05. **(c)** 1.67 **(d)** p-value $= 0.095$ **(e)** Since the p-value is not ≤ 0.05, we do not reject H_0. There is insufficient evidence that the population proportion is not equal to 0.5.
22. (a) $np_0 = 1000(0.9) = 900 \geq 5$ and $n(1 - p_0) = 1000(1 - 0.9) = 100 \geq 5$, so we may use the Z test for proportions. **(b)** $H_0 : p = 0.9$ vs. $H_a : p > 0.9$. Reject H_0 if p-value ≤ 0.05. **(c)** $Z_{\text{data}} = 2.64$. **(d)** p-value $= 0.0041$. **(e)** Since p-value ≤ 0.05, we reject H_0. There is evidence that the population proportion is greater than 0.9.

23.

	Value of p_0	Form of hypothesis test, with $\alpha = 0.05$	Where p_0 lies in relation to 95% confidence interval (0.1, 0.9)	Conclusion of hypothesis test
(a)	0	$H_0 : p = 0$ vs. $H_a : p \neq 0$	Outside	Reject H_0
(b)	1	$H_0 : p = 1$ vs. $H_a : p \neq 1$	Outside	Reject H_0
(c)	0.5	$H_0 : p = 0.5$ vs. $H_a : p \neq 0.5$	Inside	Do not reject H_0

24.

	Value of p_0	Form of hypothesis test, with $\alpha = 0.01$	Where p_0 lies in relation to 99% confidence interval (0.51, 0.52)	Conclusion of hypothesis test
(a)	0.511	$H_0 : p = 0.511$ vs. $H_a : p \neq 0.511$	Inside	Do not reject H_0
(b)	0.521	$H_0 : p = 0.521$ vs. $H_a : p \neq 0.521$	Outside	Reject H_0
(c)	0.519	$H_0 : p = 0.519$ vs. $H_a : p \neq 0.519$	Inside	Do not reject H_0

25.

	Value of p_0	Form of hypothesis test, with $\alpha = 0.10$	Where p_0 lies in relation to 90% confidence interval (0.1, 0.2)	Conclusion of hypothesis test
(a)	0.09	$H_0 : p = 0.09$ vs. $H_a : p \neq 0.09$	Outside	Reject H_0
(b)	0.9	$H_0 : p = 0.9$ vs. $H_a : p \neq 0.9$	Outside	Reject H_0
(c)	0.19	$H_0 : p = 0.19$ vs. $H_a : p \neq 0.19$	Inside	Do not reject H_0

26.

	Value of p_0	Form of hypothesis test, with $\alpha = 0.05$	Where p_0 lies in relation to 95% confidence interval (0.05, 0.95)	Conclusion of hypothesis test
(a)	0.01	$H_0 : p = 0.01$ vs. $H_a : p \neq 0.01$	Outside	Reject H_0
(b)	0.5	$H_0 : p = 0.5$ vs. $H_a : p \neq 0.5$	Inside	Do not reject H_0
(c)	0.06	$H_0 : p = 0.06$ vs. $H_a : p \neq 0.06$	Inside	Do not reject H_0

27. $np_0 = 500(0.172) = 86 \geq 5$ and $n(1 - p_0) = 500(1 - 0.172) = 414 \geq 5$, so we may use the Z test for proportions. $H_0 : p = 0.172$ vs. $H_a : p \neq 0.172$. Reject H_0 if p-value ≤ 0.10. $Z_{\text{data}} = -0.12$. p-value $= 0.9044$. Since p-value is not ≤ 0.10, we do not reject H_0. There is insufficient evidence that the population proportion of Americans who identified themselves as Baptists is not equal to 0.172.
28. $np_0 = 1000(0.368) = 368 \geq 5$ and $n(1 - p_0) = 1000(1 - 0.368) = 632 \geq 5$, so we may use the Z test for proportions. $H_0 : p = 0.368$ vs. $H_a : p > 0.368$. Reject H_0 if p-value ≤ 0.05. $Z_{\text{data}} = 0.79$. p-value $= 0.2148$. Since p-value is not ≤ 0.05, we do not reject H_0. There is insufficient evidence that the population proportion of births to unmarried women is greater than 0.368.
29. $np_0 = 400(0.071) = 28.4 \geq 5$ and $n(1 - p_0) = 400(1 - 0.071) = 371.6 \geq 5$, so we may use the Z test for proportions. $H_0 : p = 0.071$ vs. $H_a : p \neq 0.071$. Reject H_0 if p-value ≤ 0.01. $Z_{\text{data}} = 1.28$. p-value $= 0.2006$. Since p-value is not ≤ 0.01, we do not reject H_0. There is insufficient evidence that the population proportion of Americans aged 20–24 is not equal to 0.071.
30. $np_0 = 900(0.048) = 43.2 \geq 5$ and $n(1 - p_0) = 900(1 - 0.048) = 856.8 \geq 5$, so we may use the Z test for proportions. $H_0 : p = 0.048$ vs. $H_a : p > 0.048$. Reject H_0 if p-value ≤ 0.01. $Z_{\text{data}} = 1.68$. p-value $= 0.0465$. Since p-value is not ≤ 0.01, we do not reject H_0. There is insufficient evidence that the population proportion of persons 12 or older that have used a prescription pain reliever non-medically is greater than 0.048.
31. (a) We have $np_0 = 400(0.123) = 49.2 \geq 5$ and $n(1 - p_0) = 400(1 - 0.123) = 350.8 \geq 5$, so we can use the Z test for proportions. **(b)** 0.43; $\hat{p} = 0.13$ is not extreme. **(c)** $H_0 : p = 0.123$ vs. $H_a : p > 0.123$. Reject H_0 if p-value ≤ 0.05. $Z_{\text{data}} = -0.43$. p-value $= 0.3336$. Since p-value is not ≤ 0.05, we do not reject H_0. There is insufficient evidence that the population proportion of California residents of Asian ethnicity is greater than 0.123.
32. $np_0 = 1000(0.07) = 70 \geq 5$ and $n(1 - p_0) = 1000(1 - 0.07) = 930 \geq 5$, so we may use the Z test for proportions. $H_0 : p = 0.07$ vs. $H_a : p \neq 0.07$. Reject H_0 if p-value ≤ 0.10. $Z_{\text{data}} = 1.24$. p-value $= 0.2150$. Since p-value is not ≤ 0.10, we do not reject H_0. There is insufficient evidence that the population proportion of hospitalizations of 18- to 44-year-old American women for affective disorders is not equal to 0.07.
33. (a) Yes. We have $np_0 = 100(0.153) = 15.3 \geq 5$ and $n(1 - p_0) = 100(1 - 0.153) = 84.7 \geq 5$. **(b)** 2.14; mildly extreme **(c)** $H_0 : p = 0.153$ vs. $H_a : p \neq 0.153$. Reject H_0 if the P-value ≤ 0.01. $Z_{\text{data}} = 2.14$. p-value $= 0.0324$. Since the p-value is not ≤ 0.01, we do not reject H_0. There is insufficient evidence that the population proportion of Hispanic families that had a household income of at least \$75,000 is not equal to 0.153.

34. (a) We have $np_0 = 100 (0.456) = 45.6 \geq 5$ and $n(1 - p_0) = 100(1 - 0.456) = 54.4 \geq 5$, so we can use the Z test for proportions. **(b)** 0.92; $\hat{p} = 0.41$ is not extreme. **(c)** $H_0 : p = 0.456$ vs. $H_a : p \neq 0.456$. Reject H_0 if p-value ≤ 0.05. $Z_{\text{data}} = 0.92$. p-value $= 0.3576$. Since p-value is not ≤ 0.05, we do not reject H_0. There is insufficient evidence that the population proportion of eighth-graders who have used alcohol is not equal to 0.456.
35. (a) There is no evidence against the null hypothesis.
(b) Do not reject H_0 because the two methods for performing the hypothesis test are equivalent. **(c)** Since the conclusion is do not reject H_0, the 95% confidence interval will contain 0.456.
(d) We did not test whether or not this proportion has decreased. Therefore our hypothesis test does not support this headline.
36. (a)–(c) Increase **(d)–(e)** Unchanged
37. (a) We have $np_0 = 100(0.11) = 11 \geq 5$ and $n(1 - p_0) = 100(1 - 0.11) = 89 \geq 5$, so we can use the Z test for proportions. **(b)** $H_0 : p = 0.11$ vs. $H_a : p < 0.11$. $Z_{\text{crit}} = -1.645$. Reject H_0 if $Z_{\text{data}} \leq -1.645$. $Z_{\text{data}} = -1.60$. Since Z_{data} is not ≤ -1.645, we do not reject H_0. There is insufficient evidence that the population proportion of children age 6 and under exposed to ETS at home on a regular basis is less than 0.11.
38. (a) Type II; answers will vary. **(b)** Since we did not reject H_0, our hypothesis test does not support this headline.
39. (a) Since the p-value ≤ 0.10, we reject H_0. There is evidence that the population proportion of children age 6 and underexposed to environmental tobacco smoke at home on a regular basis is less than 0.11. **(b)** The difference is because we changed the value of α and not because we used different methods for the two different hypothesis tests. **(c)** Since $0.05 \leq p$-value ≤ 0.10, there is mild evidence against the null hypothesis that the population proportion of children age 6 and underexposed to environmental tobacco smoke at home on a regular basis is greater than or equal to 0.11.
40. (a) Unchanged **(b)–(c)** Decrease **(d)** Unchanged **(e)** Depends on new value of $\hat{p}$.

41.

	Value of p_0	Form of hypothesis test, with $\alpha = 0.05$	Where p_0 lies in relation to 95% confidence interval (0.330, 0.596)	Conclusion of hypothesis test
(a)	0.3	$H_0 : p = 0.3$ vs. $H_a : p \neq 0.3$	Outside	Reject H_0
(b)	0.4	$H_0 : p = 0.4$ vs. $H_a : p \neq 0.4$	Inside	Do not reject H_0
(c)	0.5	$H_0 : p = 0.5$ vs. $H_a : p \neq 0.5$	Inside	Do not reject H_0
(d)	0.6	$H_0 : p = 0.6$ vs. $H_a : p \neq 0.6$	Outside	Reject H_0

42. (a) Decrease **(b)** Increase by a factor of $\sqrt{2}$ **(c)** Decrease **(d)** Unchanged **(e)** The conclusion will now be to reject H_0.
43. (a) Increase **(b)** Decrease **(c)** Increase **(d)** Unchanged **(e)** Will still be "Do not reject H_0."

Section 9.6
1. Answers will vary.
2. σ is the actual population standard deviation and σ_0 is the hypothesized population standard deviation.
3. No, σ will never be less than 0.
4. The population must be normal.

5. Answers will vary.
6. The confidence level is $(1 - \alpha) 100\%$.
7. $H_0 : \sigma = 10$ vs. $H_a : \sigma > 10$
8. $H_0 : \sigma = 5$ vs. $H_a : \sigma < 5$
9. $H_0 : \sigma = 3$ vs. $H_a : \sigma \neq 3$
10. $H_0 : \sigma = 100$ vs. $H_a : \sigma > 100$
11. $\chi^2_{\text{data}} = 60$
12. 10
13. $\chi^2_{\text{data}} = 10.417$
14. 18.72
15. $\chi^2_{\text{data}} = 6.125$
16. 25
17. $\chi^2_{\alpha} = \chi^2_{0.05} = 31.410$
18. $\chi^2_{1-\alpha} = \chi^2_{0.95} = 3.940$
19. $\chi^2_{\alpha/2} = \chi^2_{0.025} = 27.488$ and $\chi^2_{1-\alpha/2} = \chi^2_{0.975} = 6.262$
20. $\chi^2_{\alpha} = \chi^2_{0.01} = 27.688$
21. $\chi^2_{1-\alpha} = \chi^2_{0.90} = 2.833$
22. $\chi^2_{\alpha/2} = \chi^2_{0.025} = 40.646$ and $\chi^2_{1-\alpha/2} = \chi^2_{0.975} = 13.120$
23. (a) Reject H_0 if $\chi^2_{\text{data}} \geq 31.410$ **(b)** Since $\chi^2_{\text{data}} \geq 31.410$, we reject H_0. There is evidence that the population standard deviation is greater than 1.
24. (a) Reject H_0 if $\chi^2_{\text{data}} \leq 3.940$. **(b)** Since χ^2_{data} is not ≤ 3.940, we do not reject H_0. There is insufficient evidence that the population standard deviation is less than 5.
25. (a) Reject H_0 if $\chi^2_{\text{data}} \leq 6.262$ or $\chi^2_{\text{data}} \geq 27.488$. **(b)** Since χ^2_{data} is not ≤ 6.262 and χ^2_{data} is not ≥ 27.488, we do not reject H_0. There is insufficient evidence that the population standard deviation is different from 3.
26. (a) Reject H_0 if $\chi^2_{\text{data}} \geq 27.688$. **(b)** Since χ^2_{data} is not ≥ 27.688, we do not reject H_0. There is insufficient evidence that the population standard deviation is greater than 10.
27. (a) Reject H_0 if $\chi^2_{\text{data}} \leq 2.833$. **(b)** Since χ^2_{data} is not ≤ 2.833, we do not reject H_0. There is insufficient evidence that the population standard deviation is less than 20.
28. (a) Reject H_0 if $\chi^2_{\text{data}} < 13.120$ or $\chi^2_{\text{data}} \geq 40.646$. **(b)** Since χ^2_{data} is not ≤ 13.120 and χ^2_{data} is not ≥ 40.646, we do not reject H_0. There is insufficient evidence that the population standard deviation is different than 50.
29. (a)

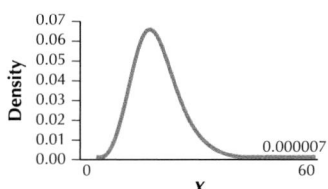

(b) p-value $= 7.121750863 \times 10^{-6}$ **(c)** Since the p-value ≤ 0.05, we reject H_0. There is evidence that the population standard deviation is greater than 1.
30. (a) and **(b)** p-value $= 0.5595067149$

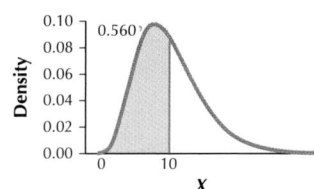

(c) Since the p-value is not ≤ 0.05, we do not reject H_0. There is insufficient evidence that the population standard deviation is less than 5.

31. (a)

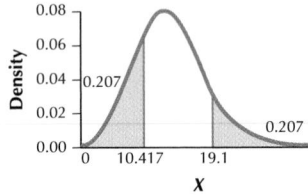

(b) p-value = 0.4145552434 **(c)** Since the p-value is not ≤ 0.05, we do not reject H_0. There is insufficient evidence that the population standard deviation is different from 3.

32. (a) and **(b)** p-value = 0.1320442389

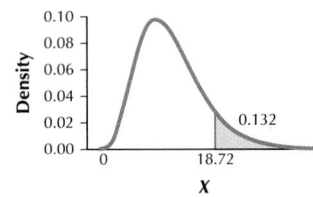

(c) Since the p-value is not ≤ 0.05, we do not reject H_0. There is insufficient evidence that the population standard deviation is greater than 10.

33. (a)

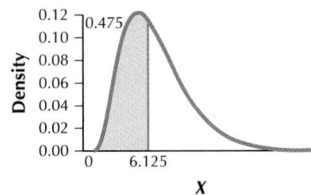

(b) p-value = 0.4747679539 **(c)** Since the p-value is not ≤ 0.05, we do not reject H_0. There is insufficient evidence that the population standard deviation is less than 20.

34. (a) and **(b)** p-value = 0.9247473258

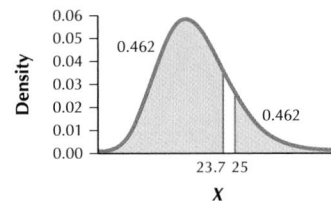

(c) Since the p-value is not ≤ 0.05, we do not reject H_0. There is insufficient evidence that the population standard deviation is different than 5.

35.

	Value of σ_0	Form of hypothesis test, with $\alpha = 0.05$	Where σ_0 lies in relation to 95% confidence interval (1, 4)	Conclusion of hypothesis test
(a)	0	$H_0 : \sigma = 0$ vs. $H_a : \sigma \neq 0$	Outside	Reject H_0
(b)	2	$H_0 : \sigma = 2$ vs. $H_a : \sigma \neq 2$	Inside	Do not reject H_0
(c)	5	$H_0 : \sigma = 5$ vs. $H_a : \sigma \neq 5$	Outside	Reject H_0

36.

	Value of σ_0	Form of hypothesis test, with $\alpha = 0.01$	Where σ_0 lies in relation to 99% confidence interval (10, 25)	Conclusion of hypothesis test
(a)	15	$H_0 : \sigma = 15$ vs. $H_a : \sigma \neq 15$	Inside	Do not reject H_0
(b)	26	$H_0 : \sigma = 26$ vs. $H_a : \sigma \neq 26$	Outside	Reject H_0
(c)	5	$H_0 : \sigma = 5$ vs. $H_a : \sigma \neq 5$	Outside	Reject H_0

37.

	Value of σ_0	Form of hypothesis test, with $\alpha = 0.10$	Where σ_0 lies in relation to 90% confidence interval (100, 200)	Conclusion of hypothesis test
(a)	150	$H_0 : \sigma = 150$ vs. $H_a : \sigma \neq 150$	Inside	Do not reject H_0
(b)	250	$H_0 : \sigma = 250$ vs. $H_a : \sigma \neq 250$	Outside	Reject H_0
(c)	0	$H_0 : \sigma = 0$ vs. $H_a : \sigma \neq 0$	Outside	Reject H_0

38.

	Value of σ_0	Form of hypothesis test, with $\alpha = 0.05$	Where σ_0 lies in relation to 95% confidence interval (127, 698)	Conclusion of hypothesis test
(a)	125	$H_0 : \sigma = 125$ vs. $H_a : \sigma \neq 125$	Outside	Reject H_0
(b)	128	$H_0 : \sigma = 128$ vs. $H_a : \sigma \neq 128$	Inside	Do not reject H_0
(c)	700	$H_0 : \sigma = 700$ vs. $H_a : \sigma \neq 700$	Outside	Reject H_0

39. (a) 982.75 **(b)** $H_0 : \sigma = 36.5$ vs. $H_a : \sigma > 36.5$. Reject H_0 if the p-value ≤ 0.01. p-value ≈ 0. Since the p-value ≤ 0.01, we reject H_0. There is evidence that the population standard deviation of DDT level in the breast milk of Hispanic women in the Yakima valley is greater than 36.5 parts per billion.
40. (a) 48.51 **(b)** $H_0 : \sigma = 0.8$ vs. $H_a : \sigma = 0.8$. $\chi^2_{1-\alpha} = \chi^2_{0.95} = 69.126$. Since $\chi^2_{data} \leq 69.126$, we reject H_0. There is evidence that the population standard deviation of annual ring growth is less than 0.8 millimeters per year.
41. (a) 0.00001497113333 **(b)** $H_0 : \sigma = 30{,}000$ vs. $H_a : \sigma \neq 30{,}000$. Reject H_0 if the p-value ≤ 0.05. p-value ≈ 0. Since the p-value ≤ 0.05, we reject H_0. There is evidence that the population standard deviation of union membership differs from 30,000. **(c)** No, since the conclusion for the hypothesis test is reject H_0
42. $H_0 : \sigma = 1$ vs. $H_a : \sigma < 1$. $\chi^2_{1-\alpha} = \chi^2_{0.95} = 10.117$. $\chi^2_{data} = 31.13$. Since χ^2_{data} is not ≤ 10.117, we do not reject H_0. There is insufficient evidence that the population standard deviation of the foot lengths of fourth-graders is less than 1 centimeter.
43. *p*-Value method: $H_0 : \sigma = 50$ vs. $H_a : \sigma > 50$. Reject H_0 if p-value ≤ 0.05. $\chi^2_{data} = 104$. p-value = 0.3721497012. Since p-value is not ≤ 0.05, we do not reject H_0. There is

insufficient evidence that the population standard deviation of test scores for boys is greater than 50 points. **Critical-value method:** $H_0 : \sigma = 50$ vs. $H_a : \sigma \geq 50$. $\chi^2_\alpha = \chi^2_{0.05} = 124.342$. Reject H_0 if $\chi^2_{data} \geq 124.342$. $\chi^2_{data} = 104$. Since χ^2_{data} is not ≥ 124.342, we do not reject H_0. There is insufficient evidence that the population standard deviation of test scores for boys is greater than 50 points.
44. $H_0 : \sigma = 20$ vs. $H_a : \sigma < 20$. Reject H_0 if p-value ≤ 0.05. $\chi^2_{data} = 24.5$. p-value $= 0.0013251562$. Since p-value ≤ 0.05, we reject H_0. There is evidence that the population standard deviation of heart rates of people leading high-stress lives is less than 20 beats per minute.

Section 9.7

1. A Type II error is not rejecting H_0 when H_0 is false.
2. $\bar{x}_{crit}$ is the value of the sample mean $\bar{x}$ associated with Z_{crit}.
3. The probability of rejecting H_0 when H_0 is false
4. $1 - \beta$, where β is the probability of a Type II error
5. (a) 51.024

(b)

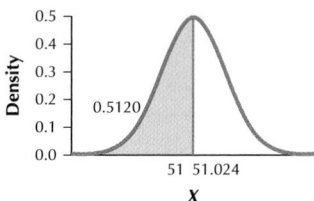

(c) 0.5120 **(d)** 0.4880
6. (a) 51.024

(b)

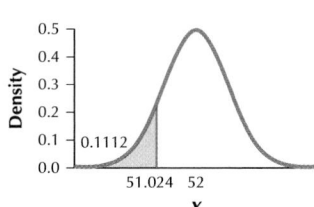

(c) 0.1112 **(d)** 0.8888
7. (a) 51.024

(b)

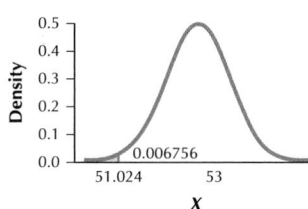

(c) 0.0068 **(d)** 0.9932
8. (a) 51.024

(b)

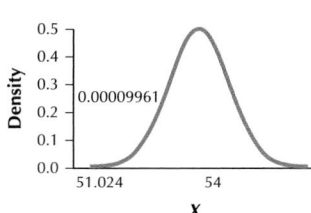

(c) TI-83/84: 0.00009964 **(d)** 0.99990036
9. (a) 51.024

(b)

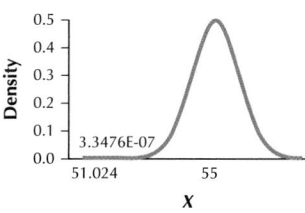

(c) TI-83/84: 0.0000003353 **(d)** 0.9999996647
10. (a) 51.024

(b)

(c) TI-83/84: 0.0000000002496 **(d)** 0.9999999997504
11. (a) 96.71

(b)

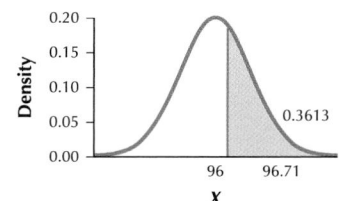

(c) 0.3613 **(d)** 0.6387
12. (a) 96.71

(b)

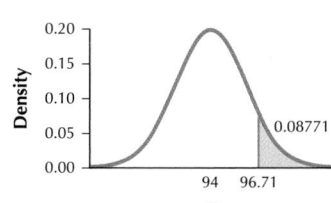

(c) 0.0877 **(d)** 0.9123
13. (a) 96.71

(b)

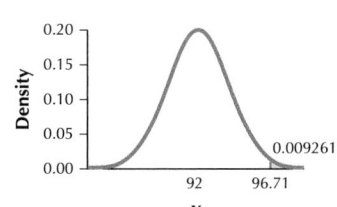

(c) 0.0093 **(d)** 0.9907
14. (a) 96.71

(b)

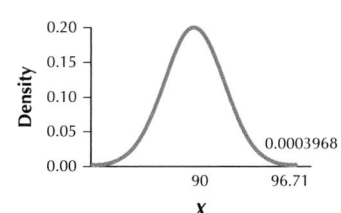

(c) 0.0003969 **(d)** 0.9996031

15. (a) 96.71

(b)

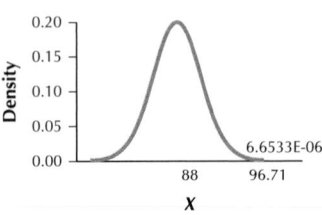

(c) 0.000006658 **(d)** 0.999993342

16. (a) 96.71

(b)

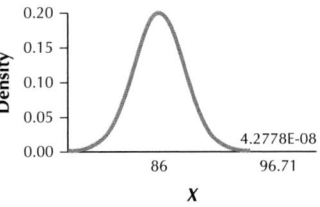

(c) 0.00000004287 **(d)** 0.99999995713

17.

18.

19. (a) A Type II error would be to conclude that the population mean daily number of shares traded is 1.6 billion when it actually is more than 1.6 billion. **(b)** TI-83/84: 0.8520 **(c)** TI-83/84: 0.6718 **(d)** TI-83/84: 0.4384 **(e)** TI-83/84: 0.2251 **(f)** 0.1480, 0.3282, 0.5616, 0.7749

(g)

20. (a) A Type II error is concluding that the population mean credit score in Florida is 673 when it is actually less than 673. **(b)** TI-83/84: 0.8520 **(c)** TI-83/84: 0.5179 **(d)** TI-83/84: 0.1698 **(e)** TI-83/84: 0.0253 **(f)** 0.1480, 0.4821, 0.8302, 0.9747

(g)

21. (a) A Type II error would be concluding that the population mean salary for entry-level accountants is \$41,560 when it is actually different from \$41,560. **(b)** TI-83/84: 0.8577 **(c)** TI-83/84: 0.1788 **(d)** TI-83/84: 0.00175 **(e)** TI-83/84: 0.0000004334 **(f)** 0.1423, 0.8212, 0.99825, 0.9999995666

(g)

22. (a) A Type II error would be concluding that the population mean tax deduction for itemizers who claim mortgage interest is \$11,350 when it is actually less than \$11,350. **(b)** TI-83/84: 0.4582 **(c)** TI-83/84: 0.0000001657 **(d)** TI-83/84: 0 **(e)** TI-83/84: 0 **(f)** 0.5418, 0.9999998343, 1, 1

(g)

23. (a) A Type II error would be to conclude that the population mean price for a gallon of milk is \$3.24 when it is actually greater than \$3.24. **(b)** TI-83/84: 0.8708 **(c)** TI-83/84: 0.0021 **(d)** TI-83/84: 0 **(e)** TI-83/84: 0 **(f)** 0.1292, 0.9979, 1, 1

(g)

24. (a) A Type II error would be to conclude that the population mean time that it takes owners of hybrid cars to recoup their initial cost is 3 years when it actually is less than 3 years. **(b)** TI-83/84: 0.0000001173 **(c)** TI-83/84: 0 **(d)** TI-83/84: 0 **(e)** TI-83/84: 0 **(f)** 0.9999998827, 1, 1, 1

(g)

Chapter 9 Review

1. $H_0 : \mu = 12$ vs. $H_a : \mu < 12$
2. $H_0 : \mu = 10$ vs. $H_a : \mu > 10$
3. $H_0 : \mu = 0$ vs. $H_a : \mu < 0$
4. **(a)** $H_0 : \mu = 2.58$ vs. $H_a : \mu \neq 2.58$ **(b)** Concluding that the population mean has changed from 2.58 when it actually is different from 2.58, and concluding that the population mean has not changed from 2.58 when it actually is not different from 2.58 **(c)** Concluding that the population mean has changed from 2.58 when it hasn't **(d)** Concluding that the population mean has not changed from 2.58 when it actually has changed from 2.58
5. **(a)** $H_0 : \mu = 202.7$ vs. $H_a : \mu < 202.7$ **(b)** We conclude that (1) the population mean number of speeding-related fatalities is less than 202.7 when it actually is and (2) the mean number of speeding-related fatalities is greater than or equal to 202.7 when it actually is. **(c)** The population mean number of speeding-related fatalities is less than 202.7 when it actually is greater than or equal to 202.7. **(d)** The population mean number of speeding-related fatalities is greater than or equal to 202.7 when it actually is less than 202.7.
6. **(a)** $H_0 : \mu = 50,000$ vs. $H_a : \mu > 50,000$ **(b)** Concluding that the population mean salary is greater than $50,000 when it actually is, and concluding that the population mean is less than or equal to $50,000 when it actually is **(c)** Concluding that the population mean salary is greater than $50,000 when it actually isn't **(d)** Concluding that the population mean is less than or equal to $50,000 when it actually isn't
7. -1
8. -2
9. -10
10. **(a)** 2.58 **(b)** Reject H_0 if $Z_{data} \leq -2.58$ or $Z_{data} \geq 2.58$.

(c)

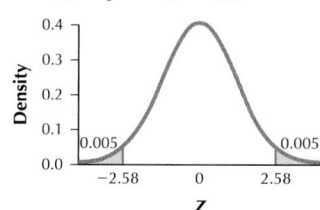

(d) Since Z_{data} is not ≤ -2.58 and Z_{data} is not ≥ 2.58, we do not reject H_0. There is insufficient evidence that the population mean is different from μ_0.
11. **(a)** 1.28 **(b)** Reject H_0 if $Z_{data} \geq 1.28$.

(c)

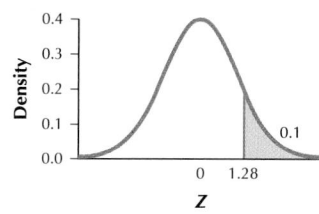

(d) Since $Z_{data} \geq 1.28$, we reject H_0. There is evidence that the population mean is greater than μ_0.
12. **(a)** 1.645 **(b)** Reject H_0 if $Z_{data} \geq 1.645$.

(c)

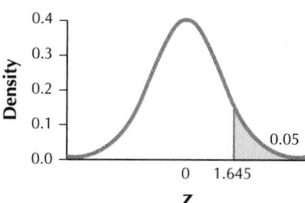

(d) Since Z_{data} is not ≥ 1.645, we do not reject H_0. There is insufficient evidence that the population mean is greater than μ_0.
13. **(a)** $H_0 : \mu = 673$ vs. $H_a : \mu < 673$ **(b)** -1.645; reject H_0 if $Z_{data} \leq -1.645$. **(c)** $Z_{data} = -5.52$

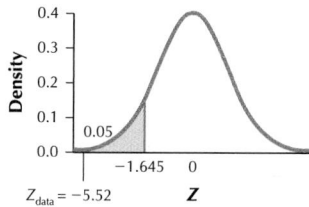

(d) Since $Z_{data} \leq -1.645$, we reject H_0. There is evidence that the population mean credit score in Florida is less than 673.
14. **(a)** $H_0 : \mu = 52,200$ vs. $H_a : \mu > 52,200$ **(b)** $Z_{crit} = 1.28$. Reject H_0 if $Z_{data} \geq 1.28$. **(c)** $Z_{data} = 9.33$

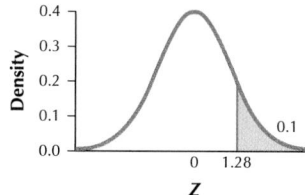

(d) Since $Z_{data} \geq 1.28$, we reject H_0. There is evidence that the population mean salary of college graduates is greater than $52,200.
15. **(a)** $H_0 : \mu = 500$ vs. $H_a : \mu \neq 500$. Reject H_0 if the p-value ≤ 0.05. **(b)** 4 **(c)** $6.337206918 \times 10^{-5}$

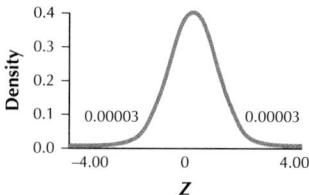

(d) Since the p-value ≤ 0.05, reject H_0. There is evidence that the population mean is different than 500.
16. **(a)** $H_0 : \mu = -10$ vs. $H_a : \mu < -10$. Reject H_0 if the p-value ≤ 0.01. **(b)** -5 **(c)** p-value $= 2.87105 \times 10^{-7}$

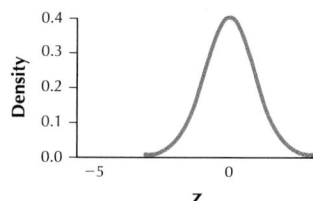

(d) Since the p-value ≤ 0.01, reject H_0. There is evidence that the population mean is less than -10.

17. $H_0 : \mu = 6{,}096$ vs. $H_a : \mu > 6{,}096$. Reject H_0 if the p-value ≤ 0.01. $Z_{\text{data}} = 11.9$; p-value $= 6.09738351 \times 10^{-33}$. Since the p-value ≤ 0.01, reject H_0. There is evidence that the population mean per capita annual expenditures on health care is greater than \$6096.

18. (a) (6.67, 7.33) (b) (i) There is insufficient evidence that the population mean amount of coffee dispensed by the old coffee machine is different than 6.9 ounces. (ii) There is evidence that the population mean amount of coffee dispensed by the old coffee machine is different than 7.5 ounces. (iii) There is insufficient evidence that the population mean amount of coffee dispensed by the old coffee machine is different than 6.7 ounces. (iv) There is insufficient evidence that the population mean amount of coffee dispensed by the old coffee machine is different than 7 ounces.

19. $t_{\text{crit}} = 1.415$

20. $t_{\text{crit}} = 1.895$

21. $t_{\text{crit}} = 2.998$

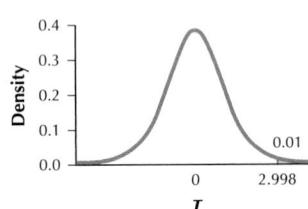

22. For right-tailed tests, t_{crit} increases as α decreases.

23. $H_0 : \mu = 9$ vs. $H_a : \mu \neq 9$. $t_{\text{crit}} = 1.753$. Reject H_0 if $t_{\text{data}} \leq -1.753$ or $t_{\text{data}} \geq 1.753$. $t_{\text{data}} = 1.33$. Since t_{data} is not ≤ -1.753 and t_{data} is not ≥ 1.753, we do not reject H_0. There is insufficient evidence that the population mean is different from 9.

24. $H_0 : \mu = 45$ vs. $H_a : \mu \neq 45$. Reject H_0 if p-value ≤ 0.10. $t_{\text{data}} = 0$. p-value $= 0.5$. Since p-value is not ≤ 0.10, we do not reject H_0. There is insufficient evidence that the population mean differs from 45.

25. (a) We have $np_0 = 1000(0.8) = 800 \geq 5$ and $n(1 - p_0) = 1000(1 - 0.8) = 200 \geq 5$. (b) $H_0 : p = 0.8$ vs. $H_a : p > 0.8$ (c) $Z_{\text{crit}} = 1.28$. Reject H_0 if $Z_{\text{data}} \geq 1.28$. (d) $Z_{\text{data}} = 2.37$ (e) Since $Z_{\text{data}} \geq 1.28$, we reject H_0. There is evidence that the population proportion is greater than 0.8.

26. (a) We have $np_0 = 900(0.2) = 180 \geq 5$ and $n(1 - p_0) = 900(1 - 0.2) = 720 \geq 5$. (b) $H_0 : p = 0.2$ vs. $H_a : p < 0.2$

(c) 1.645; reject H_0 if $Z_{\text{data}} \leq -1.645$. (d) -1.67 (e) Since $Z_{\text{data}} \leq -1.645$, we reject H_0. There is evidence that the population proportion is less than 0.2.

27. (a) We have $np_0 = 100(0.4) = 40 \geq 5$ and $n(1 - p_0) = 100(1 - 0.4) = 60 \geq 5$. (b) $H_0 : p = 0.4$ vs. $H_a : p \neq 0.4$ (c) $Z_{\text{crit}} = 2.58$. Reject H_0 if $Z_{\text{data}} \leq -2.58$ or $Z_{\text{data}} \geq 2.58$. (d) $Z_{\text{data}} = 3.06$ (e) Since $Z_{\text{data}} \geq 2.58$, we reject H_0. There is evidence that the population proportion is not equal to 0.4.

28. (a) We have $np_0 = 144(0.7) = 100.8 \geq 5$ and $n(1 - p_0) = 144(1 - 0.7) = 43.2 \geq 5$. (b) $H_0 : p = 0.7$ vs. $H_a : p \neq 0.7$. Reject H_0 if the p-value ≤ 0.05. (c) $Z_{\text{data}} = 1.67$ (d) p-value $= 0.095$ (e) Since the p-value is not ≤ 0.05, we do not reject H_0. There is insufficient evidence that the population proportion is different than 0.7.

29. (a) We have $np_0 = 100(0.25) = 25 \geq 5$ and $n(1 - p_0) = 100(1 - 0.25) = 75 \geq 5$. (b) $H_0 : p = 0.25$ vs. $H_a : p < 0.25$. Reject H_0 if the p-value ≤ 0.05. (c) 0 (d) 0.5 (e) Since the p-value is not ≤ 0.05, we do not reject H_0. There is insufficient evidence that the population proportion is less than 0.25.

30. $np_0 = 1000\,(0.416) = 416 \geq 5$ and $n(1 - p_0) = 1000(1 - 0.416) = 584 \geq 5$. Thus we can use the Z test. $H_0 : p = 0.416$ vs. $H_a : p < 0.416$. $Z_{\text{crit}} = -1.645$. Reject H_0 if $Z_{\text{data}} \leq -1.645$. $Z_{\text{data}} = -4.23$. Since $Z_{\text{data}} \leq -1.645$, we reject H_0. There is evidence that the population proportion who prefer DSL is less than 0.416.

31. (a) $H_0 : \sigma = 6$ vs. $H_a : \sigma > 6$ (b) $\chi_\alpha^2 = \chi_{0.05}^2 = 30.144$. Reject H_0 if $\chi_{\text{data}}^2 \geq 30.144$ (c) $\chi_{\text{data}}^2 = 42.75$

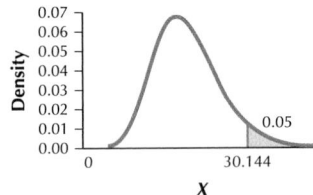

(d) Since $\chi_{\text{data}}^2 \geq 30.144$, we reject H_0. There is evidence that the population standard deviation is greater than 6.

32. (a) $H_0 : \sigma = 10$ vs. $H_a : \sigma \neq 10$ (b) $\chi_{\alpha/2}^2 = \chi_{0.025}^2 = 40.646$ and $\chi_{1-\alpha/2}^2 = \chi_{0.975}^2 = 13.120$. Reject H_0 if $\chi_{\text{data}}^2 \geq 40.646$ or $\chi_{\text{data}}^2 \leq 13.120$. (c) 22.5

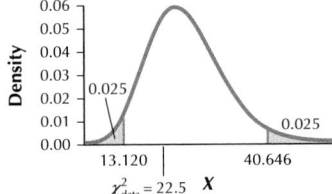

(d) Since χ_{data}^2 is not ≤ 13.120 and χ_{data}^2 is not ≥ 40.646, we do not reject H_0. There is insufficient evidence that the population standard deviation differs from 10.

33. (a) $H_0 : \sigma = 35$ vs. $H_a : \sigma < 35$. Reject H_0 if the p-value ≤ 0.05. (b) 6.857 (c) p-value $= 0.5560805474$

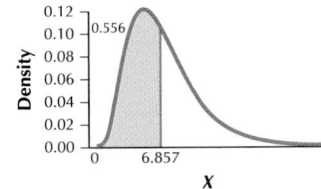

(d) Since the p-value is not ≤ 0.05, we do not reject H_0. There is insufficient evidence that the population standard deviation is less than 35.

34. (a) $H_0 : \sigma = 50$ vs. $H_a : \sigma \neq 50$. Reject H_0 if the p-value ≤ 0.05. **(b)** 20.25 **(c)** 0.5328172862

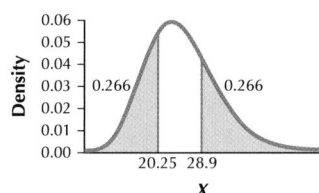

(d) Since the p-value is not ≤ 0.05 for $\alpha = 0.01$, 0.05, and 0.10, we do not reject H_0. There is insufficient evidence that the population standard deviation is not equal to 50.

35. $H_0 : \sigma = 50$ vs. $H_a : \sigma \neq 50$. Reject H_0 if the p-value ≤ 0.01. $\chi^2_{\text{data}} = 0.690$. p-value $= 0.094887$. Since the p-value is not ≤ 0.01, we do not reject H_0. There is insufficient evidence that the population standard deviation differs from 50.

36. (a) $\bar{x}_{\text{critical, lower}} = 95.1625$, $\bar{x}_{\text{critical, upper}} = 104.8375$

(b)

(c) TI-83/84: 0.8364 **(d)** 0.1636

37. (a) $\bar{x}_{\text{critical, lower}} = 95.1625$, $\bar{x}_{\text{critical, upper}} = 104.8375$

(b)

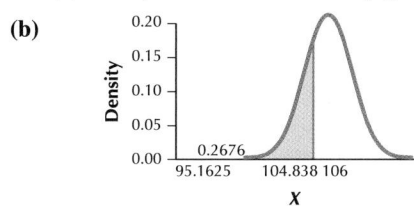

(c) 0.2676 **(d)** 0.7324

38. (a) $\bar{x}_{\text{critical, lower}} = 95.1625$, $\bar{x}_{\text{critical, upper}} = 104.8375$

(b)

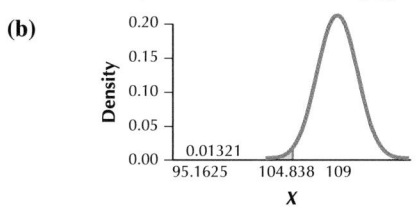

(c) TI-83/84: 0.0132 **(d)** 0.9868

39. (a) $\bar{x}_{\text{critical, lower}} = 95.1625$, $\bar{x}_{\text{critical, upper}} = 104.8375$

(b)

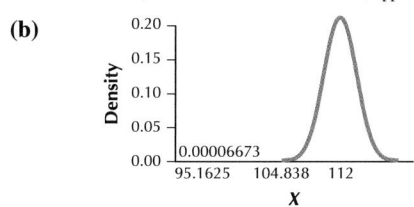

(c) 0.00006675 **(d)** 0.99993325

40. (a) $\bar{x}_{\text{critical, lower,}} = 95.1625$, $\bar{x}_{\text{critical, upper}} = 104.8375$

(b)

(c) 0 **(d)** 1

41.

Chapter 9 Quiz

1. False
2. True
3. True
4. I
5. small
6. α
7. $np_0 \geq 5$ and $n(1 - p_0) \geq 5$
8. A small p-value indicates that there is strong evidence against the null hypothesis. A large p-value indicates that there is no evidence against the null hypothesis.
9. No
10. (a) $H_0 : \mu = 1.14$ vs. $H_a : \mu < 1.14$. -1.645. Reject H_0 if $Z_{\text{data}} \leq -1.645$. $Z_{\text{data}} = -1.68$. Since $Z_{\text{data}} \leq -1.645$, we reject H_0. There is evidence that the population mean fee charged by banks when you withdraw funds from an ATM machine not owned by your bank is less than \$1.14. **(b)** Type I error, Type II error
11. (a) No, since the population standard deviation is not known. $H_0 : \mu = 32$ vs. $H_a : \mu \neq 32$. 1.690. Reject H_0 if $t_{\text{data}} \leq -1.690$ or $t_{\text{data}} \geq 1.690$. $\chi^2_{\text{data}} = 1.80$. Since $t_{\text{data}} \geq 1.690$, we reject H_0. There is evidence that the population mean years of potential life lost in alcohol-related fatal automobile accidents is different from 32 years. **(b)** p-value $= 0.0805$, so there is moderate evidence against the null hypothesis.
12. $H_0 : p = 0.127$ vs. $H_a : p > 0.127$. Reject H_0 if the p-value ≤ 0.05. $Z_{\text{data}} = 0.93$. p-value $= 0.1762$. Since $0.15 \leq p$-value, there is no evidence against the null hypothesis that the population proportion of preterm births is less than or equal to 0.127. Since the p-value ≤ 0.05, we do not reject H_0. There is insufficient evidence that the population proportion of preterm births is greater than 0.127.
13. $H_0 : \sigma = 0.25$ vs. $H_a : \sigma < 0.25$. $\chi^2_{1-\alpha} = \chi^2_{0.90} = 4.168$. Reject H_0 if $\chi^2_{\text{data}} \leq 4.168$. $\chi^2_{\text{data}} = 16.992$. Since χ^2_{data} is not ≤ 4.168, we do not reject H_0. There is insufficient evidence that the population standard deviation of net price change is less than 25 cents.

Chapter 10

Section 10.1

1. When the subjects selected for the first sample do not determine the subjects in the second sample

2. When the subjects in the first sample determine the subjects in the second sample

3. Matched pairs or paired samples

4. μ_d is the population mean of the differences of matched-pairs data.

5. Since both samples of games were based on the same players, this is an example of dependent sampling.

6. Independent sampling; the selection of the first group of females does not depend on the selection of the second group and vice versa.

7. Since the same students are taking both tests, this is an example of dependent sampling.

8. Independent sampling; the sampled speeds on the first road do not depend on the speeds on the second road and vice versa.

9. $\bar{x}_d = 1.1$, $s_d = 0.9618$

10. $\bar{x}_d = 0.6667$, $s_d = 1.3663$

11. $\bar{x}_d = -7.1429$, $s_d = 2.6726$

12. $\bar{x}_d = 0.3286$, $s_d = 0.2690$

13. $\bar{x}_d = -0.00625$, $s_d = 0.2095$

14. $\bar{x}_d = -3.25$, $s_d = 2.3146$

15. $H_0 : \mu_d = 0$ vs. $H_a : \mu_d > 0$. $t_{\text{crit}} = 2.132$. Reject H_0 if $t_{\text{data}} \geq 2.132$. $t_{\text{data}} = 2.557$. Since $t_{\text{data}} = 2.557$ is ≥ 2.132, we reject H_0. There is evidence at the $\alpha = 0.05$ level of significance that the population mean difference is greater than 0.

16. $H_0 : \mu_d = 0$ vs. $H_a : \mu_d \neq 0$. $t_{\text{crit}} = 4.032$. Reject H_0 if $t_{\text{data}} \leq -4.032$ or if $t_{\text{data}} \geq 4.032$. $t_{\text{data}} = 1.195$. Since $t_{\text{data}} = 1.195$ is not ≤ -4.032 and is not ≥ 4.032, we do not reject H_0. There is insufficient evidence at the $\alpha = 0.01$ level of significance that the population mean difference is not equal to 0.

17. $H_0 : \mu_d = 0$ vs. $H_a : \mu_d < 0$. $t_{\text{crit}} = -1.440$. Reject H_0 if $t_{\text{data}} \leq -1.440$. $t_{\text{data}} = -7.071$. Since $t_{\text{data}} = -7.071$ is ≤ -1.440, we reject H_0. There is evidence at the $\alpha = 0.10$ level of significance that the population mean difference is less than 0.

18. $H_0 : \mu_d = 0$ vs. $H_a : \mu_d > 0$. Reject H_0 if the p-value ≤ 0.01. $t_{\text{data}} = 3.232$ (TI-83/84: 3.231). p-value $= 0.0089$. Since the p-value $= 0.0089$ is ≤ 0.01, we reject H_0. There is evidence at the $\alpha = 0.01$ level of significance that the population mean difference is greater than 0.

19. $H_0 : \mu_d = 0$ vs. $H_a : \mu_d \neq 0$. Reject H_0 if the p-value ≤ 0.05. $t_{\text{data}} = -0.084$. p-value $= 0.9351$. Since the p-value $= 0.9351$ is not ≤ 0.05, we do not reject H_0. There is insufficient evidence at the $\alpha = 0.05$ level of significance that the population mean difference is not equal to 0.

20. $H_0 : \mu_d = 0$ vs. $H_a : \mu_d < 0$. Reject H_0 if the p-value ≤ 0.10. $t_{\text{data}} = -3.971$ (TI-83/84: -3.972). p-value $= 0.0027$. Since the p-value $= 0.0027$ is ≤ 0.10, we reject H_0. There is evidence at the $\alpha = 0.10$ level of significance that the population mean difference is less than 0.

21. $(-0.0940, 2.294)$. We are 95% confident that the population mean difference lies between -0.0040 and 2.294.

22. $(-1.582, 2.916)$. We are 99% confident that the population mean difference lies between -1.582 and 2.916.

23. $(-9.106, -5.180)$. We are 90% confident that the population mean difference lies between -9.106 and -5.180.

24. $(-0.048, 0.705)$. TI-83/84: $(-0.048, 0.706)$. We are 99% confident that the population mean difference lies between -0.048 and 0.705 (0.706).

25. $(-0.181, 0.169)$. We are 95% confident that the population mean difference lies between -0.181 and 0.169.

26. $(-4.801, -1.699)$. TI-83/84: $(-4.8, -1.7)$. We are 90% confident that the population mean difference lies between $-4.801(-4.8)$ and $-1.699(-1.7)$.

27. (a) $H_0 : \mu_d = 0$ vs. $H_a : \mu_d \neq 0$. $\mu_0 = 0$ lies inside of the interval $(-5, 5)$, so we do not reject H_0 at the $\alpha = 0.05$ level of significance. **(b)** $H_0 : \mu_d = -6$ vs. $H_a : \mu_d \neq -6$. $\mu_0 = -6$ lies outside of the interval $(-5, 5)$, so we reject H_0 at the $\alpha = 0.05$ level of significance. **(c)** $H_0 : \mu_d = 4$ vs. $H_a : \mu_d \neq 4$. $\mu_0 = 4$ lies inside of the interval $(-5, 5)$, so we do not reject H_0 at the $\alpha = 0.05$ level of significance.

28. (a) $H_0 : \mu_d = -12$ vs. $H_a : \mu_d \neq -12$. $\mu_0 = -12$ lies outside of the interval $(-10, -4)$, so we reject H_0 at the $\alpha = 0.01$ level of significance. **(b)** $H_0 : \mu_d = 0$ vs. $H_a : \mu_d \neq 0$. $\mu_0 = 0$ lies outside of the interval $(-10, -4)$, so we reject H_0 at the $\alpha = 0.01$ level of significance. **(c)** $H_0 : \mu_d = 4$ vs. $H_a : \mu_d \neq 4$. $\mu_0 = 4$ lies outside of the interval $(-10, -4)$, so we reject H_0 at the $\alpha = 0.01$ level of significance.

29. (a) $H_0 : \mu_d = -10$ vs. $H_a : \mu_d \neq -10$. $\mu_0 = -10$ lies outside of the interval $(10, 20)$, so we reject H_0 at the $\alpha = 0.10$ level of significance. **(b)** $H_0 : \mu_d = 25$ vs. $H_a : \mu_d \neq 25$. $\mu_0 = 25$ lies outside of the interval $(10, 20)$, so we reject H_0 at the $\alpha = 0.10$ level of significance. **(c)** $H_0 : \mu_d = 0$ vs. $H_a : \mu_d \neq 0$. $\mu_0 = 0$ lies outside of the interval $(10, 20)$, so we reject H_0 at the $\alpha = 0.10$ level of significance.

30. (a) $H_0 : \mu_d = 0.41$ vs. $H_a : \mu_d \neq 0.41$. $\mu_0 = 0.41$ lies inside of the interval $(0, 1)$, so we do not reject H_0 at the $\alpha = 0.05$ level of significance. **(b)** $H_0 : \mu_d = 0.29$ vs. $H_a : \mu_d \neq 0.29$. $\mu_0 = 0.29$ lies inside of the interval $(0, 1)$, so we do not reject H_a at the $\alpha = 0.05$ level of significance. **(c)** $H_0 : \mu_d = 1.23$ vs. $H_a : \mu_d \neq 1.23$. $\mu_0 = 0.1.23$ lies outside of the interval $(0, 1)$, so we reject H_0 at the $\alpha = 0.05$ level of significance.

31. (a) $\bar{x}_d = 753.75$, $s_d = 986.1658$ **(b)** There is insufficient evidence that 2007 models are on average more expensive.

32. (a) $\bar{x}_d = 4$, $s_d = 6.519$ **(b) Critical-value method:** $H_0 : \mu_d = 0$ vs. $H_a : \mu_d > 0$. $t_{\text{crit}} = 1.533$. Reject H_0 if $t_{\text{data}} \geq 1.533$. $t_{\text{data}} = 1.372$. Since $t_{\text{data}} = 1.372$ is not ≥ 1.533, we do not reject H_0. There is insufficient evidence at the $\alpha = 0.10$ level of significance that the population mean difference is greater than 0. Therefore there is insufficient evidence that listening to Mozart improves math scores. **p-value method:** $H_0 : \mu_d = 0$ vs. $H_a : \mu_d > 0$. Reject H_0 if the p-value ≤ 0.10. $t_{\text{data}} = 1.372$. p-value $= 0.1210$. Since the p-value $= 0.1210$ is not ≤ 0.10, we do not reject H_0. There is insufficient evidence at the $\alpha = 0.10$ level of significance that the population mean difference is greater than 0. Therefore there is insufficient evidence that listening to Mozart improves math scores.

33. (a) $\bar{x}_d = 15.14$, $s_d = 3.7787$ **(b) Critical-value method:** $H_0 : \mu_d = 0$ vs. $H_a : \mu_d \neq 0$. $t_{\text{crit}} = 3.250$. Reject H_0 if $t_{\text{data}} \leq -3.250$ or if $t_{\text{data}} \geq 3.250$. $t_{\text{data}} = 12.670$. Since $t_{\text{data}} = 12.670$ is ≥ 3.250, we reject H_0. There is evidence at the $\alpha = 0.01$ level of significance that the population mean difference between high and low temperatures is different from 0. **p-value method:** $H_0 : \mu_d = 0$ vs. $H_a : \mu_d \neq 0$. Reject H_0 if the p-value ≤ 0.01. $t_{\text{data}} = 12.670$. p-value ≈ 0. Since the p-value ≈ 0 is ≤ 0.01, we reject H_0. There is evidence at the $\alpha = 0.01$ level of significance that the population mean difference between high and low temperatures is different from 0.

34. (a) $\bar{x}_d = -28,825$, $s_d = 16,806.2241$ **(b) Critical-value method:** $H_0 : \mu_d = 0$ vs. $H_a : \mu_d \neq 0$. $t_{\text{crit}} = 2.353$. Reject H_0 if $t_{\text{data}} \leq -2.353$ or if $t_{\text{data}} \geq 2.353$. $t_{\text{data}} = -3.430$. Since

$t_{\text{data}} = -3.430$ is ≤ -2.353, we reject H_0. There is evidence at the $\alpha = 0.10$ level of significance that the population mean difference between home sale prices in 2008 and 2007 is different from 0. **p-value method:** $H_0 : \mu_d = 0$ vs. $H_a : \mu_d \ne 0$. Reject H_0 if the p-value ≤ 0.10. $t_{\text{data}} = -3.430$. p-value $= 0.0415$. Since the p-value $= 0.0415$ is ≤ 0.10, we reject H_0. There is evidence at the $\alpha = 0.10$ level of significance that the population mean difference between home sale prices in 2008 and 2007 is different from 0.

35. $(-815.2398, 2322.7398)$. We are 95% confident that the population mean difference in car prices lies between $-\$815.2398$ and $\$2322.7398$.

36. $(-4.093, 12.093)$. TI-83/84: $(-4.095, 12.095)$. We are 95% confident that the population mean difference in math quiz scores before and after listening to Mozart lies between -4.0953 (-4.095) and 12.093 (12.095).

37. (a) $(12.437, 17.843)$. We are 95% confident that the population mean difference between high and low temperatures lies between 12.437 and 17.843 degrees. (b) $\mu_0 = 0$ lies outside of the interval $(12.437, 17.8430)$, so we reject H_0. This is the same conclusion we reached in the hypothesis test in Exercise 33.

38. (a) $(-\$55,563.70, -\$2086.30)$. TI-83/84: $(-\$55,567, -\$2083)$. We are 95% confident that the population mean difference between 2008 and 2007 home prices lies between $-\$55,563.70$ $(-\$55,567)$ and $-\$2086.30$ $(-\$2083)$. (b) $\mu_0 = 0$ lies outside of the interval $(-\$55,563.70, -\$2086.30)$ (TI-83/84: $(-\$55,567, -\$2083)$), so we reject H_0. This is the same conclusion we reached in the hypothesis test in Exercise 34.

39. $H_0 : \mu_d = 0$ vs. $H_a : \mu_d < 0$. Reject H_0 if p-value ≤ 0.10. $t_{\text{data}} = -2.892$. p-value $= 0.0100686368$. Since p-value ≤ 0.10, we reject H_0. There is evidence that the manufacturer's spelling checker software reduces the population mean number of spelling errors.

40. (a) $(1.9618, 23.5048)$ (b) Since 0 is not in the interval, there is evidence that the 2003 science test scores for fourth-graders are higher than the 1995 science test scores for fourth-graders.

41. (a) $(2.6796, 13.5704)$ (b) No, the manufacturer's claim is a one-tailed test and the confidence interval can be used only for a two-tailed test. (c) $H_0 : \mu_d = 0$ vs. $H_a : \mu_d > 0$. Reject H_0 if p-value ≤ 0.05. $t_{\text{data}} = 3.529$. p-value $= 0.0048053601$. Since the p-value ≤ 0.05, we reject H_0. There is evidence that the population mean of the differences between the post-test and pre-test reading scores of students who play the phonetics game is greater than 0.

42. (a) -10.92 collisions per year (b) $(-18.3465, -3.4935)$. TI-83/84: $(-18.61, -3.234)$. (c) **Critical-value method:** $H_0 : \mu_d = 0$ vs. $H_a : \mu_d < 0$. $t_{\text{crit}} = -2.624$. Reject H_0 if $t_{\text{data}} \le -2.624$. $t_{\text{data}} = -3.074$. Since $t_{\text{data}} = -3.074$ is ≤ -2.624, we reject H_0. There is evidence at the $\alpha = 0.01$ level of significance that the population mean difference is less than 0. Therefore there is evidence that the road improvements have lowered the number of collisions per year on these sections of highway. **p-value method:** $H_0 : \mu_d = 0$ vs. $H_a : \mu_d < 0$. Reject H_0 if the p-value ≤ 0.01. $t_{\text{data}} = -3.074$. p-value $= 0.0044$. Since the p-value $= 0.0044$ is ≤ 0.01, we reject H_0. There is evidence at the $\alpha = 0.01$ level of significance that the population mean difference is less than 0. Therefore there is evidence that the road improvements have lowered the number of collisions per year on these sections of highway.

43. **Critical-value method:** $H_0 : \mu_d = 0$ vs. $H_a : \mu_d < 0$. $t_{\text{crit}} = 3.365$. Reject H_0 if $t_{\text{data}} \le -3.365$. $t_{\text{data}} = -4.843$. Since $t_{\text{data}} \le$

-3.365, we reject H_0. There is evidence that the population mean number of goals scored per game has increased.

44. The conclusion would still be to reject H_0.

45. Because we are taking home sales of the same counties in 2006 and 2007

46. (a) $\bar{x}_d = -10.9333$ (b) $s_d = 22.8425$ (c) $t_{\text{data}} = -1.854$

47. There is insufficient evidence that the population mean number of home sales differed from 2006 to 2007.

48. $(-1.7177, 23.5843)$

49. The conclusion would remain the same.

Section 10.2

1. The two populations are normally distributed. The sample sizes are large (at least 30).

2. We do not reject the null hypothesis.

3. (a) $H_0 : \mu_1 = \mu_2$ vs. $H_a : \mu_1 \ne \mu_2$ (b) $t_{\text{crit}} = 1.690$. Reject H_0 if $t_{\text{data}} \le -1.690$ or $t_{\text{data}} \ge 1.690$. (c) $t_{\text{data}} = 4.243$. (d) Since $t_{\text{data}} \ge 1.690$, we reject H_0. There is evidence that the population mean for Population 1 is different from the population mean for Population 2.

4. (a) $H_0 : \mu_1 = \mu_2$ vs. $H_a : \mu_1 > \mu_2$ (b) $t_{\text{crit}} = 1.671$. Reject H_0 if $t_{\text{data}} \ge 1.671$. (c) $t_{\text{data}} = 4.438$. (d) Since $t_{\text{data}} = 4.438$ is ≥ 1.671, we reject H_0. There is evidence at the $\alpha = 0.05$ level of significance that the population mean of Population 1 is greater than the population mean of Population 2.

5. (a) $H_0 : \mu_1 = \mu_2$ vs. $H_a : \mu_1 < \mu_2$ (b) $t_{\text{crit}} = -2.423$. Reject H_0 if $t_{\text{data}} \le -2.423$. (c) $t_{\text{data}} = -5.077$ (d) Since $t_{\text{data}} = -5.077$ is ≤ -2.423, we reject H_0. There is evidence at the $\alpha = 0.01$ level of significance that the population mean of Population 1 is less than the population mean of Population 2.

6. (a) $H_0 : \mu_1 = \mu_2$ vs. $H_a : \mu_1 > \mu_2$ (b) $t_{\text{crit}} = 1.685$. Reject H_0 if $t_{\text{data}} \ge 1.685$. (c) $t_{\text{data}} = 3.303$. (d) Since $t_{\text{data}} = 3.303 \ge 1.685$, we reject H_0. There is evidence at the $\alpha = 0.05$ level of significance that the population mean of Population 1 is greater than the population mean of Population 2.

7. (a) $H_0 : \mu_1 = \mu_2$ vs. $H_a : \mu_1 \ne \mu_2$. Reject H_0 if the p-value ≤ 0.10. (b) $t_{\text{data}} = -2.492$. (c) p-value $= 0.0162$. (d) Since the p-value is ≤ 0.10, we reject H_0. There is evidence at the $\alpha = 0.10$ level of significance that the population mean of Population 1 is different from the population mean of Population 2.

8. (a) $H_0 : \mu_1 = \mu_2$ vs. $H_a : \mu_1 > \mu_2$. Reject H_0 if the p-value ≤ 0.05. (b) $t_{\text{data}} = 6.676$ (c) p-value ≈ 0. (d) Since the p-value ≈ 0 is ≤ 0.05, we reject H_0. There is evidence at the $\alpha = 0.05$ level of significance that the population mean of Population 1 is greater than the population mean of Population 2.

9. (a) $H_0 : \mu_1 = \mu_2$ vs. $H_a : \mu_1 < \mu_2$. Reject H_0 if the p-value ≤ 0.05. (b) $t_{\text{data}} = -13.868$ (c) p-value ≈ 0. (d) Since the p-value ≈ 0 is ≤ 0.05, we reject H_0. There is evidence at the $\alpha = 0.05$ level of significance that the population mean of Population 1 is less than the population mean of Population 2.

10. (a) $H_0 : \mu_1 = \mu_2$ vs. $H_a : \mu_1 \ne \mu_2$. Reject H_0 if the p-value ≤ 0.01. (b) $t_{\text{data}} = -5.085$ (c) p-value $= 0.00002$. (d) Since the p-value $= 0.00002$ is ≤ 0.01, we reject H_0. There is evidence that the population mean of Population 1 is different from the population mean of Population 2.

11. (a) $\bar{x}_1 - \bar{x}_2 = 2$ (b) $E = 0.797$. We can estimate the difference in the population means of Population 1 and Population 2 to within 0.797 with 90% confidence. (c) $(1.203, 2.797)$. We are 90% confident that the difference in the population means of Population 1 and Population 2 lies between 1.203 and 2.797.

12. (a) $\bar{x}_1 - \bar{x}_2 = 2$ (b) $E = 0.901$. We can estimate the difference in the population means of Population 1 and Population 2 to within 0.901 with 95% confidence. (c) (1.099, 2.901). We are 95% confident that the difference in the population means of Population 1 and Population 2 lies between 1.099 and 2.901.

13. (a) $\bar{x}_1 - \bar{x}_2 = -10$ (b) $E = 5.326$. We can estimate the difference in the population means of Population 1 and Population 2 to within 5.326 with 99% confidence. (c) $(-15.326, -4.674)$. We are 99% confident that the difference in the population means of Population 1 and Population 2 lies between -15.326 and -4.674.

14. (a) $\bar{x}_1 - \bar{x}_2 = 10$ (b) $E = 6.125$. We can estimate the difference in the population means of Population 1 and Population 2 to within 6.125 with 95% confidence. (c) (3.875, 16.125). We are 95% confident that the difference in the population means of Population 1 and Population 2 lies between 3.875 and 16.125.

15. (a) $\bar{x}_1 - \bar{x}_2 = -1$ (b) $E = 0.811$. We can estimate the difference in the population means of Population 1 and Population 2 to within 0.811 with 95% confidence. (c) $(-1.811, -0.189)$. We are 95% confident that the difference in the population means of Population 1 and Population 2 lies between -1.811 and -0.189.

16. (a) $\bar{x}_1 - \bar{x}_2 = 8$ (b) $E = 1.989$. We can estimate the difference in the population means of Population 1 and Population 2 to within 1.989 with 90% confidence. (c) (6.011, 9.989). We are 90% confident that the difference in the population means of Population 1 and Population 2 lies between 6.011 and 9.989.

17. (a) $H_0: \mu_1 - \mu_2 = 0$ vs. $H_a: \mu_1 - \mu_2 \neq 0$. $\mu_0 = 0$ lies outside of the interval (10, 15), so we reject H_0 at the $\alpha = 0.05$ level of significance. (b) $H_0: \mu_1 - \mu_2 = 12$ vs. $H_a: \mu_1 - \mu_2 \neq 12$. $\mu_0 = 12$ lies inside of the interval (10, 15), so we do not reject H_0 at the $\alpha = 0.05$ level of significance. (c) $H_0: \mu_1 - \mu_2 = 16$ vs. $H_a: \mu_1 - \mu_2 \neq 16$. $\mu_0 = 16$ lies outside of the interval (10, 15), so we reject H_0 at the $\alpha = 0.05$ level of significance.

18. (a) $H_0: \mu_1 - \mu_2 = 1$ vs. $H_a: \mu_1 - \mu_2 \neq 1$. $\mu_0 = 1$ lies inside of the interval (0, 100), so we do not reject H_0 at the $\alpha = 0.01$ level of significance. (b) $H_0: \mu_1 - \mu_2 = 99$ vs. $H_a: \mu_1 - \mu_2 \neq 99$. $\mu_0 = 99$ lies inside of the interval (0, 100), so we do not reject H_0 at the $\alpha = 0.01$ level of significance. (c) $H_0: \mu_1 - \mu_2 = 101$ vs. $H_a: \mu_1 - \mu_2 \neq 101$. $\mu_0 = 101$ lies outside of the interval (0, 100), so we reject H_0 at the $\alpha = 0.01$ level of significance.

19. (a) $H_0: \mu_1 - \mu_2 = -10.1$ vs. $H_a: \mu_1 - \mu_2 \neq -10.1$. $\mu_0 = -10.1$ lies outside of the interval $(-10, 10)$, so we reject H_0 at the $\alpha = 0.10$ level of significance. (b) $H_0: \mu_1 - \mu_2 = -9.9$ vs. $H_a: \mu_1 - \mu_2 \neq -9.9$. $\mu_0 = -9.9$ lies inside of the interval $(-10, 10)$, so we do not reject H_0 at the $\alpha = 0.10$ level of significance. (c) $H_0: \mu_1 - \mu_2 = 0$ vs. $H_a: \mu_1 - \mu_2 \neq 0$. $\mu_0 = 0$ lies inside of the interval $(-10, 10)$, so we do not reject H_0 at the $\alpha = 0.10$ level of significance.

20. (a) $H_0: \mu_1 - \mu_2 = -16$ vs. $H_a: \mu_1 - \mu_2 \neq -16$. $\mu_0 = -16$ lies inside of the interval $(-25, -15)$, so we do not reject H_0 at the $\alpha = 0.05$ level of significance. (b) $H_0: \mu_1 - \mu_2 = -26$ vs. $H_a: \mu_1 - \mu_2 \neq -26$. $\mu_0 = -26$ lies outside of the interval $(-25, -15)$, so we reject H_0 at the $\alpha = 0.05$ level of significance. (c) $H_0: \mu_1 - \mu_2 = 0$ vs. $H_a: \mu_1 - \mu_2 \neq 0$. $\mu_0 = 0$ lies outside of the interval $(-25, -15)$, so we reject H_0 at the $\alpha = 0.05$ level of significance.

21. $H_0: \mu_1 = \mu_2$ vs. $H_a: \mu_1 > \mu_2$. $t_{\text{crit}} = 1.294$. Reject H_0 if $t_{\text{data}} \geq 1.294$. $s^2_{\text{pooled}} = 110.5$. $t_{\text{data}} \approx 0.807$. Since $t_{\text{data}} \approx 0.807$ is not ≥ 1.294, we do not reject H_0. There is insufficient evidence at the $\alpha = 0.10$ level of significance that the population mean of Population 1 is greater than the population mean of Population 2.

22. $H_0: \mu_1 = \mu_2$ vs. $H_a: \mu_1 < \mu_2$, $t_{\text{crit}} = -1.660$. Reject H_0 if $t_{\text{data}} \leq -1.660$. $s^2_{\text{pooled}} \approx 0.0728$. $t_{\text{data}} \approx -7.177$. Since $t_{\text{data}} \approx -7.177$ is ≤ -1.660, we reject H_0. There is evidence at the $\alpha = 0.05$ level of significance that the population mean of Population 1 is less than the population mean of Population 2.

23. $(-2.940, 6.940)$. We are 95% confident that the difference in the population means of Population 1 and Population 2 lies between -2.940 and 6.940.

24. $(-0.255, -0.145)$. We are 95% confident that the difference in the population means of Population 1 and Population 2 lies between -0.255 and -0.145.

25. $H_0: \mu_1 = \mu_2$ vs. $H_a: \mu_1 > \mu_2$. $Z_{\text{crit}} = 1.645$. Reject H_0 if $Z_{\text{data}} \geq 1.645$. $Z_{\text{data}} \approx 2.757$. Since $Z \approx 2.757$ is ≥ 1.645, we reject H_0. There is evidence at the $\alpha = 0.05$ level of significance that the population mean of Population 1 is greater than the population mean of Population 2.

26. $H_0: \mu_1 = \mu_2$ vs. $H_a: \mu_1 < \mu_2$. $Z_{\text{crit}} = -1.28$. Reject H_0 if $Z_{\text{data}} \leq -1.28$. $Z_{\text{data}} = -6.4$. Since $Z_{\text{data}} = -6.4$ is ≤ -1.28, we reject H_0. There is evidence at the $\alpha = 0.10$ level of significance that the population mean of Population 1 is less than the population mean of Population 2.

27. (0.289, 1.711). We are 95% confident that the difference in the population means of Population 1 and Population 2 lies between 0.289 and 1.711.

28. $(-5.225, -2.775)$. We are 95% confident that the difference in the population means of Population 1 and Population 2 lies between -5.225 and -2.775.

29. Since both sample sizes are less than 30 and the distribution of both populations is unknown, it is not appropriate to use Welch's t test.

30. Since both populations are normally distributed, it is appropriate to use Welch's t test. **Critical-value method:** $H_0: \mu_1 = \mu_2$ vs. $H_a: \mu_1 < \mu_2$. $t_{\text{crit}} = -1.729$. Reject H_0 if $t_{\text{data}} \leq -1.729$. $t_{\text{data}} = -2.233$. Since $t_{\text{data}} = -2.233$ is ≤ -1.729, we reject H_0. There is evidence at the $\alpha = 0.05$ level of significance that the population mean number of foreclosures on single-family residences in 2007 was less than the population mean number of foreclosures on single-family residences in 2008. **p-value method:** $H_0: \mu_1 = \mu_2$ vs $H_1: \mu_1 < \mu_2$. Reject H_0 if the p-value ≤ 0.05. $t_{\text{data}} = -2.233$. p-value $= 0.0189$. Since the p-value $= 0.0189 \leq 0.05$, we reject H_0. There is evidence at the $\alpha = 0.05$ level of significance that the population mean number of foreclosures on single-family residences in 2007 was less than the population mean number of foreclosures on single-family residences in 2008.

31. (a) -1192 (b) 2,426.795 (c) $(-3,618.795, 1,234.795)$. We are 95% confident that the interval captures the difference of the population mean incomes for Sacramento County and Los Angeles County, California. (d) $H_0: \mu_1 = \mu_2$ vs. $H_a: \mu_1 < \mu_2$. $t_{\text{crit}} = -1.690$. Reject H_0 if $t_{\text{data}} \leq -1.690$. $t_{\text{data}} = -0.997$. Since $t_{\text{data}} = -0.997$ is not ≤ -1.690, we do not reject H_0. There is insufficient evidence at the $\alpha = 0.05$ level of significance that the population mean income in Sacramento County, California, in 2004 was less than the population mean income in Los Angeles County, California, in 2004. (e) The confidence interval in (c) could not have been used to perform the hypothesis test in

(d) because the hypothesis test in (d) is a one-tailed test and confidence intervals can only be used to perform two-tailed tests. **32. (a)** -57 **(b)** 59.3489 **(c)** $(-116.3489, 2.3489)$. We are 95% confident that the interval captures the difference of the population mean math scores of students from the United States and Hong Kong. **(d)** $H_0 : \mu_1 = \mu_2$ vs. $H_a : \mu_1 < \mu_2$. $t_{\text{crit}} = -2.821$. Reject H_0 if $t_{\text{data}} \leq -2.821$. $t_{\text{data}} = -1.760$. Since $t_{\text{data}} = -1.760$ is not ≤ -2.821, we do not reject H_0. There is insufficient evidence at the $\alpha = 0.01$ level of significance that the population mean math score for students from the United States in 2003 was less than the population mean math score for students from Hong Kong in 2003. **(e)** The confidence interval in (c) could not have been used to perform the hypothesis test in (d) because the hypothesis test in (d) is a one-tailed test and confidence intervals can only be used to perform two-tailed tests. Also, a 90% confidence interval can only be used to perform a two-tailed test for level of significance $\alpha = 0.10$.
33. (a) $(-1.047, 4.247)$. We are 95% confident that the interval captures the difference in the population mean number of children per teacher in the towns of Cupertino, California, and Santa Rosa, California. **(b)** $H_0 : \mu_1 - \mu_2 = 0$ vs. $H_a : \mu_1 - \mu_2 \neq 0$. $\mu_0 = 0$ lies inside of the interval $(-1.047, 4.247)$, so we do not reject H_0. There is insufficient evidence at the $\alpha = 0.01$ level of significance that the population mean number of children per teacher in the town of Cupertino, California, differs from the population mean number of children per teacher in the town of Santa Rosa, California.
34. (a) Since both sample sizes are large ($n_1 \geq 30$ and $n_2 \geq 30$), Case 2 applies. **(b)** $(-13.9365, 33.9365)$. We are 95% confident that the interval captures the difference between the population mean verbal SAT score of males and the population mean verbal SAT score of females. **(c)** Since 0 is in the 95% confidence interval $(-13.9365, 33.9365)$, we would not reject H_0.
35. $H_0 : \mu_1 = \mu_2$ vs. $H_a : \mu_1 \neq \mu_2$. $t_{\text{crit}} = 2.201$. Reject H_0 if $t_{\text{data}} \leq -2.201$ or if $t_{\text{data}} \geq 2.201$. $t_{\text{data}} = -5.829$. Since $t_{\text{data}} \leq -2.201$, we reject H_0. There is sufficient evidence that the difference between mean property taxes in Ohio and North Carolina is significant.
36. (a) Since both sample sizes are large ($n_1 \geq 30$ and $n_2 \geq 30$), Case 2 applies. **(b)** $(11,442.85, 15,479.15)$. We are 95% confident that the interval captures the difference between the population mean starting salary for college graduates majoring in information systems and the population mean starting salary for college graduates majoring in psychology. **(c)** Wider; the higher the confidence level, the wider the confidence interval
37. (a) $(-74.6747, -5.3253)$. We are 95% confident that the interval captures the difference in the population mean number of daily visitors to Windvale Park and Cranebrook Park. **(b)** $H_0 : \mu_1 = \mu_2$ vs. $H_a : \mu_1 < \mu_2$. Reject H_0 if p-value ≤ 0.05. $t_{\text{data}} = -2.359$. p-value $= 0.0126370393$. Since the p-value ≤ 0.05, we reject H_0. There is evidence that the population mean number of daily visitors to Windvale Park is less than the population mean number of daily visitors to Cranebrook Park. **Critical-value method:** $H_0 : \mu_1 = \mu_2$ vs. $H_1 : \mu_1 < \mu_2$. $t_{\text{crit}} = -1.699$. Reject H_0 if $t_{\text{data}} \leq -1.699$. $t_{\text{data}} = -2.359$. Since $t_{\text{data}} = -2.359$ is ≤ -1.699, we reject H_0. There is evidence at the $\alpha = 0.05$ level of significance that the population mean number of daily visitors to Windvale Park is less than the population mean number of daily visitors to Cranebrook Park. **(c)** No, since confidence intervals can be used only for two-tailed tests and this is a one-tailed test.

38. $H_0 : \mu_1 \leq \mu_2$ vs. $H_a : \mu_1 > \mu_2$. Reject H_0 if p-value ≤ 0.05. $t_{\text{data}} = 1.017$. p-value $= 0.1558$. Since p-value is not ≤ 0.05, we do not reject H_0. There is insufficient evidence that the population coached SAT score improvement is greater than the population noncoached SAT score improvement. **Critical-value method:** $H_0 : \mu_1 = \mu_2$ vs. $H_a : \mu_1 > \mu_2$. $t_{\text{crit}} = 1.662$. Reject H_0 if $t_{\text{data}} \geq 1.662$. $t_{\text{data}} = 1.017$. Since $t_{\text{data}} = 1.017$ is not ≥ 1.662, we do not reject H_0. There is insufficient evidence at the $\alpha = 0.05$ level of significance that the population mean coached SAT improvement is greater than the population mean noncoached improvement.
39. (a) $\bar{x}_1 - \bar{x}_2 = 8$ **(b)** $(-12.699, 28.699)$ **(c)** $H_0 : \mu_1 = \mu_2$ vs. $H_a : \mu_1 \neq \mu_2$. Reject H_0 if p-value ≤ 0.01. $t_{\text{data}} = 1.017$. p-value $= 0.3116$. Since the p-value is not ≤ 0.01, we do not reject H_0. There is insufficient evidence that the mean coached SAT score improvement is different from the mean noncoached SAT score improvement. **Critical-value method:** $H_0 : \mu_1 = \mu_2$ vs. $H_a : \mu_1 \neq \mu_2$. $t_{\text{crit}} = 2.632$. Reject H_0 if $t_{\text{data}} \leq -2.632$ or if $t_{\text{data}} \geq 2.632$. $t_{\text{data}} = 1.017$. Since $t_{\text{data}} = 1.017$ is not ≤ -2.632 and is not ≥ 2.632, we do not reject H_0. There is insufficient evidence at the $\alpha = 0.01$ level of significance that the population mean coached SAT improvement differs from the population mean noncoached improvement. Since this is a two-tailed test, we can use the confidence interval found in (b) to perform the hypotheses test. Our hypothesized value of 0 lies in the interval, so we do not reject H_0. There is insufficient evidence that the population mean coached SAT improvement is less than the population mean noncoached improvement.
40. (a) Since the width of the confidence interval is $2 \cdot t_{\alpha/2} \cdot \sqrt{\frac{s_1^2}{n_1} + \frac{s_2^2}{n_2}}$, an increase in the sample sizes will result in a decrease in the width of the confidence interval. This is good because smaller confidence intervals give a more precise estimate. **(b)** It depends on how large the new sample sizes are.
41. (a) $\bar{x}_1 - \bar{x}_2 = -498.5238$ **(b)** $(-791.006, -206.042)$. We are 90% confident that the interval captures the difference in the population mean daily calorie intake of children in the inner city and the suburbs. **(c)** $H_0 : \mu_1 = \mu_2$ vs. $H_a : \mu_1 < \mu_2$. Reject H_0 if p-value ≤ 0.10. $t_{\text{data}} = -3.434$. p-value $= 0.0092775929$. Since the p-value ≤ 0.10, we reject H_0. There is evidence that the population mean daily calorie intake of inner-city children is less than that of children from the suburbs. **(d)** There is very strong evidence against the null hypothesis.
42. (a) $(-1000.24, 4346.24)$. We are 95% confident that the interval captures the difference between the population mean teacher salary in California and the population mean teacher salary in Michigan. **(b)** $H_0 : \mu_1 = \mu_2$ vs. $H_a : \mu_1 > \mu_2$. Reject H_0 if p-value ≤ 0.05. $t_{\text{data}} = 1.244$. p-value $= 0.1082$. Since p-value is not ≤ 0.05, we do not reject H_0. There is insufficient evidence that the population mean teacher salary in California is greater than the population mean teacher salary in Michigan. **(c)** Since $0.10 \leq p$-value ≤ 0.15, there is slight evidence against the null hypothesis.
43. (a) $(-3.161, 0.561)$. We are 99% confident that the interval captures the difference of the population mean number of hours worked in 2003 and 1994. **(b)** $H_0 : \mu_1 = \mu_2$ vs. $H_a : \mu_1 < \mu_2$. Reject H_0 if p-value ≤ 0.01. $t_{\text{data}} = -1.838$. p-value $= 0.0342678723$. Since the p-value is not ≤ 0.01, we do not reject H_0. There is insufficient evidence that the population mean number of hours worked in 2003 is less than the population mean number of hours worked in 1994. **(c)** Answers will vary.

44. (a) This will result in an increase in $\bar{x}_1 - \bar{x}_2$, but $\bar{x}_1 - \bar{x}_2$ will still be negative. **(b)** This will result in an increase in t_{data}, but t_{data} will still be negative. **(c)** Increase in p-value **(d)** Unchanged
45. (a) $(-1.750, 727.750)$. TI-83/84: $(-1.743, 727.740)$. We are 95% confident that the difference of the population mean birth weight of the babies lies between -1.750 (-1.743) grams and 727.750 (727.740) grams. **(b) Critical-value method:** $H_0 : \mu_1 = \mu_2$ vs. $H_a : \mu_1 \neq \mu_2$. $Z_{\text{crit}} = 1.96$. Reject H_0 if $Z_{\text{data}} \leq -1.96$ or if $Z_{\text{data}} \geq 1.96$. $Z_{\text{data}} = 1.95$. Since $Z_{\text{data}} = 1.95$ is not ≤ -1.96 and is not ≥ 1.96, we do not reject H_0. There is insufficient evidence at the $\alpha = 0.05$ level of significance that the population mean birth weight of the babies differs. **p-value method:** $H_0 : \mu_1 = \mu_2$ vs. $H_a : \mu_1 \neq \mu_2$. Reject H_0 if p-value ≤ 0.05. $Z_{\text{data}} = 1.95$. p-value $= 0.0512$. Since p-value $= 0.0512$ is not ≤ 0.05, we do not reject H_0. There is insufficient evidence at the $\alpha = 0.05$ level of significance that the population mean birth weight of the babies differs. **(c)** Since $0.05 < p$-value < 0.10, there is mild evidence against the null hypothesis.
46. (a)–(d) Unchanged
47. (a) $\bar{x}_1 = 31,363$, $s_1 = 135,270$ **(b)** $\bar{x}_2 = 18,305$, $s_2 = 260,938$ **(c)** $H_0 : \mu_1 = \mu_2$ vs. $H_a : \mu_1 \neq \mu_2$. Reject H_0 if the p-value ≤ 0.05. $t_{\text{data}} = 1.259$; p-value $= 0.2084026891$. Since the p-value is not ≤ 0.05, we do not reject H_0. There is insufficient evidence that the population mean number of residents in towns and cities in California is different than the population mean number of residents is towns and cities in New York.
48. (a) $\bar{x}_1 = 129.81$, $s_1 = 204.63$ **(b)** $\bar{x}_2 = 274.7$, $s_2 = 381.8$ **(c)** No, because the amount of phosphorus and the amount of potassium are measured for the same foods. **(d)** $H_0 : \mu_d = 0$ vs. $H_a : \mu_d \neq 0$. Reject H_0 if p-value ≤ 0.05. $t_{\text{data}} = -15.222$. p-value ≈ 0. Since the p-value ≤ 0.05, we reject H_0. There is evidence that the population mean of the differences between the amount of phosphorus and the amount of potassium in foods is different from 0.

Section 10.3

1. $\hat{p}_1$ and $\hat{p}_2$
2. No, because the confidence interval is not based on the assumption that $p_1 = p_2$.
3. Z_{data} measures the standardized distance between sample proportions. Extreme values of Z_{data} indicate evidence against the null hypothesis.
4. We can either assess the strength of the evidence against the null hypothesis or conduct further studies involving larger samples.
5. (a) $H_0 : p_1 = p_2$ vs. $H_a : p_1 \neq p_2$; $Z_{\text{crit}} = 1.645$. Reject H_0 if $Z_{\text{data}} \leq -1.645$ or $Z_{\text{data}} \geq 1.645$. **(b)** 0.7857 **(c)** 0.65 **(d)** Since $Z_{\text{data}} \geq -1.645$ and $Z_{\text{data}} \leq 1.645$, we do not reject H_0. There is insufficient evidence that the population proportion from Population 1 is different from the population proportion from Population 2.
6. (a), (b), (c), and **(d)** are not appropriate since $x_1 = 4$ is not ≥ 5.
7. (a) $H_0 : p_1 = p_2$ vs. $H_a : p_1 > p_2$. $Z_{\text{crit}} = 2.33$. Reject H_0 if $Z_{\text{data}} \geq 2.33$. **(b)** $\hat{p}_{\text{pooled}} = 100/450 \approx 0.2222$. **(c)** $Z_{\text{data}} = 3.550$. **(d)** Since $Z_{\text{data}} = 3.550$ is ≥ 2.33, we reject H_0. There is evidence at the $\alpha = 0.01$ level of significance that the population proportion of Population 1 is greater than the population proportion of Population 2.
8. (a) $H_0 : p_1 = p_2$ vs. $H_a : p_1 \neq p_2$. $Z_{\text{crit}} = 2.58$. Reject H_0 if $Z_{\text{data}} \leq -2.58$ or $Z_{\text{data}} \geq 2.58$ **(b)** $\hat{p}_{\text{pooled}} = 100/450 \approx 0.2222$
(c) $Z_{\text{data}} \approx 3.550$ **(d)** Since $Z_{\text{data}} \approx 3.550$ is ≥ 2.58, we reject H_0. There is evidence at the $\alpha = 0.01$ level of significance that

the population proportion of Population 1 is different from the population proportion of Population 2.
9. (a) $H_0 : p_1 = p_2$ vs. $H_a : p_1 > p_2$. Reject H_0 if p-value ≤ 0.05. **(b)** $\hat{p}_{\text{pooled}} = 450/800 = 0.5625$ **(c)** $Z_{\text{data}} = 3.563$
(d) p-value $= 0.0002$ **(e)** Since p-value $= 0.0002$ is ≤ 0.05, we reject H_0. There is evidence at the $\alpha = 0.05$ level of significance that the population proportion of Population 1 is greater than the population proportion of Population 2.
10. (a) $H_0 : p_1 = p_2$ vs. $H_a : p_1 < p_2$. Reject H_0 if p-value ≤ 0.05 **(b)** $\hat{p}_{\text{pooled}} = 1110/2000 = 0.555$ **(c)** $Z_{\text{data}} = -5.849$
(d) p-value ≈ 0 **(e)** Since p-value ≈ 0 is ≤ 0.05, we reject H_0. There is evidence at the $\alpha = 0.05$ level of significance that the population proportion of Population 1 is less than the population proportion of Population 2.
11. (a) $H_0 : p_1 = p_2$ vs. $H_a : p_1 \neq p_2$. Reject H_0 if p-value ≤ 0.10. **(b)** $\hat{p}_{\text{pooled}} = 910/1140 \approx 0.7982$ **(c)** $Z_{\text{data}} \approx -1.284$
(d) p-value ≈ 0.1991 **(e)** Since p-value ≈ 0.1991 is not ≤ 0.10, we do not reject H_0. There is insufficient evidence at the $\alpha = 0.10$ level of significance that the population proportion of Population 1 is different from the population proportion of Population 2.
12. (a) $H_0 : p_1 = p_2$ vs. $H_a : p_1 < p_2$. Reject H_0 if p-value ≤ 0.10. **(b)** $\hat{p}_{\text{pooled}} = 910/1140 \approx 0.7982$ **(c)** $Z_{\text{data}} = -1.284$
(d) p-value $= 0.0996$ **(e)** Since p-value $= 0.0996$ is ≤ 0.10, we reject H_0 There is evidence at the $\alpha = 0.10$ level of significance that the population proportion of Population 1 is less than the population proportion of Population 2.
13. (a) $x_1 = 80 \geq 5$, $n_1 - x_1 = 20 \geq 5$, $x_2 = 30 \geq 5$, and $n_2 - x_2 = 10 \geq 5$, so it is appropriate. **(b)** 0.05 **(c)** 0.1554. The point estimate $\hat{p}_1 - \hat{p}_2$ will lie within $E = 0.1554$ of the difference in population proportions $p_1 - p_2$ 95% of the time. **(d)** $(-0.1054, 0.2054)$. We are 95% confident that the difference in population proportions lies between -0.1054 and 0.2054.
14. (a) Since $x_1 = 4 \leq 5$, it is not appropriate to construct a 95% confidence interval for $p_1 - p_2$. **(b)–(d)** Cannot be done since the conditions are not met.
15. (a) $x_1 = 60 \geq 5$, $n_1 - x_1 = 140 \geq 5$, $x_2 = 40 \geq 5$, and $n_2 - x_2 = 210 \geq 5$, so it is appropriate. **(b)** 0.14 **(c)** 0.078. The point estimate $\hat{p}_1 - \hat{p}_2$ will lie within $E = 0.078$ of the difference in population proportions $p_1 - p_2$ 95% of the time. **(d)** $(0.062, 0.218)$. We are 95% confident that the difference in population proportions lies between 0.062 and 0.218.
16. (a) Yes, because $x_1 = 250 \geq 5$, $n_1 - x_1 = 150 \geq 5$, $x_2 = 200 \geq 5$, and $n_2 - x_2 = 200 \geq 5$. **(b)** 0.125 **(c)** 0.0682. The point estimate will lie within 0.0682 of the difference in population proportions $p_1 - p_2$ 95% of the time. **(d)** $(0.0568, 0.1932)$. We are 95% confident that the difference in population proportions lies between 0.0568 and 0.1932.
17. (a) $x_1 = 490 \geq 5$, $n_1 - x_1 = 510 \geq 5$, $x_2 = 620 \geq 5$, and $n_2 - x_2 = 380 \geq 5$, so it is appropriate. **(b)** -0.13 **(c)** 0.0431. The point estimate $\hat{p}_1 - \hat{p}_2$ will lie within $E = 0.0431$ of the difference in population proportions $p_1 - p_2$ 95% of the time. **(d)** $(-0.1731, -0.0869)$. We are 95% confident that the difference in population proportions lies between -0.1731 and -0.0869.
18. (a) Yes, because $x_1 = 412 \geq 5$, $n_1 - x_1 = 115 \geq 5$, $x_2 = 498 \geq 5$, and $n_2 - x_2 = 115 \geq 5$. **(b)** -0.0306 **(c)** 0.0468. The point estimate will lie within 0.0468 of the difference in population proportions $p_1 - p_2$ 95% of the time. **(d)** $(-0.0774, 0.0162)$. We are 95% confident that the difference in population proportions lies between -0.0774 and 0.0162.
19. (a) $H_0 : p_1 - p_2 = 0$ vs. $H_a : p_1 - p_2 \neq 0$. The hypothesized value of 0 lies outside the interval $(0.5, 0.6)$, so we reject H_0 at

the $\alpha = 0.05$ level of significance. **(b)** $H_0 : p_1 - p_2 = 0.1$ vs. $H_a : p_1 - p_2 \neq 0.1$. The hypothesized value of 0.1 lies outside the interval (0.5, 0.6), so we reject H_0 at the $\alpha = 0.05$ level of significance. **(c)** $H_0 : p_1 - p_2 = 0.57$ vs. $H_a : p_1 - p_2 \neq 0.57$. The hypothesized value of 0.57 lies inside the interval (0.5, 0.6), so we do not reject H_0 at the $\alpha = 0.05$ level of significance.

20. (a) $H_0 : p_1 - p_2 = 0.2$ vs. $H_a : p_1 - p_2 \neq 0.2$. The hypothesized value of 0.2 lies inside of the interval (0.01, 0.99), so we do not reject H_0 at the $\alpha = 0.01$ level of significance. **(b)** $H_0 : p_1 - p_2 = 0$ vs. $H_a : p_1 - p_2 \neq 0$. The hypothesized value of 0 lies outside of the interval (0.01, 0.99), so we reject H_0 at the $\alpha = 0.01$ level of significance. **(c)** $H_0 : p_1 - p_2 = 0.999$ vs. $H_a : p_1 - p_2 \neq 0.999$. The hypothesized value of 0.999 lies outside of the interval (0.01, 0.99), so we reject H_0 at the $\alpha = 0.01$ level of significance.

21. (a) $H_0 : p_1 - p_2 = 0.151$ vs $H_a : p_1 - p_2 \neq 0.151$. The hypothesized value of 0.151 lies outside of the interval (0.1, 0.11), so we reject H_0 at the $\alpha = 0.10$ level of significance. **(b)** $H_0 : p_1 - p_2 = 0.115$ vs. $H_a : p_1 - p_2 \neq 0.115$. The hypothesized value of 0.115 lies outside of the interval (0.1, 0.11), so we reject H_0 at the $\alpha = 0.10$ level of significance. **(c)** $H_0 : p_1 - p_2 = 0.105$ vs. $H_a : p_1 - p_2 \neq 0.105$. The hypothesized value of 0.105 lies inside of the interval (0.1, 0.11), so we do not reject H_0 at the $\alpha = 0.10$ level of significance.

22. (a) $H_0 : p_1 - p_2 = 0.41$ vs. $H_a : p_1 - p_2 \neq 0.41$. The hypothesized value of 0.41 lies outside of the interval (0.43, 0.57), so we reject H_0 at the $\alpha = 0.05$ level of significance. **(b)** $H_0 : p_1 - p_2 = 0.51$ vs. $H_a : p_1 - p_2 \neq 0.51$. The hypothesized value of 0.51 lies inside of the interval (0.43, 0.57), so we do not reject H_0 at the $\alpha = 0.05$ level of significance. **(c)** $H_0 : p_1 - p_2 = 0.61$ vs. $H_a : p_1 - p_2 \neq 0.61$. The hypothesized value of 0.61 lies outside of the interval (0.43, 0.57), so we reject H_0 at the $\alpha = 0.05$ level of significance.

23. (a) $x_1 = 0.74 (500) = 370 \geq 5$, $(n_1 - x_1) = 130 \geq 5$, $x_2 = 0.83 (500) = 415 \geq 5$, and $(n_2 - x_2) = 85 \geq 5$. Therefore it is appropriate to perform the Z test for the difference in population proportions. **(b)** p_1 is the population proportion of teenage boys who posted their photo on their online profile and p_2 is the population proportion of teenage girls who posted their photo on their online profile. **(c) Critical-value method:** $H_0 : p_1 = p_2$ vs. $H_a : p_1 \neq p_2$. $Z_{\text{crit}} = 1.96$. Reject H_0 if $Z_{\text{data}} \leq -1.96$ or if $Z_{\text{data}} \geq 1.96$. $\hat{p}_{\text{pooled}} = 785/1000 = 0.785$. $Z_{\text{data}} = -3.464$. Since $Z_{\text{data}} = -3.464$ is ≤ -1.96, we reject H_0. There is evidence at the $\alpha = 0.05$ level of significance that the population proportion of teenage boys who posted their photo on their online profile differs from the population proportion of teenage girls who posted their photo on their online profile. **p-value method:** $H_0 : p_1 = p_2$ vs. $H_a : p_1 \neq p_2$. Reject H_0 if the p-value ≤ 0.05. $\hat{p}_{\text{pooled}} = 785/1000 = 0.785$. $Z_{\text{data}} = -3.464$. p-value $= 0.0005$. Since the p-value $= 0.0005$ is ≤ 0.05, we reject H_0. There is evidence at the $\alpha = 0.05$ level of significance that the population proportion of teenage boys who posted their photo on their online profile differs from the population proportion of teenage girls who posted their photo on their online profile.

24. (a) $\hat{p}_1 = X_1/n_1 = 3{,}305/50{,}350 \approx 0.0656$ and $\hat{p}_2 = X_2/n_2 = 73{,}289/754{,}642 \approx 0.0971$. $\hat{p}_1 - \hat{p}_2 \approx -0.0315$ **(b)** p_1 is the population proportion of Medicare recipients living in Alaska who are age 85 or over and $\hat{p}_1$ is the sample proportion of Medicare recipients living in Alaska who are age 85 or over. **(c) Critical-value method:** $H_0 : p_1 = p_2$ vs. $H_a : p_1 \neq p_2$. $Z_{\text{crit}} = 1.96$. Reject H_0 if $Z_{\text{data}} \leq -1.96$ or if $Z_{\text{data}} \geq 1.96$. $\hat{p}_{\text{pooled}} = 76{,}594/804{,}992 \approx 0.0951$. $Z_{\text{data}} = -23.328$ (TI-83/84:

-23.307). Since $Z_{\text{data}} = -23.329$ is ≤ -1.96, we reject H_0. There is evidence at the $\alpha = 0.05$ level of significance that the population proportion of Medicare recipients living in Alaska who are age 85 or over differs from the population proportion of Medicare recipients living in Arizona who are age 85 or older. **p-value method:** $H_0 : p_1 = p_2$ vs. $H_a : p_1 \neq p_2$. Reject H_0 if the p-value ≤ 0.05. $\hat{p}_{\text{pooled}} = 76{,}594/804{,}992 \approx 0.0951$. $Z_{\text{data}} = -23.329$ (TI-83/84: -23.207). p-value ≈ 0. Since the p-value ≈ 0 is ≤ 0.05, we reject H_0. There is evidence at the $\alpha = 0.05$ level of significance that the population proportion of Medicare recipients living in Alaska who are age 85 or over differs from the population proportion of Medicare recipients living in Arizona who are age 85 or older.

25. (a) $x_1 = 34 \geq 5$, $(n_1 - x_1) = 66 \geq 5$, $x_2 = 64 \geq 5$, and $(n_2 - x_2) = 136 \geq 5$. Therefore it is appropriate to perform the Z test for the difference in population proportions. **(b)** p_1 is the population proportion of Ohio businesses that are owned by women and p_2 is the population proportion of New Jersey businesses that are owned by women. **(c) Critical-value method:** $H_0 : p_1 = p_2$ vs. $H_a : p_1 > p_2$. $Z_{\text{crit}} = 1.28$. Reject H_0 if $Z_{\text{data}} \geq 1.28$. $\hat{p}_{\text{pooled}} = 98/300 \approx 0.3267$. $Z_{\text{data}} = 0.348$. Since $Z_{\text{data}} = 0.348$ is not ≥ 1.28, we do not reject H_0. There is insufficient evidence at the $\alpha = 0.10$ level of significance that the population proportion of Ohio businesses that are owned by women is greater than the population proportion of New Jersey businesses that are owned by women. **p-value method:** $H_0 : p_1 = p_2$ vs. $H_a: p_1 > p_2$. Reject H_0 if the p-value ≤ 0.10. $\hat{p}_{\text{pooled}} = 98/300 \approx 0.3267$. $Z_{\text{data}} = 0.348$. p-value $= 0.3639$. Since the p-value $= 0.3639$ is not ≤ 0.10, we do not reject H_0. There is insufficient evidence at the $\alpha = 0.10$ level of significance that the population proportion of Ohio businesses that are owned by women is greater than the population proportion of New Jersey businesses that are owned by women.

26. (a) $\hat{p}_1 = X_1/n_1 = 14/54 \approx 0.2593$ and $\hat{p}_2 = X_2/n_2 = 25/45 \approx 0.5556$. $\hat{p}_1 - \hat{p}_2 \approx -0.2963$ **(b)** p_1 is the population proportion of women with breast cancer who have fetal cells and $\hat{p}_1$ is the sample proportion of women with breast cancer who have fetal cells. **(c) Critical-value method:** $H_0 : p_1 = p_2$ vs. $H_a : p_1 < p_2$. $Z_{\text{crit}} = -2.33$. Reject H_0 if $Z_{\text{data}} \leq -2.33$. $\hat{p}_{\text{pooled}} = 39/99 \approx 0.3939$. $Z_{\text{data}} = -3.004$. Since $Z_{\text{data}} = -3.004$ is ≤ -2.33, we reject H_0. There is evidence at the $\alpha = 0.01$ level of significance that the population proportion of women with breast cancer who have fetal cells is less than the population proportion of women without breast cancer with fetal cells. **p-value method:** $H_0 : p_1 = p_2$ vs. $H_a: p_1 < p_2$. Reject H_0 if the p-value ≤ 0.01. $\hat{p}_{\text{pooled}} = 39/99 \approx 0.3939$. $Z_{\text{data}} = -3.004$. p-value $= 0.0013$. Since the p-value $= 0.0013$ is ≤ 0.01, we reject H_0. There is evidence at the $\alpha = 0.01$ level of significance that the population proportion of women with breast cancer who have fetal cells is less than the population proportion of women without breast cancer with fetal cells.

27. (a) $E = 0.0509$. We may estimate the difference of the population proportion of teenage boys who post their photo on their online profile and the population proportion of teenage girls who post their photo on their online profile to within 0.0509 with 95% confidence. **(b)** $(-0.1409, -0.0391)$. TI-83/84: $(-0.1406, -0.0394)$. We are 95% confident that the difference of the population proportion of teenage boys who post their photo on their online profile and the population proportion of teenage girls who post their photo on their online profile lies between $-0.1409 (-0.1406)$ and -0.0391 (-0.0394). **(c)** $H_0 :$ $p_1 = p_2$ vs. $H_a: p_1 \neq p_2$. The hypothesized value of 0 lies outside of the interval in (b), so we reject H_0. There is evidence that the population proportion of teenage boys who post their photo on their online profile differs from the population proportion of teenage girls who post their photo on their online profile. (d) Yes, it agrees.

28. (a) $E = 0.0026$. We may estimate the difference of the population proportion of Medicare recipients living in Alaska who are age 85 and older and the population proportion of Medicare recipients living in Arizona who are age 85 and older to within 0.0026 with 95% confidence. (b) $(-0.0341, -0.0289)$. TI-83/84: $(-0.0337, -0.0292)$. We are 95% confident that the difference of the population proportion of Medicare recipients living in Alaska who are age 85 and older and the population proportion of Medicare recipients living in Arizona who are age 85 and older lies between $-0.0341(-0.0337)$ and $-0.0289(-0.0292)$. (c) $H_0 : p_1 = p_2$ vs. $H_a : p_1 \neq p_2$. Our hypothesized value of 0 lies outside of the interval in (b), so we reject H_0. There is evidence that the population proportion of Medicare recipients living in Alaska who are age 85 and older differs from the population proportion of Medicare recipients living in New Jersey who are age 85 and older. (d) Yes, it agrees.

29. (a) $(-0.0745, 0.1145)$. TI-83/84: $(-0.0749, 0.1150)$. We are 90% confident that the difference of the population proportion of Ohio businesses that are owned by women and the population proportion of New Jersey businesses that are owned by women lies between $-0.0745(-0.0749)$ and $0.1145 (0,1150)$. (b) H_0: $p_1 = p_2$ vs. $H_a : p_1 \neq p_2$. Our hypothesized value of 0 lies inside the interval in (a), so we do not reject H_0. There is insufficient evidence that the population proportion of Ohio businesses that are owned by women differs from the population proportion of New Jersey businesses that are owned by women. (c) No, it is a one-sided test and confidence intervals can only be used to perform two-sided tests.

30. (a) $(-0.5507, -0.0419)$. TI-83/84: $(-0.5412, -0.0513)$. We are 99% confident that the difference of the population proportion of women with breast cancer who have fetal cells and the population proportion of women without breast cancer who have fetal cells lies between $-0.5507(-0.5412)$ and -0.0419 (-0.0513). (b) $H_0 : p_1 = p_2$ vs. $H_a : p_1 \neq p_2$. The hypothesized value of 0 lies outside the interval in (a), so we reject H_0. There is evidence that the population proportion of women with breast cancer who have fetal cells differs from the population proportion of women without breast cancer who have fetal cells. (c) No, it is a one-sided test and confidence intervals can only be used to perform two-sided tests.

31. $H_0 : p_1 = p_2$ vs. $H_a : p_1 \neq p_2$. Reject H_0 if p-value < 0.05. $\hat{p}_{pooled} = 0.195$. $Z_{data} = -2.37$. p-value $= 0.0178$. Since p-value ≤ 0.05, we reject H_0. There is evidence that the proportion of Americans under 35 years old owning stocks is different from the proportion of Americans aged 35–44 owning stocks.

32. $H_0 : p_1 = p_2$ vs. $H_a : p_1 \neq p_2$. Reject H_0 if p-value ≤ 0.05. $\hat{p}_{pooled} = 0.7705$. $Z_{data} = 0.21$. p-value $= 0.8336$. Since p-value is not ≥ 0.05, we do not reject H_0. There is insufficient evidence that the proportion of the people who wore the ionized bracelets who reported improvement in their maximum pain index is different from the proportion of the people who wore the placebo bracelets who reported improvement in their maximum pain index.

33. $x_1 = 920 \geq 5$, $n_1 - x_1 = 80 \geq 5$, $x_2 = 870 \geq 5$, and $n_2 - x_2 = 130 \geq 5$, so it is appropriate.

34. $p_1 = $ the population proportion of 18- to 24-year-old males who listen to the radio each week and $p_2 = $ the population proportion of males age 65 or older who listen to the radio each week.

35. p_1 is the population proportion of 18- to 24-year-old males who listen to radio each week and $\hat{p}_1$ is the sample proportion of 18- to 24-year old males who listen to radio each week.

36. 0.0269. The point estimate of the difference in the population proportion of 18- to 24-year-old males who listen to the radio each week and the population proportion of males 65 years and older who listen to the radio each week will lie within $E = 0.0269$ of the difference in population proportions $p_1 - p_2$ 95% of the time.

37. $(0.0231, 0.0769)$. We are 95% confident that the difference in the population proportion of 18- to 24-year-old males who listen to the radio each week and the population proportion of males 65 years and older who listen to the radio each week lies between 0.0231 and 0.0769.

38. (a) $H_0 : p_1 - p_2 = 0$ vs. $H_a : p_1 - p_2 \neq 0$. The hypothesized value of 0 does not lie in the interval from Exercise 37, so we reject H_0. There is evidence that the difference in the population proportion of 18- to-24-year-old males who listen to the radio each week and the population proportion of males 65 years and older who listen to the radio each week differs from 0. (b) $H_0 : p_1 - p_2 = 0.01$ vs. $H_a : p_1 - p_2 \neq 0.01$. The hypothesized value of 0.01 does not lie in the interval from Exercise 37, so we reject H_0. There is evidence that the difference in the population proportion of 18- to 24-year-old males who listen to the radio each week and the population proportion of males 65 years and older who listen to the radio each week differs from 0.01. (c) $H_0 : p_1 - p_2 = 0.05$ vs. $H_a : p_1 - p_2 \neq 0.05$. The hypothesized value of 0.05 lies in the interval from Exercise 37, so we do not reject H_0. There is insufficient evidence that the difference in the population proportion of 18- to 24-year-old males who listen to the radio each week and the population proportion of males 65 years and older who listen to the radio each week differs from 0.05.

39. We can't because it is a one-tailed test and confidence intervals can only be used to perform two-tailed test.

40. **Critical-value method:** $H_0 : p_1 = p_2$ vs. $H_a : p_1 > p_2$. $Z_{crit} = 1.645$. Reject H_0 if $Z_{data} \geq 1.645$. $\hat{p}_{pooled} = 1790/2000 = 0.895$. $Z_{data} = 3.647$. Since $Z_{data} = 3.647$ is ≥ 1.645, we reject H_0. There is evidence at the $\alpha = 0.05$ level of significance that the population proportion of 18- to 24-year-old males who listen to the radio each week is greater than the population proportion of males 65 years and older who listen to the radio each week. **p-value method:** $H_0 : p_1 = p_2$ vs. $H_a : p_1 > p_2$. Reject H_0 if the p-value ≤ 0.05. $\hat{p}_{pooled} = 1790/2000 = 0.895$. $Z_{data} = 3.647$. p-value $= 0.00013$. Since the p-value $= 0.00013$ is ≤ 0.05, we reject H_0. There is evidence at the $\alpha = 0.05$ level of significance that the population proportion of 18- to 24-year-old males who listen to the radio each week is greater than the population proportion of males 65 years and older who listen to the radio each week.

41. (a) $E = 0.085$. It would increase. (b) It would increase. $Z_{data} = 1.153$. p-value $= 0.1245$. (c) It would change to "Do not reject H_0" since p-value $= 0.124 \geq 0.05$.

Section 10.4

1. Two population standard deviations

2. False

3. True

4. $F_{data} = s_1^2/s_2^2$

5. An F distribution with $n_1 - 1$ degrees of freedom in the numerator and $n_2 - 1$ degrees of freedom in the denominator.

6. False

7. The F-value with $df_1 = n_1 - 1$ numerator degrees of freedom and $df_2 = n_2 - 1$ denominator degrees of freedom, with area α to the right of $F_{\alpha,\, n_1-1,\, n_2-1}$.
8. Switch the values of df_1 and df_2. Find $F_{\alpha,\, n_1-1,\, n_2-1}$ using the F table. Calculate $F_{\text{crit}} = F_{1-\alpha,\, n_1-1,\, n_2-1} = 1/F_{\alpha,\, n_1-1,\, n_2-1}$.

9. $F_{\alpha,\, n_1-1,\, n_2-1} = F_{0.05,\, 10,\, 9} = 3.14$.
10. $F_{\alpha,\, n_1-1,\, n_2-1} = F_{0.10,\, 10,\, 9} = 2.42$.
11. $F_{\alpha,\, n_1-1,\, n_2-1} = F_{0.01,\, 5,\, 4} = 15.52$.
12. $F_{\alpha,\, n_1-1,\, n_2-1} = F_{0.01,\, 5,\, 20} = 4.10$.
13. $F_{1-\alpha,\, n_1-1,\, n_2-1} = F_{0.95,\, 20,\, 3} = 0.3226$.
14. $F_{1-\alpha,\, n_1-1,\, n_2-1} = F_{0.99,\, 20,\, 3} = 0.2024$.
15. $F_{1-\alpha,\, n_1-1,\, n_2-1} = F_{0.95,\, 3,\, 20} = 0.1155$.
16. $F_{1-\alpha,\, n_1-1,\, n_2-1} = F_{0.99,\, 3,\, 20} = 0.0375$.
17. $F_{\alpha/2,\, n_1-1,\, n_2-1} = F_{0.025,\, 15,\, 6} = 5.27$, $F_{1-\alpha/2,\, n_1-1,\, n_2-1} = F_{0.975,\, 15,\, 6} = 0.2933$.
18. $F_{\alpha/2,\, n_1-1,\, n_2-1} = F_{0.05,\, 30,\, 100} = 1.57$, $F_{1-\alpha/2,\, n_1-1,\, n_2-1} = F_{0.95,\, 30,\, 100} = 0.5495$.
19. $F_{\alpha/2,\, n_1-1,\, n_2-1} = F_{0.025,\, 6,\, 15} = 3.41$, $F_{1-\alpha/2,\, n_1-1,\, n_2-1} = F_{0.975,\, 15,\, 6} = 0.1898$.
20. $F_{\alpha/2,\, n_1-1,\, n_2-1} = F_{0.05,\, 60,\, 100} = 1.45$, $F_{1-\alpha/2,\, n_1-1,\, n_2-1} = F_{0.95,\, 60,\, 100} = 0.6329$.
21. (a) $H_0 : \sigma_1 = \sigma_2$ vs. $H_a : \sigma_1 > \sigma_2$ (b) $F_{\text{crit}} = F_{\alpha,\, n_1-1,\, n_2-1} = F_{0.05,\, 10,\, 6} = 4.06$. Reject H_0 if $F_{\text{data}} \geq 4.06$. (c) $F_{\text{data}} = 4$. (d) Since $F_{\text{data}} = 4$ is not ≥ 4.06, we do not reject H_0. There is insufficient evidence at the $\alpha = 0.05$ level of significance that the population standard deviation of Population 1 is greater than the population standard deviation of Population 2.
22. (a) $H_0 : \sigma_1 = \sigma_2$ vs. $H_a : \sigma_1 < \sigma_2$ (b) $F_{\text{crit}} = F_{1-\alpha,\, n_1-1,\, n_2-1} = F_{0.95,\, 15,\, 7} = 0.3690$. Reject H_0 if $F_{\text{data}} \leq 0.3690$. (c) $F_{\text{data}} = 0.4444$. (d) Since $F_{\text{data}} = 0.4444$ is not ≤ 0.3690, we do not reject H_0. There is insufficient evidence at the $\alpha = 0.05$ level of significance that the population standard deviation of Population 1 is less than the population standard deviation of Population 2.
23. (a) $H_0 : \sigma_1 = \sigma_2$ vs. $H_a : \sigma_1 < \sigma_2$ (b) $F_{\text{crit}} = F_{1-\alpha,\, n_1-1,\, n_2-1} = F_{0.90,\, 9,\, 20} = 0.4348$. Reject H_0 if $F_{\text{data}} \leq 0.4348$. (c) $F_{\text{data}} = 0.5102$. (d) Since $F_{\text{data}} = 0.5102$ is not ≤ 0.4348, we do not reject H_0. There is insufficient evidence at the $\alpha = 0.10$ level of significance that the population standard deviation of Population 1 is less than the population standard deviation of Population 2.
24. (a) $H_0 : \sigma_1 = \sigma_2$ vs. $H_a : \sigma_1 > \sigma_2$ (b) $F_{\text{crit}} = F_{\alpha,\, n_1-1,\, n_2-1} = F_{0.10,\, 30,\, 6} = 2.80$. Reject H_0 if $F_{\text{data}} \geq 2.80$. (c) $F_{\text{data}} = 4$ (d) Since $F_{\text{data}} = 4$ is ≥ 2.80, we reject H_0. There is evidence at the $\alpha = 0.10$ level of significance that the population standard deviation of Population 1 is greater than the population standard deviation of Population 2.
25. (a) $H_0 : \sigma_1 = \sigma_2$ vs. $H_a : \sigma_1 \neq \sigma_2$ (b) $F_{\text{crit}} = F_{\alpha/2,\, n_1-1,\, n_2-1} = F_{0.025,\, 5,\, 12} = 3.89$ and $F_{\text{crit}} = F_{1-\alpha/2,\, n_1-1,\, n_2-1} = F_{0.975,\, 5,\, 12} = 0.1511$. Reject H_0 if $F_{\text{data}} \geq 3.89$ or if $F_{\text{data}} \leq 0.1511$. (c) $F_{\text{data}} = 5.686$ (d) Since $F_{\text{data}} = 5.686$ is ≥ 3.89, we reject H_0. There is evidence at the $\alpha = 0.05$ level of significance that the population standard deviation of Population 1 differs from the population standard deviation of Population 2.
26. (a) $H_0 : \sigma_1 = \sigma_2$ vs. $H_a : \sigma_1 \neq \sigma_2$ (b) $F_{\text{crit}} = F_{\alpha/2,\, n_1-1,\, n_2-1} = F_{0.025,\, 20,\, 6} = 5.17$ and $F_{\text{crit}} = F_{1-\alpha/2,\, n_1-1,\, n_2-1} = F_{0.975,\, 20,\, 6} = 0.3195$. Reject H_0 if $F_{\text{data}} \geq 5.17$ or if $F_{\text{data}} \leq 0.3195$. (c) $F_{\text{data}} = 1.168$ (d) Since $F_{\text{data}} = 1.168$ is not ≥ 5.17 and is not ≤ 0.3195, we do not reject H_0. There is insufficient evidence at the $\alpha = 0.05$ level of significance that the population standard deviation of Population 1 differs from the population standard deviation of Population 2.

27. (a) $H_0 : \sigma_1 = \sigma_2$ vs. $H_a : \sigma_1 > \sigma_2$. Reject H_0 if the p-value ≤ 0.01. (b) $F_{\text{data}} = 2.778$ (c) p-value $= 0.0420$. (d) Since the p-value $= 0.0420$ is not ≤ 0.01, we do not reject H_0. There is insufficient evidence at the $\alpha = 0.01$ level of significance that the population standard deviation of Population 1 is greater than the population standard deviation of Population 2.
28. (a) $H_0 : \sigma_1 = \sigma_2$ vs. $H_a : \sigma_1 < \sigma_2$. Reject H_0 if the p-value ≤ 0.01. (b) $F_{\text{data}} = 0.3265$ (c) p-value $= 0.0272$. (d) Since the p-value $= 0.0272$ is not ≤ 0.01, we do not reject H_0. There is insufficient evidence at the $\alpha = 0.01$ level of significance that the population standard deviation of Population 1 is less than the population standard deviation of Population 2.
29. (a) $H_0 : \sigma_1 = \sigma_2$ vs. $H_a : \sigma_1 < \sigma_2$. Reject H_0 if the p-value ≤ 0.05. (b) $F_{\text{data}} = 0.2899$ (c) p-value $= 0.0090$. (d) Since the p-value $= 0.0090$ is ≤ 0.05, we reject H_0. There is evidence at the $\alpha = 0.05$ level of significance that the population standard deviation of Population 1 is less than the population standard deviation of Population 2.
30. (a) $H_0 : \sigma_1 = \sigma_2$ vs. $H_a : \sigma_1 > \sigma_2$. Reject H_0 if the p-value ≤ 0.05. (b) $F_{\text{data}} = 3.906$ (c) p-value ≈ 0. (d) Since the p-value ≈ 0 is ≤ 0.05, we reject H_0. There is evidence at the $\alpha = 0.05$ level of significance that the population standard deviation of Population 1 is greater than the population standard deviation of Population 2.
31. (a) $H_0 : \sigma_1 = \sigma_2$ vs. $H_a : \sigma_1 \neq \sigma_2$. Reject H_0 if the p-value ≤ 0.10. (b) $F_{\text{data}} = 1$. (c) p-value ≈ 1. (d) Since the p-value ≈ 1 is not ≤ 0.10, we do not reject H_0. There is insufficient evidence at the $\alpha = 0.10$ level of significance that the population standard deviation of Population 1 is different from the population standard deviation of Population 2.
32. (a) $H_0 : \sigma_1 = \sigma_2$ vs. $H_a : \sigma_1 \neq \sigma_2$. Reject H_0 if the p-value ≤ 0.10. (b) $F_{\text{data}} = 0.5373$. (c) p-value $= 0.3056$. (d) Since the p-value $= 0.3056$ is not ≤ 0.10, we do not reject H_0. There is insufficient evidence at the $\alpha = 0.10$ level of significance that the population standard deviation of Population 1 is different from the population standard deviation of Population 2.
33. Critical-value method: $H_0 : \sigma_1 = \sigma_2$ vs. $H_a : \sigma_1 < \sigma_2$. $F_{\text{crit}} = F_{1-\alpha,\, n_1-1,\, n_2-1} = F_{0.95,\, 1159,\, 1570} = 0.9009$. Reject H_0 if $F_{\text{data}} \leq 0.9009$. $F_{\text{data}} = 0.5890$. Since $F_{\text{data}} = 0.5890$ is ≤ 0.9009, we reject H_0. There is evidence at the $\alpha = 0.05$ level of significance that the population standard deviation of the males' BMI is less than the population standard deviation of the females' BMI. **p-value method:** $H_0 : \sigma_1 = \sigma_2$ vs. $H_a : \sigma_1 < \sigma_2$. Reject H_0 if the p-value ≤ 0.05. $F_{\text{data}} = 0.5890$. p-value $= 0$. Since the p-value $= 0$ is ≤ 0.05, we reject H_0. There is evidence at the $\alpha = 0.05$ level of significance that the population standard deviation of the males' BMI is less than the population standard deviation of the females' BMI.
34. Critical-value method: $H_0 : \sigma_1 = \sigma_2$ vs. $H_a : \sigma_1 > \sigma_2$. $F_{\text{crit}} = F_{\alpha,\, n_1-1,\, n_2-1} = F_{0.10,\, 42,\, 246} = 1.34$. Reject H_0 if $F_{\text{data}} \geq 1.34$. $F_{\text{data}} = 1.8595$. Since $F_{\text{data}} = 1.8595$ is ≥ 1.34, we reject H_0. There is evidence at the $\alpha = 0.10$ level of significance that the population standard deviation of the number of cigarettes smoked per day of the Morning High group is greater than the population standard deviation of the number of cigarettes smoked per day of the Flatline group. **p-value method:** $H_0 : \sigma_1 = \sigma_2$ vs. $H_a : \sigma_1 > \sigma_2$. Reject H_0 if the p-value ≤ 0.10. $F_{\text{data}} = 1.8595$. p-value $= 0.0021$. Since the p-value $= 0.0021$ is ≤ 0.10, we reject H_0. There is evidence at the $\alpha = 0.10$ level of significance that the population standard deviation of the number of cigarettes smoked per day of the Morning High group is greater than the population standard deviation of the number of cigarettes smoked per day of the Flatline group.

35. Critical-value method: $H_0 : \sigma_1 = \sigma_2$ vs. $H_a : \sigma_1 \neq \sigma_2$. $F_{\text{crit}} = F_{\alpha/2, n_1-1, n_2-1} = F_{0.05, 84, 340} = 1.39$ and $F_{\text{crit}} = F_{1-\alpha/2, n_1-1, n_2-1} = F_{0.95, 84, 340} = 0.6623$. Reject H_0 if $F_{\text{data}} \leq 0.6623$ or if $F_{\text{data}} \geq 1.39$. $F_{\text{data}} = 0.8292$. Since $F_{\text{data}} = 0.8292$ is not ≤ 0.6623 and not ≥ 1.39, we do not reject H_0. There is insufficient evidence at the $\alpha = 0.10$ level of significance that the population standard deviation of the IQ scores of children with autism differs from the population standard deviation of the IQ scores of children with Asperger's syndrome. **p-value method:** $H_0 : \sigma_1 = \sigma_2$ vs. $H_a : \sigma_1 \neq \sigma_2$. Reject H_0 if the p-value ≤ 0.10. $F_{\text{data}} = 0.8292$. p-value $= 0.3030$. Since the p-value $= 0.3030$ is not ≤ 0.10, we do not reject H_0. There is insufficient evidence at the $\alpha = 0.10$ level of significance that the population standard deviation of the IQ scores of children with autism differs from the population standard deviation of the IQ scores of children with Asperger's syndrome.

36. Critical-value method: $H_0 : \sigma_1 = \sigma_2$ vs. $H_a : \sigma_1 < \sigma_2$. $F_{\text{crit}} = F_{1-\alpha, n_1-1, n_2-1} = F_{0.95, 99, 99} = 0.6329$. Reject H_0 if $F_{\text{data}} \leq 0.6329$. $F_{\text{data}} = 0.1479$. Since $F_{\text{data}} = 0.1479$ is ≤ 0.6329, we reject H_0. There is evidence at the $\alpha = 0.05$ level of significance that the population standard deviation of the blood pressures of adults aged 30–44 is less than the population standard deviation of the blood pressures of adults aged 70–79. **p-value method:** $H_0 : \sigma_1 = \sigma_2$ vs. $H_a : \sigma_1 < \sigma_2$. Reject H_0 if the p-value ≤ 0.05. $F_{\text{data}} = 0.1479$. p-value $= 0$. Since the p-value $= 0$ is ≤ 0.05, we reject H_0. There is evidence at the $\alpha = 0.05$ level of significance that the population standard deviation of the blood pressures of adults aged 30–44 is less than the population standard deviation of the blood pressures of adults aged 70–79.

37. (a) No **(b) Critical-value method:** $H_0 : \sigma_1 = \sigma_2$ vs. $H_a : \sigma_1 > \sigma_2$. $F_{\text{crit}} = F_{\alpha, n_1-1, n_2-1} = F_{0.01, 13, 13} = 4.16$. Reject H_0 if $F_{\text{data}} \geq 4.16$. $F_{\text{data}} = 3173.62408/1.164810989 \approx 2724.5829$. Since $F_{\text{data}} \approx 2724.58829$ is ≥ 4.16, we reject H_0. There is evidence at the $\alpha = 0.01$ level of significance that the population standard deviation of gold prices is greater than the population standard deviation of silver prices. **p-value method:** $H_0 : \sigma_1 = \sigma_2$ vs. $H_a : \sigma_1 > \sigma_2$. Reject H_0 if the p-value ≤ 0.01. $F_{\text{data}} = 3173.62408/1.164810989 \approx 2724.5829$. p-value ≈ 0. Since the p-value ≈ 0 is ≤ 0.01, we reject H_0. There is evidence at the $\alpha = 0.01$ level of significance that the population standard deviation of gold prices is greater than the population standard deviation of silver prices.

38. Critical-value method: $H_0 : \sigma_1 = \sigma_2$ vs. $H_a : \sigma_1 \neq \sigma_2$. $F_{\text{crit}} = F_{\alpha/2, n_1-1, n_2-1} = F_{0.025, 6, 6} = 5.82$ and $F_{\text{crit}} = F_{1-\alpha/2, n_1-1, n_2-1} = F_{0.975, 6, 6} = 0.1718$. Reject H_0 if $F_{\text{data}} \leq 0.1718$ or if $F_{\text{data}} \geq 5.82$. $F_{\text{data}} = 4733.333333/2534.952381 \approx 1.8672$. Since $F_{\text{data}} \approx 1.8672$ is not $F_{\text{data}} \leq 0.1718$ and not $F_{\text{data}} \geq 5.82$, we do not reject H_0. There is insufficient evidence at the $\alpha = 0.05$ level of significance that the population standard deviation of the number of runs scored by the American League differs from the population standard deviation of the number of runs scored by National League teams. **p-value method:** $H_0 : \sigma_1 = \sigma_2$ vs. $H_a : \sigma_1 \neq \sigma_2$. Reject H_0 if the p-value ≤ 0.05. $F_{\text{data}} = 4733.333333/2534.952381 \approx 1.8672$. p-value $= 0.4665$. Since the p-value $= 0.4665$ is not ≤ 0.05, we do not reject H_0. There is insufficient evidence at the $\alpha = 0.05$ level of significance that the population standard deviation of the number of runs scored by the American League differs from the population standard deviation of the number of runs scored by National League teams.

39. (a) Different. The box and the whiskers of the boxplot for Honda cars are much longer than the box and whiskers of the boxplot for Lexus cars. **(b) Critical-value method:** $H_0 : \sigma_1 =$

σ_2 vs. $H_a : \sigma_1 \neq \sigma_2$. $F_{\text{crit}} = F_{\alpha/2, n_1-1, n_2-1} = F_{0.05, 6, 5} = 4.95$ and $F_{\text{crit}} = F_{1-\alpha/2, n_1-1, n_2-1} = F_{0.95, 6, 5} = 0.2278$. Reject H_0 if $F_{\text{data}} \leq 0.2020$ or if $F_{\text{data}} \geq 4.95$. $F_{\text{data}} = 76.47619048/10.96666667 \approx 6.9735$. Since $F_{\text{data}} \approx 6.9735$ is ≥ 4.95, we reject H_0. There is evidence at the $\alpha = 0.10$ level of significance that the population standard deviation of the number of the combined mpg of Honda cars differs from the population standard deviation of the combined mpg of Lexus cars. **p-value method:** $H_0 : \sigma_1 = \sigma_2$ vs. $H_a : \sigma_1 \neq \sigma_2$. Reject H_0 if the p-value ≤ 0.10. $F_{\text{data}} = 76.47619048/10.96666667 \approx 6.9735$. p-value $= 0.0501$. Since the p-value $= 0.0501$ is ≤ 0.10, we reject H_0. There is evidence at the $\alpha = 0.10$ level of significance that the population standard deviation of the number of the combined mpg of Honda cars differs from the population standard deviation of the combined mpg of Lexus cars.

Chapter 10 Review

1. (a) $\bar{x}_d = -2.6875$, $s_d = 1.6146$ **(b)** $(-4.0376, -1.3374)$
2. $H_0 : \mu_d = 0$ vs. $H_a : \mu_d < 0$. $t_{\text{crit}} = -1.895$. Reject H_0 if $t_{\text{data}} \leq -1.895$. $t_{\text{data}} = -4.708$. Since $t_{\text{data}} \leq -1.895$, we reject H_0. There is evidence that the population mean of the differences is less than 0.
3. $H_0 : \mu_d = 0$ vs. $H_a : \mu_d < 0$. Reject H_0 if p-value < 0.05. $t_{\text{data}} = -4.708$. p-value $= 0.0010939869$. Since the p-value ≤ 0.05, we reject H_0. There is evidence that the population mean of the differences is less than 0.
4. Since both sample sizes are large ($n_1 \geq 30$ and $n_2 \geq 30$), it is appropriate to construct a 95% confidence interval for $\mu_1 - \mu_2$.
5. 0.1
6. 0.005684
7. (0.094, 0.106). We are 95% confident that the interval captures the difference in population means.
8. (a) $H_0 : \mu_1 = \mu_2$ vs. $H_a : \mu_1 > \mu_2$. $t_{\text{crit}} = 1.306$. Reject H_0 if $t_{\text{data}} \geq 1.306$. $t_{\text{data}} = 5.117$. Since $t_{\text{data}} \leq 1.306$, we reject H_0. There is evidence that the population mean salary of young persons with a college degree is greater than the population mean salary of young persons without a college degree.
(b) (3348.77, 6651.23). We are 90% confident that the difference in the population mean salaries of young persons with and without college degrees lies between \$3348.77 and \$6651.23.
9. (a) $H_0 : p_1 = p_2$ vs. $H_a : p_1 \neq p_2$. Reject H_0 if the p-value ≤ 0.05. $\hat{p}_{\text{pooled}} = 10/157 \approx 0.0636942675$. $Z_{\text{data}} = 2.40$. p-value $= 0.0163$. Since the p-value $= 0.0163$ is ≤ 0.05, we reject H_0. There is evidence at the $\alpha = 0.05$ level of significance that the population proportion of packet loss from Asian Web sites differs from the population proportion of packet loss from North American Web sites. **(b)** (0.0096, 0.2304)
10. (a) $(-0.0716, 0.0322)$ **(b)** Since the p-value is not ≥ 0.01, we do not reject H_0. There is insufficient evidence that the population proportion of new mothers in Florida who took their babies in for a checkup within one week of delivery is different from the proportion of new mothers in North Carolina who took their babies in for a checkup within one week of delivery.
11. $H_0 : \sigma_1 = \sigma_2$ vs. $H_a : \sigma_1 > \sigma_2$. $F_{\text{crit}} = F_{\alpha, n_1-1, n_2-1} = F_{0.01, 54, 106} = 1.74$. Reject H_0 if $F_{\text{data}} \geq 1.74$. $F_{\text{data}} = 13.011$. Since $F_{\text{data}} = 13.011$ is ≥ 1.74, we reject H_0. There is evidence at the $\alpha = 0.01$ level of significance that the population standard deviation of Population 1 is greater than the population standard deviation of Population 2.
12. $H_0 : \sigma_1 = \sigma_2$ vs. $H_a : \sigma_1 < \sigma_2$. $F_{\text{crit}} = F_{1-\alpha, n_1-1, n_2-1} = F_{0.95, 124, 26} = 0.6173$. Reject H_0 if $F_{\text{data}} \leq 0.6173$. $F_{\text{data}} = 0.3123$. Since $F_{\text{data}} = 0.3123$ is ≤ 0.6173, we reject H_0. There is evidence

at the $\alpha = 0.05$ level of significance that the population standard deviation of Population 1 is less than the population standard deviation of Population 2.
13. $H_0 : \sigma_1 = \sigma_2$ vs. $H_a : \sigma_1 > \sigma_2$. Reject H_0 if the p-value $\leq$ 0.05. $F_{\text{data}} = 5.112$. p-value ≈ 0. Since the p-value ≈ 0 is $\leq$ 0.05, we reject H_0. There is evidence at the $\alpha = 0.05$ level of significance that the population standard deviation of Population 1 is greater than the population standard deviation of Population 2.
14. $H_0 : \sigma_1 = \sigma_2$ vs. $H_a : \sigma_1 < \sigma_2$. Reject H_0 if the p-value ≤ 0.01. $F_{\text{data}} = 0.4916$. p-value $= 0.0001$. Since the p-value $= 0.0001$ is ≤ 0.01, we reject H_0. There is evidence at the $\alpha = 0.01$ level of significance that the population standard deviation of Population 1 is less than the population standard deviation of Population 2.

Chapter 10 Quiz
1. True
2. True
3. False
4. normal; large (greater than or equal to 30)
5. margin of error
6. $\bar{x}_d$
7. $\mu_1 - \mu_2$
8. $\hat{p}_{\text{pooled}}$
9. No difference
10. (a) (6.6680, 21.3320) **(b)** Since 0 does not lie in the confidence interval, we reject H_0. There is evidence that the population mean difference in the number of cigarettes smoked before and after attending Butt-Enders is different from 0.
11. (a) Critical-value method: $H_0 : \mu_1 = \mu_2$ vs. $H_a : \mu_1 < \mu_2$. $t_{\text{crit}} = -1.690$. Reject H_0 if $t_{\text{data}} \leq -1.690$. $t_{\text{data}} = -3.667$. Since $t_{\text{data}} = -3.667$ is ≤ -1.690, we reject H_0. There is evidence at the $\alpha = 0.05$ level of significance that the population mean income in Suburb A is less than the population mean income in Suburb B. **p-value method:** $H_0 : \mu_1 = \mu_2$ vs. $H_a : \mu_1 < \mu_2$. Reject H_0 if p-value ≤ 0.05. $t_{\text{data}} = -3.667$. p-value $= 0.0004$. Since p-value $= 0.0004$ is ≤ 0.05, we reject H_0. There is evidence at the $\alpha = 0.05$ level of significance that the population mean income in Suburb A is less than the population mean income in Suburb B. **(b)** $(-23{,}304.69, -6{,}695.31)$. We are 95% confident that the interval captures the difference of the population mean income of Suburb A and the population mean income of Suburb B.
12. (2.2406, 17.7594). We are 95% confident that the interval captures the difference of the population mean number of bottles processed by the updated machine and the population mean number of bottles processed by the non-updated machine.
13. (a) Since $t_{\text{data}} \geq 1.662$, we reject H_0. There is evidence that the population mean number of bottles processed by the updated machine is greater than the population mean number of bottles processed by the non-updated machine. **(b)** Since confidence intervals can be used only to perform two-tailed tests and the hypothesis test in **(a)** is a one-tailed test, the confidence interval in Exercise 12 cannot be used to perform the hypothesis test in **(a)**.
14. (a) $H_0 : \mu_1 = \mu_2$ vs. $H_a : \mu_1 \neq \mu_2$. $t_{\text{crit}} = 1.662$. Reject H_0 if $t_{\text{data}} \leq -1.662$ or $t_{\text{data}} \geq 1.662$. $t_{\text{data}} = -6.129$. Since $t_{\text{data}} \leq -1.662$, we reject H_0. There is evidence that the population mean income of people 18 to 24 years old who never married is different from the population mean income of people 18 to 24 years old who are married. **(b)** No, the conclusion of the two-tailed hypothesis test for $\alpha = 0.10$ is "Reject H_0."

(c) $(-\$7349.928, -\$4214.072)$. The confidence interval does not include 0.
15. $H_0 : p_1 = p_2$; $H_a : p_1 < p_2$. Reject H_0 if the p-value ≤ 0.05. $Z_{\text{data}} = 0.28$; p-value $= 0.3897$. Since the p-value is not ≥ 0.05, we do not reject H_0. There is insufficient evidence that the population proportion of 18- to 20-year-olds who used an illicit drug decreased from 2004 to 2005.
16. $H_0 : p_1 = p_2$ vs. $H_a : p_1 > p_2$. $Z_{\text{crit}} = 1.645$. Reject H_0 if $Z_{\text{data}} \geq 1.645$. $\hat{p}_1 - \hat{p}_2 = 0.051$, $\hat{p}_{\text{pooled}} = 0.7155$, $Z_{\text{data}} = 2.53$. Since $Z_{\text{data}} \leq 1.645$, we reject H_0. There is evidence that the population proportion of people aged 35 to 44 who were married was lower in 2000 than in 1990.
17. Critical-value method: $H_0 : \sigma_1 = \sigma_2$ vs. $H_a : \sigma_1 < \sigma_2$. $F_{\text{crit}} = F_{1-\alpha, n_1 - 1, n_2 - 1} = F_{0.95, 10, 10} = 0.3356$. Reject H_0 if $F_{\text{data}} \leq 0.3356$. $F_{\text{data}} = 0.1387$. Since $F_{\text{data}} = 0.1387$ is ≤ 0.3356, we reject H_0. There is evidence at the $\alpha = 0.05$ level of significance that the population standard deviation of fine particulate particle pollution in the air inside closed taxi cabs during the Olympics is less than the population standard deviation of fine particulate particle pollution in the air inside closed taxi cabs after the Olympics. **p-value method:** $H_0 : \sigma_1 = \sigma_2$ vs. $H_a : \sigma_1 < \sigma_2$. Reject H_0 if p-value ≤ 0.05. $F_{\text{data}} = 0.1387$. p-value $= 0.0022$. Since p-value $= 0.0022$ is ≤ 0.05, we reject H_0. There is evidence at the $\alpha = 0.05$ level of significance that the population standard deviation of fine particulate particle pollution in the air inside closed taxi cabs during the Olympics is less than the population standard deviation of fine particulate particle pollution in the air inside closed taxi cabs after the Olympics.

Chapter 11

Section 11.1
1. (1) Each independent trial of the experiment has k possible outcomes, $k = 2, 3, \ldots$ (2) The ith outcome (category) occurs with probability p_i, where $i = 1, 2, \ldots, k$ (3) $\sum_{i=1}^{k} p_i = 1$.
2. Answers will vary.
3. It is the long-run mean of that random variable after an arbitrarily large number of trials.
4. H_0 : The random variable follows a particular distribution. H_a : The random variable does not follow the distribution specified in H_0.
5. Multinomial
6. Not multinomial
7. Multinomial
8. Not multinomial
9. (a) $E_1 = 50, E_2 = 25, E_3 = 25$ **(b)** Conditions are met.
10. (a) $E_1 = 2, E_2 = 3, E_3 = 4, E_4 = 1$ **(b)** χ^2 goodness of fit conditions are not met.
11. (a) $E_1 = 90, E_2 = 5, E_3 = 4, E_4 = 1$ **(b)** Conditions are not met.
12. (a) $E_1 = 80, E_2 = 70, E_3 = 20, E_4 = 20, E_5 = 10$ **(b)** χ^2 goodness of fit conditions are met.
13. 0.667
14. 3.5
15. 7.333
16. 2.183
17. 17.667
18. 8.8535
19. (a) $E_1 = 40, E_2 = 30, E_3 = 30$; conditions are met. **(b)** $\chi^2_{\text{crit}} = \chi^2_{0.05} = 5.991$. Reject H_0 if $\chi^2_{\text{data}} \geq 5.991$. **(c)** 4.167 **(d)** Since χ^2_{data} is not ≥ 5.991, we do not reject H_0. There is

insufficient evidence that the random variable does not follow the distribution specified in H_0.

20. (a) $E_1 = 30$, $E_2 = 30$, $E_3 = 30$. Since none of the expected frequencies is less than 1 and none of the expected frequencies is less than 5, the conditions for performing the χ^2 goodness of fit test are met. **(b)** $\chi^2_{crit} = \chi^2_{0.01} = 9.210$. Reject H_0 if $\chi^2_{data} \geq 9.210$. **(c)** $\chi^2_{data} = 6.667$ **(d)** Since χ^2_{data} is not ≥ 9.210, we do not reject H_0. There is insufficient evidence that the random variable does not follow the distribution specified in H_0.

21. (a) $E_1 = 80$, $E_2 = 70$, $E_3 = 20$, $E_4 = 20$, $E_5 = 10$; conditions are met. **(b)** $\chi^2_{crit} = \chi^2_{0.10} = 7.779$. Reject H_0 if $\chi^2_{data} \geq 7.779$. **(c)** 6.607 **(d)** Since χ^2_{data} is not ≥ 7.779, we do not reject H_0. There is insufficient evidence that the random variable does not follow the distribution specified in H_0.

22. (a) $E_1 = 60$, $E_2 = 40$, $E_3 = 40$, $E_4 = 40$, $E_5 = 20$. Since none of the expected frequencies is less than 1 and none of the expected frequencies is less than 5, the conditions for performing the χ^2 goodness of fit test are met. **(b)** $\chi^2_{crit} = \chi^2_{0.05} = 9.488$. Reject H_0 if $\chi^2_{data} \geq 9.488$. **(c)** $\chi^2_{data} = 0.8$ **(d)** Since χ^2_{data} is not ≤ 9.488 we do not reject H_0. There is insufficient evidence that the random variable does not follow the distribution specified in H_0.

23. (a) Reject H_0 if the p-value ≤ 0.05. $E_1 = 50$, $E_2 = 50$; conditions are met. **(b)** 4 **(c)** p-value $= 0.0455$. **(d)** Since the p-value ≤ 0.05, we reject H_0. There is evidence that the random variable does not follow the distribution specified in H_0.

24. (a) Reject H_0 if the p-value ≤ 0.10. $E_1 = 50$, $E_2 = 25$, $E_3 = 25$. Since none of the expected frequencies is less than 1 and none of the expected frequencies is less than 5, the conditions for performing the χ^2 goodness of fit test are met. **(b)** 0.24 **(c)** p-value $= 0.8869$. **(d)** Since the p-value is not ≤ 0.10, we do not reject H_0. There is insufficient evidence that the random variable does not follow the distribution specified in H_0.

25. (a) Reject H_0 if the p-value ≤ 0.10. $E_1 = 100$, $E_2 = 50$, $E_3 = 30$, $E_4 = 20$; conditions are met. **(b)** 6.083 **(c)** p-value $= 0.1076$. **(d)** Since the p-value is not ≤ 0.10, we do not reject H_0. There is insufficient evidence that the random variable does not follow the distribution specified in H_0.

26. (a) Reject H_0 if the p-value ≤ 0.05. $E_1 = 80$, $E_2 = 40$, $E_3 = 40$, $E_4 = 20$, $E_5 = 20$. Since none of the expected frequencies is less than 1 and none of the expected frequencies is less than 5, the conditions for performing the χ^2 goodness of fit test are met. **(b)** 8.125 **(c)** p-value $= 0.0871$ **(d)** Since the p-value is not ≤ 0.05, we do not reject H_0. There is insufficient evidence that the random variable does not follow the distribution specified in H_0.

27. Since χ^2_{data} is not ≥ 9.488, we do not reject H_0. There is insufficient evidence that the distribution of education levels has changed since 2005.

28. $H_0 : p_{fastfood} = 0.30$, $p_{foodcourts} = 0.46$, $p_{restaurants} = 0.24$. H_a : The random variable does not follow the distribution specified in H_0. $E_{fastfood} = 30$, $E_{foodcourts} = 46$, $E_{restaurants} = 24$. Since none of the expected frequencies is less than 1 and none of the expected frequencies is less than 5, the conditions for performing the χ^2 goodness of fit test are met. $\chi^2_{crit} = \chi^2_{0.05} = 4.605$. Reject H_0 if $\chi^2_{data} \leq 4.605$. $\chi^2_{data} = 1.371$. Since χ^2_{data} is not ≥ 4.605, we do not reject H_0. There is insufficient evidence that the random variable does not follow the distribution specified in H_0.

29. $H_0 : p_{phip} = 0.30$, $p_{mm} = 0.556$, $p_{other} = 0.144$. H_a : The random variable does not follow the distribution specified in H_0. $E_{phip} = 300$, $E_{mm} = 556$, $E_{other} = 144$. Since none of the expected frequencies is less than 1 and none of the expected frequencies is less than 5, the conditions for performing the χ^2 goodness of fit test are met. $\chi^2_{crit} = \chi^2_{0.05} = 5.991$. Reject H_0 if $\chi^2_{data} \geq 5.991$.

$\chi^2_{data} = 14.224$. Since $\chi^2_{data} \geq 5.991$, we reject H_0. There is evidence that the population proportions of minority patients who suffered spinal cord injuries, who had a private health insurance provider, Medicare, Medicaid, or other arrangements, have changed.

30. $H_0 : p_{excellent} = 0.54$, $p_{good} = 0.39$, $p_{fair} = 0.06$, $p_{poor} = 0.01$. H_a : The random variable does not follow the distribution specified in H_0. $E_{excellent} = 270$, $E_{good} = 195$, $E_{fair} = 30$. $E_{poor} = 5$. Since none of the expected frequencies is less than 1 and none of the expected frequencies is less than 5, the conditions for performing the χ^2 goodness of fit test are met. $\chi^2_{crit} = \chi^2_{0.05} = 7.815$. Reject H_0 if $\chi^2_{data} \geq 7.815$. $\chi^2_{data} = 3.554$. Since χ^2_{data} is not ≥ 7.815, we do not reject H_0. There is insufficient evidence that the proportions have changed since 2007.

31. $H_0 : p_{males} = 0.4641403733$, $p_{females} = 0.5358596267$. H_a : The random variable does not follow the distribution specified in H_0. $E_{males} = 1129.25$, $E_{females} = 1303.75$. Since none of the expected frequencies is less than 1 and none of the expected frequencies is less than 5, the conditions for performing the χ^2 goodness of fit test are met. $\chi^2_{crit} = \chi^2_{0.05} = 3.841$. Reject H_0 if $\chi^2_{data} \geq 3.841$. $\chi^2_{data} = 17.278$. Since $\chi^2_{data} \geq 3.841$, we reject H_0. There is evidence that the population proportions of males and females living in college dormitories have changed.

32. $H_0 : p_{pizza} = 0.25$, $p_{cheeseburger} = 0.25$, $p_{quiche} = 0.25$, $p_{sushi} = 0.25$. H_a : The random variable does not follow the distribution specified in H_0. $E_{pizza} = 125$, $E_{cheeseburger} = 125$, $E_{quiche} = 125$, $E_{sushi} = 125$. Since none of the expected frequencies is less than 1 and none of the expected frequencies is less than 5, the conditions for performing the χ^2 goodness of fit test are met. $\chi^2_{crit} = \chi^2_{0.01} = 11.345$. Reject H_0 if $\chi^2_{data} \geq 11.345$. $\chi^2_{data} = 377.2$. Since $\chi^2_{data} \geq 11.345$, we reject H_0. There is evidence that there is a difference in student preference among the four entries.

33. $H_0 : p_{Hertz} = 0.28$, $p_{Avis} = 0.214$, $p_{National} = 0.121$, $p_{Budget} = 0.105$, $p_{Alamo} = 0.105$, $p_{Dollar} = 0.085$, $p_{Others} = 0.09$. H_a : The random variable does not follow the distribution specified in H_0. $E_{Hertz} = 28$, $E_{Avis} = 21.4$, $E_{National} = 12.1$, $E_{Budget} = 10.5$, $E_{Alamo} = 10.5$, $E_{Dollar} = 8.5$, $E_{Others} = 9$. Since none of the expected frequencies is less than 1 and none of the expected frequencies is less than 5, the conditions for performing the χ^2 goodness of fit test are met. $\chi^2_{crit} = \chi^2_{0.05} = 12.592$. Reject H_0 if $\chi^2_{data} \geq 12.592$. $\chi^2_{data} = 0.2058$. Since χ^2_{data} is not ≥ 9.488, we do not reject H_0. There is insufficient evidence that the population proportions of market shares held by the largest car rental agencies have changed.

34. $H_0 : p_{White} = 0.8068$, $p_{Black} = 0.1274$, $p_{Indian} = 0.0095$, $p_{Asian} = 0.0401$, $p_{Hawaiian} = 0.0017$, $p_{Twomore} = 0.0145$. H_a : The random variable does not follow the distribution specified in H_0. $E_{White} = 806.8$, $E_{Black} = 127.4$, $E_{Indian} = 9.5$, $E_{Asian} = 40.1$, $E_{Hawaiian} = 1.7$, $E_{Twomore} = 14.5$. Since none of the expected frequencies is less than 1 and only one of the six expected frequencies is less than 5, the conditions for performing the χ^2 goodness of fit test are met. Reject H_0 if p-value ≤ 0.10. $\chi^2_{data} = 45.887$. p-value ≈ 0. Since p-value ≤ 0.10, we reject H_0. There is evidence that the population proportions have changed since 2002.

35. $H_0 : p_{every} = 0.31$, $p_{almost} = 0.12$, $p_{onceortwice} = 0.14$, $p_{few} = 0.24$, $p_{never} = 0.19$. H_a : The random variable does not follow the distribution specified in H_0. $E_{every} = 31$, $E_{almost} = 12$, $E_{onceortwice} = 14$, $E_{few} = 24$, $E_{never} = 19$. Since none of the expected frequencies is less than 1 and none of the expected frequencies is less than 5, the conditions for performing the χ^2 goodness of fit test are met. $\chi^2_{crit} = \chi^2_{0.10} = 7.779$. Reject H_0 if $\chi^2_{data} \geq 7.779$. $\chi^2_{data} = 0.531$. Since χ^2_{data} is not ≥ 7.779, we do not reject H_0. There is insufficient evidence that the population proportions of how often Americans attend religious services have changed.

36. $H_0 : p_{\text{sawadv}} = 0.50, p_{\text{notseeadv}} = 0.41, p_{\text{notrecall}} = 0.09. H_a :$ The random variable does not follow the distribution specified in H_0. $E_{\text{sawadv}} = 500, E_{\text{notseeadv}} = 410, E_{\text{notrecall}} = 90$. Since none of the expected frequencies is less than 1 and none of the expected frequencies is less than 5, the conditions for performing the χ^2 goodness of fit test are met. Reject H_0 if p-value ≤ 0.05. $\chi^2_{\text{data}} = 10.014$. p-value $= 0.0069$. Since p-value ≤ 0.05, we reject H_0. There is evidence that the population proportions have changed since 2007.

37. $H_0 : p_{\text{believe}} = 0.78, p_{\text{notsure}} = 0.12, p_{\text{didnotbelieve}} = 0.10. H_a :$ The random variable does not follow the distribution specified in H_0. $E_{\text{believe}} = 780, E_{\text{notsure}} = 120, E_{\text{didnotbelieve}} = 100$. Since none of the expected frequencies is less than 1 and none of the expected frequencies is less than 5, the conditions for performing the χ^2 goodness of fit test are met. $\chi^2_{\text{crit}} = \chi^2_{0.05} = 5.991$. Reject H_0 if $\chi^2_{\text{data}} \geq 5.991$. $\chi^2_{\text{data}} = 11.885$. Since $\chi^2_{\text{data}} \geq 5.991$, we reject H_0. There is evidence that the population proportions of people who either believe, are not sure, or don't believe in angels have changed.

38. $H_0 : p_{\text{Caucasian}} = 0.67, p_{\text{Asian}} = 0.20, p_{\text{AfricanAmerican}} = 0.08, p_{\text{Hispanic}} = 0.05. H_a :$ The random variable does not follow the distribution specified in H_0. $E_{\text{Caucasian}} = 67, E_{\text{Asian}} = 20, E_{\text{AfricanAmerican}} = 8, E_{\text{Hispanic}} = 5$. Since none of the expected frequencies is less than 1 and none of the expected frequencies is less than 5 the conditions for performing the χ^2 goodness of fit test are met. Reject H_0 if p-value ≤ 0.05. $\chi^2_{\text{data}} = 8.018$. p-value $= 0.0456$. Since p-value ≤ 0.05, we reject H_0. There is evidence that the ethnic composition of the university faculty has changed since 1990.

39. $H_0 : p_{\text{personnel}} = 0.24, p_{\text{operations}} = 0.28, p_{\text{other}} = 0.48. H_a :$ The random variable does not follow the distribution specified in H_0. $E_{\text{personnel}} = 91.056, E_{\text{operations}} = 106.232, E_{\text{other}} = 182.112$. Since none of the expected frequencies is less than 1 and none of the expected frequencies is less than 5, the conditions for performing the χ^2 goodness of fit test are met. $\chi^2_{\text{crit}} = \chi^2_{0.05} = 5.991$. Reject H_0 if $\chi^2_{\text{data}} \geq 5.991$. $\chi^2_{\text{data}} = 3.7072$. Since χ^2_{data} is not ≥ 5.991, we do not reject H_0. There is insufficient evidence that the population proportions of budget items have changed from 1985 to 2004.

40. **(a)–(c)** Insufficient information

Section 11.2

1. Tabular summary of the relationship between two categorical variables

2. Answers will vary.

3. The two-sample Z test for the difference in proportions from Chapter 10 is for comparing proportions of two independent populations, and the χ^2 test for homogeneity of proportions is for comparing proportions of k independent populations.

4. Under the assumption that the variables are independent, $P(A \cap B) = P(A) \cdot P(B) = \left(\frac{\text{row total}}{n}\right) \cdot \left(\frac{\text{column total}}{n}\right)$. Thus the expected frequency of A and B is $n \cdot P(A \cap B) = n \cdot \left(\frac{\text{row total}}{n}\right) \cdot \left(\frac{\text{column total}}{n}\right)$.

5.

	A1	A2	Total
B1	11	19	30
B2	11	19	30
Total	22	38	60

6.

	C1	C2	Total
D1	55	95	150
D2	55	95	150
Total	110	190	300

7.

	E1	E2	E3	Total
F1	30.71	20.79	8.50	60
F2	34.29	23.21	9.50	67
Total	65	44	18	127

8.

	G1	G2	Total
H1	9	9	18
H2	9	9	18
H3	9	9	18
Total	27	27	54

9.

	I1	I2	I3	Total
J1	99.2788	93.6058	102.1154	295
J2	55.5288	52.3558	57.1154	165
J3	20.1923	19.0385	20.7692	60
Total	174.9999	165.0001	180	520

10.

	K1	K2	K3	K4	Total
L1	37.5	72.92	89.58	100	300
L2	23.75	46.18	56.74	63.33	190
L3	28.75	55.90	68.68	76.67	230
Total	90	175	215	240	720

11. **(a)** $H_0 :$ Variable A and Variable B are independent. $H_a :$ Variable A and Variable B are not independent.

(b)

	A1	A2	Total
B1	11	19	30
B2	11	19	30
Total	22	38	60

Since none of the expected frequencies is less than 1 and none of the expected frequencies is less than 5, the conditions for performing the χ^2 test for independence are met. **(c)** 3.841. Reject H_0 if $\chi^2_{\text{data}} \geq 3.841$. **(d)** 0.2871 **(e)** Since χ^2_{data} is not ≥ 3.841, we do not reject H_0. There is insufficient evidence that variable A and variable B are not independent.

12. **(a)** $H_0 :$ Variables E and F are independent. $H_a :$ Variables E and F are not independent.

(b)

	E1	E2	E3	Total
F1	30.71	20.79	8.50	60
F2	34.29	23.21	9.50	67
Total	65	44	18	127

Since none of the expected frequencies is less than 1 and none of the expected frequencies is less than 5, the conditions for performing the χ^2 test for independence are met. **(c)** $\chi^2_{\text{crit}} = \chi^2_{0.10} = 4.605$. Reject H_0 if $\chi^2_{\text{data}} \geq 4.605$. **(d)** 0.590 **(e)** Since χ^2_{data} is not ≥ 4.605, we do not reject H_0. There is insufficient evidence that variable E and variable F are not independent.

13. **(a)** $H_0:$ Variable I and Variable J are independent. $H_a :$ Variable I and Variable J are not independent.

(b)

	I1	I2	I3	Total
J1	99.2788	93.6058	102.1154	295
J2	55.5288	52.3558	57.1154	165
J3	20.1923	19.0385	20.7692	60
Total	174.9999	165.0001	180	520

Since none of the expected frequencies is less than 1 and none of the expected frequencies is less than 5, the conditions for performing the χ^2 test for independence are met. **(c)** 13.277. Reject H_0 if $\chi^2_{data} \geq 13.277$. **(d)** 4.000 **(e)** Since χ^2_{data} is not $\geq$ 13.277, we do not reject H_0. There is insufficient evidence that variable I and variable J are not independent.
14. (a) H_0 : Variables I and J are independent. H_a : Variables I and J are not independent.

(b)

	I1	I2	I3	Total
J1	99.2788	93.6058	102.1154	295
J2	55.5288	52.3558	57.1154	165
J3	20.1923	19.0385	20.7692	60
Total	174.9999	165.0001	180	520

Since none of the expected frequencies is less than 1 and none of the expected frequencies is less than 5, the conditions for performing the χ^2 test for independence are met. **(c)** $\chi^2_{crit} = \chi^2_{0.10} = 7.779$. Reject H_0 if $\chi^2_{data} \geq 7.779$. **(d)** 4.000 **(e)** Since χ^2_{data} is not $\geq$ 7.779, we do not reject H_0. There is insufficient evidence that variable I and variable J are not independent.
15. (a) H_0 : Variable C and Variable D are independent. H_a: Variable C and Variable D are not independent. Reject H_0 if the p-value ≤ 0.05.

	C1	C2	Total
D1	55	95	150
D2	55	95	150
Total	110	190	300

Since none of the expected frequencies is less than 1 and none of the expected frequencies is less than 5, the conditions for performing the χ^2 test for independence are met. **(b)** 1.4354 **(c)** p-value $= 0.2309$ **(d)** Since the p-value is not ≤ 0.05, we do not reject H_0. There is insufficient evidence that variable C and variable D are not independent.
16. (a) H_0 : Variables G and H are independent. H_a : Variables G and H are not independent.

	G1	G2	Total
H1	9	9	18
H2	9	9	18
H3	9	9	18
Total	27	27	54

Since none of the expected frequencies is less than 1 and none of the expected frequencies is less than 5, the conditions for performing the χ^2 test for independence are met. Reject H_0 if the p-value ≤ 0.10. **(b)** 0.444 **(c)** p-value $= 0.8009$ **(d)** Since the p-value is not ≤ 0.10, we do not reject H_0. There is insufficient evidence that variables G and H are not independent.
17. (a) H_0 : Variable K and Variable L are independent. H_a : Variable K and Variable L are not independent. Reject H_0 if p-value ≤ 0.01.

	K1	K2	K3	K4	Total
L1	37.5	72.92	89.58	100	300
L2	23.75	46.18	56.74	63.33	190
L3	28.75	55.90	68.68	76.67	230
Total	90	175	215	240	720

Since none of the expected frequencies is less than 1 and none of the expected frequencies is less than 5, the conditions for performing the χ^2 test for independence are met. **(b)** $\chi^2_{data} = 4.906$ **(c)** p-value $= 0.5560$ **(d)** Since p-value is not ≤ 0.01, we do not reject H_0. There is insufficient evidence that variable K and variable L are not independent.
18. (a) H_0 : Variables K and L are independent. H_a : Variables K and L are not independent.

(b)

	K1	K2	K3	K4	Total
L1	37.5	72.92	89.58	100	300
L2	23.75	46.18	56.74	63.33	190
L3	28.75	55.90	68.68	76.67	230
Total	90	175	215	240	720

Since none of the expected frequencies is less than 1 and none of the expected frequencies is less than 5, the conditions for performing the χ^2 test for independence are met. Reject H_0 if the p-value ≤ 0.10. **(b)** $\chi^2_{data} = 4.906$ **(c)** p-value $= 0.5560$ **(d)** Since the p-value is not ≤ 0.10, we do not reject H_0. There is insufficient evidence that variables K and L are not independent.
19. (a) $H_0 : p_1 = p_2 = p_3$. H_a : Not all the proportions in H_0 are equal.

(b)

	Sample 1	Sample 2	Sample 3	Total
Successes	9.63	20.86	29.52	60.01
Failures	20.37	44.14	62.48	126.99
Total	30	65	92	187

Since none of the expected frequencies is less than 1 and none of the expected frequencies is less than 5, the conditions for performing the χ^2 test for homogeneity of proportions are met. **(c)** 5.991. Reject H_0 if $\chi^2_{data} \geq 5.991$. **(d)** 0.0846 **(e)** Since χ^2_{data} is not $\geq$ 5.991, we do not reject H_0. There is insufficient evidence that not all the proportions in H_0 are equal.
20. (a) $H_0 : p_1 = p_2 = p_3$. H_a : Not all the proportions in H_0 are equal.

(b)

	Sample 1	Sample 2	Sample 3	Total
Successes	48.3092	50.2415	101.4493	200
Failures	201.6908	209.7585	423.5507	835
Total	250	260	525	1035

Since none of the expected frequencies is less than 1 and none of the expected frequencies is less than 5, the conditions for performing the χ^2 test for homogeneity of proportions are met. **(c)** $\chi^2_{crit} = \chi^2_{0.05} = 5.991$. Reject H_0 if $\chi^2_{data} \geq 5.991$. **(d)** 0.100 **(e)** Since χ^2_{data} is not $\geq$ 5.991, we do not reject H_0. There is insufficient evidence that not all of the proportions in H_0 are equal.
21. (a) $H_0 : p_1 = p_2 = p_3 = p_4$. H_a : Not all the proportions in H_0 are equal.

(b)

	Sample 1	Sample 2	Sample 3	Sample 4	Total
Successes	9.67	15.08	20.11	25.14	70
Failures	15.33	23.92	31.89	39.86	111
Total	25	39	52	65	181

Since none of the expected frequencies is less than 1 and none of the expected frequencies is less than 5, the conditions for performing the χ^2 test for homogeneity of proportions are met. **(c)** 7.815. Reject H_0 if $\chi^2_{\text{data}} \geq 7.815$. **(d)** 0.0213 **(e)** Since χ^2_{data} is not ≥ 7.815, we do not reject H_0. There is insufficient evidence that not all the proportions in H_0 are equal.
22. (a) $H_0: p_1 = p_2 = p_3 = p_4$. H_a: Not all the proportions in H_0 are equal.

(b)

	Sample 1	Sample 2	Sample 3	Sample 4	Total
Successes	96.6851	150.8287	201.1050	251.3812	700
Failures	153.3149	239.1713	318.8950	398.6188	1110
Total	250	390	520	650	1810

Since none of the expected frequencies is less than 1 and none of the expected frequencies is less than 5, the conditions for performing the χ^2 test for homogeneity of proportions are met. **(c)** $\chi^2_{\text{crit}} = \chi^2_{0.05} = 7.815$. Reject H_0 if $\chi^2_{\text{data}} \geq 7.815$. **(d)** 0.2150 **(e)** Since χ^2_{data} is not ≥ 7.815, we do not reject H_0. There is insufficient evidence that not all the proportions in H_0 are equal.
23. (a) $H_0: p_1 = p_2 = p_3$. H_a: Not all the proportions in H_0 are equal. Reject H_0 if the p-value ≤ 0.05.

	Sample 1	Sample 2	Sample 3	Total
Successes	27.17	57.74	95.09	180
Failures	12.83	27.26	44.91	85
Total	40	85	140	265

Since none of the expected frequencies is less than 1 and none of the expected frequencies is less than 5, the conditions for performing the χ^2 test for homogeneity of proportions are met. **(b)** 2.0442 **(c)** p-value = 0.3598. **(d)** Since the p-value is not ≤ 0.05, we do not reject H_0. There is insufficient evidence that not all the proportions in H_0 are equal.
24. (a) $H_0: p_1 = p_2 = p_3$. H_a: Not all the proportions in H_0 are equal. Reject H_0 if the p-value ≤ 0.05.

	Sample 1	Sample 2	Sample 3	Total
Successes	99.3103	120	140.6897	360
Failures	20.6897	25	29.3103	75
Total	120	145	170	435

Since none of the expected frequencies is less than 1 and none of the expected frequencies is less than 5, the conditions for performing the χ^2 test for homogeneity of proportions are met. **(b)** 0.047 **(c)** p-value = 0.9768. **(d)** Since the p-value is not ≤ 0.05, we do not reject H_0. There is insufficient evidence that not all the proportions in H_0 are equal.
25. (a) $H_0: p_1 = p_2 = p_3 = p_4$. H_a: Not all the proportions in H_0 are equal. Reject H_0 if the p-value ≤ 0.05.

	Sample 1	Sample 2	Sample 3	Sample 4	Total
Successes	8.98	12.35	21.88	34.79	78
Failures	7.02	9.65	17.12	27.21	61
Total	16	22	39	62	139

Since none of the expected frequencies is less than 1 and none of the expected frequencies is less than 5, the conditions for performing the χ^2 test for homogeneity of proportions are met. **(b)** 1.264 **(c)** p-value = 0.7377. **(d)** Since the p-value is not ≤ 0.05, we do not reject H_0. There is insufficient evidence that not all the proportions in H_0 are equal.
26. (a) $H_0: p_1 = p_2 = p_3 = p_4$. H_a: Not all the proportions H_0 in are equal. Reject H_0 if the p-value ≤ 0.05.

	Sample 1	Sample 2	Sample 3	Sample 4	Total
Successes	83.8710	174.1935	290.3226	451.6129	1000
Failures	46.1290	95.8065	159.6774	248.3871	550
Total	130	270	450	700	1550

Since none of the expected frequencies is less than 1 and none of the expected frequencies is less than 5, the conditions for performing the χ^2 test for homogeneity of proportions are met. **(b)** 37.048 **(c)** p-value ≈ 0. **(d)** Since the p-value ≤ 0.05, we reject H_0. There is evidence that not all the proportions in H_0 are equal.
27. H_0: *Type of stimulus* and *type of mouse* are independent. H_a: *Type of stimulus* and *type of mouse* are not independent. Reject H_0 if p-value ≤ 0.05. Since none of the expected frequencies is less than 1 and none of the expected frequencies is less than 5, the conditions for performing the χ^2 test for independence are met. $\chi^2_{\text{data}} = 0.7937$. p-value = 0.3730. Since p-value is not ≤ 0.05, we do not reject H_0. There is insufficient evidence that *type of stimulus* and *type of mouse* are not independent.
28. H_0: *Year* and *level* are independent. H_a: *Year* and *level* are not independent. Since none of the expected frequencies is less than 1 and none of the expected frequencies is less than 5, the conditions for performing the χ^2 test for independence are met. $\chi^2_{\text{crit}} = \chi^2_{0.05} = 5.991$. Reject H_0 if $\chi^2_{\text{data}} \geq 5.991$. $\chi^2_{\text{data}} = 17.570$. Since $\chi^2_{\text{data}} \geq 5.991$, we reject H_0. There is evidence that *year* and *level* are not independent.
29. $H_0: p_{\text{Republicans}} = p_{\text{Independents}} = p_{\text{Democrats}}$. H_a: Not all the proportions in H_0 are equal. Since none of the expected frequencies is less than 1 and none of the expected frequencies is less than 5, the conditions for performing the χ^2 test for homogeneity of proportions are met. $\chi^2_{\text{crit}} = \chi^2_{0.05} = 5.991$. Reject H_0 if $\chi^2_{\text{data}} \geq 5.991$. $\chi^2_{\text{data}} = 1.1568$. Since χ^2_{data} is not ≥ 5.991, we do not reject H_0. There is insufficient evidence that the population proportion favoring restriction is not the same for all three groups.
30. H_0: *Type of course* and *ethnic group* are independent. H_a: *Type of course* and *ethnic group* are not independent. Since none of the expected frequencies is less than 1 and none of the expected frequencies is less than 5, the conditions for performing the χ^2 test for independence are met. $\chi^2_{\text{crit}} = \chi^2_{0.05} = 12.592$. Reject H_0 if $\chi^2_{\text{data}} \geq 12.592$. $\chi^2_{\text{data}} = 43.622$. Since $\chi^2_{\text{data}} \geq 12.592$, we reject H_0. There is evidence that *type of course* and *ethnic group* are not independent.
31. H_0: *Gender* and *political party preference* are independent. H_a: *Gender* and *political party preference* are not independent. Reject H_0 if p-value ≤ 0.01. Since none of the expected frequencies is less than 1 and none of the expected frequencies is less than 5, the conditions for performing the χ^2 test for independence are met. $\chi^2_{\text{data}} = 33.333$. p-value ≈ 0. Since p-value ≤ 0.01, we reject H_0. There is evidence that *gender* and *political party preference* are not independent.

32. H_0 : *Continent of origin* and *state of settlement* are independent. H_a : *Continent of origin* and *state of settlement* are not independent. Since none of the expected frequencies is less than 1 and none of the expected frequencies is less than 5, the conditions for performing the χ^2 test for independence are met. $\chi^2_{crit} = \chi^2_{0.05} = 13.277$. Reject H_0 if $\chi^2_{data} \geq 13.277$. $\chi^2_{data} = 54.874$. Since $\chi^2_{data} \geq 13.277$, we reject H_0. There is evidence that *continent of origin* and *state of settlement* are not independent.

33. H_0 : $p_{edit} = p_{arrange}$. H_a : Not all the proportions in H_0 are equal. Reject H_0 if p-value ≤ 0.05. Since none of the expected frequencies is less than 1 and none of the expected frequencies is less than 5, the conditions for performing the χ^2 test for homogeneity of proportions are met. $\chi^2_{data} = 3.5165$. p-value = 0.0608. Since p-value is not ≤ 0.05, we do not reject H_0. There is insufficient evidence that the proportions who favor email differ between the two tasks.

34. No. For the work email group the dark green bar is longer, and for the personal email group the light green bar is longer. This means that no spam is more common for the work email group and that some spam is more common for the personal email group.

35. H_0 : $p_{work} = p_{personal}$. H_a : Not all the proportions in H_0 are equal. Reject H_0 if p-value ≤ 0.01. Since none of the expected frequencies is less than 1 and none of the expected frequencies is less than 5, the conditions for performing the χ^2 test for homogeneity of proportions are met. $\chi^2_{data} = 23.3325$. p-value ≈ 0. Since p-value ≤ 0.01, we reject H_0. There is evidence that the population proportions who report "a lot of spam" are not the same for work email and personal email. Yes.

36. **(a)** The type of game with the highest frequency for males is video games and the type of game with the highest frequency for females is computer games. We see some evidence that the most frequently played type of of game depends in part on gender and that the two variables may not be independent. We thus might expect to reject H_0. **(b)** Since the p-value ≤ 0.01, we reject H_0. There is evidence that *gender* and *type of game* are not independent.

37. H_0 : $p_{urban} = p_{suburban} = p_{rural}$. H_a : Not all the proportions in H_0 are equal. Reject H_0 if p-value ≤ 0.05. Since none of the expected frequencies is less than 1 and none of the expected frequencies is less than 5, the conditions for performing the χ^2 test for homogeneity of proportions are met. $\chi^2_{data} = 9.095$. p-value = 0.0106. Since p-value ≤ 0.05, we reject H_0. There is evidence that the population proportions of residents from the three categories who use online dating are not all the same.

38. 478 observations, 11 variables.

39. **(a)** Dependent **(b)** Since the p-value ≈ 0, p-value ≤ 0.05. Thus we reject H_0. There is evidence that *gender* and *goals* are not independent.

40. **(a)** Independent **(b)** Since the p-value = 0.841, the p-value is not ≤ 0.05. Thus we do not reject H_0. There is insufficient evidence that *gender* and *grade* are not independent.

41. **(a)** Dependent **(b)** Since the p-value ≈ 0.001, p-value ≤ 0.10. Thus we reject H_0. There is evidence that *urb_rural* and *goals* are not independent.

42. **(a)** Yes; yes **(b)** H_0 : *Grade* and *goals* are independent. H_0 : *Grade* and *goals* are not independent. Reject H_0 if p-value ≤ 0.01. Since the p-value = 0.859, the p-value is not ≤ 0.01. Thus we do not reject H_0. There is insufficient evidence that *grade* and *goals* are not independent.

43. H_0 : $p_{Jan} = p_{Feb} = p_{Mar} = p_{Apr} = p_{May} = p_{June} = p_{July} = p_{Aug} = p_{Sept} = p_{Oct} = p_{Nov} = p_{Dec}$. H_a : Not all the proportions in H_0 are

equal. Reject H_0 if p-value ≤ 0.01. $\chi^2_{data} = 30.2571$. p-value ≤ 0.005. Since p-value ≤ 0.01, we reject H_0. There is evidence that the population proportion of "drafted dates" is not equal for all months.

44. H_0 : $p_{Jan} = p_{Feb} = p_{Mar} = p_{Apr} = p_{May} = p_{June} = p_{July} = p_{Aug} = p_{Sept} = p_{Oct} = p_{Nov} = p_{Dec}$. H_a : Not all the proportions in H_0 are equal. Since none of the expected frequencies is less than 1 and none of the expected frequencies is less than 5, the conditions for performing the χ^2 test for homogeneity of proportions are met. $\chi^2_{crit} = \chi^2_{0.10} = 17.275$. Reject H_0 if $\chi^2_{data} \geq 17.275$. $\chi^2_{data} = 6.617$. Since χ^2_{data} is not ≥ 17.275, we do not reject H_0. There is insufficient evidence that not all the proportions in H_0 are equal.

Chapter 11 Review

1. H_0 : $p_{USCan} = 0.32$, $p_{USMex} = 0.22$, $p_{CanUS} = 0.31$, $p_{MexUS} = 0.15$. H_a : The random variable does not follow the distribution specified in H_0. $E_{USCan} = \$22.4$ billion, $E_{USMex} = \$15.4$ billion, $E_{CanUS} = \$21.7$ billion, $p_{MexUS} = \$10.5$ billion. Since none of the expected frequencies is less than 1 and none of the expected frequencies is less than 5, the conditions for performing the χ^2 goodness of fit test are met. Reject H_0 if p-value ≤ 0.05. $\chi^2_{data} = 0.469$. p-value = 0.9256. Since p-value is not ≤ 0.05, we do not reject H_0. There is insufficient evidence that the population proportions of truck-hauled trade have changed since 2002.

2. H_0 : $p_{Black} = 0.42$, $p_{White} = 0.46$, $p_{Hispanic} = 0.10$, $p_{Other} = 0.02$. H_a : The random variable does not follow the distribution specified in H_0. $E_{Black} = 1501.5$, $E_{White} = 1644.5$, $E_{Hispanic} = 357.5$, $E_{Other} = 71.5$. Since none of the expected frequencies is less than 1 and none of the expected frequencies is less than 5, the conditions for performing the χ^2 goodness of fit test are met. $\chi^2_{crit} = \chi^2_{0.10} = 6.251$. Reject H_0 if $\chi^2_{data} \geq 6.251$. $\chi^2_{data} = 13.422$. Since $\chi^2_{data} \geq 6.251$, we reject H_0. There is evidence that the population proportions have changed since 2004.

3. H_0 : $p_{rock} = 0.40$, $p_{rap/hip-hop} = 0.25$, $p_{country} = 0.15$, $p_{blues} = 0.08$, $p_{jazz} = 0.07$, $p_{classical} = 0.05$. H_a : The random variable does not follow the distribution specified in H_0. $E_{rock} = 80$, $E_{rap/hip-hop} = 50$, $E_{country} = 30$, $E_{blues} = 16$, $E_{jazz} = 14$, $E_{classical} = 10$. Since none of the expected frequencies is less than 1 and none of the expected frequencies is less than 5, the conditions for performing the χ^2 goodness of fit test are met. $\chi^2_{crit} = \chi^2_{0.05} = 11.071$. Reject H_0 if $\chi^2_{data} \geq 11.071$. $\chi^2_{data} = 12.4762$. Since $\chi^2_{data} \geq 11.071$, we reject H_0. There is evidence that the music preferences of college students have changed since 1995.

4. H_0 : $p_{abusedalcohol} = 0.25$, $p_{alcoholdependent} = 0.06$, $p_{other} = 0.69$. H_a : The random variable does not follow the distribution specified in H_0. $E_{abusedalcohol} = 250$, $E_{alcoholdependent} = 60$, $E_{other} = 690$. Since none of the expected frequencies is less than 1 and none of the expected frequencies is less than 5, the conditions for performing the χ^2 goodness of fit test are met. Reject H_0 if p-value ≤ 0.10. $\chi^2_{data} = 4.493$. p-value = 0.1057687682. Since p-value is not ≤ 0.10, we do not reject H_0. There is insufficient evidence that the population proportions have changed since 2002.

5. H_0 : $p_0 = 0.10$, $p_1 = 0.10$, $p_2 = 0.10$, $p_3 = 0.10$, $p_4 = 0.10$, $p_5 = 0.10$, $p_6 = 0.10$, $p_7 = 0.10$, $p_8 = 0.10$, $p_9 = 0.10$. H_a : Not all the proportions in H_0 are equal. Reject H_0 if p-value ≤ 0.05. $E_0 = 21.8$, $E_1 = 21.8$, $E_2 = 21.8$, $E_3 = 21.8$, $E_4 = 21.8$, $E_5 = 21.8$, $E_6 = 21.8$, $E_7 = 21.8$, $E_8 = 21.8$, $E_9 = 21.8$. Since none of the expected frequencies is less than 1 and none of the expected frequencies is less than 5, the conditions for performing the χ^2 goodness of fit test are met. Reject H_0 if p-value ≤ 0.05. $\chi^2_{data} = 12.4587$. p-value = 0.18866727. Since p-value is not ≤ 0.05, we do not reject H_0. There is insufficient evidence that the population proportions of digits are not all 0.10.

6. $H_0 : p_{18-34} = 0.057, p_{35-49} = 0.207, p_{50-64} = 0.388, p_{over65} = 0.348$. H_a : The random variable does not follow the distribution specified in H_0. $E_{18-34} = 57, E_{35-49} = 207, E_{50-64} = 388, E_{over65} = 348$. Since none of the expected frequencies is less than 1 and none of the expected frequencies is less than 5, the conditions for performing the χ^2 goodness of fit test are met. $\chi^2_{crit} = \chi^2_{0.05} = 7.815$. Reject H_0 if $\chi^2_{data} \geq 7.815$. $\chi^2_{data} = 28.233$. Since $\chi^2_{data} \geq 7.815$, we reject H_0. There is evidence that the proportions have changed since 2006.

7. (a) A higher proportion of the females with high GPAs take the SAT exam than the proportion of the females with lower GPAs. **(b)** $H_0 : p_{A+} = p_A = p_{A-} = p_B = p_C = p_{D/F}$. H_a : Not all the proportions in H_0 are equal. Reject H_0 if p-value ≤ 0.05. Since none of the expected frequencies is less than 1 and none of the expected frequencies is less than 5, the conditions for performing the χ^2 test for homogeneity of proportions are met. $\chi^2_{data} = 15.0850$. p-value $= 0.0100052538$. Since p-value ≤ 0.05, we reject H_0. There is evidence that the proportion of females is not all across the six grade categories.

8. H_0 : *Gender* and *race* are independent. H_a : *Gender* and *race* are not independent. Since none of the expected frequencies is less than 1 and none of the expected frequencies is less than 5, the conditions for performing the χ^2 test for independence are met. $\chi^2_{crit} = \chi^2_{0.05} = 4.605$. Reject H_0 if $\chi^2_{data} \geq 4.605$. $\chi^2_{data} = 16.918$. Since $\chi^2_{data} \geq 4.605$, we reject H_0. There is evidence that *gender* and *race* are not independent.

9. $H_0 : p_{Northeast} = p_{Midwest} = p_{South} = p_{West}$. H_a : Not all the proportions in H_0 are equal. Reject H_0 if p-value ≤ 0.01. Since none of the expected frequencies is less than 1 and none of the expected frequencies is less than 5, the conditions for performing the χ^2 test for homogeneity of proportions are met. $\chi^2_{data} = 25.846$. p-value ≈ 0. Since p-value ≤ 0.01, we reject H_0. There is evidence that the population proportions of pregnant women who have had an HIV test in the past 12 months are not the same across all four regions.

10. H_0 : *Poll response* and *gender* are independent. H_a : *Poll response* and *gender* are not independent. Reject H_0 if p-value ≤ 0.01. Since none of the expected frequencies is less than 1 and none of the expected frequencies is less than 5, the conditions for performing the χ^2 test for independence are met. $\chi^2_{data} = 11.472$. p-value $= 0.0094291366$. Since p-value ≤ 0.01, we reject H_0. There is evidence that *poll response* and *gender* are not independent.

11. H_0 : Age and radio station type are independent. H_a : Age and radio station type are not independent. Reject H_0 if p-value ≤ 0.05. Since none of the expected frequencies is less than 1 and none of the expected frequencies is less than 5, the conditions for performing the χ^2 test for independence are met. $\chi^2_{data} = 8.269$. p-value $= 0.0040$. Since p-value ≤ 0.05, we reject H_0. There is evidence that age and radio station type are not independent.

12. H_0 : *Happiness in marriage* and *gender* are independent. H_a : *Happiness in marriage* and *gender* are not independent. Since none of the expected frequencies is less than 1 and none of the expected frequencies is less than 5, the conditions for performing the χ^2 test for independence are met. $\chi^2_{crit} = \chi^2_{0.05} = 5.991$. Reject H_0 if $\chi^2_{data} \geq 5.991$. $\chi^2_{data} = 3.190$. Since χ^2_{data} is not ≥ 5.991, we do not reject H_0. There is insufficient evidence that *happiness in marriage* and *gender* are not independent.

13. $H_0 : p_{Whites} = p_{Blacks} = p_{Hispanics}$. H_a : Not all the proportions in H_0 are equal. Reject H_0 if p-value ≤ 0.05. Since none of the

expected frequencies is less than 1 and none of the expected frequencies is less than 5, the conditions for performing the χ^2 test for homogeneity of proportions are met. $\chi^2_{data} = 42.658$. p-value ≈ 0. Since p-value ≤ 0.05, we reject H_0. There is evidence that Internet use levels is not the same for all races.

Chapter 11 Quiz

1. True
2. False
3. False
4. 1, 5
5. equal
6. expected frequency
7. (a) Critical value method, **(b)** exact p-value method, or **(c)** estimated p-value method
8. H_a, the alternative hypothesis
9. Degrees of freedom $= (r - 1)(c - 1)$, where $r =$ the number of categories in the row variable and $c =$ the number of categories in the column variable.
10. $E_1 = 10, E_2 = 10, E_3 = 10, E_4 = 10, E_5 = 10$. Conditions are met. $\chi^2_{crit} = 9.488$. Reject H_0 if $\chi^2_{data} \geq 9.488$. $\chi^2_{data} = 1$. Since χ^2_{data} is not ≥ 9.488, we do not reject H_0. There is insufficient evidence that the random variable does not follow the distribution specified in H_0.
11. $E_1 = 48, E_2 = 40, E_3 = 32, E_4 = 24, E_5 = 9.6, E_6 = 6.4$. Conditions are met. $\chi^2_{crit} = 11.071$. Reject H_0 if $\chi^2_{data} \geq 11.071$. $\chi^2_{data} = 2.917$. Since χ^2_{data} is not ≥ 11.071, we do not reject H_0. There is sufficient evidence that the random variable does not follow the distribution specified in H_0.
12. $E_1 = 20, E_2 = 20, E_3 = 20, E_4 = 20, E_5 = 20$. Conditions are met. $\chi^2_{crit} = 13.277$. Reject H_a if $\chi^2_{data} \geq 13.277$. $\chi^2_{data} = 0.5$. Since χ^2_{data} is not ≥ 13.277, we do not reject H_0. There is insufficient evidence that the random variable does not follow the distribution specified in H_0.
13. $E_1 = 60, E_2 = 50, E_3 = 40, E_4 = 30, E_5 = 12, E_6 = 8$. Conditions are met. $\chi^2_{crit} = 11.071$. Reject H_a if $\chi^2_{data} \geq 11.071$. $\chi^2_{data} = 5.5$. Since χ^2_{data} is not ≥ 11.071, we do not reject H_0. There is insufficient evidence that the random variable does not follow the distribution specified in H_0.
14. (a) The higher the grade level, the higher the proportion of students who have used an illicit drug. **(b)** $H_0 : p_{8th-graders} = p_{10th-graders} = p_{12th-graders}$. H_a : Not all the proportions in H_0 are equal. Reject H_0 if p-value ≤ 0.01. Since none of the expected frequencies is less than 1 and none of the expected frequencies is less than 5, the conditions for performing the χ^2 test for homogeneity of proportions are met. $\chi^2_{data} = 3060.14226$. p-value ≈ 0. Since p-value ≤ 0.01, we reject H_0. There is evidence that the proportions of children in those grades that have ever used an illicit drug are not all the same.
15. H_0 : *Gender* and *sport preference* are independent. H_a : *Gender* and *sport preference* are not independent. Reject H_0 if p-value ≤ 0.05. Since none of the expected frequencies is less than 1 and none of the expected frequencies is less than 5, the conditions for performing the χ^2 test for independence are met. $\chi^2_{data} = 19.857$. p-value $= 0.00004876$. Since p-value ≤ 0.05, we reject H_0. There is evidence that *gender* and *sport preference* are not independent.
16. $H_0 : p_{Texas} = p_{Oklahoma} = p_{Pennsylvania}$. H_a : Not all the proportions in H_0 are equal. Reject H_0 if p-value ≤ 0.05. Since none of the expected frequencies is less than 1 and none of the expected frequencies is less than 5, the conditions for performing the χ^2 test for homogeneity of proportions are met.

$\chi^2_{data} = 81,246.70827$. p-value ≈ 0. Since p-value ≤ 0.01, we reject H_0. There is evidence that the population proportions of cattle on smaller farms are not the same across all three states.

Chapter 12

Section 12.1

1. No. If the sample sizes are not all the same, then we need to calculate the overall sample mean by calculating the weighted mean of the sample means where the weights are the sample sizes.

2. MSTR measures the variability in the sample means. MSE measures the variability within the samples.

3. Answers will vary.

4. Each of the k populations is normally distributed, the variances of the populations are all equal, and the samples are independently drawn.

5. Against.

6. False. It means that at least one of the population means is different from the rest.

7. (a) $df_1 = 2$, $df_2 = 12$ (b) 10 (c) 40 (d) 12 (e) 52

8. (a) $df_1 = 3$, $df_2 = 16$ (b) 11 (c) 100 (d) 16 (e) 116

9. (a) $df_1 = 3$, $df_2 = 696$ (b) 96.42857143 (c) 491,071.4286 (d) 18,248 (e) 509,319.4286

10. (a) $df_1 = 3$, $df_2 = 296$ (b) $\bar{\bar{x}} = 10$ (c) SSTR = 10,000 (d) SSE = 1157.50 (e) SST = 11,157.50

11. (a) 20 (b) 1 (c) 20

(d)

Source of variation	Sum of squares	Degrees of freedom	Mean square	F
Treatments	40	2	20	20
Error	12	12	1	
Total	52			

12. (a) 33.3333 (b) 1 (c) 33.3333

(d)

Source of variation	Sum of squares	Degrees of freedom	Mean square	F
Treatments	100	3	33.3333	33.3333
Error	16	16	1	
Total	116			

13. (a) 163,690.4762 (b) 26.2183908 (c) 6243.343

(d)

Source of variation	Sum of squares	Degrees of freedom	Mean square	F
Treatments	491,071.4286	3	163,690.4762	6243.3435
Error	18,248	696	26.2184	
Total	509,319.4286			

14. (a) MSTR = 3,333.3333 (b) MSE = 3.9105 (c) F = 852.4118

(d)

Source of variation	Sum of squares	Degrees of freedom	Mean square	F
Treatments	10,000	3	3,333.3333	852.4118
Error	1,157.50	296	3.9105	
Total	11,157.50			

15. (a) $H_0 : \mu_1 = \mu_2 = \mu_3$. H_a : Not all the population means are equal. Reject H_0 if the p-value ≤ 0.05. (b) 20 (c) p-value =

0.00015. (d) Since the p-value ≤ 0.05, we reject H_0. There is evidence that not all the population means are equal.

16. (a) $H_0 : \mu_A = \mu_B = \mu_C = \mu_D$. H_a : Not all the population means are equal. Reject H_0 if the p-value ≤ 0.05. (b) 33.333333 (c) p-value ≈ 0 (d) Since the p-value ≤ 0.05, we reject H_0. There is evidence that not all the population means are equal.

17. (a) $H_0 : \mu_A = \mu_B = \mu_C = \mu_D$. H_a : Not all the population means are equal. Reject H_0 if the p-value ≤ 0.05. (b) $F_{data} = 6243.3435$ (c) p-value = 0 (d) Since the p-value ≤ 0.05, we reject H_0. There is evidence that not all of the population means are equal.

18. $H_0 : \mu_A = \mu_B = \mu_C = \mu_D$. H_a : Not all the population means are equal. Reject H_0 if the p-value ≤ 0.05. (b) $F_{data} = 842.4118$ (c) p-value = 0 (d) Since p-value ≤ 0.05, we reject H_0. There is evidence that not all of the population means are equal.

19. (a) Missing values are in red.

Source of variation	Sum of squares	Degrees of freedom	Mean square	F-test statistic
Treatment	SSTR = 120	$df_1 = 6$	MSTR = 20	$F_{data} = 44$
Error	SSE = 315	$df_2 = 693$	MSE = 0.4545454545	
Total	SST = 435			

(b) $H_0 : \mu_1 = \mu_2 = \mu_3 = \mu_4 = \mu_5 = \mu_6 = \mu_7$. H_a : Not all the population means are equal. Reject H_0 if the p-value ≤ 0.05. $F_{data} = 44$; p-value ≈ 0. Since the p-value ≤ 0.05, we reject H_0. There is evidence that not all the population means are equal.

20. (a) Missing values are in red.

Source of variation	Sum of squares	Degrees of freedom	Mean square	F-test statistic
Treatment	SSTR = 60	$df_1 = 2$	MSTR = 30	$F_{data} = 5$
Error	SSE = 90	$df_2 = 15$	MSE = 6	
Total	SST = 150			

(b) $H_0 : \mu_1 = \mu_2 = \mu_3$; H_a: Not all the population means are equal. $F_{crit} = 6.36$. Reject H_0 if $F_{data} \geq 6.36$. $F_{data} = 5$. Since F_{data} is not ≥ 6.36, we do not reject H_0. There is insufficient evidence that not all the population means are equal.

21. (a) Missing values are in red.

Source of variation	Sum of squares	Degrees of freedom	Mean square	F-test statistic
Treatment	SSTR = 40	$df_1 = 4$	MSTR = 10	$F_{data} = 1.0$
Error	SSE = 400	$df_2 = 40$	MSE = 10	
Total	SST = 440			

(b) $H_0 : \mu_1 = \mu_2 = \mu_3 = \mu_4 = \mu_5$. H_a : Not all the population means are equal. $F_{crit} = 2.06$. Reject H_0 if $F_{data} \geq 2.06$. $F_{data} = 1.0$. Since F_{data} is not ≥ 2.06, we do not reject H_0. There is insufficient evidence that not all the population means are equal.

22. (a) Missing values are in red.

Source of variation	Sum of squares	Degrees of freedom	Mean square	F-test statistic
Treatment	SSTR = 96	$df_1 = 2$	MSTR = 48	$F_{data} = 2.0$
Error	SSE = 480	$df_2 = 20$	MSE = 24	
Total	SST = 576			

(b) $H_0 : \mu_1 = \mu_2 = \mu_3$. H_a : Not all the population means are equal. Reject H_0 if the p-value ≤ 0.05. $F_{data} = 2.0$; p-value $= 0.1615$. Since the p-value is not ≤ 0.05, we do not reject H_0. There is insufficient evidence that not all the population means are equal.
23. (a) The largest sample standard deviation $S_{online} = 15.0555$ is not more than twice the smallest sample standard deviation $2 \cdot S_{hybrid} = 2(12.6491) = 25.2982$. **(b)** (i) df$_1 = 2$, df$_2 = 15$; (ii) $\bar{\bar{x}} = 75.27777778$; (iii) SSTR $= 219.4444444$; (iv) SSE $= 2804.16667$; (v) SST $= 3023.611111$; (vi) MSTR $= 109.7222222$; (vii) MSE $= 186.9444444$; (viii) $F_{data} = 0.5869$
(c)

Source of variation	Sum of squares	Degrees of freedom	Mean square	F
Treatment	219.4444444	2	109.7222222	0.5869
Error	2804.16667	15	186.9444444	
Total	3023.611111			

(d) $H_0 : \mu_{online} = \mu_{traditional} = \mu_{hybrid}$ vs. H_a : Not all the population means are equal. Reject H_0 if $F_{data} \geq 6.36$. $F_{data} = 0.5869$. Since $F_{data} = 0.5869$ is not ≥ 6.36, we do not reject H_0. There is insufficient evidence that not all the population mean grades of the three classes are equal.
24. (a) The largest sample standard deviation $s_{StoreA} = 5$ is not more than twice the smallest sample standard deviation $2 \cdot s_{StoreC} = 2(2.7749) = 5.5498$. **(b)** (i) df$_1 = 3$, df$_2 = 16$ (ii) $\bar{\bar{x}} = 17.7$ (iii) SSTR $= 1527.4$ (iv) SSE $= 230.798362$ (v) SST $= 1758.198362$ (vi) MSTR $= 509.1333333$ (vii) MSE $= 14.42489763$ (viii) $F_{data} = 35.29545558$
(c)

Source of variation	Sum of squares	Degrees of freedom	Mean square	F
Treatment	1527.4	3	509.1333333	35.29546668
Error	230.798362	16	14.42489763	
Total	1758.198362			

(d) $H_0 : \mu_{StoreA} = \mu_{StoreB} = \mu_{StoreC} = \mu_{StoreD}$ versus H_a : Not all the population means are equal. Reject H_0 if $F_{data} \geq 3.29$. $F_{data} = 35.29546668$. Since $F_{data} = 35.29546668$ is ≥ 3.29, we reject H_0. There is evidence that not all the population mean sales at the four stores are equal.
25. (a) The largest sample standard deviation $s_{none} = 3.22$ is not more than twice the smallest sample standard deviation $2 \cdot s_{Catholic} = 2(2.74) = 5.48$. **(b)** (i) df$_1 = 4$, df$_2 = 2886$ (ii) $\bar{\bar{x}} = 13.36583535$ (iii) SSTR $= 581.5002576$ (iv) SSE $= 24,230.7355$ (v) SST $= 24,812.23576$ (vi) MSTR $= 145.3750644$ (vii) MSE $= 8.395958247$ (viii) $F_{data} = 17.31488654$
(c)

Source of variation	Sum of squares	Degrees of freedom	Mean square	F
Treatment	581.5002576	4	145.3750644	17.31488654
Error	24,230.7355	2886	8.395958247	
Total	24,812.23576			

(d) $H_0 : \mu_{Protestant} = \mu_{Catholic} = \mu_{Jewish} = \mu_{none} = \mu_{other}$ versus H_a : Not all the population means are equal. Reject H_0 if $F_{data} \geq 2.38$. $F_{data} = 17.31488654$. Since $F_{data} = 17.31488654$ is ≥ 2.38, we reject H_0. There is evidence that not all the population mean number of years are equal.
26. Using the TI-83/84: Before: $\bar{x} = 10.91666667$, $s^2 = 13.10333333$, $s = 3.619852667$. During: $\bar{x} = 13.41666667$, $s^2 = 30.26515152$, $s = 5.501377238$. After: $\bar{x} = 11.45833333$,

$s^2 = 9.668106061$, $s = 3.109357821$. **(a)** The largest sample standard deviation $s_{during} = 5.501377238$ is not more than twice the smallest sample standard deviation $2 \cdot s_{after} = 2(3.109357821) = 6.218715642$. **(b)** (i) df$_1 = 2$, df$_2 = 33$ (ii) $\bar{\bar{x}} = 11.93055556$ (iii) SSTR $= 41.51388896$ (iv) SSE $= 583.4025$ (v) SST $= 21,121.61084$ (vi) MSTR $= 20.75694448$ (vii) MSE $= 17.67886364$ (viii) $F_{data} = 1.74110786$
(c)

Source of variation	Sum of squares	Degrees of freedom	Mean square	F
Treatment	20,538.20834	2	20.75694448	1.74110786
Error	583.4025	33	17.67886364	
Total	21,121.61084			

(d) $H_0 : \mu_{before} = \mu_{during} = \mu_{after}$ versus H_a : Not all the population means are equal. Reject H_0 if $F_{data} \geq 3.39$. $F_{data} = 1.74110786$. Since $F_{data} = 1.74110786$ is ≥ 3.39, we reject H_0. There is evidence that not all the population mean numbers of emergency room visits are equal.
27. (a) $H_0 : \mu_{Females} = \mu_{Males}$. H_a : The two population means are not equal. $\mu_{Females} = $ the population mean heart rate for females; $\mu_{Males} = $ the population mean heart rate for males. Reject H_0 if the p-value ≤ 0.05. 4.896939413, p-value $= 0.0287$. Since the p-value is ≤ 0.05, we reject H_0. There is evidence that the population mean heart rates are not equal. **(b)** Inference for Two Independent Means, Section 10.2.
28. No evidence
29. Since the p-value is ≤ 0.01, we reject H$_0$. There is evidence that not all the population mean heights are equal.
30. (a) Since one of the boxplots overlaps only 2 of the 5 other boxplots, the comparison boxplot of the nutritional ratings may be considered as evidence against the null hypothesis that all population mean nutritional ratings were equal. **(b)** Rejected
31. Since $S_{QuakerOats} = 10.603 \leq 11.018 = 2 S_{Nabisco}$, the equal variance requirement is satisfied.
32. Yes, since the cereals were selected randomly from the manufacturers so that the selection of a cereal from one manufacturer did not affect the selection of cereals from other manufacturers.
33. $H_0 : \mu_{GeneralMills} = \mu_{Kelloggs} = \mu_{Nabisco} = \mu_{Post} = \mu_{QuakerOats} = \mu_{RalstonPurina}$. H_a : Not all the population means are equal. Reject H_0 if the p-value ≤ 0.05. $F_{data} = 15.71$; p-value ≈ 0. Since the p-value is ≤ 0.05 we reject H_0. There is evidence that the population mean nutritional ratings of the cereals made by the different manufacturers are not all equal.
34. (a) (i) n_t would stay the same. (ii) k would stay the same. (iii) SSTR would decrease. (iv) SSE would decrease. (v) SST would decrease. (vi) MSTR would decrease. (vii) MSE would decrease. (viii) F_{data} would decrease. **(b)** The conclusion remains the same.
35. (a) (i) n_t would stay the same. (ii) k would stay the same. (iii) SSTR would increase. (iv) SSE stays the same. (v) SST will increase. (vi) MSTR will increase. (vii) MSE will stay the same. (vii) F_{data} will increase. **(b)** Since the original F_{data} was less than 6.36, our conclusion was "Do not reject H_0." From (vii) we know that F_{data} is increased. The new value for F_{data} is 2.346449094. This is still less than 6.36, so our conclusion would still be "Do not reject H_0."
36. (a) SSTR $= 0$; MSTR $= 0$; $F_{data} = 0$. **(b)** p-value $= 1$. **(c)** Since the p-value ≥ 0.05, we would not reject H_0.
37. (a) Since the boxplot for the gas mileage of automobiles manufactured in the United States does not overlap the other boxplots, the conclusion might be to reject H_0. **(b)** $H_0 : \mu_{Europe} = \mu_{Japan} = \mu_{USA}$. H_a : Not all of the population means are equal. Reject H_0 if the p-value ≤ 0.01. $F_{data} = 96.6250761$. p-value $= 8.53843292 \times 10^{-35}$.

Since the p-value is ≤ 0.01, we reject H_0. There is evidence that not all the population mean gas mileages are equal. **(c)** Yes
38. (a) (i) (25.4805, 29.7255) (ii) (28.6366, 32.2654)
(iii) (18.9526, 21.1134) **(b)** The confidence interval for the population mean gas mileage of American cars does not overlap the other two confidence intervals. This is evidence against the null hypothesis that all the population means are equal.
39. (a)–(b) No change **(c)** Increase **(d)** No change **(e)–(f)** Increase **(g)** No change **(h)** Increase **(i)** Decrease **(j)** No change
40. (a) $H_0 : \mu_1 = \mu_2 = \mu_3 = \mu_4 = \mu_5 = \mu_6 = \mu_7 = \mu_8$. H_a : Not all the population means are equal. **(b)** Reject H_0 if the p-value ≤ 0.05. **(c)** 8.27 **(d)** p-value ≈ 0 **(e)** Since the p-value is ≤ 0.05, we reject H_0. **(f)** There is evidence that not all the population means are equal.

(g)

```
Source     DF        SS        MS      F      P
SIZE2       7  10879518   1554217   8.27  0.000
Error     330  62003922    187891
Total     337  72883441
```

41. (a) $H_0 : \mu_{87} = \mu_{88} = \mu_{89} = \mu_{90} = \mu_{91}$. H_a : Not all the population means are equal. **(b)** Reject H_0 if the p-value ≤ 0.05. **(c)** $F_{\text{data}} = 1.34$ **(d)** p-value $= 0.255$ **(e)** Since the p-value is ≤ 0.05, we do not reject H_0. **(f)** There is insufficient evidence that not all the population means are equal.

(g)

Source	df	SS	MS	F	P
Year	4	1155151	288788	1.34	0.255
Error	333	71728290	215400		
Total	337	72883441			

42. (a) $H_0 : \mu_1 = \mu_2 = \mu_3 = \mu_4$. H_a : Not all the population means are equal. **(b)** Reject H_0 if the p-value ≤ 0.01. **(c)** 3.12 **(d)** p-value $= 0.026$ **(e)** Since the p-value is not ≤ 0.01, we do not reject H_0. **(f)** There is insufficient evidence that not all the population means are equal.

(g)

```
Source       DF        SS      MS      F      P
PROTECT2      3     844.4   281.5   3.12  0.026
Error       334   30168.7    90.3
Total       337   31013.1
```

43. (a) $H_0 : \mu_1 = \mu_2 = \mu_3 = \mu_4$. H_a : Not all the population means are equal. **(b)** Reject H_0 if the p-value ≤ 0.05. **(c)** $F_{\text{data}} = 3.12$ **(d)** p-value $= 0.026$ **(e)** Since the p-value is ≤ 0.05, we reject H_0. **(f)** There is evidence that not all the population means are equal.

(g)

Source	df	SS	MS	F	P
Protect2	3	844.4	281.5	3.12	0.026
Error	334	30168.7	90.3		
Total	337	31013.1			

44. (a, b) Decreases
45. (a) Decreases **(b)** Decreases. Since the within-sample variability is increased, SSE and MSE are increased. Since the sample means remain the same, SSTR and MSTR remain unchanged. Thus $F_{\text{data}} = \dfrac{\text{MSTR}}{\text{MSE}}$ decreases.

Section 12.2

1. ANOVA only tests for whether or not all of the population means are equal. It does not test for which pairs of means are not equal.
2. If the ANOVA does not indicate any differences in the means, then there is no point in performing multiple comparisons to test which pairs of means are different.
3. It is performing a hypothesis test to determine whether two mean are different. $C = {}_kC_2 = k!/[2! (k - 2)!]$, where k is the number of populations.

4. The probability of making at least one Type I error in the set of hypothesis tests when performing multiple comparisons
5. By multiplying the p-value of each pairwise hypothesis test by the number of comparisons being made
6. Set it equal to 1. The p-value is a probability and probabilities cannot be greater than 1.
7. The requirements for ANOVA have been met and the null hypothesis that the population means are all equal has been rejected.
8. If a $100(1 - \alpha)\%$ confidence interval for $\mu_1 - \mu_2$ contains zero, then at level of significance α we do not reject the null hypothesis $H_0 : \mu_1 = \mu_2$. If the interval does not contain zero, then we do reject H_0.
9. $t_{\text{data}} = 4.472$
10. $t_{\text{data}} = 8.944$
11. $t_{\text{data}} = 4.472$
12. $t_{\text{data}} = -1$
13. $t_{\text{data}} = 3$
14. $t_{\text{data}} = 4$
15. (a) Test 1: $H_0 : \mu_1 = \mu_2$ vs. $H_a : \mu_1 \neq \mu_2$; Test 2: $H_0 : \mu_1 = \mu_3$ vs. $H_a : \mu_1 \neq \mu_3$; Test 3: $H_0 : \mu_2 = \mu_3$ vs. $H_a : \mu_2 \neq \mu_3$. For each hypothesis test, reject H_0 if the Bonferroni-adjusted p-value $\leq \alpha = 0.05$. **(b)** Test 1: $t_{\text{data}} = 4.472$; Test 2: $t_{\text{data}} = 8.944$; Test 3: $t_{\text{data}} = 4.472$ **(c)** Test 1: Bonferroni-adjusted p-value $= 0.0004$; Test 2: Bonferroni-adjusted p-value $= 0$; Test 3: Bonferroni-adjusted p-value $= 0.0004$ **(d)** Test 1: The adjusted p-value $= 0.0004$, which is ≤ 0.05; therefore we reject H_0. There is evidence at the $\alpha = 0.05$ level of significance that the population mean of Population 1 differs from the population mean of Population 2. Test 2: The adjusted p-value $= 0$, which is ≤ 0.05; therefore we reject H_0. There is evidence at the $\alpha = 0.05$ level of significance that the population mean of Population 1 differs from the population mean of Population 3. Test 3: The adjusted p-value $= 0.004$, which is ≤ 0.05; therefore we reject H_0. There is evidence at the $\alpha = 0.05$ level of significance that the population mean of Population 2 differs from the population mean of Population 3.
16. (a) Test 1: $H_0 : \mu_1 = \mu_2$ vs. $H_a : \mu_1 \neq \mu_2$; Test 2: $H_0 : \mu_1 = \mu_3$ vs. $H_a : \mu_1 \neq \mu_3$; Test 3: $H_0 : \mu_2 = \mu_3$ vs. $H_a : \mu_2 \neq \mu_3$. For each hypothesis test, reject H_0 if the Bonferroni-adjusted p-value $\leq \alpha = 0.05$ **(b)** Test 1: $t_{\text{data}} = -1$; Test 2: $t_{\text{data}} = 3$; Test 3: $t_{\text{data}} = 4$ **(c)** Test 1: Bonferroni-adjusted p-value $= 0.9861$; Test 2: Bonferroni-adjusted p-value $= 0.0205$; Test 3: Bonferroni-adjusted p-value $= 0.0019$ **(d)** Test 1: The adjusted p-value $= 0.9861$, which is not ≤ 0.05; therefore we do not reject H_0. There is insufficient evidence at the $\alpha = 0.05$ level of significance that the population mean of Population 1 differs from the population mean of Population 2. Test 2: The adjusted p-value $= 0.0205$, which is ≤ 0.05; therefore we reject H_0. There is evidence at the $\alpha = 0.05$ level of significance that the population mean of Population 1 differs from the population mean of Population 3. Test 3: The adjusted p-value $= 0.0019$, which is ≤ 0.05; therefore we reject H_0. There is evidence at the $\alpha = 0.05$ level of significance that the population mean of Population 2 differs from the population mean of Population 3.
17. $q_{\text{data}} = 0.707$
18. $q_{\text{data}} = 3.536$
19. $q_{\text{data}} = 2.828$
20. $q_{\text{data}} = 4.714$
21. $q_{\text{data}} = 2.357$
22. $q_{\text{data}} = 2.357$
23. $q_{\text{crit}} = 3.356$
24. $q_{\text{crit}} = 3.399$
25. (a) Test 1: $H_0 : \mu_1 = \mu_2$ vs. $H_a : \mu_1 \neq \mu_2$; Test 2: $H_0 : \mu_1 = \mu_2$ vs. $H_a : \mu_1 \neq \mu_3$; Test 3: $H_0 : \mu_2 = \mu_3$ vs. $H_a : \mu_2 \neq \mu_3$ **(b)** $q_{\text{crit}} = 3.356$. Reject H_0 if $q_{\text{data}} \geq 3.356$; **(c)** Test 1: $q_{\text{data}} = 0.707$;

Test 2: $q_{data} = 3.536$; Test 3: $q_{data} = 2.828$ **(d)** Test 1: $q_{data} = 0.707$, which is not ≥ 3.356; therefore we do not reject H_0. There is insufficient evidence at the $\alpha = 0.05$ level of significance that the population mean of Population 1 differs from the population mean of Population 2. Test 2: $q_{data} = 3.536$, which is ≥ 3.356; therefore we reject H_0. There is evidence at the $\alpha = 0.05$ level of significance that the population mean of Population 1 differs from the population mean of Population 3. Test 3: $q_{data} = 2.828$, which is not ≥ 3.356; therefore we do not reject H_0. There is insufficient evidence at the $\alpha = 0.05$ level of significance that the population mean of Population 2 differs from the population mean of Population 3.

26. (a) Test 1: $H_0 : \mu_1 = \mu_2$ vs. $H_a : \mu_1 \neq \mu_2$; Test 2: $H_0 : \mu_1 = \mu_3$ vs. $H_a : \mu_1 \neq \mu_3$; Test 3: $H_0 : \mu_2 = \mu_3$ vs. $H_a : \mu_2 \neq \mu_3$ **(b)** $q_{crit} = 3.399$. Reject H_0 if $q_{data} \geq 3.399$ **(c)** Test 1: $q_{data} = 4.714$; Test 2: $q_{data} = 2.357$; Test 3: $q_{data} = 2.357$ **(d)** Test 1: $q_{data} = 4.714$, which is ≥ 3.399; therefore we reject H_0. There is evidence at the $\alpha = 0.05$ level of significance that the population mean of Population 1 differs from the population mean of Population 2. Test 2: $q_{data} = 2.357$, which is not ≥ 3.399; therefore we do not reject H_0. There is insufficient evidence at the $\alpha = 0.05$ level of significance that the population mean of Population 1 differs from the population mean of Population 3. Test 3: $q_{data} = 2.357$, which is not ≥ 3.399; therefore we do not reject H_0. There is insufficient evidence at the $\alpha = 0.05$ level of significance that the population mean of Population 2 differs from the population mean of Population 3.

27. Test 1: $H_0 : \mu_A = \mu_B$ vs. $H_a : \mu_A \neq \mu_B$; Test 2: $H_0 : \mu_A = \mu_C$ vs. $H_a : \mu_A \neq \mu_C$; Test 3: $H_0 : \mu_B = \mu_C$ vs. $H_a : \mu_B \neq \mu_C$. For each hypothesis test, reject H_0 if the Bonferroni-adjusted p-value $\leq \alpha = 0.01$. Test 1: $t_{data} = -3.162$; Test 2: $t_{data} = 3.162$; Test 3: $t_{data} = 6.325$. Test 1: Bonferroni-adjusted p-value = 0.0246; Test 2: Bonferroni-adjusted p-value = 0.0246; Test 3: Bonferroni-adjusted p-value = 0.0001. Test 1: The adjusted p-value = 0.0246, which is not ≤ 0.01; therefore we do not reject H_0. There is insufficient evidence at the $\alpha = 0.01$ level of significance that the population mean of Population A differs from the population mean of Population B. Test 2: The adjusted p-value = 0.0246, which is not ≤ 0.01; therefore we do not reject H_0. There is insufficient evidence at the $\alpha = 0.01$ level of significance that the population mean of Population A differs from the population mean of Population C. Test 3: The adjusted p-value = 0.0001, which is ≤ 0.01; therefore we reject H_0. There is evidence at the $\alpha = 0.01$ level of significance that the population mean of Population B differs from the population mean of Population C.

28. See Instructor's Guide with Solutions

29. Test 1: $H_0 : \mu_A = \mu_B$ vs. $H_a : \mu_A \neq \mu_B$; Test 2: $H_0 : \mu_A = \mu_C$ vs. $H_a : \mu_A \neq \mu_C$; Test 3: $H_0 : \mu_A = \mu_D$ vs. $H_a : \mu_A \neq \mu_D$; Test 4: $H_0 : \mu_B = \mu_C$ vs. $H_a : \mu_B \neq \mu_C$; Test 5: $H_0 : \mu_B = \mu_D$ vs. $H_a : \mu_B \neq \mu_D$; Test 6: $H_0 : \mu_C = \mu_D$ vs. $H_a : \mu_C \neq \mu_D$; $q_{crit} = 3.685$. For each hypothesis test, reject H_0 if $q_{data} \geq 3.685$. Test 1: $q_{data} = 53.484$, which is ≥ 3.685; therefore we reject H_0. There is evidence at the $\alpha = 0.05$ level of significance that the population mean of Population A differs from the population mean of Population B. Test 2: $q_{data} = 112.755$, which is ≥ 3.685; therefore we reject H_0. There is evidence at the $\alpha = 0.05$ level of significance that the population mean of Population A differs from the population mean of Population C. Test 3: $q_{data} = 175.069$, which is ≥ 3.685; therefore we reject H_0. There is evidence at the $\alpha = 0.05$ level of significance that the population mean of Population A differs from the population mean of Population D. Test 4: $q_{data} = 63.926$, which is ≥ 3.685; therefore we reject H_0. There is evidence at the $\alpha = 0.05$ level of significance that the population mean of Population B differs from the population mean of Population C. Test 5: $q_{data} = 133.711$, which is ≥ 3.685;

therefore we reject H_0. There is evidence at the $\alpha = 0.05$ level of significance that the population mean of Population B differs from the population mean of Population D. Test 6: $q_{data} = 72.783$, which is ≥ 3.685; therefore we reject H_0. There is evidence at the $\alpha = 0.05$ level of significance that the population mean of Population C differs from the population mean of Population D.

30. See Instructor's Guide with Solutions

31. Test 1: $H_0 : \mu_A = \mu_B$ vs. $H_a : \mu_A \neq \mu_B$. 95% confidence interval for $\mu_B = \mu_A$ is $(-5.642, 0.309)$, which does contain zero, so we do not reject $H_0 : \mu_A = \mu_B$ for level of significance $\alpha = 0.05$. Test 2: $H_0 : \mu_A = \mu_C$ vs. $H_a : \mu_A \neq \mu_C$. 95% confidence interval for $\mu_C - \mu_A$ is $(-7.642, -1.691)$, which does not contain zero, so we reject $H_0 : \mu_A = \mu_C$ for level of significance $\alpha = 0.05$. Test 3: $H_0 : \mu_B = \mu_C$ vs. $H_a : \mu_B \neq \mu_C$. 95% confidence interval for $\mu_C - \mu_B$ is $(-4.976, 0.976)$, which does contain zero, so we do not reject $H_0 : \mu_B = \mu_C$ for level of significance $\alpha = 0.05$.

32. Test 1: $H_0 : \mu_A = \mu_B$ vs. $H_a : \mu_A \neq \mu_B$. 95% confidence interval for $\mu_B = \mu_A$ is $(-10.385, -1.615)$, which does not contain zero, so we reject $H_0 : \mu_A = \mu_B$ for level of significance $\alpha = 0.05$. Test 2: $H_0 : \mu_A = \mu_C$ vs. $H_a : \mu_A \neq \mu_C$. 95% confidence interval for $\mu_C - \mu_A$ is $(-4.719, 4.052)$, which does contain zero, so we do not reject $H_0 : \mu_A = \mu_C$ for level of significance $\alpha = 0.05$. Test 3: $H_0 : \mu_B = \mu_C$ vs. $H_a : \mu_B \neq \mu_C$. 95% confidence interval for $\mu_C - \mu_A$ is $(1.281, 10.052)$, which does not contain zero, so we reject $H_0 : \mu_B = \mu_C$ for level of significance $\alpha = 0.05$.

33. Since the conclusion of the ANOVA is do not reject H_0, it is not appropriate to perform multiple comparisons.

34. See Instructor's Guide with Solutions.

35. See Student Solutions Manual.

36. Test 1: $H_0 : \mu_{Europe} = \mu_{Japan}$ vs. $H_a : \mu_{Europe} \neq \mu_{Japan}$; Test 2: $H_0 : \mu_{Europe} = \mu_{USA}$ vs. $H_a : \mu_{Europe} \neq \mu_{USA}$; Test 3: $H_0 : \mu_{Japan} = \mu_{USA}$ vs. $H_a : \mu_{Japan} \neq \mu_{USA}$. For each hypothesis test, reject H_0 if the Bonferroni-adjusted p-value $\leq \alpha$ 0.01. Test 1: $t_{data} = -2.692$; Test 2: $t_{data} = 8.635$; Test 3: $t_{data} = 12.589$. Test 1: The Bonferroni-adjusted p-value = 0.0222, which is not ≤ 0.01; therefore we do not reject H_0. There is insufficient evidence at the $\alpha = 0.01$ level of significance that the population mean gas mileage of cars manufactured in Europe differs from the population mean gas mileage of cars manufactured in Japan. Test 2: The Bonferroni-adjusted p-value = 0, which is ≤ 0.01; therefore we reject H_0. There is evidence at the $\alpha = 0.01$ level of significance that the population mean gas mileage of cars manufactured in Europe differs from the population mean gas mileage of cars manufactured in the United States. Test 3: The Bonferroni-adjusted p-value = 0, which is ≤ 0.01; therefore we reject H_0. There is evidence at the $\alpha = 0.01$ level of significance that the population mean gas mileage of cars manufactured in Japan differs from the population mean gas mileage of cars manufactured in the United States.

37. See Student Solutions Manual.

38. The conclusion was do not reject H_0, so it is not appropriate to perform multiple comparisons.

39. See Student Solutions Manual.

40. See Instructor's Guide with Solutions.

Section 12.3

1. The variable of interest is the variable we are interested in studying, and the blocking factor is a variable that is not of primary interest to the researcher but is included in the ANOVA in order to improve the ability of the ANOVA to find significant differences among the treatment means. Treatment. Nuisance factor.

2. In a randomized block design ANOVA, we test for differences among the treatment means, while accounting for the variability among the levels in the blocking factor.

3. We reject H_0 when the p-value is small. The smaller SSE, the larger F is and therefore the smaller the p-value is.

4. The larger F is, the smaller the p-value is. Smaller p-values will more likely lead us to reject the null hypothesis.

5. (a) 4 treatments, 4 blocks (b) $F = 7.03$ (c) **Fcdf** (7.03, 1E99, 3, 9) = 0.0098363901 ≈ 0.010.

6. (a) 3 treatments, 5 blocks (b) $F = 2.64$ (c) **Fcdf** (2.64, 1E99, 2, 8) = 0.1316945031 ≈ 0.132

7. (a) 4 treatments, 8 blocks (b) $F = 5.03$ (c) **Fcdf** (5.03, 1E99, 3, 21) = 0.0087858268 ≈ 0.009

8. (a) 4 treatments, 7 blocks (b) $F = 1.70$ (c) **Fcdf** (1.70, 1E99, 3, 18) = 0.2027174288 ≈ 0.203

9. (a) $H_0 : \mu_1 = \mu_2 = \mu_3 = \mu_4$ vs. H_a : Not all of the population means are equal. Reject H_0 if p-value ≤ 0.05. (b) The p-value = 0.010, which is ≤ 0.05; therefore we reject H_0. There is evidence at level of significance $\alpha = 0.05$ that the population means are not all equal.

10. (a) $H_0 : \mu_1 = \mu_2 = \mu_3$ vs. H_a : Not all of the population means are equal. Reject H_0 if p-value ≤ 0.05. (b) The p-value = 0.132, which is not ≤ 0.05; therefore we do not reject H_0. There is insufficient evidence at level of significance $\alpha = 0.05$ that the population means are not all equal.

11. (a) $H_0 : \mu_1 = \mu_2 = \mu_3 = \mu_4$ vs. H_a : Not all of the population means are equal. Reject H_0 if p-value ≤ 0.05. (b) The p-value = 0.009, which is ≤ 0.05; therefore we reject H_0. There is evidence at level of significance $\alpha = 0.05$ that the population means are not all equal.

12. (a) $H_0 : \mu_1 = \mu_2 = \mu_3 = \mu_4$ vs. H_a : Not all of the population means are equal. Reject H_0 if p-value ≤ 0.05. (b) The p-value = 0.204, which is not ≤ 0.05; therefore we do not reject H_0. There is insufficient evidence at level of significance $\alpha = 0.05$ that the population means are not all equal.

13. (a) $H_0 : \mu_1 = \mu_2 = \mu_3$ vs. H_a : Not all of the population means are equal. Reject H_0 if p-value ≤ 0.05. (b) Answers to missing values are in red.

Source	Sum of squares	Degrees of freedom	Mean square	F
Treatments	90	2	45	6
Blocks	50	5	10	
Error	60	8	7.5	
Total	200	15		

(c) The p-value = 0.0256, which is ≤ 0.05; therefore we reject H_0. There is evidence at level of significance $\alpha = 0.05$ that the population means are not all equal.

14. (a) $H_0 : \mu_1 = \mu_2 = \mu_3 = \mu_4$ vs. H_a : Not all of the population means are equal. Reject H_0 if p-value ≤ 0.05.
(b) Answers to missing values are in red.

Source	Sum of squares	Degrees of freedom	Mean square	F
Treatments	180	3	60	5
Blocks	240	6	40	
Error	216	18	12	
Total	636	27		

(c) The p-value = 0.0107, which is ≤ 0.05; therefore we reject H_0. There is evidence at level of significance $\alpha = 0.05$ that the population means are not all equal.

15. (a)

Source	Sum of squares	Degrees of freedom	Mean square	F
Treatments	90	2	45	5.3182
Error	110	13	8.4615	
Total	200	15		

(b) $H_0 : \mu_1 = \mu_2 = \mu_3$ vs. H_a : Not all of the population means are equal. Reject H_0 if p-value ≤ 0.05. The p-value = 0.0205, which is ≤ 0.05; therefore we reject H_0. There is evidence at level of significance $\alpha = 0.05$ that the population means are not all equal. (c) The conclusions are the same for both tests. No.

16. (a)

Source	Sum of squares	Degrees of freedom	Mean square	F
Treatments	180	3	60	3.1579
Error	456	24	19	
Total	636	27		

(b) $H_0 : \mu_1 = \mu_2 = \mu_3 = \mu_4$ vs. H_a : Not all of the population means are equal. Reject H_0 if p-value ≤ 0.05. The p-value = 0.0431, which is ≤ 0.05; therefore we reject H_0. There is evidence at level of significance $\alpha = 0.05$ that the population means are not all equal. (c) The conclusions are the same for both tests. No.

17. $b - 1 + (k - 1)(b - 1) = b - 1 + k \cdot b - k - b + 1 = k \cdot b - k = n_T - k$

18. $H_0 : \mu_{2006} = \mu_{2007} = \mu_{2008}$ vs. H_a : Not all of the population means are equal. Reject H_0 if p-value ≤ 0.05. The p-value = 0.319, which is not ≤ 0.05; therefore we do not reject H_0. There is insufficient evidence at level of significance $\alpha = 0.05$ that the population mean price per pound of strawberries differs in these three years.

19. $H_0 : \mu_{1995} = \mu_{2003} = \mu_{2007}$ vs. H_a : Not all of the population means are equal. Reject H_0 if p-value ≤ 0.10. The p-value = 0.218, which is not ≤ 0.10; therefore we do not reject H_0. There is insufficient evidence at level of significance $\alpha = 0.10$ that the population mean math score is different in these three years.

20. $H_0 : \mu_{1990} = \mu_{2000} = \mu_{2005}$ vs. H_a : Not all of the population means are equal. Reject H_0 if p-value ≤ 0.10. The p-value = 0.011, which is ≤ 0.10; therefore we reject H_0. There is evidence at level of significance $\alpha = 0.10$ that the population mean number of people living in cities and towns in Oregon differs in these three years.

21. (a) $H_0 : \mu_{2006} = \mu_{2007} = \mu_{2008}$ vs. H_a : Not all of the population means are equal. Reject H_0 if p-value ≤ 0.05. The p-value = 0.983, which is not ≥ 0.05; therefore we do not reject H_0. There is insufficient evidence at level of significance $\alpha = 0.05$ that the population mean price per pound of strawberries differs in these three years. (b) No, the conclusions are the same.

22. (a) $H_0 : \mu_{1995} = \mu_{2003} = \mu_{2007}$ vs. H_a : Not all of the population means are equal. Reject H_0 if p-value ≤ 0.10. The p-value = 0.870, which is not ≤ 0.10; therefore we do not reject H_0. There is insufficient evidence at level of significance $\alpha = 0.10$ that the population mean math score is different in these three years. (b) No, the conclusions are the same.

23. $H_0 : \mu_{1990} = \mu_{2000} = \mu_{2005}$ vs. H_a : Not all of the population means are equal. Reject H_0 if p-value ≤ 0.10. The p-value $= 0.976$, which is not ≤ 0.10; therefore we do not reject H_0. There is insufficient evidence at level of significance $\alpha = 0.10$ that the population mean number of people living in cities and towns in Oregon differs in these three years. **(b)** Yes, the conclusions are different.

24. (a) $H_0 : \mu_{FY05} = \mu_{FY06} = \mu_{FY07} = \mu_{FY08}$ vs. H_a : Not all of the population means are equal. Reject H_0 if p-value ≤ 0.05. The p-value $= 0.259$, which is not ≤ 0.05; therefore we do not reject H_0. There is insufficient evidence at level of significance $\alpha = 0.05$ that the population mean amount of economic assistance sent to foreign countries and earmarked for child survival and health was not the same for these four fiscal years. **(b)** $H_0 : \mu_{FY05} = \mu_{FY06} = \mu_{FY07} = \mu_{FY08}$ vs. H_a : Not all of the population means are equal. Reject H_0 if p-value ≤ 0.05. The p-value $= 0.024$, which is ≤ 0.05; therefore we reject H_0. There is evidence at level of significance $\alpha = 0.05$ that the population mean amount of economic assistance sent to foreign countries and earmarked for child survival and health was not the same for these four fiscal years. **(c)** Yes

25. (a) $H_0 : \mu_{MarketCap} = \mu_{FirmValue} = \mu_{EnterpriseValue}$ vs. H_a : Not all of the population means are equal. Reject H_0 if p-value ≤ 0.05. The p-value $= 0.435$, which is not ≤ 0.05; therefore we do not reject H_0. There is insufficient evidence at level of significance $\alpha = 0.05$ that the population mean values differ among the three measures. **(b)** $H_0 : \mu_{MarketCap} = \mu_{FirmValue} = \mu_{EnterpriseValue}$ vs. H_a : Not all of the population means are equal. Reject H_0 if p-value ≤ 0.05. The p-value $= 0.019$, which is ≤ 0.05; therefore we reject H_0. There is evidence at level of significance $\alpha = 0.05$ that the population mean values differ among the three measures. **(c)** Yes

Section 12.4

1. We are interested in testing for the significance of both factors and we need to test for interaction of the two factors.
2. The main effects
3. Factor interaction
4. Answers will vary.
5. It is a graphical representation of the cell means for each cell in the contingency table. It is used to investigate the presence of interaction between the two factors.
6. (a) Significant interaction **(b)** No interaction **(c)** Some interaction
7. Test for interaction between the factors, test for Factor A effect, Test for Factor B effect
8. Do not perform the test for either Factor A or Factor B. If there is an interaction between factors, then we cannot draw conclusions about the main effects.
9. Significant interaction
10. No interaction
11. Some interaction
12. Significant interaction
13. The lines are parallel, so there is no interaction between Factor A and Factor B.

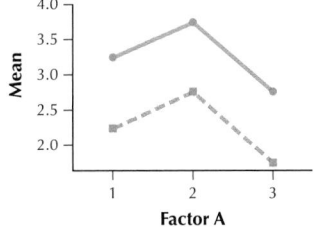

14. There appears to be significant interaction between Factor A and Factor B.

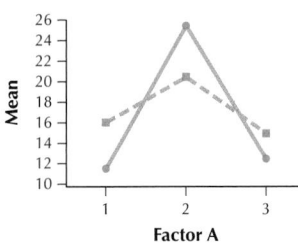

15. The lines are nearly parallel, so there is no interaction between Factors A and B.

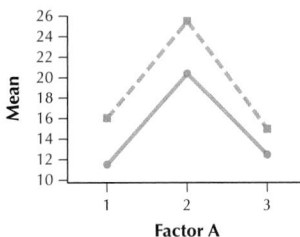

16. The graphs don't intersect, but they are not parallel. Therefore there may be a slight interaction between Factors A and B.

17. (a) H_0 : There is no interaction between carrier (Factor A) and type (Factor B). H_a : There is interaction between carrier (Factor A) and type (Factor B). Reject H_0 if the p-value ≤ 0.05. The p-value $= 1.00$, which is not ≤ 0.05; therefore we do not reject H_0. There is insufficient evidence of interaction between carrier (Factor A) and type (Factor B) at level of significance $\alpha = 0.05$. This result agrees with the interaction plot in Exercise 13. **(b)** H_0 : There is no carrier (Factor A) effect. That is, the population means do not differ by carrier. H_0 : There is a carrier (Factor A) effect. That is, the population means do differ by carrier. Reject H_0 if the p-value ≤ 0.05. The p-value $= 0.020$, which is ≤ 0.05; therefore we reject H_0. There is evidence for a carrier (Factor A) effect. In other words, there is evidence at level of significance $\alpha = 0.05$ that the population means do differ by carrier. **(c)** H_0 : There is no type (Factor B) effect. That is, the population means do not differ by type. H_a : There is a type (Factor B) effect. That is, the population means do differ by type. Reject H_0 if the p-value ≤ 0.05. The p-value $= 0.003$, which is ≤ 0.05; therefore we reject H_0. There is evidence for a type (Factor B) effect. In other words, there is evidence at level of significance $\alpha = 0.05$ that the population means do differ by type.

18. (a) H_0 : There is no interaction between carrier (Factor A) and type (Factor B). H_a : There is interaction between carrier (Factor A) and type (Factor B). Reject H_0 if the p-value ≤ 0.05. The p-value $= 0.001$, which is ≤ 0.05; therefore we reject H_0. There is evidence of interaction between carrier (Factor A) and type (Factor B) at level of significance $\alpha = 0.05$. This result agrees with the interaction plot in Exercise 14. **(b)** Not appropriate **(c)** Not appropriate

19. (a) H_0 : There is no interaction between carrier (Factor A) and type (Factor B). H_a : There is interaction between carrier (Factor A) and type (Factor B). Reject H_0 if the p-value ≤ 0.05. The p-value $= 0.252$, which is not ≤ 0.05; therefore we do not reject H_0. There is insufficient evidence of interaction between carrier (Factor A) and type (Factor B) at level of significance $\alpha = 0.05$. This result agrees with the interaction plot in Exercise 15. **(b)** H_0 : There is no carrier (Factor A) effect. That is, the population means do not differ by carrier. H_a : There is a carrier (Factor A) effect. That is, the population means do differ by carrier. Reject H_0 if the p-value ≤ 0.05. The p-value $= 0$, which is ≤ 0.05; therefore we reject H_0. There is evidence for a carrier (Factor A) effect. In other words, there is evidence at level of significance $\alpha = 0.05$ that the population means do differ by carrier. **(c)** H_0 : There is no type (Factor B) effect. That is, the population means do not differ by type. H_a : There is a type (Factor B) effect. That is, the population means do differ by type. Reject H_0 if the p-value ≤ 0.05. The p-value $= 0$, which is ≤ 0.05; therefore we reject H_0. There is evidence for a type (Factor B) effect. In other words, there is evidence at level of significance $\alpha = 0.05$ that the population means do differ by type.

20. (a) H_0 : There is no interaction between carrier (Factor A) and type (Factor B). H_a : There is interaction between carrier (Factor A) and type (Factor B). Reject H_0 if the p-value ≤ 0.05. The p-value $= 0.332$, which is not ≤ 0.05; therefore we do not reject H_0. There is insufficient evidence of interaction between carrier (Factor A) and type (Factor B) at level of significance $\alpha = 0.05$. This result agrees with the interaction plot in Exercise 16. **(b)** H_0 : There is no carrier (Factor A) effect. That is, the population means do not differ by carrier. H_a : There is a carrier (Factor A) effect. That is, the population means do differ by carrier. Reject H_0 if the p-value ≤ 0.05. The p-value $= 0.729$, which is not ≤ 0.05; therefore we do not reject H_0. There is insufficient evidence for a carrier (Factor A) effect. In other words, there is insufficient evidence at level of significance $\alpha = 0.05$ that the population means do differ by carrier. **(c)** H_0 : There is no type (Factor B) effect. That is, the population means do not differ by type. H_a : There is a type (Factor B) effect. That is, the population means do differ by type. Reject H_0 if the p-value ≤ 0.05. The p-value $= 0.001$, which is ≤ 0.05; therefore we reject H_0. There is evidence for a type (Factor B) effect. In other words, there is evidence at level of significance $\alpha = 0.05$ that the population means do differ by type.

21. (a) H_0 : There is no interaction between hypertension (Factor A) and gender (Factor B). H_a : There is interaction between hypertension (Factor A) and gender (Factor B). Reject H_0 if the p-value ≤ 0.05. The p-value $= 0.443$, which is not ≤ 0.05; therefore we do not reject H_0. There is insufficient evidence of interaction between hypertension (Factor A) and gender (Factor B) at level of significance $\alpha = 0.05$. **(b)** H_0 : There is no hypertension (Factor A) effect. That is, the population means do not differ by whether or not the person has hypertension. H_a : There is a hypertension (Factor A) effect. That is, the population means do not differ by whether or not the person has hypertension. Reject H_0 if the p-value ≤ 0.05. The p-value $= 0.014$, which is ≤ 0.05; therefore we reject H_0. There is evidence for a hypertension (Factor A) effect. Thus we can conclude at level of significance $\alpha = 0.05$ that there is a significant difference in mean cardiac output between patients who have hypertension and patients who don't. **(c)** H_0 : There is no gender (Factor B)

effect. That is, the population means do not differ by gender. H_a : There is a gender (Factor B) effect, that is, the population means do differ by gender. Reject H_0 if the p-value ≤ 0.05. The p-value $= 0.105$, which is not ≤ 0.05; therefore we do not reject H_0. There is insufficient evidence for a gender (Factor B) effect. Thus we can conclude at level of significance $\alpha = 0.05$ that there is no significant difference in mean cardiac output between females and males.

22. (a) H_0 : There is no interaction between problem type (Factor A) and course (Factor B). H_a : There is interaction between problem type (Factor A) and course (Factor B). Reject H_0 if the p-value ≤ 0.05. The p-value $= 0.887$, which is not ≤ 0.05; therefore we do not reject H_0. There is insufficient evidence of interaction between problem type (Factor A) and course (Factor B) at level of significance $\alpha = 0.05$. **(b)** H_0 : There is no problem type (Factor A) effect. That is, the population means do not differ by problem type. H_a : There is a problem type (Factor A) effect. That is, the population means do differ by problem type. Reject H_0 if the p-value ≤ 0.05. The p-value $= 0.140$, which is not ≤ 0.05; therefore we do not reject H_0. There is insufficient evidence for a problem type (Factor A) effect. Thus we can conclude at level of significance $\alpha = 0.05$ that there is no significant difference in mean test scores between multiple-choice tests, short-answer tests, and word-problem tests. **(c)** H_0 : There is no course (Factor B) effect. That is, the population means do not differ by course. H_a : There is a course (Factor B) effect, that is, the population means do differ by course. Reject H_0 if the p-value ≤ 0.05. The p-value $= 0.933$, which is not ≤ 0.05; therefore we do not reject H_0. There is insufficient evidence for a course (Factor B) effect. Thus we can conclude at level of significance $\alpha = 0.05$ that there is no significant difference in mean test scores between statistics tests and algebra tests.

23. H_0 : There is no interaction between brand (Factor A) and fiber (Factor B). H_a : There is interaction between brand (Factor A) and fiber (Factor B). Reject H_0 if the p-value ≤ 0.05. The p-value $= 0.888$, which is not ≤ 0.05; therefore we do not reject H_0. There is insufficient evidence of interaction between brand (Factor A) and fiber (Factor B) at level of significance $\alpha = 0.05$. H_0 : There is no brand (Factor A) effect. That is, the population means do not differ by brand. H_a : There is a brand (Factor A) effect. That is, the population means do differ by brand. Reject H_0 if the p-value ≤ 0.05. The p-value $= 0.045$, which is ≤ 0.05; therefore we reject H_0. There is evidence for a brand (Factor A) effect. Thus we can conclude at level of significance $\alpha = 0.05$ that there is a significant difference in mean nutritional ratings between Kellogg's cereals and General Mills cereals. H_0 : There is no fiber (Factor B) effect. That is, the population means do not differ by whether or not the cereal has fiber. H_a : There is a fiber (Factor B) effect. That is, the population means do differ by whether or not the cereal has fiber. Reject H_0 if the p-value ≤ 0.05. The p-value $= 0.006$, which is ≤ 0.05; therefore we reject H_0. There is evidence for a fiber (Factor B) effect. Thus we can conclude at level of significance $\alpha = 0.05$ that there is a significant difference in mean nutritional ratings between cereals with a high fiber content and cereals with a low fiber content.

24. (a) H_0 : There is no interaction between industry (Factor A) and exchange (Factor B). H_a : There is interaction between industry (Factor A) and exchange (Factor B). Reject H_0 if the p-value ≤ 0.01. The p-value $= 0.142$, which is not ≤ 0.01; therefore we do not reject H_0. There is insufficient evidence of interaction between industry (Factor A) and exchange (Factor B) at level of significance $\alpha = 0.01$. **(b)** H_0: There is no industry (Factor A) effect. That is, the population means do not differ by industry. H_a: There is an industry (Factor A) effect. That is, the population means do differ by industry. Reject H_0 if the p-value ≤ 0.01. The p-value $= 0.042$, which is not ≤ 0.01; therefore we do not reject H_0. There is insufficient evidence for an industry (Factor A) effect. Thus we can conclude at level of significance $\alpha = 0.01$ that there is no significant difference in mean stock price between the three industries. **(c)** H_0: There is no exchange (Factor B) effect. That is, the population means do not differ by exchange. H_a: There is an exchange (Factor B) effect. That is, the population means do differ by exchange. Reject H_0 if the p-value ≤ 0.01. The p-value $= 0.002$, which is ≤ 0.01; therefore we reject H_0. There is evidence for an exchange (Factor B) effect. Thus we can conclude at level of significance $\alpha = 0.01$ that there is a significant difference in mean stock prices for the NYSE and the NASDAQ. **(d)** The conclusion in part **(b)** would change to reject H_0, there is an industry effect. The conclusion in part **(c)** would remain the same.

25. H_0: There is no interaction between position (Factor A) and team (Factor B). H_a: There is interaction between position (Factor A) and team (Factor B). Reject H_0 if the p-value ≤ 0.05. The p-value $= 0.289$, which is not ≤ 0.05; therefore we do not reject H_0. There is insufficient evidence of interaction between position (Factor A) and team (Factor B) at level of significance $\alpha = 0.05$. H_0: There is no position (Factor A) effect. That is, the population means do not differ by position. H_a: There is a position (Factor A) effect. That is, the population means do differ by position. Reject H_0 if the p-value ≤ 0.05. The p-value $= 0.019$, which is ≤ 0.05; therefore we reject H_0. There is evidence for a position (Factor A) effect. Thus we can conclude at level of significance $\alpha = 0.05$ that there is a significant difference in mean batting averages between infielders and outfielders. H_0: There is no team (Factor B) effect. That is, the population means do not differ by team. H_a: There is a team (Factor B) effect. That is, the population means do differ by team. Reject H_0 if the p-value ≤ 0.05. The p-value $= 0.063$, which is not ≤ 0.05; therefore we do not reject H_0. There is insufficient evidence for a team (Factor B) effect. Thus we can conclude at level of significance $\alpha = 0.05$ that there is no significant difference in mean batting averages between the New York Yankees and the Los Angeles Angels.

Chapter 12 Review

1. (a) $df_1 = 3$, $df_2 = 296$ **(b)** 10 **(c)** 10,000 **(d)** 1,157.5 **(e)** 11,157.5 **(f)** 3,333.3333 **(g)** 3.910472973 **(h)** 852.4117985
2.

Source of variation	Sum of squares	Degrees of freedom	Mean square	F-test statistic
Treatment	SSTR = 10,000	$df_1 = 3$	MSTR = 3333.3333	F_{data} = 852.4117985
Error	SSE = 1157.5	$df_2 = 296$	MSE = 3.910472973	
Total	SST = 11,157.5			

3. $H_0 : \mu_A = \mu_B = \mu_C$. H_a : Not all the population means are equal. μ_A population mean test score for Branch A, μ_B = population mean test score for Branch B, and μ_C = population mean test score for Branch C. $F_{crit} = 3.49$. Reject H_0 if $F_{data} \geq 3.49$. $F_{data} = 1.57$. Since $F_{data} \leq 3.49$, we do not reject H_0. There is insufficient evidence that not all the population means are equal.

Source	df	SS	MS	F	P
Factor	2	569	284	1.57	0.231
Error	21	3797	181		
Total	23	4366			

4. $H_0 : \mu_1 = \mu_2 = \mu_3$. H_a : Not all the population means are equal. μ_1 = population mean level of satisfaction for Medical Treatment 1. μ_2 = population mean level of satisfaction for Medical Treatment 2. μ_3 = population mean level of satisfaction for Medical Treatment 3. $F_{crit} = 3.49$. Reject H_0 if $F_{data} \geq 3.49$. $F_{data} = 3.19$. Since $F_{data} \leq 3.49$, we do not reject H_0. There is insufficient evidence that not all of the population means are equal.

```
Source    DF        SS        MS      F      P
Factor     2      4114      2057   3.19  0.065
Error     18     11600       644
Total     20     15714
```

5. $H_0 : \mu_A = \mu_B = \mu_C = \mu_D$. H_a : Not all the population means are equal. μ_A = the population mean customer satisfaction at Store A, μ_B = the population mean customer satisfaction at Store B, μ_C = the population mean customer satisfaction at Store C, and μ_D = the population mean customer satisfaction at Store D. Reject H_0 if the p-value < 0.05. $F_{data} = 25.47$. p-value ≈ 0. Since the p-value ≤ 0.05, we reject H_0. There is evidence that not all the population means are equal.

Source	df	SS	MS	F	P
Factor	3	7321.4	2440.5	25.47	0.000
Error	24	2300.0	95.8		
Total	27	9621.4			

6. $t_{data} = -2.5$
7. $t_{data} = -1.5$
8. $t_{data} = 1$
9. (a) Test 1: $H_0 : \mu_1 = \mu_2$ vs. $H_a : \mu_1 \neq \mu_2$; Test 2: $H_0 : \mu_1 = \mu_3$ vs. $H_a : \mu_1 \neq \mu_3$; Test 3: $H_0 : \mu_2 = \mu_3$ vs. $H_a : \mu_2 \neq \mu_3$. For each hypothesis test, reject H_0 if the Bonferroni-adjusted p-value $\leq \alpha = 0.05$. **(b)** Test 1: $t_{data} = -2.5$; Test 2: $t_{data} = -1.5$; Test 3: $t_{data} = 1$ **(c)** Test 1: Bonferroni-adjusted p-value $= 0.0441$; Test 2: Bonferroni-adjusted p-value $= 0.4140$; Test 3: Bonferroni-adjusted p-value $= 0.9620$ **(d)** Test 1: The adjusted p-value $= 0.0441$, which is ≤ 0.05; therefore we reject H_0. There is evidence at the $\alpha = 0.05$ level of significance that the population mean of Population 1 differs from the population mean of Population 2. Test 2: The adjusted p-value $= 0.4140$, which is not ≤ 0.05; therefore we do not reject H_0. There is insufficient evidence at the $\alpha = 0.05$ level of significance that the population mean of Population 1 differs from the population mean of Population 3. Test 3: The adjusted p-value $= 0.9620$, which is not ≤ 0.05, therefore we do not reject H_0. There is insufficient evidence at the $\alpha = 0.05$ level of significance that the population mean of Population 2 differs from the population mean of Population 3.
10. $q_{data} = 2$
11. $q_{data} = 4$
12. $q_{data} = 2$
13. $q_{crit} = 3.356$
14. (a) Test 1: $H_0 : \mu_1 = \mu_2$ vs. $H_a : \mu_1 \neq \mu_2$; Test 2: $H_0 : \mu_1 = \mu_3$ vs. $H_a : \mu_1 \neq \mu_3$; Test 3: $H_0 : \mu_2 = \mu_3$ vs. $H_a : \mu_2 \neq \mu_3$ **(b)** $q_{crit} = 3.356$. Reject H_0 if $q_{data} \geq 3.356$.

(c) Test 1: $q_{data} = 2$; Test 2: $q_{data} = 4$; Test 3: $q_{data} = 2$
(d) Test 1: $q_{data} = 2$, which is not ≥ 3.356; therefore we do not reject H_0. There is insufficient evidence at the $\alpha = 0.05$ level of significance that the population mean of Population 1 differs from the population mean of Population 2. Test 2: $q_{data} = 4$, which is ≥ 3.356; therefore we reject H_0. There is evidence at the $\alpha = 0.05$ level of significance that the population mean of Population 1 differs from the population mean of Population 3. Test 3: $q_{data} = 2$, which is not ≥ 3.356; therefore we do not reject H_0. There is insufficient evidence at the $\alpha = 0.05$ level of significance that the population mean of Population 2 differs from the population mean of Population 3.
15. (a) $H_0 : \mu_1 = \mu_2 = \mu_3 = \mu_4 = \mu_5$ vs. H_a : Not all of the population means are equal. Reject H_0 if p-value ≤ 0.05.
(b) Answers to missing values are in red.

Source	Sum of squares	Degrees of freedom	Mean fquare	F
Treatments	80	4	20	2
Blocks	420	5	84	
Error	200	20	10	
Total	700	29		

(c) The p-value $= 0.1333$, which is not ≤ 0.05; therefore we do not reject H_0. There is insufficient evidence at level of significance $\alpha = 0.05$ that the population means are not all equal.
16. $H_0 : \mu_{women} = \mu_{men}$ vs. H_a : Not all of the population means are equal. Reject H_0 if p-value ≤ 0.05. The p-value $= 1.000$, which is not ≤ 0.05; therefore we do not reject H_0. There is insufficient evidence at level of significance $\alpha = 0.05$ that the population mean number of small businesses owned by women differs from the population mean number of small businesses owned by men.
17. The lines are not parallel, so there is some interaction between Factor A and Factor B.

18. There is significant interaction between Factor A and Factor B.

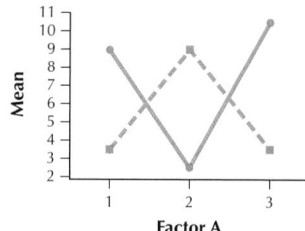

19. (a) H_0 : There is no interaction between carrier (Factor A) and type (Factor B). H_a : There is interaction between carrier (Factor A) and type (Factor B). Reject H_0 if the p-value ≤ 0.05. The p-value $= 0.020$, which is ≤ 0.05; therefore we reject H_0. There is evidence of interaction between carrier (Factor A) and type (Factor B) at level of significance $\alpha = 0.05$. This result

agrees with the interaction plot in Exercise 17. **(b)** Not appropriate **(c)** Not appropriate
20. (a) H_0 : There is no interaction between carrier (Factor A) and type (Factor B). H_a : There is interaction between carrier (Factor A) and type (Factor B). Reject H_0 if the p-value ≤ 0.05. The p-value $= 0.004$, which is ≤ 0.05; therefore we reject H_0. There is evidence of interaction between carrier (Factor A) and type (Factor B) at level of significance $\alpha = 0.05$. This result agrees with the interaction plot in Exercise 18. **(b)** Not appropriate **(c)** Not appropriate

Chapter 12 Quiz

1. False
2. True
3. False
4. Mean square
5. Mean square treatment
6. Mean square error
7. $\bar{\bar{x}}$
8. Mean square equals the sum of squares divided by the degrees of freedom.
9. F_{data}
10. $H_0 : \mu_4 = \mu_6 = \mu_8$. H_a : Not all the population means are equal. μ_4 = population mean miles per gallon for 4-cylinder cars. μ_6 = population mean miles per gallon for 6-cylinder cars. μ_8 = population mean miles per gallon for 8-cylinder cars. Reject H_0 if the p-value ≤ 0.05. $F_{data} = 341.4931564$. p-value $= 0$. Since the p-value ≤ 0.05, we reject H_0. There is evidence that not all the population mean gas mileages are equal.
11. $H_0 : \mu_{married} = \mu_{widowed} = \mu_{divorced} = \mu_{separated} = \mu_{nevermarried}$. H_a : Not all the population means are equal. $\mu_{married}$ = population mean number of hours worked by people who are married. $\mu_{widowed}$ = population mean number of hours worked by people who are widowed. $\mu_{divorced}$ = population mean number of hours worked by people who are divorced. $\mu_{separated}$ = population mean number of hours worked by people who are separated. $\mu_{nevermarried}$ = population mean number of hours worked by people who have never been married. Reject H_0 if the p-value ≤ 0.05. $F_{data} = 2.510227871$. p-value $= 0.0401$. Since the p-value ≤ 0.05, we reject H_0. There is evidence that not all the population mean numbers of hours worked are equal.
12. $H_0 : \mu_{Kelloggs} = \mu_{Quaker} = \mu_{RalstonPurina}$. H_a : Not all the population means are equal. $\mu_{Kelloggs}$ = population mean number of calories per serving in breakfast cereals made by Kellogg's. μ_{Quaker} = population mean number of calories per serving in breakfast cereals made by Quaker. $\mu_{RalstonPurina}$ = population mean number of calories per serving in breakfast cereals made by Ralston Purina. $F_{crit} = 3.18$. Reject H_0 if $F_{data} \geq 3.18$. $F_{data} = 1.557344523$. Since F_{data} is not ≥ 3.18, we do not reject H_0. There is insufficient evidence that not all the population mean numbers of calories per serving are equal.

Chapter 13

Section 13.1
1. The regression equation is calculated from a sample and is valid only for values of x in the range of the sample data. The population regression equation may be used to approximate the relationship between the predictor variable x and the response variable y for the entire population of (x, y) pairs.
2. (1) Zero mean assumption (2) Constant variance assumption (3) Independence assumption (4) Normality assumption

3. We construct a scatterplot of the residuals against the fitted values and a normal probability plot of the residuals. We must make sure that the scatterplot contains no strong evidence of any unhealthy patterns and that the normal probability plot indicates no evidence of departures from normality in residuals.

4. b_0 and b_1 are statistics and β_0 and β_1 are parameters.

5. There is no relationship between x and y.

6. $s = \sqrt{MSE/(n) - 2} = \sqrt{\sum(y - \hat{y})^2/(n) - 2}$ is the standard error of the estimate and $s_x = \sqrt{\sum(x - \bar{x})^2/(n) - 1}$ is the sample standard deviation of x.

7. **(a)** and **(b)**

x	y	Predicted value $\hat{y} = 13.5 + 2.5x$	Residual $(y - \hat{y})$
1	15	16	−1
2	20	18.5	1.5
3	20	21	−1
4	25	23.5	1.5
5	25	26	−1

(c) and **(d)** See Student Solutions Manual. **(e)** The scatterplot of the residuals contains an unhealthy pattern, so the regression assumptions are not verified.

8. **(a)** and **(b)**

x	y	Predicted value $\hat{y} = 8 + 3.2x$	Residual $(y - \hat{y})$
0	10	8	2
5	20	24	−4
10	45	40	5
15	50	56	−6
20	75	72	3

(c) and **(d)** See Instructor's Guide with Solutions. **(e)** The scatterplot of the residuals contains strong evidence of an unhealthy pattern. Therefore we conclude that the regression assumptions are not verified.

9. **(a)** and **(b)**

x	y	Predicted value $\hat{y} = 21.6 + 4x$	Residual $(y - \hat{y})$
−5	0	1.6	−1.6
−4	8	5.6	2.4
−3	8	9.6	−1.6
−2	16	13.6	2.4
−1	16	17.6	−1.6

(c) and **(d)** See Student Solutions Manual. **(e)** The scatterplot of the residuals contains an unhealthy pattern, so the regression assumptions are not verified.

10. **(a)** and **(b)**

x	y	Predicted value $\hat{y} = -16 - 3x$	Residual $(y - \hat{y})$
−3	−5	−7	2
−1	−15	−13	−2
1	−20	−19	−1
3	−25	−25	0
5	−30	−31	1

(c) and **(d)** See Instructor's Guide with Solutions. **(e)** The scatterplot of the residuals contains strong evidence of an unhealthy pattern. Therefore, we conclude that the regression assumptions are not verified.

11. **(a)** and **(b)**

x	y	Predicted value $\hat{y} = 104 - 0.5x$	Residual $(y - \hat{y})$
10	100	99	1
20	95	94	1
30	85	89	−4
40	85	84	1
50	80	79	1

(c) and **(d)** See Student Solutions Manual. **(e)** The scatterplot of the residuals contains an unhealthy pattern, so the regression assumptions are not verified.

12. **(a)** and **(b)**

x	y	Predicted value $\hat{y} = 9 + 0.2x$	Residual $(y - \hat{y})$
0	11	9	2
20	11	13	−2
40	16	17	−1
60	21	21	0
80	26	25	1

(c) and **(d)** See Instructor's Guide with Solutions **(e)** The scatterplot of the residuals contains no strong evidence of unhealthy patterns and the normal probability plot indicates no evidence of departures from normality in the residuals. Therefore we conclude that the regression assumptions are verified.

13. **(a)** and **(b)**

x	y	$\hat{y} = 0.6x + 0.2$	$y - \hat{y}$
1	1	0.8	0.2
2	1	1.4	−0.4
3	2	2	0
4	3	2.6	0.4
5	3	3.2	−0.2

(c)

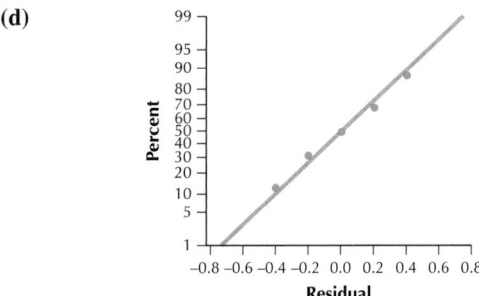

(d)

(e) The scatterplot in **(c)** of the residuals versus fitted values shows no strong evidence of unhealthy patterns. Thus, the independence assumption, the constant variance assumption, and the zero-mean assumption are verified. Also, the normal probability plot of the residuals in **(d)** indicates no evidence of departure from normality of the residuals. Therefore we conclude that the regression assumptions are verified.

14. (a) and **(b)**

x	y	$\hat{y} = -2x + 8$	$y - \hat{y}$
1	6	6	0
2	5	4	1
2	4	4	0
2	3	4	-1
3	2	2	0

(c)

(d)

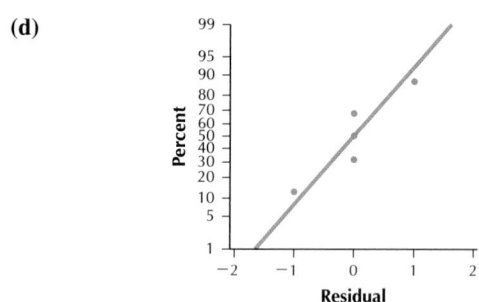

(e) The scatterplot in **(c)** of the residuals versus fitted values shows no strong evidence of unhealthy patterns. Thus, the independence assumption, the constant variance assumption, and the zero-mean assumption are verified. Also, the normal probability plot of the residuals in **(d)** indicates no evidence of departure from normality of the residuals. Therefore we conclude that the regression assumptions are verified.

15. (a) $t_{crit} = 3.182$ **(b)** $s = 1.58113883$ **(c)** $\sum(x - \bar{x})^2 = 10$ **(d)** $t_{data} = 5$ **(e)** $H_0 : \beta_1 = 0$: There is no linear relationship between x and y. $H_a : \beta_1 \neq 0$: There is a linear relationship between x and y. Reject H_0 if $t_{data} \geq 3.182$ or $t_{data} \leq -3.182$. Since $t_{data} = 5 \geq 3.182$, we reject H_0. There is evidence at level of significance $\alpha = 0.05$ that $\beta_1 \neq 0$ and that there is a linear relationship between x and y.

16. (a) $t_{crit} = 3.182$ **(b)** $s = 5.477225575$ **(c)** $\sum(x - \bar{x})^2 = 250$ **(d)** $t_{data} = 9.2376$ **(e)** $H_0 : \beta_1 = 0$: There is no linear relationship between x and y. $H_a : \beta_1 \neq 0$: There is a linear relationship between x and y. Reject H_0 if $t_{data} \geq 3.182$ or $t_{data} \leq -3.182$. Since $t_{data} = 9.2376 \geq 3.182$, we reject H_0. There is evidence at level of significance $\alpha = 0.05$ that $\beta_1 \neq 0$ and that there is a linear relationship between x and y.

17. (a) $t_{crit} = 3.182$ **(b)** $s = 2.529822128$. **(c)** $\sum(x - \bar{x})^2 = 10$ **(d)** $t_{data} = 5$ **(e)** $H_0 : \beta_1 = 0$: There is no linear relationship between x and y. $H_a : \beta_1 \neq 0$: There is a linear relationship

between x and y. Reject H_0 if $t_{data} \geq 3.182$ or $t_{data} \leq -3.182$. Since $t_{data} = 5 \geq 3.182$, we reject H_0. There is evidence at level of significance $\alpha = 0.05$ that $\beta_1 \neq 0$ and that there is a linear relationship between x and y.

18. (a) $t_{crit} = 3.182$ **(b)** $s = 1.825741858$ **(c)** $\sum(x - \bar{x})^2 = 40$ **(d)** $t_{data} = -10.3923$ **(e)** $H_0 : \beta_1 = 0$: There is no linear relationship between x and y. $H_a : \beta_1 \neq 0$: There is a linear relationship between x and y. Reject H_0 if $t_{data} \geq 3.182$ or $t_{data} \leq -3.182$. Since $t_{data} = -10.3923 \leq -3.182$, we reject H_0. There is evidence at level of significance $\alpha = 0.05$ that $\beta_1 \neq 0$ and that there is a linear relationship between x and y.

19. (a) $s = 2.581988897$ **(b)** $\sum(x - \bar{x})^2 = 1000$ **(c)** $t_{data} = -6.1237$ **(d)** p-value $= 0.0088$ **(e)** $H_0 : \beta_1 = 0$: There is no linear relationship between x and y. $H_a : \beta_1 \neq 0$: There is a linear relationship between x and y. Reject H_0 if p-value ≤ 0.05. Since p-value $= 0.0088 \leq 0.05$, we reject H_0. There is evidence at level of significance $\alpha = 0.05$ that $\beta_1 \neq 0$ and that there is a linear relationship between x and y.

20. (a) $s = 1.825741858$ **(b)** $\sum(x - \bar{x})^2 = 4000$ **(c)** $t_{data} = 6.9282$ **(d)** p-value $= 0.0062$ **(e)** $H_0 : \beta_1 = 0$: There is no linear relationship between x and y. $H_a : \beta_1 \neq 0$: There is a linear relationship between x and y. Reject H_0 if p-value ≤ 0.05. Since p-value $= 0.0062 \leq 0.05$, we reject H_0. There is evidence at level of significance $\alpha = 0.05$ that $\beta_1 \neq 0$ and that there is a linear relationship between x and y.

21. (a) $s = 0.3651483717$ **(b)** $\sum(x - \bar{x})^2 = 10$ **(c)** $t_{data} = 5.1962$ **(d)** p-value $= 0.0138$ **(e)** $H_0 : \beta_1 = 0$: There is no linear relationship between x and y. $H_a : \beta_1 \neq 0$: There is a linear relationship between x and y. Reject H_0 if p-value ≤ 0.05. Since p-value $= 0.0138 \leq 0.05$, we reject H_0. There is evidence at level of significance $\alpha = 0.05$ that $\beta_1 \neq 0$ and that there is a linear relationship between x and y.

22. (a) $s = 0.8164965809$ **(b)** $\sum(x - \bar{x})^2 = 2$ **(c)** $t_{data} = -3.4641$ **(d)** p-value $= 0.0405$ **(e)** $H_0 : \beta_1 = 0$: There is no linear relationship between x and y. $H_a : \beta_1 \neq 0$: There is a linear relationship between x and y. Reject H_0 if p-value ≤ 0.05. Since p-value $= 0.0405 \leq 0.05$, we reject H_0. There is evidence at level of significance $\alpha = 0.05$ that $\beta_1 \neq 0$ and that there is a linear relationship between x and y.

23. (a) $t_{\alpha/2} = 3.182$ **(b)** $E = 1.591$ **(c)** $(0.909, 4.091)$ **(d)** $H_0 : \beta_1 = 0$: There is no linear relationship between x and y. $H_a : \beta_1 \neq 0$: There is a linear relationship between x and y. Since the confidence interval from **(c)** does not contain zero, we may conclude that $\beta_1 \neq 0$ and that a linear relationship exists between x and y, at level of significance $\alpha = 0.05$.

24. (a) $t_{\alpha/2} = 3.182$ **(b)** $E = 1.1023$ **(c)** $(2.0977, 4.3023)$, TI-83/84: $(2.0978, 4.3022)$ **(d)** $H_0 : \beta_1 = 0$: There is no linear relationship between x and y. $H_a : \beta_1 \neq 0$: There is a linear relationship between x and y. Since the confidence interval from **(c)** does not contain zero, we may conclude that $\beta_1 \neq 0$ and that a linear relationship exists between x and y, at level of significance $\alpha = 0.05$.

25. (a) $t_{\alpha/2} = 3.182$ **(b)** $E = 2.5456$ **(c)** $(1.4544, 6.5456)$ **(d)** $H_0 : \beta_1 = 0$: There is no linear relationship between x and y. $H_a : \beta_1 \neq 0$: There is a linear relationship between x and y. Since the confidence interval from **(c)** does not contain zero, we may conclude that $\beta_1 \neq 0$ and that a linear relationship exists between x and y, at level of significance $\alpha = 0.05$.

26. (a) $t_{\alpha/2} = 3.182$ (b) $E = 0.9186$ (c) $(-3.9186, -2.0814)$
(d) $H_0 : \beta_1 = 0$: There is no linear relationship between x
and y. $H_a : \beta_1 \neq 0$: There is a linear relationship between
x and y. Since the confidence interval from (c) does not
contain zero, we may conclude that $\beta_1 \neq 0$ and that a linear
relationship exists between x and y, at level of significance
$\alpha = 0.05$.
27. (a) $t_{\alpha/2} = 3.182$ (b) $E = 0.2598$ (c) $(-0.7598, -0.2402)$
(d) $H_0 : \beta_1 = 0$: There is no linear relationship between x
and y. $H_a : \beta_1 \neq 0$: There is a linear relationship between
x and y. Since the confidence interval from (c) does not
contain zero, we may conclude that $\beta_1 \neq 0$ and that a linear
relationship exists between x and y, at level of significance
$\alpha = 0.05$.
28. (a) $t_{\alpha/2} = 3.182$ (b) $E = 0.0919$ (c) $(0.1081,$
$0.2919)$. TI-83/84: $(0.1080, 0.2920)$ (d) $H_0 : \beta_1 = 0$:
There is no linear relationship between x and y.
$H_a : \beta_1 \neq 0$: There is a linear relationship between
x and y. Since the confidence interval from (c) does not
contain zero, we may conclude that $\beta_1 \neq 0$ and that a linear
relationship exists between x and y, at level of significance
$\alpha = 0.05$.
29. (a) $t_{\alpha/2} = 3.182$ (b) $E = 0.3674$ (c) $(0.2326, 0.9674)$.
TI-83/84: $(0.2325, 0.9675)$ (d) $H_0 : \beta_1 = 0$: There is no linear
relationship between x and y. $H_a : \beta_1 \neq 0$: There is a linear
relationship between x and y. Since the confidence interval from
(c) does not contain zero, we may conclude that $\beta_1 \neq 0$ and that a
linear relationship exists between x and y, at level of significance
$\alpha = 0.05$.
30. (a) $t_{\alpha/2} = 3.182$ (b) $E = 1.8371$ (c) $(-3.8371, -0.1629)$.
TI-83/84: $(-3.8370, -0.1626)$ (d) $H_0 : \beta_1 = 0$: There is no
linear relationship between x and y. $H_a : \beta_1 \neq 0$: There is a linear
relationship between x and y. Since the confidence interval from
(c) does not contain zero, we may conclude that $\beta_1 \neq 0$ and that a
linear relationship exists between x and y, at level of significance
$\alpha = 0.05$.
31. (a) See Student Solutions Manual. The scatterplot of
the residuals contains an unhealthy pattern, so the regression
assumptions are not verified. (b) $H_0 : \beta_1 = 0$: There is no
relationship between volume (x) and weight (y). $H_a : \beta_1 \neq 0$:
There is a linear relationship between volume (x) and weight (y).
Reject H_0 if the p-value ≤ 0.05. Since the p-value ≤ 0.05, we
reject H_0. There is evidence for a linear relationship between
volume (x) and weight (y).
32. (a) See Student Solutions Manual. The scatterplot of
the residuals contains an unhealthy pattern, so the regression
assumptions are not verified. (b) $H_0 : \beta_1 = 0$: There is no
relationship between *Family Size* (x) and *Pets* (y). $H_a : \beta_1 \neq 0$:
There is a linear relationship between *Family Size* (x) and *Pets* (y).
Reject H_0 if $t_{\text{data}} \leq -3.182$ or $t_{\text{data}} \geq 3.182$. Since $t_{\text{data}} \geq 3.182$,
we reject H_0. There is evidence for a linear relationship between
Family Size (x) and *Pets* (y).
33. (a) See the Instructor's Guide with Solutions.
The scatterplot of the residuals contains no strong
evidence of unhealthy patterns and the normal probability
plot indicates no evidence of departures from normality
in the residuals. Therefore we conclude that the regression
assumptions are verified. (b) Since $t_{\text{data}} \geq 2.776$, we reject H_0.
There is evidence for a linear relationship between *Low* (x) and
High (y).

34. (a)

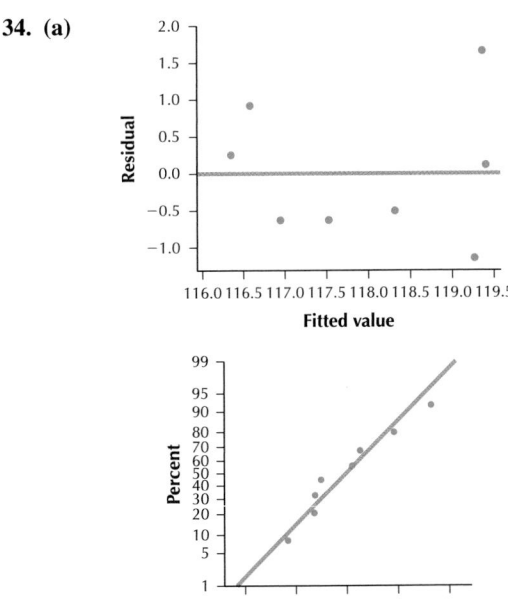

The scatterplot above of the residuals versus fitted values shows
no strong evidence of unhealthy patterns. Thus, the independence
assumption, the constant variance assumption, and the zero-mean
assumption are verified. Also, the normal probability plot of the
residuals above indicates no evidence of departure from normality of the residuals. Therefore we conclude that the regression
assumptions are verified.
(b) $H_0 : \beta_1 = 0$: There is no linear relationship between
Win % (x) and *Rating* (y). $H_a : \beta_1 \neq 0$: There is a linear relationship between *Win %* (x) and *Rating* (y). Reject H_0 if p-value $\leq$
0.05. $t_{\text{data}} = 3.3881$. Since p-value $= 0.0147 \leq 0.05$, we reject
H_0. There is evidence at level of significance $\alpha = 0.05$, that
$\beta_1 \neq 0$ and that there is a linear relationship between *Win %* (x)
and *Rating* (y).

35. (a)

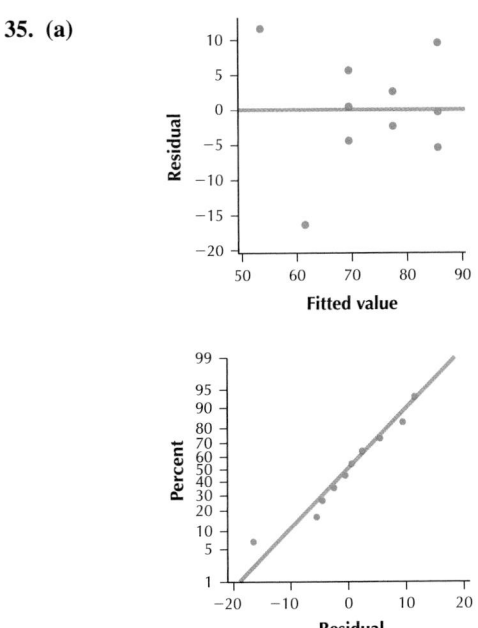

The scatterplot above of the residuals versus fitted values shows
no strong evidence of unhealthy patterns. Thus, the independence

assumption, the constant variance assumption, and the zero-mean assumption are verified. Also, the normal probability plot of the residuals above indicates no evidence of departure from normality of the residuals. Therefore we conclude that the regression assumptions are verified.

(b) $H_0 : \beta_1 = 0$: There is no linear relationship between *Midterm* exam score (*x*) and *Overall* grade (*y*). $H_a : \beta_1 \neq 0$: There is a linear relationship between *Midterm* exam score (*x*) and *Overall* grade (*y*). Reject H_0 if *p*-value ≤ 0.05. $t_{\text{data}} = 3.8032$. Since *p*-value $= 0.0052 \leq 0.05$, we reject H_0. There is evidence at level of significance $\alpha = 0.05$ that $\beta_1 \neq 0$ and that there is a linear relationship between *Midterm* exam score (*x*) and *Overall* grade (*y*).

36. (a)

The scatterplot above of the residuals versus fitted values shows no strong evidence of unhealthy patterns. Thus, the independence assumption, the constant variance assumption, and the zero-mean assumption are verified. Also, the normal probability plot of the residuals above indicates no evidence of departure from normality of the residuals. Therefore we conclude that the regression assumptions are verified.

(b) $H_0 : \beta_1 = 0$: There is no linear relationship between price (*x*) and change (*y*). $H_a : \beta_1 \neq 0$: There is a linear relationship between price (*x*) and change (*y*). Reject H_0 if *p*-value ≤ 0.05. $t_{\text{data}} = -2.4412$. Since *p*-value $= 0.0504$, which is not ≤ 0.05, we do not reject H_0. There is insufficient evidence at level of significance $\alpha = 0.05$ that $\beta_1 \neq 0$ and that there is a linear relationship between price (*x*) and change (*y*).

37. (a) $E = 0.3312$ **(b)** (1.2688, 1.9312) **(c)** We are 95% confident that the interval (1.2688, 1.9312) captures the population slope β_1 of the relationship between volume and weight.

38. (a) $E = 0.3182$ **(b)** (0.1818, 0.8182) **(c)** We are 95% confident that the interval (0.1818, 0.8182) captures the population slope β_1 of the relationship between *Family Size* and *Pets*.

39. (a) $E = 0.2402$ **(b)** (0.8063, 1.2868) **(c)** We are 95% confident that the interval (0.8063, 1.2868) captures the population slope β_1 of the relationship between *Low* and *High*.

40. (a) $E = 0.1393$ **(b)** (0.0536, 0.3322). TI-83/84: (0.0536, 0.3323) **(c)** We are 95% confident that the interval (0.0536, 0.3322) ((0.0536, 0.3323)) captures the slope β_1 of the regression line. That is, we are 95% confident that, for each additional percent of games won, the increase in the rating of the team lies between 0.0536 and 0.3322 (0.3323).

41. (a) $E = 0.4869$ **(b)** (0.3161, 1.2899) **(c)** We are 95% confident that the interval (0.3161, 1.2899) captures the slope β_1 of the regression line. That is, we are 95% confident that, for each additional point on the midterm grade, the increase in the overall grade lies between 0.3161 and 1.2899.

42. (a) $E = 0.0152$ **(b)** $(-0.0304, 0)$ TI-83/84: $(-0.0304, 0.000036)$ **(c)** We are 95% confident that the interval $(-0.0304, 0)$ $((-0.0304, 0.000036))$ captures the slope β_1 of the regression line. That is, we are 95% confident that, for each additional point on the midterm grade, the change in the overall grade lies between -0.0304 and 0 (0.000036).

43. Against; the points appear to lie near a line with a positive slope.

44. No, the regression assumptions are not violated.

45. $H_0 : \beta_1 = 0$: There is no linear relationship between SAT Reading score (*x*) and SAT Math score (*y*). $H_a : \beta_1 \neq 0$: There is a linear relationship between SAT Reading score (*x*) and SAT Math score (*y*). Reject H_0 if $t_{\text{data}} \geq 2.353$ or $t_{\text{data}} \leq -2.353$. Since $t_{\text{data}} = 3.1963 \geq 2.353$, we reject H_0. There is evidence at level of significance $\alpha = 0.10$ that $\beta_1 \neq 0$ and that there is a linear relationship between SAT Reading score (*x*) and SAT Math score (*y*).

46. (0.1125, 0.7403) TI-83/84: (0.1125, 0.7404). We are 90% confident that the interval (0.1125, 0.7403) ((0.1125, 0.7404)) captures the slope β_1 of the regression line. That is, we are 90% confident that, for each additional point on the SAT Reading score, the increase in the SAT Math score lies between 0.1125 and 0.7403 (0.7404).

47. Yes. Since the confidence interval from Exercise 46 does not contain zero, we may conclude that $\beta_1 \neq 0$ and that a linear relationship exists between SAT Reading score (*x*) and SAT Math score (*y*), at level of significance $\alpha = 0.10$.

48. (a) See Student Solutions Manual. The residuals vs. predicted values plot shows a funnel pattern. **(b)** The funnel pattern in the residuals vs. predicted values plot violates the constant variance assumption. **(c)** No, because one of the regression assumptions is violated. **(d)** Yes. It is appropriate to perform the descriptive statistics we learned in Section 4.2 and 4.3. These are just calculations based on the data. It is inferential statistics that it is not appropriate to perform. We cannot make any inferences using the regression equation if the regression equation is not valid.

49. (a) Increase by 5 **(b)** Remain unchanged **(c)–(d)** Remain unchanged **(e)** Decrease **(f)** Remain unchanged

50. (a) t_{data} increases if b_1 is positive and decreases if b_1 is negative. **(b)** r^2 remains the same. **(c)** *s* decreases. **(d)** *p*-value decreases. **(e)** Since we don't know what the new *p*-value will be, we don't know if the *p*-value will decrease enough to change the conclusion from "Do not reject H_0" to "Reject H_0."

51. (a) Increase by 10 **(b)** Remain unchanged **(c)–(d)** Increase **(e)** Decrease **(f)** Increase **(k)** Decreases **(l)** Remain unchanged

52. (a) t_{data} increases if b_1 is positive and decreases if b_1 is negative. **(b)** r^2 increases. **(c)** *s* decreases. **(d)** *p*-value decreases. **(e)** Unchanged.

53. (a) Unchanged **(b)** Increase **(c)** Unchanged **(d)** Decrease **(e)** Increase **(f)–(g)** Decrease

54. (a–b) Decrease **(c–d)** Increase **(e)** Depends on the new *p*-value.

55. (a) See the Instructor's Guide with Solutions. The scatterplot of the residuals contains no strong evidence of unhealthy patterns and the normal probability plot indicates no evidence of departures from normality in the residuals. Therefore we conclude that the regression assumptions are verified. **(b)** (1.0203, 1.9577).

We are 95% confident that the interval (1.0203, 1.9577) captures the population slope β_1 of the relationship between *Dow Jones Industrial Average* (x) and *pros' performance* (y). **(c)** Since 0 does not lie in the confidence interval, we would expect to reject the null hypothesis that $\beta_1 = 0$. **(d)** $H_0 : \beta_1 = 0$. There is no relationship between *Dow Jones Industrial Average* (x) and *pros' performance* (y). $H_a : \beta_1 \neq 0$. There is a linear relationship between *Dow Jones Industrial Average* (x) and *pros' performance* (y). Reject H_0 if p-value ≤ 0.05. $t_{\text{data}} = 6.31$. p-value ≈ 0. Since the p-value ≤ 0.05, we reject H_0. There is evidence for a linear relationship between *Dow Jones Industrial Average* (x) and *pros' performance* (y).

56. (a) The scatterplot of the residuals contains evidence of an unhealthy pattern and the normal probability plot indicates evidence of departures from normality in the residuals. Therefore we conclude that the regression assumptions are not verified. **(b)** (13.5483, 14.6201). We are 95% confident that the interval (13.5483, 14.6201) captures the population slope β_1 of the relationship between fat per gram and calories per gram. **(c)** Yes **(d)** $H_0 : \beta_1 = 0$: There is no relationship between fat per gram (x) and calories per gram (y). $H_a : \beta_1 \neq 0$: There is a linear relationship between fat per gram (x) and calories per gram (y). Reject H_0 if the p-value ≤ 0.05. $t_{\text{data}} = 52.15$. p-value ≈ 0. Since the p-value ≤ 0.05, we reject H_0. There is evidence for a linear relationship between fat per gram (x) and calories per gram (y).

57. (a) See the Instructor's Guide with Solutions. The scatterplot of the residuals contains no strong evidence of unhealthy patterns and the normal probability plot indicates no evidence of departures from normality in the residuals. Therefore we conclude that the regression assumptions are verified. **(b)** (0.0087, 0.0439). We are 95% confident that the interval (0.0087, 0.0439) captures the population slope β_1 of the relationship between *heart rate* and *body temperature*. **(c)** Since 0 does not lie in the confidence interval, we would expect to reject the null hypothesis that $\beta_1 = 0$. **(d)** $H_0 : \beta_1 = 0$. There is no relationship between *heart rate* (x) and *body temperature* (y). $H_a : \beta_1 \neq 0$. There is a linear relationship between *heart rate* (x) and *body temperatue* (y). Reject H_0 if p-value ≤ 0.05. $t_{\text{data}} = 2.97$. p-value $= 0.004$. Since the p-value ≤ 0.05, we reject H_0. There is evidence for a linear relationship between *heart rate* (x) and *body temperature* (y).

58. (a) No **(b)** Positive relationship **(c)** Unclear
59. (a) The predicted severity of a head injury from a car crash equals -438.0 plus 27.653 times the severity of a chest injury from the crash. **(b)** $H_0 : \beta_1 = 0$. There is no relationship between *chest injury severity* (x) and *head injury severity* (y). $H_a : \beta_1 \neq 0$. There is a linear relationship between *chest injury severity* (x) and *head injury severity* (y). Reject H_0 if p-value ≤ 0.01. $t_{\text{data}} = 12.59$. p-value ≈ 0. Since the p-value ≤ 0.01, we reject H_0. There is evidence for a linear relationship between *chest injury severity* (x) and *head injury severity* (y). **(c)** $b_1 = 27.653$ means that for each 1-point increase in the chest injury severity, the head injury severity increases by 27.653. **(d)** (21.8863, 33.4197). We are 99% confident that the interval (21.8863, 33.4197) captures the population slope β_1 of the relationship between *chest injury severity* and *head injury severity*. Since 0 does not lie in the confidence interval, we would expect to reject the null hypothesis that $\beta_1 = 0$. In **(b)**, we rejected the null hypothesis.
60. (a) No **(b)** No apparent relationship between the variables **(c)** The weight of vehicles is the predictor variable and the severity of the leg injuries should be the response variable.
61. (a) The predicted severity of a left leg injury from a car crash equals 569.4 plus 0.16531 times the weight of the car in

pounds. **(b)** Since the p-value ≤ 0.05, we reject H_0. There is evidence for a linear relationship between *weight of the car* (x) and *severity of left leg injury* (y). **(c)** $b_1 = 0.16531$ means that for every additional pound the car weighs, the estimated severity of the left leg injury increases by 0.16531.

Section 13.2
1. The confidence interval is for the mean value of y for a given x and the prediction interval is for a randomly selected value of y for a given x.
2. False
3. Lower bound: 18.7500 (Minitab: 18.7497); Upper bound: 23.5000 (Minitab: 23.2500)
4. Lower bound: 32.2057 (Minitab: 32.2046); Upper bound: 47.7943 (Minitab: 47.7954)
5. Lower bound: 1.1909 (Minitab: 1.19027); Upper bound: 10.0091 (Minitab: 10.0097)
6. Lower bound: -28.182 (Minitab: -28.1824); Upper bound: -21.818 (Minitab: -21.8176)
7. Lower bound: 92.636 (Minitab: 92.6351); Upper bound: 105.364 (Minitab: 105.365)
8. Lower bound: 9.818 (Minitab: 9.81755); Upper bound: 16.182 (Minitab: 16.1824)
9. Lower bound: 15.4886 (Minitab: 15.4878); Upper bound: 26.5114 (Minitab: 26.5122)
10. Lower bound: 20.9080 (Minitab: 20.9053); Upper bound: 59.0920 (Minitab: 59.0947)
11. Lower bound: -3.5783 (Minitab: -3.57958); Upper bound: 14.7783 (Minitab: 14.7796)
12. Lower bound: -31.6239 (Minitab: -31.6248); Upper bound: -18.3761 (Minitab: -18.3752)
13. Lower bound: 88.6076 (Minitab: 88.6062); Upper bound: 109.3924 (Minitab: 109.394)
14. Lower bound: 6.3761 (Minitab: 6.37521); Upper bound: 19.6239 (Minitab: 19.6248)
15. The interval in Exercise 9 is wider. Individual values are more variable than their mean. The interval in Exercise 3 is a 95% confidence interval for the mean value of y for the given value $x = 3$ and the interval in Exercise 9 is a prediction interval for a randomly chosen value of y for the given value $x = 3$.
16. The interval in Exercise 10 is wider. Individual values are more variable than their mean. The interval in Exercise 4 is a 95% confidence interval for the mean value of y for the given value $x = 10$ and the interval in Exercise 10 is a prediction interval for a randomly chosen value of y for the given value $x = 10$.
17. (a) 10.4 kilograms **(b)** Lower bound: 7.1550 kilograms (Minitab: 7.15453); Upper bound: 13.6450 kilograms (Minitab: 13.6455)
18. (a) 2.7 pets **(b)** Lower bound: 2.1489 pets (Minitab: 2.14878); Upper bound: 3.2511 pets (Minitab: 3.25122)
19. (a) 512.0628 **(b)** Lower bound: 507.5287 (Minitab: 507.545); Upper bound: 516.5969 (Minitab: 516.615)
20. (a) 43.345 degrees **(b)** Lower bound: 34.4495 degrees (Minitab: 34.4486); Upper bound: 52.2405 degrees (Minitab: 52.2400)
21. (a) Lower bound: 5.1009 kilograms (Minitab: 5.1009); Upper bound: 15.6991 kilograms (Minitab: 15.6998) **(b)** The interval in **(a)** is wider. Individual values are more variable than their mean. The interval in Exercise 17**(b)** is a 95% confidence interval for the mean value of y for the given value $x = 4$ cubic meters and the interval in **(a)** is a prediction interval for a randomly chosen value of y for the given value $x = 4$ cubic meters.

22. (a) Lower bound: 1.5527 pets (Minitab: 1.5255); Upper bound: 3.8473 pets (Minitab: 3.84745) **(b)** The interval in **(a)** is wider. Individual values are more variable than their mean. The interval in Exercise 18**(b)** is a 95% confidence interval for the mean value of y for the given value $x = 5$ and the interval in **(a)** is a prediction interval for a randomly chosen value of y for the given value $x = 5$.
23. (a) Lower bound: 503.8178 (Minitab: 503.834); Upper bound: 520.3078 (Minitab: 520.326) **(b)** The interval in **(a)** is wider. Individual values are more variable than their mean. The interval in Exercise 19**(b)** is a 90% confidence interval for the mean value of y for the given value $x = 500$ and the interval in **(a)** is a prediction interval for a randomly chosen value of y for the given value $x = 500$.
24. (a) Lower bound: 22.1576 degrees (Minitab: 22.1564); Upper bound: 64.5324 degrees (Minitab: 64.5322) **(b)** The interval in **(a)** is wider. Individual values are more variable than their mean. The interval in Exercise 20**(b)** is a 99% confidence interval for the mean value of y for the given value $x = 30$ degrees and the interval in **(a)** is a prediction interval for a randomly chosen value of y for the given value $x = 30$ degrees.
25. (a) Lower bound: 117.8439 (Minitab: 117.847); Upper bound: 120.1257 (Minitab: 120.128) **(b)** Lower bound: 116.2773 (Minitab: 116.280); Upper bound: 121.6923 (Minitab: 121.695)
26. (a) Lower bound: 33.5120 (Minitab: 33.5112); Upper bound: 73.3334 (Minitab: 73.3373) **(b)** Lower bound: 18.4308 (Minitab: 18.4283); Upper bound: 88.4146 (Minitab: 88.4202) **(c)** It would be extrapolation since $x = 40$ is outside of the range of the data set. The danger in extrapolation is that the relationship between the variables may not be linear outside of the range of the data set. Thus the regression equation may not be valid outside of the range of the data set.
27. (a) Lower bound: -0.3080 (Minitab: -0.308027); Upper bound: -0.0256 (Minitab: -0.0255747) **(b)** Lower bound: -0.5234 (Minitab: -0.523393); Upper bound: 0.1898 (Minitab: 0.189792) **(c)** It would be extrapolation since $x = \$50$ is outside of the range of the data set. The danger in extrapolation is that the relationship between the variables may not be linear outside of the range of the data set. Thus the regression equation may not be valid outside of the range of the data set.
28. (a) It would become wider. The higher the confidence level, the wider the confidence interval. The confidence interval needs to be wider to be more confident that the true value is in the confidence interval. **(b)** It would become wider. The higher the confidence level, the wider the prediction interval. The prediction interval needs to be wider to be more confident that the true value is in the prediction interval.
29. (a) (98.153, 98.521) **(b)** (96.891, 99.783)
30. (a) (5.2140, 5.4798) **(b)** (3.3932, 7.3006)

Section 13.3

1. $\hat{y} = b_0 + b_1 x_1 + b_2 x_2 + b_3 x_3$
2. R_{adj}^2 is preferable to R^2 as a measure of the goodness of a regression equation, because R_{adj}^2 will decrease if an unhelpful x variable is added to the regression equation.
3. The F test for the overall significance of the multiple regression
4. Yes. If the conclusion of the F test is that our multiple regression is useful, then we can conclude that at least one of the β_i's is not equal to zero. This does not indicate that all of the β_i's are not equal to zero.
5. The F test is for the overall significance of the multiple regression and the t test is for testing whether a particular x-variable has a significant relationship with the response variable y.

6. k (One for each predictor x variable).
7. The coefficient of a dummy variable can be interpreted as the estimated increase in y for those observations with the value of the dummy variable equal to 1 as compared to those with the value of the dummy variable equal to 0 when all of the other x variables are held constant.
8. The F Test, the t tests, verify the assumptions, report and interpret your final model
9. For each increase in one unit of the variable x_1, the estimated value of y increases by 5 units when the value of x_2 is held constant.
10. For each increase in one unit of the variable x_2, the estimated value of y decreases by 8 units when the value of x_1 is held constant.
11. The estimated value of y when $x_1 = 0$ and $x_2 = 0$ is $b_0 = 10$.
12. 50% of the variability in y is accounted for by this multiple regression equation.
13. 0.4412
14. (a) 8 **(b)** -4
15. For each increase in one unit of the variable x_1, the estimated value of y decreases by 0.1 unit when the value of x_2 is held constant.
16. For each increase in one unit of the variable x_2, the estimated value of y increases by 0.9 unit when the value of x_1 is held constant.
17. The estimated value of y when $x_1 = 0$ and $x_2 = 0$ is $b_0 = 0.5$.
18. 75% of the variability in y is accounted for by this multiple regression equation.
19. 0.7394
20. (a) 5.4 **(b)** 2.8
21. $\hat{y} = -37.8 + 4.50x_1 + 3.37x_2 + 0.306x_3$
22. The estimated value of y when $x_1 = 0$, $x_2 = 0$, and $x_3 = 0$ is $b_0 = -37.8$. For each increase in one unit of the variable x_1, the estimated value of y increases by 4.50 units when the values of x_2 and x_3 are held constant. For each increase in one unit of the variable x_2, the estimated value of y increases by 3.37 units when the values of x_1 and x_2 are held constant. For each increase in one unit of the variable x_3, the estimated value of y increases by 0.306 unit when the values of x_1 and x_2 are held constant.
23. (a) $H_0 : \beta_1 = \beta_2 = \beta_3 = 0$: There is no linear relationship between y and the set x_1, x_2, and x_3. The overall multiple regression is not significant. H_a : At least one of the β's $\neq 0$: There is a linear relationship between y and the set x_1, x_2, and x_3. The overall multiple regression is significant. Reject H_0 if the p-value $\leq \alpha = 0.05$. **(b)** $F = 14.37$. p-value $= 0.004$ **(c)** The p-value $= 0.004 \leq \alpha = 0.05$, so we reject H_0. There is evidence at level of significance $\alpha = 0.05$ for a linear relationship between y and the set x_1, x_2, and x_3. The overall multiple regression is significant.
24. (a) Test 1: $H_0 : \beta_1 = 0$: There is no linear relationship between y and x_1. $H_a : \beta_1 \neq 0$: There is a linear relationship between y and x_1. Reject H_0 if the p-value $\leq \alpha = 0.05$. Test 2: $H_0 : \beta_2 = 0$: There is no linear relationship between y and x_2. $H_a : \beta_2 \neq 0$: There is a linear relationship between y and x_2. Reject H_0 if the p-value $\leq \alpha = 0.05$. Test 3: $H_0 : \beta_3 = 0$: There is no linear relationship between y and x_3. $H_a : \beta_3 \neq 0$: There is a linear relationship between y and x_3. Reject H_0 if the p-value $\leq \alpha = 0.05$. **(b)** Test 1: $t = 3.72$, with p-value $= 0.010$. Test 2: $t = 2.75$, with p-value $= 0.034$. Test 3: $t = 0.87$, with p-value $= 0.418$. **(c)** Test 1: The p-value $= 0.010$, which is $\leq \alpha = 0.05$. Therefore we reject H_0. There is evidence of a linear relationship between y and x_1. Test 2: The p-value $= 0.034$, which is $\leq \alpha = 0.05$. Therefore we reject H_0. There is evidence of a

linear relationship between y and x_2. Test 3: The p-value $= 0.418$, which is not $\leq \alpha = 0.05$. Therefore we do not reject H_0. There is insufficient evidence of a linear relationship between y and x_3.
25. The p-value for x_3 is the only p-value greater than $\alpha = 0.05$, so we eliminate x_3 from the multiple regression equation. The new regression equation is $\hat{y} = -37.3 + 4.46x_1 + 3.31x_2$.
(a) Test 1: $H_0 : \beta_1 = 0$: There is no linear relationship between y and x_1. $H_a : \beta_1 \neq 0$: There is a linear relationship between y and x_1. Reject H_0 if the p-value $\leq \alpha = 0.05$. Test 2: $H_0 : \beta_2 = 0$: There is no linear relationship between y and x_2. $H_a : \beta_2 \neq 0$ There is a linear relationship between y and x_2. Reject H_0 if the p-value $\leq \alpha = 0.05$. **(b)** Test 1: $t = 3.76$, with p-value $= 0.007$. Test 2: $t = 2.75$, with p-value $= 0.029$ **(c)** Test 1: The p-value $= 0.002$, which is $\leq \alpha = 0.05$. Therefore we reject H_0. There is evidence of a linear relationship between y and x_1. Test 2: The p-value $= 0.029$, which is $\leq \alpha = 0.05$. Therefore we reject H_0. There is evidence of a linear relationship between y and x_2. Since all variables are significant, we have our final multiple regression equation.

26.

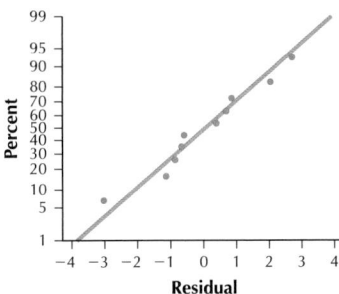

The scatterplot above of the residuals versus fitted values shows no strong evidence of unhealthy patterns. Thus, the independence assumption, the constant variance assumption, and the zero-mean assumption are verified. Also, the normal probability plot of the residuals above indicates no evidence of departure from normality of the residuals. Therefore we conclude that the regression assumptions are verified.
27. (a) $\hat{y} = -37.3 + 4.46x_1 + 3.31x_2$ **(b)** The estimated value of y when $x_1 = 0$ and $x_2 = 0$ is $b_0 = -37.3$. For each increase in one unit of the variable x_1, the estimated value of y increases by 4.46 units when the value of x_2 is held constant. For each increase in one unit of the variable x_2, the estimated value of y increases by 3.31 units when the value of x_1 is held constant. **(c)** Using the multiple regression equation in **(a)**, the size of the typical prediction error will be about 1.87731. 82.3% of the variability in y is accounted for by this multiple regression equation.
28. The regression equation is $\hat{y} = -2.98 + 1.13x_1 - 0.175x_2 + 3.55x_3$.
29. The estimated value of y when $x_1 = 0$, $x_2 = 0$, and $x_3 = 0$ is $b_0 = -2.98$. For each increase in one unit of the variable x_1, the estimated value of y increases by 1.13 units when the values of x_2 and x_3 are held constant. For each increase in one

unit of the variable x_2, the estimated value of y decreases by 0.175 unit when the values of x_1 and x_3 are held constant. For each increase in one unit of the variable x_3, the estimated value of y increases by 3.55 units when the values of x_1 and x_2 are held constant.
30. (a) $H_0 : \beta_1 = \beta_2 = \beta_3 = 0$: There is no linear relationship between y and the set x_1, x_2, and x_3. The overall multiple regression is not significant. H_a: At least one of the β's $\neq 0$. There is a linear relationship between y and the set x_1, x_2, and x_3. The overall multiple regression is significant. Reject H_0 if the p-value $\leq \alpha = 0.01$. **(b)** $F = 185.68$. p-value $= 0.000$ **(c)** The p-value $= 0.000 \leq \alpha = 0.01$, so we reject H_0. There is evidence at level of significance $\alpha = 0.01$ for a linear relationship between y and the set x_1, x_2, and x_3. The overall multiple regression is significant. For $x_2 = 0$, the regression equation is $\hat{y} = -2.98 + 1.13x_1 - 0.175x_2$. For $x_3 = 1$, the regression equation is $\hat{y} = 0.57 + 1.13x_1 - 0.175x_2$.
31. (a) Test 1: $H_0 : \beta_1 = 0$: There is no linear relationship between y and x_1. $H_a : \beta_1 \neq 0$: There is a linear relationship between y and x_1. Reject H_0 if the p-value $\leq \alpha = 0.01$. Test 2: $H_0 : \beta_2 = 0$: There is no linear relationship between y and x_2. $H_a : \beta_2 \neq 0$: There is a linear relationship between y and x_2. Reject H_0 if the p-value $\leq \alpha = 0.01$. Test 3: $H_0 : \beta_3 = 0$: There is no linear relationship between y and x_3. $H_a : \beta_3 \neq 0$: There is a linear relationship between y and x_3. Reject H_0 if the p-value $\leq \alpha = 0.01$. **(b)** Test 1: $t = 20.81$ with p-value $= 0.000$; Test 2: $t = -1.03$, with p-value $= 0.344$; Test 3: $t = 5.76$, with p-value $= 0.001$ **(c)** Test 1: The p-value $= 0.000$, which is $\leq \alpha = 0.01$. Therefore we reject H_0. There is evidence of a linear relationship between y and x_1. Test 2: The p-value $= 0.344$, which is not $\leq \alpha = 0.01$. Therefore we do not reject H_0. There is insufficient evidence of a linear relationship between y and x_2. Test 3: The p-value $= 0.001$, which is $\leq \alpha = 0.01$. Therefore we reject H_0. There is evidence of a linear relationship between y and x_3.
32. The p-value for x_2 is the only p-value greater than $\alpha = 0.01$, so we eliminate x_2 from the regression equation. The new regression equation is $\hat{y} = -3.12 + 1.15x_1 + 3.61x_3$.
(a) Test 1: $H_0 : \beta_1 = 0$: There is no linear relationship between y and x_1. $H_a : \beta_1 \neq 0$: There is a linear relationship between y and x_1. Reject H_0 if the p-value $\leq \alpha = 0.01$. Test 2: $H_0 : \beta_2 = 0$: There is no linear relationship between y and x_2. $H_a : \beta_2 \neq 0$: There is a linear relationship between y and x_3. Reject H_0 if the p-value $\leq \alpha = 0.01$. **(b)** Test 1: $t = 21.38$, with p-value $= 0.000$; Test 2: $t = 5.86$, with p-value $= 0.001$ **(c)** Test 1: The p-value $= 0.000$, which is $\leq \alpha = 0.01$. Therefore we reject H_0. There is evidence of a linear relationship between y and x_1. Test 2: The p-value $= 0.001$, which is $\leq \alpha = 0.01$. Therefore we reject H_0. There is evidence of a linear relationship between y and x_3. Since all of the variables are significant, we have our final multiple regression equation.
33.

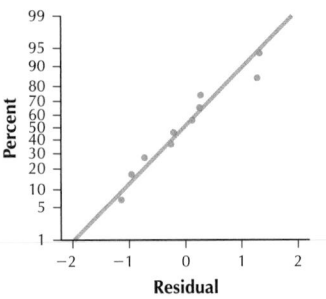

The scatterplot above of the residuals versus fitted values shows no strong evidence of unhealthy patterns. Thus, the independence assumption, the constant variance assumption, and the zero-mean assumption are verified. Also, the normal probability plot of the residuals above indicates no evidence of departure from normality of the residuals. Therefore we conclude that the regression assumptions are verified.

34. (a) The final multiple regression equation is $\hat{y} = -3.12 + 1.15x_1 + 3.61x_3$. For $x_2 = 0$, the regression equation is $\hat{y} = -3.12 + 1.15x_1$. For $x_2 = 1$, the regression equation is $\hat{y} = 0.49 + 1.15x_1$.

(b) For each increase in one unit of the variable x_1, the estimated value of y increases by 1.15 units. The estimated increase in y for those observations with $x_2 = 1$, as compared to those with $x_2 = 0$, when x_1 is held constant, is 3.61.

(c) Using the multiple regression equation in **(a)**, the size of the typical prediction error will be about 0.959129. 98.4% of the variability in y is accounted for by this multiple regression equation.

35. (a) $H_0 : \beta_1 = \beta_2 = \beta_3 = 0$: There is no linear relationship between *Overall Dating Score* and the set *Percentage 18–24 years old*, *Percentage 18–24 and single*, and *Online Dating Score*. The overall multiple regression is not significant. H_a : At least one of the β's $\neq 0$. There is a linear relationship between *Overall Dating Score* and the set *Percentage 18–24 years old*, *Percentage 18–24 and single*, and *Online Dating Score*. The overall multiple regression is significant. Reject H_0 if the p-value $\leq \alpha = 0.05$. $F = 3.22$. p-value $= 0.104$. The p-value $= 0.104$, which is not $\leq \alpha = 0.05$, so we do not reject H_0. There is insufficient evidence at level of significance $\alpha = 0.05$ for a linear relationship between *Overall Dating Score* and the set *Percentage 18–24 years old*, *Percentage 18–24 and single*, and *Online Dating Score*. The overall multiple regression is not significant. **(b)–(d)** Not appropriate to perform.

36. See Instructor's Guide with Solutions.

37. See Student Solutions Manual.

38. See Instructor's Guide with Solutions.

39. (a) $H_0 : \beta_1 = \beta_2 = \beta_3 = 0$: There is no linear relationship between *Current Ratio* and the set *Price-Earnings Ratio*, *Assets*, and *Liabilities*. The overall multiple regression is not significant. H_a: At least one of the β's $\neq 0$: There is a linear relationship between *Current Ratio* and the set *Price-Earnings Ratio*, *Assets*, and *Liabilities*. The overall multiple regression is significant. Reject H_0 if the p-value $\leq \alpha = 0.10$. $F = 0.56$. p-value $= 0.728$. The p-value $= 0.728$, which is not $\leq \alpha = 0.10$, so we do not reject H_0. There is insufficient evidence at level of significance $\alpha = 0.10$ for a linear relationship between *Current Ratio* and the set *Price-Earnings Ratio*, *Assets*, and *Liabilities*. The overall multiple regression is not significant. **(b)** There is no linear relationship between *Current Ratio* and the set *Price-Earnings Ratio*, *Assets*, and *Liabilities*. Therefore there is no final regression model. **(c)** $H_0 : \beta_1 = \beta_2 = \beta_3 = 0$: There is no linear relationship between

Current Ratio and the set of *Price-Earnings Ratio*, *Assets*, and *Liabilities*. The overall multiple regression is not significant. H_a: At least one of the β's $\neq 0$: There is a linear relationship between *Current Ratio* and the set *Price-Earnings Ratio*, *Assets*, and *Liabilities*. The overall multiple regression is significant. Reject H_0 if the p-value $\leq \alpha = 0.13$. $F = 0.56$. p-value $= 0.728$. The p-value $= 0.728$, which is not $\leq \alpha = 0.13$, so we do not reject H_0. There is insufficient evidence at level of significance $\alpha = 0.13$ for a linear relationship between *Current Ratio* and the set *Price-Earnings Ratio*, *Assets*, and *Liabilities*. The overall multiple regression is not significant. **(d)** Not applicable.

40. See Instructor's Guide with Solutions.

41. See Student Solutions Manual.

42. See Instructor's Guide with Solutions.

Chapter 13 Review

1. $H_0 : \beta_1 = 0$: There is no linear relationship between *Number of Years of Education* (x) and *Annual Earnings* (y). $H_a : \beta_1 \neq 0$ There is a linear relationship between Number of Years of Education (x) and Annual Earnings (y). Reject H_0 if $t_{\text{data}} \geq 2.571$ or $t_{\text{data}} \leq -2.571$. Since $t_{\text{data}} = 7.542 \geq 2.571$, we reject H_0. There is evidence at level of significance $\alpha = 0.05$ that $\beta_1 \neq 0$ and that there is a linear relationship between *Number of Years of Education* (x) and *Annual Earnings* (y).

2. $H_0 : \beta_1 = 0$: There is no linear relationship between *High school GPA* (x) and *First-year college GPA* (y). $H_a : \beta_1 \neq 0$ There is a linear relationship between *High school GPA* (x) and *First-year college GPA* (y). Reject H_0 if $t_{\text{data}} \geq 2.306$ or $t_{\text{data}} \leq -2.306$. Since $t_{\text{data}} = 4.5727 \geq 2.306$, we reject H_0. There is evidence at level of significance $\alpha = 0.05$ that $\beta_1 \neq 0$ and that there is a linear relationship between *High school GPA* (x) and *First-year college GPA* (y).

3. $H_0 : \beta_1 = 0$: There is no linear relationship between *Age* (x) and *Price* (y). $H_a : \beta_1 \neq 0$: There is a linear relationship between *Age* (x) and *Price* (y). Reject H_0 if $t_{\text{data}} \geq 2.306$ or $t_{\text{data}} \leq -2.306$. Since $t_{\text{data}} = -15.0124 \leq -2.306$, we reject H_0. There is evidence at level of significance $\alpha = 0.05$ that $\beta_1 \neq 0$ and that there is a linear relationship between *Age* (x) and *Price* (y).

4. (2.9453, 5.9919). We are 95% confident that the interval (2.9453, 5.9919) captures the population slope β_1 of the relationship between Education and Annual Earnings.

5. (0.3390, 1.0290). We are 95% confident that the interval (0.3390, 1.0290) captures the population slope β_1 of the relationship between high school GPA and first-year college GPA.

6. (-1.8728, -1.3742). We are 95% confident that the interval (-1.8728, -1.3742) captures the population slope β_1 of the relationship between *Age* and *Price*.

7. (a) 20.9231 thousand dollars **(b)** (14.2832, 27.5630) Minitab: (14.28, 27.56). We are 95% confident that the mean annual salary for people with 10 years of education lies between 14.28 thousand dollars and 27.56 thousand dollars. **(c)** (6.5524, 35.2938) Minitab: (6.55, 35.29). We are 95% confident that the annual salary for a randomly selected person with 10 years of education lies between 6.55 thousand dollars and 35.29 thousand dollars.

8. (a) 2.6484 **(b)** (2.4833, 2.8135) Minitab: (2.4834, 2.8135). We are 95% confident that the mean first-year college GPA for students with a high school GPA of 3.0 lies between 2.4834 and 2.8135. **(c)** (2.1098, 3.1870) Minitab: (2.1098, 3.1871). We are 95% confident that the first-year college GPA for a randomly selected student with a high school GPA of 3.0 lies between 2.1098 and 3.1871.

9. (a) 6.8179 thousand dollars **(b)** (5.8049, 7.8309) Minitab: (5.805, 7.831). We are 95% confident that the mean price for

8-year-old cars of this make and model lies between 5.805 thousand dollars and 7.831 thousand dollars **(c)** (4.9023, 8.7335) Minitab: (4.902, 8.733). We are 95% confident that the price for a randomly selected 8-year-old car of this make and model lies between 4.902 thousand dollars and 8.733 thousand dollars.

10. (a) $H_0 : \beta_1 = \beta_2 = \beta_3 = 0$: There is no linear relationship between y and the set x_1, x_2, and x_3. The overall multiple regression is not significant. H_a: At least one of the β's $\neq 0$: There is a linear relationship between y and the set x_1, x_2, and x_3. The overall multiple regression is significant. Reject H_0 if the p-value $\leq \alpha = 0.05$. **(b)** $F = 72.24$. p-value $= 0.000$ **(c)** The p-value $= 0.000 \leq \alpha = 0.05$, so we reject H_0. There is evidence at level of significance $\alpha = 0.05$ for a linear relationship between y and the set x_1, x_2, and x_3. The overall multiple regression is significant.

11. (a) Test 1: $H_0 : \beta_1 = 0$: There is no linear relationship between y and x_1. $H_a : \beta_1 \neq 0$: There is a linear relationship between y and x_1. Reject H_0 if the p-value $\leq \alpha = 0.05$. Test 2: $H_0 : \beta_2 = 0$: There is no linear relationship between y and x_2. $H_a : \beta_2 \neq 0$: There is a linear relationship between y and x_2. Reject H_0 if the p-value $\leq \alpha = 0.05$. Test 3: $H_0 : \beta_2 = 0$: There is no linear relationship between y and x_2. $H_a : \beta_2 \neq 0$ There is a linear relationship between y and x_2. Reject H_0 if the p-value $\leq \alpha = 0.05$. **(b)** Test 1: $t = 1.86$, with p-value $= 0.112$; Test 2: $t = -0.27$, with p-value $= 0.798$; Test 3: $t = -1.07$, with p-value $= 0.326$ **(c)** Test 1: The p-value $= 0.112$, which is not $\leq \alpha = 0.05$. Therefore we do not reject H_0. There is insufficient evidence of a linear relationship between y and x_1. Test 2: The p-value $= 0.798$, which is not $\leq \alpha = 0.05$. Therefore we do not reject H_0. There is insufficient evidence of a linear relationship between y and x_2. Test 3: The p-value $= 0.326$, which is not $\leq \alpha = 0.05$. Therefore we do not reject H_0. There is insufficient evidence of a linear relationship between y and x_2.

12. See Instructor's Guide with Solutions

13.

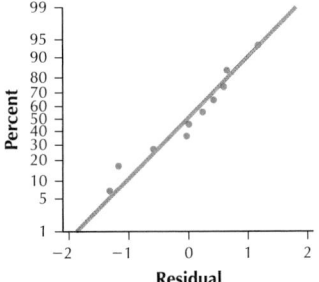

The preceding scatterplot above of the residuals versus fitted values shows no strong evidence of unhealthy patterns. Thus, the independence assumption, the constant variance assumption, and the zero-mean assumption are verified. Also, the normal probability plot of the residuals preceding indicates no evidence of departure from normality of the residuals. Therefore we conclude that the regression assumptions are verified.

Chapter 13 Quiz

1. False
2. False
3. True
4. Estimated, predicted y
5. β_1, b_1
6. Dummy
7. Zero-mean assumption $E(\varepsilon) = 0$, constant variance assumption, independence assumption, normality assumption
8. The t test for the slope β_1
9. R^2_{adj} is preferable to R^2 as a measure of the goodness of a regression equation, because R^2_{adj} will decrease if an unhelpful x variable is added to the regression equation.
10. $H_0 : \beta_1 = 0$: There is no linear relationship between *Height* (x) and *Weight* (y). $H_a : \beta_1 \neq 0$: There is a linear relationship between *Height* (x) and *Weight* (y). Reject H_0 if p-value $\leq \alpha = 0.01$. $t_{\text{data}} = 8.47$. p-value $= 0.000$. Since p-value $= 0.000 \leq \alpha = 0.01$, we reject H_0. There is evidence at level of significance $\alpha = 0.01$ that $\beta_1 \neq 0$ and that there is a linear relationship between *Height* (x) and *Weight* (y).
11. (a) No. Since H_0 was rejected at level of significance $\alpha = 0.01$ in the hypothesis test in Exercise 10, the conclusion is that $\beta_1 \neq 0$. **(b)** (4.3998, 10.17). We are 99% confident that the interval (4.3998, 10.17) captures the slope β_1 of the regression line. That is, we are 99% confident that, for each additional inch in height of a male student, the increase in the weight lies between 4.3998 and 10.17.
12. (a) 168.1314 pounds **(b)** (163.1156, 173.1472) Minitab: (163.11, 173.14). We are 95% confident that the mean weight for male college students 70 inches tall lies between 163.11 pounds and 173.14 pounds **(c)** (151.9267, 184.3361). Minitab: (151.92, 184.33). We are 95% confident that the weight for a randomly selected male college student with a height of 70 inches lies between 151.92 pounds and 184.33 pounds.
13. (a) The regression equation is $\hat{y} = 16.8 + 0.718x_1$.
(b) The estimated value of y when $x_1 = 0$ is 16.8. For each increase in one unit of the variable x_1, the estimated value of y increases by 0.718. **(c)** Using the multiple regression equation above, the size of the typical prediction error will be about 0.854028. 96.3% of the variability in y is accounted for by this multiple regression equation.

Tables Appendix

Table A Random numbers

10480	15011	01536	02011	81647	91646	67179	14194	62590	36207	20969	99570	91291	90700
22368	46573	25595	85393	30995	89198	27982	53402	93965	34095	52666	19174	39615	99505
24130	48360	22527	97265	76393	64809	15179	24830	49340	32081	30680	19655	63348	58629
42167	93093	06243	61680	07856	16376	39440	53537	71341	57004	00849	74917	97758	16379
37570	39975	81837	16656	06121	91782	60468	81305	49684	60672	14110	06927	01263	54613
77921	06907	11008	42751	27756	53498	18602	70659	90655	15053	21916	81825	44394	42880
99562	72905	56420	69994	98872	31016	71194	18738	44013	48840	63213	21069	10634	12952
96301	91977	05463	07972	18876	20922	94595	56869	69014	60045	18425	84903	42508	32307
89579	14342	63661	10281	17453	18103	57740	84378	25331	12566	58678	44947	05584	56941
85475	36857	43342	53988	53060	59533	38867	62300	08158	17983	16439	11458	18593	64952
28918	69578	88231	33276	70997	79936	56865	05859	90106	31595	01547	85590	91610	78188
63553	40961	48235	03427	49626	69445	18663	72695	52180	20847	12234	90511	33703	90322
09429	93969	52636	92737	88974	33488	36320	17617	30015	08272	84115	27156	30613	74952
10365	61129	87529	85689	48237	52267	67689	93394	01511	26358	85104	20285	29975	89868
07119	97336	71048	08178	77233	13916	47564	81056	97735	85977	29372	74461	28551	90707
51085	12765	51821	51259	77452	16308	60756	92144	49442	53900	70960	63990	75601	40719
02368	21382	52404	60268	89368	19885	55322	44819	01188	65255	64835	44919	05944	55157
01011	54092	33362	94904	31273	04146	18594	29852	71585	85030	51132	01915	92747	64951
52162	53916	46369	58586	23216	14513	83149	98736	23495	64350	94738	17752	35156	35749
07056	97628	33787	09998	42698	06691	76988	13602	51851	46104	88916	19509	25625	58104
48663	91245	85828	14346	09172	30168	90229	04734	59193	22178	30421	61666	99904	32812
54164	58492	22421	74103	47070	25306	76468	26384	58151	06646	21524	15227	96909	44592
32639	32363	05597	24200	13363	38005	94342	28728	35806	06912	17012	64161	18296	22851
29334	27001	87637	87308	58731	00256	45834	15398	46557	41135	10367	07684	36188	18510
02488	33062	28834	07351	19731	92420	60952	61280	50001	67658	32586	86679	50720	94953
81525	72295	04839	96423	24878	82651	66566	14778	76797	14780	13300	87074	79666	95725
29676	20591	68086	26432	46901	20849	89768	81536	86645	12659	92259	57102	80428	25280
00742	57392	39064	66432	84673	40027	32832	61362	98947	96067	64760	64584	96096	98253
05366	04213	25669	26422	44407	44048	37937	63904	45766	66134	75470	66520	34693	90449
91921	26418	64117	94305	26766	25940	39972	22209	71500	64568	91402	42416	07844	69618
00582	04711	87917	77341	42206	35126	74087	99547	81817	42607	43808	76655	62028	76630
00725	69884	62797	56170	86324	88072	76222	36086	84637	93161	76038	65855	77919	88006
69011	65797	95876	55293	18988	27354	26575	08625	40801	59920	29841	80150	12777	48501
25976	57948	29888	88604	67917	48708	18912	82271	65424	69774	33611	54262	85963	03547
09763	83473	73577	12908	30883	18317	28290	35797	05998	41688	34952	37888	38917	88050
91567	42595	27958	30134	04024	86385	29880	99730	55536	84855	29080	09250	79656	73211
17955	56349	90999	49127	20044	59931	06115	20542	18059	02008	73708	83517	36103	42791
46503	18584	18845	49618	02304	51038	20655	58727	28168	15475	56942	53389	20562	87338
92157	89634	94824	78171	84610	82834	09922	25417	44137	48413	25555	21246	35509	20468
14577	62765	35605	81263	39667	47358	56873	56307	61607	49518	89656	20103	77490	18062
98427	07523	33362	64270	01638	92477	66969	98420	04880	45585	46565	04102	46880	45709
34914	63976	88720	82765	34476	17032	87589	40836	32427	70002	70663	88863	77775	69348
70060	28277	39475	46473	23219	53416	94970	25832	69975	94884	19661	72828	00102	66794
53976	54914	06990	67245	68350	82948	11398	42878	80287	88267	47363	46634	06541	97809
76072	29515	40980	07391	58745	25774	22987	80059	39911	96189	41151	14222	60697	59583
90725	52210	83974	29992	65831	38857	50490	83765	55657	14361	31720	57375	56228	41546
64364	67412	33339	31926	14883	24413	59744	92351	97473	89286	35931	04110	23726	51900
08962	00358	31662	25388	61642	34072	81249	35648	56891	69352	48373	45578	78547	81788
95012	68379	93526	70765	10593	04542	76463	54328	02349	17247	28865	14777	62730	92277
15664	10493	20492	38391	91132	21999	59516	81652	27195	48223	46751	22923	32261	85653

Reprinted with permission from W. H. Beyer, *Handbook of Tables for Probability and Statistics*, 2nd ed. Copyright CRC Press, Boca Raton, Fla., 1986.

Table B Binomial distribution

n	X	0.10	0.15	0.20	0.25	0.30	0.35	0.40	0.45	0.50
2	0	0.8100	0.7225	0.6400	0.5625	0.4900	0.4225	0.3600	0.3025	0.2500
	1	0.1800	0.2550	0.3200	0.3750	0.4200	0.4550	0.4800	0.4950	0.5000
	2	0.0100	0.0225	0.0400	0.0625	0.0900	0.1225	0.1600	0.2025	0.2500
3	0	0.7290	0.6141	0.5120	0.4219	0.3430	0.2746	0.2160	0.1664	0.1250
	1	0.2430	0.3251	0.3840	0.4219	0.4410	0.4436	0.4320	0.4084	0.3750
	2	0.0270	0.0574	0.0960	0.1406	0.1890	0.2389	0.2880	0.3341	0.3750
	3	0.0010	0.0034	0.0080	0.0156	0.0270	0.0429	0.0640	0.0911	0.1250
4	0	0.6561	0.5220	0.4096	0.3164	0.2401	0.1785	0.1296	0.0915	0.0625
	1	0.2916	0.3685	0.4096	0.4219	0.4116	0.3845	0.3456	0.2995	0.2500
	2	0.0486	0.0975	0.1536	0.2109	0.2646	0.3105	0.3456	0.3675	0.3750
	3	0.0036	0.0115	0.0256	0.0469	0.0756	0.1115	0.1536	0.2005	0.2500
	4	0.0001	0.0005	0.0016	0.0039	0.0081	0.0150	0.0256	0.0410	0.0625
5	0	0.5905	0.4437	0.3277	0.2373	0.1681	0.1160	0.0778	0.0503	0.0312
	1	0.3280	0.3915	0.4096	0.3955	0.3602	0.3124	0.2592	0.2059	0.1562
	2	0.0729	0.1382	0.2048	0.2637	0.3087	0.3364	0.3456	0.3369	0.3125
	3	0.0081	0.0244	0.0512	0.0879	0.1323	0.1811	0.2304	0.2757	0.3125
	4	0.0004	0.0022	0.0064	0.0146	0.0284	0.0488	0.0768	0.1128	0.1562
	5		0.0001	0.0003	0.0010	0.0024	0.0053	0.0102	0.0185	0.0312
6	0	0.5314	0.3771	0.2621	0.1780	0.1176	0.0754	0.0467	0.0277	0.0156
	1	0.3543	0.3993	0.3932	0.3560	0.3025	0.2437	0.1866	0.1359	0.0938
	2	0.0984	0.1762	0.2458	0.2966	0.3241	0.3280	0.3110	0.2780	0.2344
	3	0.0146	0.0415	0.0819	0.1318	0.1852	0.2355	0.2765	0.3032	0.3125
	4	0.0012	0.0055	0.0154	0.0330	0.0595	0.0951	0.1382	0.1861	0.2344
	5	0.0001	0.0004	0.0015	0.0044	0.0102	0.0205	0.0369	0.0609	0.0938
	6			0.0001	0.0002	0.0007	0.0018	0.0041	0.0083	0.0156
7	0	0.4783	0.3206	0.2097	0.1335	0.0824	0.0490	0.0280	0.0152	0.0078
	1	0.3720	0.3960	0.3670	0.3115	0.2471	0.1848	0.1306	0.0872	0.0547
	2	0.1240	0.2097	0.2753	0.3115	0.3177	0.2985	0.2613	0.2140	0.1641
	3	0.0230	0.0617	0.1147	0.1730	0.2269	0.2679	0.2903	0.2918	0.2734
	4	0.0026	0.0109	0.0287	0.0577	0.0972	0.1442	0.1935	0.2388	0.2734
	5	0.0002	0.0012	0.0043	0.0115	0.0250	0.0466	0.0774	0.1172	0.1641
	6		0.0001	0.0004	0.0013	0.0036	0.0084	0.0172	0.0320	0.0547
	7				0.0001	0.0002	0.0006	0.0016	0.0037	0.0078
8	0	0.4305	0.2725	0.1678	0.1001	0.0576	0.0319	0.0168	0.0084	0.0039
	1	0.3826	0.3847	0.3355	0.2670	0.1977	0.1373	0.0896	0.0548	0.0312
	2	0.1488	0.2376	0.2936	0.3115	0.2965	0.2587	0.2090	0.1569	0.1094
	3	0.0331	0.0839	0.1468	0.2076	0.2541	0.2786	0.2787	0.2568	0.2188
	4	0.0046	0.0185	0.0459	0.0865	0.1361	0.1875	0.2322	0.2627	0.2734
	5	0.0004	0.0026	0.0092	0.0231	0.0467	0.0808	0.1239	0.1719	0.2188
	6		0.0002	0.0011	0.0038	0.0100	0.0217	0.0413	0.0703	0.1094
	7			0.0001	0.0004	0.0012	0.0033	0.0079	0.0164	0.0313
	8					0.0001	0.0002	0.0007	0.0017	0.0039

Note: Blank entries indicate a binomial probability of less than 0.00005.

(Continued)

Table B Binomial distribution (*continued*)

						p				
n	*X*	0.10	0.15	0.20	0.25	0.30	0.35	0.40	0.45	0.50
9	0	0.3874	0.2316	0.1342	0.0751	0.0404	0.0207	0.0101	0.0046	0.0020
	1	0.3874	0.3679	0.3020	0.2253	0.1556	0.1004	0.0605	0.0339	0.0176
	2	0.1722	0.2597	0.3020	0.3003	0.2668	0.2162	0.1612	0.1110	0.0703
	3	0.0446	0.1069	0.1762	0.2336	0.2668	0.2716	0.2508	0.2119	0.1641
	4	0.0074	0.0283	0.0661	0.1168	0.1715	0.2194	0.2508	0.2600	0.2461
	5	0.0008	0.0050	0.0165	0.0389	0.0735	0.1181	0.1672	0.2128	0.2461
	6	0.0001	0.0006	0.0028	0.0087	0.0210	0.0424	0.0743	0.1160	0.1641
	7			0.0003	0.0012	0.0039	0.0098	0.0212	0.0407	0.0703
	8				0.0001	0.0004	0.0013	0.0035	0.0083	0.0176
	9						0.0001	0.0003	0.0008	0.0020
10	0	0.3487	0.1969	0.1074	0.0563	0.0282	0.0135	0.0060	0.0025	0.0010
	1	0.3874	0.3474	0.2684	0.1877	0.1211	0.0725	0.0403	0.0207	0.0098
	2	0.1937	0.2759	0.3020	0.2816	0.2335	0.1757	0.1209	0.0763	0.0439
	3	0.0574	0.1298	0.2013	0.2503	0.2668	0.2522	0.2150	0.1665	0.1172
	4	0.0112	0.0401	0.0881	0.1460	0.2001	0.2377	0.2508	0.2384	0.2051
	5	0.0015	0.0085	0.0264	0.0584	0.1029	0.1536	0.2007	0.2340	0.2461
	6	0.0001	0.0012	0.0055	0.0162	0.0368	0.0689	0.1115	0.1596	0.2051
	7		0.0001	0.0008	0.0031	0.0090	0.0212	0.0425	0.0746	0.1172
	8			0.0001	0.0004	0.0014	0.0043	0.0106	0.0229	0.0439
	9					0.0001	0.0005	0.0016	0.0042	0.0098
	10							0.0001	0.0003	0.0010
12	0	0.2824	0.1422	0.0687	0.0317	0.0138	0.0057	0.0022	0.0008	0.0002
	1	0.3766	0.3012	0.2062	0.1267	0.0712	0.0368	0.0174	0.0075	0.0029
	2	0.2301	0.2924	0.2835	0.2323	0.1678	0.1088	0.0639	0.0339	0.0161
	3	0.0853	0.1720	0.2362	0.2581	0.2397	0.1954	0.1419	0.0923	0.0537
	4	0.0213	0.0683	0.1329	0.1936	0.2311	0.2367	0.2128	0.1700	0.1208
	5	0.0038	0.0193	0.0532	0.1032	0.1585	0.2039	0.2270	0.2225	0.1934
	6	0.0005	0.0040	0.0155	0.0401	0.0792	0.1281	0.1766	0.2124	0.2256
	7		0.0006	0.0033	0.0115	0.0291	0.0591	0.1009	0.1489	0.1934
	8		0.0001	0.0005	0.0024	0.0078	0.0199	0.0420	0.0762	0.1208
	9			0.0001	0.0004	0.0015	0.0048	0.0125	0.0277	0.0537
	10					0.0002	0.0008	0.0025	0.0068	0.0161
	11						0.0001	0.0003	0.0010	0.0029
	12								0.0001	0.0002
15	0	0.2059	0.0874	0.0352	0.0134	0.0047	0.0016	0.0005	0.0001	
	1	0.3432	0.2312	0.1319	0.0668	0.0305	0.0126	0.0047	0.0016	0.0005
	2	0.2669	0.2856	0.2309	0.1559	0.0916	0.0476	0.0219	0.0090	0.0032
	3	0.1285	0.2184	0.2501	0.2252	0.1700	0.1110	0.0634	0.0318	0.0139
	4	0.0428	0.1156	0.1876	0.2252	0.2186	0.1792	0.1268	0.0780	0.0417
	5	0.0105	0.0449	0.1032	0.1651	0.2061	0.2123	0.1859	0.1404	0.0916
	6	0.0019	0.0132	0.0430	0.0917	0.1472	0.1906	0.2066	0.1914	0.1527
	7	0.0003	0.0030	0.0138	0.0393	0.0811	0.1319	0.1771	0.2013	0.1964
	8		0.0005	0.0035	0.0131	0.0348	0.0710	0.1181	0.1647	0.1964
	9		0.0001	0.0007	0.0034	0.0016	0.0298	0.0612	0.1048	0.1527
	10			0.0001	0.0007	0.0030	0.0096	0.0245	0.0515	0.0916
	11				0.0001	0.0006	0.0024	0.0074	0.0191	0.0417
	12					0.0001	0.0004	0.0016	0.0052	0.0139
	13						0.0001	0.0003	0.0010	0.0032
	14								0.0001	0.0005
	15									

Note: Blank entries indicate a binomial probability of less than 0.00005.

Table B Binomial distribution (*continued*)

n	X	0.10	0.15	0.20	0.25	0.30	0.35	0.40	0.45	0.50
18	0	0.1501	0.0536	0.0180	0.0056	0.0016	0.0004	0.0001		
	1	0.3002	0.1704	0.0811	0.0338	0.0126	0.0042	0.0012	0.0003	0.0001
	2	0.2835	0.2556	0.1723	0.0958	0.0458	0.0190	0.0069	0.0022	0.0006
	3	0.1680	0.2406	0.2297	0.1704	0.1046	0.0547	0.0246	0.0095	0.0031
	4	0.0700	0.1592	0.2153	0.2130	0.1681	0.1104	0.0614	0.0291	0.0117
	5	0.0218	0.0787	0.1507	0.1988	0.2017	0.1664	0.1146	0.0666	0.0327
	6	0.0052	0.0301	0.0816	0.1436	0.1873	0.1941	0.1655	0.1181	0.0708
	7	0.0010	0.0091	0.0350	0.0820	0.1376	0.1792	0.1892	0.1657	0.1214
	8	0.0002	0.0022	0.0120	0.0376	0.0811	0.1327	0.1734	0.1864	0.1669
	9		0.0004	0.0033	0.0139	0.0386	0.0794	0.1284	0.1694	0.1855
	10		0.0001	0.0008	0.0042	0.0149	0.0385	0.0771	0.1248	0.1669
	11			0.0001	0.0010	0.0046	0.0151	0.0374	0.0742	0.1214
	12				0.0002	0.0012	0.0047	0.0145	0.0354	0.0708
	13					0.0002	0.0012	0.0045	0.0134	0.0327
	14						0.0002	0.0011	0.0039	0.0117
	15							0.0002	0.0009	0.0031
	16								0.0001	0.0006
	17									0.0001
	18									
20	0	0.1216	0.0388	0.0115	0.0032	0.0008	0.0002			
	1	0.2702	0.1368	0.0576	0.0211	0.0068	0.0020	0.0005	0.0001	
	2	0.2852	0.2293	0.1369	0.0669	0.0278	0.0100	0.0031	0.0008	0.0002
	3	0.1901	0.2428	0.2054	0.1339	0.0716	0.0323	0.0123	0.0040	0.0011
	4	0.0898	0.1821	0.2182	0.1897	0.1304	0.0738	0.0350	0.0139	0.0046
	5	0.0319	0.1028	0.1746	0.2023	0.1789	0.1272	0.0746	0.0365	0.0148
	6	0.0089	0.0454	0.1091	0.1686	0.1916	0.1712	0.1244	0.0746	0.0370
	7	0.0020	0.0160	0.0545	0.1124	0.1643	0.1844	0.1659	0.1221	0.0739
	8	0.0004	0.0046	0.0222	0.0609	0.1144	0.1614	0.1797	0.1623	0.1201
	9	0.0001	0.0011	0.0074	0.0271	0.0654	0.1158	0.1597	0.1771	0.1602
	10		0.0002	0.0020	0.0099	0.0308	0.0686	0.1171	0.1593	0.1762
	11			0.0005	0.0030	0.0120	0.0336	0.0710	0.1185	0.1602
	12			0.0001	0.0008	0.0039	0.0136	0.0355	0.0727	0.1201
	13				0.0002	0.0010	0.0045	0.0146	0.0366	0.0739
	14					0.0002	0.0012	0.0049	0.0150	0.0370
	15						0.0003	0.0013	0.0049	0.0148
	16							0.0003	0.0013	0.0046
	17								0.0002	0.0011
	18									0.0002
	19									
	20									

Note: Blank entries indicate a binomial probability of less than 0.00005.

(*Continued*)

Table B Binomial distribution (*continued*)

n	X	0.55	0.60	0.65	0.70	0.75	0.80	0.85	0.90	0.95
2	0	0.2025	0.1600	0.1225	0.0900	0.0625	0.0400	0.0225	0.0100	0.0025
	1	0.4950	0.4800	0.4550	0.4200	0.3750	0.3200	0.2550	0.1800	0.0950
	2	0.3025	0.3600	0.4225	0.4900	0.5625	0.6400	0.7225	0.8100	0.9025
3	0	0.0911	0.0640	0.0429	0.0270	0.0156	0.0080	0.0034	0.0010	0.0001
	1	0.3341	0.2880	0.2389	0.1890	0.1406	0.0960	0.0574	0.0270	0.0071
	2	0.4084	0.4320	0.4436	0.4410	0.4219	0.3840	0.3251	0.2430	0.1354
	3	0.1664	0.2160	0.2746	0.3430	0.4219	0.5120	0.6141	0.7290	0.8574
4	0	0.0410	0.0256	0.0150	0.0081	0.0039	0.0016	0.0005	0.0001	
	1	0.2005	0.1536	0.1115	0.0756	0.0469	0.0256	0.0115	0.0036	0.0005
	2	0.3675	0.3456	0.3105	0.2646	0.2109	0.1536	0.0975	0.0486	0.0135
	3	0.2995	0.3456	0.3845	0.4116	0.4219	0.4096	0.3685	0.2916	0.1715
	4	0.0915	0.1296	0.1785	0.2401	0.3164	0.4096	0.5220	0.6561	0.8145
5	0	0.0185	0.0102	0.0053	0.0024	0.0010	0.0003	0.0001		
	1	0.1128	0.0768	0.0488	0.0284	0.0146	0.0064	0.0022	0.0005	
	2	0.2757	0.2304	0.1811	0.1323	0.0879	0.0512	0.0244	0.0081	0.0011
	3	0.3369	0.3456	0.3364	0.3087	0.2637	0.2048	0.1382	0.0729	0.0214
	4	0.2059	0.2592	0.3124	0.3601	0.3955	0.4096	0.3915	0.3281	0.2036
	5	0.0503	0.0778	0.1160	0.1681	0.2373	0.3277	0.4437	0.5905	0.7738
6	0	0.0083	0.0041	0.0018	0.0007	0.0002	0.0001			
	1	0.0609	0.0369	0.0205	0.0102	0.0044	0.0015	0.0004	0.0001	
	2	0.1861	0.1382	0.0951	0.0595	0.0330	0.0154	0.0055	0.0012	0.0001
	3	0.3032	0.2765	0.2355	0.1852	0.1318	0.0819	0.0415	0.0146	0.0021
	4	0.2780	0.3110	0.3280	0.3241	0.2966	0.2458	0.1762	0.0984	0.0305
	5	0.1359	0.1866	0.2437	0.3025	0.3560	0.3932	0.3993	0.3543	0.2321
	6	0.0277	0.0467	0.0754	0.1176	0.1780	0.2621	0.3771	0.5314	0.7351
7	0	0.0037	0.0016	0.0006	0.0002	0.0001				
	1	0.0320	0.0172	0.0084	0.0036	0.0013	0.0004	0.0001		
	2	0.1172	0.0774	0.0466	0.0250	0.0115	0.0043	0.0012	0.0002	
	3	0.2388	0.1935	0.1442	0.0972	0.0577	0.0287	0.0109	0.0026	0.0002
	4	0.2918	0.2903	0.2679	0.2269	0.1730	0.1147	0.0617	0.0230	0.0036
	5	0.2140	0.2613	0.2985	0.3177	0.3115	0.2753	0.2097	0.1240	0.0406
	6	0.0872	0.1306	0.1848	0.2471	0.3115	0.3670	0.3960	0.3720	0.2573
	7	0.0152	0.0280	0.0490	0.0824	0.1335	0.2097	0.3206	0.4783	0.6983
8	0	0.0017	0.0007	0.0002	0.0001					
	1	0.0164	0.0079	0.0033	0.0012	0.0004	0.0001			
	2	0.0703	0.0413	0.0217	0.0100	0.0038	0.0011	0.0002		
	3	0.1719	0.1239	0.0808	0.0467	0.0231	0.0092	0.0026	0.0004	
	4	0.2627	0.2322	0.1875	0.1361	0.0865	0.0459	0.0185	0.0046	0.0004
	5	0.2568	0.2787	0.2786	0.2541	0.2076	0.1468	0.0839	0.0331	0.0054
	6	0.1569	0.2090	0.2587	0.2965	0.3115	0.2936	0.2376	0.1488	0.0515
	7	0.0548	0.0896	0.1373	0.1977	0.2670	0.3355	0.3847	0.3826	0.2793
	8	0.0084	0.0168	0.0319	0.0576	0.1001	0.1678	0.2725	0.4305	0.6634

Note: Blank entries indicate a binomial probability of less than 0.00005.

Table B Binomial distribution (*continued*)

n	X	0.55	0.60	0.65	0.70	0.75	0.80	0.85	0.90	0.95
9	0	0.0008	0.0003	0.0001						
	1	0.0083	0.0035	0.0013	0.0004	0.0001				
	2	0.0407	0.0212	0.0098	0.0039	0.0012	0.0003			
	3	0.1160	0.0743	0.0424	0.0210	0.0087	0.0028	0.0006	0.0001	
	4	0.2128	0.1672	0.1181	0.0735	0.0389	0.0165	0.0050	0.0008	
	5	0.2600	0.2508	0.2194	0.1715	0.1168	0.0661	0.0283	0.0074	0.0006
	6	0.2119	0.2508	0.2716	0.2668	0.2336	0.1762	0.1069	0.0446	0.0077
	7	0.1110	0.1612	0.2162	0.2668	0.3003	0.3020	0.2597	0.1722	0.0629
	8	0.0339	0.0605	0.1004	0.1556	0.2253	0.3020	0.3679	0.3874	0.2985
	9	0.0046	0.0101	0.0207	0.0404	0.0751	0.1342	0.2316	0.3874	0.6302
10	0	0.0003	0.0001							
	1	0.0042	0.0016	0.0005	0.0001					
	2	0.0229	0.0106	0.0043	0.0014	0.0004	0.0001			
	3	0.0746	0.0425	0.0212	0.0090	0.0031	0.0008	0.0001		
	4	0.1596	0.1115	0.0689	0.0368	0.0162	0.0055	0.0012	0.0001	
	5	0.2340	0.2007	0.1536	0.1029	0.0584	0.0264	0.0085	0.0015	0.0001
	6	0.2384	0.2508	0.2377	0.2001	0.1460	0.0881	0.0401	0.0112	0.0010
	7	0.1665	0.2150	0.2522	0.2668	0.2503	0.2013	0.1298	0.0574	0.0105
	8	0.0763	0.1209	0.1757	0.2335	0.2816	0.3020	0.2759	0.1937	0.0746
	9	0.0207	0.0403	0.0725	0.1211	0.1877	0.2684	0.3474	0.3874	0.3151
	10	0.0025	0.0060	0.0135	0.0282	0.0563	0.1074	0.1969	0.3487	0.5987
12	0	0.0001								
	1	0.0010	0.0003	0.0001						
	2	0.0068	0.0025	0.0008	0.0002					
	3	0.0277	0.0125	0.0048	0.0015	0.0004	0.0001			
	4	0.0762	0.0420	0.0199	0.0078	0.0024	0.0005	0.0001		
	5	0.1489	0.1009	0.0591	0.0291	0.0115	0.0033	0.0006		
	6	0.2124	0.1766	0.1281	0.0792	0.0401	0.0155	0.0040	0.0005	
	7	0.2225	0.2270	0.2039	0.1585	0.1032	0.0532	0.0193	0.0038	0.0002
	8	0.1700	0.2128	0.2367	0.2311	0.1936	0.1329	0.0683	0.0213	0.0021
	9	0.0923	0.1419	0.1954	0.2397	0.2581	0.2362	0.1720	0.0852	0.0173
	10	0.0339	0.0639	0.1088	0.1678	0.2323	0.2835	0.2924	0.2301	0.0988
	11	0.0075	0.0174	0.0368	0.0712	0.1267	0.2062	0.3012	0.3766	0.3413
	12	0.0008	0.0022	0.0057	0.0138	0.0317	0.0687	0.1422	0.2824	0.5404
15	0									
	1	0.0001								
	2	0.0010	0.0003	0.0001						
	3	0.0052	0.0016	0.0004	0.0001					
	4	0.0191	0.0074	0.0024	0.0006	0.0001				
	5	0.0515	0.0245	0.0096	0.0030	0.0007	0.0001			
	6	0.1048	0.0612	0.0298	0.0116	0.0034	0.0007	0.0001		
	7	0.1647	0.1181	0.0710	0.0348	0.0131	0.0035	0.0005		
	8	0.2013	0.1771	0.1319	0.0811	0.0393	0.0138	0.0030	0.0003	
	9	0.1914	0.2066	0.1906	0.1472	0.0917	0.0430	0.0132	0.0019	
	10	0.1404	0.1859	0.2123	0.2061	0.1651	0.1032	0.0449	0.0105	0.0006
	11	0.0780	0.1268	0.1792	0.2186	0.2252	0.1876	0.1156	0.0428	0.0049

Note: Blank entries indicate a binomial probability of less than 0.00005.

(Continued)

Table B Binomial distribution (*continued*)

n	X	0.55	0.60	0.65	0.70	0.75	0.80	0.85	0.90	0.95
	12	0.0318	0.0634	0.1110	0.1700	0.2252	0.2501	0.2184	0.1285	0.0307
	13	0.0090	0.0219	0.0476	0.0916	0.1559	0.2309	0.2856	0.2669	0.1348
	14	0.0016	0.0047	0.0126	0.0305	0.0668	0.1319	0.2312	0.3432	0.3658
	15	0.0001	0.0005	0.0016	0.0047	0.0134	0.0352	0.0874	0.2059	0.4633
18	0									
	1									
	2	0.0001								
	3	0.0009	0.0002							
	4	0.0039	0.0011	0.0002						
	5	0.0134	0.0045	0.0012	0.0002					
	6	0.0354	0.0145	0.0047	0.0012	0.0002				
	7	0.0742	0.0374	0.0151	0.0046	0.0010	0.0001			
	8	0.1248	0.0771	0.0385	0.0149	0.0042	0.0008	0.0001		
	9	0.1694	0.1284	0.0794	0.0386	0.0139	0.0033	0.0004		
	10	0.1864	0.1734	0.1327	0.0811	0.0376	0.0120	0.0022	0.0002	
	11	0.1657	0.1892	0.1792	0.1376	0.0820	0.0350	0.0091	0.0010	
	12	0.1181	0.1655	0.1941	0.1873	0.1436	0.0816	0.0301	0.0052	0.0002
	13	0.0666	0.1146	0.1664	0.2017	0.1988	0.1507	0.0787	0.0218	0.0014
	14	0.0291	0.0614	0.1104	0.1681	0.2130	0.2153	0.1592	0.0700	0.0093
	15	0.0095	0.0246	0.0547	0.1046	0.1704	0.2297	0.2406	0.1680	0.0473
	16	0.0022	0.0069	0.0190	0.0458	0.0958	0.1723	0.2556	0.2835	0.1683
	17	0.0003	0.0012	0.0042	0.0126	0.0338	0.0811	0.1704	0.3002	0.3763
	18		0.0001	0.0004	0.0016	0.0056	0.0180	0.0536	0.1501	0.3972
20	0									
	1									
	2									
	3	0.0002								
	4	0.0013	0.0003							
	5	0.0049	0.0013	0.0003						
	6	0.0150	0.0049	0.0012	0.0002					
	7	0.0366	0.0146	0.0045	0.0010	0.0002				
	8	0.0727	0.0355	0.0136	0.0039	0.0008	0.0001			
	9	0.1185	0.0710	0.0336	0.0120	0.0030	0.0005			
	10	0.1593	0.1171	0.0686	0.0308	0.0099	0.0020	0.0002		
	11	0.1771	0.1597	0.1158	0.0654	0.0271	0.0074	0.0011	0.0001	
	12	0.1623	0.1797	0.1614	0.1144	0.0609	0.0222	0.0046	0.0004	
	13	0.1221	0.1659	0.1844	0.1643	0.1124	0.0545	0.0160	0.0020	
	14	0.0746	0.1244	0.1712	0.1916	0.1686	0.1091	0.0454	0.0089	0.0003
	15	0.0365	0.0746	0.1272	0.1789	0.2023	0.1746	0.1028	0.0319	0.0022
	16	0.0139	0.0350	0.0738	0.1304	0.1897	0.2182	0.1821	0.0898	0.0133
	17	0.0040	0.0123	0.0323	0.0716	0.1339	0.2054	0.2428	0.1901	0.0596
	18	0.0008	0.0031	0.0100	0.0278	0.0669	0.1369	0.2293	0.2852	0.1887
	19	0.0001	0.0005	0.0020	0.0068	0.0211	0.0576	0.1368	0.2702	0.3774
	20			0.0002	0.0008	0.0032	0.0115	0.0388	0.1216	0.3585

Note: Blank entries indicate a binomial probability of less than 0.00005.

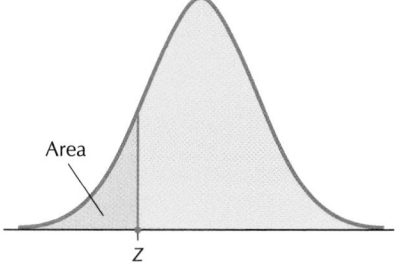

Area

Z

Table C Standard normal distribution

Z	0.00	0.01	0.02	0.03	0.04	0.05	0.06	0.07	0.08	0.09
−3.4	0.0003	0.0003	0.0003	0.0003	0.0003	0.0003	0.0003	0.0003	0.0003	0.0002
−3.3	0.0005	0.0005	0.0005	0.0004	0.0004	0.0004	0.0004	0.0004	0.0004	0.0003
−3.2	0.0007	0.0007	0.0006	0.0006	0.0006	0.0006	0.0006	0.0005	0.0005	0.0005
−3.1	0.0010	0.0009	0.0009	0.0009	0.0008	0.0008	0.0008	0.0008	0.0007	0.0007
−3.0	0.0013	0.0013	0.0013	0.0012	0.0012	0.0011	0.0011	0.0011	0.0010	0.0010
−2.9	0.0019	0.0018	0.0018	0.0017	0.0016	0.0016	0.0015	0.0015	0.0014	0.0014
−2.8	0.0026	0.0025	0.0024	0.0023	0.0023	0.0022	0.0021	0.0021	0.0020	0.0019
−2.7	0.0035	0.0034	0.0033	0.0032	0.0031	0.0030	0.0029	0.0028	0.0027	0.0026
−2.6	0.0047	0.0045	0.0044	0.0043	0.0041	0.0040	0.0039	0.0038	0.0037	0.0036
−2.5	0.0062	0.0060	0.0059	0.0057	0.0055	0.0054	0.0052	0.0051	0.0049	0.0048
−2.4	0.0082	0.0080	0.0078	0.0075	0.0073	0.0071	0.0069	0.0068	0.0066	0.0064
−2.3	0.0107	0.0104	0.0102	0.0099	0.0096	0.0094	0.0091	0.0089	0.0087	0.0084
−2.2	0.0139	0.0136	0.0132	0.0129	0.0125	0.0122	0.0119	0.0116	0.0113	0.0110
−2.1	0.0179	0.0174	0.0170	0.0166	0.0162	0.0158	0.0154	0.0150	0.0146	0.0143
−2.0	0.0228	0.0222	0.0217	0.0212	0.0207	0.0202	0.0197	0.0192	0.0188	0.0183
−1.9	0.0287	0.0281	0.0274	0.0268	0.0262	0.0256	0.0250	0.0244	0.0239	0.0233
−1.8	0.0359	0.0351	0.0344	0.0336	0.0329	0.0322	0.0314	0.0307	0.0301	0.0294
−1.7	0.0446	0.0436	0.0427	0.0418	0.0409	0.0401	0.0392	0.0384	0.0375	0.0367
−1.6	0.0548	0.0537	0.0526	0.0516	0.0505	0.0495	0.0485	0.0475	0.0465	0.0455
−1.5	0.0668	0.0655	0.0643	0.0630	0.0618	0.0606	0.0594	0.0582	0.0571	0.0559
−1.4	0.0808	0.0793	0.0778	0.0764	0.0749	0.0735	0.0721	0.0708	0.0694	0.0681
−1.3	0.0968	0.0951	0.0934	0.0918	0.0901	0.0885	0.0869	0.0853	0.0838	0.0823
−1.2	0.1151	0.1131	0.1112	0.1093	0.1075	0.1056	0.1038	0.1020	0.1003	0.0985
−1.1	0.1357	0.1335	0.1314	0.1292	0.1271	0.1251	0.1230	0.1210	0.1190	0.1170
−1.0	0.1587	0.1562	0.1539	0.1515	0.1492	0.1469	0.1446	0.1423	0.1401	0.1379
−0.9	0.1841	0.1814	0.1788	0.1762	0.1736	0.1711	0.1685	0.1660	0.1635	0.1611
−0.8	0.2119	0.2090	0.2061	0.2033	0.2005	0.1977	0.1949	0.1922	0.1894	0.1867
−0.7	0.2420	0.2389	0.2358	0.2327	0.2296	0.2266	0.2236	0.2206	0.2177	0.2148
−0.6	0.2743	0.2709	0.2676	0.2643	0.2611	0.2578	0.2546	0.2514	0.2483	0.2451
−0.5	0.3085	0.3050	0.3015	0.2981	0.2946	0.2912	0.2877	0.2843	0.2810	0.2776
−0.4	0.3446	0.3409	0.3372	0.3336	0.3300	0.3264	0.3228	0.3192	0.3156	0.3121
−0.3	0.3821	0.3783	0.3745	0.3707	0.3669	0.3632	0.3594	0.3557	0.3520	0.3483
−0.2	0.4207	0.4168	0.4129	0.4090	0.4052	0.4013	0.3974	0.3936	0.3897	0.3859
−0.1	0.4602	0.4562	0.4522	0.4483	0.4443	0.4404	0.4364	0.4325	0.4286	0.4247
−0.0	0.5000	0.4960	0.4920	0.4880	0.4840	0.4801	0.4761	0.4721	0.4681	0.4641

(Continued)

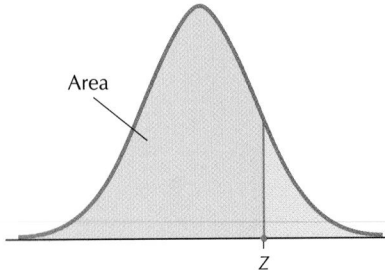

Area

z

Table C Standard normal distribution (*continued*)

z	0.00	0.01	0.02	0.03	0.04	0.05	0.06	0.07	0.08	0.09
0.0	0.5000	0.5040	0.5080	0.5120	0.5160	0.5199	0.5239	0.5279	0.5319	0.5359
0.1	0.5398	0.5438	0.5478	0.5517	0.5557	0.5596	0.5636	0.5675	0.5714	0.5753
0.2	0.5793	0.5832	0.5871	0.5910	0.5948	0.5987	0.6026	0.6064	0.6103	0.6141
0.3	0.6179	0.6217	0.6255	0.6293	0.6331	0.6368	0.6406	0.6443	0.6480	0.6517
0.4	0.6554	0.6591	0.6628	0.6664	0.6700	0.6736	0.6772	0.6808	0.6844	0.6879
0.5	0.6915	0.6950	0.6985	0.7019	0.7054	0.7088	0.7123	0.7157	0.7190	0.7224
0.6	0.7257	0.7291	0.7324	0.7357	0.7389	0.7422	0.7454	0.7486	0.7517	0.7549
0.7	0.7580	0.7611	0.7642	0.7673	0.7704	0.7734	0.7764	0.7794	0.7823	0.7852
0.8	0.7881	0.7910	0.7939	0.7967	0.7995	0.8023	0.8051	0.8078	0.8106	0.8133
0.9	0.8159	0.8186	0.8212	0.8238	0.8264	0.8289	0.8315	0.8340	0.8365	0.8389
1.0	0.8413	0.8438	0.8461	0.8485	0.8508	0.8531	0.8554	0.8577	0.8599	0.8621
1.1	0.8643	0.8665	0.8686	0.8708	0.8729	0.8749	0.8770	0.8790	0.8810	0.8830
1.2	0.8849	0.8869	0.8888	0.8907	0.8925	0.8944	0.8962	0.8980	0.8997	0.9015
1.3	0.9032	0.9049	0.9066	0.9082	0.9099	0.9115	0.9131	0.9147	0.9162	0.9177
1.4	0.9192	0.9207	0.9222	0.9236	0.9251	0.9265	0.9279	0.9292	0.9306	0.9319
1.5	0.9332	0.9345	0.9357	0.9370	0.9382	0.9394	0.9406	0.9418	0.9429	0.9441
1.6	0.9452	0.9463	0.9474	0.9484	0.9495	0.9505	0.9515	0.9525	0.9535	0.9545
1.7	0.9554	0.9564	0.9573	0.9582	0.9591	0.9599	0.9608	0.9616	0.9625	0.9633
1.8	0.9641	0.9649	0.9656	0.9664	0.9671	0.9678	0.9686	0.9693	0.9699	0.9706
1.9	0.9713	0.9719	0.9726	0.9732	0.9738	0.9744	0.9750	0.9756	0.9761	0.9767
2.0	0.9772	0.9778	0.9783	0.9788	0.9793	0.9798	0.9803	0.9808	0.9812	0.9817
2.1	0.9821	0.9826	0.9830	0.9834	0.9838	0.9842	0.9846	0.9850	0.9854	0.9857
2.2	0.9861	0.9864	0.9868	0.9871	0.9875	0.9878	0.9881	0.9884	0.9887	0.9890
2.3	0.9893	0.9896	0.9898	0.9901	0.9904	0.9906	0.9909	0.9911	0.9913	0.9916
2.4	0.9918	0.9920	0.9922	0.9925	0.9927	0.9929	0.9931	0.9932	0.9934	0.9936
2.5	0.9938	0.9940	0.9941	0.9943	0.9945	0.9946	0.9948	0.9949	0.9951	0.9952
2.6	0.9953	0.9955	0.9956	0.9957	0.9959	0.9960	0.9961	0.9962	0.9963	0.9964
2.7	0.9965	0.9966	0.9967	0.9968	0.9969	0.9970	0.9971	0.9972	0.9973	0.9974
2.8	0.9974	0.9975	0.9976	0.9977	0.9977	0.9978	0.9979	0.9979	0.9980	0.9981
2.9	0.9981	0.9982	0.9982	0.9983	0.9984	0.9984	0.9985	0.9985	0.9986	0.9986
3.0	0.9987	0.9987	0.9987	0.9988	0.9988	0.9989	0.9989	0.9989	0.9990	0.9990
3.1	0.9990	0.9991	0.9991	0.9991	0.9992	0.9992	0.9992	0.9992	0.9993	0.9993
3.2	0.9993	0.9993	0.9994	0.9994	0.9994	0.9994	0.9994	0.9995	0.9995	0.9995
3.3	0.9995	0.9995	0.9995	0.9996	0.9996	0.9996	0.9996	0.9996	0.9996	0.9997
3.4	0.9997	0.9997	0.9997	0.9997	0.9997	0.9997	0.9997	0.9997	0.9997	0.9998

Table D *t*-Distribution

		Confidence level				
		80%	90%	95%	98%	99%
				Area in one tail		
		0.10	0.05	0.025	0.01	0.005
				Area in two tails		
		0.20	0.10	0.05	0.02	0.01
df	1	3.078	6.314	12.706	31.821	63.657
	2	1.886	2.920	4.303	6.965	9.925
	3	1.638	2.353	3.182	4.541	5.841
	4	1.533	2.132	2.776	3.747	4.604
	5	1.476	2.015	2.571	3.365	4.032
	6	1.440	1.943	2.447	3.143	3.707
	7	1.415	1.895	2.365	2.998	3.499
	8	1.397	1.860	2.306	2.896	3.355
	9	1.383	1.833	2.262	2.821	3.250
	10	1.372	1.812	2.228	2.764	3.169
	11	1.363	1.796	2.201	2.718	3.106
	12	1.356	1.782	2.179	2.681	3.055
	13	1.350	1.771	2.160	2.650	3.012
	14	1.345	1.761	2.145	2.624	2.977
	15	1.341	1.753	2.131	2.602	2.947
	16	1.337	1.746	2.120	2.583	2.921
	17	1.333	1.740	2.110	2.567	2.898
	18	1.330	1.734	2.101	2.552	2.878
	19	1.328	1.729	2.093	2.539	2.861
	20	1.325	1.725	2.086	2.528	2.845
	21	1.323	1.721	2.080	2.518	2.831
	22	1.321	1.717	2.074	2.508	2.819
	23	1.319	1.714	2.069	2.500	2.807
	24	1.318	1.711	2.064	2.492	2.797
	25	1.316	1.708	2.060	2.485	2.787
	26	1.315	1.706	2.056	2.479	2.779
	27	1.314	1.703	2.052	2.473	2.771
	28	1.313	1.701	2.048	2.467	2.763
	29	1.311	1.699	2.045	2.462	2.756
	30	1.310	1.697	2.042	2.457	2.750
	31	1.309	1.696	2.040	2.453	2.744
	32	1.309	1.694	2.037	2.449	2.738
	33	1.308	1.692	2.035	2.445	2.733
	34	1.307	1.691	2.032	2.441	2.728
	35	1.306	1.690	2.030	2.438	2.724
	36	1.306	1.688	2.028	2.435	2.719
	37	1.305	1.687	2.026	2.431	2.715
	38	1.304	1.686	2.024	2.429	2.712
	39	1.304	1.685	2.023	2.426	2.708
	40	1.303	1.684	2.021	2.423	2.704
	50	1.299	1.676	2.009	2.403	2.678
	60	1.296	1.671	2.000	2.390	2.660
	70	1.294	1.667	1.994	2.381	2.648
	80	1.292	1.664	1.990	2.374	2.639
	90	1.291	1.662	1.987	2.368	2.632
	100	1.290	1.660	1.984	2.364	2.626
	1000	1.282	1.646	1.962	2.330	2.581
	z	1.282	1.645	1.960	2.326	2.576

Table E Chi-square (χ^2) distribution

Degrees of freedom	Area to the right of critical value									
	0.995	0.99	0.975	0.95	0.90	0.10	0.05	0.025	0.01	0.005
1	—	—	0.001	0.004	0.016	2.706	3.841	5.024	6.635	7.879
2	0.010	0.020	0.051	0.103	0.211	4.605	5.991	7.378	9.210	10.597
3	0.072	0.115	0.216	0.352	0.584	6.251	7.815	9.348	11.345	12.838
4	0.207	0.297	0.484	0.711	1.064	7.779	9.488	11.143	13.277	14.860
5	0.412	0.554	0.831	1.145	1.610	9.236	11.071	12.833	15.086	16.750
6	0.676	0.872	1.237	1.635	2.204	10.645	12.592	14.449	16.812	18.548
7	0.989	1.239	1.690	2.167	2.833	12.017	14.067	16.013	18.475	20.278
8	1.344	1.646	2.180	2.733	3.490	13.362	15.507	17.535	20.090	21.955
9	1.735	2.088	2.700	3.325	4.168	14.684	16.919	19.023	21.666	23.589
10	2.156	2.558	3.247	3.940	4.865	15.987	18.307	20.483	23.209	25.188
11	2.603	3.053	3.816	4.575	5.578	17.275	19.675	21.920	24.725	26.757
12	3.074	3.571	4.404	5.226	6.304	18.549	21.026	23.337	26.217	28.299
13	3.565	4.107	5.009	5.892	7.042	19.812	22.362	24.736	27.688	29.819
14	4.075	4.660	5.629	6.571	7.790	21.064	23.685	26.119	29.141	31.319
15	4.601	5.229	6.262	7.261	8.547	22.307	24.996	27.488	30.578	32.801
16	5.142	5.812	6.908	7.962	9.312	23.542	26.296	28.845	32.000	34.267
17	5.697	6.408	7.564	8.672	10.085	24.769	27.587	30.191	33.409	35.718
18	6.265	7.015	8.231	9.390	10.865	25.989	28.869	31.526	34.805	37.156
19	6.844	7.633	8.907	10.117	11.651	27.204	30.144	32.852	36.191	38.582
20	7.434	8.260	9.591	10.851	12.443	28.412	31.410	34.170	37.566	39.997
21	8.034	8.897	10.283	11.591	13.240	29.615	32.671	35.479	38.932	41.401
22	8.643	9.542	10.982	12.338	14.042	30.813	33.924	36.781	40.289	42.796
23	9.260	10.196	11.689	13.091	14.848	32.007	35.172	38.076	41.638	44.181
24	9.886	10.856	12.401	13.848	15.659	33.196	36.415	39.364	42.980	45.559
25	10.520	11.524	13.120	14.611	16.473	34.382	37.652	40.646	44.314	46.928
26	11.160	12.198	13.844	15.379	17.292	35.563	38.885	41.923	45.642	48.290
27	11.808	12.879	14.573	16.151	18.114	36.741	40.113	43.194	46.963	49.645
28	12.461	13.565	15.308	16.928	18.939	37.916	41.337	44.461	48.278	50.993
29	13.121	14.257	16.047	17.708	19.768	39.087	42.557	45.722	49.588	52.336
30	13.787	14.954	16.791	18.493	20.599	40.256	43.773	46.979	50.892	53.672
40	20.707	22.164	24.433	26.509	29.051	51.805	55.758	59.342	63.691	66.766
50	27.991	29.707	32.357	34.764	37.689	63.167	67.505	71.420	76.154	79.490
60	35.534	37.485	40.482	43.188	46.459	74.397	79.082	83.298	88.379	91.952
70	43.275	45.442	48.758	51.739	55.329	85.527	90.531	95.023	100.425	104.215
80	51.172	53.540	57.153	60.391	64.278	96.578	101.879	106.629	112.329	116.321
90	59.196	61.754	65.647	69.126	73.291	107.565	113.145	118.136	124.116	128.299
100	67.328	70.065	74.222	77.929	82.358	118.498	124.342	129.561	135.807	140.169

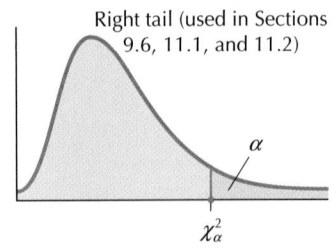

Right tail (used in Sections 9.6, 11.1, and 11.2)

α

χ^2_α

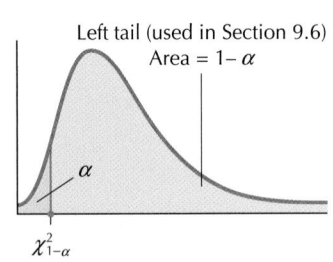

Left tail (used in Section 9.6)
Area = $1 - \alpha$

α

$\chi^2_{1-\alpha}$

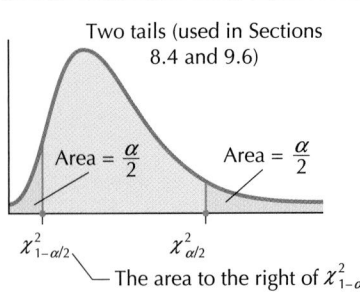

Two tails (used in Sections 8.4 and 9.6)

Area = $\dfrac{\alpha}{2}$ Area = $\dfrac{\alpha}{2}$

$\chi^2_{1-\alpha/2}$ $\chi^2_{\alpha/2}$

The area to the right of $\chi^2_{1-\alpha/2}$ is $1 - \dfrac{\alpha}{2}$.

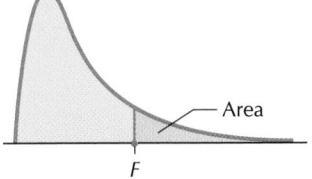
Area

F

Table F F-Distribution critical values

					df₁				
	Area in right tail	**1**	**2**	**3**	**4**	**5**	**6**	**7**	**8**
	0.100	39.86	49.59	53.59	55.83	57.24	58.20	58.91	59.44
	0.050	161.45	199.50	215.71	224.58	230.16	233.99	236.77	238.88
1	0.025	647.79	799.50	864.16	899.58	921.85	937.11	948.22	956.66
	0.010	4052.20	4999.50	5403.40	5624.60	5763.60	5859.00	5928.40	5981.10
	0.001	405284.00	500000.00	540379.00	562500.00	576405.00	585937.00	592873.00	598144.00
	0.100	8.53	9.00	9.16	9.24	9.29	9.33	9.35	9.37
	0.050	18.51	19.00	19.16	19.25	19.30	19.33	19.35	19.37
2	0.025	38.51	39.00	39.17	39.25	39.30	39.33	39.36	39.37
	0.010	98.50	99.00	99.17	99.25	99.30	99.33	99.36	99.37
	0.001	998.50	999.00	999.17	999.25	999.30	999.33	999.36	999.37
	0.100	5.54	5.46	5.39	5.34	5.31	5.28	5.27	5.25
	0.050	10.13	9.55	9.28	9.12	9.01	8.94	8.89	8.85
3	0.025	17.44	16.04	15.44	15.10	14.88	14.73	14.62	14.54
	0.010	34.12	30.82	29.46	28.71	28.24	27.91	27.67	27.49
	0.001	167.03	148.50	141.11	137.10	134.58	132.85	131.58	130.62
	0.100	4.54	4.32	4.19	4.11	4.05	4.01	3.98	3.95
	0.050	7.71	6.94	6.59	6.39	6.26	6.16	6.09	6.04
4	0.025	12.22	10.65	9.98	9.60	9.36	9.20	9.07	8.98
	0.010	21.20	18.00	16.69	15.98	15.52	15.21	14.98	14.80
	0.001	74.14	61.25	56.18	53.44	51.71	50.53	49.66	49.00
	0.100	4.06	3.78	3.62	3.52	3.45	3.40	3.37	3.34
	0.050	6.61	5.79	5.41	5.19	5.05	4.95	4.88	4.82
5	0.025	10.01	8.43	7.76	7.39	7.15	6.98	6.85	6.76
	0.010	16.26	13.27	12.06	11.39	10.97	10.67	10.46	10.29
	0.001	47.18	37.12	33.20	31.09	29.75	28.83	28.16	27.65
	0.100	3.78	3.46	3.29	3.18	3.11	3.05	3.01	2.98
	0.050	5.99	5.14	4.76	4.53	4.39	4.28	4.21	4.15
6	0.025	8.81	7.26	6.60	6.23	5.99 ‘	5.82	5.70	5.60
	0.010	13.75	10.92	9.78	9.15	8.75	8.47	8.26	8.10
	0.001	35.51	27.00	23.70	21.92	20.80	20.03	19.46	19.03
	0.100	3.59	3.26	3.07	2.96	2.88	2.83	2.78	2.75
	0.050	5.59	4.74	4.35	4.12	3.97	3.87	3.79	3.73
7	0.025	8.07	6.54	5.89	5.52	5.29	5.12	4.99	4.90
	0.010	12.25	9.55	8.45	7.85	7.46	7.19	6.99	6.84
	0.001	29.25	21.69	18.77	17.20	16.21	15.52	15.02	14.63
	0.100	3.46	3.11	2.92	2.81	2.73	2.67	2.62	2.59
	0.050	5.32	4.46	4.07	3.84	3.69	3.58	3.50	3.44
8	0.025	7.57	6.06	5.42	5.05	4.82	4.65	4.53	4.43
	0.010	11.26	8.65	7.59	7.01	6.63	6.37	6.18	6.03
	0.001	25.41	18.49	15.83	14.39	13.48	12.86	12.40	12.05

df₂

(Continued)

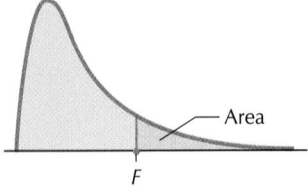

Area

F

Table F *F*-Distribution critical values (*continued*)

		df₁							
df₂	Area in right tail	9	10	15	20	30	60	120	1000
1	0.100	59.86	60.19	61.22	61.74	62.26	62.79	63.06	63.30
	0.050	240.54	241.88	245.95	248.01	250.10	252.20	253.25	254.19
	0.025	963.28	968.63	984.87	993.10	1001.4	1009.8	1014.0	1017.7
	0.010	6022.5	6055.8	6157.3	6208.7	6260.6	6313.0	6339.4	6362.7
	0.001	602284.0	605621.0	615764.0	620908.0	626099.0	631337.0	633972.0	636301.0
2	0.100	9.38	9.39	9.42	9.44	9.16	9.47	9.48	9.49
	0.050	19.38	19.40	19.43	19.45	19.46	19.48	19.49	19.49
	0.025	39.39	39.40	39.43	39.45	39.46	39.48	39.49	39.50
	0.010	99.39	99.40	99.43	99.45	99.47	99.48	99.49	99.50
	0.001	999.39	999.40	999.43	999.45	999.47	999.48	999.49	999.50
3	0.100	5.24	5.23	5.20	5.18	5.17	5.15	5.14	5.13
	0.050	8.81	8.79	8.70	8.66	8.62	8.57	8.55	8.53
	0.025	14.47	14.42	14.25	14.17	14.08	13.99	13.95	13.91
	0.010	27.35	27.23	26.87	26.69	26.50	26.32	26.22	26.14
	0.001	129.86	129.25	127.37	126.42	125.45	124.47	123.97	123.53
4	0.100	3.94	3.92	3.87	3.84	3.82	3.79	3.78	3.76
	0.050	6.00	5.96	5.86	5.80	5.75	5.69	5.66	5.63
	0.025	8.90	8.84	8.66	8.56	8.46	8.36	8.31	8.26
	0.010	14.66	14.55	14.20	14.02	13.84	13.65	13.56	13.47
	0.001	48.47	48.05	46.76	46.10	45.43	44.75	44.40	44.09
5	0.100	3.32	3.30	3.24	3.21	3.17	3.14	3.12	3.11
	0.050	4.77	4.74	4.62	4.56	4.50	4.43	4.40	4.37
	0.025	6.68	6.62	6.43	6.33	6.23	6.12	6.07	6.02
	0.010	10.16	10.05	9.72	9.55	9.38	9.20	9.11	9.03
	0.001	27.24	26.92	25.91	25.39	24.87	24.33	24.06	23.82
6	0.100	2.96	2.94	2.87	2.84	2.80	2.76	2.74	2.72
	0.050	4.10	4.06	3.94	3.87	3.81	3.74	3.70	3.67
	0.025	5.52	5.46	5.27	5.17	5.07	4.96	4.90	4.86
	0.010	7.98	7.87	7.56	7.40	7.23	7.06	6.97	6.89
	0.001	18.69	18.41	17.56	17.12	16.67	16.21	15.98	15.77
7	0.100	2.72	2.70	2.63	2.59	2.56	2.51	2.49	2.47
	0.050	3.68	3.64	3.51	3.44	3.38	3.30	3.27	3.23
	0.025	4.82	4.76	4.57	4.47	4.36	4.25	4.20	4.15
	0.010	6.72	6.62	6.31	6.16	5.99	5.82	5.74	5.66
	0.001	14.33	14.08	13.32	12.93	12.53	12.12	11.91	11.72
8	0.100	2.56	2.54	2.46	2.42	2.38	2.34	2.32	2.30
	0.050	3.39	3.35	3.22	3.15	3.08	3.01	2.97	2.93
	0.025	4.36	4.30	4.10	4.00	3.89	3.78	3.73	3.68
	0.010	5.91	5.81	5.52	5.36	5.20	5.03	4.95	4.87
	0.001	11.77	11.54	10.84	10.48	10.11	9.73	9.53	9.36

Table F *F*-Distribution critical values (*continued*)

						df$_1$					
	Area in right tail	**1**	**2**	**3**	**4**	**5**	**6**	**7**	**8**	**9**	**10**
9	0.100	3.36	3.01	2.81	2.69	2.61	2.55	2.51	2.47	2.44	2.42
	0.050	5.12	4.26	3.86	3.63	3.48	3.37	3.29	3.23	3.18	3.14
	0.025	7.21	5.71	5.08	4.72	4.48	4.32	4.20	4.10	4.03	3.96
	0.010	10.56	8.02	6.99	6.42	6.06	5.80	5.61	5.47	5.35	5.26
	0.001	22.86	16.39	13.90	12.56	11.71	11.13	10.70	10.37	10.11	9.89
10	0.100	3.29	2.92	2.73	2.61	2.52	2.46	2.41	2.38	2.35	2.32
	0.050	4.96	4.10	3.71	3.48	3.33	3.22	3.14	3.07	3.02	2.98
	0.025	6.94	5.46	4.83	4.47	4.24	4.07	3.95	3.85	3.78	3.72
	0.010	10.04	7.56	6.55	5.99	5.64	5.39	5.20	5.06	4.94	4.85
	0.001	21.04	14.91	12.55	11.28	10.48	9.93	9.52	9.20	8.96	8.75
12	0.100	3.18	2.81	2.61	2.48	2.39	2.33	2.28	2.24	2.21	2.19
	0.050	4.75	3.89	3.49	3.26	3.11	3.00	2.91	2.85	2.80	2.75
	0.025	6.55	5.10	4.47	4.12	3.89	3.73	3.61	3.51	3.44	3.37
	0.010	9.33	6.93	5.95	5.41	5.06	4.82	4.64	4.50	4.39	4.30
	0.001	18.64	12.97	10.80	9.63	8.89	8.38	8.00	7.71	7.48	7.29
15	0.100	3.07	2.70	2.49	2.36	2.27	2.21	2.16	2.12	2.09	2.06
	0.050	4.54	3.68	3.29	3.06	2.90	2.79	2.71	2.64	2.59	2.54
	0.025	6.20	4.77	4.15	3.80	3.58	3.41	3.29	3.20	3.12	3.06
	0.010	8.68	6.36	5.42	4.89	4.56	4.32	4.14	4.00	3.89	3.80
	0.001	16.59	11.34	9.34	8.25	7.57	7.09	6.74	6.47	6.26	6.08
20	0.100	2.97	2.59	2.38	2.25	2.16	2.09	2.04	2.00	1.96	1.94
	0.050	4.35	3.49	3.10	2.87	2.71	2.60	2.51	2.45	2.39	2.35
	0.025	5.87	4.46	3.86	3.51	3.29	3.13	3.01	2.91	2.84	2.77
	0.010	8.10	5.85	4.94	4.43	4.10	3.87	3.70	3.56	3.46	3.37
	0.001	14.82	9.95	8.10	7.10	6.46	6.02	5.69	5.44	5.24	5.08
25	0.100	2.92	2.53	2.32	2.18	2.09	2.02	1.97	1.93	1.89	1.87
	0.050	4.24	3.39	2.99	2.76	2.60	2.49	2.40	2.34	2.28	2.24
	0.025	5.69	4.29	3.69	3.35	3.13	2.97	2.85	2.75	2.68	2.61
	0.010	7.77	5.57	4.68	4.18	3.85	3.63	3.46	3.32	3.22	3.13
	0.001	13.88	9.22	7.45	6.49	5.89	5.46	5.15	4.91	4.71	4.56
50	0.100	2.81	2.41	2.20	2.06	1.97	1.90	1.84	1.80	1.76	1.73
	0.050	4.03	3.18	2.79	2.56	2.40	2.29	2.20	2.13	2.07	2.03
	0.025	5.34	3.97	3.39	3.05	2.83	2.67	2.55	2.46	2.38	2.32
	0.010	7.17	5.06	4.20	3.72	3.41	3.19	3.02	2.89	2.78	2.70
	0.001	12.22	7.96	6.34	5.46	4.90	4.51	4.22	4.00	3.82	3.67
100	0.100	2.76	2.36	2.14	2.00	1.91	1.83	1.78	1.73	1.69	1.66
	0.050	3.94	3.09	2.70	2.46	2.31	2.19	2.10	2.03	1.97	1.93
	0.025	5.18	3.83	3.25	2.92	2.70	2.54	2.42	2.32	2.24	2.18
	0.010	6.90	4.82	3.98	3.51	3.21	2.99	2.82	2.69	2.59	2.50
	0.001	11.50	7.41	5.86	5.02	4.48	4.11	3.83	3.61	3.44	3.30
200	0.100	2.73	2.33	2.11	1.97	1.88	1.80	1.75	1.70	1.66	1.63
	0.050	3.89	3.04	2.65	2.42	2.26	2.14	2.06	1.98	1.93	1.88
	0.025	5.10	3.76	3.18	2.85	2.63	2.47	2.35	2.26	2.18	2.11
	0.010	6.76	4.71	3.88	3.41	3.11	2.89	2.73	2.60	2.50	2.41
	0.001	11.15	7.15	5.63	4.81	4.29	3.92	3.65	3.43	3.26	3.12
1000	0.100	2.71	2.31	2.09	1.95	1.85	1.78	1.72	1.68	1.64	1.61
	0.050	3.85	3.00	2.61	2.38	2.22	2.11	2.02	1.95	1.89	1.84
	0.025	5.04	3.70	3.13	2.80	2.58	2.42	2.30	2.20	2.13	2.06
	0.010	6.66	4.63	3.80	3.34	3.04	2.82	2.66	2.53	2.43	2.34
	0.001	10.89	6.96	5.46	4.65	4.14	3.78	3.51	3.30	3.13	2.99

df$_2$

(Continued)

Table F *F*-Distribution critical values (*continued*)

	Area in right tail	12	15	20	25	30	40	50	60	120	1000
						df₁					
9	0.100	2.38	2.34	2.30	2.27	2.25	2.23	2.22	2.21	2.18	2.16
	0.050	3.07	3.01	2.94	2.89	2.86	2.83	2.80	2.79	2.75	2.71
	0.025	3.87	3.77	3.67	3.60	3.56	3.51	3.47	3.45	3.39	3.34
	0.010	5.11	4.96	4.81	4.71	4.65	4.57	4.52	4.48	4.40	4.32
	0.001	9.57	9.24	8.90	8.69	8.55	8.37	8.26	8.19	8.00	7.84
10	0.100	2.28	2.24	2.20	2.17	2.16	2.13	2.12	2.11	2.08	2.06
	0.050	2.91	2.85	2.77	2.73	2.70	2.66	2.64	2.62	2.58	2.54
	0.025	3.62	3.52	3.42	3.35	3.31	3.26	3.22	3.20	3.14	3.09
	0.010	4.71	4.56	4.41	4.31	4.25	4.17	4.12	4.08	4.00	3.92
	0.001	8.45	8.13	7.80	7.60	7.47	7.30	7.19	7.12	6.94	6.78
12	0.100	2.15	2.10	2.06	2.03	2.01	1.99	1.97	1.96	1.93	1.91
	0.050	2.69	2.62	2.54	2.50	2.47	2.43	2.40	2.38	2.34	2.30
	0.025	3.28	3.18	3.07	3.01	2.96	2.91	2.87	2.85	2.79	2.73
	0.010	4.16	4.01	3.86	3.76	3.70	3.62	3.57	3.54	3.45	3.37
	0.001	7.00	6.71	6.40	6.22	6.09	5.93	5.83	5.76	5.59	5.44
15	0.100	2.02	1.97	1.92	1.89	1.87	1.85	1.83	1.82	1.79	1.76
	0.050	2.48	2.40	2.33	2.28	2.25	2.20	2.18	2.16	2.11	2.07
	0.025	2.96	2.86	2.76	2.69	2.64	2.59	2.55	2.52	2.46	2.40
	0.010	3.67	3.52	3.37	3.28	3.21	3.13	3.08	3.05	2.96	2.88
	0.001	5.81	5.54	5.25	5.07	4.95	4.80	4.70	4.64	4.47	4.33
20	0.100	1.89	1.84	1.79	1.76	1.74	1.71	1.69	1.68	1.64	1.61
	0.050	2.28	2.20	2.12	2.07	2.04	1.99	1.97	1.95	1.90	1.85
	0.025	2.68	2.57	2.46	2.40	2.35	2.29	2.25	2.22	2.16	2.09
	0.010	3.23	3.09	2.94	2.84	2.78	2.69	2.64	2.61	2.52	2.43
	0.001	4.82	4.56	4.29	4.12	4.00	3.86	3.77	3.70	3.54	3.40
25	0.100	1.82	1.77	1.72	1.68	1.66	1.63	1.61	1.59	1.56	1.52
	0.050	2.16	2.09	2.01	1.96	1.92	1.87	1.84	1.82	1.77	1.72
	0.025	2.51	2.41	2.30	2.23	2.18	2.12	2.08	2.05	1.98	1.91
	0.010	2.99	2.85	2.70	2.60	2.54	2.45	2.40	2.36	2.27	2.18
	0.001	4.31	4.06	3.79	3.63	3.52	3.37	3.28	3.22	3.06	2.91
50	0.100	1.68	1.63	1.57	1.53	1.50	1.46	1.44	1.42	1.38	1.33
	0.050	1.95	1.87	1.78	1.73	1.69	1.63	1.60	1.58	1.51	1.45
	0.025	2.22	2.11	1.99	1.92	1.87	1.80	1.75	1.72	1.64	1.56
	0.010	2.56	2.42	2.27	2.17	2.10	2.01	1.95	1.91	1.80	1.70
	0.001	3.44	3.20	2.95	2.79	2.68	2.53	2.44	2.38	2.21	2.05
100	0.100	1.61	1.56	1.49	1.45	1.42	1.38	1.35	1.34	1.28	1.22
	0.050	1.85	1.77	1.68	1.62	1.57	1.52	1.48	1.45	1.38	1.30
	0.025	2.08	1.97	1.85	1.77	1.71	1.64	1.59	1.56	1.46	1.36
	0.010	2.37	2.22	2.07	1.97	1.89	1.80	1.74	1.69	1.57	1.45
	0.001	3.07	2.84	2.59	2.43	2.32	2.17	2.08	2.01	1.83	1.64
200	0.100	1.58	1.52	1.46	1.41	1.38	1.34	1.31	1.29	1.23	1.16
	0.050	1.80	1.72	1.62	1.56	1.52	1.46	1.41	1.39	1.30	1.21
	0.025	2.01	1.90	1.78	1.70	1.64	1.56	1.51	1.47	1.37	1.25
	0.010	2.27	2.13	1.97	1.87	1.79	1.69	1.63	1.58	1.45	1.30
	0.001	2.90	2.67	2.42	2.26	2.15	2.00	1.90	1.83	1.64	1.43
1000	0.100	1.55	1.49	1.43	1.38	1.35	1.30	1.27	1.25	1.38	1.08
	0.050	1.76	1.68	1.58	1.52	1.47	1.41	1.36	1.31	1.24	1.11
	0.025	1.96	1.85	1.72	1.64	1.58	1.50	1.45	1.41	1.29	1.13
	0.010	2.20	2.06	1.90	1.79	1.72	1.61	1.54	1.50	1.35	1.16
	0.001	2.77	2.54	2.30	2.14	2.02	1.87	1.77	1.69	1.49	1.22

df₂

Table G Critical values for correlation coefficient

n	
3	0.997
4	0.950
5	0.878
6	0.811
7	0.754
8	0.707
9	0.666
10	0.632
11	0.602
12	0.576
13	0.553
14	0.532
15	0.514
16	0.497
17	0.482
18	0.468
19	0.456
20	0.444
21	0.433
22	0.423
23	0.413
24	0.404
25	0.396
26	0.388
27	0.381
28	0.374
29	0.367
30	0.361

Table H Critical values for Tukey's test

$\alpha_{EW} = 0.05$

df	k: 2	3	4	5	6	7	8	9	10	11	12	13	14	15	16	17	18	19
1	17.97	26.98	32.82	37.08	40.41	43.12	45.40	47.36	49.07	50.59	51.96	53.20	54.33	55.36	56.32	57.22	58.04	58.83
2	6.085	8.331	9.798	10.88	11.74	12.44	13.03	13.54	13.99	14.39	14.75	15.08	15.38	15.65	15.91	16.14	16.37	16.37
3	4.501	5.910	6.825	7.502	8.037	8.478	8.853	9.177	9.462	9.717	9.946	10.15	10.35	10.53	10.69	10.84	10.98	11.11
4	3.927	5.040	5.757	6.287	6.707	7.053	7.347	7.602	7.826	8.027	8.208	8.373	8.525	8.664	8.794	8.914	9.028	9.134
5	3.635	4.602	5.218	5.673	6.033	6.330	6.582	6.802	6.995	7.168	7.324	7.466	7.596	7.717	7.828	7.932	8.030	8.122
6	3.461	4.339	4.896	5.305	5.628	5.895	6.122	6.319	6.493	6.649	6.789	6.917	7.034	7.143	7.244	7.338	7.426	7.508
7	3.344	4.165	4.681	5.060	5.359	5.606	5.815	5.998	6.158	6.302	6.431	6.550	6.658	6.759	6.852	6.939	7.020	7.097
8	3.261	4.041	4.529	4.886	5.167	5.399	5.597	5.767	5.918	6.054	6.175	6.287	6.389	6.483	6.571	6.653	6.729	6.802
9	3.199	3.949	4.415	4.756	5.024	5.244	5.432	5.595	5.739	5.867	5.983	6.089	6.186	6.276	6.359	6.437	6.510	6.579
10	3.151	3.877	4.327	4.654	4.912	5.124	5.305	5.461	5.599	5.722	5.833	5.935	6.028	6.114	6.194	6.269	6.339	6.405
11	3.113	3.820	4.256	4.574	4.823	5.028	5.202	5.353	5.487	5.605	5.713	5.811	5.901	5.984	6.062	6.134	6.202	6.265
12	3.082	3.773	4.199	4.508	4.751	4.950	5.119	5.265	5.395	5.511	5.615	5.710	5.798	5.878	5.953	6.023	6.089	6.151
13	3.055	3.735	4.151	4.453	4.690	4.885	5.049	5.192	5.318	5.431	5.533	5.625	5.711	5.789	5.862	5.931	5.995	6.055
14	3.033	3.702	4.111	4.407	4.639	4.829	4.990	5.131	5.254	5.364	5.463	5.554	5.637	5.714	5.786	5.852	5.915	5.974
15	3.014	3.674	4.076	4.367	4.595	4.782	4.940	5.077	5.198	5.306	5.404	5.493	5.574	5.649	5.720	5.785	5.846	5.904
16	2.998	3.649	4.046	4.333	4.557	4.741	4.897	5.031	5.150	5.256	5.352	5.439	5.520	5.593	5.662	5.727	5.786	5.843
17	2.984	3.628	4.020	4.303	4.524	4.706	4.858	4.991	5.108	5.212	5.307	5.392	5.471	5.544	5.612	5.675	5.734	5.790
18	2.971	3.609	3.997	4.277	4.495	4.673	4.824	4.956	5.071	5.174	5.267	5.352	5.429	5.501	5.568	5.630	5.688	5.743
19	2.960	3.593	3.977	4.253	4.469	4.645	4.794	4.924	5.038	5.140	5.231	5.315	5.391	5.462	5.528	5.589	5.647	5.701
20	2.950	3.578	3.958	4.232	4.445	4.620	4.768	4.896	5.008	5.108	5.199	5.282	5.357	5.427	5.493	5.553	5.610	5.663
24	2.919	3.532	3.901	4.166	4.373	4.541	4.684	4.807	4.915	5.012	5.099	5.179	5.251	5.319	5.381	5.439	5.494	5.545
30	2.888	3.486	3.845	4.102	4.302	4.464	4.602	4.720	4.824	4.917	5.001	5.077	5.147	5.211	5.271	5.327	5.379	5.429
40	2.858	3.442	3.791	4.039	4.232	4.389	4.521	4.635	4.735	4.824	4.904	4.977	5.044	5.106	5.163	5.216	5.266	5.313
60	2.829	3.399	3.737	3.977	4.163	4.314	4.441	4.550	4.646	4.732	4.808	4.878	4.942	5.001	5.056	5.107	5.154	5.199
120	2.800	3.356	3.685	3.917	4.096	4.241	4.363	4.468	4.560	4.641	4.714	4.781	4.842	4.898	4.950	4.998	5.044	5.086
∞	2.772	3.314	3.633	3.858	4.030	4.170	4.286	4.387	4.474	4.552	4.622	4.685	4.743	4.796	4.845	4.891	4.934	4.974

(Continued)

Table H Critical values for Tukey's test (*continued*)

$\alpha_{EW} = 0.05$

df	k: 20	22	24	26	28	30	32	34	36
1	59.56	60.91	62.12	63.22	64.23	65.15	66.01	66.81	67.56
2	16.77	17.13	17.45	17.75	18.02	18.27	18.50	18.72	18.92
3	11.24	11.47	11.68	11.87	12.05	12.21	12.36	12.50	12.63
4	9.233	9.418	9.584	9.736	9.875	10.00	10.12	10.23	10.34
5	8.208	8.368	8.512	8.643	8.764	8.875	8.979	9.075	9.165
6	7.587	7.730	7.861	7.979	8.088	8.189	8.283	8.370	8.452
7	7.170	7.303	7.423	7.533	7.634	7.728	7.814	7.895	7.972
8	6.870	6.995	7.109	7.212	7.307	7.395	7.477	7.554	7.625
9	6.644	6.763	6.871	6.970	7.061	7.145	7.222	7.295	7.363
10	6.467	6.582	6.686	6.781	6.868	6.948	7.023	7.093	7.159
11	6.326	6.436	6.536	6.628	6.712	6.790	6.863	6.930	6.994
12	6.209	6.317	6.414	6.503	6.585	6.660	6.731	6.796	6.858
13	6.112	6.217	6.312	6.398	6.478	6.551	6.620	6.684	6.744
14	6.029	6.132	6.224	6.309	6.387	6.459	6.526	6.588	6.647
15	5.958	6.059	6.149	6.233	6.309	6.379	6.445	6.506	6.564
16	5.897	5.995	6.084	6.166	6.241	6.310	6.374	6.434	6.491
17	5.842	5.940	6.027	6.107	6.181	6.249	6.313	6.372	6.427
18	5.794	5.890	5.977	6.055	6.128	6.195	6.258	6.316	6.371
19	5.752	5.846	5.932	6.009	6.081	6.147	6.209	6.267	6.321
20	5.714	5.807	5.891	5.968	6.039	6.104	6.165	6.222	6.275
24	5.594	5.683	5.764	5.838	5.906	5.968	6.027	6.081	6.132
30	5.475	5.561	5.638	5.709	5.774	5.833	5.889	5.941	5.990
40	5.358	5.439	5.513	5.581	5.642	5.700	5.753	5.803	5.849
60	5.241	5.319	5.389	5.453	5.512	5.566	5.617	5.664	5.708
120	5.126	5.200	5.266	5.327	5.382	5.434	5.481	5.526	5.568
∞	5.012	5.081	5.144	5.201	5.253	5.301	5.346	5.388	5.427

df	k: 38	40	50	60	70	80	90	100
1	68.26	68.92	71.73	73.97	75.82	77.40	78.77	79.98
2	19.11	19.28	20.05	20.66	21.16	21.59	21.96	22.29
3	12.75	12.87	13.36	13.76	14.08	14.36	14.61	14.82
4	10.44	10.53	10.93	11.24	11.51	11.73	11.92	12.09
5	9.250	9.330	9.674	9.949	10.18	10.38	10.54	10.69
6	8.529	8.601	8.913	9.163	9.370	9.548	9.702	9.839
7	8.043	8.110	8.400	8.632	8.824	8.989	9.133	9.261
8	7.693	7.756	8.029	8.248	8.430	8.586	8.722	8.843
9	7.428	7.488	7.749	7.958	8.132	8.281	8.410	8.526
10	7.220	7.279	7.529	7.730	7.897	8.041	8.166	8.276
11	7.053	7.110	7.352	7.546	7.708	7.847	7.968	8.075
12	6.916	6.970	7.205	7.394	7.552	7.687	7.804	7.909
13	6.800	6.854	7.083	7.267	7.421	7.552	7.667	7.769
14	6.702	6.754	6.979	7.159	7.309	7.438	7.550	7.650
15	6.618	6.669	6.888	7.065	7.212	7.339	7.449	7.546
16	6.544	6.594	6.810	6.984	7.128	7.252	7.360	7.457
17	6.479	6.529	6.741	6.912	7.054	7.176	7.283	7.377
18	6.422	6.471	6.680	6.848	6.989	7.109	7.213	7.307
19	6.371	6.419	6.626	6.792	6.930	7.048	7.152	7.244
20	6.325	6.373	6.576	6.740	6.877	6.994	7.097	7.187
24	6.181	6.226	6.421	6.579	6.710	6.822	6.920	7.008
30	6.037	6.080	6.267	6.417	6.543	6.650	6.744	6.827
40	5.893	5.934	6.112	6.255	6.375	6.477	6.566	6.645
60	5.750	5.789	5.958	6.093	6.206	6.303	6.387	6.462
120	5.607	5.644	5.802	5.929	6.035	6.126	6.205	6.275
∞	5.463	5.498	5.646	5.764	5.863	5.947	6.020	6.085

Notes and Data Sources

Chapter 1

1. T. J. Scanlon, R. N. Luben, F. L. Scanlon, and N. Singleton, "Is Friday the 13th bad for your health?" *British Medical Journal* 307 (December 1993).

2. U.S. Census Bureau, *The Population Profile of the United States: 2000*, www.consensus.gov/population/www/pop-profile/profile2000.

3. Pew Internet and American Life Project, "Cyberbullying and online teens," June 2007, www.pewinternet.org.

4. National Agricultural Statistics Service.

5. Iain McGregor and Wayne Hall, "MDMA (Ecstasy) neurotoxicity: assessing and communicating the risks," *Lancet* 355 (9217, May 20, 2000): 1818–21.

6. Michel de Lorgeril, Patricia Salen, Jean-Louis Martin, Isabelle Monjaud, Jacques Delaye, and Nicole Mamelle, "Mediterranean diet, traditional risk factors, and the rate of cardiovascular complications after myocardial infarction, final report of the Lyon Diet Heart Study," *Circulation: Journal of the American Heart Association* 99 (1999): 779–85. The American Heart Association (www.americanheart.org) identifies the following characteristics as common to most Mediterranean diets. There is a "high consumption of fruits, vegetables, bread and other cereals, potatoes, beans, nuts and seeds. Olive oil is an important monounsaturated fat source. Dairy products, fish and poultry are consumed in low to moderate amounts, and little red meat is eaten."

7. U.S. Department of Health and Human Services, *The Health Consequences of Involuntary Exposure to Tobacco Smoke: A Report of the Surgeon General—Executive Summary* (U.S. Department of Health and Human Services, Centers for Disease Control and Prevention, Coordinating Center for Health Promotion, National Center for Chronic Disease Prevention and Health Promotion, Office on Smoking and Health, 2006).

8. R. L. Bratton et al., "Effect of 'ionized' wrist bracelets on musculoskeletal pain: a randomized, double-blind, placebo-controlled trial," *Mayo Clinic Proceedings* 77 (2002):1164–68.

Chapter 2

1. Roper Center, University of Connecticut.

2. National Health Interview Survey, U.S. Centers for Disease Control and Prevention, 2005.

3. M. A. Chase and G. M. Dummer, "The role of sports as a social determinant for children," *Research Quarterly for Exercise and Sport* 63 (1992): 418–24.

4. U.S. Bureau of Labor Statistics.

5. U.S. Centers for Disease Control and Prevention.

Chapter 3

1. For more on clickstream analysis, see Zdravko Markov and Daniel Larose, *Data Mining the Web: Uncovering Patterns in Web Content, Structure, and Usage* (John Wiley and Sons, 2007).

2. U.S. Census Bureau.

3. Michael Brett and Charles Goldman, "A meta-analysis of the freshwater trophic cascade," *Proceedings of the National Academy of Sciences* 93 (July 1996).

4. Dr. Peter Nonacs, "Foraging habits of thatch ants," Department of Statistics, University of California at Los Angeles and the Sierra Nevada Aquatic Research Laboratory, www.stat.ucla.edu/datasets/.

5. Children's Bureau, Administration for Children and Families, U.S. Department of Health and Human Services.

6. National Water and Climate Center, U.S. Department of Agriculture.

7. B. S. Glenn et al., "Changes in systolic blood pressure associated with lead in blood and bone," *Epidemiology* 17 (September 2006).

8. National Center for Education Statistics, 2005.

9. M. Donald Thomas and William L. Bainbridge, "Grade inflation: the current fraud," *Effective School Research*, January 1997.

10. National Center for Health Statistics, *Health*, 2006.

Chapter 4

1. United Nations Educational, Scientific, and Cultural Organization (UNESCO).

2. *Crime in the United States, 2004*, www.fbi.gov.

Chapter 5

1. Amanda Lenhart et al., *Writing, Technology, and Teens*, Pew Internet and American Life Project, December 2007.

2. U.S. Census Bureau, 2004 American Community Survey.

3. Andrew Rocco Tresolini Fiore, "Romantic regressions: an analysis of behavior in online dating systems," master's thesis, Massachusetts Institute of Technology, 2004.

4. *Percentage Baseball* (MIT Press, 1966).

5. Kristen Purcell, Roger Enner, and Nicole Henderson, *The Rise of Apps Culture*, Pew Research Center's Internet and American Life Project. www.pewinternet.org.

6. Washington Initiative (greaterwashington.org).

7. *Profile of Hired Farmworkers, a 2008 Update/ERR-60*, Economic Research Service/USDA.

Chapter 6

1. U.S. Census Bureau. The category "3 or more" has been changed to "3" for this exercise.

2. U.S. National Center for Education Statistics. The category "5 or more" has been changed to "5" for this exercise.

3. U.S. Census Bureau.

4. Gunter Hitsch, Ali Hortacsu, and Dan Ariely, "What makes you click: an empirical analysis of online dating"; available online at www.aeaweb.org/annual_mtg_papers/2006/0106_0800_0502.pdf.

5. www.networkworld.com/news/2010/062310-20-percent-of-android-apps.html.

6. Stephen J. Blumberg and Julian V. Luke, *Wireless Substitution: Early Release of Estimates from the National Health Interview*

Survey, July–December 2009, National Center for Health Statistics, Centers for Disease Control and Prevention.

7. *Women in Management: Analysis of Female Managers' Representation, Characteristics, and Pay*, Government Accountability Office publication GAO-10-892R, September 20, 2010.

8. M. J. Bull, K. B. Stroup, S. Gerhart, et al., "Misuse of car safety seats," *Pediatrics* 81 (January 1988): 98–101.

9. E. Skogvoll and B. H. Lindqvist, "Modeling the occurrence of cardiac arrest as a Poisson process," *Annals of Emergency Medicine* 33 (4, 1999): 409–17.

10. Sue McAlister, "Santa Clara County median home price plunges, sales rise," *Mercury News*, March 19, 2009. www.mercurynews.com.

11. "British Airways joins RBS and Ethoca in the collaborative fight against fraud," press release, *Marketwire*, February 19, 2009.

12. "Herger-Feinstein Quincy Library Group Forest Recovery Act Implementation on the Eagle Lake Ranger District, Lassen NF," www.qlg.org/pub/act/lnf/lnf1.htm.

13. Zdravko Markov and Daniel T. Larose, *Data Mining the Web: Uncovering Patterns in Web Content, Structure, and Usage* (John Wiley and Sons, 2007).

14. F. Giannelli, T. Anagnostopolous, and P. M. Green, "Mutation rates in humans. II. Sporadic mutation-specific rates and rate of detrimental human mutations inferred from hemophilia B," *American Journal of Human Genetics* 65 (6, December 1, 1999): 1550–87.

15. Edwin R. Van Teijlingen, George W. Lowis, Maureen Porter, and Peter McCaffery, eds., *Midwifery and the Medicalization of Childbirth: Comparative Perspectives* (Nova Publishers, 2004).

16. Department of Health and Human Services, www.Mass.gov.

17. www.mlb.com.

18. The Campus Security Data Analysis Cutting Tool, www.ope.ed.gov, 2008.

19. Frederick Mueller and Robert Cantu, *Annual Survey of Football Injury Research*, National Center for Catastrophic Sport Injury Research, 2008.

20. NickBurcher.com.

21. Amanda Lenhart et al., *Teens, Video Games, and Civics*, Pew Internet and American Life Project, September 2008. http://www.pewinternet.org/Reports/2008/Teens-Video-Games-and-Civics.aspx.

22. D. L. Olds, C. R. Henderson Jr., R. Tatelbaum, et al., "Improving the delivery of prenatal care and outcomes of pregnancy: a randomized trial of nurse home visitation," *Pediatrics* 77 (1986): 16–28.

23. Allen J. Wilcox, National Institutes of Health, "The analysis of birth weight and infant mortality," *International Journal of Epidemiology* (December 2001). eb.niehs.nih.gov/bwt/subcfreq.htm.

24. Lynn Unruh and Myron Fottler, "Patient turnover and nursing staff adequacy," *Health Services Research*, April 2006.

25. M. Donald Thomas and William L. Bainbridge, "Grade inflation: the current fraud," *Effective School Research*, January 1997.

26. Harvard School of Public Health, survey of 5046 adults in hurricane high-risk areas, June–July 2007.

27. The Associated Press/Ipsos Poll actually contacted 1000 adults in June 2007.

28. Aviation Accident Data and Synopses, National Transportation Safety Board.

29. Barbara Alving et al., "Trends in blood pressure among children and adolescents," *Journal of the American Medical Association* 291 (May 2004): 2107–13.

30. Phillida Bunkle and John Lepper, "Women's participation in gambling: whose reality? A public health issue," paper presented to the European Association for the Study of Gambling Conference, Barcelona, Spain, October 2002.

Chapter 7

1. "The magical number seven, plus or minus two: some limits on our capacity for processing information," *Psychological Review* 63 (1956), 81–97.

2. United States Geological Survey, neic.usgs.gov/neis/qed/.

3. A small business is defined by the SBA as having fewer than 20 employees.

4. Sloan Burke, Michele Wallen, Karen Vail-Smith, and David Knox, "Using technology to control intimate partners: An exploratory study of college undergraduates," *Computers in Human Behavior* 27 (3, May 2011): 1162–67.

5. Murray Mittleman et al., "Determinants of myocardial onset study," *Circulation: Journal of the American Heart Association*, June 1999.

Chapter 8

1. Adapted from A. Johnson, "Results from analyzing metals in 1999 Spokane River fish and crayfish samples," Quantitative Environmental Learning Project, Washington State Department of Ecology report 00-03-017, www.seattlecentral.edu/qelp/sets/021/021.html.

2. Kevin Crowley et al., "Parents explain more often to boys than girls during shared scientific thinking," *Psychological Science* 12 (3, May 2001): 258–61.

3. U.S. Energy Information Administration, 2005.

4. Florida Department of Financial Services, 2011.

5. www.vgchartz.com, April 1, 2011.

6. National Weather Service.

7. George Miller, "The magical number seven, plus or minus two: some limits on our capacity for processing information," *Psychological Review* 63 (1956): 81–97.

8. Mary H. Ward et al., "Proximity to crops and residential exposure to agricultural herbicides in Iowa," *Environmental Health Perspectives* 114 (6, June 2006): 893–97.

9. Irene Yen et al., "Perceived neighborhood problems and quality of life, physical functioning, and depressive symptoms among adults with asthma," *American Journal of Public Health* 96 (5, May 2006): 873–79.

10. Gary Bennett et al., "Television viewing and pedometer-determined physical activity among multiethnic residents of low-income housing," *American Journal of Public Health* 96 (9, September 2006), 1681–85.

11. Mary C. Meyer, "Wider shoes for wider feet?" *Journal of Statistics Education* 14 (1, 2006), www.amstat.org/publications/jse/v14n1/datasets.meyer.html.

12. Clive Lipchin, "Report from the field: perceptions of water use in the Arava Valley of Israel and Jordan," *Journal of the International Institute, University of Michigan* (Summer 2004). A cubic meter of water is equivalent to 264 gallons.

13. Robert J. Pianta et al., "Teaching: opportunities to learn in America's elementary classroom," *Science* 315 (March 30, 2007): 1795–96.

14. See Note 3.

15. See Note 4.

16. See Note 5.

17. See Note 6.

18. Community College Survey of Student Engagement (CCSSE), 2007, www.ccsse.org. The survey reported that 178 of 307 (57.98045603%) students worked with classmates outside class to prepare a group assignment during the current academic year. The sample results in Example 8.16 (174 of 300, or 58%) were chosen for ease of calculation.

19. Christopher Reynolds, "Prey tell," *American Demographics* 25 (8, October 2003): 48.

20. www.gallup.com/poll/146885/Positivity-Optimism-Norm-Thriving-States.aspx.

21. *MDMA (Ecstacy) Abuse*, National Institute on Drug Abuse Research Report Series, U.S. Department of Health and Human Services, February 2006.

22. http://hosted.ap.org/specials/interactives/wdc/debt_stress/index.html.

23. Mildred Cho and Lisa Bero, "The quality of drug studies published in symposium proceedings," *Annals of Internal Medicine*, 124 (5, March 1996): 485–89.

24. See Note 11.

25. See Note 3.

26. See Note 4.

27. Karen Avenoso, "Erasing the passed," *Boston Globe*, July 14, 1996. (Thanks to *Chance News* www.dartmouth.edu/~chance/).

Chapter 9

1. Y. Kvach and C. A. Stepien, "The invasive round goby *Apollonia melanostoma* (Actinopterygii: Gobiidae)—a new intermediate host of the trematode *Neochasmus umbellus* (Trematoda: Cryptogonimidae) in Lake Erie, Ohio, USA," *Journal of Applied Ichthyology* 24 (1, February 2008), 103–05.

2. Press release, August 23, 2007: "Consumers report eating at home more in the wake of high gas prices," NPD Group, Inc., 900 West Shore Road, Port Washington, NY 11050.

3. "When it comes to height, Americans no longer stand tallest," *Research News*, The Ohio State University, researchnews.osu.edu/.

4. *Digital Transactions News*, September 2007.

5. K. Marien, A. Conseur, and M. Sanderson, "The effect of fish consumption on DDT and DDE levels in breast milk among Hispanic immigrants," *Journal of Human Lactation* 14 (3, 1998): 237–42.

6. C. J. Earle, L. B. Brubaker, and G. Segura, International Tree Ring Data Base, NOAA/NGDC Paleoclimatology Program, Boulder, CO.

7. See Note 3.

8. "Online shoppers will pay extra to protect privacy, Carnegie Mellon study shows," *ScienceDaily*, www.sciencedaily.com/releases/2007/06/070606235316.htm. (Accessed January 20, 2008.)

9. Caroline Davis, Elizabeth Blackmore, Deborah Katzman, and John Fox, "Anorexia nervosa case study," paper presented at Statistical Society of Canada Annual Conference, Montreal, 2004. We have reversed the research question from that of the original case study.

10. health.usnews.com/sections/health/west-hospitals.

11. Courtesy American Heritage Center, University of Wyoming.

12. Data courtesy of OzDASL (Australian Data and Story Library) at statsci.org. The original source is Cara Dubois, ed., *Lowie's Selected Papers in Anthropology* (University of California Press, 1960).

13. http://moconews.net/article/419-average-number-of-apps-downloaded-to-iphone-40-android-25/.

14. *Vital Signs: Current Cigarette Smoking, Morbidity and Mortality Weekly Report*, September 10, 2010. http://www.cdc.gov/mmwr/preview/mmwrhtml/mm5935a3.htm.

15. Mary Madden and Amanda Lenhart "Online dating," Pew Internet and American Life Project, 2006.

16. Barry Kosmin and Egon Mayer, "Principal investigators," American Religious Identification Survey, Graduate Center, City University of New York.

17. Brady Hamilton, Joyce Martin, and Stephanie Ventura, "Births: preliminary data for 2005," *National Vital Statistics Reports* 55 (11), U.S. Department of Health and Human Services.

18. "Patterns and trends in nonmedical prescription pain reliever use: 2002 to 2005," in *NSDUH Report*, Substance Abuse and Mental Health Services Administration, April 6, 2007.

19. Jeff Humphries, "The multicultural economy: minority buying power in the new century," Selig Center for Economic Growth, Terry College of Business, University of Georgia, 2006.

20. "Trends in the prevalence of alcohol use among eighth graders: Monitoring the Future Study, 1991–2003," NIAAA, National Institutes of Health.

21. "Fact sheet: National Survey on Environmental Management of Asthma and Children's Exposure to Environmental Tobacco Smoke," U.S. Environmental Protection Agency, May 17, 2005.

22. Based on data from the U.S. Census Bureau.

23. Energy Information Administration, "Annual electric generator report," Form EIA-906.

24. See Note 5.

25. See Note 6.

26. U.S. Bureau of Labor Statistics.

27. Mary C. Meyer, "Wider shoes for wider feet?" *Journal of Statistics Education* 14 (1, 2006).

28. Steve Strand, Ian Deary, and Pauline Smith, "Sex differences in cognitive abilities test scores: a UK national picture," *British Journal of Educational Psychology* 76 (2006): 463–80.

29. Siobhan Banks and David Dinges, "Behavioral and physiological consequences of sleep restriction," *Journal of Clinical Sleep Medicine* 15 (2007): 519–28.

30. U.S. Census Bureau.

31. "A nation online: entering the broadband age," Economics and Statistics Administration, U.S. Department of Commerce.

32. U.S. Bureau of Justice Statistics.

33. Joyce A. Martin et al., "Births: final data for 2005," *National Vital Statistics Reports*, 56 (6, December 5, 2007).

Chapter 10

1. Kelley, H. H., "The warm-cold variable in first impression of persons," *Journal of Personality* 18 (1950): 431–39.

2. A. Towler and R. L. Dipboye, "The effect of instructor reputation and need for cognition on student behavior," poster presented at American Psychological Society conference, May 1998.

3. K. J. Thomas et al., "Randomized controlled trial of a short course of traditional acupuncture compared with usual care for persistent non-specific low back pain," *British Medical Journal* 23 (September 2006).

4. Karin Olson and John Hanson, "Using reiki to manage pain," *Cancer Prevention and Control* 1 (2, 1997): 108–13.

5. "Highway safety projects—before and after study update," *Measures, Markers, and Mileposts*, Washington State Department of Transportation, December 2005.

6. P. A. Mackowiak, S. S. Wasserman, and M. M. Levine, "A critical appraisal of 98.6 degrees F, the upper limit of the normal body temperature, and other legacies of Carl Reinhold August Wunderlich," *Journal of the American Medical Association* 268 (1992): 1578–80.

7. George W. Snedecor and William G. Cochran, *Statistical Methods*, 8th Ed. (Iowa State University Press, 1989).

8. See Barry K. Moser and Gary R. Stevens, "Homogeneity of variance in the two-sample means test," *American Statistician* 46 (1, February 1992): 19–21.

9. Steven Reinberg, "U.S. kids using media almost 8 hours a day: survey finds few parents set rules as use of 'smart' phones, computers soars," *Bloomberg Business Week: Executive Health*, January 20, 2010. www.businessweek.com/lifestyle/content/healthday/635134.html.

10. D. L. Olds, C. R. Henderson Jr, R. Tatelbaum et al., "Improving the delivery of prenatal care and outcomes of pregnancy: a randomized trial of nurse home visitation," *Pediatrics* 77 (1986): 16–28.

11. Amanda Lenhart and Mary Madden, "Teens, privacy, and online social networks: how teens manage their online identities and personal information in the age of MySpace," Pew Internet and American Life Project, April 2007.

12. Vijayakrishna K. Gadi et al., "Case-control study of fetal microchimerism and breast cancer," *PLoS one* 3 (March 5, 2008). (plos one, doi; 10:1371/journal.pone.0001706).

13. R. L. Bratton et al., "Effect of 'ionized' wrist bracelets on musculoskeletal pain: a randomized, double-blind, placebo-controlled trial," *Mayo Clinic Proceedings* 77 (2002): 1164–68.

14. D. B. Allison et al., "Weight loss increases and fat loss decreases all cause mortality rate: results from two independent cohort studies," *International Journal of Obesity* 23 (1999): 603–11.

15. Siddharth Chandra et al., "Daily smoking patterns, their determinants, and implications for quitting," *Experimental and Clinical Psychopharmacology* 15 (1, 2007): 67–80.

16. Eric Zander and Sven Olof Dahlgren, "WISC–III index score profiles of 520 Swedish children with pervasive developmental disorders, *Psychological Assessment* 22 (2, 2010): 213–22.

17. G. Danaei et al., "The promise of prevention: The effects of four preventable risk factors and national life expectancy disparities by race and county in the United States," *PLoS Medicine* 7 (3, 2010): 1–14.

18. Shaowei Wu et al., "Association of heart rate variability in taxi drivers with marked changes in particulate air pollution in Beijing in 2008," *Environmental Health Perspectives* 118 (2010): 87–91.

Chapter 11

1. Mary Madden and Amanda Lenhart, *Online Dating*, Pew Internet and American Life Project, 2005.

2. U.S. Department of Education, National Center for Education Statistics, Adult Education Survey of the 2005 National Household Education Surveys Program.

3. Derek M. Burnett et al., "Impact of minority status following traumatic spinal cord injury," *NeuroRehabilitation* 17 (2002): 187–94.

4. Pew Research Center for the People and the Press, *How Young People View Their Lives, Futures, and Politics: A Portrait of "Generation Next"* (Washington, D.C., 2007).

5. Andrew Rocco Tresolini Fiore, "Romantic regressions: an analysis of behavior in online dating systems," master's thesis, Program in Media Arts and Sciences, Massachusetts Institute of Technology, 2004.

6. See Note 1.

7. M. A. Chase and G. M. Dummer, "The role of sports as a social determinant for children," *Research Quarterly for Exercise and Sport* 63 (1992): 418–24.

8. J. R. Knight, H. Wechsler, M. Kuo, M. Seibring, E. R. Weitzman, and M. Schuckit, "Alcohol abuse and dependence among U.S. college students," *Journal of Studies on Alcohol* 63, (3, 2002): 263–70.

9. Donald Garrow and Leonard Egede, "National patterns and correlates of complementary and alternative medicine use in adults with diabetes," *Journal of Alternative and Complementary Medicine* 12 (2006): 895–902.

10. J. E. Anderson and S. Sansom, "HIV testing in a national sample of pregnant US women: who is not getting tested?" *AIDS Care* 19 (March 2007): 375–80.

11. National Agricultural Statistics Service, *Agricultural Statistics*, www.usda.gov/nass 2006.

Chapter 12

1. Joseph Maze, Richard Murphy, and Cheri Simonds, "I'll see you on Facebook: the effects of computer-mediated teacher self-disclosure on student motivation, affective learning, and classroom climate," *Communication Edition* 56 (2007): 1–17.

2. S. Blackman and D. Catalina, "The moon and the emergency room," *Perceptual and Motor Skills* 37 (1973): 624–26.

3. William S. Cleveland, *Visualizing Data* (Hobart Press, 1993).

4. The data set is adapted from the *cereals* data set from the Data and Story Library, ib.stat.cmu.edu/DASL.

Chapter 13

None.

Index

boldface indicates a definition   *italics* indicates a figure   *t* indicates a table

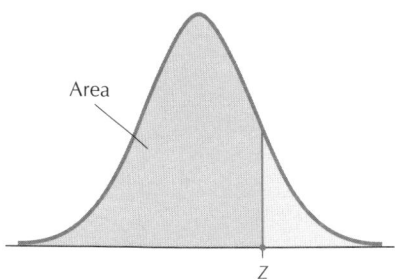

Area

Z

Table C Standard normal distribution (*continued*)

Z	0.00	0.01	0.02	0.03	0.04	0.05	0.06	0.07	0.08	0.09
0.0	0.5000	0.5040	0.5080	0.5120	0.5160	0.5199	0.5239	0.5279	0.5319	0.5359
0.1	0.5398	0.5438	0.5478	0.5517	0.5557	0.5596	0.5636	0.5675	0.5714	0.5753
0.2	0.5793	0.5832	0.5871	0.5910	0.5948	0.5987	0.6026	0.6064	0.6103	0.6141
0.3	0.6179	0.6217	0.6255	0.6293	0.6331	0.6368	0.6406	0.6443	0.6480	0.6517
0.4	0.6554	0.6591	0.6628	0.6664	0.6700	0.6736	0.6772	0.6808	0.6844	0.6879
0.5	0.6915	0.6950	0.6985	0.7019	0.7054	0.7088	0.7123	0.7157	0.7190	0.7224
0.6	0.7257	0.7291	0.7324	0.7357	0.7389	0.7422	0.7454	0.7486	0.7517	0.7549
0.7	0.7580	0.7611	0.7642	0.7673	0.7704	0.7734	0.7764	0.7794	0.7823	0.7852
0.8	0.7881	0.7910	0.7939	0.7967	0.7995	0.8023	0.8051	0.8078	0.8106	0.8133
0.9	0.8159	0.8186	0.8212	0.8238	0.8264	0.8289	0.8315	0.8340	0.8365	0.8389
1.0	0.8413	0.8438	0.8461	0.8485	0.8508	0.8531	0.8554	0.8577	0.8599	0.8621
1.1	0.8643	0.8665	0.8686	0.8708	0.8729	0.8749	0.8770	0.8790	0.8810	0.8830
1.2	0.8849	0.8869	0.8888	0.8907	0.8925	0.8944	0.8962	0.8980	0.8997	0.9015
1.3	0.9032	0.9049	0.9066	0.9082	0.9099	0.9115	0.9131	0.9147	0.9162	0.9177
1.4	0.9192	0.9207	0.9222	0.9236	0.9251	0.9265	0.9279	0.9292	0.9306	0.9319
1.5	0.9332	0.9345	0.9357	0.9370	0.9382	0.9394	0.9406	0.9418	0.9429	0.9441
1.6	0.9452	0.9463	0.9474	0.9484	0.9495	0.9505	0.9515	0.9525	0.9535	0.9545
1.7	0.9554	0.9564	0.9573	0.9582	0.9591	0.9599	0.9608	0.9616	0.9625	0.9633
1.8	0.9641	0.9649	0.9656	0.9664	0.9671	0.9678	0.9686	0.9693	0.9699	0.9706
1.9	0.9713	0.9719	0.9726	0.9732	0.9738	0.9744	0.9750	0.9756	0.9761	0.9767
2.0	0.9772	0.9778	0.9783	0.9788	0.9793	0.9798	0.9803	0.9808	0.9812	0.9817
2.1	0.9821	0.9826	0.9830	0.9834	0.9838	0.9842	0.9846	0.9850	0.9854	0.9857
2.2	0.9861	0.9864	0.9868	0.9871	0.9875	0.9878	0.9881	0.9884	0.9887	0.9890
2.3	0.9893	0.9896	0.9898	0.9901	0.9904	0.9906	0.9909	0.9911	0.9913	0.9916
2.4	0.9918	0.9920	0.9922	0.9925	0.9927	0.9929	0.9931	0.9932	0.9934	0.9936
2.5	0.9938	0.9940	0.9941	0.9943	0.9945	0.9946	0.9948	0.9949	0.9951	0.9952
2.6	0.9953	0.9955	0.9956	0.9957	0.9959	0.9960	0.9961	0.9962	0.9963	0.9964
2.7	0.9965	0.9966	0.9967	0.9968	0.9969	0.9970	0.9971	0.9972	0.9973	0.9974
2.8	0.9974	0.9975	0.9976	0.9977	0.9977	0.9978	0.9979	0.9979	0.9980	0.9981
2.9	0.9981	0.9982	0.9982	0.9983	0.9984	0.9984	0.9985	0.9985	0.9986	0.9986
3.0	0.9987	0.9987	0.9987	0.9988	0.9988	0.9989	0.9989	0.9989	0.9990	0.9990
3.1	0.9990	0.9991	0.9991	0.9991	0.9992	0.9992	0.9992	0.9992	0.9993	0.9993
3.2	0.9993	0.9993	0.9994	0.9994	0.9994	0.9994	0.9994	0.9995	0.9995	0.9995
3.3	0.9995	0.9995	0.9995	0.9996	0.9996	0.9996	0.9996	0.9996	0.9996	0.9997
3.4	0.9997	0.9997	0.9997	0.9997	0.9997	0.9997	0.9997	0.9997	0.9997	0.9998

Chapter 9   Hypothesis Testing

- The test statistic used for the Z test for the mean (p. 432):

$$Z_{\text{data}} = \frac{\bar{x} - \mu_0}{\sigma_{\bar{x}}} = \frac{\bar{x} - \mu_0}{\sigma/\sqrt{n}}$$

- The test statistic used for the *t* test for the mean (p. 454):

$$t_{\text{data}} = \frac{\bar{x} - \mu_0}{s_{\bar{x}}} = \frac{\bar{x} - \mu_0}{s/\sqrt{n}}$$

- The test statistic used for the Z test for the proportion (p. 469):

$$Z_{\text{data}} = \frac{(\hat{p} - p_0)}{\sigma_{\hat{p}}} = \frac{(\hat{p} - p_0)}{\sqrt{\dfrac{p_0(1 - p_0)}{n}}}$$

- The test statistic used for the χ^2 test for σ (p. 479):

$$\chi^2_{\text{data}} = \frac{(n - 1)s^2}{\sigma_0^2}$$

The three possible forms for the hypotheses for a test for μ

Form	Null and alternative hypotheses
Right-tailed test	$H_0: \mu = \mu_0$ versus $H_a: \mu > \mu_0$
Left-tailed test	$H_0: \mu = \mu_0$ versus $H_a: \mu < \mu_0$
Two-tailed test	$H_0: \mu = \mu_0$ versus $H_a: \mu \neq \mu_0$

Finding the *p*-value

Type of hypothesis test
Right-tailed test
$H_0: \mu = \mu_0$ versus $H_a: \mu > \mu_0$
p-value $= P(Z > Z_{\text{data}})$
Area to right of Z_{data}
Left-tailed test
$H_0: \mu = \mu_0$ versus $H_a: \mu < \mu_0$
p-value $= P(Z < Z_{\text{data}})$
Area to left of Z_{data}
Two-tailed test
$H_0: \mu = \mu_0$ versus $H_a: \mu \neq \mu_0$
p-value $= P\big(Z > |Z_{\text{data}}|\big) + P\big(Z < -|Z_{\text{data}}|\big)$
$\qquad = 2 \cdot P\big(Z > |Z_{\text{data}}|\big)$
Sum of the two tail areas.

Rejection rules for Z test for the mean

Form of test		Rejection rules: "Reject H_0 if…"
Right-tailed	$H_0: \mu = \mu_0$ vs. $H_a: \mu > \mu_0$	$Z_{\text{data}} > Z_{\text{crit}}$
Left-tailed	$H_0: \mu = \mu_0$ vs. $H_a: \mu < \mu_0$	$Z_{\text{data}} < Z_{\text{crit}}$
Two-tailed	$H_0: \mu = \mu_0$ vs. $H_a: \mu \neq \mu_0$	$Z_{\text{data}} > Z_{\text{crit}}$ or $Z_{\text{data}} < -Z_{\text{crit}}$

The three possible forms for the hypotheses for a test for *p*

Form	Null and alternative hypotheses
Right-tailed test, one-tailed test	$H_0: p = p_0$ versus $H_a: p > p_0$
Left-tailed test, one-tailed test	$H_0: p = p_0$ versus $H_a: p < p_0$
Two-tailed test	$H_0: p = p_0$ versus $H_a: p \neq p_0$

The three possible forms for the hypotheses for a test for σ

Form	Null and alternative hypotheses
Right-tailed test, one-tailed test	$H_0: \sigma = \sigma_0$ versus $H_a: \sigma > \sigma_0$
Left-tailed test, one-tailed test	$H_0: \sigma = \sigma_0$ versus $H_a: \sigma < \sigma_0$
Two-tailed test	$H_0: \sigma = \sigma_0$ versus $H_a: \sigma \neq \sigma_0$

Chapter 10   Two-Sample Inference

- $100(1 - \alpha)\%$ confidence interval for μ_d (matched-pair data) (p. 506): Lower Bound: $\bar{x}_d - (t_{\alpha/2})(s_d/\sqrt{n})$, Upper Bound: $\bar{x}_d + (t_{\alpha/2})(s_d/\sqrt{n})$, where $\bar{x}_d$ and s_d represent the sample mean and sample standard deviation of the differences, and $t_{\alpha/2}$ is found using $n - 1$ degrees of freedom.

- Test statistic for the paired sample *t* test (p. 502): $t_{\text{data}} = \dfrac{\bar{x}_d}{s_d/\sqrt{n}}$

- $100(1 - \alpha)\%$ Welch's confidence interval for $\mu_1 - \mu_2$ (p. 518):

  Lower Bound: $(\bar{x}_1 - \bar{x}_2) - t_{\alpha/2}\sqrt{\dfrac{s_1^2}{n_1} + \dfrac{s_2^2}{n_2}}$

  Upper Bound: $(\bar{x}_1 - \bar{x}_2) + t_{\alpha/2}\sqrt{\dfrac{s_1^2}{n_1} + \dfrac{s_2^2}{n_2}}$ where $t_{\alpha/2}$ is found using degrees of freedom the smaller of $n_1 - 1$ and $n_2 - 1$.

- $100(1 - \alpha)\%$ confidence interval for $p_1 - p_2$ (p. 535):

  Lower Bound: $\hat{p}_1 - \hat{p}_2 \pm (Z_{\alpha/2})\sqrt{\dfrac{\hat{p}_1 \cdot \hat{q}_1}{n_1} + \dfrac{\hat{p}_2 \cdot \hat{q}_2}{n_2}}$

  Upper Bound: $\hat{p}_1 - \hat{p}_2 \pm (Z_{\alpha/2})\sqrt{\dfrac{\hat{p}_1 \cdot \hat{q}_1}{n_1} + \dfrac{\hat{p}_2 \cdot \hat{q}_2}{n_2}}$

- Test statistic for the independent samples Z test for $p_1 - p_2$ (p. 530):

$$Z_{\text{data}} = \frac{(\hat{p}_1 - \hat{p}_2)}{\sqrt{\hat{p}_{\text{pooled}} \cdot (1 - \hat{p}_{\text{pooled}})\left(\dfrac{1}{n_1} + \dfrac{1}{n_2}\right)}}$$

  when the following conditions are satisfied: $x_1 \geq 5$, $(n_1 - x_1) \geq 5$, $x_2 \geq 5$, and $(n_2 - x_2) \geq 5$, and where $\hat{p}_{\text{pooled}} = \dfrac{x_1 + x_2}{n_1 + n_2}$.

Chapter 11 Categorical Data Analysis

- The expected frequency of the *i*th category when testing goodness of fit (p. 556): $E_i = n \cdot p_i$ where n is the number of trials, and p_i is the population proportion for the *i*th category.
- Test statistic for the goodness of fit test (p. 559):

$$\chi^2_{\text{data}} = \sum \frac{(O_i - E_i)^2}{E_i}$$ assuming the following conditions are true:
(a) None of the expected frequencies is less than 1, and (b) at most 20% of the expected frequencies are less than 5. Use $k - 1$ degrees

of freedom for the goodness of fit test, and $(r - 1)(c - 1)$ degrees of freedom for the test for independence or homogeneity of proportions.
- Expected frequencies for a χ^2 test for independence or for testing homogeneity of proportions (p. 569):

$$\text{Expected frequency} = \frac{(\text{row total})(\text{column total})}{\text{grand total}}$$

Chapter 12 Analysis of Variance

- Overall sample mean, $\bar{\bar{x}}$ (p. 592): The mean of all the observations from all the samples:

$$\bar{\bar{x}} = \frac{(n_1\bar{x}_1 + n_2\bar{x}_2 + \cdots + n_k\bar{x}_k)}{n_t}$$

- Test statistic for performing a one-way ANOVA (p. 593):

$$F_{\text{data}} = \frac{\text{MSTR}}{\text{MSE}}$$

- Mean square error (MSE) (p. 593):

$$\text{MSE} = \frac{\sum (n_i - 1)s_i^2}{n_t - k}$$

- Mean square treatment (MSTR) (p. 593):

$$\text{MSTR} = \frac{\sum n_i (\bar{x}_i - \bar{\bar{x}})^2}{k - 1}$$

One-way ANOVA table

Source of variation	Sum of squares	Degrees of freedom	Mean square	F test statistic
Treatment	SSTR	$df_1 = k - 1$	$\text{MSTR} = \dfrac{\text{SSTR}}{k - 1}$	$F_{\text{data}} = \dfrac{\text{MSTR}}{\text{MSE}}$
Error	SSE	$df_2 = n_t - k$	$\text{MSE} = \dfrac{\text{SSE}}{n_t - k}$	
Total	SST			

Chapter 13 Regression Analysis

- Standard error of the estimate (p. 639):

$$s = \sqrt{\text{MSE}} = \sqrt{\frac{\text{SSE}}{n - 2}}$$

- The regression model, or the regression equation (p. 635):
$y = \beta_1 x + \beta_0 + \varepsilon$, where: β_0 is the y intercept of the population regression line, β_1 is the slope of the population regression line, and ε is the error term.

- Confidence interval for the population slope β_1 of the regression line (p. 642): $b_1 \pm (t_{\text{crit}})(s_{b_1})$, where t_{crit} is based on $n - 2$ degrees of freedom.
- Test statistic (p. 638): $t_{\text{data}} = b_1 / s_{b_1}$

IMPORTANT TABLES
for Larose, *Discovering Statistics*
© 2013 by W.H. Freeman and Company

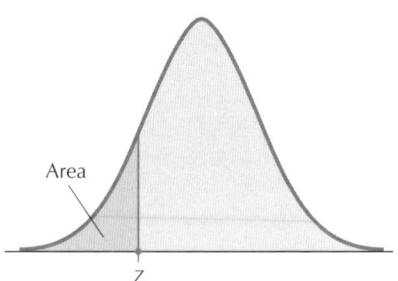

Area

Z

Table C Standard normal distribution

Z	0.00	0.01	0.02	0.03	0.04	0.05	0.06	0.07	0.08	0.09
−3.4	0.0003	0.0003	0.0003	0.0003	0.0003	0.0003	0.0003	0.0003	0.0003	0.0002
−3.3	0.0005	0.0005	0.0005	0.0004	0.0004	0.0004	0.0004	0.0004	0.0004	0.0003
−3.2	0.0007	0.0007	0.0006	0.0006	0.0006	0.0006	0.0006	0.0005	0.0005	0.0005
−3.1	0.0010	0.0009	0.0009	0.0009	0.0008	0.0008	0.0008	0.0008	0.0007	0.0007
−3.0	0.0013	0.0013	0.0013	0.0012	0.0012	0.0011	0.0011	0.0011	0.0010	0.0010
−2.9	0.0019	0.0018	0.0018	0.0017	0.0016	0.0016	0.0015	0.0015	0.0014	0.0014
−2.8	0.0026	0.0025	0.0024	0.0023	0.0023	0.0022	0.0021	0.0021	0.0020	0.0019
−2.7	0.0035	0.0034	0.0033	0.0032	0.0031	0.0030	0.0029	0.0028	0.0027	0.0026
−2.6	0.0047	0.0045	0.0044	0.0043	0.0041	0.0040	0.0039	0.0038	0.0037	0.0036
−2.5	0.0062	0.0060	0.0059	0.0057	0.0055	0.0054	0.0052	0.0051	0.0049	0.0048
−2.4	0.0082	0.0080	0.0078	0.0075	0.0073	0.0071	0.0069	0.0068	0.0066	0.0064
−2.3	0.0107	0.0104	0.0102	0.0099	0.0096	0.0094	0.0091	0.0089	0.0087	0.0084
−2.2	0.0139	0.0136	0.0132	0.0129	0.0125	0.0122	0.0119	0.0116	0.0113	0.0110
−2.1	0.0179	0.0174	0.0170	0.0166	0.0162	0.0158	0.0154	0.0150	0.0146	0.0143
−2.0	0.0228	0.0222	0.0217	0.0212	0.0207	0.0202	0.0197	0.0192	0.0188	0.0183
−1.9	0.0287	0.0281	0.0274	0.0268	0.0262	0.0256	0.0250	0.0244	0.0239	0.0233
−1.8	0.0359	0.0351	0.0344	0.0336	0.0329	0.0322	0.0314	0.0307	0.0301	0.0294
−1.7	0.0446	0.0436	0.0427	0.0418	0.0409	0.0401	0.0392	0.0384	0.0375	0.0367
−1.6	0.0548	0.0537	0.0526	0.0516	0.0505	0.0495	0.0485	0.0475	0.0465	0.0455
−1.5	0.0668	0.0655	0.0643	0.0630	0.0618	0.0606	0.0594	0.0582	0.0571	0.0559
−1.4	0.0808	0.0793	0.0778	0.0764	0.0749	0.0735	0.0721	0.0708	0.0694	0.0681
−1.3	0.0968	0.0951	0.0934	0.0918	0.0901	0.0885	0.0869	0.0853	0.0838	0.0823
−1.2	0.1151	0.1131	0.1112	0.1093	0.1075	0.1056	0.1038	0.1020	0.1003	0.0985
−1.1	0.1357	0.1335	0.1314	0.1292	0.1271	0.1251	0.1230	0.1210	0.1190	0.1170
−1.0	0.1587	0.1562	0.1539	0.1515	0.1492	0.1469	0.1446	0.1423	0.1401	0.1379
−0.9	0.1841	0.1814	0.1788	0.1762	0.1736	0.1711	0.1685	0.1660	0.1635	0.1611
−0.8	0.2119	0.2090	0.2061	0.2033	0.2005	0.1977	0.1949	0.1922	0.1894	0.1867
−0.7	0.2420	0.2389	0.2358	0.2327	0.2296	0.2266	0.2236	0.2206	0.2177	0.2148
−0.6	0.2743	0.2709	0.2676	0.2643	0.2611	0.2578	0.2546	0.2514	0.2483	0.2451
−0.5	0.3085	0.3050	0.3015	0.2981	0.2946	0.2912	0.2877	0.2843	0.2810	0.2776
−0.4	0.3446	0.3409	0.3372	0.3336	0.3300	0.3264	0.3228	0.3192	0.3156	0.3121
−0.3	0.3821	0.3783	0.3745	0.3707	0.3669	0.3632	0.3594	0.3557	0.3520	0.3483
−0.2	0.4207	0.4168	0.4129	0.4090	0.4052	0.4013	0.3974	0.3936	0.3897	0.3859
−0.1	0.4602	0.4562	0.4522	0.4483	0.4443	0.4404	0.4364	0.4325	0.4286	0.4247
−0.0	0.5000	0.4960	0.4920	0.4880	0.4840	0.4801	0.4761	0.4721	0.4681	0.4641

- Factorial symbol $n!$ (p. 245): $0! = 1$; $1! = 1$;
  $n! = n(n - 1)(n - 2) \cdots 3 \cdot 2 \cdot 1$
- Permutation of r items chosen from n distinct items (p. 245):

  $_nP_r = \dfrac{n!}{(n - r)!}$

- Combination of r items chosen from n distinct items (p. 247):

  $_nC_r = \dfrac{n!}{r!(n - r)!}$

- Permutations of nondistinct items (p. 249): $\dfrac{n!}{n_1! \cdot n_2! \cdots \cdots n_k!}$

Chapter 6 Probability Distributions

- Mean μ of a discrete random variable X (p. 264):

  $\mu = \sum X \cdot P(X)$

- Variance of a discrete random variable X (p. 267):

  $\sigma^2 = \sum (X - \mu)^2 \cdot P(X)$ or

  $\sigma^2 = \sum (X^2 \cdot P(X)) - \mu^2$

- Standard deviation of a discrete random variable X (p. 267):

  $\sigma = \sqrt{\sum (X - \mu)^2 \cdot P(X)}$ or $\sigma = \sqrt{\sum (X^2 \cdot P(X)) - \mu^2}$

- The binomial probability distribution formula (p. 277):
  $P(X) = (_nC_X) \, p^n \, (1 - p)^{n-X}$
- Mean of a binomial random variable (p. 280): $\mu = n \cdot p$
- Variance of a binomial random variable (p. 280):

  $\sigma^2 = n \cdot p \cdot (1 - p)$

- Standard deviation of a binomial random variable (p. 280):

  $\sigma = \sqrt{n \cdot p \cdot (1 - p)}$

- Standardizing a normal random variable (p. 313): $Z = \dfrac{X - \mu}{\sigma}$
- Calculating the X-value, given a Z-value (p. 302): $X = Z\sigma + \mu$

Chapter 7 Sampling Distributions

- Mean of the sampling distribution of the sample mean $\bar{x}$ (p. 339):
  $\mu_{\bar{x}} = \mu$
- Standard error of the mean (p. 340):

  $\sigma_{\bar{x}} = \dfrac{\sigma}{\sqrt{n}}$

- Standardizing a normal sampling distribution for means (p. 341):

  $Z = \dfrac{\bar{x} - \mu_{\bar{x}}}{\sigma_{\bar{x}}} = \dfrac{\bar{x} - \mu}{\sigma/\sqrt{n}}$

- Central Limit Theorem for Means (p. 350): Given a population with mean μ and standard deviation σ, the sampling distribution of the sample mean $\bar{x}$ becomes approximately normal $(\mu, \sigma/\sqrt{n})$ as the sample size gets larger, regardless of the shape of the population.

- Mean of the sampling distribution of the sample proportion $\hat{p}$ (p. 359):
  $\mu_{\hat{p}} = p$
- Standard error of the proportion (p. 360):

  $\sigma_{\hat{p}} = \sqrt{\dfrac{p \cdot (1 - p)}{n}}$

- Central Limit Theorem for Proportions (p. 361): The sampling distribution of the sample proportion $\hat{p}$ follows an approximately normal distribution with mean $\mu_{\hat{p}} = p$ and standard deviation

  $\sigma_{\hat{p}} = \sqrt{\dfrac{p \cdot (1 - p)}{n}}$ when both the following conditions are satisfied: (1) $np \geq 5$ and (2) $n(1 - p) \geq 5$.

- Standardizing a normal sampling distribution for proportions (p. 362):

  $Z = \dfrac{\hat{p} - \mu_{\hat{p}}}{\sigma_{\hat{p}}} = \dfrac{\hat{p} - p}{\sqrt{\dfrac{p(1 - p)}{n}}}$

Chapter 8 Confidence Intervals

- $100(1 - \alpha)\%$ Z confidence interval for μ (p. 373):

  Lower Bound $= \bar{x} - Z_{\alpha/2}(\sigma/\sqrt{n})$, Upper Bound $= \bar{x} + Z_{\alpha/2}(\sigma/\sqrt{n})$

  provided either the original population is normal, and σ is known, or the sample size is large ($n \geq 30$), and σ is known.
- Sample size for estimating the population mean (p. 380):

  $n = \left(\dfrac{(Z_{\alpha/2})\sigma}{E} \right)^2$

  where $Z_{\alpha/2}$ is associated with the desired confidence level, and E is the desired margin of error. Round up to the next integer.
- $100(1 - \alpha)\%$ t confidence interval for μ (p. 389):

  Lower Bound $= \bar{x} - t_{\alpha/2}(s/\sqrt{n})$, Upper Bound $= \bar{x} + t_{\alpha/2}(s/\sqrt{n})$

  where $t_{\alpha/2}$ is based on $n - 1$ degrees of freedom and either the population is normal or the sample size is large ($n \geq 30$).
- $100(1 - \alpha)\%$ Z confidence interval for p (p. 402): Lower Bound $=$

  $\hat{p} - Z_{\alpha/2}\sqrt{\dfrac{\hat{p}(1 - \hat{p})}{n}}$, Upper Bound $= \hat{p} + Z_{\alpha/2}\sqrt{\dfrac{\hat{p}(1 - \hat{p})}{n}}$

  The Z interval for p may be used only if *both* of the following conditions apply: $n\hat{p} \geq 5$ and $n(1 - \hat{p}) \geq 5$.
- Sample size for estimating a population proportion when $\hat{p}$ is known (p. 405):

  $n = \hat{p}(1 - \hat{p})\left(\dfrac{Z_{\alpha/2}}{E} \right)^2$

  where $Z_{\alpha/2}$ is associated with the desired confidence level, and E is the desired margin of error. Round up to the next integer.
- Sample size for estimating a population proportion when $\hat{p}$ is not known (p. 405):

  $n = \left(\dfrac{(0.5)(Z_{\alpha/2})}{E} \right)^2$

  where $Z_{\alpha/2}$ is associated with the desired confidence level, and E is the desired margin of error. Round up to the next integer.
- $100(1 - \alpha)\%$ χ^2 confidence interval for the population variance σ^2 (p. 414):

  Lower Bound $= \sqrt{\dfrac{(n - 1)s^2}{\chi^2_{\alpha/2}}}$, Upper Bound $= \sqrt{\dfrac{(n - 1)s^2}{\chi^2_{1-\alpha/2}}}$

  where $\chi^2_{1-\alpha/2}$ and $\chi^2_{\alpha/2}$ are the critical values for a χ^2 distribution with $n - 1$ degrees of freedom, and provided that the sample is taken from a normal population.
- $100(1 - \alpha)\%$ χ^2 confidence interval for the population standard deviation σ (p. 414):

  Lower Bound $= \sqrt{\dfrac{(n - 1)s^2}{\chi^2_{\alpha/2}}}$, Upper Bound $= \sqrt{\dfrac{(n - 1)s^2}{\chi^2_{1-\alpha/2}}}$

  where $\chi^2_{1-\alpha/2}$ and $\chi^2_{\alpha/2}$ are the critical values for a χ^2 distribution with $n - 1$ degrees of freedom, and provided that the sample is taken from a normal population.

Table D *t*-Distribution

| | | Confidence level | | | | |
		80%	90%	95%	98%	99%
				Area in one tail		
		0.10	0.05	0.025	0.01	0.005
				Area in two tails		
		0.20	0.10	0.05	0.02	0.01
df	1	3.078	6.314	12.706	31.821	63.657
	2	1.886	2.920	4.303	6.965	9.925
	3	1.638	2.353	3.182	4.541	5.841
	4	1.533	2.132	2.776	3.747	4.604
	5	1.476	2.015	2.571	3.365	4.032
	6	1.440	1.943	2.447	3.143	3.707
	7	1.415	1.895	2.365	2.998	3.499
	8	1.397	1.860	2.306	2.896	3.355
	9	1.383	1.833	2.262	2.821	3.250
	10	1.372	1.812	2.228	2.764	3.169
	11	1.363	1.796	2.201	2.718	3.106
	12	1.356	1.782	2.179	2.681	3.055
	13	1.350	1.771	2.160	2.650	3.012
	14	1.345	1.761	2.145	2.624	2.977
	15	1.341	1.753	2.131	2.602	2.947
	16	1.337	1.746	2.120	2.583	2.921
	17	1.333	1.740	2.110	2.567	2.898
	18	1.330	1.734	2.101	2.552	2.878
	19	1.328	1.729	2.093	2.539	2.861
	20	1.325	1.725	2.086	2.528	2.845
	21	1.323	1.721	2.080	2.518	2.831
	22	1.321	1.717	2.074	2.508	2.819
	23	1.319	1.714	2.069	2.500	2.807
	24	1.318	1.711	2.064	2.492	2.797
	25	1.316	1.708	2.060	2.485	2.787
	26	1.315	1.706	2.056	2.479	2.779
	27	1.314	1.703	2.052	2.473	2.771
	28	1.313	1.701	2.048	2.467	2.763
	29	1.311	1.699	2.045	2.462	2.756
	30	1.310	1.697	2.042	2.457	2.750
	31	1.309	1.696	2.040	2.453	2.744
	32	1.309	1.694	2.037	2.449	2.738
	33	1.308	1.692	2.035	2.445	2.733
	34	1.307	1.691	2.032	2.441	2.728
	35	1.306	1.690	2.030	2.438	2.724
	36	1.306	1.688	2.028	2.435	2.719
	37	1.305	1.687	2.026	2.431	2.715
	38	1.304	1.686	2.024	2.429	2.712
	39	1.304	1.685	2.023	2.426	2.708
	40	1.303	1.684	2.021	2.423	2.704
	50	1.299	1.676	2.009	2.403	2.678
	60	1.296	1.671	2.000	2.390	2.660
	70	1.294	1.667	1.994	2.381	2.648
	80	1.292	1.664	1.990	2.374	2.639
	90	1.291	1.662	1.987	2.368	2.632
	100	1.290	1.660	1.984	2.364	2.626
	1000	1.282	1.646	1.962	2.330	2.581
	z	1.282	1.645	1.960	2.326	2.576

Chapter 3 Describing Data Numerically

- Sample mean (p. 91): $\bar{x} = \sum x / n$
- Population mean (p. 92): $\mu = \sum x / N$
- Range (p. 105): Largest data value – smallest data value

- Population variance (p. 108):
$$\sigma^2 = \frac{\sum (x - \mu)^2}{N} \text{ or } \sigma^2 = \frac{\sum x^2 - \left(\sum x\right)^2 / N}{N}$$

- Population standard deviation (p. 109):
$$\sigma = \sqrt{\sigma^2} = \sqrt{\frac{\sum (x - \mu)^2}{N}} \text{ or } \sigma = \sqrt{\frac{\sum x^2 - \left(\sum x\right)^2 / N}{N}}$$

- Sample variance (p. 110):
$$s^2 = \frac{\sum (x - \bar{x})^2}{n - 1} \text{ or } s^2 = \frac{\sum x^2 - \left(\sum x\right)^2 / n}{n - 1}$$

- Sample standard deviation (p. 110):
$$s = \sqrt{s^2} = \sqrt{\frac{\sum (x - \bar{x})^2}{n - 1}} \text{ or } s = \sqrt{\frac{\sum x^2 - \left(\sum x\right)^2 / n}{n - 1}}$$

- Weighted mean (p. 118):
$$\bar{x}_w = \frac{\sum w_i x_i}{\sum w_i} = \frac{w_1 x_1 + w_2 x_2 + \cdots + w_n x_n}{w_1 + w_2 + \cdots + w_n}$$

- Estimated mean for data grouped into a frequency distribution
(p. 119): $\hat{\mu} = \dfrac{\sum m_i f_i}{N} = \dfrac{m_1 f_1 + m_2 f_2 + \cdots + m_k f_k}{N}$

- Estimated variance for data grouped into a frequency distribution
(p. 120): $\hat{\sigma}^2 = \sqrt{\dfrac{\sum \left(m_i - \hat{\mu}\right)^2 \cdot f_i}{N}}$

- Estimated standard deviation for data grouped into a frequency
distribution (p. 120): $\hat{\sigma} = \sqrt{\hat{\sigma}^2} = \sqrt{\dfrac{\sum \left(m_i - \hat{\mu}\right)^2 \cdot f_i}{N}}$

- Percentile (position of pth percentile) (p. 128): $i = (p/100)n$
- Z-score for sample data (p. 124): $\dfrac{x - \bar{x}}{s}$
- Z-score for population data (p. 124): $\dfrac{x - \mu}{\sigma}$
- Chebyshev's Rule (p. 146): *At least* $\left(1 - \dfrac{1}{k^2}\right)100\%$ of the values
from any data set will fall within k standard deviations of the mean,
where $k > 1$.
- The Empirical Rule: If the data distribution is bell-shaped (p. 148):
  - About 68% of the data values will fall within one standard
  deviation of the mean.
  - About 95% of the data values will fall within two standard
  deviations of the mean.
  - About 99.7% of the data values will fall within three standard
  deviations of the mean.
- Interquartile range (p. 133): IQR = Q3 − Q1
- Five-number summary (p. 137): Minimum, Q1, Median, Q3,
Maximum
- Lower fence (for box plot) (p. 138): Q1 − 1.5(IQR)
- Upper fence (for box plot) (p. 138): Q3 + 1.5(IQR)

Chapter 4 Correlation and Regression

- Correlation coefficient r (p. 161 or p. 165):
$$r = \frac{\sum (x - \bar{x})(y - \bar{y})}{(n - 1)s_x s_y} \text{ or } r = \frac{\sum xy - \left(\sum x \sum y\right)/n}{\sqrt{\left(\sum x^2 - \left(\sum x\right)^2 / n\right)\left(\sum y^2 - \left(\sum y\right)^2 / n\right)}}$$

- Regression equation (regression line) (p. 172): $\hat{y} = b_1 x + b_0$

- Slope of the regression line (p. 172 or p. 174): $b_1 = \dfrac{\sum (x - \bar{x})(y - \bar{y})}{\sum (x - \bar{x})^2}$ or
$$b_1 = \frac{\sum xy - \left(\sum x \sum y\right)/n}{\sum x^2 - \left(\sum x\right)^2 / n}$$

- y Intercept (p. 172): $b_0 = \bar{y} - (b_1 \cdot \bar{x})$
- Prediction error or residual (p. 177): $(y - \hat{y})$
- SSE, sum of squares error (p. 186): $\sum (y - \hat{y})^2$

- Standard error of the estimate (p. 187):
$$s = \sqrt{\text{MSE}} = \sqrt{\frac{\text{SSE}}{n - 2}}$$

- SST, sum of squares total (p. 188 or p. 191): $\text{SST} = \sum (y - \bar{y})^2$ or
$$\text{SST} = \sum y^2 - \left(\sum y\right)^2 / n$$

- The coefficient of determination (p. 190): $r^2 = \text{SSR}/\text{SST}$
- SSR, sum of squares regression (p. 189 or p. 191): $\text{SSR} = \sum (\hat{y} - \bar{y})^2$
or $\text{SSR} = \dfrac{\left[\sum xy - \left(\sum x\right)\left(\sum y\right)/n\right]^2}{\sum x^2 - \left(\sum x\right)^2 / n}$

- Correlation coefficient r (p. 161): Can be expressed as
$r = \pm \sqrt{r^2}$, taking the positive or negative sign of the slope b_1.

Chapter 5 Probability

- Classical method for assigning probabilities (p. 204):
$$P(E) = \frac{\text{number of outcomes in } E}{\text{number of outcomes in sample space}} = \frac{N(E)}{N(S)}$$

- Relative frequency method of assigning probabilities (p. 209):
$$P(E) \approx \frac{\text{frequency of } E}{\text{number of trials of experiment}}$$

- Probabilities for complements (p. 218): $P(A) + P(A^C) = 1$,
$P(A) = 1 - P(A^C)$, and $P(A^C) = 1 - P(A)$
- Addition Rule (p. 219):
$P(A \text{ or } B) = P(A \cup B) = P(A) + P(B) - P(A \cap B)$
- Addition Rule for mutually exclusive events (p. 221):
$P(A \cup B) = P(A) + P(B)$

- Conditional probability (p. 226):
$$P(B|A) = \frac{P(A \cap B)}{P(A)} = \frac{N(A \cap B)}{N(A)}$$

- Independent events (p. 228): Events A and B are *independent* if
$P(A|B) = P(A)$ or if $P(B|A) = P(B)$.
- Multiplication Rule (p. 230): $P(A \cap B) = P(B)\,P(A|B)$, or
$P(A \cap B) = P(A)\,P(B|A)$
- Alternate method for determining independence (p. 228):
  - If $P(A)\,P(B) = P(A \cap B)$, then events A and B are *independent*.
  - If $P(A)\,P(B) \neq P(A \cap B)$, then events A and B are *dependent*.
- Multiplication Rule for n independent events (p. 235):
$P(A \cap B \cap C \cap \ldots) = P(A)\,P(B)\,P(C) \ldots$

Table E Chi-square (χ^2) distribution

Degrees of freedom	Area to the right of critical value									
	0.995	0.99	0.975	0.95	0.90	0.10	0.05	0.025	0.01	0.005
1	—	—	0.001	0.004	0.016	2.706	3.841	5.024	6.635	7.879
2	0.010	0.020	0.051	0.103	0.211	4.605	5.991	7.378	9.210	10.597
3	0.072	0.115	0.216	0.352	0.584	6.251	7.815	9.348	11.345	12.838
4	0.207	0.297	0.484	0.711	1.064	7.779	9.488	11.143	13.277	14.860
5	0.412	0.554	0.831	1.145	1.610	9.236	11.071	12.833	15.086	16.750
6	0.676	0.872	1.237	1.635	2.204	10.645	12.592	14.449	16.812	18.548
7	0.989	1.239	1.690	2.167	2.833	12.017	14.067	16.013	18.475	20.278
8	1.344	1.646	2.180	2.733	3.490	13.362	15.507	17.535	20.090	21.955
9	1.735	2.088	2.700	3.325	4.168	14.684	16.919	19.023	21.666	23.589
10	2.156	2.558	3.247	3.940	4.865	15.987	18.307	20.483	23.209	25.188
11	2.603	3.053	3.816	4.575	5.578	17.275	19.675	21.920	24.725	26.757
12	3.074	3.571	4.404	5.226	6.304	18.549	21.026	23.337	26.217	28.299
13	3.565	4.107	5.009	5.892	7.042	19.812	22.362	24.736	27.688	29.819
14	4.075	4.660	5.629	6.571	7.790	21.064	23.685	26.119	29.141	31.319
15	4.601	5.229	6.262	7.261	8.547	22.307	24.996	27.488	30.578	32.801
16	5.142	5.812	6.908	7.962	9.312	23.542	26.296	28.845	32.000	34.267
17	5.697	6.408	7.564	8.672	10.085	24.769	27.587	30.191	33.409	35.718
18	6.265	7.015	8.231	9.390	10.865	25.989	28.869	31.526	34.805	37.156
19	6.844	7.633	8.907	10.117	11.651	27.204	30.144	32.852	36.191	38.582
20	7.434	8.260	9.591	10.851	12.443	28.412	31.410	34.170	37.566	39.997
21	8.034	8.897	10.283	11.591	13.240	29.615	32.671	35.479	38.932	41.401
22	8.643	9.542	10.982	12.338	14.042	30.813	33.924	36.781	40.289	42.796
23	9.260	10.196	11.689	13.091	14.848	32.007	35.172	38.076	41.638	44.181
24	9.886	10.856	12.401	13.848	15.659	33.196	36.415	39.364	42.980	45.559
25	10.520	11.524	13.120	14.611	16.473	34.382	37.652	40.646	44.314	46.928
26	11.160	12.198	13.844	15.379	17.292	35.563	38.885	41.923	45.642	48.290
27	11.808	12.879	14.573	16.151	18.114	36.741	40.113	43.194	46.963	49.645
28	12.461	13.565	15.308	16.928	18.939	37.916	41.337	44.461	48.278	50.993
29	13.121	14.257	16.047	17.708	19.768	39.087	42.557	45.722	49.588	52.336
30	13.787	14.954	16.791	18.493	20.599	40.256	43.773	46.979	50.892	53.672
40	20.707	22.164	24.433	26.509	29.051	51.805	55.758	59.342	63.691	66.766
50	27.991	29.707	32.357	34.764	37.689	63.167	67.505	71.420	76.154	79.490
60	35.534	37.485	40.482	43.188	46.459	74.397	79.082	83.298	88.379	91.952
70	43.275	45.442	48.758	51.739	55.329	85.527	90.531	95.023	100.425	104.215
80	51.172	53.540	57.153	60.391	64.278	96.578	101.879	106.629	112.329	116.321
90	59.196	61.754	65.647	69.126	73.291	107.565	113.145	118.136	124.116	128.299
100	67.328	70.065	74.222	77.929	82.358	118.498	124.342	129.561	135.807	140.169

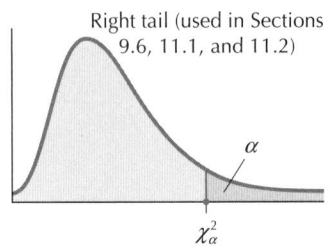

Right tail (used in Sections 9.6, 11.1, and 11.2)

χ^2_α

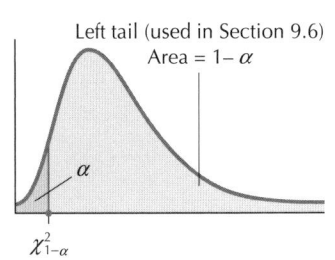

Left tail (used in Section 9.6)
Area = $1 - \alpha$

$\chi^2_{1-\alpha}$

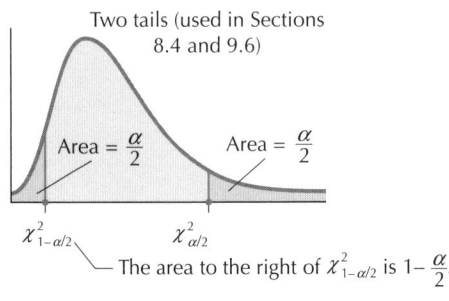

Two tails (used in Sections 8.4 and 9.6)

Area = $\dfrac{\alpha}{2}$ Area = $\dfrac{\alpha}{2}$

$\chi^2_{1-\alpha/2}$ $\chi^2_{\alpha/2}$

The area to the right of $\chi^2_{1-\alpha/2}$ is $1 - \dfrac{\alpha}{2}$.

Table D t-Distribution

		Confidence level				
		80%	90%	95%	98%	99%
		Area in one tail				
		0.10	0.05	0.025	0.01	0.005
		Area in two tails				
		0.20	0.10	0.05	0.02	0.01
df	1	3.078	6.314	12.706	31.821	63.657
	2	1.886	2.920	4.303	6.965	9.925
	3	1.638	2.353	3.182	4.541	5.841
	4	1.533	2.132	2.776	3.747	4.604
	5	1.476	2.015	2.571	3.365	4.032
	6	1.440	1.943	2.447	3.143	3.707
	7	1.415	1.895	2.365	2.998	3.499
	8	1.397	1.860	2.306	2.896	3.355
	9	1.383	1.833	2.262	2.821	3.250
	10	1.372	1.812	2.228	2.764	3.169
	11	1.363	1.796	2.201	2.718	3.106
	12	1.356	1.782	2.179	2.681	3.055
	13	1.350	1.771	2.160	2.650	3.012
	14	1.345	1.761	2.145	2.624	2.977
	15	1.341	1.753	2.131	2.602	2.947
	16	1.337	1.746	2.120	2.583	2.921
	17	1.333	1.740	2.110	2.567	2.898
	18	1.330	1.734	2.101	2.552	2.878
	19	1.328	1.729	2.093	2.539	2.861
	20	1.325	1.725	2.086	2.528	2.845
	21	1.323	1.721	2.080	2.518	2.831
	22	1.321	1.717	2.074	2.508	2.819
	23	1.319	1.714	2.069	2.500	2.807
	24	1.318	1.711	2.064	2.492	2.797
	25	1.316	1.708	2.060	2.485	2.787
	26	1.315	1.706	2.056	2.479	2.779
	27	1.314	1.703	2.052	2.473	2.771
	28	1.313	1.701	2.048	2.467	2.763
	29	1.311	1.699	2.045	2.462	2.756
	30	1.310	1.697	2.042	2.457	2.750
	31	1.309	1.696	2.040	2.453	2.744
	32	1.309	1.694	2.037	2.449	2.738
	33	1.308	1.692	2.035	2.445	2.733
	34	1.307	1.691	2.032	2.441	2.728
	35	1.306	1.690	2.030	2.438	2.724
	36	1.306	1.688	2.028	2.435	2.719
	37	1.305	1.687	2.026	2.431	2.715
	38	1.304	1.686	2.024	2.429	2.712
	39	1.304	1.685	2.023	2.426	2.708
	40	1.303	1.684	2.021	2.423	2.704
	50	1.299	1.676	2.009	2.403	2.678
	60	1.296	1.671	2.000	2.390	2.660
	70	1.294	1.667	1.994	2.381	2.648
	80	1.292	1.664	1.990	2.374	2.639
	90	1.291	1.662	1.987	2.368	2.632
	100	1.290	1.660	1.984	2.364	2.626
	1000	1.282	1.646	1.962	2.330	2.581
	z	1.282	1.645	1.960	2.326	2.576

Table E Chi-square (χ^2) distribution

Degrees of freedom	Area to the right of critical value									
	0.995	0.99	0.975	0.95	0.90	0.10	0.05	0.025	0.01	0.005
1	—	—	0.001	0.004	0.016	2.706	3.841	5.024	6.635	7.879
2	0.010	0.020	0.051	0.103	0.211	4.605	5.991	7.378	9.210	10.597
3	0.072	0.115	0.216	0.352	0.584	6.251	7.815	9.348	11.345	12.838
4	0.207	0.297	0.484	0.711	1.064	7.779	9.488	11.143	13.277	14.860
5	0.412	0.554	0.831	1.145	1.610	9.236	11.071	12.833	15.086	16.750
6	0.676	0.872	1.237	1.635	2.204	10.645	12.592	14.449	16.812	18.548
7	0.989	1.239	1.690	2.167	2.833	12.017	14.067	16.013	18.475	20.278
8	1.344	1.646	2.180	2.733	3.490	13.362	15.507	17.535	20.090	21.955
9	1.735	2.088	2.700	3.325	4.168	14.684	16.919	19.023	21.666	23.589
10	2.156	2.558	3.247	3.940	4.865	15.987	18.307	20.483	23.209	25.188
11	2.603	3.053	3.816	4.575	5.578	17.275	19.675	21.920	24.725	26.757
12	3.074	3.571	4.404	5.226	6.304	18.549	21.026	23.337	26.217	28.299
13	3.565	4.107	5.009	5.892	7.042	19.812	22.362	24.736	27.688	29.819
14	4.075	4.660	5.629	6.571	7.790	21.064	23.685	26.119	29.141	31.319
15	4.601	5.229	6.262	7.261	8.547	22.307	24.996	27.488	30.578	32.801
16	5.142	5.812	6.908	7.962	9.312	23.542	26.296	28.845	32.000	34.267
17	5.697	6.408	7.564	8.672	10.085	24.769	27.587	30.191	33.409	35.718
18	6.265	7.015	8.231	9.390	10.865	25.989	28.869	31.526	34.805	37.156
19	6.844	7.633	8.907	10.117	11.651	27.204	30.144	32.852	36.191	38.582
20	7.434	8.260	9.591	10.851	12.443	28.412	31.410	34.170	37.566	39.997
21	8.034	8.897	10.283	11.591	13.240	29.615	32.671	35.479	38.932	41.401
22	8.643	9.542	10.982	12.338	14.042	30.813	33.924	36.781	40.289	42.796
23	9.260	10.196	11.689	13.091	14.848	32.007	35.172	38.076	41.638	44.181
24	9.886	10.856	12.401	13.848	15.659	33.196	36.415	39.364	42.980	45.559
25	10.520	11.524	13.120	14.611	16.473	34.382	37.652	40.646	44.314	46.928
26	11.160	12.198	13.844	15.379	17.292	35.563	38.885	41.923	45.642	48.290
27	11.808	12.879	14.573	16.151	18.114	36.741	40.113	43.194	46.963	49.645
28	12.461	13.565	15.308	16.928	18.939	37.916	41.337	44.461	48.278	50.993
29	13.121	14.257	16.047	17.708	19.768	39.087	42.557	45.722	49.588	52.336
30	13.787	14.954	16.791	18.493	20.599	40.256	43.773	46.979	50.892	53.672
40	20.707	22.164	24.433	26.509	29.051	51.805	55.758	59.342	63.691	66.766
50	27.991	29.707	32.357	34.764	37.689	63.167	67.505	71.420	76.154	79.490
60	35.534	37.485	40.482	43.188	46.459	74.397	79.082	83.298	88.379	91.952
70	43.275	45.442	48.758	51.739	55.329	85.527	90.531	95.023	100.425	104.215
80	51.172	53.540	57.153	60.391	64.278	96.578	101.879	106.629	112.329	116.321
90	59.196	61.754	65.647	69.126	73.291	107.565	113.145	118.136	124.116	128.299
100	67.328	70.065	74.222	77.929	82.358	118.498	124.342	129.561	135.807	140.169

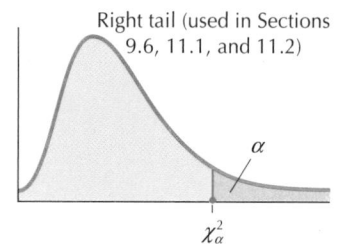

Right tail (used in Sections 9.6, 11.1, and 11.2)

α

χ^2_α

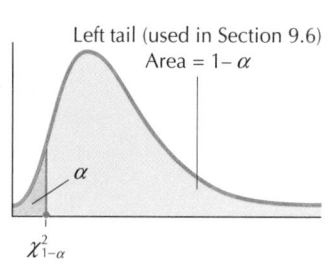

Left tail (used in Section 9.6)

Area = $1-\alpha$

α

$\chi^2_{1-\alpha}$

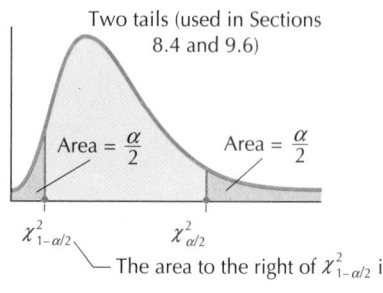

Two tails (used in Sections 8.4 and 9.6)

Area = $\dfrac{\alpha}{2}$

Area = $\dfrac{\alpha}{2}$

$\chi^2_{1-\alpha/2}$

$\chi^2_{\alpha/2}$

The area to the right of $\chi^2_{1-\alpha/2}$ is $1-\dfrac{\alpha}{2}$.